171 BHT corrections

212 sec. migration, map depth to top carrier

The Petroleum System—
From Source to Trap

edited by

Leslie B. Magoon

Wallace G. Dow

AAPG Memoir 60

Published by
The American Association of Petroleum Geologists
Tulsa, Oklahoma, U.S.A. 74101

Association Editor: Kevin T. Biddle
Science Director: Gary D. Howell
Publications Manager: Cathleen P. Williams
Special Projects Editor: Anne H. Thomas
Production, Design, and Layout: Kathy A. Walker, Editorial Technologies

Dust jacket photo: computer simulation of seismic and well data with interpreted stratigraphic horizons in color. Photo provided by Steven P. Buck, Senior Staff Geologist, Mobil Exploration Norway Inc.

FOREWORD

For years, petroleum geologists, whether working for themselves, small or large companies, or research, academic, or governmental institutions, have struggled to come up with a more reliable and logical way to judge and describe the petroleum potential and attendant exploration risks of undrilled prospects, plays, and basins. The volume you are holding, *The Petroleum System—From Source to Trap,* finally solves this problem. In a collection of individually authored papers, including case studies and analogs, it describes the petroleum system approach.

While not a panacea, this exciting, if not totally new, approach can significantly help geologists evaluate and communicate the petroleum potential and exploration risks involved in an area of investigation. Perhaps equally important, it can provide both the data and a logical basis for constructive discussion among petroleum geologists knowledgeable in that particular area.

As a petroleum geologist with over 40 years experience, I have seen this approach successfully employed. It is my hope that more and more petroleum geologists around the world will not only embrace and use the petroleum system approach but will build upon and improve it.

Jack C. Threet
Retired Vice President Exploration
Shell Oil Company, Houston, Texas

The editors and authors dedicate this volume to the worldwide community of geologists, geophysicists, geochemists, and managers who have applied the scientific method in their search for petroleum.

CONTENTS

Part IV. Identification and Characterization

Part V. Case Studies—Western Hemisphere

PREFACE

Wallace G. Dow

The petroleum system concept was first developed in 1970 at the Amoco research laboratory in Tulsa, Oklahoma. In my first major geochemical study, I described three "oil systems" in the Williston basin based on analytical data generated by Jack Williams and the geochemical research group, headed by Jim Momper. The purpose was to reduce risk by predicting the most likely places where oil would be found and where it most likely would be absent.

After graduating from Rutgers University in 1959 with a B.A. in geology, three years in the military, and receiving an M.S. in geology from the University of North Dakota under Wilson Laird, I took a job with the Pan American Petroleum Corporation (now Amoco) in their Denver Division office. I was an exploration geologist, alternating between project and well site work in the northern Rocky Mountain area. Jim Momper, a senior geologist I knew in Denver, had been transferred to the Tulsa geochemical research group and asked me to collect crude oils whenever possible because they needed samples to analyze. I collected over 250 oil samples between 1966 and 1969, about half of which were from the Williston basin. Because of my interest in geochemistry, Jim offered me a transfer to the Tulsa Research Laboratory to help him bring geologic insight into the then new science of petroleum geochemistry. I accepted the challenge and arrived in Tulsa with my family on a snowy New Year's Eve in 1969 with little idea of what the future would bring. I have been involved in geochemistry ever since.

Jack Williams analyzed the oils I had collected using techniques that were far less sophisticated than those in use today. The Williston basin oils were clearly divided into three major genetic types with several subtypes and mixtures. The oil compositional differences indicated that three separate source rocks were involved. Cores from all available organic-rich rocks in the basin were solvent extracted, and the extracts were analyzed with the same techniques used on the oils. Ordovician rock extracts positively correlated with the oil found in Ordovician and Silurian reservoirs rocks, Bakken shale extracts were very similar to the oils in Mississippian and Devonian reservoirs, and extracts from Tyler shales compared favorably to oils produced from Pennsylvanian Tyler reservoirs. Extracts from other organic-rich rocks lacked similarity to any of the oils I had collected. These analytical results and our interpretation demonstrated that oils from different source rocks can be different and that oil–source rock correlations are geologically meaningful.

In the early 1970s, it was generally known, but largely ignored, that traps, reservoirs, seals, and source rocks were all required to make an oil accumulation. Most geologists knew a lot about traps and reservoirs, little about seals, and virtually nothing about source rocks. A few source rock papers had appeared in the 1960s by workers now accepted as pioneers in the field—Hunt, Philippi, Tissot, and Vassoyevich—which served as a foundation for our work. We did the best we could in an era before biomarkers, vitrinite reflectance, Rock-Eval pyrolysis, capillary gas chromatography, and most of the analytical techniques we take for granted today. Despite these difficulties, Jack's oil–source rock correlations have survived the test of time.

My job was to find ways to make this new geochemical information useful to Amoco's exploration effort in the Williston basin and eventually to all petroleum provinces around the world. I reasoned that if we knew where the oils came from and how they migrated, we could better predict where they would be found in the future. Geochemistry could then be used to high-grade areas in which to concentrate exploration activity, thereby reducing risk.

The first step was to map the stratigraphic and areal distribution of each oil type. We were fortunate to start with the Williston basin because the three oil types are distinct here and the accumulations of each type are isolated by evaporite seals. I identified three source–reservoir packages that I called "oil systems" and named them after their principal source and reservoir rocks. Each oil system had an area of mature source rock, migration pathways, reservoirs, traps, and seals. The concept depended on the ability to separate oils into genetic types, correlate each type of a specific source rock, estimate the quantity of oil generated and expelled from the source rock, and map the vertical and lateral migration pathways through which the oil moved. This study led us to conclude that the combination of geology and geochemistry would become a powerful exploration tool. We did not know it at the time, but our work had predicted most of the successful Williston basin oil plays of the 1970s and 1980s and that little or no oil would be found in areas that we considered high risk.

After presenting our work within Amoco, we were granted permission to share our concept with the petroleum industry. Jim Momper and I organized a session on "New Ideas: Origin, Migration, and Entrapment of Oil" for the 1972 AAPG Annual Convention in Denver, Colorado. Jack Williams presented a paper on "Characterization of oil types in the Williston basin" and I followed with a paper on "The Application of oil correlation and source rock data to exploration in the Williston basin." These papers were later published in the July 1974 AAPG Bulletin. Our approach of combining geochemical data into a complete geological framework formed the basis for the petroleum system concept. Subsequent work by Perrodon, Meissner, and Ulmishek developed these ideas further and set the stage for Les Magoon's rigorous definition and application of the petroleum system concept, beginning in 1986.

Don Mathews, vice-president of the Superior Oil Company, heard my Williston basin paper in Denver and offered me the opportunity to start a geochemical group at their research center in Houston. Superior had just acquired a new kerogen maturity technique called "vitrinite reflectance" that was being used at the time only by Shell and Tenneco. One of our biggest geochemical limitations in those days was the lack of a reliable way to measure thermal maturity of organic matter independent of kerogen type. I immediately recognized the potential of this new and largely undeveloped technique, and after considerable soul searching, I reluctantly left Amoco in the fall of 1972 to begin a new adventure.

The petroleum system concept blends petroleum geology and geochemistry together in a way that can substantially increase exploration success. It is a tool that has evolved during the past 25 years and will continue to be improved in the future. This book makes our current state of knowledge available to every company involved in the search for oil and gas, and we hope many will benefit from the ideas it contains.

Leslie B. Magoon

For the editors, this book has a two-fold purpose—to describe the petroleum system and to provide a mechanism for evaluating migration from the active source rock to the trap. Wally and I developed the petroleum system for different reasons.

After graduation, I went to work for Shell Oil Company in Los Angeles as an exploration geologist with emphasis on petroleum geochemistry. Although I lacked previous experience, because I had more chemistry than most geologists I became immersed in source rock geochemistry to carry out my assignment, which was to participate in the evaluation of the offshore lease sale area in the Santa Barbara Channel. When I entered Shell, the company was taking the geochemical research work of Phillippi from the laboratory to the field. Since little published literature was available, I relied mostly on company documents and a small cadre of Shell geologists and geochemists who understood source rock geochemistry, such as John T. Smith, Adrian Maaskant, Marlan Downey, Archie Hood, and John Castaño, all of whom willingly shared their knowledge with me.

The source rock study of the Ventura basin–Santa Barbara Channel area was completed in 1968, and I was transferred to Farmington, New Mexico, then on to Denver in 1971 where I carried out similar source rock studies to support new plays in both the southern and northern Rocky Mountain states. In addition to getting well site experience, I also had the opportunity to develop a play and evaluate prospects that could be drilled. With company training classes, my experience with exploration tools and techniques, such as paleontology, wireline logs, and geophysical data, grew quickly. In 1972 while in Denver, I attended the AAPG session on "New Ideas: Origin, Migration, and Entrapment of Oil." Wally Dow presented one of two papers on source rock geochemistry of the Williston basin. Afterward, my colleagues at Shell and I commented on how similar our approaches and interpretations were for understanding the distribution of hydrocarbons in the Williston basin. At the time, I was working a little farther west in the Big Snowy trough so I could relate to their interpretation in the Williston basin. In late 1973, I was transferred to Shell Pectin and moved to Houston.

In 1974, I took a job with the USGS in Menlo Park, California, and had the opportunity to work on the Cook Inlet area in Alaska. My first assignment was to evaluate the Federal OCS of Lower Cook Inlet in preparation for an offshore lease sale. In 1977, I was assigned to work on the North Slope in the newly named National Petroleum Reserve in Alaska (NPRA) on an evaluation effort of the previously named Naval Petroleum Reserve no. 4 (NPR-4). With George Claypool, we carried out an in-depth source rock and migration study. Around 1981, my involvement in the Arctic National Wildlife Refuge (ANWR) began. During this time, I was involved in both national resource assessments and the third was being organized.

I had the privilege of participating on Leg 77 of the *Deep Sea Drilling Project* (DSDP) in the Caribbean in December 1982. Here, I was able to reflect and read a great deal about petroleum geochemistry. Because I was involved in the national resource assessments of undiscovered oil and gas and because I realized how difficult it is to incorporate geologic information into the assessment process, I felt it would be worthwhile to develop a scheme that would better serve our purposes. Because our organization was without reflection seismic data that could map potential hydrocarbon traps, we needed a method to evaluate the entire country systematically without seismic data. In addition, our geologic staff was much smaller and less focused than in industry. Obviously, a different approach than industry used was needed to get science into the assessment process.

I began by reflecting on the way evaluations were carried out while I was with Shell and the way petroleum geology and geochemistry were being presented in the literature. Through many discussions with colleagues, it became apparent that basin studies was a catch-all phrase for any type of work relating to sedimentary rocks and petroleum and that source rock and migration studies were poorly defined. In addition, mass balance calculations seemed to be the best approach to determine the upper limit of petroleum available to trap, but it was unclear which factors should be included in the mass balance equation. With the problem outlined, I presented the solution in several ways

In 1986, I circulated internally a brochure about the petroleum system and how it could be used to set up the mass balance equation. That same year, I presented a poster session at the Gordon Conference on Organic Geochemistry where Wally Dow reminded me that he had already defined such an "oil system" in 1972 in Denver and that he had published it in the AAPG Bulletin in 1974. From

1987 to 1991, I developed the petroleum system concept and presented these ideas as a poster session during the 1987 AAPG Annual meeting in Los Angeles, at the 28th International Geological Congress in Washington, D.C., during 1989, and in the 1990–1991 AAPG Distinguished Lecture tour. Wally Dow and I teamed up to co-convene the successful oral session (by the same name as this volume) for the 1991 AAPG Annual meeting in Dallas. Over this same time period, I have edited three U.S. Geological Survey Bulletins on the petroleum system. During 1992 and 1993, Wally and I have visited many oil companies to acquaint their staffs with the petroleum system concept.

The help and support of many people, those mentioned above and others, are acknowledged. Ken Bird and George Claypool have always been open and direct in their suggestions and criticisms during the development of the concept. I thank Gary Hill and Don Gautier for approving the USGS petroleum system project so that I could develop the concept. The authors and co-authors of every chapter ensured the success of this book by allowing the editors sufficient latitude to incorporate the petroleum system concept. Zenon Valin is gratefully acknowledged for his help on proofreading each chapter and with other duties as well. The editors appreciate the reviewers, Gerard Demaison, Miner Long, John T. Smith, and Peter van de Kamp, who read and made valuable suggestions that improved the volume. We thank all those geoscientists who spoke up and criticized the petroleum system concept and made it more useful. Lastly, the petroleum system concept will evolve as more case studies are published, which will undoubtedly require that the concept be continually improved.

CONTRIBUTORS

DONALD E. ANDERS, U.S. Geological Survey, Federal Center Box 25046, MS 977, Denver, Colorado 80225, U.S.A., Tel. 303 236-9381. Fax 303 236-3202.

G. BACOCCOLI, Petróleo Brasileiro S/A Petrobras Depex, Rio de Janeiro, Brazil.

S. K. BHATTACHARYA, Basin Research Division, KDMIPE, ONGC, 9 Kaulagarh Road, Dehradun 248195, India, Tel. 0135 23193, Fax 0135 25265

KEVIN T. BIDDLE, Exxon Exploration Company, P.O. Box 146, Houston, TX, U.S.A., 77001-0146, Tel. 713 973 3049, Fax 713 935 6031.

KENNETH J. BIRD, Branch of Petroleum Geology, U.S. Geological Survey, 345 Middle-field Road, MS 999, Menlo Park, CA, U.S.A., 94025, Tel. 415 354 3006, Fax 415 354 3224.

S. K. BISWAS, Director KDMIPE, Oil & Natural Gas Commission, 9 Kaulagarh Road, Dehradun 248195, India, Tel. 135 23193, Fax 135 25265.

PHILIPPE BLANC, Elf Aquitaine, CSTJF-L2109 Avenue Larribau, 64018 Pau Cedex, France, Tel. 33-59834000, Fax 33-59834369.

STEVEN P. BUCK, Mobil Exploration Norway, P.O. Box 510, 4001 Stavanger, Norway, Tel. 47-4-568294, Fax 47-4-568071.

JAIME BUITRAGO, Exxon Exploration Company, P.O. Box 4279, Houston, TX, 77210-4279, U.S.A.; Tel. 713 591 5254.

MARY ROSE CASSA, State of California Environ-mental Protection Agency, Department of Toxic Substances Control, 700 Heinz Ave., Suite 200, Berkeley, CA, 94710-2737, U.S.A., Tel. 510 540 3771, Fax 510 540 3819.

JERRY L. CLAYTON, Branch of Petroleum Geology, U.S. Geological Survey, MS 977, Federal Center Box 25046, Denver, CO 80225, U.S.A., Tel. 303 236 9379. Fax 303 236 3202.

GARY A. COLE, Badge 197340, c/o Saudi Aramco, P.O. Box 11987, Dhahran 31311, Saudi Arabia, Tel. 9663 878 1896, Fax 9663 873 7766.

JACQUES CONNAN, Elf Aquitaine, CSTJF-L2109 Avenue Larribau, 64018 Pau Cedex, France, Tel. 33 598340 00, Fax 33 59834369.

CHRIS CORNFORD, Integrated Geochem. Inter-national Ltd., Hallsannery, Bideford, Devon EX39 5HE, U.K., Tel. 0237 471749, Fax 0237 421700.

JOSEPH A. CURIALE, Unocal Inc., P.O. Box 76, Brea, CA 92621, U.S.A., Tel. 714 577 2312.

E.M. DAUKORU, Nigerian National Petroleum Corporation, Lagos, Nigeria.

W.C. DAWSON, Texaco EPTD, 3901 Briarpark, Houston, TX 77042, U.S.A., Tel. 713 954 6086, Fax 713 954 6113.

GERARD DEMAISON, 1575 Prospect Avenue, Capitola, CA 95010, U.S.A., Tel. 408 476 2903.

DAVID DEMING, School of Geology and Geophysics, University of Oklahoma, Norman, OK 73019-0628, U.S.A., Tel. 405 325 6304, Fax 405 325 3140.

WALLACE G. DOW, DGSI, 8701 New Trails Drive, The Woodlands, TX 77381, U.S.A., Tel. 713 363 2176, Fax 713 292 3528.

MARLAN W. DOWNEY, President, ARCO Inter-national Oil & Gas, 2300 West Plano Parkway, Plano, TX 75075, U.S.A., Tel. 214 754 4002, Fax 214 754 4057.

RICHARD J. DROZD, Westport Technology International, 6700 Portwest Dr., Houston, TX 77024, U.S.A., Tel. 713 560 8530, Fax 713 864 9357.

CHUKWUEMEKA M. EKWEOZOR, Petroleum Geochemistry Research Group, University of Ibadan, Ibadan, Nigeria, Tel. 234 1 400550.

TIMOTHY D. ELAM, Chevron U.S.A. Inc., 5001 California Avenue, Room C211, Bakersfield, CA 93309, U.S.A., Tel. 805 395 6330, Fax 805 395 6304.

LEWIS W. ELROD, Texaco EPTD, 3901 Briarpark, Houston, TX 77042, U.S.A., Tel. 713 954 6278, Fax 713 954 6113.

WILLIAM A. ENGLAND, BP Research Centre, Building 101.141A, Sunbury-on-Thames, Middlesex, TW16 7LN, United Kingdom, Tel. 932 762855, Fax 932 763824.

THOMAS D. FOUCH, U.S. Geological Survey, Federal Center Box 25046, MS 940, Denver, CO 80225, U.S.A., Tel. 303 236 7064, Fax 303 236 8822.

PETER GERLING, Federal Institute for Geosciences and Natural Resources (BGR), Stilleweg Z, D-3000 Hannover 51, Germany, Tel. 0511 643 2631, Fax 0511 643 2304.

BRIAN HORSFIELD, Forschungszentrum Jülich, ICG-4, Postfach 1913, W-5170 Jülich, Germany, Tel. 2461 61 3670, Fax 2461 61 2484.

BRADLEY J. HUIZINGA, ARCO International Oil & Gas Co., Plano, Texas, U.S.A., Tel. 214 754 6077, Fax 214 754 6687.

CLIFTON F. JORDAN, JR., Integrated Data Services, 6878 Cedar Lane, Bonne Terre, Missouri 63628, U.S.A., Tel. 314 431 0425, Fax 314 431 2933.

B. J. KATZ, Texaco EPTD, 3901 Briarpark, Houston, TX 77042, U.S.A., Tel. 713 954 6093, Fax 713 954 6113.

H. DOUGLAS KLEMME, RR1, Box 179B, Bondville, VT 05340, U.S.A., Tel. 802 297 1821, Fax 802 297 3221.

FRANZ KOCKEL, Federal Institute for Geosciences and Natural Resources (BGR), Stilleweg Z, D-3000 Hannover 51, Germany, Tel. 0511 643 2631, Fax 0511 643 2304.

ISTAVAN KONCZ, MOL Rt., H-8801 Nagykanizsa, P.O. Box 194, Hungary.

E.A.M. KOUTSOUKOS, Petrobras R & D Center, Petrobras/CENPES, Cidade University Quadra 7, Ilha Do Fundao 21910, Rio de Janeiro, Brazil, Tel. 21 598 6460, Fax 21 280 0226.

MICHAEL D. LEWAN, U.S. Geological Survey, Federal Center Box 25046 MS 977, Denver CO 80225, U.S.A., Tel. 303 236 9391, Fax 303 236 3202.

PAUL G. LILLIS, Branch of Petroleum Geology, U.S. Geological Survey, MS 977, Federal Center Box 25046, Denver, CO 80225, U.S.A., Tel. 303 236 9382, Fax 303 236 3202.

LESLIE B. MAGOON, Branch of Petroleum Geology, U.S. Geological Survey, 345 Middlefield Road, MS 999, Menlo Park, CA 94025, U.S.A., Tel. 415 354 3010, Fax 415 354 3224.

FERNANDO MARCANO, Maravan, S.A., Edif. Maraven, Chuao, Caracas 1060, Venezuela, Tel. 2 908 2479, Fax 2 908 3150.

RICHARD F. MAST, Branch of Resource Analysis, U.S. Geological Survey, Federal Center Box 54026, MS 937, Denver, CO 80225, U.S.A., Tel. 303 236 5330, Fax 303 776 5448.

THANE H. McCULLOH, 7136 Aberdeen, Dallas, TX 75230-5407, U.S.A., Tel. 214 951 3089.

MARCIO R. MELLO, Petrobras R & D Center, Petrobras/CENPES, Cidade University Quadra 7, Ilha Do Fundao 21910, Rio de Janeiro, Brazil, Tel. 21 598 6460, Fax 21 280 0226.

JENNIFER A. MILES, Optimisers Limited, Halfway House, Asthall Leigh Road, Fordwells, Oxon OX8 5PP, U.K.d, Tel. 0235 811237, Fax 0235 811237.

W.U. MOHRIAK, Petróleo Brasileiro S/A Petrobras Depex, Rio de Janeiro, Brazil.

DAVID G. MORSE, Environmental Quality Div., Watervliet Arsenal–PWQ, Watervliet, NY 12189, U.S.A., Tel. 518 266 5731.

VITO F. NUCCIO, Branch of Sedimentary Processes, U.S. Geological Survey, MS 939, Federal Center Box 25046, Denver, CO 80225, U.S.A., Tel. 303 236 1654, Fax 303 236 0459.

KENNETH E. PETERS, Mobil Exploration & Producing Technical Center, 3033 Irving Blvd., Dallas, TX 75247, U.S.A., Tel. 214 951 3272, Fax 214 951 2265.

JANET K. PITMAN, Branch of Sedimentary Processes, U.S. Geological Survey, MS 939, Federal Center Box 25046, Denver, CO 80225, U.S.A., Tel. 303 236 7745, Fax 303 236 0459.

MARGARET H. PYTTE, B-2224, Chevron Overseas Petroleum Inc., P.O. Box 5046, San Ramon, CA 94583-0946, USA; 6001 Bollinger Canyon Road, San Ramon, CA 94583, U.S.A., Tel. 510 842 3586, Fax 510 842 3442.

M. K. RANGARAJU, Exploration Business Group, SRBC, Oil & Natural Gas Commission, MMDA Building, N. 8, Gandhi Irvin Road, Egmorem Madras 600 008.

DUDLEY D. RICE, Branch of Petroleum Geology, U.S. Geological Survey, Federal Center Box 25046, MS 971, Denver, CO 80225, U.S.A., Tel. 303 236 5771, Fax 303 236 8822.

V.D. ROBISON, Texaco EPTD, 3901 Briarpark, Houston, TX 77042, U.S.A., Tel. 713 954 6355, Fax 713 954 6113.

JÜRGEN RULLKÖTTER, Universität Oldenburg, ICLM, P.O. Box 2503, Oldenburg D2900, Germany, Tel. 49 7983262, Fax 49 7983384.

JAMES W. SCHMOKER, Branch of Petroleum Geology, U.S. Geological Survey, MS 970, Federal Center Box 25046, Denver, CO 80225, U.S.A., Tel. 303 236 5794, Fax 303 236 8822.

JOHN T. SMITH, Shell Development Company, P.O. Box 481, Houston, TX 77001, U.S.A., Tel. 713 245 7569.

CHARLES W. SPENCER, Branch of Petroleum Geology, U.S. Geological Survey, MS 940, Federal Center Box 25046, Denver, CO 80225, U.S.A., Tel. 303 236 5761, Fax 303 236 8822.

P. SUNDARARAMAN, Chevron Petroleum Technology Company, 1300 Beach Boulevard, P.O. Box 446, La Habra, CA 90633-0446, U.S.A., Tel. 403 234 6211, Fax 310 694 7178.

SUHAS C. TALUKDAR, DGSI, 8701 New Trails Drive, The Woodlands, TX 77381, U.S.A., Tel. 713 363 2176, Fax 713 292 3528.

J. THOMAS, Basin Research Division, KDMIPE, ONGC 9, Kaulagarh Road, Dehradun 248195, India, Tel. 0135 23193, Fax 0135 25265

JACK C. THREET, Tealstone, 150 Gessner, #9D, Houston, TX 77024, U.S.A.

CARLOS M. URIEN, Consultant, Paraguay 609, Buenos Aires 1642, Argentina, Tel. 1 312 7645, Fax 1 312 7645.

ZENON C. VALIN, Branch of Petroleum Geology, U.S. Geological Survey, 345 Middlefield Road, MS 999, Menlo Park, CA 94025, U.S.A., Tel. 415 354 3012, Fax 415 354 3224.

DOUGLAS W. WAPLES, Platte River Associates, Inc., 2000 W. 120th, Suite 10, Denver, CO 80234, U.S.A., Tel. 303 469 7765, Fax 303 469 7770.

HERMANN WEHNER, Federal Institute for Geosciences and Natural Resources (BGR), Stilleweg Z, D-3000 Hannover 51, Germany, Tel. 0511 643 2631, Fax 0511 643 2304.

CHARLES WIELCHOWSKY, EXXON Exploration Company, P.O. Box 146, Houston, TX 77001-0146, U.S.A., Tel. 713 591 5407.

MICHAEL J. WHITICAR, Centre for Earth and Ocean Studies, University of Victoria, P.O. Box 1700, Victoria, B.C., V8W 2Y2, Canada, Tel. 604 721 7334, Fax 604 721 7715.

JAMES LEE WILSON, Consultant, 1316 Patio Drive, New Braunfels, TX, 78130-8505, U.S.A., Tel. 512 625 6612.

JUVENAL J. ZAMBRANO, Consultant, Du Rioja 489, San Juan, Argentina.

AAPG
wishes to thank the following for their generous contributions to

The Petroleum System—From Source to Trap

Amoco Production Company
ARCO International Oil & Gas Co.
Chevron Overseas Petroleum, Inc.
DGSI
Elf Aquitaine Production—France
Mobil Exploration Norway
Petrobrás S.A.
Shell Oil Company
Unocal

Contributions are applied against the production costs of the publication,
thus directly reducing the book's purchase price and increasing its
availability to a greater audience.

Part I

Introduction

Magoon, L. B, and W. G. Dow, eds., 1994, The petroleum
system—from source to trap: AAPG Memoir 60.

Chapter 1

The Petroleum System

Leslie B. Magoon

Branch of Petroleum Geology
U.S. Geological Survey
Menlo Park, California, U.S.A.

Wallace G. Dow

DGSI
The Woodlands, Texas, U.S.A.

Abstract

Sedimentary basins, petroleum systems, plays, and prospects can be viewed as separate levels of investigation, all of which are needed to better understand the genesis and habitat of hydrocarbons. *Sedimentary basin* investigations emphasize the stratigraphic sequence and structural style of sedimentary rocks. *Petroleum system* studies describe the genetic relationship between a pod of active source rock and the resulting oil and gas accumulations. Investigations of *plays* describe the present-day geologic similarity of a series of present-day traps, and studies of *prospects* describe the individual present-day trap. Except for the petroleum system, these terms are widely used by petroleum geologists. The procedure to identify, characterize, name, and determine its level of certainty is discussed.

A petroleum system encompasses a pod of active source rock and all related oil and gas and includes all the essential elements and processes needed for oil and gas accumulations to exist. The essential elements are the source rock, reservoir rock, seal rock, and overburden rock, and the processes include trap formation and the generation–migration–accumulation of petroleum. All essential elements must be placed in time and space such that the processes required to form a petroleum accumulation can occur.

The petroleum system has a stratigraphic, geographic, and temporal extent. Its name combines the names of the source rock and the major reservoir rock and also expresses a level of certainty—known, hypothetical, or speculative. Four figures and a table that best depict the geographic, stratigraphic, and temporal evolution of a petroleum system include a burial history chart to establish the age and critical moment of the system, a map and a cross section drawn at the critical moment, an events chart to summarize the formation of the petroleum system, and a table of related accumulations. The petroleum system can be used as an effective model to investigate discovered hydrocarbon accumulations.

INTRODUCTION

New ideas are constantly being developed and put to use in oil and gas exploration. Even more common than the development of new ideas is the revival of older concepts, which are then put to use in new ways. The concept of the petroleum system is one that many geologists are intuitively familiar with and may feel that they have been using all along. There are several reasons why we are now proposing to revive, expand, define, and formalize this concept. First, the ability to identify a petroleum system uniquely depends on geochemical techniques needed to map organic facies, to understand and map hydrocarbon shows, and to carry out petroleum–petroleum and petroleum–source rock correlations, some of which were put into widespread use

only in the past 10–15 years. Second, the petroleum system approach is a way of organizing information that uniquely lends itself to efficient investigations for purposes of exploration, resource appraisal, and research. Third, the role of petroleum system investigations in basin analysis, play analysis, and prospect appraisal has never been adequately clarified.

In addition to providing an introduction to this volume, the purposes of this paper are as follows: (1) to define, compare, and contrast the different levels of petroleum investigations; (2) to describe the history of the petroleum system model; (3) to identify, name, and determine the level of certainty of a petroleum system; (4) to describe those figures that best depict the geographic, stratigraphic, and temporal extent of a petroleum system; and (5) to describe how a petroleum system study is implemented.

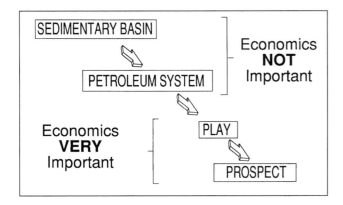

Figure 1.1. Four levels of petroleum investigation.

LEVELS OF PETROLEUM INVESTIGATIONS

Investigations of sedimentary basins, petroleum systems, plays, and prospects can be viewed as separate levels of hydrocarbon investigation, all of which are needed to better understand the genesis and habitat of hydrocarbons. Investigations of sedimentary basins describe the stratigraphic sequence and structural style of sedimentary rocks. Petroleum system studies describe the genetic relation between a particular pod of generating source rock and the resulting petroleum. Investigations of plays describe a series of present-day traps, and of prospects, an individual trap, and determine whether they have economic value and are exploitable with available technology and tools (Figure 1.1 and Table 1.1).

Economic considerations are unimportant in sedimentary basin and petroleum system investigations, but are essential in play or prospect evaluation. Whenever plays or prospects are discussed, economically producible hydrocarbons are implied or anticipated. Stated in another way, without favorable economics, a commercial petroleum play or prospect does not exist. In contrast, a sedimentary basin and a petroleum system exist regardless of economic considerations because these phenomena are based on natural processes. Proof of a sedimentary basin is sedimentary rock; proof of a petroleum system is the presence of hydrocarbons, even a puff of gas or a drop of oil (low volume but high concentration).

Historical aspects have differing importance for each level of investigation. Investigations of sedimentary basins and petroleum systems are relative to the geologic time when processes are occurring, that is, when sediments are being deposited and when hydrocarbons are migrating to their traps. In contrast, the present-day existence of a play or prospect is the important factor. There is little interest in a play or prospect that existed at the end of the Paleozoic but has since been eroded or destroyed. A prospect is conceptual because a successful prospect turns into an oil or gas field when drilled or disappears when the prospect is unsuccessful.

In addition, as the focus of investigation on hydrocarbon occurrence moves from the sedimentary basin to the prospect level, the cost of the investigation per unit surface area generally increases. Investigation of sedimentary basins requires a low-density information grid that covers a large area, such as widely spaced seismic lines, a few strategically placed exploratory wells, and small-scale geologic maps. In contrast, prospect evaluation requires a relatively high-density information grid that covers a small area, such as closely spaced seismic lines on a large-scale map. Eventually, the cost to acquire drilling rights and to drill wells must also be included in the economics of the prospect.

For the purpose of this volume, each level of petroleum investigation has its own descriptive term, such as basin *analysis* for the investigation of a sedimentary basin. Also, modeling has a similar set of terms, such as basin *modeling*. The difference between analysis and modeling is that in analysis, an existing item is dissected to determine how it functions, whereas in modeling, a hypothetical item is dissected to determine how it should function. For example, prospect modeling is used on a prospect to justify drilling, whereas a prospect analysis is carried out after drilling to understand why it lacked commercial hydrocarbons.

A historical summary of geologic models relevant to the different levels of petroleum investigations is outlined in Table 1.2. A descriptive comment for each reference is followed by eight items divided into two broad categories: geologic factors and evaluation criteria. These references discuss the eight items in the two categories at various levels of detail. Although this table is incomplete, it is shown to contrast and demonstrate the relationship of a petroleum system study with other levels of investigation.

Table 1.1. Factor Comparison in the Four Levels of Petroleum Investigation

Factor	Sedimentary Basin	Petroleum System	Play	Prospect
Investigation	Sedimentary rocks	Petroleum	Traps	Trap
Economics	None	None	Essential	Essential
Geologic time	Time of deposition	Critical moment	Present-day	Present-day
Existence	Absolute	Absolute	Conditional	Conditional
Cost	Very low	Low	High	Very high
Analysis and modeling	Basin	System	Play	Prospect

Table 1.2. Summary of Geologic Models That Incorporate Sedimentary, Structural, and Organic Geochemical Processes To Explain the Distribution of Petroleum in Nature[a]

Reference	Description	Geologic Factors[b]					Evaluation Criteria[c]		
		Geol	Gen	Mig	Acc	Tim	Nom	Crt	Cls
Sedimentary basin analysis									
Weeks (1952)	Basin development	++	−	−	−	−	−	−	++
Knebel and Rodriguez-Eraso (1956)	Oil habitat	+	−	−	++	−	−	−	++
Uspenskaya (1967)	Accumulation categories	+	−	−	++	−	−	−	++
Halbouty et al. (1970a,b)	Basin classification	++	−	−	++	−	−	−	++
Klemme (1971a,b, 1975, 1986)	Basin classification	++	−	−	−	−	−	−	++
Bally (1975)	Geodynamic scenario	++	−	−	+	−	++	−	++
Huff (1978, 1980)	Basin type	++	−	−	−	−	−	−	++
Zieglar and Spotts (1978)	Reservoir and source bed	+	+	+	++	−	−	−	−
Bally and Snelson (1980)	Realms of subsidence	++	−	−	−	−	−	−	++
Welte and Yukler (1981)	Deterministic model	+	++	++	++	+	−	−	−
Bois et al. (1982)	Geotectonic classification	++	+	−	++	+	−	−	+
Kingston et al. (1983a)	Global basin classification	++	−	−	−	++	−	−	++
Demaison (1984)	Generative basin	+	++	+	+	+	−	−	−
Ungerer et al. (1984)	Deterministic model	+	++	++	++	++	−	−	−
Tissot et al. (1987)	Kinetic model	+	++	+	++	++	−	−	−
Petroleum system study									
Dow (1974)	Oil system	+	++	+	++	+	+	−	−
Perrodon (1980, 1983a,b)	Petroleum system	++	−	−	−	−	−	−	−
Perrodon and Masse (1984)	Petroleum system	++	−	−	−	−	−	−	−
Meissner et al. (1984)	Hydrocarbon machine	+	++	+	+	+	−	−	−
Ulmishek (1986)	Independent petroliferous system	+	++	+	++	+	−	−	−
Magoon (1987, 1988, 1989a,b, 1992a,b)	Petroleum system	−	+	+	+	+	++	++	++
Demaison and Huizinga (1991)	Petroleum system	++	++	++	++	+	−	−	++
Perrodon (1992)	Petroleum system	++	+	+	+	+	−	−	++
Play evaluation									
Bois (1975)	Petroleum zone	−	+	+	++	−	−	−	−
White (1980)	Facies cycle wedges	++	+	+	++	+	−	−	−
Kingston et al. (1983b)	Hydrocarbon plays	++	−	−	−	−	−	−	++
Dolton et al. (1987)	Play	+	+	+	+	+	−	−	−
Bird (1988)	Play appraisal method	++	+	+	+	+	+	−	−
Podruski et al. (1988)	Resource endowment	++	+	+	++	+	+	−	−
White (1988)	Play map	++	+	+	+	+	+	−	−
Prospect evaluation									
Bishop et al. (1983)	Trapped hydrocarbon	−	+	+	++	−	−	−	−
Sluijk and Nederlof (1984)	Systematic appraisal	+	+	+	++	−	−	−	−
Callahan et al. (1987)	PRESTO	−	−	−	++	−	−	−	−
Mackenzie and Quigley (1988)	Geochemical appraisal	+	++	++	++	++	−	−	−

[a]++, discussed in detail; +, only mentioned; −, not mentioned.

[b]Geol = geology, including structure, stratigraphy, and geologic history of sedimentary rocks; Gen = generation, including the necessary organic matter richness, type, and maturity to generate petroleum from a source rock; Mig = migration, including the movement of oil, gas, or other hydrocarbon through the country rock; Acc = accumulation, including the presence of a reservoir rock, seal, trap, and high concentration of hydrocarbons; Tim = timing, meaning trap formation relative to hydrocarbon migration.

[c]Nom = nomenclature or name; Crt = level of certainty; Cls = classification scheme.

Sedimentary Basin Investigations

Over the last several decades, investigations of sedimentary basins have emphasized plate tectonics or structural evolution. Basin classification schemes evolved from descriptive geology (Weeks, 1952; Knebel and Rodriguez-Eraso, 1956) to genetic interpretations (Halbouty et al., 1970a,b; Klemme, 1971a,b, 1975, 1986; Bally, 1975; Huff, 1978, 1980; Bally and Snelson, 1980; Bois et al., 1982; Kingston et al., 1983a) with the advent of plate tectonics theory. With increased understanding of organic geochemistry, work on the occurrence of oil and gas also has gone from the descriptive (Weeks, 1952; Knebel and Rodriguez-Eraso, 1956) to the deterministic (Tissot, 1969; Tissot and Pelet, 1971; Zieglar and Spotts, 1978; Welte and Yukler, 1981; Demaison, 1984; Ungerer et al., 1984; Tissot et al., 1987).

Each new approach to the analysis of petroliferous sedimentary basins becomes more focused on the genesis of petroleum. Bally (1975) pointed out that sedimentary basin type does little to improve our ability to forecast the volume of petroleum from a particular type of basin. However, as more petroleum geochemistry is incorporated into the analysis of a sedimentary basin, the success ratio goes up (Demaison, 1984) and the forecast of petroleum occurrence becomes more certain (Tissot et al., 1987).

When sedimentary basins with uncomplicated geologic histories are studied, a basin analysis approach that promotes organic geochemistry works well. However, when similar studies are carried out in fold and thrust belts (such as in Wyoming, U.S.A.), in areas of complex geology (such as the Basin and Range of Nevada and Utah, U.S.A.), or in areas of uncommon heat source (such as in the mid-Pacific Ridge) (Kvenvolden et al., 1988), basin analysis techniques are more difficult to apply because the original sedimentary basin is severely deformed or incomplete. In fact, for maps that show oil and gas fields and basin outlines together, the petroleum accumulations occur within the basin outline as often as they occur on the adjacent highs or arches that are outside the basin outline (Vissides and Quirin, 1964; Wilkerson and Reed, 1982). Oil and gas fields usually (but not always) occur in sedimentary rocks, but not necessarily within the boundary of basins. Therefore, to understand the occurrence of these accumulations, at least two items need clarification. First, a working definition is needed for the sedimentary basin and what is being investigated, and second, a different type of investigation is needed that is separate from basin analysis and deals only with oil and gas.

First, the term *basin* has different implications to different specialties. A paleontologist uses the term in reference to where in the water column fossils live, such as benthic or planktonic. A petroleum geochemist visualizes the most anoxic part of a paleoocean or continental basin where organic matter accumulates and refers to that as the basin. Carbonate and siliciclastic stratigraphers refer to the sedimentary fill that was deposited sometime in the past as the basin. Structural geologists refer to the container that is created in response to a tectonic process, such as rifting, as a basin. On interpreting a seismic profile, a geophysicist refers to a thick package (measured in two-way time) of sedimentary rocks as a basin. Geologists frequently use the term geographically, that is, to name and locate a province, such as the Williston basin, which is separate from the genetic use of basin to mean any sedimentary basin. In some cases, the water column is implied as the basin, in others the sedimentary rock contents are the basin, and in yet others, the container is the basin. None of these meanings is incorrect, and specialists from different disciplines are usually aware that *basin* has more than one meaning.

For this volume, the *sedimentary basin* is a depression filled with sedimentary rocks. The depression, formed by any tectonic process, is lined by basement rock, which can be igneous, metamorphic, and/or sedimentary rock. The basin includes the rock matter, organic matter, and water deposited in this depression. In certain cases, such as with coal and some carbonate deposits, the sedimentary material is formed in situ. Basin used by itself refers to the sedimentary basin.

The term *basin* used with a proper noun refers to a petroleum province, such as the Williston basin. Sometimes basin is capitalized, such as in the Green River Basin, when it is a proper geographic name that usually refers to the present-day river drainage. A petroleum province is sometimes referred to as a petroleum basin, which is different from a petroleum system.

A sedimentary basin analysis investigates, in a myriad of ways, the formation and contents of this depression. Structural and stratigraphic studies are the most conventional way to study a sedimentary basin. More recent techniques include seismic stratigraphy and sequence stratigraphy. Sequence stratigraphy, for example, can be used to understand the distribution of sandstone and shale in a particular area as a package of related sedimentary rock. For the petroleum geologist, in certain areas the reservoir properties of this sandstone can be mapped as well as the organic facies of the shale. Sedimentary basin analysis includes all aspects of basin formation and the basin fill up to the time petroleum is generated, at which time a petroleum system investigation is required. Because petroleum is mobile, fragile, and responds to different physiochemical parameters than does basin fill, this second type of investigation, the petroleum system, is needed.

Petroleum System Investigations

Each investigative procedure has an appropriate starting point. For the prospect analysis, the starting point is the trap, for the play, a series of traps, and for a basin analysis, a tectonic setting and sedimentary rocks. Similarly, the investigative procedure for the petroleum system starts with discovered hydrocarbon accumulations, regardless of size. Because of this, shows or traces of oil and gas take on new importance. Petroleum geochemical analysis of oil and gas traces can provide critical information as to the nature of the responsible petroleum system. After the system is identified, the rest of the investigation is devoted to determining the stratigraphic, geographic, and temporal extent of the petroleum system. The bigger the petroleum system, the more likely it will have generated and accumulated commercial quantities of hydrocarbons. As indicated earlier, the petroleum system defines a level of investigation that usually lies between that of a sedimentary basin and a play.

The term *oil system* was first introduced by Dow (1974) and is based on the concept of oil–source rock correlation. The term *petroleum system* was first used by Perrodon (1980). Independently, Demaison (1984) devised the *generative basin,* Meissner et al. (1984) described their *hydrocarbon machine,* and Ulmishek (1986) identified an *independent petroliferous system.* All of these concepts are similar to Dow's oil system. Expanding upon previous work, Magoon (1987, 1988, 1989a,b) attempted to formalize criteria for identifying, naming, and determining the level of certainty for the petroleum system. This volume further refines the petroleum system concept and shows how the system is mapped and used to evaluate exploration opportunities (see later sections).

Play and Prospect Investigations

Beyond sedimentary basin and petroleum system analysis, the remaining levels of investigation are play and prospect analysis. *Prospects* were first used by exploration geologists to describe present-day structural or stratigraphic features that could be mapped and drilled. A series of related prospects is a *play.* As information about petroleum geochemistry increased, the definition of a play became broader. For example, Bois (1975) defined a *petroleum zone,* which he considered to be similar to a play (Bois et al., 1982), to include hydrocarbon mixtures of similar composition. More rigorous definitions of a play and a prospect have included a source rock as well as a migration path (White, 1980, 1988; Bishop et al., 1983; Sluijk and Nederlof, 1984; Dolton et al., 1987; Bird, 1988). The use of quantitative petroleum geochemistry (Mackenzie and Quigley, 1988) with play and prospect evaluation provides important volumetric information for economic analysis.

Plays and prospects are defined more traditionally in this volume, that is, to include present-day exploration potential for undiscovered commercial oil and gas accumulations (Table 1.1). The *play* is one or more prospects, and a *prospect* is a potential trap that must be evaluated to see if it contains commercial quantities of hydrocarbons. The presence of reservoir rock, seal rock, trap volume, hydrocarbon charge, and timing are usually involved in this evaluation. For example, if the reservoir rock in the play is eolian sandstone, then the distribution and quality of this sandstone is mapped from outcrop and well control so that it can be projected into the play area using seismic information. The probability that this eolian sandstone occurs in the play area can be evaluated in any aspect, e.g., thickness. Regardless of whether this sandstone is penetrated when the prospect is drilled, the existence of this eolian sandstone outside the play area is still valid. In the same way, already discovered oil and gas fields as well as other noncommercial quantities of hydrocarbons that are genetically related can be mapped as a petroleum system, which can then be projected into the play area as hydrocarbon charge. This hydrocarbon charge can then be evaluated with respect to the play or prospect.

PETROLEUM SYSTEM HISTORY

Dow's Oil System

The concept of an oil system was presented in 1972 at the AAPG annual meeting in Denver (Dow, 1972) and was later published (Dow, 1974). The oil system, as Dow (1974, p. 1254) presented it, was based on oil–oil and oil–source rock correlations

> to develop an understanding of the distribution of the three major oil types in the Williston basin . . ., and where each type is most likely to be found in the future. The focus of the paper is on geology and interpretation of geochemical data, not on the presentation of new geochemical data.

Dow (1974, p. 1254–1255) goes on to state that because the source rocks are isolated by evaporites,

> The distribution of oil in the basin therefore can be described in terms of three major source–reservoir oil systems. Each system contains a source rock and a group of reservoir rocks and is isolated from other oil systems by an evaporite seal.

He then names the oil systems. In Dow's (1974, p. 1261) summary section he states,

> The model developed in the Williston basin depends on the ability to (1) separate oils into genetic types, (2) relate each type to a specific source sequence, (3) understand the quantity of organic matter and the degree of thermal maturation required for generation and expulsion of oil in commercial quantities, and (4) map the distribution of both vertical and horizontal migration pathways and seals. The most likely distribution of each oil type in the subsurface can be mapped with the foregoing approach. Plays then can be made in these high-grade areas where the chance of finding oil is greatest.

Dow's (1974) paper is important for the following reasons: (1) oil–source rock correlation was the keystone to identifying the system; (2) the name included the source and reservoir rock separated by a hyphen; (3) the term *play* was used as a distinct concept; (4) in each oil system description, a mass balance comparison was carried out on the theoretical amount of oil generated and reserves (the calculations were left out of the paper); (5) the use of the term *oil system* excluded gas and condensate; and (6) the criteria for applying this concept beyond the Williston basin was only implied, not stated.

Perrodon's Petroleum System

Perrodon (1980, 1983a,b) and Perrodon and Masse (1984) first used the term *petroleum system*. Since Perrodon (1980, 1983b) are in French, and the same material is covered in a revised and updated version (Perrodon, 1983a) and in Perrodon and Masse (1984), which are in English, we quote these latter publications.

Perrodon (1983a, p. 187) states that

The geologic criteria governing the distribution of pools, and in particular, the combined presence of source rocks, reservoirs and seals, generally exhibit a certain geographic extension which is reflected by the formation of a family of pools, or even better, a petroleum system, a structured set of natural elements of the same species or having the same function. From the geographic standpoint, and according to their dimensions and complexity, these sets are reflected by the existence of a petroleum zone or province.

In Perrodon and Masse (1984), *petroleum system* is used in the title and they define it (p. 5) as follows:

Therefore, a petroleum province can be considered as the final result of an organized set of geologic events (in space and in time) that can be called a petroleum system. In such a system, the sequence of subsidence movements and associated flows is just as decisive as lithologic and geometric factors in the formation of a group of pools. This concept of the succession of geodynamics and sedimentary processes which affect petroleum potential is developed, and specific examples of petroleum systems from the North Sea, the Arabian Platform and the Congo Basin are presented.

Concerning basin geodynamics, Perrodon and Masse (p. 5) go on to say that

In a sedimentary basin it is not only the source rocks, reservoirs and seals, but the whole sedimentary column which plays an active and decisive role in the genesis, entrapment, and conservation of hydrocarbons. The formation of a petroleum system is the result of a succession of physical and chemical transformations (diagenesis, tectonic deformations, compaction, etc.) which affect these sediments and closely control the genesis, concentration and dispersion of hydrocarbons. Important factors which control these transformations and even initiate them are the movements of uplift and subsidence. We will stress the conditions which affect the genesis and growth of these movements, and note that together they conform to a small number of basic mechanisms: tectonics, heat flow and gravity.

Their paper then discusses thermotectonic areas, subsidence, sedimentation rates, and sedimentary and climatic factors. With regards to petroleum systems and provinces, Perrodon and Masse (1984, p. 18) state the following:

The petroleum potential of a basin (the formation and preservation of hydrocarbon pools) is the result of the organization of the sedimentary volume and of its evolution in time. Furthermore, special attention must be paid to the characteristics and relationships of the flows passing through the sedimentary space: geothermal flows rising from the mantle and the crust, and flows of the different fluids circulating due to differences in pressure and available pathways. In the final analysis, all these transfers of energy and fluids themselves appear to be controlled by the geodynamics of the basin, i.e., by the characteristics of subsidence, whose mechanisms are reflected by different types of petroleum systems. Some examples follow.

These examples include rift basins, platform basins, passive margin basins, and pull-apart basins.

Demaison's Generative Basin

In Demaison (1984, p. 1), the term *generative basin* is defined as follows:

Areas underlain by mature source rocks are called "petroleum generative depressions" or "hydrocarbon kitchens." A "generative basin" is defined as a sedimentary basin that contains one or more petroleum generative depressions. Mapping generative depressions is achieved by integrating geochemical data relevant to maturation and organic facies with structural and stratigraphic information derived from seismic and deep wells.

Demaison (1984, p. 1) describes the success ratios in exploration of petroleum provinces:

Locales of high success ratios in finding petroleum are called "areas of high potential," "plays," or "petroleum zones." A rapid worldwide review of 12 sedimentary basins, described in order of geotectonic style, reveals the following regularities:
   1. The zones of concentrated petroleum occurrence ("areas of high potential") and high success ratios are genetically related to oil generative depressions or basins. These depressions are mappable by integrated methods (geology, geophysics, and geochemistry).
   2. The largest petroleum accumulations tend to be located close to the center of the generative basins or on structurally high trends neighboring deep generative depressions.
   3. Migration distances commonly range in tens rather than hundreds of miles and are limited by the drainage areas of individual structures. Thus the outlines of generative depressions commonly include most of the producible hydrocarbon accumulations and the largest fields. Unusual cases of long distance migration are documented on certain foreland basin plates where stratigraphy and structure permitted uninterrupted updip movement of oil.
   These three regularities provide powerful analogs for forecasting areas of high petroleum potential in undrilled or sparsely drilled basins.

Demaison (1984, p. 3) continues his discussion of the generative basin concept by stating that

Recognition of generative depressions is achieved by overlaying organic facies maps and maturation maps of each key petroleum source horizon. Maturation maps are compiled from seismic depth maps, near the potential source horizons, and from maturation gradients derived from well data and calibrated time–temperature models. . . . . Organic facies maps reflect the stratigraphic distribution of organic matter types within a given source rock unit. They are compiled by integrating kerogen type data in the known paleographic and paleooceanographic context.
   The geochemical approach, in prospect appraisal, begins by investigating whether mature source beds are present in the drainage area of a trap. A further step consists of mapping areas of mature source beds and calculating both mature source rock volumes and petroleum yield. Lastly, migration pathways can be modeled between the mature source-rocks and the trap. This type of geologic exercise permits a ranking of prospects by the criterion of degree-of-access to mature source rocks.
   The geochemical approach to basin evaluation consists of mapping oil generative depressions or basins and erecting a matrix of drilling success ratios, volumes of discovered hydrocarbons and "kitchen" potential. When these correlations have been established they may be used for comparative purposes and for future evaluation of geologic risk. Application of the "generative basin concept," leading to recognition and prediction of areas of high potential, is the object of this contribution.

Demaison (1984) makes the following points. First, the

accumulated hydrocarbons whose provenance was the mature source rock is shown to apply for generative basins worldwide. Second, risk can be reduced by staying close to the mature source rock where the drilling success ratio is highest. Three, unlike the oil system, the generative basin can have one or more petroleum generating depressions as well as one or more source rocks.

Meissner's Hydrocarbon Machine

In Meissner et al. (1984, p. 1), the term *hydrocarbon machine* is defined as follows:

> Sequences which contain all of the elements involved in the process of hydrocarbon generation from source rock to consequent migration and accumulation constitute what may be termed natural geologic hydrocarbon machines.

They go on to say (1984, p. 1) that

> Use of this conceptual framework will allow the prediction of generation/migration/accumulation *cells* or *hydrocarbon machines* operative in certain portions of the stratigraphic section. This predictive ability, when used in conjunction with regional source rock distribution maps, will explain the distribution of hydrocarbon accumulations already found and lead to the further delineation of prospective areas.

Meissner et al. (1984, p. 1–2) expand on their definition of hydrocarbon machine in the explanation of a figure:

> The starting point of the diagram concerns the existence of a source rock from which the hydrocarbons originate, the factors controlling its deposition and composition, and the types of hydrocarbons it may generate under conditions of thermal maturity. The following parts of the diagram concern the controls that time, stratigraphy, structure, and fluid dynamics exert on the processes of hydrocarbon migration and accumulation.
> All of the factors which affect the processes of hydrocarbon generation, migration, and accumulation constitute elements of a total system which may be described as a *machine*. These elements are placed in their interdependent cause-and-effect context in the schematic diagram of Figure 2. The illustration of a plumbing system involving a typical hydrocarbon machine depicts the movement of fluids outward from their site of generation within an area of thermal maturity to carrier/reservoir beds in which they migrate and to sites of accumulation in traps.

Figure 2 of Meissner et al. (1984, p. 3) shows a diagram of the hydrocarbon machine, which is captioned as follows:

> Diagrammatic model of a hydrocarbon machine showing geometric arrangement of essential elements and fluid migration patterns characterizing the internal "plumbing" system. The function of such a machine is to turn organic matter in a source rock (raw material) into a hydrocarbon accumulation (finished product).

Meissner et al. (1984) make the following points. First, the "generation/migration/accumulation *cells* or *hydrocarbon machines*" are very similar to the oil systems of Dow (1974) (although they fail to reference his work) and to the petroleum system of Perrodon (1980, 1983a,b) and Perrodon and Masse (1984). Second, the processes of

hydrocarbon generation, migration, and accumulation are distinguished from essential elements and are expressed as a single process. Last, the essential elements are shown in their figure 2 to be the source rock, reservoir rock, seal rock, and trap.

Ulmishek's Independent Petroliferous System

In Ulmishek (1986), the term *independent petroliferous system (IPS)* was used to describe the "stratigraphic aspects of petroleum resource assessment." In the abstract (p. 59), they state that IPS is

> . . . understood here as a body of rocks separated from surrounding rocks by regional barriers to lateral and vertical migration of fluids, including oil and gas. Stratigraphically, an IPS is essentially homogeneous. It includes source rocks, reservoir rocks, traps, and a regional seal, and thus, it is a suitable unit for comparative analysis of the factors and petroleum genetic studies. For oil and gas resource assessment in poorly known regions, an IPS has certain advantages over a basin or play as an assessment unit. The concept of an IPS can also be used in statistical methods of resource appraisal and can increase reliability of these results.

In expanding his definition, Ulmishek (1986, p. 61–62) goes on to say that

> It is evident that three of the four major factors controlling a region's petroleum richness (source, reservoir, and seal) contain much more stratigraphic than tectonic information. The fourth, the trap factor, tends to reflect both stratigraphy and tectonics depending on the type of trap. It seems reasonable, therefore, that a unit chosen for comparative assessment of petroleum resources should be more related to the stratigraphy of an area than to the tectonics. The analysis of factors of richness in such a unit will be an easier task than the analysis of these factors in any tectonic unit that is "heterogeneous" from a stratigraphic point of view. Because the four listed factors reflect the conditions for successive processes of generation, accumulation, and preservation of oil and gas, such a unit must meet two major requirements: (1) it must be a confined system in which these processes take place independently from surrounding rocks, and (2) it must be the simplest of these systems, to provide maximum internal geologic uniformity and to permit sufficient depth of analysis. Such an assessment unit is here called an independent petroliferous system (IPS), which is defined as a continuous body of rocks separated from surrounding rocks by regional barriers to lateral and vertical migration of liquids and gases (including hydrocarbons) and within which the processes of generation, accumulation, and preservation of oil and gas are essentially independent from those occurring in surrounding rocks.

At the end of this same section, he (1986, p. 62) states the following:

> The most important task in developing the proposed approach is the determination, for analog purposes, of IPSs in well-explored basins. At present, 40–50 well-explored basins worldwide certainly contain not less than 150–200 IPSs. These could provide an excellent file of analogs with most combinations of factor types. Volumetric yields of the well-studied IPSs could serve as a basis for the evaluation of undiscovered resources of the forecast IPSs.

In a discussion of an IPS as an assessment unit, Ulmishek (1986, p. 62) states that

> An IPS is purely an assessment unit; its application for other purposes is limited. As an assessment unit, however, it has significant advantages over two other such units that are widely used in practice: the play, or petroleum zone, and the basin.

He later observes (1986, figure 3D, p. 66) that when an analysis of drilling statistics is carried out by IPS, rather than by drilling depth in a basin, it becomes clear that poorly explored IPSs have potential for undiscovered commerical oil and gas accumulations.

Ulmishek's (1986) paper either states or implies several points. (1) The IPS is similar to the oil system of Dow (1974) and the hydrocarbon machine of Meissner et al. (1984) (although neither is referenced). (2) The major *factors* (source rock, trap, reservoir rock, and seal) are the same as the essential elements of Meissner et al. (1984). (3) All major factors are stratigraphic in nature except for trap, which is mainly structural. (4) Major factors are distinguished from *processes* (generation, accumulation, and preservation) when referring to the assessment unit (IPS). The process of migration is absent, and preservation is an addition when compared to Meissner et al. (1984). (5) The IPS is only considered an assessment unit. (6) The paper points to "two other such units that are widely used in practice: the play, or petroleum zone, and the basin." (7) Breaking out the drilling statistics so that new IPSs are more clearly identified is a sage observation.

Magoon's Petroleum System

Magoon (1987) first used the term *elements* to refer to source rock, migration path, reservoir rock, seal, and trap and explains that the elements "must be placed in time and space such that a petroleum deposit can occur." To identify a petroleum system, Magoon (1987) relied on oil–source rock correlation. The name of the petroleum system included the name of the source rock and major reservoir rock followed by the level of certainty. He classified the systems using certain criteria.

In Magoon (1988, table 1, p. 3), an attempt was made to put the petroleum system into historical perspective using a table that summarized the contribution of Dow (1974), Bois (1975), White (1980), Bois et al. (1982), Demaison (1984), Meissner et al. (1984), Ulmishek (1986), and Magoon (1987). The table specified the geologic parameters and evaluation criteria discussed by each author. Magoon (1988, p. 2) states that

> The petroleum system emphasizes the genetic relation between a particular source rock and the resulting petroleum accumulation; basin studies emphasize structural depressions and the included sedimentary rocks regardless of the relation to any petroleum deposits; and the play or prospect approach emphasizes whether the present-day trap is detectable with available technology or tools.

The most recent definition of a petroleum system and classification scheme can be found in Magoon (1989a). The definition incorporates previous contributions and adds new words where necessary to clarify a petroleum system. The levels of petroleum investigation (Magoon, 1989b) are introduced to distinguish the petroleum system from the sedimentary basin, play, and prospect.

Magoon and Dow's Petroleum System

The petroleum system is predicated on the synthesis of previous work (Table 1.2). The terms *sedimentary basin, play,* and *prospect* have been informally used by petroleum geologists prior to the advent of modern-day organic geochemistry to explain the habitat of hydrocarbons. Early work in organic geochemistry by Trask and Wu (1930), Triebs (1936), Hunt and Jamieson (1956), and Phillipi (1957) provided ways to measure and map source rocks and associated products. To understand a petroleum system, a working knowledge of petroleum geochemistry is essential.

Dow (1974) distinguished a play from the oil system based on geochemistry. Ulmishek (1986) recognized the (independent) petroliferous system as a separate unit distinct from the sedimentary basin and play. Magoon (1989b) identified the levels of petroleum investigation as basin studies, petroleum systems, plays, and prospects. The present volume refers to the sedimentary basin, petroleum system, prospect, and play.

The term *petroleum system* was chosen because *petroleum* includes all forms of hydrocarbons (solid, liquid, or gaseous) (Levorsen, 1967) and *system* accounts for the interdependence of the essential elements (source rock, reservoir rock, seal rock, and overburden rock) and processes (trap formation and generation–migration–accumulation of petroleum). The term has been used before by Perrodon (1980, 1983a,b) and Perrodon and Masse (1984) in a way that is consistent with our use. The term *essential elements* originates from Meissner et al. (1984) and Ulmishek (1986), and *processes* are formalized in Meissner et al. (1984) and Ulmishek (1986).

The uniqueness of a petroleum system is based on petroleum–source rock correlation and is named according to Dow (1974), whereas the *level of certainty* is according to Magoon (1987, 1988, 1989a,b). The geographic and stratigraphic distribution as well as the preservation time of the petroleum system is specified by Magoon (1988). The definition of the petroleum system used in this volume is a refinement of previous work.

PETROLEUM SYSTEM DEFINITIONS AND CHARACTERISTICS

A *petroleum system* is defined here as a natural system that encompasses a pod of active source rock and all related oil and gas and which includes all the geologic elements and processes that are essential if a hydrocarbon accumulation is to exist. This once-active source rock may now be inactive or spent (depleted). *Petroleum* here includes high concentrations of (1) thermal or biogenic gas found in conventional reservoirs or in gas hydrate, tight reservoirs, fractured shale, and coal; or (2) condensates, crude oils, and asphalts found in nature.

Table 1.3. Oil and Gas Fields in the Fictitious Deer–Boar(.) Petroleum System, or the Accumulations Related to One Pod of Active Source Rock

Field Name	Discovery Date	Reservoir Rock	API gravity (°API)	Cumulative Oil Production (million bbl)	Remaining Reserves (million bbl)
Big Oil	1954	Boar Ss	32	310	90
Raven	1956	Boar Ss	31	120	12
Owens	1959	Boar Ss	33	110	19
Just	1966	Boar Ss	34	160	36
Hardy	1989	Boar Ss	29	85	89
Lucky	1990	Boar Ss	15	5	70
Marginal	1990	Boar Ss	18	12	65
Teapot	1992	Boar Ss	21	9	34

The term *system* describes the interdependent elements and processes that form the functional unit that creates hydrocarbon accumulations. The *essential elements* include a petroleum source rock, reservoir rock, seal rock, and overburden rock, and the *processes* are trap formation and the generation–migration–accumulation of petroleum. These essential elements and processes must occur in time and space so that organic matter included in a source rock can be converted to a petroleum accumulation. A petroleum system exists wherever the essential elements and processes occur.

Characteristics and Limits

The geographic, stratigraphic, and temporal extent of the petroleum system is specific and is best depicted using a table (Table 1.3) and the following four figures (Figures 1.2–1.5): (1) a burial history chart depicting the critical moment, age, and essential elements at a specified location; (2) a map and (3) a cross section drawn at the critical moment depicting the spatial relationship of the essential elements; and (4) a petroleum system events chart showing the temporal relationship of the essential elements and processes and the preservation time and critical moment for the system. The table lists all the oil and gas fields in the petroleum system.

The *critical moment* is that point in time selected by the investigator that best depicts the generation–migration–accumulation of most hydrocarbons in a petroleum system. A map or cross section drawn at the critical moment best shows the geographic and stratigraphic extent of the system. If properly constructed, the burial history chart shows that time when most of the petroleum in the system is generated and accumulating in its primary trap. For biogenic gas, the critical moment is related to low temperatures (Whiticar, Chapter 16, this volume). Geologically, generation, migration, and accumulation of petroleum at one location usually occur over a short time span (England, Chapter 12, this volume). When included with the burial history curve, the essential elements show the function of each rock unit and lithology in the petroleum system. In the example of Figure 1.2 (using fictitious rock units), the so-called Deer Shale is the source rock, the Boar Sandstone is the

reservoir rock, the George Shale is the seal rock, and all the rock units above the Deer Shale comprise the overburden rock. The burial history chart is located where the overburden rock is thickest and indicates that the source rock started through the oil window 260 Ma in Permian time (time scale from Palmer, 1983) and was at its maximum burial depth 255 Ma. The critical moment is 250 Ma, and the time of generation, migration, and accumulation ranges from 260 to 240 Ma, which is also the age of the petroleum system.

The *geographic extent* of the petroleum system at the critical moment is defined by a line that circumscribes the pod of active source rock and includes all the discovered petroleum shows, seeps, and accumulations that originated from that pod. A plan map, drawn at the end of Paleozoic time in our example, includes a line that circumscribes the pod of active source rock and all related discovered hydrocarbons. This map best depicts the geographic extent or known extent of the petroleum system (Figure 1.3)

Stratigraphically, the petroleum system includes the following rock units or essential elements within the geographic extent: a petroleum source rock, reservoir rock, seal rock, and overburden rock at the critical moment. The functions of the first three rock units are obvious. However, the function of the overburden rock is more subtle because, in addition to providing the overburden necessary to thermally mature the source rock, it can also have considerable impact on the geometry of the underlying migration path and trap. The cross section of Figure 1.4, drawn to represent the end of the Paleozoic (250 Ma), shows the geometry of the essential elements at the time of hydrocarbon accumulation and best depicts the *stratigraphic extent* of the system.

The petroleum system *events chart* shows eight different events (Figure 1.5). The top four events record the time of deposition from stratigraphic studies of the essential elements, and the next two events record the time the petroleum system processes took place. The formation of traps is investigated using geophysical data and structural geologic analysis. The generation–migration–accumulation of hydrocarbons, or age of the petroleum system, is based on stratigraphic and petroleum geochemical studies and on the burial history

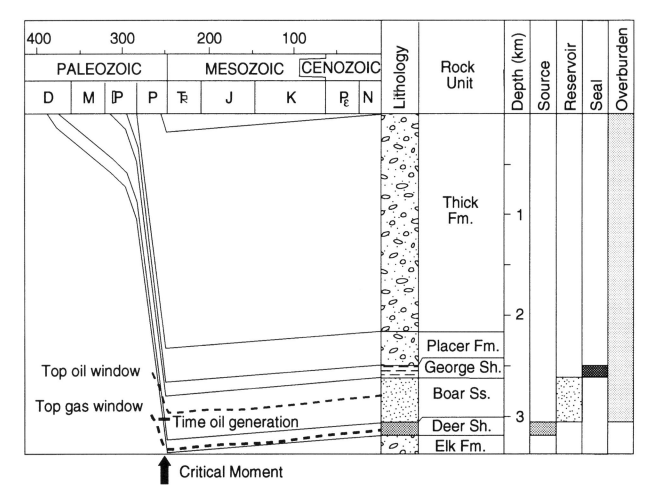

Figure 1.2. Burial history chart showing the critical moment (250 Ma) and the time of oil generation (260–240 Ma) for the fictitious Deer–Boar(.) petroleum system. This information is used on the events chart (Figure 1.5). Neogene (N) includes the Quaternary here. All rock unit names used here are fictitious. Location used for burial history chart is shown on Figures 1.3 and 1.4. (Time scale from Palmer, 1983.)

chart. These two processes are followed by the preservation time, which takes place after the generation–migration–accumulation of hydrocarbons occur, and is the time when hydrocarbons within that petroleum system are preserved, modified, or destroyed. When the generation–migration–accumulation of the petroleum system extends to the present day, there is no preservation time, and it would be expected that most of the petroleum is preserved and that comparatively little has been biodegraded or destroyed. The last event is the critical moment as determined by the investigator from the burial history chart, and it shows the time represented on the map and cross section.

Table 1.3 shows all the discovered accumulations included in the petroleum system, provides a basis for mass balance equations, and is a basis for ranking a system.

Level of Certainty

A petroleum system can be identified at three levels of certainty: known, hypothetical, or speculative. The level of certainty indicates the confidence for which a particular pod of active source rock has generated the hydrocarbons in an accumulation. In a *known* petroleum system, a good geochemical match exists between the active source rock and the oil or gas accumulations. In a *hypothetical* petroleum system, geochemical information identifies a source rock, but no geochemical match exists between the source rock and the petroleum accumulation. In a *speculative* petroleum system, the existence of either a source rock or petroleum is postulated entirely on the basis of geologic or geophysical evidence. At the end of the system's name, the level of certainty is indicated by (!) for known, (.) for hypothetical, and (?) for speculative (Table 1.4).

Petroleum System Name

The name of the petroleum system includes the source rock, followed by the name of the major reservoir rock, and then the symbol expressing the level of certainty. For example, the Deer–Boar(.) is a hypothetical petroleum system consisting of the Devonian Deer Shale as the oil

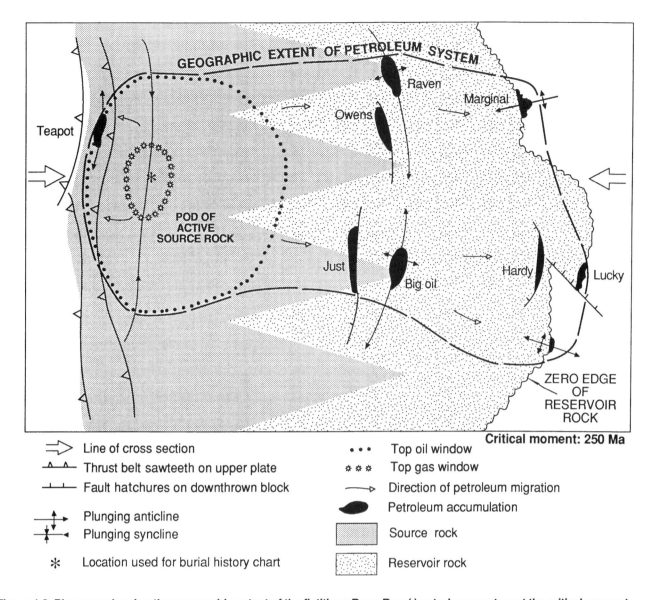

Figure 1.3. Plan map showing the geographic extent of the fictitious Deer–Boar(.) petroleum system at the critical moment (250 Ma). Thermally immature source rock is outside the oil window. The pod of active source rock lies within the oil and gas windows. (Present-day source rock maps and hydrocarbon shows are shown on Figures 5.12 and 5.13, Peters and Cassa, Chapter 5, this volume.)

source rock and the Boar Sandstone as the major reservoir rock. The major reservoir rock contains the largest volume of hydrocarbons in the petroleum system (see, e.g., La Luna–Misoa(!) petroleum system in Talukdar and Marcano, Chapter 29, this volume).

Discussion

Because our description here of a petroleum system attempts to incorporate previous work, it is written in a way that gives some words specific meanings, so that all petroleum types and occurrences are included in the definition. These specific meanings are purposely chosen to address the so-called exceptions in petroleum occurrence, such as biogenic gas and immature oil. The reader is referred to other chapters in this volume and to the glossary for clarification of terms. Here, terms important to the petroleum system definition are discussed.

Pod of Active Source Rock

A pod of active source rock indicates that a contiguous volume of organic matter is creating petroleum, either through biological activity or temperature, at a specified time. The volume or pod of active source rock is determined by mapping the organic facies (quantity, quality, and thermal maturity) considered to be the presently active, inactive, or spent source rock using organic geochemical data displayed as geochemical logs (Peters and Cassa, Chapter 5, this volume). Organic matter generates petroleum either biologically (Whiticar, Chapter 16, this volume) or thermally (Lewan, Chapter 11). From the time a petroleum phase is created, a

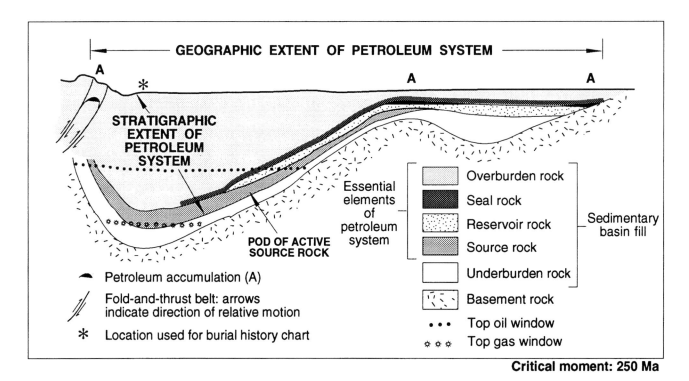

Figure 1.4. Geologic cross section showing the stratigraphic extent of the fictitious Deer–Boar(.) petroleum system at the critical moment (250 Ma). Thermally immature source rock lies updip of the oil window. The pod of active source rock is downdip of the oil window. (The present-day cross section is shown in Figure 5.12F, Peters and Cassa, Chapter 5, this volume.)

petroleum system exists. A source rock is active when it is generating this petroleum, whereas an inactive or spent source rock was at some time in the past an active source rock. For example, the Deer Shale source rock was an active source rock in Late Paleozoic time, but is presently an inactive source rock. The *pod of active source* rock is that contiguous volume of source rock that is generating gas biologically or oil and gas thermally. The active time can be present day or any time in the past.

Petroleum Synonyms

As used in this volume, the terms *petroleum, hydrocarbons*, and *oil and gas* are synonyms. Petroleum originally referred to crude oil, but its definition was broadened by Levorsen (1967) to include all naturally occurring hydrocarbons, whether gaseous, liquid, or solid. Geochemically, hydrocarbon compounds are those containing only hydrogen and carbon, such as aromatic or saturated hydrocarbons. Hydrocarbon compounds are in contrast to nonhydrocarbon compounds, or those containing nitrogen, sulfur, and oxygen. Hydrocarbon and nonhydrocarbon compounds are both found in crude oil and natural gas, but hydrocarbon compounds usually predominate. Over the past 10–15 years, whenever the term *hydrocarbons* has been used without modifiers, it is usually meant to be synonymous with petroleum. When *oil and gas* are used together as a term, it collectively refers to crude oil and natural gas in any proportion. *Condensate* is in a gas phase in the accumulation and in a liquid phase at the surface, but either way it is consid-

ered petroleum, as are solid petroleum materials such as natural bitumen, natural asphalt, and bituminous sands.

Major and Minor Reservoir Rocks

Major and minor reservoir rocks are determined from the percentage of in-place petroleum that originated from a particular pod of active source rock. If the volume of in-place petroleum is unavailable, recoverable hydrocarbons are the next best volume. All the discovered oil and gas fields included in a petroleum system are listed and the original in-place (recoverable) hydrocarbons are determined by stratigraphic interval. The volumes of in-place hydrocarbons for each stratigraphic interval are added up, and the percentage for each is determined. Reservoir rocks that contain minor amounts of in-place hydrocarbons are the minor reservoir rocks. Usually one stratigraphic interval contains most of the in-place hydrocarbons, so this interval is the major reservoir rock. The name of this unit is the one used in the second part of the petroleum system name.

The major reservoir rock indicates the optimum migration path for the petroleum between the pod of active source rock and the traps that include the major reservoir rock. The minor reservoir rock indicates the least effective migration path or one that should be studied for overlooked prospects. Major and minor reservoir rocks should be included on the events chart.

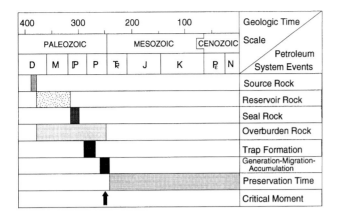

Figure 1.5. The events chart showing the relationship between the essential elements and processes as well as the preservation time and critical moment for the fictitious Deer–Boar(.) petroleum system. Neogene (N) includes the Quaternary here. (Time scale from Palmer, 1983.)

Evolution of a Petroleum System

The time of hydrocarbon generation for a petroleum system can span considerable time and cover a large area. The time span over which petroleum generation occurs can be determined for a series of locations to show how the petroleum system evolves in time and space. At given time increments within this time span, maps and cross sections can be drawn to show the kinematic evolution of the petroleum system. Knowing the age of various horizons within the overburden rock is the key to determining when and where a source rock first starts generating petroleum and when and where it finishes generating petroleum.

For example, for a petroleum system whose overburden rock has been deposited over a broad area (such as a prograding deltaic sequence), the time span over which petroleum generation–migration–accumulation occurs is quite large. If this deltaic sequence, which is the overburden rock, has prograded over a 50-m.y. period from west to east, then the underlying source rock in this petroleum system will generate petroleum first on the west and last on the east. The geologist knows that it is not always practical to show from start to finish the kinematic development of this petroleum system in 5-m.y. increments, as it would require up to 11 maps and cross sections. However, one map and cross section can be drawn to represent the time when the west end of the cross section shows the source rock at maximum burial depth, and an other map and cross section can be drawn to represent the time when the east end of the cross section shows the source rock at maximum burial depth. If more detail is required to better understand how the system evolved, then additional maps and cross sections can be drawn. The critical moment is defined as a single moment because, in most instances, the exploration geologist has only enough time to construct and present one map and cross section to depict a petroleum system.

Table 1.4. Definitions of Levels of Certainty

Level of Certainty	Symbol	Criteria
Known	(!)	Oil–source rock or gas–source rock correlation
Hypothetical	(.)	In absence of petroleum–source rock correlation, geochemical evidence indicates the origin of the oil and gas
Speculative	(?)	Geologic or geophysical evidence

Preservation Time

The preservation time of a petroleum system starts after oil and gas generation, migration, and accumulation processes are complete. Processes that occur during the preservation time are remigration, physical or biological degradation, and/or complete destruction of the hydrocarbons (Blanc and Connan, Chapter 14, this volume). During the preservation time, remigrated petroleum can accumulate in traps formed after hydrocarbon generation has ceased in the petroleum system. If insignificant tectonic activity occurs during the preservation time, accumulations will remain in their original position. Remigration occurs during the preservation time only if folding, faulting, uplift, or erosion occurs. If all accumulations and essential elements are destroyed during the preservation time, then the evidence that a petroleum system existed is removed. An actively forming or just completed petroleum system is without a preservation time.

Comparison with Sedimentary Basin and Play

Aspects of the petroleum system can also be compared with the sedimentary basin and the play. If the critical moment of 250 Ma used in our example (Figure 1.4) was instead present-day, then two sedimentary basins, three plays, and one petroleum system would be shown on the map and cross section. The interface between the sedimentary rock and the basement rock on the cross section would show two lenticular bodies of sedimentary rock or two basins. The three plays that would be shown on the map and cross section are (1) a series of suspected traps along an anticlinal trend, (2) a series of suspected traps along a stratigraphic pinch-out trend, or (3) suspected traps within a stratigraphic interval. However, if all these accumulations were discovered, there would be only one petroleum system on the cross section because one pod of active source rock generated all the hydrocarbons in the discovered accumulations.

EXAMPLES OF PETROLEUM SYSTEMS

One way to better understand what is meant by a petroleum system is to categorize or classify as many systems as possible. Magoon (1989b) classified petroleum systems in the United States based on the complexity of the overburden rock (purebred versus hybrid), reservoir lithology (siliciclastic versus carbonate), and kerogen type (type I, II, and III kerogen). Later, these same petroleum systems were classified according to the age of their source rock (Magoon, 1992b). Demaison and Huizinga (1991; Chapter 4, this volume) classified 38 petroleum systems found throughout the world by hydrocarbon charge (supercharged, normally charged, and undercharged), migration drainage style (vertically versus laterally drained), and entrapment style (high versus low impedance).

Another way to classify petroleum systems is to designate them as either typical or atypical. A *typical* petroleum system is an oil system whose source rock is thermally matured during deep burial by the overburden rock. Most the case studies in this volume are of typical petroleum systems. An *atypical* petroleum system is one in which hydrocarbons were generated in other ways. For example, a petroleum system can occur when an immature source rock within a thin sequence of sedimentary rocks that overlays continental crust is intruded by a dike (Figure 1.6). The dike's heat thermally matures the source rock and generates oil that seeps into the adjacent sedimentary rock and river valley. Another example is the oil generated from the heat related to the ridge vent in the Escanaba trough (Kvenvolden et al., 1988). Yet another example is biogenic gas generated at a shallow depth through biological activity (Whiticar, Chapter 16, this volume), such as the gas in the shallow Tertiary sedimentary rock in the Cook Inlet, Alaska (Claypool et. al, 1980; Chapter 22, this volume).

Typical petroleum systems are shown on Figures 1.7 and 1.8 using maps and cross sections that are each drawn at the critical moment. Notice that the source rock in each case has been deposited in a much larger sedimentary basin than the overburden rock. Although all the essential elements and a trap are included in Figure 1.7A, a petroleum system is absent because hydrocarbons have not been generated. Given the same situation in Figure 1.7B but with a source rock now generating hydrocarbons, you have one petroleum system (Cornford, Chapter 33, this volume). If two or more source rocks are superimposed on one another and are both thermally mature by the same overburden rock within the same basin fill (Figure 1.7C), then more than one petroleum system occurs in the same basin fill (Dow, 1972; Talukdar and Marcano, Chapter 29, and Kockel et al., Chapter 34, this volume). If each source rock expels hydrocarbons with unique compositions, then an analysis of these hydrocarbons from seeps or accumulations will indicate how many systems are in the area. At this point, the investigator should map the stratigraphic and geographic extent of the seeps and accumulations of

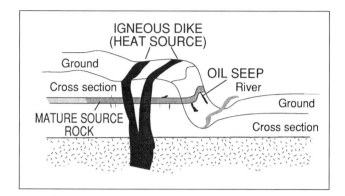

Figure 1.6. An atypical petroleum system whose oil originates from a source rock that is thermally matured by an igneous dike.

the same composition as a halo of hydrocarbons that encase a pod of active source rock, which also should be mapped (Peters and Cassa, Chapter 5, this volume).

A corollary to the area with stacked or multiple active source rocks that form more than one petroleum system is the one source rock that extends over a wide area and has sufficient overburden rock in more than one area to form pods of active source rock (Klemme, Chapter 3; Buitrago, Chapter 30; and Mello et al., Chapter 31, this volume).

Upper Devonian of United States

More than one petroleum system can form when a source rock extends beyond one package of overburden rock to another package (Figures 1.8B and 1.9). For example, when the sedimentary basin of a source rock is on the scale of a continent, such as the Upper Devonian of the United States, that one organic-rich interval can be the source rock for more than one petroleum system. However, the stratigraphic nomenclature for this Upper Devonian source rock is different depending on the location (in parentheses): Ohio Shale and Devonian black shale (Appalachian basin), Antrim Shale (Michigan basin), New Albany Shale (Illinois basin), Woodford Shale (mid-Continent provinces), Aneth Formation (Paradox basin), Pilot Shale (Great Basin), Bakken Formation (Williston basin), and Exshaw Formation (Sweetgrass arch). Wherever this Upper Devonian source rock is buried enough by overburden rock (basin) to generate hydrocarbons, a petroleum system exists.

What eventually matures the Upper Devonian organic-rich interval is increased heat from additional burial by overburden rock deposited in smaller post-Devonian sedimentary basins (successor basins) located on or along the edge of the North American craton. Sedimentary basins on the craton are sags or rifts, whereas basins at the edge of the craton are foreland basins. Unless the sediments are created in situ (e.g., carbonate rocks, evaporites, and coals), the provenance for the sediments deposited in all three basin types is the craton (as well as the fold-and-thrust belt for the foreland basin). The reservoir and seal rocks are either in the Upper

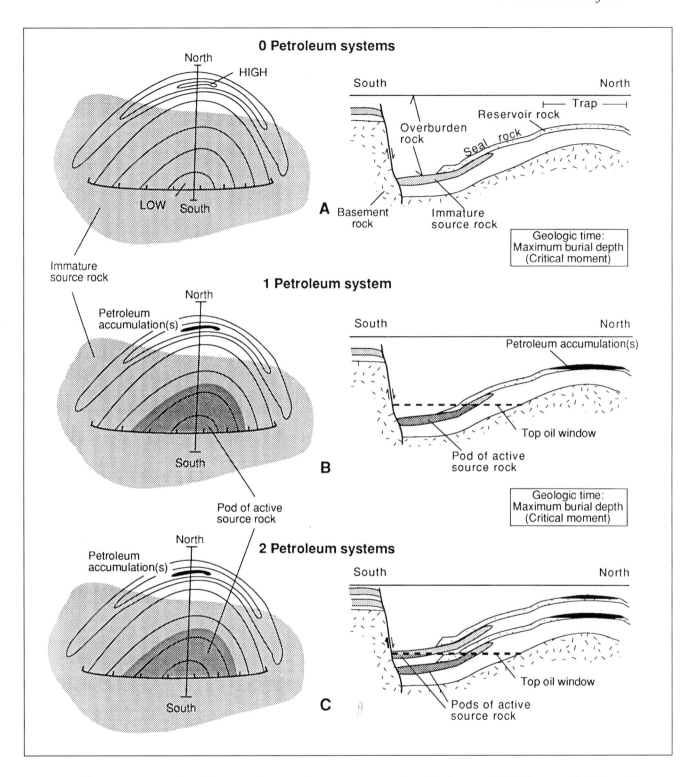

Figure 1.7. Three examples of partial or complete petroleum systems at the critical moment. (A) The essential elements are present, but the system is incomplete (thus no petroleum system); (B) one petroleum system; and (C) two petroleum systems. Notice that the overburden rock creates the geometry of the most recent sedimentary basin and that the source rock was deposited in a larger, older sedimentary basin.

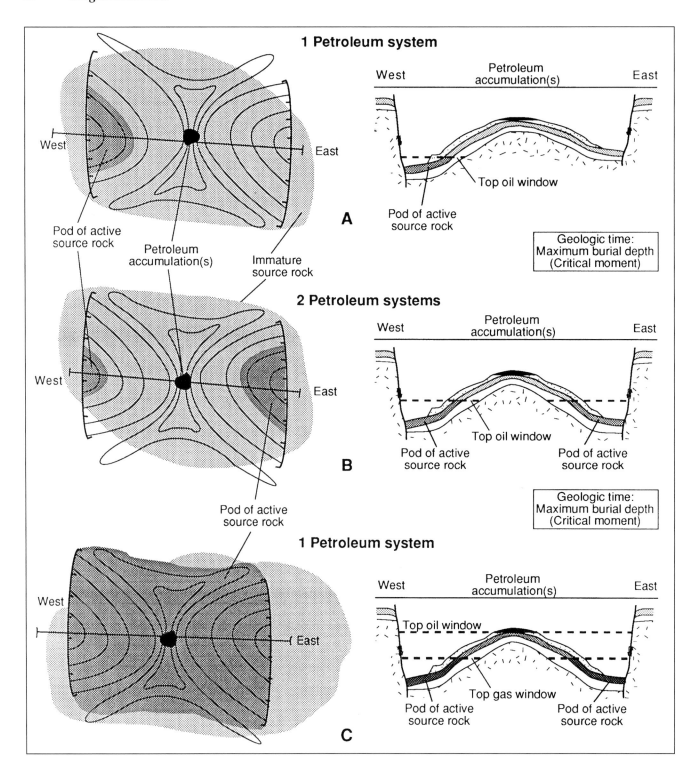

Figure 1.8. The number of petroleum systems is determined by the number of pods of active source, as shown by these three examples. Petroleum accumulation is charged by **(A)** a single pod of source rock, or one petroleum system; **(B)** two pods, or two petroleum systems; and **(C)** one pod, or one petroleum system.

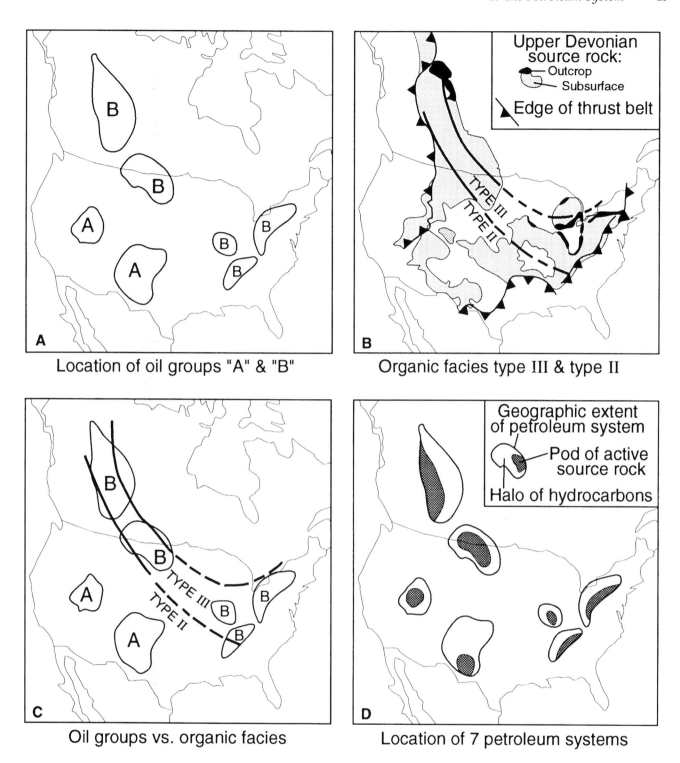

A Location of oil groups "A" & "B"

B Organic facies type III & type II

Upper Devonian source rock:
— Outcrop
— Subsurface

Edge of thrust belt

C Oil groups vs. organic facies

D Location of 7 petroleum systems

Geographic extent of petroleum system

Pod of active source rock

Halo of hydrocarbons

Figure 1.9. Fictitious example #1, in which one source rock deposited over a continent (North America) forms seven different petroleum systems where the overburden rock is thick enough to form a pod of active source rock. Using oil–oil and oil–source rock correlations, geochemical logs, and petroleum accumulations and shows, seven petroleum systems can be mapped.

Devonian strata or are within the overburden rock. The trap and petroleum forming processes occur during deposition of the overburden rock.

Over the area of the North American continent, the age of these petroleum systems that have Upper Devonian source rocks varies with the location of the system. Along the eastern and southern edge of the North American craton, these late Paleozoic foreland basins (including the Appalachian, Warrior, and Anadarko basins) received only minor amounts of post-Paleozoic sediments. Since the present-day petroleum accumulations must have generated and migrated around the end of Permian time or earlier (when maximum burial was achieved), the age (generation–migration–accumulation) of these petroleum systems having Upper Devonian source rocks ranged from Mississippian to Permian time. The preservation time extended through the Mesozoic and Cenozoic. In contrast, the western edge of the craton includes foreland basin sedimentary rocks as young as Cretaceous or early Tertiary, and one of the cratonic interior basin sags may be as young as Tertiary. The age of these systems ranged from the Cretaceous to Tertiary.

Miocene of California, U.S.A.

Another organic-rich interval that is involved in many petroleum systems is the Miocene of California. In California, numerous strike-slip basins formed in the Miocene and continue to develop to the present day. At first, conditions in the basins were conducive to the formation and preservation of organic matter along with abundant biogenic silica and relatively little siliciclastic material. Deposition of coarser siliciclastic material became progressively more rapid during Pliocene–Pleistocene time. This sediment provided the necessary overburden that heated the source rock to generate hydrocarbons that formed petroleum systems within the Los Angeles basin, Ventura basin (Santa Barbara offshore), Santa Maria basin, San Joaquin basin, and several other coastal basins. Again, what started out as organic-rich deposits over a large area eventually developed into smaller sedimentary basins that acquired sufficient overburden rock to generate hydrocarbons, thus forming separate petroleum systems.

INVESTIGATIVE TECHNIQUE

A petroleum system investigation should begin with hydrocarbons (Smith, Chapter 2, this volume), such as a show of oil or gas. In the same way that sedimentary rock requires a sedimentary basin, an oil or gas show requires a petroleum system. With this line of investigation, it is necessary to understand the smallest accumulations or shows because they are clues to whether commercial accumulations are possible. In addition, the petroleum system investigation approach requires that the focus of work is on the stratigraphic and structural studies of the essential elements and processes. If an exploratory well penetrates and successfully tests the plumbing of the petroleum system (within the stratigraphic and geographic extent), the chance of finding commercial hydrocarbons is improved.

Ideally, a petroleum system analysis begins with an oil and gas (show) map. Geochemical analyses of those hydrocarbon shows are needed to understand the origin of the oil or gas (biogenic versus thermal). Comparing oil to oil and gas to gas can indicate whether more than one petroleum system is involved. The line of inquiry can be expanded to include the type of organic matter responsible for those shows and the overburden rock required to thermally mature the source rock. To determine the geographic, stratigraphic, and temporal extent of the petroleum system, the investigator will need to acquire specific information to make the burial history chart, map, cross section, and events chart that define the system (Figures 1.2–1.5) (see also Peters and Cassa, Figures 5.12 and 5.13, Chapter 5, this volume).

Fictitious Example #1

To explain the investigative technique more graphically, two fictitious examples are provided (see also Smith, Chapter 2, this volume).

From the United States and Canada, 300 oils were collected and analyzed. The oils were collected from rocks that range in age from Precambrian to Holocene, from a depth range of 0–3000 m, and from many lithologies, such as fractured granite and shale, sandstone, and dolomite. Many different types of analyses were carried out on the oils. Oil–oil correlations indicate two groups, A and B, that form clusters in seven areas (Figure 1.9A).

A geochemical profile (Peters and Cassa, Chapter 5, this volume) of a well in each area indicates that each well penetrated more than one source rock and that an Upper Devonian source rock was common to all seven areas. Reexamining the vertical distribution of the oils indicates that one-third of the oils are from Carboniferous reservoirs. Using kerogen studies from the literature and other data, an organic facies map indicates two kerogen types, type II and III, in the Upper Devonian source rock (Figure 1.9B). In areas where the Upper Devonian source rock was eroded across the transcontinental arch, regional mapping allowed the organic facies to be mapped where it was absent or too deeply buried.

By use of hydrous pyrolysis (Lewan, Chapter 11, this volume) on immature source rock samples, oil–source rock correlations indicate that the two organic facies in the Upper Devonian are responsible for the two oil groups. Furthermore, the two clusters of group A oil are within the type II kerogen, and the four clusters of group B oil are within the type III kerogen (Figure 1.9C).

Additional well and outcrop control and burial history diagrams can be used to map the the thermal maturity of the Upper Devonian source rock. A pod of active source rock occurs with each of the seven oil clusters. Computerized exploratory well and field files are used to map the distribution of oil, which is found to be within the oil clusters, further confirming the geographic and stratigraphic extent of these seven petroleum systems.

This example shows the use and limitations of oil–oil and oil–source rock correlations. First, if two oils are identical, they may not necessarily be in the same petroleum system even though the oil–source rock correlations indicate that they are from the same source rock. Second, if two oils are different, they can still be from the same source rock. For example, if the organic facies changes within a pod of active source rock, the oils may be from the same petroleum system. Finally, to identify a petroleum system uniquely, the extent of hydrocarbon shows must be mapped relative to the pod of active source rock. This example also shows why the distribution as well as the quality, quantity, and thermal maturity of source rock should be mapped worldwide at the time of deposition (Klemme, Chapter 3, this volume).

Fictitious Example #2

The previous example identified and mapped the geographic and stratigraphic extent of seven petroleum systems. The next example investigates and describes one petroleum system (see Peters and Cassa, Chapter 5, this volume).

To demonstrate how the four figures and one table work together to characterize a petroleum system, we illustrate a petroleum system study with a specific example. Figures 1.2–1.5 and Table 1.3 depict a fictitious petroleum system, the so-called Deer–Boar(.) petroleum system. The oil accumulations and shows prove the existence of at least one system, but if there is more than one group of oils, there could be two or more systems present. To identify and name each system, oil and source rock samples were collected and analyzed for the following reasons: (1) to establish oil families, (2) to determine which family originated from which source rock, (3) to map the quantity and type of organic matter in the source rock, and (4) to map the thermal maturity of the source rock. On a map, we have shown the present-day location of each oil accumulation attributed to each group (Table 1.3) and have indicated the pod of active source rock. Much of this information is included in Figures 1.3 and 1.4.

In our fictitious example, sufficient information was collected to identify and map the thermal maturity of the Deer Shale as the most likely source for the oil accumulations in the Boar Sandstone (Peters and Cassa, Chapter 5, Figure 5.12, this volume). However, because of a lack of thermally mature samples of the Deer Formation, an oil–source rock correlation was inconclusive (see Lewan, Chapter 11, this volume, for solution). Therefore, our level of certainty is hypothetical because we are unable to demonstrate geochemically that the oil originated from the Deer Shale. However, geographic and stratigraphic evidence is sufficient to assign a name and level of certainty—the Deer–Boar(.) petroleum system.

At the location of the most thermally mature source rock, a burial history chart has to be made to determine the critical moment (Figure 1.2). The critical moment, in this case, is when the source rock is at maximum burial depth and is near the time when most hydrocarbons migrated into primary traps. (If the critical moment were the present day, the source rock would presently be at maximum burial depth; see Magoon, Chapter 22; Cole and Drozd, Chapter 33, this volume.) Various articles and computer programs exist to model petroleum generation and migration; most use the burial history curve or geohistory chart (Waples, Chapter 17, this volume). The essential elements of the system should be shown on the burial history chart.

Next, a map and cross section are drawn for the critical moment (Figures 1.3 and 1.4), and all accumulations are itemized (Table 1.3). The critical moment is important because the geometry of the migration paths and traps are reconstructed for about the time the oil and gas accumulated. If the critical moment is prior to present-day, then the location of present-day traps on a play or prospect map (not shown) can be compared to the location of traps at the critical moment to determine if oil and gas have remigrated. If the traps have shifted from the critical moment to the present day, the shifted trap or prospect would have to be charged with remigrated oil or gas. These maps can also be compared to determine if physical or microbial alteration (or destruction) occurred during the preservation time. A table of accumulations for this petroleum system indicates its size and is the basis for further calculations and comparisons carried out in the case studies.

Last, a petroleum system events chart is constructed to summarize the essential elements, processes, preservation time, and critical moment (Figure 1.5). In our fictitious example, the description is as follows. The Deer Shale, a Devonian (390–380 Ma) source rock is buried by Devonian–Permian (380–250 Ma) rocks to its maximum depth in the Late Permian (250 Ma). The process of generation–migration–accumulation of hydrocarbons occur during the Permian (260–240 Ma), and the critical moment is 250 Ma. These hydrocarbons accumulated under the George Shale (300–286 Ma) and in the Boar Sandstone, reservoirs of Pennsylvanian age (315–300 Ma) that formed into traps during the Late Pennsylvanian–Early Permian (290–270 Ma). The preservation time is 240 m.y. (Figures 1.3 and 1.4).

The events chart can be viewed as a team organizational tool. For example, geologic time is studied by the paleontologist and stratigrapher, the reservoir by the petrophysicist and stratigrapher, and trap formation by the structural geologist and geophysicist.

These four figures and table are simplified to make important points about a single petroleum system. Each figure could be drawn to include additional information unique to a particular petroleum system. Once a petroleum system is named, mapped, and described, it can be analyzed in many ways. For example, this volume contains case studies that describe petroleum migration from the pod of active source rock to a trap.

SUMMARY

Sedimentary basins, petroleum systems, plays, and prospects can be viewed as separate levels of petroleum investigations, all of which are needed to better understand the genesis and habitat of hydrocarbons. Investigations of sedimentary basins describe the stratigraphic sequence and structural style of sedimentary rocks. Petroleum system studies describe the genetic relationship between a pod of active source rock and an accumulation. Investigations of plays describe the present-day geologic similarity of a series of traps, and of prospects, describe individual traps. Except for the petroleum system, these terms are widely used by petroleum geologists.

A petroleum system encompasses a pod of active source rock and all generated oil and gas and includes all the elements that are essential for an oil and gas accumulation to exist: petroleum source rock, reservoir rock, seal rock, and overburden rock. All essential elements must be placed in time and space such that the processes required to form a petroleum accumulation can occur. These processes include trap formation and generation–migration–accumulation of hydrocarbons. The petroleum system has a stratigraphic limit, geographic extent, and an age. Its name combines the names of the source rock and the major reservoir rock with a symbol that expresses a level of certainty—known (!), hypothetical (.), and speculative (?). Along with its name, four figures and a table best depict the geographic, stratigraphic, and temporal evolution of the petroleum system: a burial history chart to establish the age and critical moment for the system, a map and cross section drawn at the critical moment, an events chart to summarize the formation of the petroleum system, and a table listing the accumulations in the system.

A petroleum system investigation is different from the other three levels of investigation in at least three ways. First, every petroleum system investigation commences with hydrocarbons regardless of amount. Second, hydrocarbons of a particular composition are related back to a pod of active source rock. Third, the pod of active source rock and related hydrocarbons are mapped. In addition, investigating each essential element of a petroleum system individually prevents the investigator from overemphasizing basin, play, or prospect analysis before the plumbing of the petroleum system has been unraveled.

This chapter describes the petroleum system; how it is used is limited only by the readers imagination. Some of the ways to characterize and use the petroleum system are shown in the remainder of this volume.

Acknowledgments   The authors wish to acknowledge the many people who have over the last five years contributed to the evolution of the petroleum system. Numerous colleagues from ARCO, Chevron, Exxon, Shell, Elf Aquitaine, Total, Unocal, Mobil, and the U.S. Geologic Survey have openly discussed and encouraged the publication of this chapter. We gratefully acknowledge Kenneth J. Bird, C. M. Molenaar, Douglas Klemme, R. J. Murris, and David A. White, who critically reviewed an earlier version of this chapter; George E. Claypool, Jennifer A. Miles, and James G. Palacas who reviewed a later version; and Gerard Demaison, Miner Long, John T. Smith, and Peter van de Kamp who reviewed the latest version. Their reviews were positive and helpful, and many of their suggestions are incorporated into this chapter. As helpful as everyone has been, the authors take full responsibility for the content of this work.

References Cited

Bally, A. W., 1975, A geodynamic scenario for hydrocarbon occurrences: Tokyo, Proceedings, Ninth World Petroleum Congress, v. 2, p. 33–44.

Bally, A. W., and S. Snelson, 1980, Realms of subsidence, *in* A. D. Miall, ed., Facts and principles of world petroleum occurrence: Canadian Society of Petroleum Geologists Memoir 6, p. 9–75.

Bird, K. J., 1988, The geologic basis for appraising undiscovered hydrocarbon resources in the National Petroleum Reserve of Alaska by the play-appraisal method, *in* G. Gryc, ed., Geology of the National Petroleum Reserve in Alaska: USGS Professional Paper 1399, p. 81–116.

Bishop, R. S., H. M. Gehman, Jr., and A. Young, 1983, Concepts for estimating hydrocarbon accumulation and dispersion: AAPG Bulletin, v. 67, p. 337–348.

Bois, C., 1975, Petroleum-zone concept and the similarity analysis contribution to resource appraisal, *in* J. D. Haun, ed., Methods of estimating the volume of undiscovered oil and gas resources: AAPG Studies in Geology 1, p. 87–89.

Bois, C., P. Bouche, and R. Pelet, 1982, Global geologic history and distribution of hydrocarbon reserves: AAPG Bulletin, v. 66, n. 9, p. 1248–1270.

Callahan, J. E., G. W. Brougham, and R. J. Bascle, 1987, Economically recoverable oil resources, *in* K. J. Bird and L. B. Magoon, eds., Petroleum geology of the northern part of the Arctic National Wildlife Refuge, northeastern Alaska: USGS Bulletin 1778, p. 299–307.

Claypool, G. E., C. N. Threlkeld, and L. B. Magoon, 1980, Biogenic and thermogenic origins of natural gas in Cook Inlet basin, Alaska: AAPG Bulletin, v. 64, p. 1131–1139.

Demaison, G., 1984, The generative basin concept, *in* G. Demaison and R. J. Murris, eds., Petroleum geochemistry and basin evaluation: AAPG Memoir 35, p. 1–14.

Demaison, G. J., A. J. J. Holck, R. W. Jones, and G. T. Moore, 1984, Predictive source bed stratigraphy; a guide to regional petroleum occurrence: London, Proceedings, 11th World Petroleum Congress, v. 11, n. 2, p. 17.

Demaison, G., and B. J. Huizinga, 1991, Genetic classification of petroleum systems: AAPG Bulletin, v. 75, n. 10, p. 1626–1643.

Demaison, G., and R. J. Murris, eds., 1984, Petroleum geochemistry and basin evaluation: AAPG Memoir 35, 426 p.

Dolton, G. L., K. J. Bird, and R. A. Crovelli, 1987, Assessment of in-place oil and gas resources, *in* K. J. Bird and L. B. Magoon, eds., Petroleum geology of the northern part of the Arctic National Wildlife Refuge, northeastern Alaska: U.S. Geologic Survey Bulletin 1778, p. 277–298.

Dow, W. G., 1972, Application of oil correlation and source rock data to exploration in Williston basin (abs.): AAPG Bulletin, v. 56, p. 615.

Dow, W. G., 1974, Application of oil correlation and source rock data to exploration in Williston basin: AAPG Bulletin, v. 58, n. 7, p. 1253–1262.

Halbouty, M. T., A. A. Meyerhoff, R. E. King, R. H. Dott, Sr., H. D. Klemme, and T. Shabad, 1970a, World's giant oil and gas fields, geologic factors affecting their formation, and basin classification, Part I—giant oil and gas fields, *in* M. T. Halbouty, ed., Geology of giant petroleum fields: AAPG Memoir 14, p. 502–528.

Halbouty, M. T., R. T. King, H. D. Klemme, R. H. Dott, Sr., and A. A. Meyerhoff, 1970b, World's giant oil and gas fields, geologic factors affecting their formation, and basin classification, Part II—factors affecting formation of giant oil and gas fields, and basin classification, M. T. Halbouty, ed., Geology of giant petroleum fields: AAPG Memoir 14, p. 528–555.

Huff, K. F., 1978, Frontiers of world oil exploration: Oil and Gas Journal, v. 76, n. 40, p. 214–220.

Huff, K. F., 1980, Frontiers of world oil exploration, *in* A. D. Miall, ed., Facts and principles of world petroleum occurrence: Canadian Society of Petroleum Geologists Memoir 6, p. 343–362.

Hunt, J. M., and G. W. Jamieson, 1956, Oil and organic matter in source rocks of petroleum: AAPG Bulletin, v. 40, n. 3, p. 477–488.

Kingston, D. R., C. P. Dishroon, and P. A. Williams, 1983a, Global basin classification system: AAPG Bulletin, v. 67, p. 2175–2193.

Kingston, D. R., C. . Dishroon, and P. A. Williams, 1983b, Hydrocarbon plays and global basin classification: AAPG Bulletin, v. 67, p. 2194–2198.

Klemme, H. D., 1971a, What giants and their basins have in common: Oil and Gas Journal, v. 69, n. 9, p. 85–90.

Klemme, H. D., 1971b, To find a giant, find the right basin: Oil and Gas Journal, v. 69, n. 10, p. 103–110.

Klemme, H. D., 1975, Giant oil fields related to their geologic setting—a possible guide to exploration: Bulletin of Canadian Petroleum Geology, v. 23, p. 30–66.

Klemme, H. D., 1986, Field size distribution related to basin characteristics, *in* D. D. Rice, ed., Oil and gas assessment—methods and applications: AAPG Special Studies in Geology 21, p. 85–99.

Knebel, G. M., and G. Rodriguez-Eraso, 1956, Habitat of some oil: AAPG Bulletin, v. 40, p. 547–561.

Kvenvolden, K. A., J. B. Rapp, F. D. Hostettler, J. D. King, and G. E. Claypool, 1988, Organic geothermometry of petroleum from Escanaba trough, offshore northern California, *in* L. Mattavelli and L. Novelli, eds., Advances in organic geochemistry 1987, Part I, Organic geochemistry in petroleum exploration: Organic Geochemistry, v. 13, p. 351–355.

Levorsen, A. I., 1967, Geology of Petroleum, 2nd ed.: San Francisco, Freeman, 724 p.

Mackenzie, A. S., and T. M. Quigley, 1988, Principles of geochemical prospect appraisal: AAPG Bulletin, v. 72, p. 399–415.

Magoon, L. B., 1987, The petroleum system—a classification scheme for research, resource assessment, and exploration (abs.): AAPG Bulletin, v. 71, n. 5, p. 587.

Magoon, L. B., 1988, The petroleum system—a classification scheme for research, exploration, and resource assessment, *in* L. B. Magoon, ed., Petroleum systems of the United States: USGS Bulletin 1870, p. 2–15.

Magoon, L. B., ed., 1989a, The petroleum system—status of research and methods, 1990: USGS Bulletin 1912, 88 p.

Magoon, L. B., 1989b, Identified petroleum systems within the United States—1990, *in* L. B. Magoon, ed., The petroleum system—status of research and methods, 1990: USGS Bulletin 1912, p. 2–9.

Magoon, L. B., ed., 1992a, The petroleum system—status of research and methods, 1992: USGS Bulletin 2007, 98 p.

Magoon, L. B., 1992b, Identified petroleum systems within the United States—1992, *in* L. B. Magoon, ed., The petroleum system—status of research and methods, 1992: USGS Bulletin 2007, p. 2–11.

Meissner, F. F., 1984, Petroleum geology of the Bakken Formation, Williston basin, North Dakota and Montana, *in* G. Demaison and R. J. Murris, eds., Petroleum geochemistry and basin evaluation: AAPG Memoir 35, p. 159–179.

Meissner, F. F., J. Woodward, and J. L. Clayton, 1984, Stratigraphic relationships and distribution of source rocks in the greater Rocky Mountain region, *in* J. Woodward, F. F. Meissner, and J. L. Clayton, eds., Hydrocarbon source rocks of the greater Rocky Mountain region: Denver, CO, Rocky Mountain Association of Geologists, p. 1–34.

Palmer, A. R., 1983, The decade of North American geology—1983 geologic time scale: Geology, v. 11, p. 503–504.

Perrodon, A., 1980, Géodynamique pétrolière. Genèse et répartition des gisements d'hydrocarbures: Paris, Masson–Elf Aquitaine, 381 p.

Perrodon, A., 1983a, Dynamics of oil and gas accumulations: Pau, Elf Aquitaine, p. 187–210.

Perrodon, A., 1983b, Géodynamique des bassins sedimentaires et systemes petroliers: Bulletin des Centres de Recherches Exploration–Production Elf Aquitaine, v. 7, p. 645–676.

Perrodon, A., 1992, Petroleum systems: models and applications: Journal of Petroleum Geology, v. 15, n. 3, p. 319–326.

Perrodon, A., and P. Masse, 1984, Subsidence, sedimentation and petroleum systems: Journal of Petroleum Geology, v. 7, n. 1, p. 5–26.

Philippi, G. T., 1957, Identification of oil–source beds by chemical means: Mexico City, Proceedings, 20th International Geologic Congress, 1956, sec. 3, p. 25–38.

Podruski, J. A., J. E. Barclay, A. P. Hamblin, P. J. Lee, K. G. Osadetz, R. M. Procter, and G. C. Taylor, 1988, Resource endowment: Geologic Survey of Canada Paper 87-26, pt. I, p. 7–125.

Sluijk, D., and M. H. Nederlof, 1984, Worldwide geologic experience as a systematic basis for prospect appraisal, *in* G. Demaison and R. J. Murris, eds., Petroleum geochemistry and basin evaluation: AAPG Memoir 35, p. 15–26.

Tissot, B. P., 1969, Premières données sur les mecanismes et la cinetique de la formation du petrole dans les sediments: simulation d'un schema reactionnel sur ordinateur: Revue de l'Institut français, du Petrole, v. 24, p. 470–501.

Tissot, B. P., and R. Pelet, 1971, Nouvelles données sur les mecanismes de genése et de migration du petrole: simulation mathematique et application à la prospection: Proceedings, Eighth World Petroleum Congress, Moscow, v. 2, p. 35–46.

Tissot, B. P., R. Pelet, and P. Ungerer, 1987, Thermal history of sedimentary basins, maturation indices, and kinetics of oil and gas generation: AAPG Bulletin, v. 71, p. 1445–1466.

Trask, P. D., and C. C. Wu, 1930, Does petroleum form in sediments at time of deposition?: AAPG Bulletin, v. 14, p. 1451–1463.

Triebs, A., 1936, Chlorophyll and Haminderviate in organischen Mineralstoffen: Angew. Chemie, v. 49, p. 682–686.

Ulmishek, G., 1986, Stratigraphic aspects of petroleum resource assessment, *in* D. D. Rice, ed., Oil and gas assessment—methods and applications: AAPG Studies in Geology 21, p. 59–68.

Ungerer, P., F. Bessis, P. Y. Chenet, B. Durand, E. Nogaret, A. Chiarelli, J. L. Oudin, and J. F. Perrin, 1984, Geologic and geochemical models in oil exploration; principles and practical examples, *in* G. Demaison and R. J. Murris, eds., Petroleum geochemistry and basin evaluation: AAPG Memoir 35, p. 53–77.

Uspenskaya, N. Yu., 1967, Principles of oil and gas territories, subdivisions, and the classification of oil and gas accumulations: Amsterdam, Proceedings, Seventh World Petroleum Congress, v. 2, p. 961–969.

Vissides, S. D., and B. A. Quirin, 1964, Oil and gas fields of the United States exclusive of Alaska and Hawaii: USGS Map, scale 1:2,500,000.

Waples, D. W., 1983, Physical-chemical models for oil generation: Colorado School of Mines Quarterly, v. 78, n. 4, p. 15–30.

Weeks, L. G., 1952, Factors of sedimentary basin development that control oil occurrence: AAPG Bulletin, v. 36, p. 2071–2124.

Welte, D. H., and M. A. Yukler, 1981, Petroleum origin and accumulation in basin evolution—a quantitative model: AAPG Bulletin, v. 65, p. 1387–1396.

White, D. A., 1980, Assessing oil and gas plays in facies-cycle wedges: AAPG Bulletin, v. 64, n. 8, p. 1158–1178.

White, D. A., 1988, Oil and gas play maps in exploration and assessment: AAPG Bulletin, v. 72, n. 8, p. 944–949.

Wilkerson, R. M., and D. L. Reed, 1982, Oil and Gas Fields of the United States (map): Tulsa, PennWell Books, approximate scale 1:3,600,000.Zieglar, D. L., and J. H. Spotts, 1978, Reservoir and source-bed history of Great Valley, California: AAPG Bulletin, v. 62, n. 5, p. 813–826.

Magoon, L. B, and W. G. Dow, eds., 1994, The petroleum
system—from source to trap: AAPG Memoir 60.

Chapter **2**

Petroleum System Logic as an Exploration Tool in a Frontier Setting

John T. Smith

Shell Development Company
Houston, Texas, U.S.A.

Abstract

Petroleum system logic is the thought process required to develop an integrated interpretation of the processes of petroleum generation, migration, and accumulation. It is illustrated here in frontier area exploration with examples taken from three offshore sales. Details of the application of petroleum system logic vary widely depending on the nature of the exploration problem and the data available. The application of petroleum system logic often allows the explorer to reduce the evaluation problem to the careful assessment of a single factor. The first two examples are of this type. The third example is a comprehensive evaluation illustrating the quantitative treatment of the processes of hydrocarbon generation, migration, and accumulation.

The critical problem in the first example (1986 Offshore Texas) was the prediction of petroleum type in a new growth fault trend. The presence of gas in the new trend was correctly predicted using petroleum system logic to extrapolate information bearing on hydrocarbon type from adjacent previously explored areas. In the second example (1976 Baltimore Canyon), the critical problem was predicting a petroleum charge in a previously unexplored area. Reservoirs, seal, trap, and ease of migration from a thick, mature stratigraphic section were ensured for the Schlee dome. An adequate petroleum charge was predicted to be available because favorable environments for source rock deposition were inferred from a geologic model derived from reflection seismic data. Postsale drilling discovered no petroleum and demonstrated the risk inherent in this mode of prediction.

The third example was taken from the 1983 Norton Sound sale. In part I of this example, the critical problem was determining the likelihood of an oil charge in the area. A reliable answer was anticipated because the determination was based on analyses of samples obtained from favorably located wells that penetrated the whole sedimentary section at a thermally mature location. The most useful evidence was Rock-Eval pyrolysis measurement of the amount of oil generated in the thermally mature section and oil shows in porous rocks in the thermally mature section. These indicated that a negligible volume of oil had migrated out of the mature section. This prediction has been confirmed by drilling. Part II of this example is a comprehensive evaluation of the Stuart subbasin, where the processes of hydrocarbon generation, migration, and accumulation were quantified using rock data from a COST well. The failure of five exploratory wells drilled on four prospects around the Stuart subbasin to find any gas accumulations is explained by this evaluation.

These examples demonstrate that all pertinent data should be considered and that proper interpretation of hydrocarbon shows is often important. When there is a possibility of a limited petroleum charge, quantitative evaluation of the processes of hydrocarbon generation, migration, and accumulation should be considered to aid in prospect or play evaluation.

INTRODUCTION

This chapter illustrates the use of petroleum system logic in frontier area exploration by describing three examples taken from the author's experience as a geochemical consultant to Shell Oil Company. These examples are from the following offshore sales: 1968 Offshore Texas, 1976 Baltimore Canyon, and 1983 Norton Sound. In each case, the conclusions drawn from the application of petroleum system logic played a major role in Shell's evaluation. The characteristics assigned to each example and the ensuing interpretation based on petroleum system logic were derived from Shell's work carried out in preparation for the particular offshore sale. In each case, the postsale drilling results are compared to the presale predictions.

Petroleum system logic as used in exploration means the development of an integrated interpretation of the processes of petroleum generation, migration, and accumulation in order to evaluate an exploration opportunity or prospect. In the ideal situation, this integrated interpretation is developed from a geologic description that includes the distribution in space and time of source rocks, reservoir rocks, seal rocks, and overburden rocks. In a frontier area, the geologic description is typically derived from reflection seismic data calibrated to stratigraphic control provided by outcrop or sea bottom samples and to wells using a limited amount of rock samples and wireline log data. Paleontologic evidence from available samples and seismic stratigraphy are used in the development of the geologic description of the area.

In the ideal situation where the geologic description is essentially complete, the first step in applying petroleum system logic is to develop an understanding for the particular frontier area of where and when hydrocarbons are generated. This understanding leads directly to the choice of possible migration paths for these hydrocarbons and then to reservoirs with access to petroleum. Finally, for these particular reservoirs, entrapment situations having the proper timing are located. The Norton Sound example illustrates two applications of petroleum system logic in a situation where this approach could be followed.

The explorer in a frontier area must often deal with an incomplete geologic description. By applying petroleum system logic to such a case, the explorer can identify the critical unknown parameters and can set up a program designed to make the necessary evaluation. Often the critical unknown parameters arise in connection with the hydrocarbon generation process. The examples taken from the 1968 Offshore Texas sale and the 1976 Baltimore Canyon sale are of this type.

CORSAIR TREND: 1968 OFFSHORE TEXAS SALE

Geologic Setting

The Corsair trend is a major growth fault trend of late Miocene age on the offshore Texas shelf. Figure 2.1 shows the location of the Corsair trend along with other information pertinent to the 1968 Offshore Texas sale. No wells had been drilled in the Corsair trend prior to the 1968 sale. Figure 2.2 shows the geologic characteristics inferred for the Corsair trend from seismic data and well control north and east of the trend. Seismic velocity data indicated the presence of hydropressured conditions and thus sandstone reservoir rock in the upper part of the upper Miocene throughout the Corsair trend. It was anticipated that traps would be created along growth faults when upper Miocene reservoirs were faulted against a shale seal. Structural closure occurs on the down-dropped side where the reservoir rock, overlain by a seal rock, rolls into an upper Miocene growth fault. The Corsair trend area offered for sale encompassed

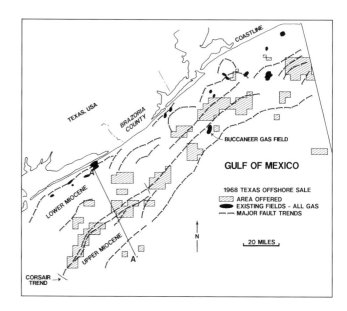

Figure 2.1. Area offered in 1968 Offshore Texas sale. Corsair trend indicated by brackets.

those prospects believed to have traps at depths less than 10,000 ft. Shell's regional maps indicated the presence of approximately 17 different structural features with trapping potential in the Corsair trend within the 1968 sale area.

Prediction of Hydrocarbon Type

The two parameters having the greatest impact on the value of a Corsair trend tract were the volume of hydrocarbons trapped on the tract and the type of hydrocarbons in the traps. The economics of oil versus gas were such that, for a given trap volume, oil was worth about seven times as much as gas. Thus, our petroleum system work focused on predicting the likelihood of oil versus gas on Corsair trend tracts.

Notice from Figure 2.1 that the only field in the upper Miocene trend in 1968 was a gas field. This field (Shell's Buccaneer gas field) has small oil rims in some reservoirs. The ultimate reserves were estimated to be 26 million bbl of oil and condensate and 736 bcf of gas for a ratio of 34 bbl of liquids per million ft^3 of gas. Also note in Figure 2.1 that all the production from the lower Miocene updip of Corsair along the coastline was gas. The question we wished to answer given the presence of gas along strike and updip was whether the source rock or thermal maturity conditions could change enough to create an oil province in the Corsair trend. Our work in onshore Texas had identified mature, oil-prone source rocks of Eocene, Cretaceous, and Jurassic ages. We had been unable to find any oil-prone source rocks in the interbedded sandstone and shale sequences deposited during the Oligocene–Miocene. We inferred that the oil present in Oligocene–Miocene reservoirs in the onshore area of Texas had migrated vertically from Eocene or older source rocks. We reasoned that the transition from

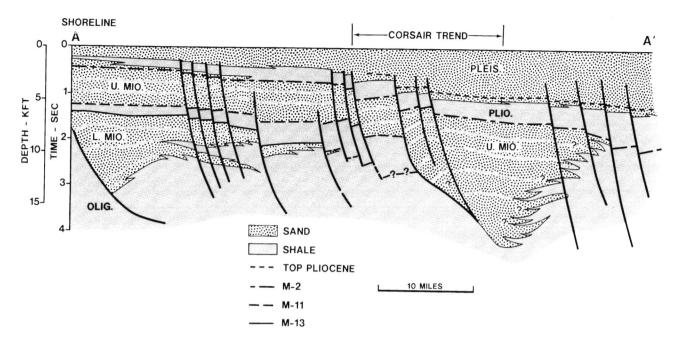

Figure 2.2. Offshore Texas cross section from the shoreline across the Corsair trend showing major growth faults, transgressive marine shales, and age markers.

an oily Oligocene province onshore to an all gas lower Miocene province offshore and updip from of the Corsair trend resulted from the fact that the oil-prone source rocks were overmature and generating gas as the lower Miocene traps were formed in offshore Texas.

From our seismic work, both reflection and refraction, we expected the oil-prone Eocene source rocks to be overmature and generating gas when the Corsair trend reservoir rocks under consideration were being deposited. Thus, the only way an oil province could have been created in the Corsair trend was the local deposition of a deep water Oligocene or Miocene oil-prone source rock below the thick or expanded upper Miocene sandstone section (Figure 2.2). We considered a deep water Oligocene oil-prone source rock to be unlikely because it would have provided oil to the offshore lower Miocene trend which, as mentioned before, is gas.

Figure 2.2 shows that the upper Miocene sandstone package is bounded by two major transgressive shales, the M-11 shale and the Pliocene shale. Thus, the updip upper Miocene sandstones are part of the same petroleum system that includes the upper Miocene growth fault system of the Corsair trend. Let us assume that an oil charge entered the upper Miocene sandstones of the Corsair trend. If the oil charge were large or followed by gas, we would expect oil to be displaced updip beneath the Pliocene shale beyond the Corsair trend. Many wells had been drilled through this upper Miocene sandstone package to reach the lower Miocene objective. There were no oil accumulations beneath the Pliocene shale, and our investigation did not reveal any reports of oil shows beneath the Pliocene shale.

Based on these three lines of evidence—gas updip and along strike, over maturity of inferred oil-prone source

rocks, and lack of oil shows in the updip extension of the upper Miocene Corsair trend—Shell bid the Corsair trend as a gas province.

Results

There had been some presale speculation that oil productive belts might lie within the sale area (Wilson, 1968a). When the sale was held, many of those present were surprised by the size of the winning bids. The highest bid in the sale was $43.8 million, the highest bid in Gulf Coast history at that time (Wilson, 1968b). This tract and the next most expensive tract ($43.5 million) were located in the Corsair trend. The winning bids on the tracts in the Corsair trend were approximately seven times larger than Shell's bids. We assume that these winning bids were based on an expectation of oil in the Corsair trend. The postsale discoveries on tracts bought in the 1968 Offshore Texas sale are shown in Figure 2.3. Note that six discoveries, all gas, were made. Later rounds of exploration and drilling have found only gas in the offshore Texas upper Miocene trend.

This example illustrates how, even without well control, one can use petroleum system logic to aid in the assignment of hydrocarbon type to a new trend in an explored province. The evaluator can provide a sound answer to the oil versus gas question by organizing geologic and geophysical information around the framework provided by petroleum system logic. In this offshore Texas example, we were able to extrapolate regional geologic and seismic information to arrive at a correct prediction of hydrocarbon type in a new trend.

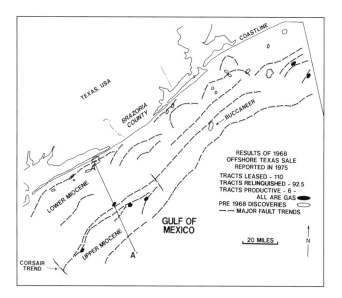

Figure 2.3. Gas discoveries made on tracts purchased in the 1968 Offshore Texas sale.

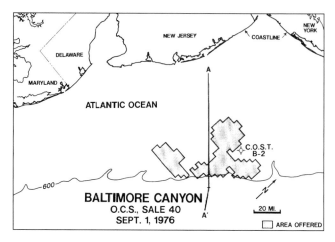

Figure 2.4. Area offered in 1976 Baltimore Canyon sale on the Atlantic coast.

SCHLEE DOME: 1976 BALTIMORE CANYON SALE

The Schlee dome is a large, deep feature located in the offshore Atlantic region about 70 mi from the New Jersey coast. Overlying sedimentary rock layers are affected by this feature. Presale evaluation showed excellent reservoir rock, seal rock, and trap geometry over and around the Schlee dome. One trap on the dome was a simple domal closure with a capacity to store about 7 billion bbl of recoverable oil. Naturally a trap of this size attracted much attention. The winning bids on the Schlee dome tracts totaled $544 million (West, 1976). Here the Schlee dome and the hydrocarbon generation and migration system that feeds it are treated as a petroleum system. No hard evidence could be developed to show that mature oil- or gas-prone source rocks were present in this petroleum system. Accordingly, a major task of the Shell evaluation team was to assess the likelihood that mature source rocks were indeed present in the Schlee dome fetch area.

Geologic Setting

The geologic setting of the Schlee dome has been thoroughly described in the literature (Schlee et al., 1976; Mattick, 1980; Prather, 1991). For purposes of this presentation, we have included the following items: an index map (Figure 2.4), a regional cross section (Figure 2.5), a reflection seismic line across Schlee dome (Figure 2.6), the stratigraphy of the COST-B-2 well (Figure 2.7), and the Schlee dome structure at the top of the Lower Cretaceous (LK) sandstone package (Figure 2.8). Figure 2.7 shows the thick Upper Cretaceous shale seal above a thick Lower Cretaceous sandstone package. Note the large area of closure at the top of the Lower Cretaceous shown in Figure 2.8, with a minimum structural closure

of 650 ft from the crest to the spill point. We estimated the total volume of this structural trap in the uppermost 600 ft of the Lower Cretaceous sandstone to be approximately 24 billion bbl. Such a trap, if full, can be expected to hold a recoverable volume of approximately 7 billion bbl of oil.

The Schlee dome was created by a Lower Cretaceous igneous intrusive. The Jurassic and part of the Lower Cretaceous were uplifted and eroded around the intrusive (Figure 2.6). It was assumed that this structural deformation caused extensive fracturing and allowed vertical communication throughout the disturbed interval. This assumption led to two conclusions. First, all hydrocarbons that had migrated to the Schlee dome area prior to the deposition of the Upper Cretaceous shale seal would be lost during the period of uplift and erosion. Second, all hydrocarbons that migrated to the Schlee dome after the deposition of the Upper Cretaceous shale seal would enter the trap in the thick Lower Cretaceous sandstone below the Upper Cretaceous shale seal. Based on these two conclusions, we have treated this trap and the stratigraphic section capable of generating hydrocarbons within the Schlee dome fetch area after the shale seal deposition as a single petroleum system.

The uncertain part of the evaluation of this petroleum system was estimating the volume and type of hydrocarbons generated within the fetch area after deposition of the shale seal. The COST-B-2 well penetrated 16,043 ft of sedimentary rocks (Figure 2.5). Mature oil- or gas-prone source rocks were not detected. The Jurassic–Lower Cretaceous intervals contained coaly material. The thermal maturity at total depth is only 0.90% R_o. Shell's estimate of the relationship between vitrinite reflectance and gas expulsion from type III kerogen is shown in Figure 2.9. Note that gas expulsion from type III kerogen is expected to start at 1.0% R_o. The problem was to estimate the probability that, within the Schlee dome fetch area, a mature oil- or gas-prone source rock exists deeper than 16,043 ft that could have charged the trap after the Upper Cretaceous shale seal was deposited.

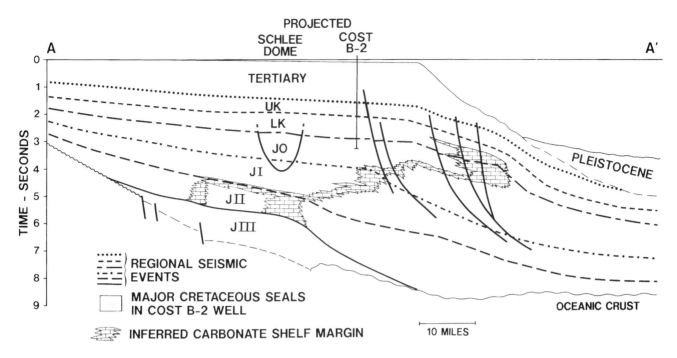

Figure 2.5. Baltimore Canyon cross section showing projected locations of Schlee dome and COST-B-2 well. See Figure 2.4 for location of cross section. Abbreviations: UK, Upper Cretaceous; LK, Lower Cretaceous; JO, JI, JII, JIII, subdivisions of Jurassic. (From McIntyre, 1976.)

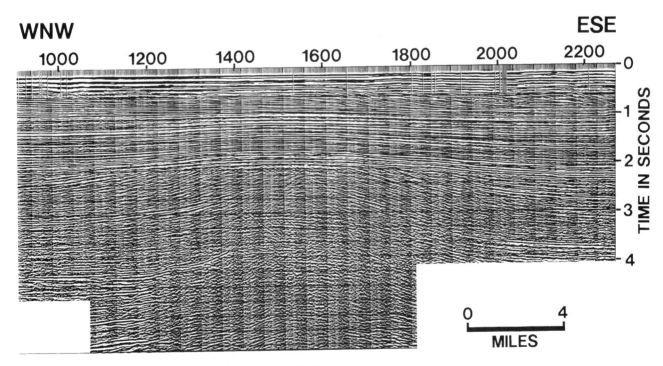

Figure 2.6. Reflection seismic line across Schlee dome, Baltimore canyon.

Maximum Depth for Effective Source Rocks

To determine from the present-day burial depth when a source rock could have contributed hydrocarbons to the petroleum system in the Schlee dome area, we estimated the relationship of thermal maturity and time

at the COST-B-2 well location for a series of stratigraphic horizons using a Lopatin type maturity model. This estimate took into account the decrease in heat flow with time of crustal cooling (Figure 2.10). The contribution of oil from oil-generating source rocks was assumed negligible for a vitrinite reflectance above 0.9% R_o, and the contribution of gas from gas-prone source rocks was

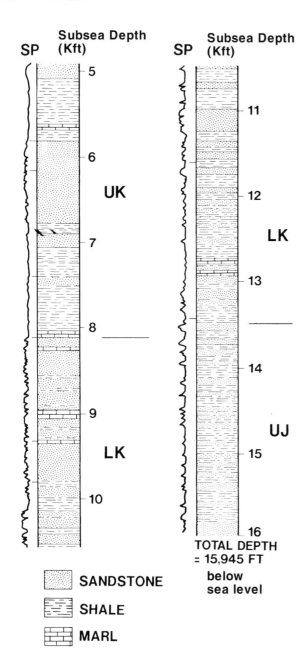

SANDSTONE

SHALE

MARL

Figure 2.7. Baltimore Canyon stratigraphy from the COST-B-2 well.

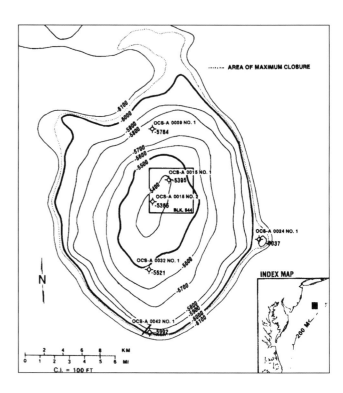

Figure 2.8. Structural map of Schlee dome on top of the Lower Cretaceous (LK). Contours are depth (in ft) converted from original seismic time maps. Postsale exploratory wells are annotated with the depth to the top of the Logan Canyon Formation equivalent (LK). (Modified from Lippert, 1983; reproduced from Prather, 1991.)

source rocks that can contribute to the Schlee dome petroleum system must lie between 19,500 and 31,500 ft. The total interval within which a contributing oil- and gas-prone source rock can lie is about 15,000 ft thick.

Source Rock Model

As just discussed, the source rock model must apply to the interval 15,000 ft thick that lies directly beneath the stratigraphic section penetrated by the COST-B-2 well. The location of the Schlee dome relative to the inferred carbonate shelf margin is shown is Figure 2.5. To develop our source rock model, we used the Cretaceous stratigraphy of the Gulf of Mexico coast as an analog. Oil-prone source rocks are found in three marine environments: transgressive shale, slope shale, and back reef lagoon. In addition, gas-prone coals and humic shales are found in the fourth environment which is transitional between marine and nonmarine. The COST-B-2 well penetrated about 7000 ft of Jurassic–Lower Cretaceous sedimentary rocks deposited in such a transitional environment.

Based on the location of the Schlee dome fetch area relative to the inferred carbonate shelf margin and the character of the seismic data, it was thought that all four of the environments favorable for source rock deposition would be found in the Schlee dome fetch area at various stratigraphic positions within the 15,000-ft thick interval below total depth of the COST-B-2 well. Accordingly,

assumed negligible above 2.2% R_o (Figure 2.9). At the time of trap formation, 0.9% R_o was attained at the stratigraphic horizon having a present depth of 22,500 ft and that 2.2% R_o was attained at the stratigraphic horizon having a present depth of 31,500 ft (Figure 2.10).

The bottom 3000 ft of the COST-B-2 well is mature for oil generation, but oil-prone source rocks are undetected within this interval. The oil-prone source rocks that could contribute to the Schlee dome petroleum system must lie between 16,043 and 22,500 ft. Significant gas expulsion from type III kerogen starts at 1.2% (Figure 2.9). A value of 1.2% R_o is reached at the stratigraphic horizon having a present depth of 19,500 ft. Therefore, the gas-prone

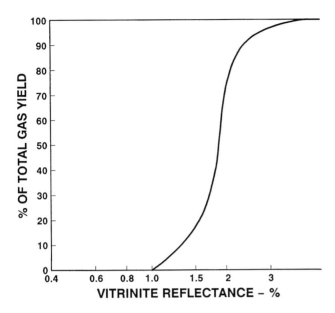

Figure 2.9. Percentage of total gas yield expelled from type III kerogen versus percentage vitrinite reflectance.

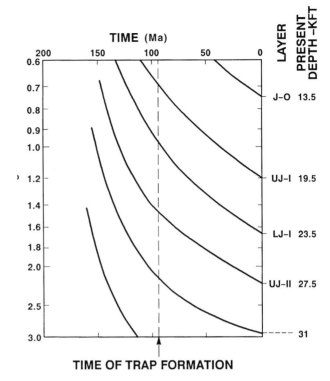

TIME OF TRAP FORMATION

Figure 2.10. Thermal maturity history at the COST-B-2 well location. Each solid line shows the percentage vitrinite reflectance versus time relationship for a particular horizon.

Shell assigned a high probability to the presence of a commercially significant volume of hydrocarbons in the Lower Cretaceous reservoirs on the Schlee dome.

Results

It was a great surprise and disappointment when the Schlee dome was drilled and found to be completely water bearing. Five wells have tested the prime objective below the Upper Cretaceous seal within the area of closure without a show of hydrocarbons. The Schlee dome petroleum system seemed to have all the ingredients required for economic success. There were thousands of feet of sedimentary rock deposited under conditions favorable for source rock development and having a thermal maturation history compatible with the timing of trap formation. There was a direct migration route from this thick stratigraphic section to a seismically well-defined structural trap having an excellent reservoir and seal combination. The only significant risk was in the existence of source rock within the fetch area. This risk seemed minor because of the favorable depositional setting and the thick package of sediments within which the source rock could lie. To explain the absence of hydrocarbons on the Schlee dome we must first assume that none of the transgressive shales in the Upper Jurassic were source rocks and, second, that the transition from carbonate reef to oxidized red beds occurred over a short distance in the Upper–Middle Jurassic section between 19,500 and 31,500 ft. When the presale evaluation was underway, this latter condition was not suspected because the COST-B-2 well had penetrated an Upper Jurassic–Lower Cretaceous section with coaly material distributed over an interval 7000 ft thick.

1983 NORTON BASIN SALE

The Norton basin is a complex of three sedimentary subbasins located off the west coast of Alaska (Figure 2.11). Two aspects of the evaluation of the Norton basin are presented here. Part I discusses the evaluation of the likelihood of a commercial oil charge in the Norton basin, and part II covers the Stuart subbasin petroleum system. Both parts provide useful examples of the types of problems encountered in applying petroleum system logic.

Economic considerations led to the conclusion that gas, if discovered, would be virtually worthless from such a remote area. Accordingly, a critical aspect of the presale evaluation effort was to assess the probability of finding significant oil reserves in the basin. Shell concluded that the important source rocks in the Norton basin area were gas prone. The work leading to this conclusion is described in part I. Once this conclusion was reached, Shell found it unnecessary to carefully evaluate the processes of hydrocarbon generation, migration, and entrapment required for rigorous application of petroleum system logic.

Exxon and Elf reached a different conclusion from that of Shell and estimated that there was a reasonable chance of finding significant oil reserves in or adjacent to the Stuart subbasin (Desautels, 1988). As a result, they

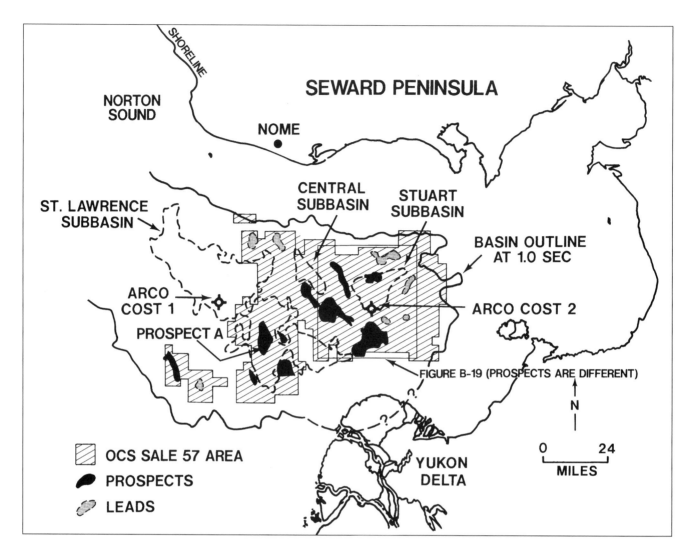

Figure 2.11. Map of Norton basin area offshore Alaska showing subbasins, prospects, COST wells, and OCS sale 57 acreage.

acquired a dominant lease position in the Stuart subbasin and drilled five wells on four structures. No hydrocarbon accumulations that merited a drill-stem test were found in these five wells. The availability of stratigraphic data and hydrocarbon indications from these wells gave us the opportunity to test the value of using petroleum system logic as an exploration tool in the Stuart subbasin. Accordingly, using only data available before the sale, we completed a "hypothetical" presale petroleum system evaluation for the Stuart subbasin and compared this evaluation to the drilling results. This material is presented in part II.

Geologic Setting

The Norton basin is located in Norton Sound under the offshore continental shelf of Alaska between the Seward Peninsula and the Yukon Delta (Figure 2.11). For our purposes, the Norton basin outline is drawn where the thickness of sedimentary rocks exceeds 1 sec on a seismic reflection profile. A *subbasin* is formed wherever

a thicker stratigraphic section is separated by a thinner section. Three subbasins are shown on Figure 2.11 along with the many prospects and leads within and between the subbasins. Also shown are the locations of the two COST wells drilled prior to the sale and the acreage put up in OCS Sale 57 that was held in March 1983.

Shell's understanding of the geology of the Norton basin at the time of the 1983 lease sale was derived from five sources: (1) publications of Fisher and co-workers of the U.S. Geologic Survey (Fisher et al. 1979, 1981, 1982; Fisher, 1982), (2) Soviet publications, (3) the two COST wells, (4) regional studies conducted by D. M. Worrall of Shell Development Company, and (5) work carried out in the Alaska Division of Shell Oil Company.

Worrall's (1991) work was done on the tectonic history of the Bering Sea and on the evolution of Tertiary strike-slip basins of the Bering shelf. Much of his work was done before the Norton basin sale. His interpretation of the geologic history of the Norton basin was incorporated into the evaluation made by the Shell Oil Alaska Division and is presented here. To avoid confusion, we

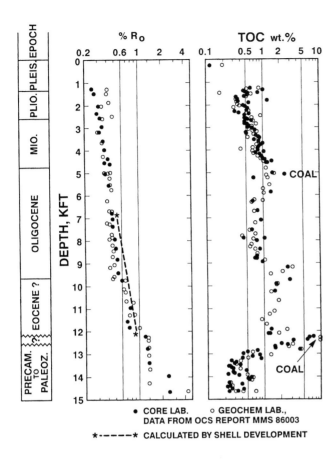

Figure 2.12. Vitrinite reflectance (R_o) and total organic carbon (TOC) for the COST-1 well in the St. Lawrence subbasin. See Figure 2.11 for well location.

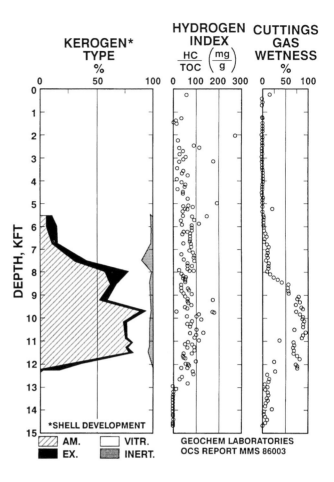

Figure 2.13. Kerogen type by visual analysis, hydrogen index by Rock-Eval pyrolysis, and cuttings gas wetness for the COST-1 well, St. Lawrence subbasin. See Figure 2.11 for well location. Abbreviations: AM, amorphous; EX, exinite; VITR, vitrinite; INERT, inertinite.

have followed the nomenclature used by Worrall (1991). The basement underlying the Norton basin consists of Precambrian–Paleozoic metamorphics intruded by Cretaceous granites. Worrall (1991) showed that there are two distinct sedimentary rock packages above the basement. The boundary between these two packages is an unconformity that Worrall calls the "red event." Here we refer to the older of these two sedimentary rock packages as the "pre-red sequence." At the time of the sale, the age of the red event was poorly established but was thought to be Paleocene. The age of the red event is now thought to be late middle Eocene (44–43 Ma) (Worrall, 1991). We refer to the younger of the two sedimentary rock packages as the "basin fill sequence." Infolded remnants of the pre-red sequence are locally present at various spots in the Norton basin and were found in both COST wells. Coals are present in the pre-red sequence in both COST wells. An abrupt increase in vitrinite reflectance to about 1.0% R_o was observed at the red event in both COST wells. We assumed that any potential for significant oil generation in the pre-red section was destroyed at the COST well locations prior to deposition of the basin fill sediments.

Slow subsidence with some associated faulting started in late Eocene and has continued to the present day. Depositional environments in the basin fill sequence include nonmarine coastal, deltaic, shallow marine, and possibly lacustrine. This sedimentary rock package forms an onlap sequence on paleobasement highs and basin margins. Traps include sedimentary rock drape over basement highs, faults, pinchouts, and onlaps.

Part I: Evaluation of Oil Charge

Initial Interpretation

Geochemical data for the COST-1 and COST-2 wells are shown in Figures 2.12–2.15. Most of these data were published by Turner et al. in 1986. The interval shallower than 7000 ft can be ignored in both wells because it does not attain the thermal maturity level required for significant oil expulsion. Visual kerogen analysis by Shell Development for COST-1 (Figure 2.13) and by Robertson Research (U.S.) for COST-2 (Figure 2.15), with which Shell concurred, suggested a large fraction of oil-prone (lipid) kerogen from about 9000 ft to the unconformity at about 12,000 ft in both wells. The vitrinite reflectance is lower in this mixed lipid and humic system than would be observed in a pure humic coal. To avoid this source of error, the calculated trend of vitrinite reflectance versus

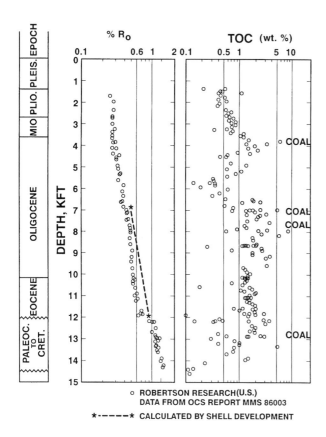

Figure 2.14. Vitrinite reflectance (R_o) and total organic carbon (TOC) for the COST-2 well in the Stuart subbasin. See Figure 2.11 for well location. (Data from Robertson Research, U.S.)

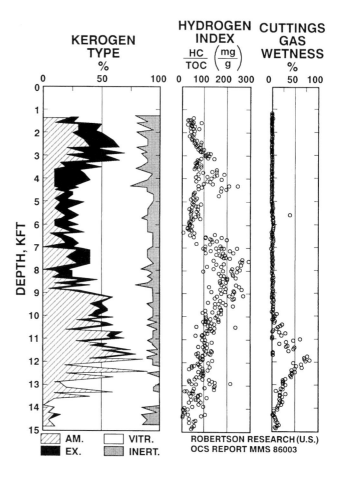

Figure 2.15. Kerogen type by visual analysis, hydrogen index by Rock-Eval pyrolysis, and cuttings gas wetness for the COST-2 well in the Stuart subbasin. See Figure 2.11 for well location. Abbreviations: AM, amorphous; EX, exinite; VITR, vitrinite; and INERT, inertinite. (Data from Robertson Research, U.S.)

depth based on the temperature gradient and burial history was used to estimate thermal maturity (Figures 2.12 and 2.14). From these calculated R_o trends, we expect oil generation from amorphous kerogen and exinite to start at a depth of about 9000 ft and be nearly complete at a depth of about 12,000 ft.

A decrease in the hydrogen index (HI) was reported in both wells over the depth interval from 9000 to 12,000 ft (Figures 2.13 and 2.15). We assumed that this decrease reflected the expected conversion of the lipid fraction of the kerogen to oil. The cuttings gas wetness level, particularly in the COST-1 well, indicated that a mature oil-generating source rock was present throughout this interval (Figures 2.13 and 2.15). The rock extracts at depths greater than 10,000 ft in COST-1 and greater than 11,000 ft in COST-2 had compositions like those of mature oils.

We estimated that this interval between 9000 ft and the unconformity contained about 1000 ft of shale that initially had about 50% type II kerogen and an average total organic carbon (TOC) content of 1.5%. From these characteristics, the initial interpretation was that the total volume of oil generated in the mature regions of all the Norton subbasins would be about 10 billion bbl.

Oil Show Evidence

The stratigraphy of the two COST wells is shown in Figure 2.16. Note the presence of many low-permeability beds throughout the interval in which oil was presumed to have been generated. In the COST-1 well, this interval contained seven thin sandstones of reservoir quality as well as the low-permeability beds. If the source rock interpretations initially accepted were valid, then at depths greater than 10,000 ft where significant oil expulsion should have occurred, the low-permeability beds should contain high saturations of oil and the sandstones should all have good oil shows.

Table 2.1 presents the results of a careful review of the evidence for shows. The quality and number of shows in the COST-1 well were judged to indicate only minor volumes of expelled oil. The thickness of mature oil generating source rock was far less than the 1000 ft initially assumed. The absence of oil shows in the COST-2 well above the red unconformity indicates that there was negligible oil expulsion above about 11,800 ft.

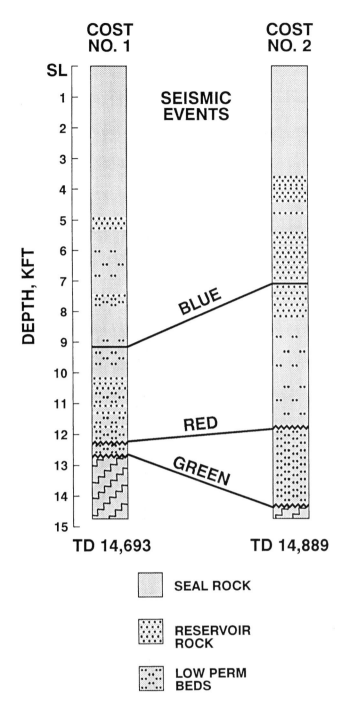

Figure 2.16. Stratigraphy of the COST-1 and COST-2 wells of the Norton basin.

Table 2.1. OCS Sale 57–Norton Basin COST Well Shows

Depth (ft)	Shows
Cost-1	
10,200	Streaming cut fluorescence
10,250	Cut fluorescence
10,910	Crush cut fluorescence
10,960–10,990 (core)	Patchy stain and cut fluorescence
Cost-2	
11,825–11,830	Trace free oil in mud
12,210–12,220	Major gas show
12,190–14,500	Gas shows in several sandstones indicated by mud gas unit and by neutron-density wireline logs

concept was that even if these coals contained lipid material, most of the oil would have been lost prior to deposition of the basin fill sequence. Thus, this show did not enhance the oil potential of the Stuart subbasin in Shell's interpretation.

Rock-Eval Pyrolysis Evidence

An indication of when enough oil has been generated to allow oil expulsion can be derived from Rock-Eval pyrolysis data. The Rock-Eval instrument measures the amount of hydrocarbons evolved from a sample as the sample temperature is increased from room temperature to 500 °C. The oil-like hydrocarbons evolved below 300 °C were present in the sample at the start of the analysis, and their total amount is reported as the S_1 peak. The magnitude of the S_1 peak is a measure of the oil content of the sample. The hydrocarbons evolved above 300 °C are largely formed by pyrolysis of kerogen in the sample. The total amount of these hydrocarbons formed by pyrolysis is reported as the S_2 peak and represents the remaining hydrocarbon-generating potential of the sample.

While the thermal maturity of a source rock is increasing and oil is being generated, the value of S_1/TOC increases until oil expulsion starts. After oil expulsion begins, the value of S_1/TOC remains approximately constant over a limited depth interval and then decreases with increasing depth and thermal maturity. For the cases we have studied, S_1/TOC must attain a value in the range of 0.1–0.2 for oil expulsion to start.

Figure 2.17 shows the plot of S_1/TOC versus depth for samples from the two COST wells. Recall that in these wells, oil generation is expected to be significant at a depth of about 9000 ft and to continue to about 12,000 ft. The values of S_1/TOC for the COST-2 sidewall core samples are low throughout. There is little indication of significant oil generation from 9000 to 10,500 ft. Even at 12,000 ft where oil generation is expected to be essentially complete, S_1/TOC is only about 0.04 compared to about 0.1 required for the onset of oil expulsion. We interpret these results to mean that the intervals sampled in COST-2 below 9000 ft are not capable of expelling oil at any thermal maturity level. At high thermal maturity (in the gas window), some liquids might be expelled

However, the observation of some free oil in the mud at 11,825–11,830 ft demonstrates that some oil was expelled in the COST-2 well. The significance of this show is discussed in the next section.

Robertson Research (U.S.) reported an oil show below the red unconformity at 12,240 ft in the COST-2 well based on a rock extract. This oil show occurred close to the major gas show observed on the mud log (Table 2.1). Both of these shows occurred below the red unconformity and are believed to be derived from coals. Shell's

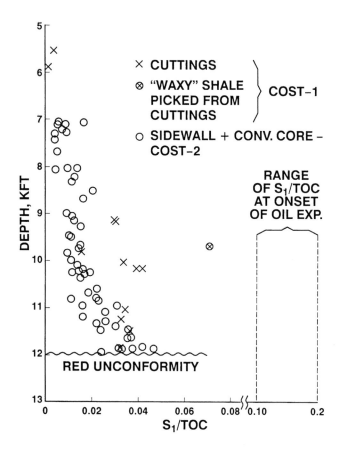

Figure 2.17. Oil content/TOC as indicated by S₁/TOC for the Norton basin COST wells.

from the sampled intervals as condensate carried in gas. A quantitative analysis leading to an estimate of the volume of this gas is presented in part II. The volume of this gas is so small relative to the area over which it must migrate to reach prospective traps on the prospects that none of this gas and condensate is expected to be observed in the exploratory wells drilled in the Stuart subbasin.

The low values observed for S_1/TOC demonstrate that the amorphous kerogen observed in the samples below 9000 ft in these Norton basin wells cannot be normal type II kerogen. To reconcile the visual kerogen observations with the Rock-Eval pyrolysis data, one can postulate the presence of a kerogen with a low HI that has a low capacity for oil generation. Subsequent to the Norton basin work described here, L. M. Pratt (1984) described the depositional conditions under which such a kerogen can be formed. She found that the HI of the marine kerogen present in the Upper Cretaceous Greenhorn Formation in the Denver basin varied from less than 100 to 600 mg HC/g TOC. The content of terrigenous organic matter was less than 15% in all of her samples. The low-HI samples were associated with deposition in a sufficiently oxic environment to allow some degree of bioturbation. We suspect that most of the kerogen present in the basin fill sequence of the Norton basin was an amorphous low-HI kerogen similar to the marine low-HI kerogen described by Pratt (1984).

The value of S_1/TOC does not provide an indication of lipid content above 9000 ft where the maturity level is too low for oil generation. However, this stratigraphic interval does not reach a high enough thermal maturity anywhere in the Stuart subbasin to generate a significant amount of oil.

The oil show at 11,825–11,830 ft in the COST-2 well demonstrates that some oil was expelled. We interpret this show to have originated from a thin lipid-rich zone that was missed by the sidewall core program. Since the presence of an oil-generating zone of appreciable thickness is not supported by source rock data, this show was judged to be insignificant. Several of the COST-1 source rock samples had S_1/TOC values indicating some oil generation. This is consistent with the scattered oil shows observed in the COST-1 well. However, S_1/TOC remained below the level expected for an oil-expelling source rock. Thus, the amount of oil expelled at the COST-1 well location was thought to be too small to be of commercial significance.

One sample from the COST-1 well (S_1/TOC = 0.07 at 9730 ft) came close to reaching the value of S_1/TOC that previous experience showed was required for the onset of oil expulsion. This sample was waxy shale picked from the cuttings for the depth interval 9690–9750 ft. This interval in the COST-1 well appeared to have the potential for oil expulsion at a higher thermal maturity. The next section describes a special study carried out to evaluate this possibility.

Before leaving this subject, we must explain the misleading decrease in HI from 9000 ft to the red unconformity. From the HI versus depth trends in Figures 2.13 and 2.15, it is evident that low values are observed in both wells in the thermally immature section. Therefore, depositional conditions in both subbasins lead to the deposition of kerogens with HI values of about 50 mg HC/g TOC. We presume that the decreases in HI below about 9000 ft were largely due to a change in the original kerogen composition rather than to the generation of oil.

Oil Generation Potential in COST-1 Well

To determine the oil generation potential of the interval from 9690 to 9750 ft in the COST-1 well, picked cuttings were thermally "matured" in the laboratory and the products were analyzed. The picked sample contained only waxy brown shale. The sample was heated with water in a sealed tube for 6 days at 300°C. These conditions are estimated to produce a conversion in the kerogen equal to that observed at 0.9% R_o. Figure 2.18 shows three normal paraffin distributions as follows: the waxy shale as received at 0.7% R_o, the waxy shale after heating for 6 days at 330°C, and a model also heated for 6 days at 330°C. The model was created from the results of laboratory maturation studies on various types of kerogen. A kerogen composition of 70% vitrinite, 17% liptinite, and 13% alginite was consistent with the conversion and product composition observed for the picked cuttings.

Visual kerogen analysis of the waxy shale indicated that it was 70% lipid and 30% vitrinite. This direct comparison of visual analysis to product generation

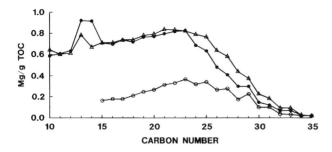

Figure 2.18. Normal paraffin distributions expressed as milligrams of each normal paraffin per grams TOC. Open circles: the waxy shale sample as received (0.7% R_o) picked from cuttings at 9690–9750 ft depth. Closed circles: the same sample after heating for 6 days at 330°C. Triangles: model kerogen containing 70% vitrinite + 17% liptinite + 13% alginite.

confirms our conclusion from the S_1/TOC data that the oil generation potential of the macerals visually identified as lipid kerogen was much less than that of type II kerogen. The final step in our evaluation of the oil potential of the Norton basin was to calculate the volume of oil that the waxy shale interval might supply to the prospect judged to have access to the largest volume of oil from this source. This prospect is identified by the letter "A" in the St. Lawrence subbasin (Figure 2.11). The measured pyrolysis yield on the picked cuttings was 0.9% by weight. Based on the model of 70% vitrinite, 17% liptinite, and 13% alginite, we estimated the total oil yield of the waxy shale at complete conversion to be 0.8% by weight. To create the source rock thickness, this oil yield was optimistically applied to the full 60-ft thickness from which the waxy shale was derived. The prospect receiving the maximum oil charge from this source was estimated to acquire about 110 million bbl of oil. Assuming favorable efficiency factors for migration to and recovery from the trap, this best prospect for oil might have a recoverable volume of 15–20 million bbl. This volume is far below the minimum required for development in the Norton basin.

Summary of the Oil Potential of the Stuart Subbasin

The COST-2 well was favorably located to penetrate any source rocks deposited above the red unconformity in the Stuart subbasin. Thermal maturity for oil generation was reached at about 9000 ft, and the red unconformity was reached at about 11,950 ft subsea. Rock-Eval pyrolysis S_1/TOC observations on sidewall cores indicated that oil had not been expelled from this mature source rock interval. Absence of oil shows in samples confirmed this interpretation. A trace of oil was observed in the mud at 11,825–11,830 ft. There was insufficient evidence for an oil source rock of significant thickness near this depth. Accordingly, it was assumed that a thin source rock of high lipid content had expelled an insignificant amount of oil at this depth. A major gas show was observed at about 12,200 ft in the section

below the red unconformity. Other gas indications were observed down to economic basement. This section contains much coal and attains a thermal maturity sufficient to generate significant volumes of gas. Shell's interpretation of these observations was that the probability of finding commercially significant oil reserves in the Stuart subbasin was very low. Thus, tracts in the area were given speculative bids in case the COST-2 well was unrepresentative or something was overlooked in the interpretation.

Summary of the Oil Potential of the St. Lawrence Subbasin

The COST-1 well was favorably located to penetrate any source rocks deposited in the St. Lawrence subbasin. Minor oil shows in samples were observed in the thermally mature section, and Rock-Eval pyrolysis S_1/TOC observations suggested that minor amounts of oil had been generated. A model was set up for the most favorable case for oil accumulation on a prospect. From this model, the most favorable prospect ("A" in Figure 2.11) was estimated to have the potential for a recoverable volume of approximately 20 million bbl of oil. This volume is below the minimum needed for development. This result, combined with the probability that there would be an inadequate thickness of reservoir rocks in the St. Lawrence subbasin, led Shell to make only speculative bids in the area.

Results

A total of six exploratory wells were drilled by others to evaluate Norton basin prospects. One well, Arco OCS-Y-0435 No. 1, was drilled on a prospect for which the hydrocarbon fetch area was near the well. Some oil shows were reported from this well, but none were worthy of a drill-stem test. Since the hydrocarbon potential of this prospect could not be predicted from either COST well, observations in the Arco OCS-Y-0435 well are not relevant to our evaluation and will receive no further attention.

No exploratory wells were drilled on prospects in or adjacent to the St. Lawrence subbasin so we lack results to compare to our prediction that oil migration from the basin fill sequence in this subbasin is quite small.

Five exploratory wells were drilled on four prospects adjacent to the Stuart subbasin (Figure 2.19). The locations of these exploratory wells are shown on the structural contour map in Figure 2.20 drawn at the top of an important reservoir rock unit. Reservoirs and seals penetrated in each well are shown relative to sea level in Figure 2.21. None of the wells found a hydrocarbon accumulation, and all of the wells were plugged and abandoned without drill-stem tests. We will go beyond these two facts and look for evidence that oil migrated out of the deep part of the Stuart subbasin to adjacent prospects. All of the wells encountered sandstones above basement overlain by a sealing rock interval (Figure 2.21). Three of the wells, Cascade OCS-Y-0398, Yellow Pup OCS-Y-0497, and Chugach OCS-Y-0425, were appropriately located to be on the migration path of hydrocarbons moving updip from the area containing

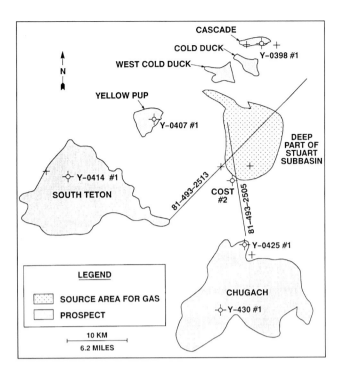

Figure 2.19. Locations of five exploratory wells, COST-2 well, two seismic lines (Figures 2.22 and 2.25), prospects, and the area of gas-expelling source rock in the Stuart subbasin area.

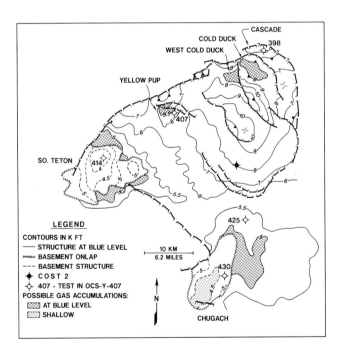

Figure 2.20. Structure map at the blue level in the Stuart subbasin showing locations of possible gas accumulations and wells.

hydrocarbons moving updip from the area containing mature source rocks in the basin fill sequence. Such hydrocarbons would be expected to migrate updip in the first sandstone above economic basement. According to Desautels (1988), these wells lacked oil shows. This absence of oil shows along expected migration paths is in agreement with Shell's interpretation that there was a low probability of finding commercial oil reserves in the prospects adjacent to the Stuart subbasin.

Part II: The Petroleum System of the Stuart Subbasin

After Shell concluded that the probability of finding commercial oil reserves anywhere in the Norton basin was very small, little effort was devoted to a rigorous evaluation of the migration and trapping characteristics for prospects in or adjacent to the different subbasins. Therefore, Shell's presale evaluation is an incomplete example of the use of the petroleum system logic as a tool in frontier exploration. However, the geology in and around the Stuart subbasin and the exploration effort expended on it (including the five wells drilled by Exxon and Elf in partnership or alone) combine to make the Stuart subbasin area an excellent place to illustrate the application of petroleum system logic in a frontier area.

For this illustration, a quantitative evaluation was completed using only data available at sale time. This evaluation included the following items:

1. Source rock units and maturity levels were quantitatively described.
2. Migration paths and expected reservoirs for gas accumulations were identified.
3. Volumes of gas expelled into the prospect fetch areas were estimated.
4. Losses along the migration path to the predicted accumulation positions were estimated for each prospect.
5. Volumes available for accumulation on each prospect were estimated.
6. These volumes were assigned to specific accumulations using the COST-2 well stratigraphy and structure at selected levels derived from reflection seismic data.

In addition to these items, which constitute a complete hypothetical presale evaluation, we conclude with a comparison of the drilling results to the predictions. To make this comparison, the predictions were modified as required by data on reservoir rock and seal rock distribution acquired from the exploratory wells.

General Characteristics of the Petroleum System in the Stuart Subbasin

Figure 2.19 is a map view of the Stuart subbasin area showing the locations of the six prospects adjacent to the subbasin, the wells that have been drilled, the area from which gas has been inferred to have migrated, and two seismic lines that will be used to illustrate structural rela-

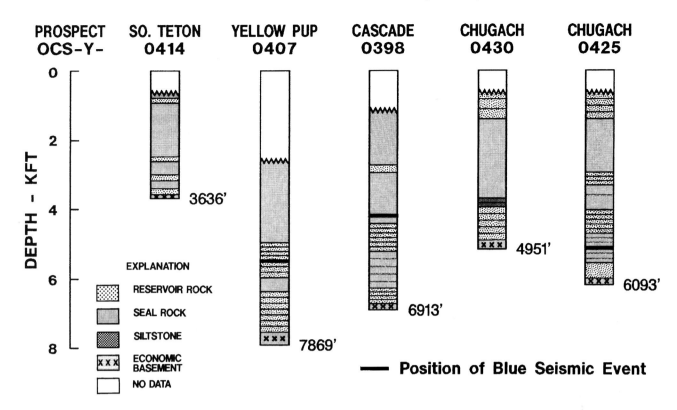

Figure 2.21. Generalized stratigraphy of Stuart subbasin tests showing distribution of seal intervals and sand-containing intervals.

tionships. The prospect names given by Exxon and Elf (Desautels, 1988) were used for the four prospects they drilled. For the other two prospects, Cold Duck and West Cold Duck, we have used the names given by Shell. As shown in Figure 2.19, gas expulsion is restricted to a relatively small central portion of the Stuart subbasin, whereas all the prospects expected to derive gas from the Stuart subbasin are located outside the gas expulsion region. Therefore, critical facets of this evaluation include determining the migration paths of the gas, the limits of the fetch areas for the various prospects, and the volumes of gas retained along the migration paths.

Figures 2.22 and 2.23 present cross-sectional views through the center of the Stuart subbasin. As indicated in Figure 2.23, some gas is expelled from the basin fill sequence. The primary source of gas is the coal in the pre-red sequence, which will be called the pre-red source rock.

The COST-2 wireline logs show the distribution of the coals (Figure 2.24). Each coal bed is characterized by increases in resistivity and sonic travel time and a decrease in density. The coals are interbedded with shales, siltstones, and low-permeability sandstones. The coal-bearing section was deposited under fluvial and paludal conditions. Under these conditions, each sandstone is expected to have a relatively narrow width and to follow a sinusoidal path providing many opportunities for stratigraphic trapping.

All of the prospects are on basement highs adjacent to the Stuart subbasin. A thick seal rock rests on the red unconformity and onlaps the basement highs (Figures 2.16, 2.22, and 2.23). To reach commercial reservoirs on the prospects, the gas must migrate along the sediment–basement contact. The gas expelled from the pre-red coals must first migrate through the fluvial sandstone either to the basement contact or to the red unconformity. The gas that migrates to the red unconformity must then migrate along the unconformity to the basement. There are migration losses along every part of the migration path, particularly in the fluvial sandstones.

The deepest sandstone reservoirs of good quality are expected to onlap the basement and be located near the "blue horizon" (Figures 2.16 and 2.22). Figure 2.20 presents the structure at the blue horizon. Note the possible onlap traps on South Teton and Chugach at this structural level. From the COST-2 well stratigraphy and the structural characteristics of these two prospects, onlap traps in good quality reservoir sandstones are possible over an interval about 1000 ft thick. Hydrocarbon migration from one onlap trap to the next higher trap would have occurred until a trap was reached beneath a top seal that extends over the basement high. Migration above this top seal may have occurred where the displacement created by a fault juxtaposes the sandstone reservoir below the seal against the sandstone reservoir immediately above the seal. This concept of hydrocarbon migration across a fault plane when two reservoirs are juxtaposed was advanced by Allan (1989) and has been used by Shell from about 1970.

The processes of generation, migration, and accumulation of hydrocarbons in the Stuart subbasin area lead to the use of a single petroleum system for evaluation of the

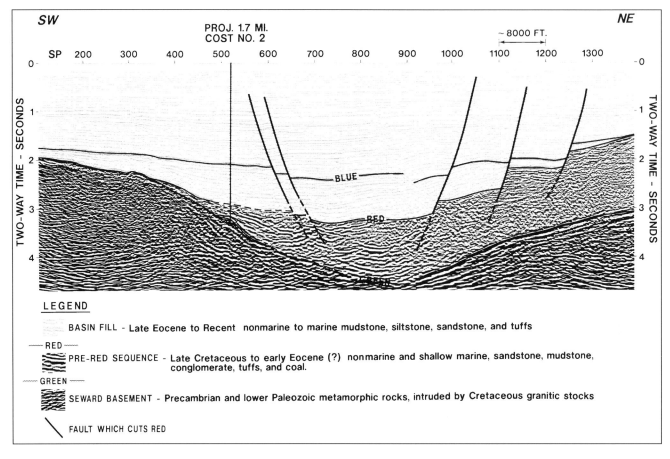

Figure 2.22. Seismic line 81-493-2513 through center of Stuart subbasin showing the pre-red sequence, the basin fill sequence, and faults cutting the pre-red unconformity.

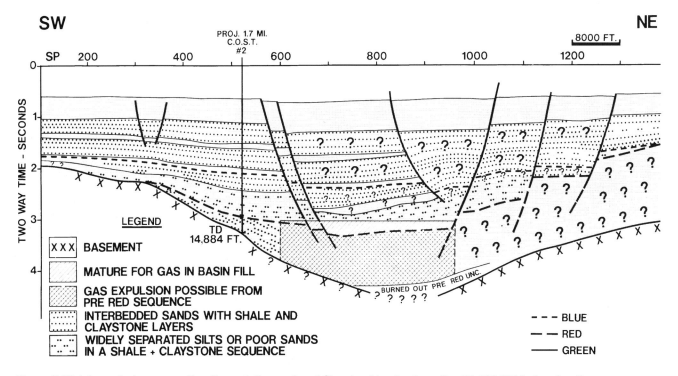

Figure 2.23. Interpreted cross section through the center of Stuart subbasin along line 81-493-2513 showing the gas-expelling region and the distribution of seals and sands.

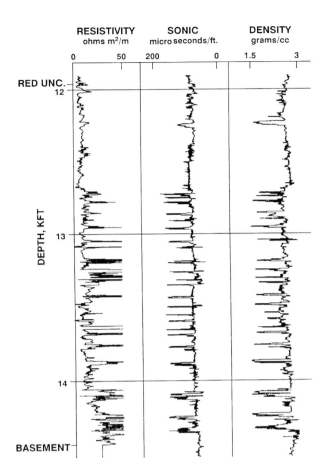

Figure 2.24. Resistivity, sonic travel time, and density logs for the COST-2 well showing the distribution of coals below the red unconformity in the Stuart subbasin.

thermally generated hydrocarbons. This petroleum system has a relatively large volume of reservoir rock in potential trapping configurations, particularly on Chugach and South Teton. However, the volume of gas available to the reservoirs may be limited because of the small area within which gas is expelled and because of losses along the migration path.

Basin Fill Source Rock Model

The section on the possibility of an oil charge in the Norton Basin concluded that gas expelled from humic (type III) kerogen would be the major product from the basin fill sequence. For a quantitative evaluation, we have used the gas expulsion curve for type III kerogen (Figure 2.9). From this curve, gas expulsion starts at 1.0% R_o and increases rapidly above 1.6% R_o. From Figures 2.14 and 2.15, it is evident that organic matter capable of generating hydrocarbons is distributed throughout the basin fill sequence. However our concern is limited to that part of the basin fill sequence having R_o greater than 1.0%.

To make estimates of thermal maturity for the 1983 Norton basin sale, Shell used an in-house calibration of a Lopatin type calculation. The COST-2 temperature gradient of 2.3°F/100 ft was used throughout the Stuart

subbasin area. For these conditions, we estimated that 1.0% R_o would be reached at 13,000 ft, and since the base of the basin fill was estimated to reach 14,500 ft, the maximum thickness of the gas-expelling section of basin fill rocks was 1500 ft.

We developed a source rock model for this lower 1500 ft of the basin fill sequence. The data in Figures 2.14, 2.15, and 2.17 were used to derive the following quantities for our model: an average TOC of 1.5 wt. %, an average HI (S_2 peak) of 120 mg HC/g TOC, and an average distillable yield (S_1 peak) of 20 mg HC/g TOC. From these values, the total hydrocarbon yield on complete conversion was found to be 2.1×10^{-3} g HC/g rock. If we assume that this total yield is obtained as gas, the yield would be 1.7×10^{11} SCF/mi^2 for a 1000-ft-thick layer of source rock. The maximum vitrinite reflectance reached at the base of the basin fill sequence is estimated to be 1.2%. At 1.2% R_o about 7% of the total potential gas yield is expelled (Figure 2.9). Under these maximum conditions, the average value of the gas yield over the entire 1500-ft sequence is about 3.5% of the total potential. Thus, the estimated gas yield from the basin fill sequence where it attains maximum burial depth and thus maximum thermal maturity is only 9×10^9 SCF/mi^2.

The total area over which the depth of the red event is greater than 13,000 ft is approximately 42 mi^2. We estimate that the total volume of gas expelled from the basin fill source rock in the Stuart subbasin is about 120×10^9 SCF, assuming the average yield from the gas-expelling area is 3×10^9 SCF/mi^2.

Pre-Red Source Rock Model

From the wireline logs on the COST-2 well (Figure 2.24), 24 coal layers with a total thickness of 161 ft were identified in the 2500-ft-thick section of pre-red sediments. We assumed that each of these coal layers had the composition of a standard humic coal. On this basis, the total gas yield at complete conversion of this thickness of standard coal was estiamted to be 1.1×10^{12} SCF/mi^2. In our Norton basin discussion, we pointed out the abrupt increase in vitrinite reflectance to 1.0% R_o at the red unconformity. In addition, there was an increase in the slope of log R_o versus depth below the unconformity. Dow (1982) also interpreted the abrupt increase in R_o at 12,100 ft to indicate the presence of an unconformity. The abrupt increase in vitrinite reflectance at the red unconformity means that gas was generated during the burial but lost when subsequent uplift and erosion created the red unconformity. To set up a quantitative model for the pre-red source rock, we must consider the distribution of coal within the gas-expelling region and correct for the loss of gas during the period of burial, uplift, and erosion that created the red unconformity.

In theory, the seismic data could be used to map the distribution of coal. Unfortunately, the data quality was inadequate for this application. We were able to use the seismic data in a qualitative manner merely to recognize the presence of coal. Coals were clearly present in the pre-red sequence basinward of Yellow Pup, South Teton,

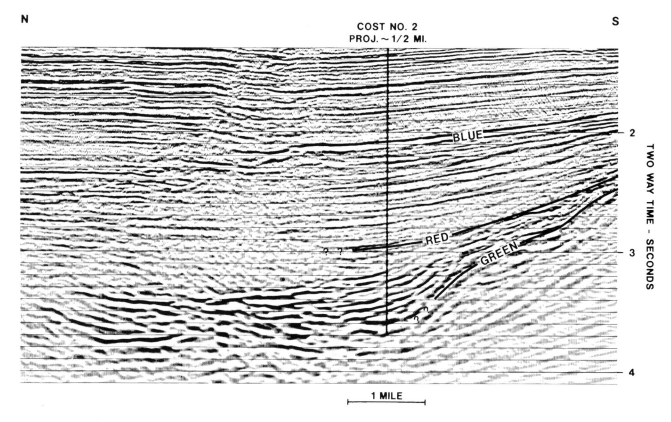

Figure 2.25. Strike line along the west flank of the Stuart subbasin showing the coal reflections below the red unconformity.

and Chugach. However, evidence was lacking for coals in the pre-red sequence in the northern and eastern quadrants of the gas-expelling area.

The seismic data (Figures 2.22 and 2.25) show that the dip and strike of the coal beds are approximately parallel to the dip and strike of the basement surface and the red unconformity on the western flank of the subbasin. The gross thickness of the coal-bearing package increases toward the thickest part of the subbasin. Given these characteristics, a model was created for the pre-red source rock using the COST-2 well and seismic line 81-493-2513 (Figure 2.22). In this model, the amount of coal was kept constant at 161 ft and was spread uniformly over an interval whose thickness increased basinward as inferred from line 81-493-2513. This source rock model was used for the western and southwestern flanks of the subbasin and included the fetch areas for the three drilled prospects we wished to evaluate—Yellow Pup, South Teton, and Chugach. A quantitative evaluation of Cascade, the fourth drilled prospect, was unnecessary for reasons that are discussed later.

Next, loss of gas during the first episode of burial for the pre-red source rock sequence was estimated. For the model, we assumed that just prior to basin fill deposition, the vitrinite reflectance was 1.0% at the red unconformity and that the slope of log R_o versus depth in the pre-red sequence was equal to the slope observed in the pre-red sequence in the COST-2 well. The slope of log R_o versus depth attained in the pre-red sequence during the first episode of burial is greater than the slope of log R_o versus depth created during the final burial episode

when the basin fill sequence was deposited (Figure 2.14). Assuming that these two conditions are constant over the fetch areas of Yellow Pup, South Teton, and Chugach seems reasonable because of the relatively simple structural relationships of the basement, the red unconformity, and the coal sequence in this area.

Under these assumptions, the thermal maturity at the end of the first burial episode was estimated at selected locations for the top, bottom, and (where necessary) middle of the coal-bearing layer. From these thermal maturity values and from Figure 2.9, we estimated the percentage of the total gas yield that had been expelled and thus lost prior to the start of the second episode of burial.

The next step of the calculation procedure was the estimation of the thermal maturity and thus the percentage gas expulsion attained at the end of basin fill deposition. We started with the structural map at the red unconformity and calculated along selected dip profiles the depths to the top, bottom, and middle of the coal-bearing source rock layers. Vitrinite reflectance values were then calculated at each of these positions assuming a temperature gradient of 2.3 °F/100 ft using Shell's 1982 version of a Lopatin type calculation. In this case, the calculations involved adding the effect of the time–temperature increment produced by the basin fill deposition to the initial thermal maturity.

The final goal was to create a map showing the volume of gas expelled from the pre-red source rock per unit area during basin fill deposition. At each location on the map, we had available from the calculations just described initial and final values for the percentage of gas expulsion at either the top and bottom or the top, middle, and bottom of the coal-bearing source rock layer. The nonlinear relationship between log vitrinite reflectance and percentage gas expulsion required the use of three values to obtain a reasonable approximation for the average of the whole layer when the percentage gas expulsion at the bottom of the layer exceeded 20%. An appropriate average was calculated for the differences between the final and initial percentage gas expulsion values at each location. The resultant average expulsion efficiency times 1.1×10^{12} SCF/mi^2 gave the volume of gas expelled from the pre-red source rock per square mile during the basin fill deposition at the given location.

As previously stated, the pre-red source rock model described here is applicable to the western and southwestern flanks of the Stuart subbasin. However, to illustrate the relative importance of the pre-red and basin fill source rocks, we have calculated a hypothetical total Stuart subbasin pre-red gas charge assuming that the model applied over the whole gas-expelling area. For this hypothetical case, the total volume of gas expelled from the pre-red source rock during the basin fill deposition period is 9×10^{12} SCF. For comparison, the estimate for the basin fill source rock was 0.12×10^{12} SCF for the total Stuart subbasin. Therefore, where the pre-red source rock is present, it will yield approximately 75 times as much gas per unit area as the basin fill source rock.

Gas Shows in the Pre-Red Sequence

Evidence for gas expulsion from the pre-red coals during the basin fill period was provided by a strong gas show in the COST-2 well in a sandstone at about 12,200 ft and by a series of weak to moderate gas shows in sandstones between 12,800 and 14,200 ft. The strong gas show was interpreted to come from a 4-ft-thick sandstone at 12,175–12,179 ft. In this show, the hydrocarbon content of the mud gas reached a maximum value of about 30%. All of the coal beds in the pre-red section gave mud gas shows. These shows interfered with the recognition of mud gas shows originating in the sandstones between 12,900 and 14,200 ft.

A careful review of the mud log along with the wireline logs showed that the mud log gas content increased during the drilling of ten sandstone intervals between 12,800 and 14,200 ft. The presence of gas in six of these sand intervals was confirmed by a lower porosity reading on the neutron log than on the density log. To make this interpretation, we used a grain density of 2.71 g/cm^3. Core data in two different pre-red sandstones had given grain density values of 2.68–2.78 g/cm^3. Therefore, the use of a grain density of 2.71 g/cm^3 may have underestimated the number of gas shows in the pre-red sandstones. In addition, some instances of gas in shaly sandstones may have been missed because of the elevated porosity reading on the neutron log.

Turner et al. (1983) made a similar interpretation regarding the presence of gas in the pre-red section.

Their comments regarding the presence of hydrocarbons in this part of the COST-2 well are as follows:

> During the drilling of this well, good gas shows consisting of methane with lesser amounts of ethane, propane, and butane were encountered between 12,190 and 14,460 ft. An examination of the geophysical logs shows neutron–density gas anomalies for much of the sandstone and interbedded coal between 12,880 and 13,942 ft. No tests were run to evaluate the degree of gas saturation in the sandstone beds with neutron–density gas anomalies. These anomalies probably represent partial saturation of the sandstone with gas generated in adjacent coal beds and unable to migrate further because of low permeability. This sequence might conceivably be productive elsewhere in the basin.

We have presented a detailed discussion of these pre-red gas shows because their occurrence provides strong support for the migration loss model presented next.

Migration Loss Model

Since we estimated that over 98% of the gas available to the evaluated prospects originated in the pre-red sequence, our major concern is to estimate the loss during migration of gas generated in the pre-red sequence. This gas must migrate through the fluvial sandstones of the pre-red sequence, along the red unconformity, and along the basement surface until a good quality sandstone reservoir onlapping a basement high is reached. There are losses due to the trapping of gas along each of these parts of the migration path. The abandoned oxbow sandstones and sinusoidal channel sandstones comprising much of the fluvial sandstone system create many stratigraphic traps. The migration paths along the red unconformity and basement surface are visualized as a series of stratigraphic traps connected by a patchy layer of permeable sand deposited at the unconformity or on the economic basement.

A reliable estimate of the volume of gas trapped along the basement surface below the reservoir section and along the red unconformity is not possible. However, per unit area, the amounts of gas trapped in these settings is probably far less than the amount trapped in the thick pre-red fluvial sandstone sequence. Furthermore, the gas show evidence provides a basis for estimating the volume trapped in the pre-red fluvial sandstones.

Because of the jump in vitrinite reflectance in the COST-2 well at the red unconformity, the boundary for the onset of gas expulsion was placed downdip from this well. Therefore, the gas observed in the COST-2 well had migrated updip. This means that some of the sandstones in the well, such as abandoned river channel sandstones, did not have access to gas. However, in the area where gas was expelled from the coals, virtually every sandstone body is charged with gas.

In the interval between 12,800 and 14,200 ft in the COST-2 well, gas shows were observed on the mud log in 10 out of a possible 20 sandstone reservoirs. These shows are gas in stratigraphic traps whose sandstone reservoir is connected to the downdip mature source rock. It seems unlikely that the small amount of gas present along a migration path would have produced a detectable show in the presence of the large background created by the coal layers in the COST-2 well.

For the pre-red sequence in the COST-2 well, Shell estimated that there were 343 net-ft of sandstone with an average porosity of 9% between the red unconformity and 12,800 ft, and 400 net-ft of sandstone with an average porosity of 11% between 12,800 and 14,200 ft. The interval above 12,800 ft contains only one coal bed, which could charge 40 net-ft of sandstone, 20 net ft-above the coal and 20 net-ft below the coal. Thus, in the COST-2 well, we estimated that the pre-red sequence contained 440 net-ft of sandstone that was available for the stratigraphic trapping of gas. If half of the sandstone traps gas, as suggested by the gas show evidence, there would be 220 net-ft of gas. For the gas-expelling region, the model thus assumes that 220 net-ft of sand contains trapped gas. An average porosity of 9% and an average gas saturation of 50% are also assumed for these accumulations. Using an average depth of 15,000 ft and an average pressure of 7500 psi for the accumulations trapped in the pre-red gas-expelling region, these parameters lead to a prediction of 60×10^9 SCF/mi^2 of trapped gas. This migration loss estimate may be conservative for the following reasons: (1) the thickness of the pre-red coal-bearing section increases in the gas-expelling region, which probably leads to an increase in net-feet of sandstone; and (2) the presence of disconnected sandstone bodies may lead to more than 50% of the net-feet of sandstone being included in the traps.

For the area updip of the gas-expelling region, we assumed that on the average there were 70 net-ft of sandstone with trapped gas. We reduced the average net-feet of trapped gas to allow for the decreasing thickness of the pre-red section and the tendency for the migrating streams to occupy a smaller fraction of the total area. For this updip area, we assumed an average porosity of 11%, an average gas saturation of 50%, an average depth of 12,000 ft and an average pressure of 6000 psi. For these conditions, the average migration loss in the pre-red area updip of the gas-expelling area is 22×10^9 SCF/mi^2.

For the evaluation of the prospects presented in the next section, the total migration loss is based on the losses in the pre-red sequence. As previously noted, additional losses are possible in traps just under the red unconformity and in onlap traps on the economic basement. However, these additional losses are immaterial to our interpretation of the hydrocarbon potential for the evaluated prospects.

Definition of Prospect Fetch Areas

Since the intent is to predict volumes of possible gas accumulations on individual prospects, we must determine the boundaries of the gas expulsion area for each prospect. To make this determination, we must decide how gas migration through the pre-red sandstones is affected by faults that displace the pre-red sequence. Five faults cut the red event along the cross section shown in Figures 2.22 and 2.23. These faults

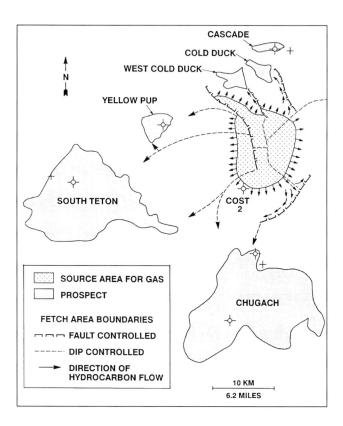

Figure 2.26. Fetch area map for Stuart subbasin showing the gas-expelling region assigned to each prospect.

divide the pre-red sequence of the Stuart subbasin into a series of fault blocks trending northwest-southeast. Our concern is whether these faults create barriers to hydrocarbon migration.

Shell estimated that there were 400 net-ft of sandstone in the bottom 1800 ft of the pre-red sequence. Only one core was taken of a sandstone in this sequence. Two samples out of thirty had an air permeability above 1 md, and the median air permeability was 0.17 md. Because of their low permeability, the gas-bearing pre-red sandstones were considered to be noncommercial. Hydrocarbon migration across a fault in this sort of stratigraphy is unlikely for two reasons. First, permeable sandstones make up less than 5% of the section and are thus unlikely to be juxtaposed across the fault. Second, even in the better sandstones the fault zone is expected to have a low permeability because of the crushing and smearing of clays, micas, and volcanic rock fragments.

For these reasons, we assumed that the faults that cut the red event divided the pre-red sequence into a series of fault blocks within each of which expelled gas is transmitted updip toward the basin margin. Combining this description of migration within the pre-red sequence with our earlier description of migration along the red unconformity and the basement, we developed the fetch map shown in Figure 2.26 for the six prospects adjacent to the Stuart subbasin. None of these prospects could derive a significant amount of thermal gas from either of the other two subbasins. Based on this fetch map,

Table 2.2. Volumes of Expelled Gas for Stuart Subbasin Prospects

	Gas Volumes (×10⁹ SCF)	
	Basin Fill	Pre-Red
Prospect	Source Rock	Source Rock
Yellow Pup	0.2	150
South Teton	3	820
Chugach	36	2070

thermally generated gas cannot migrate to the Cascade prospect. This fetch map was used to make quantitative estimates of the thermal gas available to the Yellow Pup, South Teton, and Chugach prospects.

Since there may be some doubt as to the validity of our concept that faults are barriers to hydrocarbon migration in the pre-red sequence, some comments on the impact of this concept are in order. First, if faults are not barriers, Cascade might have access to a small gas charge. Second, the fault barrier that forms the downdip limit to the South Teton fetch area transfers gas to the Chugach prospect which otherwise would have reached South Teton. Yellow Pup is unaffected because the dip of the gas-generating rocks reverses direction at the fault.

Prospect Summary

We have used the fetch map in Figure 2.26 along with the models described in previous sections to calculate the volumes of gas expelled into the fetch area for each prospect. The results are summarized in Table 2.2.

These values represent our estimates of the amount of gas expelled from the humic kerogen in the basin fill source rock and the coals in the pre-red sequence. After correction to subsurface conditions, the 36 bcf from the basin fill source rock for the Chugach would create a gas volume equivalent to that in a migration path approximately 4 ft thick in 10% porosity rock for the area required to reach the basement contact. Since there are other migration losses and several migration paths, we believe all of the Chugach basin fill gas would be lost on the migration path. The conditions for Yellow Pup and South Teton are much less favorable. Therefore, we do not believe the basin fill source could provide even a show of either gas or liquids at the prospects.

The migration loss calculations for the pre-red fluvial sandstone sequence are summarized in Table 2.3. Table 2.4 summarizes the totals from Tables 2.2 and 2.3 and lists the predicted volumes of thermal gas that could be

trapped in good quality reservoir sandstones.

The final step is to assign the gas volumes available to good quality reservoir rocks to specific traps on South Teton and Chugach. From the COST-2 well (Figure 2.16), we expect to find the deepest good quality reservoir rocks slightly deeper than the blue seismic event. Figure 2.20 shows the structure at the blue level, the locations of the blue horizon onlap on the basement, and the basement structure shallower than this onlap position. Possible gas accumulations are also shown. In the presale evaluation, the possibility of a series of onlap traps for South Teton and Chugach that started below the blue horizon and continued over a depth interval of 1000 ft or more was recognized. If such traps allowed some gas to pass through, then it was assumed that the closure below the first good seal above economic basement would have access to the gas. Thus, the presale evaluation would have predicted about 130 bcf of gas on South Teton and 1000 bcf on Chugach in some combination of onlap traps and a trap above the basement high.

For the COST-2 well, Shell estimated that there were 491 net-ft of good quality reservoir sandstone with an average porosity of 16% in an interval about 2000 ft thick extending above and below the blue event. This interval becomes thinner and is approximately 3000 ft shallower at the predicted onlap position. A reasonable presale trap model might have been to predict 100 net-ft of gas trapped in two or possibly three onlapping sandstones within a zone extending from about 500 ft below the blue horizon to about 500 ft above this horizon. The cross-hatched areas on South Teton and Chugach in Figure 2.20 represent such traps at the blue level. The trap volume on South Teton in the untested cross-hatched area, assuming 100 net-ft of gas with porosity of 20% and gas saturation of 75%, would be 475 bcf, which is far more than the 133 bcf estimated to be available. The same reservoir and trap model indicate that for Chugach, the untested cross-hatched area would hold the entire 987 bcf of gas estimated to be available. Thus, use of the presale stratigraphic information allows a reasonable explanation for the failure of the wells drilled on South Teton and Chugach to find any gas.

Drilling Results Compared to Predictions

The locations of five wells that were drilled to evaluate prospects in the Stuart subbasin are shown in Figures 2.19, 2.20, and 2.26. All of the wells were plugged and abandoned without drill-stem tests. The only significant hydrocarbon show reported by Desautels (1988) was

Table 2.3. Volumes of Gas Trapped in the Pre-Red Sequence or Migration Loss to Prospects

	Expelling Area		Migration Area		Volume Trapped on
	Area	Trapped Volume	Area	Trapped Volume	Migration Path
Prospect	(mi²)	(× 10⁹ SCF)	(mi²)	(× 10⁹ SCF)	(× 10⁹ SCF)
Yellow Pup	1.9	114	4.4	97	211
South Teton	7.3	438	11.3	249	687
Chugach	9.9	594	22.4	493	1087

Table 2.4. Volumes of Gas Available to Reservoirs or Prospects

Prospect	Gas Volumes ($\times 10^9$ SCF)		
	Expelled	Migration Loss	Available
Yellow Pup	150	211	0
South Teton	820	687	133
Chugach	2070	1087	983

oil in the mud circulated up from the basement rocks during coring operations on OCS-Y-0430 #1 on Chugach. Based on the composition of this oil, Elf inferred that it was not generated in the nonmarine source material of the Stuart subbasin area. The hydrocarbon accumulation giving rise to the oil show was judged to be of small volume and of no commercial significance.

We reviewed the wireline logs and mud logs and found no evidence for gas in any sandstones in any of the five wells. All gas shows on the mud logs could be correlated with coals.

The evaluation of the prospects using petroleum system logic predicted that there would not be thermal gas accumulations on Cascade or Yellow Pup. Therefore, the failure of the wells on these two prospects was predicted. However, accumulations of thermal gas were predicted to exist on South Teton and Chugach. Unfortunately, the structural and stratigraphic characteristics of these prospects were such that the exact locations of these accumulations could not be predicted. As we showed in the preceding section, using the COST-2 well stratigraphy, we could account for both the predicted gas volumes (133 bcf on South Teton and 987 bcf on Chugach) and the dry holes. Let us determine whether we can still reconcile the predicted gas volumes with the dry holes using the additional stratigraphic information available from the wells drilled on the prospects.

The stratigraphic section penetrated by each of these wells is shown in Figure 2.21. All of the wells bottomed in economic basement rocks and penetrated a sandstone reservoir above basement that was overlain by a seal rock. The well on South Teton was drilled on a basement high and did not penetrate the stratigraphic section within which basement onlap traps might occur. We chose the Yellow Pup well for our source of stratigraphic information for estimating the potential capacity of onlap traps on South Teton. This choice was based on the proximity of the Yellow Pup well, the inferred direction of sediment transport, and the seismic evidence for interval thicknesses and bed character.

In the Yellow Pup well, numerous sandstones occur in the interval from about 5000 to 6000 ft followed by a 400-ft-thick seal rock and a second interval with numerous sandstones from 6420 ft to the basement rock. Correcting for the elevation of the derrick floor and the structural difference between the OCS-Y-0407 well on Yellow Pup and the South Teton onlap, we would expect to have onlap traps with elevations of about 700 ft below the blue level and near the blue level.

In the Yellow Pup well, a 370-ft-thick interval across the blue level contains 68 net-ft of sandstone with an average porosity of 26%. Assuming one-half of this sand forms onlap traps having a total area equal to that shown in Figure 2.20 on South Teton, there could be 240 bcf of gas trapped at the blue level on South Teton.

We do not have a map showing the onlap at the deeper level on basement, but the structure map on basement suggests that onlap traps at the deeper level are possible. There are 82 net-ft of sandstone in an interval 170 ft thick near the top of this lower sand section in the Yellow Pup well. The average porosity of this sandstone is 21%. A 6-mi^2 area of onlap trap incorporating one-half of this net sand interval could hold 160 bcf of gas. We estimated that 133 bcf of gas would reach the reservoir interval on the South Teton prospect. This quantity is much less than the 400 bcf of gas estimated to be the amount that could be held in onlap traps in the two reservoir intervals on the South Teton prospect. Thus, the failure of gas to reach the crestal trap on South Teton is considered to be consistent with the prediction suggested by petroleum system logic.

The two wells drilled on the Chugach prospect provided us with the stratigraphic information needed to estimate the volume of both the crestal trap and an onlap trap near the blue level. Well OCS-Y-0430 located downdip of the crest penetrated a thick package of mostly seal rocks above an interval that contains numerous sandstones extending from 3952 ft to economic basement. The crest of the shallow structure is cut by a fault with a throw that decreases from about 350 ft near the crest to zero. This fault would limit the areas of the accumulations in the lower sandstones because of sand–sand contact across the fault and would allow vertical migration up to the first good seal that extends from 3952 to 3625 ft. To estimate the volume that might be trapped in this crestal trap updip of well OCS-Y-0430, we assumed a common water level of 4252 ft in all the sandstones between 4252 and 3952 ft. This places the gas–water contact about 20 ft above the level at which the hypothesized pay sandstone at 3952 ft is penetrated in well OCS-Y-0430. There is 85 ft of sandstone in this 300-ft-thick interval with an average porosity of 35%. We estimate that with a common water level this crestal trap could hold 270 bcf without any gas extending downdip to well OCS-Y-0430.

Well OCS-Y-0425 was drilled to test a potentially large onlap trap on the Chugach prospect. The well penetrated a sandstone-rich section extending from 5608 ft to the basement beneath a good seal approximately 140 ft thick. Thus, the conditions were excellent for an onlap trap. The upper 113 ft of the sandstone section contained 97 net-ft of sandstone with an average porosity of 21%. We estimate that an onlap trap that included this sandstone with the area shown in Figure 2.20 could hold 1130 bcf of gas. Thus, the total volume of trapped gas calculated using the observed stratigraphy and the trap areas proposed in Figure 2.20 is 1400 bcf compared to an estimated available volume of 987 bcf. Again, we find that the prediction made using the petroleum system logic is consistent with the results observed upon drilling.

It is evident from the nature of the problem and the quality and quantity of data available for the presale evaluation that our estimates of the volumes of expelled gas and of the volumes of gas retained in the fluvial sandstones are subject to large uncertainties. In particular, our values for the volumes of expelled gas should be viewed as estimates of the median value, with about a tenfold range from the 5% to 95% probability values. Even given this uncertainty, these estimates made in advance could provide a warning that there was a significant risk with the gas charge. These estimates could have indicated that the prospects adjacent to the Stuart subbasin were unlikely to have important gas reserves even though there were two large structures in a geologic setting that contained reservoir and seal rocks.

Summary of Norton Basin Example

The Norton basin is a complex consisting of three subbasins. For the presale evaluation, two COST wells were available, COST-1 in the St. Lawrence subbasin and COST-2 in the Stuart subbasin. Our application of petroleum system logic was restricted to the areas in and around these two subbasins and started with an assessment of the probability of finding significant oil reserves in either area.

A major unconformity, the red unconformity, occurred at approximately 12,000 ft in both wells. An abrupt increase in R_o to 1.0% occurred at this unconformity. The section below the red unconformity contained coals. Because of this increase in R_o to 1.0%, we concluded that any potential for oil generation in the pre-red section was used up and that the oil was lost prior to the deposition of the post-red basin fill sequence. Where the red unconformity was buried deeply enough under the basin fill sequence to increase the R_o above 1.0%, a second episode of gas generation and expulsion was assumed to have taken place.

Organic matter is present throughout the basin fill sequence in both COST wells and is mature for oil generation at depths greater than about 9000 ft. In this mature interval, the organic matter is a mixture of lipid and humic kerogens. Rock-Eval pyrolysis data and the poor quality of oil shows indicated that there had been an insignificant amount of oil expelled from the kerogen in the mature basin fill sediments in either well. We estimated that a subcommercial volume of oil may have been expelled from this sequence in the central part of the St. Lawrence subbasin where the overburden rocks are thickest. The COST-2 well lacked intervals with a high enough lipid content to expel oil. Where the overburden rock is thickest in the Stuart subbasin, expulsion of a minor amount of gas and condensate may have occurred from the basin fill sequence. Because of the small amount of this gas and condensate, it was most likely lost along the migration path between the gas expulsion region and the prospects.

Five wells have been drilled on four different prospects adjacent to the Stuart subbasin. Three wells on three different prospects were properly located and provided a good stratigraphic section for observing the presence of migrating oil. However, oil shows were lacking in all three wells. Therefore the evidence from the postsale drilling of these prospects is in agreement with Shell's presale evaluation that a significant oil charge was unlikely.

The second aspect of our application of petroleum system logic to the Norton basin was the development of a complete petroleum system analysis of the four drilled prospects adjacent to the Stuart subbasin. Essentially all of the hydrocarbon charge available to these prospects was judged to be gas expelled from the pre-red coals during the latter part of the basin fill period. These coals are distributed throughout a thick sedimentary package and are interbedded with fluvial sandstones and fluvial plus paludal siltstones and shales. We assigned fetch areas to each prospect so that the gas available to each prospect and the losses along the migration path could be estimated. From these estimates it was concluded using presale data that gas accumulations were unlikely to exist on two of the prospects and that the volumes of gas available to the other two prospects were small relative to the potential trapping capacity of the prospects.

The results obtained in the five exploratory wells drilled on these four prospects after the sale were in agreement with these predictions made from the petroleum system analysis. Gas accumulations were undetected on any of the prospects. The possibility of onlap traps on the flanks of the two prospects believed to have received some gas was confirmed by the stratigraphic information acquired during the drilling. Volumetric estimates made using the observed reservoir parameters indicated that, because of the locations chosen for the three wells drilled on these two prospects, failure to find accumulations of the estimated size was easily explained. Therefore, the results obtained from the postsale drilling of the five wells on four prospects are consistent with predictions made from a petroleum system logic using the COST-2 well and reflection seismic data.

CONCLUSIONS

The use of petroleum system logic in exploration means reliance on integrated interpretations of the processes of petroleum generation, migration, and accumulation for the evaluation of exploration opportunities. The accuracy of such an interpretation increases when the quality and amount of pertinent data increase. However, even in a frontier area having little well control, it is possible to make a reliable evaluation of an exploration opportunity using petroleum system logic. This conclusion was illustrated by the successful application of petroleum system logic to two aspects of the evaluation of prospects in the Stuart subbasin area of the Norton Sound in offshore Alaska. Using the COST well in the Stuart subbasin for stratigraphic control and a grid of reflection seismic lines, predictions were made that the prospects would have little or no oil and that some prospects would have gas accumulations of moderate size. Exploratory drilling confirmed these predictions.

Two kinds of evidence were particularly helpful in the evaluation of oil potential. Rock-Eval pyrolysis measurements of thermally mature samples indicated that a negligible amount of oil had been expelled from the potential source rocks. This interpretation was supported by the weakness of the oil shows in porous rocks within the thermally mature section.

Quantitative analyses of the processes of hydrocarbon generation, migration, and accumulation were required to determine which prospects might be gas productive and to estimate the size of any gas accumulations. The gas was generated in a sequence of coal beds interbedded with paludal shales and siltstones and fluvial sandstones. Significant migration losses were estimated to occur in the fluvial sandstones. Supporting evidence for these losses came from the observation of gas shows in these fluvial sands in the COST well. The Stuart subbasin example illustrates the importance of making a quantitative evaluation whenever there is a possibility that petroleum accumulation size will be limited by the available charge.

The use of petroleum system logic in the evaluation of an exploration opportunity often allows the explorer to reduce the evaluation problem to the careful assessment of a single factor. For example, often the presence of adequate reservoir and seal rocks and a trapping configuration can be demonstrated with a high level of certainty. To complete the evaluation using petroleum system logic requires demonstrating that a source rock attained maturity at the right time and expelled hydrocarbons into a migration path leading to the accumulation position. There are four factors in this part of the evaluation: source rock existence and type, source rock maturity, migration path, and timing. Study of the particular geologic characteristics may lead to the conclusion that the probability of success is dominated by the outcome of one of the factors. The final evaluation is then reduced to the assembly and careful interpretation of the evidence regarding this one factor.

Two of the examples presented in this chapter illustrate the use of petroleum system logic to reduce the evaluation problem to the consideration of a single factor. In both of these examples, the presence of adequate reservoir rock, seal rock, and structural configuration for trapping was ensured, but in each case there was an uncertainty regarding a facet of the hydrocarbon generation process. The first example was taken from the 1968 Offshore Texas lease sale. The exploration opportunity was a major growth fault trend with no previous drilling. The major unknown was whether oil would be present in the new trend as opposed to gas. The critical factor thus became the type of source rock expected in the depth intervals that could provide such an oil charge. Examination of the evidence bearing on the question led to the conclusion that oil should not be expected. Subsequent drilling proved the validity of this conclusion.

The second example was taken from the 1976 Baltimore Canyon sale. The problem was the estimation of the amount and type of hydrocarbons that were expected to accumulate in a well-defined large volume structural trap on the Schlee dome. A review of the available data showed that migration to this trap was ensured from a thick, matured, undrilled stratigraphic section. The critical remaining condition that needed to be satisfied was the presence of either oil- or gas-prone source rocks within this thick stratigraphic section. An adequate petroleum charge was predicted to be available because favorable environments for source rock deposition were inferred for this thick, undrilled interval from a geologic model derived from reflection seismic data. Postsale drilling discovered no petroleum. Although the prediction was wrong in this case, this example provides a good illustration of the use of petroleum system logic to define the critical factor in an exploration evaluation problem and of the approach used to assess the critical factor.

Petroleum system logic follows from the fundamental processes that control the creation of petroleum deposits. Because of this fundamental basis, petroleum system logic is applicable to all petroleum exploration problems. The examples chosen for review in this chapter are intended to illustrate how petroleum system logic can be applied to a diverse set of problems encountered in frontier area exploration.

Acknowledgments I thank Shell Oil Company for giving me permission to publish this paper which was based on work carried out in Shell Oil Company Exploration Divisions. A large number of Shell Oil and Shell Development personnel, far too numerous to list, contributed to the OCS sale preparations described in this paper and to the research and development work that preceded the applications described here. Of all these people, I wish to single out four individuals for particular credit. The leadership of R. E. McAdams, Vice President Exploration, Shell Oil Company, 1957–1970, was instrumental in the creation of the environment in which organic geochemical research could be effectively incorporated into the exploration program. In addition, Mr. McAdams was an inspiring personal leader to me and many others in the Shell Oil exploration organization. The research contributions of G. T. Phillippi, Archie Hood, and Pierre Mommessin provided a sound technical foundation. Finally, I thank Vic Aipperspach for his assistance in resurrecting the Alaska Division work on the Norton basin, and I give special thanks to Karee Kimbro for assuming the major responsibility for the graphics.

References Cited

Allan, U. S., 1989, Model for hydrocarbon migration and entrapment within faulted structures: AAPG Bulletin, v. 73, n. 7, p. 803–811.

Desautels, D. A., 1988, Exploration evaluation of hydrocarbon potential from Norton basin, Alaska: Bulletin des Centres de Rescherches Exploration-Production Elf-Aquitaine, v. 12, n. 2, p. 514–531.

Dow, W. G., 1982, Geochemical analysis of Norton Sound COST No. 2 well, Alaska: Houston, TX, Robertson Research (U.S.), 33 p.

Fisher, M. A., 1982, Petroleum geology of Norton basin, Alaska: AAPG Bulletin, v. 66, n. 3, p. 286–301.

Fisher, M. A., W. W. Pattan, Jr., D. R. Thor, M. L. Holmes, E. W. Scott, C. H. Nelson, and C. L. Wilson, 1979, Resource report for proposed OCS lease sale 57: Norton basin, Alaska: U.S.G.S. Open-File Report 79-720, 43 p.

Fisher, M. A., W. W. Patton, and M. L. Holmes, 1981, Geology and petroleum potential of the Norton basin area, Alaska: U.S.G.S. Open-File Report 81-1316, 51 p.

Fisher, M. A., W. W. Patton, and M. L. Holmes, 1982, Geology of Norton basin and continental shelf beneath northwestern Bering Sea, Alaska: AAPG Bulletin, v. 66, n. 3, p. 255–285.

Lippert, R. H., 1983, The "Great Stone Dome"—a compaction structure, *in* A. W. Bally, ed., Seismic expression of structural styles—a picture and work atlas: AAPG Studies in Geology 15, v. 1, p. 1.3-1 to 1.3-4.

Mattick, R. E., 1980, Petroleum geology of Baltimore Canyon trough: Society of Petroleum Engineers Eastern Regional Meeting, SPE 9525, November, 11 p.

McIntyre, L. B., 1976, Interpretation of regional seismic line, done in preparation of the Baltimore Canyon lease sale, 1976 (unpublished): Shell Oil Company.

Prather, B. E., 1991, Petroleum geology of the Upper Jurassic and Lower Cretaceous, Baltimore Canyon trough, Western North Atlantic: AAPG Bulletin, v. 75, n. 2. p. 258–277.

Pratt, L. M., 1984, Influence of paleoenvironmental factors on preservation of organic matter in middle Cretaceous Greenhorn Formation, Pueblo, Colorado: AAPG Bulletin, v. 68, n. 9, p. 1146–1159.

Schlee, J. S., J. C. Behrendt, J. A. Grow, J. M. Robb, R. E. Mattick, P. T. Taylor, and B. J. Lawson, 1976, Regional geologic framework off the northeastern United States, AAPG Bulletin, v. 60, p. 926–951.

Turner, R. F., J. G. Bolm, C. J. McCarthy, D. A. Steffy, P. Lowry, T. O. Flett, and D. Blunt, 1983, Geologic and operational summary Norton Sound COST No. 2 well, Norton Sound, Alaska: U.S.G.S. Open-File Report 83-557, p. 98.

Turner, R. F., G. C. Martin, D. E Risley, D. A. Steffy, T. O. Flett, and M. B. Lynch, 1986, Geologic report for the Norton basin planning area, Bering Sea, Alaska: OCS Report MMS 86-0033, 179 p.

West, J., 1976, U.S. operators plunge big in Baltimore Canyon sale: Oil and Gas Journal, v. 74, n. 34, August, p. 45–49.

Wilson, H. M., 1968a, Theory of oil-productive belts off Texas due for a test: Oil and Gas Journal, v. 66, n. 12, March, p. 46–48.

Wilson, H. M., 1968b, Texas size bids push offshore lease sale to near record $602.4 million: Oil and Gas Journal, v. 66, n. 22, May, p. 54–57.

Worrall, D. M., 1991, Tectonic history of the Bering Sea and the evolution of Tertiary strike-slip basins of the Bering Shelf: GSA Special Paper 257, 120 p.

"Petroleum prospecting is an art."

—E. DeGolyer

Passage from DeGolyer, E., 1940, The Development of the Art of Prospecting: Princeton University Press.

Magoon, L. B, and W. G. Dow, eds., 1994, The petroleum
system—from source to trap: AAPG Memoir 60.

Chapter **3**

Petroleum Systems of the World Involving Upper Jurassic Source Rocks

H. Douglas Klemme

Bondville, Vermont, U.S.A.

Abstract

Fourteen "mega" petroleum systems with Upper Jurassic source rocks contain one-fourth of the world's discovered petroleum. These petroleum systems, their locations in space and time, and their petroleum plumbing ingredients are reviewed, described, and tabulated. Each system's recovery efficiency is estimated. Plumbing ingredients are related to the relative magnitude of the petroleum system's estimated recovery efficency. While the presence of a source rock is a requirement of all petroleum systems—with source rock abundance and character of considerable influence on recovery efficiency—other plumbing ingredients are capable of even more influence on the magnitude of the systme's recovery efficiency. These other plumbing factors include the quality and quantity (extent) of reservoir and cap rock, trap evolution and size, and the dynamics and timing of these factors along with source rock maturation and migration. The character, quality, and quantity of these petroleum systems' plumbing are related to their plate tectonic location, palelatitudinal realms, and the structural (tectonostratigraphic) evolution of the basin or province.

INTRODUCTION

Fourteen petroleum systems with Upper Jurassic source rocks contain one-fourth of the world's discovered petroleum. Eleven other systems with Lower and Middle Jurassic source rocks presently have a minor but significant amount of discovered petroleum. These petroleum systems are geologically reviewed, their location in space and time is described and mapped on a continental scale, their relative petroleum system recovery efficiencies are estimated, and the effect their essential elements and processes have on their "petroleum plumbing" is outlined. In addition, their petroleum dynamics are discussed.

The information used to identify and map these Jurassic petroleum systems come from many references, the more important ones being Bedoes (1973), Beydoun and Dunnington (1975), Jones (1975), Weeks (1975), Nehring (1978, 1981), Kanstler et al. (1984), Carmolt and St. John (1986), Masters et al. (1987, 1991), Ziegler (1988), Creaney and Allan (1990), Hubbard et al. (1990), and Zappaterra (1990).

In mapping the world's petroleum systems that involve Upper Jurassic source rocks, continental maps (not including Antarctica) with currently accepted Upper Jurassic paleolatitudes were used as a base. Three "cut-off" margins or limits to those Upper Jurassic sedimentary rocks that include source rocks generally considered available for potential petroleum systems are outlined (Figures 3.1–3.5). These cut-offs include (1) the updip zero edge from either nondeposition or truncation of Upper Jurassic sedimentary rocks along the craton margins, (2) positive areas of either nondeposition or truncation within the Upper Jurassic depositional trend, and (3) an orogenic cut-off zone behind which any Upper Jurassic sedimentary rocks have usually been destroyed by orogenic metamorphism, intrusion, or truncation associated with Phanerozoic terrane accretion. The latter is often considered a zone of petroleum economic basement, although notable exceptions occur where the Jurassic source rock is preserved in these zones (see Cook Inlet and Vienna basin).

Tables 3.1 and 3.2 attempt to organize the petroleum plumbing ingredients, including source rock, reservoir rock, cap (seal rock), trap type, and dynamic characteristics, together with an estimate of the recovery efficiency for the petroleum systems that involve Upper Jurassic source rocks. An events chart for each of the 14 petroleum systems outlines the timing of essential elements and processes in relation to the timing of the system's plumbing dynamics (Figure 3.6). The timing of the initial development of a given trap was found to be variable dependent on the type of trap being formed. Different trap types and different ages and lithologies of reservoir rocks are the departure point for the division of petroleum systems into plays and prospects.

Difficulty in naming Upper Jurassic petroleum systems by using major source rocks and reservoir rocks was encountered in the following situations: (1) regions

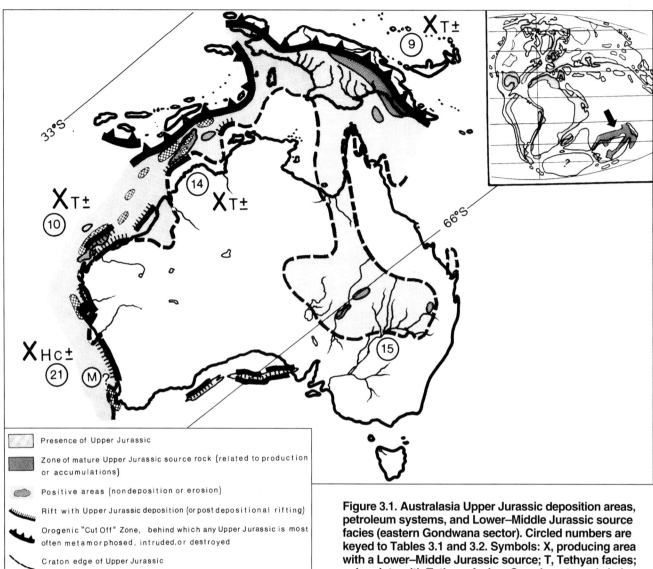

Figure 3.1. Australasia Upper Jurassic deposition areas, petroleum systems, and Lower–Middle Jurassic source facies (eastern Gondwana sector). Circled numbers are keyed to Tables 3.1 and 3.2. Symbols: X, producing area with a Lower–Middle Jurassic source; T, Tethyan facies; subscripts with Tethyan facies: C, carbonate and shales; E, evaporites; −, <40° paleolatitude; +, >40° paleolatitude. H, Humic facies (clastics); subscripts with Humic facies: C, coaly; L, lacustrine, −, <40° paleolatitude; +, >40° paleolatitude.

Legend:
Presence of Upper Jurassic

Zone of mature Upper Jurassic source rock (related to production or accumulations)

Positive areas (nondeposition or erosion)

Rift with Upper Jurassic deposition (or postdepositional rifting)

Orogenic "Cut Off" Zone, behind which any Upper Jurassic is most often metamorphosed, intruded,or destroyed

Craton edge of Upper Jurassic

Upper Jurassic volcanics   66°S   Upper Jurassic paleolatitude

(21) Petroleum System   (M) Minor Accumulation

Major lakes & drainage

of the world where there is a lack of stratigraphic names, requiring that the age of the rock units be used for source and reservoir; (2) petroleum systems so large and extensive that several stratigraphic names have been applied to the same source rock; and (3) many Upper Jurassic systems where a great deal of upward petroleum leakage occurred so that many (multiple) reservoirs, rather than one main reservoir, contain the bulk of the accumulated petroleum.

The global scale of this study requires that petroleum systems be lumped for brevity of discussion and because of the lack of detailed information (see uncited references by petroleum system at end of chapter). This is apparent in that certain petroleum system case studies included in this volume that involve Upper Jurassic source rocks do not necessarily correspond to the petroleum systems

identified in this chapter. This occurs because the case studies usually include sufficient information to map a pod of active source rock, whereas the systems identified in this chapter rely more on regional geology. It is apparent that as more attention is given to mapping each pod of active source rock and its related hydrocarbons, the 25 petroleum systems described here will probably increase in number. However, as global as this approach may be, it demonstrates the usefulness of identifying all those petroleum systems in the world that include one source rock interval.

Estimates of the key factors used to derive a petroleum system's recovery efficiency include (1) source rock area and thickness, total organic carbon (TOC), hydrogen index (HI), density, and kerogen type; (2) present discovered barrels of oil equivalent recoverable

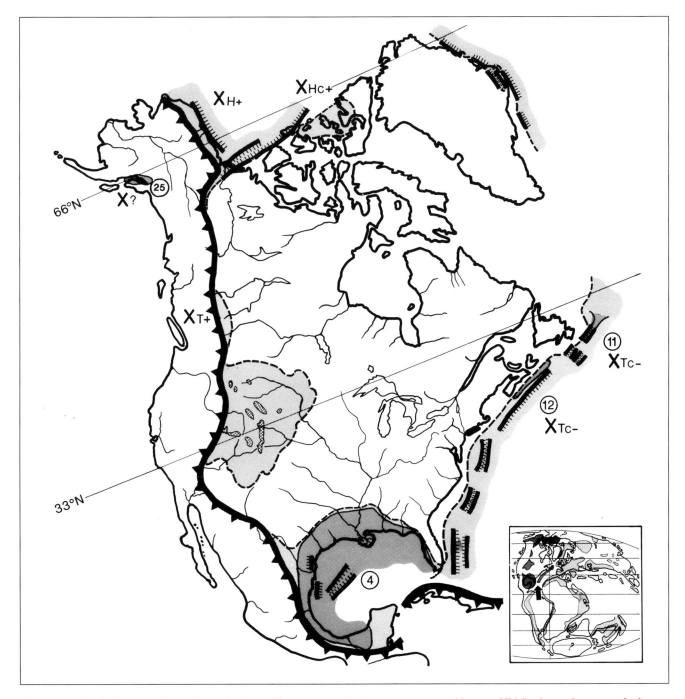

Figure 3.2. North America Upper Jurassic deposition areas, petroleum systems, and Lower–Middle Jurassic source facies (western Laurasia sector). (See Figure 3.1 for explanation of symbols.)

petroleum (BOE); and (3) the system's estimated ultimate conventionally recoverable BOE. These estimates have been accomplished with published data and are subject to more error in frontier basins. However, the calculations for the petroleum system recovery efficiency are within a magnitude believed to provide the accuracy needed for the general conclusions of this study.

Subsequent to the preparation of this paper, two other areas of Upper Jurassic source rocks have been documented: the French Aquitaine basin (Espitalié and Drouet, 1992) and the Algoa–Gamtoos basin of South Africa (Malan, 1993).

UPPER JURASSIC SOURCE ROCKS

Present-Day Geography

About 80% of the BOE generated from Upper Jurassic source rocks comes from sedimentary basins or provinces located on or in the interior of continents, while 20% of the BOE comes from basins or provinces located along continental coastal areas (Table 3.3). Interior basins or provinces contain an estimated 70% of the Upper Jurassic mature source rock area and 56% of the volume. Continental coastal areas contain 30% of the

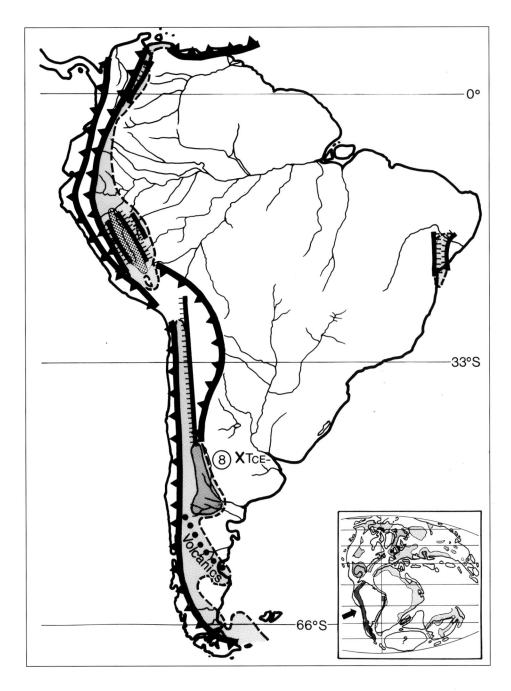

Figure 3.3. South America Upper Jurassic deposition areas, petroleum systems, and Lower–Middle Jurassic source facies (western Gondwana sector). (See Figure 3.1 for explanation of symbols.)

Upper Jurassic mature source rock area and 44% of the volume. If source rock richness is similar in both provinces, then by material balance, the continental interior would appear to contain the more efficient petroleum systems.

Plate Tectonic Location

Upper Jurassic source rocks were deposited on both Precambrian cratons and their surrounding Phanerozoic accretionary terranes. Over 50% of the BOE from Upper Jurassic source rocks comes from those rocks deposited on the Precambrian craton, mainly in northern Gondwana (Figures 3.1, 3.3, and 3.4), along the south Tethyan margin (including the Arabian–Iranian basin,

the Yemen rift province, the Papua basin, and the northwest Australian shelf). The remaining BOE from Upper Jurassic source rocks was deposited, about equally, over Hercynian and Caledonian accreted terranes around and on Laurasia (Figures 3.2 and 3.5). The eastern West Siberian basin and northwest European shelf (northern North Sea and Norwegian shelf) have Upper Jurassic source rocks deposited over Caledonian age orogenic–accreted terranes. The Gulf of Mexico, Middle Caspian, Amu Darya, and Jeane d'Arc provinces, as well as the Scotia shelf, western West Siberian basin, and Vienna basin overlie Hercynian accreted terranes. A minor amount of BOE from Upper Jurassic source rocks occurs in the Neuquen basin, which was developed on the Caledonian and Hercynian circum-Pangea and

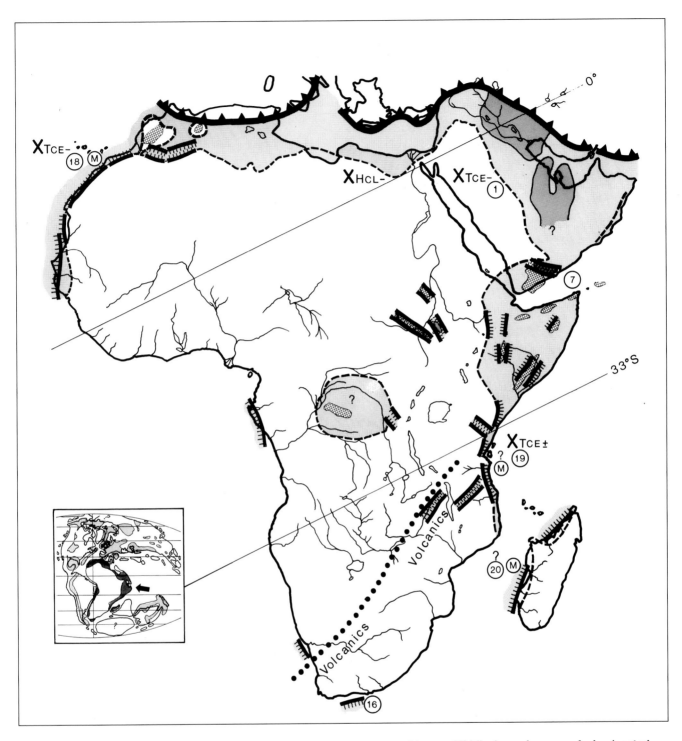

Figure 3.4. Africa Upper Jurassic deposition areas, petroleum systems, and Lower–Middle Jurassic source facies (central Gondwana sector). (See Figure 3.1 for explanation of symbols.)

Kimmerian circum-Pacific orogenic–accreted zone terranes. By material balance, the craton appears to be the locale of the more prolific petroleum systems; however, when the Arabian–Iranian and West Siberian super basins are excluded, the Hercynian and Caledonian terranes appear to underlie the more prolific petroleum systems (Table 3.4).

Petroleum Geotectonic Realm Location

Petroleum realms, as used here, consist of the Tethyan realm, which divides the southern Gondwana realm from the Boreal realm, and the Pacific realm (Klemme and Ulmishek, 1991). The Tethyan realm is related to an east-west equatorial seaway that opened and closed

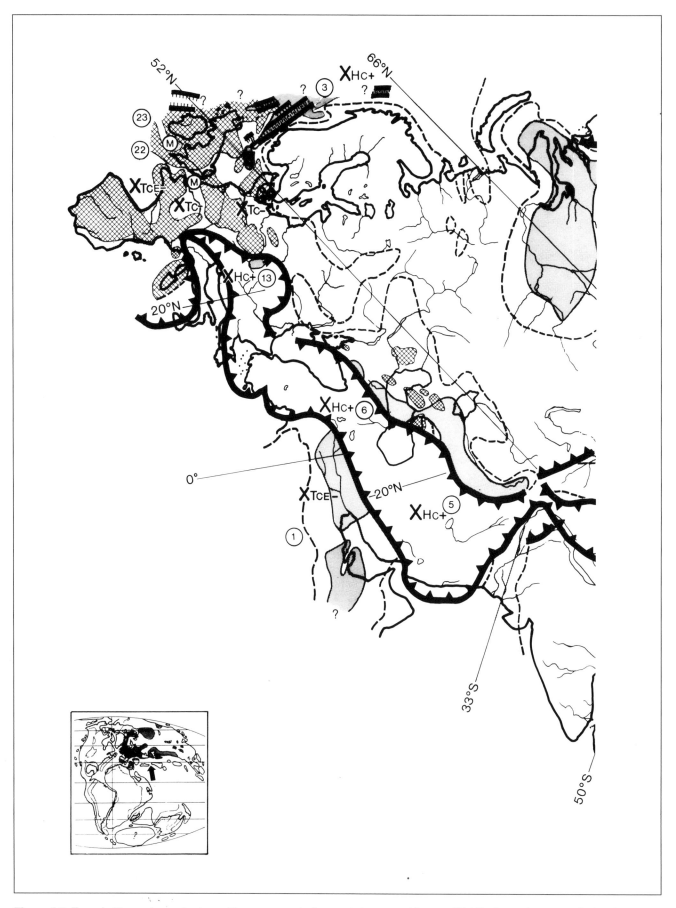

Figure 3.5. Eurasia Upper Jurassic deposition areas, petroleum systems, and Lower–Middle Jurassic source facies (eastern Laurasia sector). (See Figure 3.1 for explanation of symbols.)

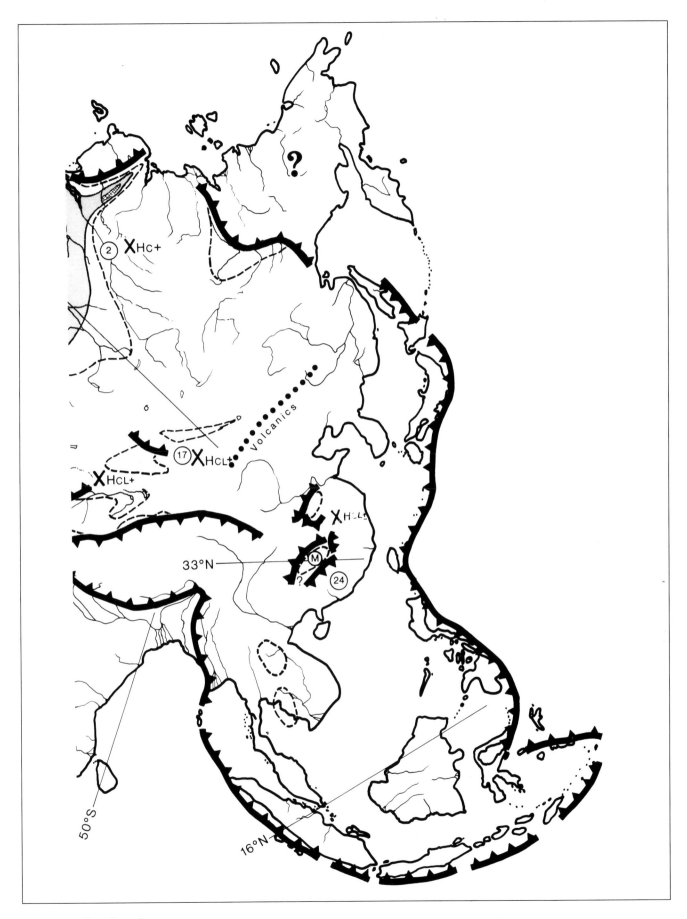

Figure 3.5. *(continued)*

Table 3.1. Petroleum Systems Involving Upper Jurassic (1–14) and Lower–Middle Jurassic (15–25) Source Rocks

Map No.[a]	Petroleum System[b]	Province or Basin	Basin Evolution[c]	Location
1	Hanifa–Arab(!)	Arabian/Iranian basin	P–R–S–F	Middle East
2	Bazhenov–Neocomian(!)	West Siberia basin	R–S	Russia
3	Kimmeridgian "hot shale"–Brent(!)	Northwest European Shelf	R–S–R–S	United Kingdom, Norway, Denmark
4	Smackover–Tamman(!)	Gulf of Mexico province	R–S–HS	USA (Texas, Alabama, Florida), Mexico
5	Khodzipaik–Shatlyk(?)	Amu Darya–Tadjik province	R–S–F	Uzbekistan, Tadjikistan, Turkmenia, Kazakhstan
6	J3 "black shales"–J3 to K2(.)	Middle Caspian–Sea of Azov province	R–S–F	Kazakhstan, Uzbekistan, Russia, Azerbaijan,
7	Lam–Amla'ah(!)	Yemen province	P–R–S	Yemen Arab Republic
8	Vaca Muerta–Sierras Blancas(?)	Neuquen basin	R–S–F	Argentina
9	Maril–Toro(.)	Greater Papua province	R–S–F	Papua New Guinea and Irian Jaya
10	Dingo–Windalia(.)	Barrow–Dampier subprovince of Northwest Shelf	R/S–R–S–HS	Australia
11	Kimmeridgian "hot shale"–Hibernia(!)	Jeane d'Arc subbasin, Grand Banks	R–S–HS	Canada
12	Verril Canyon–Mic Mac(!)	Scotia Shelf subbasin, Grand Banks	R–S–HS	Canada
13	Obermalm–Badenian(!)	Vienna basin	Complex	Austria
14	Flamingo–Plover(.)	Vulcan Graben of Northwest Shelf	R/S–R–S–HS	Australia
15	No name	Cooper subbasin, Great Aretesian basin	—	Australia
16	No name	Agulhas Bank offshore	—	South Africa
17	No name	"Rift basin province"	—	N. China and S. Mongolia
18	No name	Essaouria province	—	Morroco
19	No name	Tanzania coastal	—	Tanzania
20	No name	Morondava coastal basin	—	Malagasay
21	No name	Perth basin	—	Australia
22	No name	Western Approaches province	—	United Kingdom
23	Nno name	Celtic sea province	—	Ireland
24	No name	Sichuan basin	—	China
25	Tuxedni–Hemlock(!)	Cook Inlet	—	Alaska

[a]Map numbers correspond to numbers on Figures 3.1–3.5.

[b](!), known; (.), hypothetical; (?), speculative.

[c]F, foredeep; HS, half–sag; P, platform; R, rift; S, sag.

during the Hercynian, Kimmerian, and Alpine orogenic events while microplates were rifted or drifted from northern Gondwana and collided or docked on the southern accretionary margin of Laurasia. The southern Gondwana and Boreal realms represent the interior or continental portions of Gondwana and Laurasia. The Pacific realm was formed by the Hercynian circum-Pangea accretionary margin followed by the Kimmerian–Holocene circum-Pacific accretionary-orogenic zone. Similar to the BOE recovery averages for most of the world's source rocks, the Upper Jurassic Tethyan realm appears to have petroleum systems with the greatest recovery per unit area of mature source rock, while the Jurassic source rocks of the Boreal realm indicate a BOE recovery per unit volume similar to world total source rock recovery (Table 3.5).

Location by Type of Basin

Upper Jurassic source rocks were deposited in fold belt and foreland basins, rift basins, and divergent margin basins (Table 3.6). Fold belt and foreland basins include the Arabian–Iranian, Papua, Neuquen, Middle Caspian, and Amu Darya basins. Rifted basins include the northwest European shelf and northern North Sea province, the West Siberian basin, the Jeane d'Arc subprovince, and the Yemen rift province, while the divergent margin basins include the Gulf of Mexico, the Dampier–Bowen and Browse subprovinces of the Australian northwest shelf, and the Scotia shelf. Fold belt and foreland basins have the highest recovery, but when the super basins are excluded, the rifted basins rank highest. In either case, the divergent margin basins have lower recovery.

The same source rocks were deposited on the northwest Europe shelf as well as in the Jeane d'Arc subprovince (Kimmeridgian "hot shales") and both include sectors with structural forms resembling both rifted basins and divergent margin basins. These similar source rocks sequences were probably part of a much larger contiguous source rock sequence that extended from the Arctic to the temperate Newfoundland–Grand Banks to the Iberia sector of Laurasia, which was later separated by the late Mesozoic drift opening of the Atlantic Ocean. In the Jeane d'Arc subprovince, the Kimmeridgian hot shale was deposited, as was the Verril Canyon facies, in an anoxic environment as type I and II kerogens in the half-sag phase of the Scotia shelf. The Verril Canyon source rocks were deposited in response to the opening (drift phase) of the Atlantic south of the Newfoundland fracture zone, which eventually separated central North America from North Africa. At the same time, the area north of the fracture zone remained in the rift (predrift) phase of tectonic development (von der Dick, 1989; Foster and Rofenson, in press).

The Vienna basin contains an anomalous petroleum system in that it, like the Tuxedni–Hemlock(!) petroleum system of the Cook Inlet area (Magoon, Chapter 22, this volume), has its source rocks in a terrane that is tectonically exotic to the reservoir rocks and traps. In the Vienna basin, the Upper Jurassic source rocks were deposited in a rifted divergent margin that was later overthrust by the Alpine collisional terrane in Late Cretaceous–early Tertiary time. On this convergent margin, the collisional terrane was then superposed by the transform rifted late Tertiary movement to form the Vienna basin, which contains the system's Miocene traps and reservoir rocks (Ladwein et al., 1991). In the case of the Cook Inlet, the Middle Jurassic source rocks are believed to have been deposited in a forearc structural form which was then incorporated into an accreted zone (Ott, 1992). In both of these basins, the source rocks appear to be in what, for many years, was considered basement rock.

All of the basin types in which Upper Jurassic source rocks were deposited include in their structural evolution a time when a rift or rifts were followed by a sag, either linear or circular (Ulmishek and Klemme, 1990). The fold belt and foreland basins (of the Tethyan realm) have a rift–sag followed by a foredeep structural form. Those basins on the craton of northern Gondwana also have a prerift platform structural form, which is followed by a rift–sag–foredeep sequence of structural forms. The Neuquen basin has a tectonic evolution in which the preforedeep sequence has been labeled as either a backarc or a passive margin. In its present fold belt and foreland form, the foreland resembles a passive margin, but the backarc nature of a rift–sag tectonic sequence seems the most likely first stage for this basin's tectonic evolution. In the Papua and possibly the Neuquen basins, the rift sequence may have been partially or totally destroyed by cratonward thrusting and either orogenic uplift or subduction of much of the rift–sag sequence (a condition that might apply to the Indian continent as opposed to the Arabian subcontinent). Divergent margins develop a rift or rifts followed

by a postrift–predrift sag, while with drift, a prograding half-sag structural form is developed. Some rifts in divergent margin shelf areas remain as rifts and sags, as little drift has yet to occur in the vicinity of the rift (e.g., Jeane d'Arc subprovince and parts of the Norwegian shelf). Generally, the source rocks are deposited in the early stage of basin evolution, while the reservoir and seal rocks, and especially the overburden rocks, are deposited in the later stages of basin evolution.

Location by Structural Form

Structural form reflects the evolutionary tectonic stage of various basin types (Kingston et al., 1983; Klemme, 1983; Ulmishek and Klemme, 1990). Nearly all Upper Jurassic source rocks were deposited in the structural form of the rift–sag cycle of a basin's tectonic evolution, with 10% of the BOE coming from the source rocks deposited in the rift stage and nearly 90% from the sag stage. A minor amount of the BOE (Scotia shelf) came from source rocks deposited in the prograding sequence into a half-sag.

Other major world source rocks (Klemme and Ulmishek, 1991) include Silurian source rocks deposited only on platform structural forms, Upper Devonian source rocks with only 12% deposited on the rift–sag of Laurasia, and Pennsylvanian–Permian source rocks with 47% deposited on the rift–sag structural forms of Laurasia. In contrast, 93% of middle Cretaceous source rocks were deposited on rift–sag structural forms located in Laurasia and northern Gondwana. It is likely that the absence of the rift–sag as a depositional structural form in the Silurian source rocks and its limited presence in Devonian source rocks are due to both Caledonian and Hercynian destruction of early and middle Phanerozoic source rocks deposited in the structural forms of the rift–sag cycle and to the progressive biologic evolution from shallower to deeper water ecological niches as the habitat of bottom scavengers evolved (Ulmishek and Klemme, 1990).

Most of the Upper Jurassic source rocks occur stratigraphically close to the interface of the rift where it changes to a sag. The Bazhenov and Khodzipaik source rocks of West Siberian and Amu Darya and the Upper Dingo of the northwest shelf of Australia are generally at the base of the sag. The Kimmeridgian hot shale source rocks of the northwest European shelf, the North Sea, and the Jeane d'Arc are in the rift immediately below and in transition with the overlying sag. The Hanifa–Sargelu source rocks in the Arabian–Iranian basin are located at some stratigraphic distance above the Permian–Triassic saglike rift or riftlike sag (Koop and Stonely, 1982).

The linear nature of rifts and their overlying sags often have structural cross warps that provide barriers or sills. These barriers can cause euxinic basins where sapropelic marine and lacustrine continental deposits can accumulate in anoxic environments at all paleolatitudes. In low or equatorial paleolatitudes, type I and II kerogens, salt–evaporite seal rocks, and carbonate reservoirs are favored. High paleolatitudes tend to have more humic

Table 3.2. Detailed Characteristics of Petroleum Systems with Upper Jurassic Source Rocks

Map No.	Petroleum System Name	Size[a]	Largest Field[b]	Trap type[c]	Source Rock Age[d]	Name(s)
1	Hanifa–Arab(!)	SGS	SGF	Block, flowage, reef	UJ	Hanifa (Diyab)
		SGS	SGF	Block, flowage, reef	UJ	Hanifa (Diyab)
		SGS	SGF	Block, flowage, reef	M–UJ	Sargelu
2	Bazhenov–Neocomian(!)	SGS	SGF	Block, strat	UJ–LK	Bazhenov
3	Kimmeridgian "hot shale"–Brent(!)	SGS?	SGF	Block, flowage, strat	UJ	"Hot shale" (Local names: Draupne, Tau, Spekk, Farsund)
4	Smackover–Tamman(!)	GS	SGF	Block, flowage, strat, reef	UJ	Tamman–Smackover
5	Khodzipaik–Shatlyk(?)	LS	SGF	Block, reef, fold	UJ	Khodzipaik
6	J3 "black shales"–J3 to K2(.)	LS	GF	Block, fold, strat	UJ	"J3"
7	Lam–Amla'ah(!)	LS	LF?	Block, flowage?	UJ	Lam (Madbi, Meem, Amla'ah)
8	Vaca Muerta–Sierras Blancas(?)	LS	LF	Strat, block, fold	UJ	Vaca Meurta (Quintuco and Berrisian)
9	Maril–Toro(.)	?	LF	Fold	M–UJ	Maril
10	Dingo–Windalia(.)	LS?	LF	Fold, strat	UJ	Upper Dingo claystone
11	Kimmeridgian "hot shale"–Hibernia(!)	SS?	GF	Growth, flowage	UJ	Egret member of Raulsin Formation
12	Verril Canyon–Mic Mac(!)	?	LF?	Growth, flowage	UJ	Verrill Canyon facies
13	Obermalm–Badenian(!)	SS	GF	Block, strat	UJ	Obermalm Beds
14	Flamingo–Plover(.)	SS	LF	Block	UJ	Swan Formation or Flamingo Group

[a]SGS, super giant petroleum system, >100 × 10^9 BOE; GS, giant petroleum system, 20–100 × 10^9 BOE; LS, large petroleum system, 5–20 × 10^9 BOE; SS, significant petroleum system, 0.2–5 × 10^9 BOE.

[b]SGF, super giant field, >5000 × 10^6 BOE; GF, giant field, 500–5000 × 10^6 BOE; LF, large field, 50–500 × 10^9 BOE; SF, significant field, 1–50 × 10^6 BOE.

[c]Trap type: Block, tensional anticline; flowage, upward flowing evaporite; fold, compressional anticline; growth, roll-over anticline; reef, depositional environment; strat, purely stratigraphic.

[d]L, Lower; M, Middle; U, Upper; J, Jurassic; K, Cretaceous.

[e]R, rift; S, sag; CS, circular sag; LS, linear sag; HS, half sag.

Table 3.2 *(continued)*

Map No.	Major Reservoir Rock Age[f]	Lithology[g]	Structural Form[h]	Depositional Environment	Cap Rock (Seal) Age[f]	Lithology[g]	Structural Form[h]	Depositional Environment
1	UJ	carb	LS	Shallow water platform	UJ	anhy	LS	Restricted, silled zone
	K	carb	LS	Shallow water platform	K	sh	LS	Shale platform–shelf
	UJ	carb	LS	Shallow water platform	UJ	evap	LS	Restricted marine
2	UJ, K	ss, ml	CS	Deltaic	UJ, K	sh	CS	Restricted marine and deltaic
3	MJ, UJ, K, P	ss, chk, ml	R, LS	Continental to deltaic to marine	UJ, LK, T	sh	R, LS	Marine
4	UJ, K, P	carb, ss, ml	CS	Marine shelf, reef, deltaic	UJ, K, Mio	sh	CS, HS	Coastal marine
5	UJ, K, P	carb, ss	LS, F	Marine shelf, reef	UJ, Palc	sh	LS, F	Restricted, silled zone
6	UJ, K, P	carb, ss	LS	Marine to deltaic	UJ, Eoc	sh	LS, F	Restricted, silled zone
7	UJ, K	ss	R, LS	Deltaic, marine shelf	UJ, K	ls	R, LS	Deep marine, shelf, deltaic
8	UJ, LK	carb, ss	LS	Coastal, shelf	UJ, LK	sh	LS	Deep shelf, deltaic
9	UJ, LK, Mio	ss, carb	LS, F	Platform, reef	LK, Plio	sh	LS, F	Marine, deltaic, shelf
10	Tr, J, LK	ss, ml	R, LS	Deltaic	J, K	sh	R, LS	Restricted–openmarine
11	UJ, K	ss, ml	R, LS	Continental to marine	Neoc	sh	R, LS	Deltaic to open marine
12	UJ, K	ss, ml	LS	Delatic	UJ, K	sh	LS	Deltaic to open marine
13	Tr, Mio	ss, ml	R	Deltaic, marine	Mio	sh	R	Deltaic to estuarine
14	Tr, J	ss, ml	R	Continental to marine	LK	sh	LS, HS	Shelf to open marine

[f]U, Upper; M, Middle; L, Lower; Tr, Triassic; J, Jurassic; K, Cretaceous; T, Tertiary; P, Paleogene; Palc, Paleocene; Eoc, Eocene; Mio, Miocene; Plio, Pliocene; Neoc, Neocomian.

[g]carb, carbonate; sh, shale; ss, sandstone; ls, limestone; chk, chalk; anhy, anhydrite; evap, evaporite; ml, multiple reservoirs.

[h]CS, circular sag; LS, linear sag; HS, half sag; F, foredeep; R, rift.

[i]Est, estimated; Dis, discovery; Rec, recovery; Eff, efficiency.

Table 3.2 *(continued)*

Map No.	Kerogen Type	Paleolatitude	Structural Form[e]	Depositional Environment	Terrane
			Source Rock *(continued)*		
1	II	Equatorial	LS	Marine shelf	Craton platform
	II	Equatorial	LS	Marine shelf	Craton platform
	II	Equatorial	LS	Marine shelf	Craton platform
2	II	Boreal	CS	Lagoonal inland sea	Caledonian and Hercynian accreted
3	II	Temperate to boreal	R/S	Lagoonal troughs	Caledonian accreted
4	II, III	Equatorial to temperate	CS	Marine shelf	Hercynian accreted
5	II, III	Temperate	LS	Marine shelf	Hercynian accreted
6	II, III	Temperate	LS	Marine shelf	Hercynian accreted
7	II, III	Equatorial	R	Rift margin	Truncated craton
8	I, II	Temperate	LS	Shelf and slope deep basin	Pangea–Hercynian and Pacific–post-Hercynian
9	II, III	Temperate	LS	Marine platform/sag	Pangea–Hercynian and Pacific–post-Hercynian
10	II, III	Temperate	LS	Fluvial deltaic to marine	Craton platform
11	II, III	Temperate	R–S interface	Lagoonal to deep marine	Caledonian and Hercynian accreted
12	II, III	Temperate	HS	Deep marine	Caledonian and Hercynian accreted
13	II, III	Temperate	R	Marine shelf	Hercynian accreted
14	II, III	Temperate to high	R	Mid shelf to lagoonal	Craton platform

Table 3.2 *(continued)*

Map No.	Area (km^2)	Thickness (m)	Density (g/cm^3)	TOC (wt. %)	HI (mg HC/g TOC)	Available HC ($\times 10^9$ BOE)	Est Dis ($\times 10^9$ BOE)	Est Rec ($\times 10^9$ BOE)	Rec Eff (%)
	Active Source Rock (Estimates)						Conventionally Recoverable BOE[i]		
1	723,000	120	<2.5	4–6	500–600	57,000	410	498	0.86
2	1,600,000	35	<2.5	+6	+550	46,600	125	200	0.43
3	260,000	300	<2.5	+6	+550	54,000	60	125	0.23
4	590,000	120	>2.5	2–4	500–550	21,300	80	98	0.46
5	271,000	120	±2.5	2–4	450–500	11,700	11	16	0.13
6	259,000	120	>2.5	2–6	450–500	9,500	12	14	0.16
7	37,000	300–450	>2.5	2–4	450–550	5,500	5	13	0.23
8	63,000	200	>2.5	1–2	350–450	1,570	4	7	0.40
9	83,000	150	>2.5	1–2	350–400	1,600	1.6	>5	0.33
10	36,000	600	>2.5	1–4	350–450	3,270	1.5	>5	0.15
11	26,000	350	>2.5	2–4	350–450	2,380	2.2	>4	0.19
12	30,000	450	±2.5	1–2	350–400	1,650	0.5	>2	0.14
13	11,000	600	<2.5	1–4	350–450	430	1	>1	0.28
14	9,000	300	<2.5	2–4	350–400	630	0.2	<1	0.14

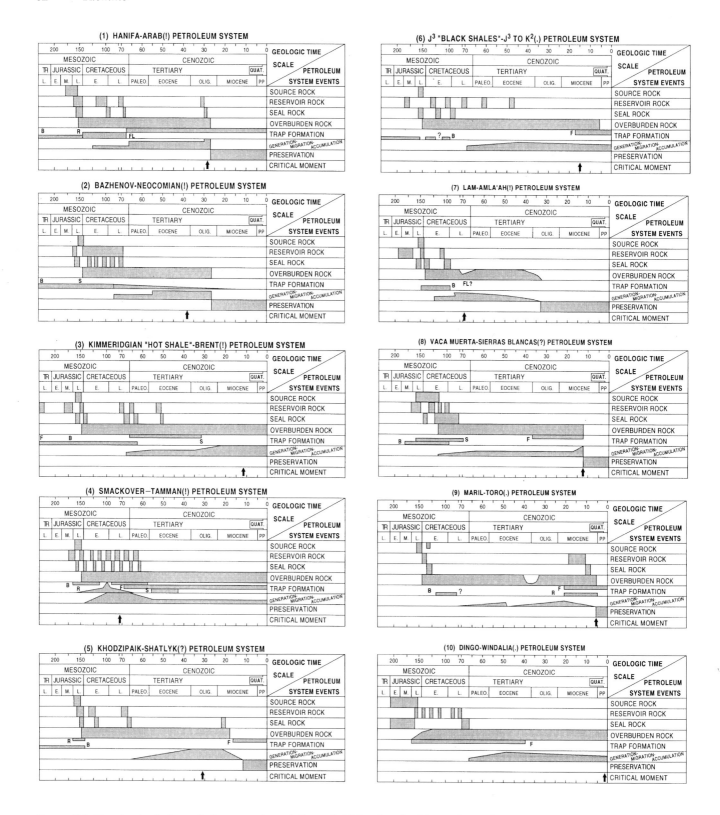

Figure 3.6. Events charts for petroleum systems 1 through 14 that involve Upper Jurassic source rocks. Numbers correspond to petroleum systems on all figures and Table 3.2. Explanation for trap formation: B, block uplift anticline; F, fold anticline; FL, flowage anticline; G, growth anticline; R, reef; S, stratigraphic.

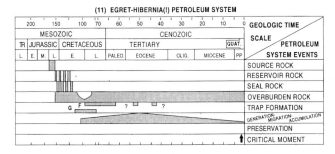

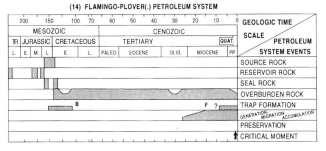

Figure 3.6. *(continued)*

Table 3.3. Present Geography of Upper Jurassic Source Rocks

Area	BOE (%)	Mature Source Rock Area (%)	Mature Source Rock Volume (%)
Interior	80	70	56
Coastal	20	30	44

Table 3.4. Plate Tectonic Location of Upper Jurassic Source Rocks[a]

Terrane	BOE (%)	Mature Source Rock Area (%)	Mature Source Rock Volume (%)
Craton	58 (9)	21 (10)	38 (18)
Hercynian	23 (45)	49 (70)	42 (57)
Caledonian	18 (44)	26 (16)	18 (20)
Pacific	1 (2)	1 (3)	2 (4)

[a]Numbers in parentheses exclude the Hanifa–Arab(!) and Bazhenov–Neocomian(!) supergiant petroleum systems.

or through the cap rocks. The supergiant and giant petroleum systems to be compared are (1) the Hanifa–Arab(!) system located in the Arabian–Iranian basin; (2) the Bazhenov–Neocomian(!) system in the West Siberia basin; (3) the Kimmeridgian hot shale–Brent(!) system in the northwest European shelf; and (4) the Smackover–Tamman(!) in the Gulf of Mexico province (Table 3.2).

The prolific nature of these petroleum systems is related to where the high percentage of the system's BOE is trapped relative to the active source rock. Here the reservoir rocks are immediately sealed by either an especially efficient cap rock or else the source and the seal for the oil are the same rock (e.g., Hith anhydrite in the Hanifa–Arab system and the Kimmeridgian hot shales in the Kimmeridgian hot shale–Brent system). Conversely, petroleum systems that include poor seals have about 80% of the BOE in reservoir rocks well above the active source rocks. When oil leaks upward to overlying reservoir rocks and structural sequences, it results in a less efficient or prolific petroleum system (e.g., Gulf of Mexico and West Siberian basin) (Table 3.7).

Plumbing and Dynamic Events

Using the distribution and volume of conventionally recoverable BOE, several observations can be made about petroleum systems with Upper Jurassic source rocks (Figure 3.6). Most of the reservoir rocks are Jurassic (63%) in age followed by Cretaceous (33%) and Tertiary (3%), and their lithologies are more likely to be carbonate (60%) rather than siliciclastic sandstone (40%). The onset of oil generation is usually Late Cretaceous–early Tertiary (76%), as opposed to Late Jurassic–Early Cretaceous (17%) or late Tertiary (7%). Most trap growth occurred before the onset of oil generation (90%) as compared to during (5%) and after (5%) oil generation.

type II and III kerogens and coal as source rocks than do low paleolatitudes. Most of the Upper Jurassic rift–sag cycles developed along paleolongitudinal north-south lineations often underlain by either the Caledonian or Hercynian orogenic–accretionary prisms present in Laurasia and in and along the Pangea break-up rifts of Gondwana (Atlantic and Indian ocean margins).

Proximity of Source, Reservoir, and Seal Rocks

In the four largest petroleum systems, the recovery efficiency is directly related to the proximity of the Upper Jurassic source rocks to the charged reservoir rocks and traps, and indirectly to the leakage of petroleum around

Table 3.5. Petroleum Geotectonic Realm of Upper Jurassic Source Rocks

| | | Mature Source Rock | | Total World | |
| | BOE | Area | Volume | BOE | Area |
Petroleum Realm	(%)	(%)	(%)	(%)	(%)
Boreal	27	49	30 ·	23	28
Tethyan	72	49	69	68	17
Southern Gondwana	0	0	0	4	38
Pacific	1	1	1	5	17

Table 3.6. Location by Basin Type of Upper Jurassic Source Rocks[a]

| | | Mature Source Rock | | Average Source Rock |
| | BOE | Area | Volume | Thickness |
Basin Type	(%)	(%)	(%)	(m)
Fold belt and foreland	60 (15)	34 (40)	43 (32)	148 (148)
Rifted	27 (47)	49 (20)	31 (25)	250 (320)
Divergent margin	12 (38)	16 (40)	26 (43)	405 (405)

[a]Numbers in parentheses exclude the Hanifa–Arab(!) and Bazhenov–Neocomian(!) supergiant petroleum systems.

LOWER–MIDDLE JURASSIC SOURCE ROCKS

Lower–Middle Jurassic sedimentary rocks occupy essentially the same position as and underlie much of the Upper Jurassic (Figures 3.1–3.5). At approximately 30 locations, Lower and Middle Jurassic source rocks occur that result in some hydrocarbon production (for locations see Figure 3.1). This represents only 5% of the total production from all Jurassic source rocks.

Two organic facies of Lower–Middle Jurassic source rocks are related to their depositional paleolatitudes (Table 3.2). Tethyan facies of shales and carbonates (X_{TC}) and evaporites (X_{TE}) were deposited in rift–sag structural forms in low paleolatitudes (0°–30°) along the margin of the Neo-Tethys (Triassic–Jurassic opening of the Tethys) (Figures 3.1–3.5). These Tethyan facies were developed on the southern margin of Laurasia and the northern margin of Gondwana and occupied the north and south sides of a seaway that was separated by a central zone of deep water with red, nodular, pelagic limestone and radiolerites located along the axis of the seaway (Wilson, 1975). The Tethyan-like facies deposited between 30° and 40° paleolatitude appears to be a mixture ("mixed facies") of the low latitude Tethyan hypersaline carbonate facies mixed with the "humic facies" of coals, humic shales (X_{HC}), and lacustrine source rocks (X_{HL}). Although it is present in minor amounts at all paleolatitudes, the Humic facies is found predominantly north of 40° paleolatitude.

Two-thirds of the area covered by Lower–Middle Jurassic source rocks is overlain by Upper Jurassic source rocks, while one-third lacks these overlying rocks. Where Upper Jurassic source rocks are absent and production came from Lower–Middle Jurassic source rocks, two-thirds of the hydrocarbon occurrences are related to regional or local uplift. This uplift is a departure from the Vail sea level curve that rises during the Upper Jurassic (Vail et al., 1977) because this is the initiation of the worldwide Neocomian regressive clastic depositional event. These regressive sequences most often occur stratigraphically above the Mixed and Humic organic facies. The other one-third of the hydrocarbon occurrences occur above the Tethyan facies where either the open marine carbonate facies or the deep marine starved basin facies were developed, but an intershelf depression, either in or on the open marine shelf, was lacking for deposition of a laminated lime mudstone in an anoxic environment to form bituminous source rocks.

LOWER CRETACEOUS SOURCE ROCKS

In certain areas, Jurassic source rocks extend up into the Lower Cretaceous. Lower Cretaceous (Berriasian–Barremian) deltaic to open marine sedimentary rocks were deposited in 30 areas where production was generated from Lower–Middle Jurassic source rocks and in 20 areas where production originated from Upper Jurassic source rocks. Where sediments were derived from the craton or continental interior, they were deposited as regressive deltaic sequences that grade to open marine. These sequences usually occur in the fold belt and foreland basins as well as in rifted basins. However, there is a tendency for more open marine sediments to occur in the divergent margin basins.

In the West Siberian basin and the northwest Europe shelf province, the deposition of Upper Jurassic source rocks continued into the Early Cretaceous (pre-Wealden or Purbeckian–Ryazanian). There are a few source rocks within the Wealden (Valangian–Barremian) stages of the Lower Cretaceous in this area (Cornford, Chapter 33, this volume).

Minor production attributed to Lower Cretaceous source rocks occurs in the (1) lacustrian shales of Lower Saxony basin (Kockel et al., Chapter 34, this volume), (2) low rank source shales in West Siberia (Peterson and Clarke, 1991), (3) marine shales of the Neuquén basin (Urien and Zambrano, Chapter 32, this volume), (4) marginal marine shales of the Cooper subbasin (Kantsler et al., 1984), and (5) possibly some of the marine shales of the Scotia shelf (Grant et al., 1986). The upper Lower Cretaceous (Barremian–Aptian) contains some source rocks (South Atlantic divergent margin basins of South America and Africa), which initiate the Cretaceous (Aptian–Turonian) "bloom" of worldwide source rocks.

Generally, the Neocomian regressive phase contains more reservoir rocks than source rocks, while the transgressive (rising sea level) Cretaceous (Aptian–Turonian) includes worldwide source rocks that have generated even more BOE than the Upper Jurassic (30% or more of the world's discovered BOE).

Table 3.7. Effect of Proximity of Reservoir Rock to Active Source Rock for These Supergiant and Giant Petroleum Systems

Petroleum System	Petroleum System BOE			BOE Recovery per Sq Mi of Mature Source Rock
	In Presource Reservoirs (%)	In Source Rock Sequence Reservoirs (%)	Leakage into Overlying Reservoirs (%)	
Hanifa–Arab(!)	minor	78[a]	22[b]	1.8×10^6
Kimmeridgian "hot shale"–Brent(!)	45[a]	30	25 (Tert)	1.2×10^6
Smackover–Tamman(!)	—	18	64 (Cret), 18 (Tert)	0.43×10^6
Bazhenov–Neocomian(!)	minor	>20	>75 (Neoc.–mid Cret)	0.32×10^6

[a]Special cap rock seal.

[b]Special seal absent.

RECOVERY EFFICIENCY OF UPPER JURASSIC SOURCE ROCKS

Petroleum system recovery efficiency is the percent of ultimately conventionally recoverable BOE (a barrel of oil is energy equivalent to 6000 ft³ of gas) to the amount of BOE that could have been generated from a pod of active source rock if the source rock was completely spent (Figure 3.7). This recovery efficiency requires the estimator to make a best guess of the ultimate conventionally recoverable BOE and to assume that the entire volume of source rocks is spent, which in many cases is untrue.

The petroleum system recovery efficiency is the percent of ultimately recoverable BOE that could be generated from a spent source rock. To determine the recovery efficiency of the 14 petroleum systems, several assumptions were necessary. The geographic extent of a given petroleum system and the area of mature or spent source rock are assumed identical, and this area is estimated using present-day hydrocarbon accumulations and the estimated burial depth of the source rocks. Even though the active source rocks range from marginally mature to spent, the volume of generated BOE is determined for a spent source rock. Each petroleum system covers a large area and may include more than one system (see Cornford, Chapter 33, this volume). The bulk properties of the source rock and its thermal maturity are estimated from the literature, as is the estimated ultimate conventionally recoverable BOE (Table 3.2). These BOE volumes, the petroleum system recovery efficiency, and other plumbing ingredients are displayed by decreasing recovery efficiency in Figure 3.7.

Obtaining an estimate of the potential BOE generated from a pod of active source rock requires the determination of its area and average thickness. It also requires an estimation of the average TOC, HI, and kerogen type for the immature source rocks. Within the Upper Jurassic source rocks, there is often considerable vertical and horizontal variation in TOC and kerogen type (and thus HI). In addition, the thickness of mature source rock is commonly quite variable, although for continental interior basins, where the source is in the sag cycle, the source rock thicknesses are much less than the thicknesses in rift sequences on coastal margin locations (see Table 3.2). Considering these possible variables and the

need to estimate the immature source rock properties, it is suggested that the petroleum system recovery efficiency (Table 3.2) values could be doubled (J. M. Hunt, oral communication, 1991) or halved (considering that published TOCs often report the highest values). However, if this correction were used, the relative magnitude of the recovery efficiencies would most likely remain in the same general order as they are given in Table 3.2.

In Figure 3.7, the petroleum system recovery efficiency is arranged in descending order from left to right, that is, 0.86–0.10% of the HC is recoverable from the spent source rocks. In other words, for every 100 BOE generated, only 0.86 BOE is recoverable. It is estimated that the world's petroleum systems have a range of recovery efficiency from 4 to 0.04% (or 8 to 0.02% if doubled and halved). For example, within the Hanifa–Arab petroleum system in the Arabian–Iranian basin, the southernmost mature source area (Figures 3.4 and 3.5) has a recovery efficiency of 2.3%, when calculated as a separate unit. The entire Gulf of Mexico's Upper Jurassic petroleum system, the Smackover–Tammam, has a calculated efficiency of 0.46%. When calculated for the area within the United States (i.e., excluding the Mexican Tampico, Chicontepec, and ReformaCampeche provinces), the recovery efficiency is only 0.18%. Thus, variability in recovery efficiency occurs not only among petroleum systems but within portions of the same system.

PETROLEUM PLUMBING INGREDIENTS RELATED TO RECOVERY EFFICIENCY

Demaison and Huizinga (Chapter 4, this volume) indicate that "a positive correlation exists between the magnitude of the SPI and province-wide petroleum reserves." SPI is the source potential index or the "cumulative hydrocarbon potential" whose measurement is similar to the potential million BOE generated per square mile of spent source rock in a petroleum system (Figure 3.7, shaded histogram). However, the ultimate (per unit) recovery of petroleum (i.e., richness) and the relative magnitude of the petroleum system recovery efficiency are not necessarily directly related to the magnitude of petroleum available from the pod of spent source rock (Figure 3.7; Tables 3.2 and 3.6).

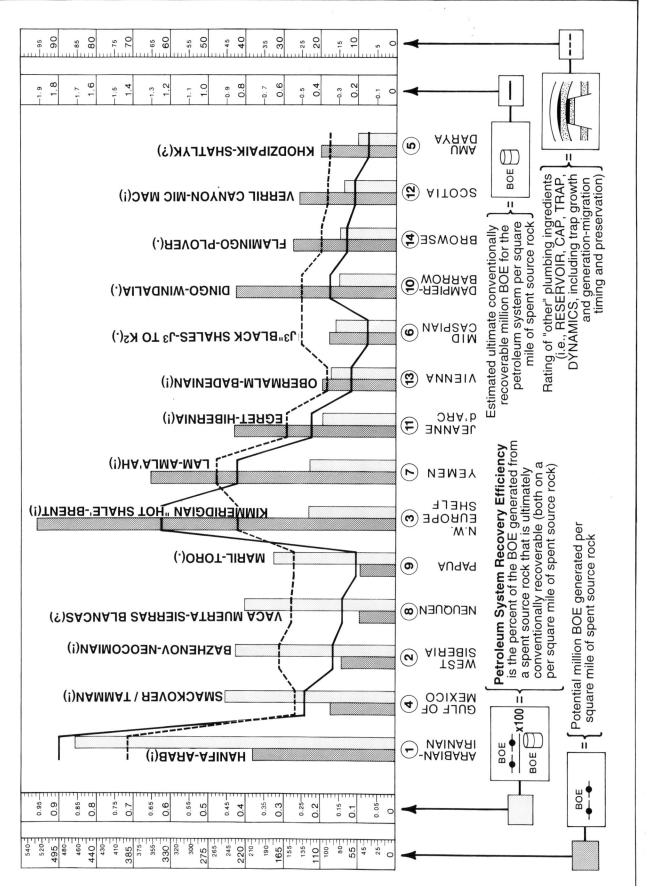

Figure 3.7. Comparison of 14 petroleum systems involving **Upper Jurassic source rocks** with respect to their recovery efficiency (light gray histogram). The amount of BOE that could be generated from a spent source rock (dark gray histogram), the amount of ultimately recoverable BOE from a spent source rock (solid line), and the rating of "other" plumbing dynamics are shown. Locations of the petroleum systems are shown on Figures 3.1–3.5.

Rather than using the petroleum system, Magara (1992, p. 71) contrasts "the ratio of the richest to the poorest petroliferous basin, in terms of average organic concentration, may be less than 20 to 1" while "the ratio of the concentration (BOE–km^2) of accumulated oil (petroleum) in the richest sedimentary basin to that in the poorest basin among those basins containing 'giant' and 'supergiant' fields is more than 500 to 1." As previously mentioned, the recovery efficiency of world class petroleum systems is estimated to range from 4 to 0.04%, or a range of 100 to 1.

Demaison and Huizinga (Chapter 4, this volume) emphasize that after the SPI, basin configuration, migration pathways, and drainage areas are the next most important factors to petroleum recovery. Magara (1992) emphasizes source rocks character and quality, including the combination of organic concentration, duration of oil generation, thickness of the oil window, source rocks age factor, dynamics, and ratio of fluid expulsion, as well as indicating other factors such as type of trap, reservoir rocks, cap rocks, and organic matter in source rocks as having great influence on the recovery efficiency. Ulmishek and Harrison (1984) in describing "independent petroliferous systems" follow Jones (1975) and Weeks (1975) by emphasizing trap, reservoir rocks, cap rocks, and dynamics as being of equal importance to that of source rocks in petroleum accumulations. Perrodon (1980; 1983) and North (1985) treat these "petroleum plumbing factors" indirectly, but in more detail.

The relative importance of the active source rock in any petroleum system is not only axiomatic; its character and plumbing greatly influence recovery efficiency. Within the limits of this study, the importance of the "plumbing ingredient" of the active source rock is noted by the widespread essentially humic (locally marine) Lower–Middle Jurassic source rock shales that have contributed only 5% of the BOE from Jurassic source rocks. These Lower–Middle Jurassic gas-prone source rocks are in the same area and presumably the same general reservoir, cap, trap, and dynamic habitat as the high rank, often anoxic Upper Jurassic source rocks that account for 95% of the BOE from Jurassic source rocks.

Another example of the relative importance of the source rock can be observed in Figure 3.7 where the Bazhenov–Neocomian(!) system in West Siberia, the Vaca Muerta–Sierras Blancas(!) system in Neuquen, and the Maril–Toro(.) system in Papua have essentially the same rating as the other plumbing ingredients (dashed line) but have a diminishing availability of potential million BOE generated per square mile from within the area of each system's mature (spent) source rocks (dark gray histogram). In this case, the petroleum system recovery efficiency (light gray histogram) and estimated ultimate conventionally recoverable million BOE (solid line) parallel the diminishing amounts of mature source rocks (dark gray histogram).

However, an even more obvious case for the greater importance of "other" plumbing ingredients and their influence on the petroleum system recovery efficiency is the comparison between the Hanifa–Arab(!) petroleum system and the Kimmeridgian hot shale–Brent(!) and possibly the Lam–Amla'ah(!) petroleum systems (Figure 3.7). In this case, the available BOE (dark gray histogram) in the Hanifa–Arab system, by unit area, is only half that of the Kimmeridgian hot shale–Brent system and only three-fourths of that estimated for the Lam–Amla'ah, yet the recovery efficiency (light gray histogram) for the Hanifa–Arab is 3.5 times higher. This anomaly coincides with a rating of the other plumbing ingredients wherein the Hanifa–Arab system is twice as high as the Kimmeridgian hot shale–Brent system.

In general, published remarks that relate to the Hanifa–Arab other plumbing ingredients include (1) a highly effective and extensive regional evaporite seal; (2) the nearly regional extent of the continuous, highly porous and permeable lime sand Arab Zone reservoir series (the extent of the reservoir rocks is nearly the size of the Alberta basin); (3) growing traps (salt-assisted block anticlines, flowage, and reefs) with areal sizes up to 900 mi^2 and HC columns over 1000 ft (Law, 1957; Wilson, 1975; Murris, 1984); and (4) plumbing dynamics that allowed for regional (>100 mi) pre-Campanian lateral migration.

In summary, there are several published comments about the Kimmeridgian hot shale–Brent petroleum system. First, effective source–seal shales provide presource reservoir rocks with a good cap, although postsource shale cap rocks apparently involve considerable vertical leakage. Second, spacially limited deltaic sandstones, marine sandstone fans, chalks, and turbiditic sandstones are locally excellent reservoir rocks but lack the continuity and extent of the Arab zone reservoir. Third, traps include excellent growing, tilted fault block, salt flowage (diapiric), and compaction and pinch-out stratigraphic traps. In general, the province has many structural traps. However, the field areal size ratio of the Kimmeridgian hot shale–Brent petroleum system area is 0.07% (field areal size to petroleum system areal extent), while the same ratio in the Hanifa–Arab is 0.20%. Finally, rift basin fault systems with vertical drainage dynamics develop considerable leakage in this system and preclude extensive BOE build-up by lateral migration.

The higher TOC values and higher gravity crude oils of the Kimmeridgian hot shales–Brent system source rocks than those of the Hanifa–Arab system indicate that a greater expulsion efficiency and relatively earlier initiation of expulsion probably occurred in the Kimmeridgian hot shale–Brent petroleum system (see Palciauskas, 1991). Although this petroleum system may have had higher rank primary migration, the closely juxtaposed regional seal, regional reservoir rocks, and regional source rocks, together with the trap size of the Hanifa–Arab plumbing ingredients, are more effective and rank above their counterparts in the Kimmeridgian hot shale–Brent system, while the vertical drainage of this system displays less effective dynamics than the extensive lateral drainage of the Hanifa–Arab petroleum system.

Another observation becomes apparent when comparing coastal rift basins with their pods of thick source rocks to the thinner source rocks of the fold belt and foreland basins such as the Arabian–Iranian basin and interior rift basins such as the West Siberian. It is that a thick sequence of source rocks most often appears to result in less petroleum (BOE) release. This is probably due to the insulation or seal effect within the central core of the source rock body. This lack of expulsion from the central core lowers the petroleum system's recovery efficiency even when the source pod is highly fractured. The interface of source rocks with reservoir rocks or carrier beds thus seems an important juxtaposition. The more of these that are interbedded ("wick" effect), the more efficient the expulsion and the greater the percent of potential BOE in the source that is able to migrate out (Cornford, Chapter 33, this volume; Leythaeuser et al., 1988a,b). These characteristic differences between thinner (<150 m) and thicker (>150 m) source rock sequences appear to be supported by the section on present-day geography, which indicates lower recovery (efficiency) from coastal areas where divergent margin and rift basins develop thicker source rocks pods, and by the section on location by type of basin, which indicates that thicker source rock sequences occur in many coastal rifted basins and in most divergent margin basins (see Figure 3.7).

Upper Jurassic petroleum system recovery efficiency is also affected by the system's petroleum realm location, by the juxtaposition of active source rock and reservoirs rock, and by the type of basin (i.e., a basin's evolution of structural forms in Ulmishek and Klemme, 1990). In the case of petroleum realms, a system's location within the low paleolatitudes of the Tethyan realm is conducive to deposition of evaporitic cap rocks and carbonate reservoir rocks at moderate to deep drill depths, which is in addition to the depth-deteriorating reservoir sandstones found at all paleolatitudes.

Both the Tethyan and Boreal realms display tectonics that incorporate the rift–sag cycle in basin development. In the Tethyan realm, rift–sag cycles developed to the south or in back of the Tethyan spreading zone. For example, the northern Gondwana–Neo-Tethys Arabian–Iranian basin evolved from a Permian–Triassic rift followed by a Jurassic sag and is preserved today, while similar structural forms and stratigraphic sequences are suspected to have occurred in northwest Africa and India but appear to have been destroyed by Tertiary collision.

The northern Tethyan margin basins display post-Hercynian collision rifting (Triassic) with platform margin sags in Jurassic time. For example, the Middle Caspian and Amu Darya basins, while similar to basins in China and Europe, appear to have been destroyed by Tertiary collisions, while in the western Tethys, the Gulf of Mexico is still in the rifted–platform to margin half-sag stage of tectonic development awaiting the Cuban–Tethyan collision.

The Boreal realm, differing from the southern Gondwana realm, has more aborted divergent marginal zones. For example, the North Sea grabens of the divergent northwest European shelf and the West Siberian–Kara Sea complex are opposed to the rift and drift margins of the Gondwana Atlantic and Indian oceans. Extensional or transpressional rift–sag cycles develop fault block traps whose trap integrity is preserved if the extension fails to proceed to the drift phase. In either rifted basins or Tethyan fold belt and foreland basins, fault block integrity is preserved as opposed to the drift phase of divergent margin basins.

CONCLUSIONS

Upper Jurassic source rocks and their petroleum systems are present in the rift–sag stages of their basins' structural evolution. The petroleum system recovery efficiency of these petroleum systems ranges from 0.10 to 0.86%. More efficient petroleum systems develop in the continental interior (rifted basins) and in those fold belt and foreland basins with a rift–sag cycle between the platform and foredeep stages of development. Less efficient systems form in continental coastal zone divergent margin basins.

Once active source rocks are present, higher petroleum system recovery efficiency is noted on average in those systems where the reservoir and cap rocks are of high quality and cover a large area and where the size of traps and the dynamics and timing of these "other" plumbing ingredients are of high rank. In the limited examples in this study of petroleum systems that involve Upper Jurassic source rocks, the influence of these other plumbing ingredients are as important as, if not more important than, the source rock quality or the amount of available petroleum from the system's active source rock. In several instances, both a higher recovery efficiency and higher recoverable petroleum (per unit area) are noted in systems with less available petroleum (per unit area) from the mature source rocks than in petroleum systems with more available petroleum in their active source rocks. These variations in recovery efficiency are also related to the geometry of the source pod within the petroleum system.

Acknowledgments   *The writer wishes to acknowledge and thank I. Maycock, R. Church, and M. Nemic for aid in data assembly; L. B. Magoon for instructive discussions and considerable aid in preparation of the data; and R. Johnson for drafting.*

References Cited

Bedoes, L. R., Jr., 1973, Oil and gas fields of Australia, Papua New Guinea, and New Zealand: Sydney, Australia, Tracer Petroleum and Mining Publications, 382 p.

Beydoun, Z. R., and H. V. Dunnington, 1975, The petroleum geology and resources of the Middle East: Beaconsfield, U.K., Scientific Press, 99 p.

Carmolt, S. W., and B. St. John, 1986, Giant oil and gas fields, *in* M. T. Halbouty, ed., Future petroleum provinces of the World: AAPG Memoir 40, p. 11–54.

Creaney, S., and J. Allan, 1990, Hydrocarbon generation and migration in the Western Canada sedimentary basin, *in* J. Brooks, ed., Classic petroleum provinces: The Geological Society Special Publication 50, p. 189–202.

Espitalié, J., and S. Drouet, 1992, Petroleum generation and accumulation in the Aquitaine basin (France), *in* A. M. Spencer, ed., Generation, accumulation, and production of Europe's hydrocarbons: Special Publication of the European Association of Petroleum Geoscientists, n. 2, p. 127–150.

Foster, D. G., and A. G. Rofenson, in press, Geologic history of the Flemish Pass basin, Offshore Newfoundland.

Grant, A. C., K. D. McAlpine, and J. A. Wade, 1986, The continental margin of eastern Canada—geological framework and petroleum potential, *in* M. J. Halbouty, ed., Future petroleum provinces of the world: AAPG Memoir 40, p. 177–206.

Hubbard, R. J., S. P. Edrich, and R. P. Rattey, 1990, Geologic evolution and hydrocarbon habitat of the "Arctic Alaska microplate" *in* J. Brooks, ed., Classic petroleum provinces: The Geological Society Special Publication 50, p. 143–188.

Jones, R. W., 1975, A quantitative geologic approach to prediction of petroleum resources, *in* J. D. Hann, ed., Methods of estimating volumes of undiscovered oil and gas resources: AAPG Studies in Geology 1, p. 186–195.

Kanstler, A. J., T. J. C. Prudence, A. C. Cook, and M. Zwigulis, 1984, Hydrocarbon habitat of the Cooper–Eromanga basin, Australia, *in* G. Demaison and R. J. Murris, eds., Petroleum geochemistry and basin evolution: AAPG Memoir 35, p. 373–390.

Kingston, D. R., et al., 1983, Global basin classification: AAPG Bulletin, v. 67, p. 2175–2193.

Klemme, H. D., 1983, Field size distribution related to basin characteristics: Oil and Gas Journal, v. 81, n. 52, p. 168–176.

Klemme, H. D., and G. F. Ulmishek, 1991, Effective petroleum source rocks of the world—stratigraphic distribution and controlling depositional factors: AAPG Bulletin, v. 75, n. 12, p. 1809–1851.

Koop, W. J., and R. Stonely, 1982, Subsidence history of the Middle East Zagros basin, Permian to Recent, *in* P. Kent et al., eds., Evolution of sedimentary basins: Philosophical Transactions of the Royal Society of London, ser. A, v. 305, n.1439, p. 149–168.

Ladwein, W., et al, 1991, Geodynamics and generation of hydrocarbons in the region of the Vienna basin, Austria *in* A. M. Spencer, ed., Generation, accumulation, and production of Europe's hydrocarbons: Special Publication of the European Association of Petroleum Geoscientists, n. 1, p. 289–303.

Law, J., 1957, Reasons for Persian Gulf oil abundance, *in* A. E. L. Morris, ed., Arabian Gulf: AAPG Foreign Reprint Series (1978), n. 2, p. 43–61.

Leythaeuser, D., R. G. Schaefer, and M. Radke, 1988a, Geochemical effects of primary migration of petroleum in Kimmeridge source rocks from Brae field area, North Sea, Part I: Geochim. Cosmochim. Acta, v. 52, p. 701–713.

Leythaeuser, D., M. Radke, and H. Willsch, 1988b, Geochemical effects of primary migration of petroleum in Kimmeridge source rocks from Brae field area, North Sea, Part II: Geochim. Cosmochim. Acta, v. 52, p. 2879–2891.

Malan, J. A., 1993, Geology, potential of Algoa, Gamtoos basins of South Africa: Oil & Gas Journal, v. 91, n. 46, p. 74–77.

Magara, 1992, Efficiency of petroleum concentration in major petroliferous basins: Journal of Petroleum Geology, v. 15, n. 1, p. 71–86.

Masters, C. D., E. D. Attanasi, W. D. Dietzman, R. F. Meyer, R. W. Mitchell, and D. H. Root, 1987, World resources of crude oil, natural gas, natural bitumen, and shale oil: Houston, TX, 12th World Petroleum Congress, preprint, 27 p.

Masters, C. D., D. H. Root, and E. D. Attanasi, 1991, World resources of crude oil and natural gas: Buenos Aires, 13th World Petroleum Congress, preprint, 23 p.

Murris, R. J., 1984, Middle East—stratigraphic evolution and oil habitat, *in* G. Demaison and R. J. Murris, eds., Petroleum geochemistry and basin evolution: AAPG Memoir 35, p. 353–372.

Nehring, R., 1978, Giant oil fields and world oil resources—Santa Monica, Calif.: Rand Corporation Report R-2284-CIA, 162 p.

Nehring, R., 1981, The discovery of significant oil and gas fields in the United States—Santa Monica, Calif.: Rand Corporation Report R2654–1-USGS–DOE, 236 p.

North, F. K., 1985, Petroleum Geology: London, Allen and Unwin, 607 p.

Ott, V. D., et al., 1992, Tectonics of the Cook Inlet Alaska revisited (abs.): AAPG 1992 Annual Convention Program with Abstracts, Calgary, Alberta.

Palciauskas, V. V., 1991, Primary migration of petroleum, *in* R. K.,Merrill, ed., Source and migration processes and evaluation techniques: AAPG Treatise of Petroleum Geology Series, p. 13–22.

Perrodon, A., 1980, Geodynamique petroliere: Bull. Cent. Rech. Exploration-Production, Memoir 2, 381 p.

Perrodon, A., 1983, Dynamics of oil and gas accumulations: Bull. Cent. Rech. Exploration-Production, Memoir 5, 354 p.

Peterson, J. A, and J. W. Clarke, 1991, Geology and hydrocarbon habitat of the West Siberian basin: AAPG Studies in Geology 32, 96 p.

Ulmishek, G. F., and W. Harrison, 1984, A quantitative technique for assessment of petroleum resources in poorly known basins: Episodes, International Union of Geological Sciences, Publication 17, p. 80–94.

Ulmishek, G. F., and H. D. Klemme, 1990, Depositional controls, distribution, and effectiveness of world's petroleum source rocks: U.S.G.S. Bulletin 1931, 59 p.

Vail, P. R., R. M. Mitchum, Jr., R. G. Todd, J. M. Widmier, S. Thompson III, J. B. Sangree, J. N. Bubb, and W. G. Hatlelid, 1977, Seismic stratigraphy and global changes in sea level, *in* C. E. Payton, ed., Seismic stratigraphy: AAPG Memoir 26, p. 49–212.

von der Dick, H., 1989, Environment of petroleum source rocks deposition in the Jeane d'Arc basin off Newfoundland, *in* A. J. Tankard and J. R. Balkwill, eds., Extensional tectonics and stratigraphy of North Atlantic margins: AAPG Memoir 46, p. 295–304.

Weeks, L. G., 1975, Potential petroleum resources—classification, estimation, and status, *in* J. D. Hann, ed., Methods of estimating volumes of undiscovered oil and gas resources: AAPG Studies in Geology 1, p. 31–49.

Wilson, J. L., 1975, Carbonate Facies in Geologic History: New York, Springer-Verlag, 471 p.

Zappaterra, E., 1990, Carbonate paleographic sequences of the Periadriatic region: Bollettino Societá Geologica Italiana, v. 109, p. 5–20.

Ziegler, P. A., 1988, Evolution of the Arctic–North Atlantic and the western Tethys: AAPG Memoir 43, 198 p., 30 pl.

Uncited References (by Petroleum System)

1. Hanifa–Arab(!)

Alsharon, A. S., 1987, Geology and reservoir characteristics of carbonate buildup in giant Bu Hassa oil field, Abu Dhabi, United Arab Emirates: AAPG Bulletin, v. 71, n. 10, p. 1304–1318.

Alsharon, A. S., and C. G. St. C. Kendall, 1986, Precambrian to Jurassic rocks of the Arabian Gulf and adjacent areas—their facies, depositional setting, and hydrocarbon habitat: AAPG Bulletin, v. 70, n. 8, p. 977–1002.

Ayers, M.G., M. Bilal, R.W. Jones, L.W. Slentz, M. Tartir, and A.O. Wilson, 1982, Hydrocarbon habitat in main producing areas, Saudi Arabia: AAPG Bulletin, v. 66, n. 1, p. 1–9.

Beydoun, Z. R., 1963, Geology of the Arabian peninsula—Eastern Aden Protectorate and part of Dhufar: U.S.G.S. Professional Paper 560-H, 49 p.

Beydoun, Z. R., 1991, Arabian plate hydrocarbon geology and potential: a plate tectonic approach: AAPG Studies in Geology 33, 77 p.

Dunnington, H. V., 1958, Generation, migration, accumulation, and dissipation of oil in northern Iraq, *in* L. G. Weeks, ed., Habitat of oil—a symposium: Tulsa, OK, AAPG, p. 1194–1251.

Dunnington, H. V., 1967, Stratigraphic distribution of oil fields in Iraq-Iran-Arabia basin: Institute of Petroleum Journal, v. 53, p. 129–153.

Ibrahim, M. W., 1983, Petroleum geology of southern Iraq: AAPG Bulletin, v. 67, p. 97–134.

Ibrahim, M. W., M. S. Khan, and H. Khatib, 1981, Structural evolution of the Harmaliyah oil field, Saudi Arabia: AAPG Bulletin, v. 65, n. 11, p. 2403–2416.

Klemme, H. D., 1984, Oil and gas maps and sections of the Arabian-Iranian basin: U.S.G.S. Open-File Report 84-0353, 13 sheets.

Koop, W. J., and R. Stonely, 1982, Subsidence history of the Middle East Zagros basin, Permian to Recent, *in* P. Kent et al., eds., Evolution of sedimentary basins: Philosophical Transactions of the Royal Society of London, ser. A, v. 305, n. 1439, p. 149–168.

Law, J., 1957, Reasons for Persian Gulf oil abundance, *in* A. E. L. Morris, ed., Arabian Gulf: AAPG Foreign Reprint Series (1978), n. 2, p. 43–61.

Morris, A. E. L., compiler, 1978, Arabian Gulf: geology and productivity: AAPG Foreign Reprint Series, n. 2, 266 p.

Murris, R. J., 1984, Middle East—stratigraphic evolution and oil habitat, *in* G. Demaison and R. J. Murris, eds., Petroleum geochemistry and basin evolution: AAPG Memoir 35, p. 353–372.

Stonely, R., 1987, A review of petroleum source rocks in parts of the Middle East, *in* J. Brooks and A. J. Fleet, eds., Marine petroleum source rocks: GSA Special Publication, n. 26, p. 263–269.

2. Bazhenov–Neocomian(!)

Clarke, J. W., O. W. Girard, Jr., J. Peterson, and J. Rachlin, 1977, Petroleum geology of the West Siberia basin and a detailed description of the Samotlor oil field: U.S.G.S. Open-File Report 77-871, 119 p.

Grace, J. D., and G. F. Hart, 1990, Urengoy gas field—U.S.S.R. West Siberia basin, Tyumen district, *in* E. A. Beaumont and N. H. Foster, eds., Structural traps III, tectonic fold and fault traps: AAPG Treatise of Petroleum Geology, Atlas of Oil and Gas Fields, p. 309–336.

Kontorovich, A. E., 1984, Geochemical methods for the quantitative evaluation of the petroleum potential of sedimentary basins, *in* G. Demaison and R. J. Murris, eds., Petroleum geochemistry and basin evaluation: AAPG Memoir 35, p. 79–110.

Kontorovich, A. E., E. E. Nesterov, F. K. Salmanov, V. S. Surkov, A. A. Trofemyk, and F. G. Ervyeh, 1975, Geology of oil and gas of West Siberia, Moscow: Nedra, 679 p.

Kulikov, P. K., 1979, Structural stages of the West Siberian platform, *in* M. V. Murator et al, eds., Tektonika territorii SSSR: Moscow, Nauka, p. 128–140.

Peterson, J. A., and J. W. Clarke, 1991, Geology and hydrocarbon habitat of the West Siberian basin: AAPG Studies in Geology 32, 96 p.

3. Kimmeridgian "Hot Shale"–Brent(!)

Baird, R. A., 1986, Maturation and source rocks evaluation of Kimmeridgian Clay, Norwegian North Sea: AAPG Bulletin, v. 66, n. 1, p. 1–9.

Colley, M. G., A. S. F. McWilliams, and R. C. Myers, 1981, Geology of the Kinsale Head gas field, Celtic Sea, Ireland, *in* L. V. Illing and G. D. Hobson, eds., Petroleum geology of the continental shelf of north-west Europe: London, Institute of Petroleum, p. 504–510.

Colter, V. S., and D. J. Havard, 1981, The Wytch Farm oil field, Doreset, *in* L. V. Illing and G. D. Hobson, eds., Petroleum geology of the continental shelf of north-west Europe: London, Institute of Petroleum, p. 494–503.

Cooper, B. S., and P. C. Barnard, 1984, Source rocks and oils of central and northern North Sea, *in* G. Demaison and R. J. Burris, eds., Petroleum geochemistry and basin evaluation: AAPG Memoir 35, p. 303–314.

D'Heur, M., 1990a, Eldfisk Field—Norway Central graben, North Sea, *in* E. A. Beaumont and N. H. Foster, eds., Structural traps IV: AAPG Treatise of Petroleum Geology, Atlas of Oil and Gas Fields, p. 27–56.

D'Heur, M., 1990b, West Ekofisk field—Norway Central graben, North Sea *in* E. A. Beaumont and N. H. Foster, eds., Structural traps IV: AAPG Treatise of Petroleum Geology, Atlas of Oil and Gas Fields, p. 57–84.

Ekern, O. F., 1990, Midgard field—Norway, southwest Central graben, North Sea, *in* E. A. Beaumont and N. H. Foster, eds., Structural traps IV: AAPG Treatise of Petroleum Geology, Atlas of Oil and Gas Fields, p. 141–172.

Feazel, C. T., I. A. Knight, and L. J. Pekot, 1990, Ekofisk field—Norway Central graben, North Sea, *in* E. A. Beaumont and N. H. Foster, eds., Structural traps IV: AAPG Treatise of Petroleum Geology, Atlas of Oil and Gas Fields, p. 1–26.

Fjaeran, T., and A. M. Spencer, 1991, Proven hydrocarbon plays, offshore Norway, *in* A. M. Spencer, ed., Generation, accumulation, and production of Europe's hydrocarbons: Special Publication of European Association of Petroleum Geoscientists, n. 1, p. 25–40.

Goff, J. C., 1948, Hydrocarbon generation and migration from Jurassic source rocks in the East Shetland basin and Viking graben of the Northern North Sea, *in* G. Demaison and R. J. Burris, eds., Petroleum geochemistry and basin evaluation: AAPG Memoir 35, p. 273–302.

Leythaeuser, D., R. G. Schaefer, and M. Radke, 1988a, Geochemical effects of primary migration of petroleum in Kimmeridge source rocks from Brae field area, North Sea, Part I: Geochim. Cosmochim. Acta, v. 52, p. 701–713.

Leythaeuser, D., M. Radke, and H. Willsch, 1988b, Geochemical effects of primary migration of petroleum in Kimmeridge source rocks from Brae field area, North Sea, Part II: Geochim. Cosmochim. Acta, v. 52, p. 2879–2891.

Mehenni, M., and W. Y. Roodenburg, 1990, Fulmar field—U.K. south central graben, North Sea, *in* E. A. Beaumont and N. H. Foster, eds., Treatise of petroleum geology—Atlas of oil and gas fields, structural traps IV: AAPG, p.113-140.

Neilsen, E.B., G. Fraselle, and L. Vianello, 1990, Tommeliten Gamma Field—Norway Central graben, North Sea, *in* E. A. Beaumont and N. H. Foster, eds., Structural traps IV: AAPG Treatise of Petroleum Geology, Atlas of Oil and Gas Fields, p. 85–112.

Østvedt, O. J., S. Evensen, and H. K. A. Ranaweera, 1990, Sliepner Øst field—Norway Viking graben, North Sea, *in* E. A. Beaumont and N. H. Foster, eds., Structural traps IV: AAPG Treatise of Petroleum Geology, Atlas of Oil and Gas Fields, p. 173–196.

Pegrum, R. M., and A. M. Spencer, 1990, Hydrocarbon plays in the Northern North Sea, *in* J. Brooks, ed., Classic petroleum provinces, Geological Society of London Special Publication, n. 50, p. 441–470.

Ranaweera, H. K. A., 1990, Sliepner Vest field—Norway, southern Viking graben, North Sea, *in* E. A. Beaumont and N. H. Foster, eds., Structural traps IV: AAPG Treatise of Petroleum Geology, Atlas of Oil and Gas Fields, p. 197–216.

Shannon, P. M., 1991, Irish offshore basins—geological development and petroleum plays, *in* A. M. Spencer, ed., Generation, accumulation, and production of Europe's hydrocarbons: European Association of Petroleum Geoscientists Special Publication, n. 1, p. 99–109.

4. Smackover–Tamman(!)

Bishop, W. F., 1980, Petroleum geology of northern Central America: Journal of Petroleum Geology, v. 3, n. 1, p. 3–59.

Dietzman, W. D., C. J. Jirik, W. E. Lyle, Jr., N. R. Rafidi, and T. A. Ross, 1983, The petroleum resources of Mexico: Washington, D.C., Energy Information Administration Report DOE–EIA-0423, Dist. category UC-98, 107 p.

Fails, T. G., 1990, The northern Gulf Coast basin—a classic petroleum province, *in* J. Brooks, ed., Classic petroleum provinces: The Geological Society Special Publication, n. 50, p. 221–248.

Garcia, R. G., and N. Halguin-Quiñones, 1992, Geochemistry tags Upper Jurassic source for most of Mexico's oil, gas: Oil and Gas Journal, v. 90, n. 22, p. 96–97.

Nehring, R., 1991, Oil and gas resources in the Gulf of Mexico basin—the geology of North America: Geological Society of America, v. J, p. 445–494.

Newkirk, T. F., 1971, Possible future petroleum potential of Jurassic, western Gulf basin, *in* I. H. Cram, ed., Future petroleum provinces of the United States—their geologic potential: AAPG Memoir 15, v. 2, p. 927–953.

Oehler, J. H., 1984, Carbonate source rocks in the Jurassic Smackover Trend of Mississippi, Alabama, and Florida, *in* J. G. Palacas, ed., Petroleum geochemistry and source rocks potential of carbonate rocks: AAPG Studies in Geology 18, p. 63–69.

Peterson , J. A., 1983, Petroleum geology and resources of southeastern Mexico, northern Guatemala, and Belize: U.S.G.S. Circular 760, 44 p.

Rainwater, E. H., 1971, Possible future petroleum potential of Lower Cretaceous, western Gulf basin, *in* I. H. Cram, ed., Future petroleum provinces of the United States—their geologic potential: AAPG Memoir 15, v. 2, p. 901–926.

Salvador, A., 1987, Late Triassic–Jurassic paleogeography and origin of Gulf of Mexico basin: AAPG Bulletin, v. 71, n. 4, p. 419–451.

Salvador, A., and A.R. Green, 1980, Opening of the Caribbean Tethys, *in* J. Aubouin, et al., eds., Geology of the Alpine chains born of the Tethys: Paris, 26th International Geologic Congress, July: Bureau de Recherches Geologiques et Minieres, Memoire 115, p. 224–229.

Sassen, R., 1990, Geochemistry of carbonate source rocks and crude oils in Jurassic salt basins of the Gulf Coast, *in* J. Brooks, Classic petroleum provinces: The Geological Society Special Publication. n. 50, p. 265–278.

Viniegra, O. F., and C. Castillo-Tejero, 1970, Golden Lane fields, Vera Cruz, Mexico, *in* M. T. Halbouty, ed., Geology of giant petroleum fields: AAPG Memoir 14, p. 309–325.

5. Khodzipaik–Shatlyk(?)

Akramkhodzhayer, A. M., and M. E. Egamberdyer, 1985, Rocks of the Upper Jurassic Khodzhoipack Suite: Geologiya Nefti i Gaza, n. 2, p. 1535–1541.

Maksimov, S. P., K. A. Kleshava, and V. S. Sheyna, eds., 1986, Geology and geodynamics of the hydrocarbon producing regions of the southern U.S.S.R.: Moscow, Nedra, 232 p.

6. J³ "Black Shales"–J³ to K²(.)

Chakhmakhchev, V. A., T. L. Venogradova, E. R. Pazumova, Z. V. Yakubson, Z. P. Kukushakeha, and A. S. Doshka, 1987, Geochemical assessment of Jurassic subsalt rocks of the East Kuban basin: Geologiya Nefti i Gaza, n. 12, p. 46–50.

Zhabrev, I. P., I. P. Zubov, N. A. Krylov, and V. V. Semenovich, 1975, Comparative evaluation of the oil and gas potential of the epi-Paleozoic basins of the U.S.S.R.: Tokyo, Ninth World Petroleum Congress, Proceedings, v. 2, n. 2, p. 82-92.

7. Lam–Amla'ah(!)

Maycock, I., 1987, Oil exploration and development in Marib–Al Jauf basin, Yemen Arab Republic: Bahrain, Proceedings Fifth Society of Petroleum Engineers Middle East Oil Technical Conference, March (unpublished).

Mills, S., 1992, Oil discoveries in the Hadramaut—how Canadian Oxy scored in Yemen: Oil and Gas Journal, v. 90, n. 10, p. 49–52.

Paul, S. K., 1990, People's Democratic Republic of Yemen—a future oil province, *in* J. Brooks, ed., Classic petroleum provinces: The Geological Society Special Publication, n. 50, p. 329–339.

8. Vaca Muerta–Sierras Blancas(?)

Urien, C. M., and J. J. Zambrana, in press, Petroleum systems in the Neuquén basin, Argentina, *in* L. B. Magoon and W. G. Dow, The petroleum system—from source to trap: AAPG Memoir (Chapter 32, this volume).

9. Maril–Toro(.)

Hobson, D. M., 1986, Papua thrust belt: Australian Petroleum Exploration Journal, v. 26, n. 1, p. 214–224.

Stewart, W. D., and E. F. Durkee, 1985, Petroleum potential of the Papuan basin: Oil and Gas Journal, v. 83, n. 13, p. 151–157.

10. Dingo–Windalia(.)

Butcher, B. P., 1989, Northwest shelf of Australia, *in* J. D. Edwards and P. A. Santogrossi, eds., Divergent–passive margin basins: AAPG Memoir 48, p. 81–115.

Purcell, P. G., and R. R. Purcell, eds., 1988, The North West shelf, Australia: Perth, Proceedings of the Petroleum Society of Australia Symposium, 651 p.

11. Kimmeridgian "Hot Shale"–Hibernia(!)

Arthur, K. R., D. R. Cole, G. G. L. Henderson, and D. W. Kushnir, 1982, Geology of the Hibernia discovery, *in* M. T. Halbouty, ed., The deliberate search for the subtle trap: AAPG Memoir 32, p. 181–196.

Foster, D. G., and A. G. Rofenson, in press, Geologic history of the Flemish Pass basin, offshore Newfoundland.

Fowler, M. G., et al., 1992, Generation and migration of oils in Jeane d'Arc basin, offshore eastern Canada (abs.): AAPG 1992 Annual Convention Program with Abstracts, Calgary, Alberta.

Meneley, R. A., 1986, Oil and gas fields in the East Coast and Arctic basins of Canada, *in* M. T. Halbouty, ed., Future petroleum provinces of the world: AAPG Memoir 40, p. 143–175.

Tankard, A. J., H. J. Welsink, and W. A. M. Jenkins, 1989, Structural styles and stratigraphy of the Jeane d'Arc basin, Grand Banks of Newfoundland, *in* A. J. Tankard and H. R. Blackwell, eds., Extensional tectonics and stratigraphy of the North Atlantic margins: AAPG Memoir 46, p. 265–282.

von der Dick, H., 1989, Environment of petroleum source rocks deposition in the Jeane d'Arc basin off Newfoundland, *in* A. J. Tankard and J. R. Balkwill, eds., Extensional tectonics and stratigraphy of North Atlantic margins: AAPG Memoir 46, p. 295–304.

12. Verril Canyon–Mic Mac(!)

Grant, A. C., K. D. McAlpine, and J. A. Wade, 1986, The continental margin of eastern Canada—geological framework and petroleum potential, *in* M. J. Halbouty, ed., Future petroleum provinces of the world: AAPG Memoir 40, p. 177–206.

Tankard, A. J., and H. J. Welsink, 1989, Mesozoic extension and styles of basin formation in Atlantic Canada, *in* A. J. Tankard and H. R. Blackwell, eds., Extensional tectonics and stratigraphy of the North Atlantic margins: AAPG Memoir 46, p. 175–196.

Welsink, H. J., J. W. Dwyer, and R. J. Knight, 1989, Tectonostratigraphy of the passive margin off Nova Scotia, *in* A. . Tankard and H. R. Blackwell, eds., Extensional tectonics and stratigraphy of the North Atlantic margins: AAPG Memoir 46, p. 215–231.

13. Obermalm–Badenian(!)

Ladwein, W., 1988, Organic geochemistry of Vienna basin—model for hydrocarbon generation in overthrust belts: AAPG Bulletin, v. 72, p. 586–599.

Ladwein, W., et al, 1991, Geodynamics and generation of hydrocarbons in the region of the Vienna basin, Austria, *in* A. M. Spencer, ed., Generation, accumulation, and production of Europe's hydrocarbons: Special Publication of the European Association of Petroleum Geoscientists, n. 1, p. 289–303.

Wessely, G., 1988, Structure and development of the Vienna basin in Austria, *in* L. H. Royden and F. Horvath, eds., The Pannonian basin—a study in basin evolution: AAPG Memoir 45, p. 333–346.

14. Flamingo–Plover(.)

Butcher, B. P., 1989, Northwest shelf of Australia, *in* J. D. Edwards and P. A. Santogrossi, eds., Divergent–passive margin basins: AAPG Memoir 48, p. 81–115.

Magoon, L. B, and W. G. Dow, eds., 1994, The petroleum
system—from source to trap: AAPG Memoir 60.

Chapter 4

Genetic Classification of Petroleum Systems Using Three Factors: Charge, Migration, and Entrapment

Gerard Demaison
Capitola, California, U.S.A.

Bradley J. Huizinga
*ARCO International Oil and Gas Co.
Plano, Texas, U.S.A.*

Abstract

Our genetic classification of petroleum systems is founded on a simple working nomenclature that consists of combining qualifiers from each of the following three categories: (1) charge factor (supercharged, normally charged, or undercharged), (2) migration drainage style (vertically drained or laterally drained), and (3) entrapment style (high impedance or low impedance).

The charge factor is estimated using the initial richness of the source rock and the volume of mature source rock. The source potential index (SPI), which combines source rock richness and net source rock thickness into a single parameter, is a convenient shortcut for comparing the petroleum potential of diverse source rocks containing dissimilar kerogen types and for rapidly estimating regional charging capacity. In extensively explored petroleum provinces that contain a single petroleum system, a positive correlation exists between the magnitude of the SPI and province-wide petroleum reserves.

Migration drainage style is determined from the structural and stratigraphic framework of the basin fill. Vertical migration drainage, which occurs mainly through faults and fractures that breach a seal, is characteristic of petroleum systems in rift basins, deltaic sequences, salt dome provinces, wrench basins, and fold and thrust belts. In contrast, lateral migration drainage is dominant wherever stratigraphically continuous seal–reservoir "doublets" or carrier beds extend over a large area in a tectonically stable province (e.g., foreland or intracratonic platform basins). Recognition of the dominant migration style helps to predict the location of zones of petroleum occurrence in relation to the pod of mature source rock.

Entrapment style, which is also dependent on the structural framework and the presence and effectiveness of seals, describes the degree of resistance (impedance) working against dispersion of the petroleum charge. Application of these working concepts should help to reduce geologic risk significantly, particularly in new ventures exploration.

INTRODUCTION

During the past 40 years, several tectonic classifications of sedimentary basins have been developed by petroleum geologists to provide a common framework of reference for the earth's sedimentary basins (e.g., Weeks, 1952; Perrodon, 1972; Klemme, 1975, 1980, 1983; Bally and Snelson, 1980; Kingston et al., 1983; Helwig, 1985). These classifications have been developed with the purpose of finding relationships between tectonic style and petroleum occurrence. The most useful outcome of these studies has been to demonstrate the statistical predominance of giant fields and major petroleum reserves in cratonic sags and foredeep basins, in contrast to lesser reserves in pull-apart and thrust-belt settings

(Klemme, 1975, 1980, 1983; Bois et al., 1982; Carmalt and St. John, 1986). Also, field size distributions in petroleum basins generally show some relationship to basin classification and basin size (Klemme, 1983). Furthermore, recognition of tectonic style helps to predict regional retention efficiency (e.g., in the evaluation of thrust belts; Vann, 1989) or abnormally high heat flow regimes affecting source rock maturation and oil preservation (e.g., in proto-oceanic rifts such as the Red Sea or Afar triangle).

Nevertheless, any degree of petroleum richness, ranging from near barren to highly prolific, can be observed among specific examples of each basin type. Bally and Snelson (1980, p. 71) recognized this point by concluding that "the classification of basins does little to improve our hydrocarbon volume forecasting ability." This sobering opinion was echoed by Ulmishek (1986, p. 63): "Tectonic basin classifications are limited in their effectiveness of rating the richness of basins." Grunau (1987, p. 254) went even further in stating, "A classification system which is based on measurable relevant criteria, and which is tuned to the needs of the explorationist, has not yet been developed." The reason the analog approach does little to improve our hydrocarbon volume forecasting ability is that source rock volumes and richness are unrelated to tectonic style. In other words, tectonically "look-alike" basins of similar size do not necessarily contain identical volumes of mature source rock and, thus, do not possess analogous regional charging potential.

Furthermore, Bois et al. (1982) and Ulmishek and Klemme (1990) have documented that paleolatitudinal and paleoclimatic considerations are more important than tectonic style in explaining the world's geographic distribution of prolific source rocks and major petroleum reserves. For instance, they show that highly favorable paleogeographic factors led to the development of prolific Upper Jurassic and middle–Upper Cretaceous source rocks in the greater Tethyan realm, which is the earth's best endowed region in terms of petroleum reserves (75% of the oil and 61% of the gas). The importance of source rock distribution, rather than tectonic style, is illustrated by the following examples.

1. In peri-Andean foreland basins, middle–Upper Cretaceous source rocks show an exponential decrease in petroleum potential from north to south. The tectonic style, which can be classified as a foreland ramp, and regional seals of each are similar. However, source rock richness and thickness, as well as discovered Cretaceous-sourced petroleum reserves, tend to wane from north to south.

2. Coastal basins along the Brazilian Atlantic margin show unequal petroleum richness, despite extensive exploration. The Campos basin alone contains 65% of all Brazilian reserves (Bacoccoli et al., 1989; Mohriak et al., 1990), whereas the neighboring Espirito Santo and Santos basins hold only minor reserves. The unequal occurrence of petroleum in Brazilian coastal basins is dependent on variations in the thickness and regional distribution of Lower Cretaceous lacustrine source rocks deposited in early rift settings. Otherwise, the tectonic style, the effectiveness of regional seals, and source rock maturity levels are similar in all the basins along this South Atlantic margin.

3. Carbonate platform systems, whether associated with passive margins or foreland basins, also show extreme variations in petroleum richness, ranging from prolific (e.g., Campeche–Reforma basin in Mexico and central Arabian basin) to marginal (e.g., South Florida basin and Adriatic basin). The differences in petroleum richness between the Campeche–Reforma basin and the South Florida basin are caused not so much by differences in tectonic styles but more by inequalities in source rock volumes and basin geothermal parameters. In the Campeche–Reforma basin, the prolific Upper Jurassic

source rock sequence is stratigraphically continuous, thick, and widespread (Gonzalez and Holguin, 1992). This source rock was deposited in a deep water anoxic environment during a major marine transgression. In contrast, the South Florida basin contains thin Lower Cretaceous source beds that are erratically distributed, both vertically and laterally. They were deposited in ponded shallow water, hypersaline, anoxic "basins" that occurred inside the carbonate platform during a period of overall low sea level. Furthermore, the geothermal gradients tend to be lower in the South Florida basin.

Because source rock volume and richness are unrelated to tectonic style, we felt that a genetic classification scheme based on the processes of petroleum formation, migration, and entrapment had to be devised to supplement conventional tectonic classifications. The geologic framework of a basin provides only the natural setting for these physicochemical processes to interact in a manner that can lead to either concentration or dispersion of petroleum. The geologic history of a basin is the "program" that sequentially activates these physicochemical processes during the passage of geologic time (Perrodon, 1980).

Three important geologic factors control the accumulation of petroleum in the subsurface and thus are essential to the existence of viable petroleum systems:

1. Volumetrically adequate petroleum generation, occurring during or after the time of trap formation;
2. Favorable migration drainage geometry, leading to the focused movement of hydrocarbons into traps rather than to dispersion and loss of hydrocarbons in either subsurface migration "waste zones" or up to the surface;
3. The existence of volumetrically adequate traps, capable of retaining their petroleum charge from the earliest time of trap filling to the present day.

Our plan is to classify genetically the main types of petroleum systems and to qualify and quantify, whenever possible, the key factors that control the occurrence, abundance, and habitat of oil and gas.

THE PETROLEUM SYSTEM

A *petroleum system* is a dynamic petroleum generating and concentrating physicochemical system, functioning in a geologic space and time scale. A petroleum system requires the timely convergence of certain geologic elements and events essential to the formation of petroleum deposits (e.g., mature source rock, expulsion, secondary migration, accumulation, and retention) (Nijhuis and Baak, 1990). This definition is similar to earlier concepts of "source–reservoir oil system" (Dow, 1974), "petroleum system" (Perrodon, 1980, 1983; Perrodon and Masse, 1984; Magoon, 1987, 1988), "hydrocarbon machine" (Meissner et al., 1984), and "independent petroliferous system" (Ulmishek, 1986). A *petroleum*

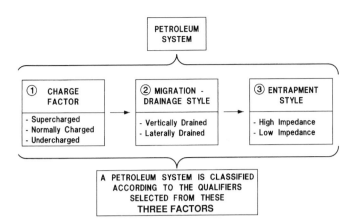

Figure 4.1. Flow diagram for the genetic classification of a petroleum system.

basin (or province) is a geologic entity containing at least one or more petroleum systems.

The concept of the petroleum system is not synonymous with *play,* which is defined by Bois (1975, p. 87) as "a continuous portion of sedimentary volume which contains pools showing the following characteristics: (1) reservoirs within the same productive sequence occur throughout the zone, (2) hydrocarbons are of similar chemical composition, and (3) traps are of the same type."

A petroleum system can be described according to three geologic factors—charge, migration, and entrapment (Figure 4.1). These three factors occur sequentially and are therefore conditional, that is, migration cannot occur without there first being a charge. The charge is dependent on the pod of mature source rock that provides a certain supply of petroleum during a given time span. The effectiveness of the charge is mainly controlled by chemical processes, consisting of biochemical transformation of dead organisms into kerogen during deposition of the source rock (Demaison et al., 1984) and thermochemical kinetics, which control the transformation of kerogen into petroleum (Tissot et al., 1987). The migration–entrapment part of the system gathers petroleum from the pod of active source rock and distributes it in a manner that may lead to either concentration of petroleum into economic accumulations or loss of petroleum due to dispersion and destruction. Migration–entrapment is predominantly controlled by physical processes, including the buoyant rise of petroleum in water, fluid flow and capillary pressure in porous media (Illing, 1939; Schowalter, 1979), and pressure–temperature–composition relationships affecting phase behavior before and during petroleum entrapment. There have been great advances made in our understanding of petroleum migration processes since the mid-1970s (Durand, 1988).

The purpose of the proposed genetic classification of petroleum systems is to describe and predict (1) the relative charging potential of a petroleum system and thus segments of the petroleum province, and (2) the geographic location of zones of petroleum occurrence or

plays in a petroleum province. As a part of this genetic classification, the source potential index (SPI) is introduced as a useful tool for approximating regional charging potential. Furthermore, patterns of regional petroleum occurrence can be predicted by delineating the pod of mature source rock and recognizing the migration style and distances (Demaison, 1984). The final result of integrating a source rock maturity map, migration style, and SPI is a more effective way to evaluate the regional petroleum potential than by using the tectonic analog approach alone. A prerequisite to the genetic approach, however, is that the tectonic framework, sequence stratigraphy, geologic history, thermal history, and a reasonably adequate geochemical database must be fully integrated using sedimentary basin analysis techniques.

The themes reviewed in this chapter do not address the prediction, before drilling, of the volume and composition of petroleum trapped in individual prospects. Advanced computer-aided methodologies for quantitative prospect evaluation have already been described by Nederlof (1979, 1981), Sluijk and Nederlof (1984), and Nijhuis and Baak (1990). Instead, the present genetic classification scheme has been devised to conduct rapid, semiquantitative regional evaluations to outline new plays, clarify research objectives, or better assess petroleum potential.

CHARGE FACTOR

In every petroleum system, the principal constraint to the petroleum richness of a province is the adequacy of the charge factor, which must be powerful enough to provide sufficient petroleum charge to the migration–entrapment part of the system. The overriding importance of the charge factor is obvious: if there is no petroleum generation in the subsurface, then there is no petroleum system, thus the migration–entrapment subsystem loses its relevance.

Charge has been defined as the hydrocarbon volumes available for entrapment (Sluijk and Nederlof, 1984). *Charge volume* equals the volume of petroleum generated in the drainage area of a trap minus the volume lost through migration processes. Overall migration losses result from the summation of primary migration losses (expulsion from the active source rock into the carrier bed) and secondary migration losses (in the carrier bed, between the active source rock and the trap).

The term *regional charge* is used to represent the total amount of petroleum from a pod of mature source rock that is available for entrapment:

Regional charge = Quantity of petroleum from a pod of
mature source rock – (expulsion
losses + migration losses)

The regional charge is dependent on the initial source rock richness and the volume of the mature source rock pod. Source rock richness is most accurately expressed in terms of the hydrocarbon genetic potential ($S_1 + S_2$

response), as measured by Rock-Eval pyrolysis on well cuttings, core, and outcrop samples. The pod of mature source rock is delineated by projecting thermal maturity data from key wells onto seismic depth maps and/or by using kinetic modeling methods. Following these delineations, the volumes of mature source rock can be estimated with the assistance of geochemical, stratigraphic, and seismic information. Finally, a gross approximation of the amount of petroleum generated in the pod of mature source rock can be obtained using genetic potentials (in kg HC/t rock), mature source rock volumes, source rock densities, and thermal maturity conversion factors (e.g., modeled transformation ratios). The resulting amount of petroleum (in kilograms) can be converted to any unit of volume required by the evaluator.

In an effort to extend beyond this point, deterministic methods using volumetric calculations have been proposed to predict the amount of petroleum present in a prospect or play. These schemes are unworkable because of the great uncertainty associated with some, or all, of the input parameters. For example, expulsion efficiency and secondary migration losses are not directly observable and thus defy accurate measurement. The calculated amounts of petroleum generated within drainage areas are invariably several orders of magnitude higher than what has already been found or can be reasonably expected in associated traps. To bring the calculated petroleum quantities to plausible proportions, the evaluator has to apply discount factors to compensate for expulsion and secondary migration losses. These discounts are either "assumed" by the evaluator, usually in response to personal biases, or are sometimes obtained from numerical modeling. Although the former approach lacks any scientific merit, we believe that the modeling of petroleum losses also leaves much to be desired in terms of geologic realism because it is oversimplified. We agree with Schowalter (1989) that

> Migration losses and trap efficiency will vary with dip angle, oil–water density, interfacial tension, wettability, and rock heterogeneity along the migration path. This ever expanding level of complexity in a realistic subsurface situation suggests that quantitative geologic modeling of this problem is complex to the point of being insolvable.

For the same fundamental reasons, mathematical modeling of expulsion efficiency from large source rock volumes of varying thickness, sedimentologic fabric, mineral matrix, kerogen richness, maturity, and pressure regime is also fraught with difficulties. Beyond the deduction that the hydrocarbon losses in petroleum systems are large, it is doubtful that operationally reliable charge predictions will ever be derived from uncalibrated deterministic models. Some calibrated methods exist for predicting the petroleum charge volumes available to undrilled traps; however, these methods require large data bases and complex, intensive statistical treatments (Sluijk and Nederlof, 1984). To sidestep the operational difficulties of calculating regional charge, we have turned to a simplified statistical method, which we refer to as the source potential index (SPI).

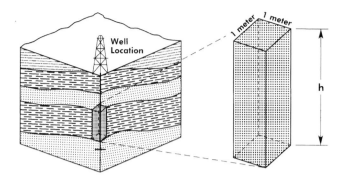

Figure 4.2. Diagram of net source rock thickness factor (*h*) in the source potential index (SPI) equation (equation 1 in the text).

Definition and Calculation of the Source Potential Index (SPI)

The *source potential index (SPI)*, or "cumulative hydrocarbon potential" (Tissot et al., 1980), is defined as the maximum quantity of hydrocarbons (in metric tons) that can be generated within a column of source rock under 1 m² of surface area (Figure 4.2). Because SPI is a measure of cumulative petroleum potential, it is important to bear in mind that (1) this parameter does not distinguish between oil-generating versus gas-generating capacity, and (2) the total quantity of petroleum will not be fully realized unless the source rock is completely matured (spent) during burial. The SPI, which effectively combines net source rock thickness and richness into a single parameter, is calculated as follows:

$$\text{SPI} = \frac{h\left(\overline{S_1 + S_2}\right)\rho}{1000} \quad (1)$$

where SPI is the source potential index (in metric tons hydrocarbons per square meter), h is the net source rock thickness (in meters), $\overline{S_1 + S_2}$ is the average genetic potential (in kilograms HC per metric ton of rock), and ρ is the source rock density (in metric tons per cubic meter). Although specific source rock densities should be used in the SPI determinations, we have simplified our calculations by arbitrarily assigning a density of 2.5 t/m³ to all source rocks.

The net source rock thickness (h) excludes intervening intervals that lack significant source potential (net source rock thickness ≤ gross source rock thickness). Therefore, multiple source beds are combined to yield a cumulative thickness at the given locality. In practice, we have generally confined each source rock sequence to include the cumulative thickness of only those source rocks with genetic potentials in excess of 2 kg HC/t rock. (In certain cases where biological markers unambiguously correlate oils to a lean source rock, this lower limit has been reduced to 1 kg HC/t rock.) Also, the net source rock thickness is corrected for well deviation, the dip of the source rock, and other structural complexities.

The genetic potential, which is a semiquantitative measure of source rock richness, is defined as the $S_1 + S_2$ yield from Rock-Eval pyrolysis (Espitalie et al., 1977). The S_1 represents the kilograms of hydrocarbons that are thermally distilled from 1 t of rock, and the S_2 represents the kilograms of hydrocarbons that are generated by pyrolytic degradation of the kerogen in 1 t of rock (Espitalie et al., 1977; Peters, 1986). Using Rock-Eval pyrolysis data of closely spaced whole-rock samples (approximately every 10 m) in a given well or measured outcrop section, the average genetic potential for a source rock is determined in the following manner. Using drill depth, the top and bottom of the gross source rock interval are determined using a geochemical log (see Figures 5.4–5.11, Chapter 5, this volume). Within this gross interval, we determined the individual source rock interval(s) on which the average genetic potential is calculated. Within each source rock interval, the $S_1 + S_2$ value for a depth (core) or depth interval (cuttings) is multiplied by the depth interval to the next deeper sample or the sample depth interval, whichever situation applies, to get the genetic potential rectangle. We calculate as many genetic potential rectangles as necessary to get through the net source rock interval. Then, the genetic potential rectangles are summed and divided by the thickness of the net source rock interval to get the average genetic potential.

For source rocks that are immature across an entire area, the acquisition of SPIs fulfills no useful purpose because hydrocarbon generation has never taken place in the subsurface. SPI calculations for a given source rock have relevance only where a thermally mature source rock has been identified. The well penetrations or measured outcrop sections selected for SPI determination should be located within or immediately adjacent to the pod of mature source rock. Since SPI is a measure of petroleum potential, the magnitude of SPI at a given location is optimal when the source rock is immature to early mature. A source rock that has reached a "middle oil window rank" or higher maturity shows a significantly reduced SPI because the average genetic potential is depleted due to oil expulsion. In certain cases, theoretical estimates of the initial SPI of a mature source rock prior to maturation can be calculated using the average genetic potential from an equivalent organic facies located in an area where it is less mature. At a given location, the difference between the initial SPI (when the source rock was immature) and present-day residual SPI (source rock is mature) can provide a rough estimate of the amount of oil expelled from the column of source rock under 1 m^2 (in metric tons HC per square meter).

Each SPI is usually obtained from an individual exploration well or measured outcrop section; thus, the resulting value is representative of the source unit at a specific location in the area of interest. Some source rocks show nearly uniform richness and thickness over long distances. Therefore, an SPI determined for an immature source rock in one area is representative of the original SPI of a thermally mature, lateral equivalent of the same source rock. Although many other source rocks show significant lateral variations in thickness and organic

facies, a general knowledge of paleogeography, source rock depositional models (Demaison et al., 1984; Jones, 1987), and possible thickness changes (e.g., derived from seismic data) allow an interpreter to determine whether the source rock in the undrilled area is likely to have shown a higher or lower SPI than those obtained from nearby wells or measured outcrop sections. Therefore, SPI calculations often serve to constrain the possible lateral changes in quantitative source rock potential.

The concept and calculations necessary to formulate cumulative hydrocarbon potential, which we have renamed SPI for practical reasons, were first applied by Tissot et al. (1980) to show the variability in hydrocarbon source potential of Cretaceous black shales in Atlantic basins. Identical calculations were later expanded to a global geochemical data base by Demaison (1988) and Demaison and Huizinga (1989). The original purpose for developing an SPI data base was to create the operational recognition that source rock volume, which is in part a function of thickness, is as important as source rock richness.

Our concept of SPI is different from the "source potential rating index" proposed by Dembicki and Pirkle (1985). Their parameter is calculated by multiplying the average total organic carbon (TOC) content of the source rock, the thickness of mature source rock, and certain maturity scaling factors. Although the method of Dembicki and Pirkle (1985) can be useful for mapping regional trends from a given source rock in a well-known basin, it is not suited for making valid comparisons of different source rock sections from basins around the world because it does not take the variability of kerogen types into account. In contrast, our SPI ranking scale has been developed for the primary purpose of making these global comparisons. We have made the ranking of very different source rocks possible by using petroleum potential, rather than relative units of effectively realized generation, and by expressing source rock richness in terms of the genetic potential (i.e., Rock-Eval $S_1 + S_2$ yield) rather than TOC. Our use of the genetic potential instead of TOC allows for a fundamentally viable ranking of the petroleum potential of diverse source rocks containing dissimilar kerogen types. Thus, a lean gas-prone source rock containing type III kerogen but having substantial thicknesses (e.g., Tertiary sequence of the Niger delta or Jurassic source rock of the Barrow–Dampier basin) can be compared on the same SPI ranking scale to oil-prone source rocks containing type I or II kerogen and having lower stratigraphic thicknesses (e.g., Upper Jurassic–Lower Cretaceous source rocks of the North Sea). SPI can also be used for mapping regional variations in a given source rock, as discussed elsewhere.

Applications of SPI to Exploration

A relative source rock ranking system has been developed by compiling the average SPIs of individual source rocks from various basins (Figure 4.3; Table 4.1). For each source rock, the result listed in Table 4.1 has been determined by calculating SPI at as many locations

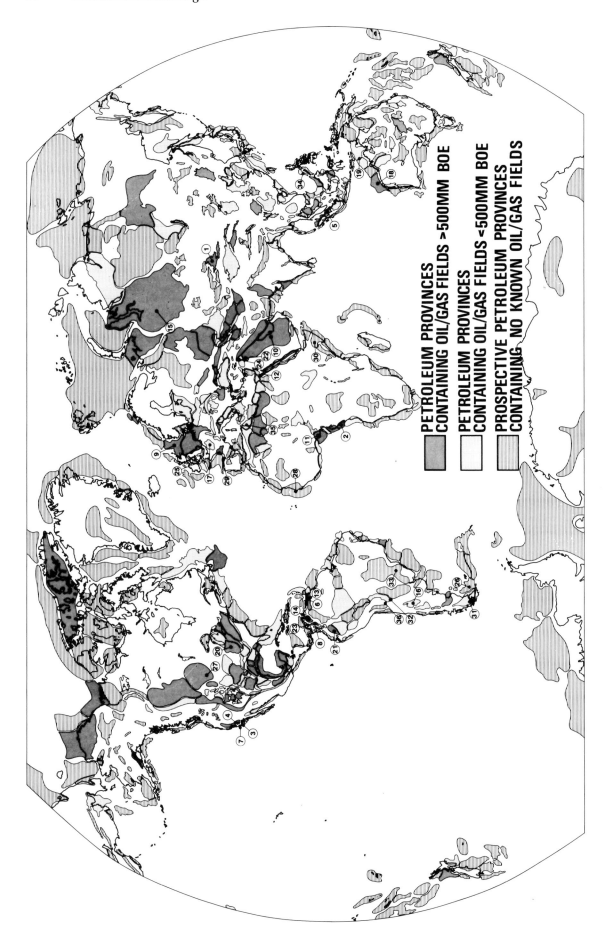

Figure 4.3. Petroleum provinces of the world containing oil or gas fields that are either larger or smaller than 500 billion bbl of oil equivalent or, based on the presence of a source rock, are prospective for oil and gas but presently nonproductive. Circle numbers refer to source rocks listed in Table 4.1. (Adapted from St. John et al., 1984.)

Table 4.1. Examples of Average Source Potential Index (SPI) by Source Rock

Map No.[a]	Petroleum Province (Country)	Field[b]	Source Rock Age	Kerogen Type	Average SPI (t HC/m^2)
1	Junggar (China)	>	Upper Permian	I	65
2	Lower Congo (Cabinda)	>	Lower Cretaceous	I	46
3	Santa Barbara Channel (U.S.A.)	>	Miocene	II	39
4	San Joaquin (U.S.A.)	>	Miocene	II	38
5	Central Sumatra (Indonesia)	>	Eocene–Oligocene	I	34[c]
6	Eastern Venezuela fold and thrust belt (Venezuela)	>	Middle–Upper Cretaceous	II	27[c]
7	Offshore Santa Maria (U.S.A.)	>	Miocene	II	21
8	Middle Magdalena (Colombia)	>	Middle–Upper Cretaceous	II	16
9	North Sea (U.K.)	>	Upper Jurassic–Lower Cretaceous	II	15
10	Central Arabia (Saudi Arabia)	>	Upper Jurassic	II	14
11	Niger Delta (Nigeria)	>	Tertiary	III	14[c]
12	Gulf of Suez (Egypt)	>	Upper Cretaceous–Eocene	II	14
4	San Joaquin (U.S.A.)	>	Eocene–Oligocene	II to II-III	14
13	Maturin (Venezuela)	>	Middle–Upper Cretaceous	II	12[c]
14	Maracaibo (Venezuela)	>	Middle–Upper Cretaceous	II	10[c]
15	West Siberia (Russia)	>	Upper Jurassic	II	8[c]
16	Cuyo (Argentina)	<	Triassic	I	8
17	Paris (France)	<	Lower Jurassic	II	7
18	Barrow-Dampier (Australia)	>	Middle–Upper Jurassic	II-III to III	6
19	E. Browse–W. Bonaparte (Australia)	<	Middle–Upper Jurassic	II-III to III	6
20	Illinois (U.S.A.)	>	Lower Carboniferous	II	6[c]
21	Oriente (Ecuador)	>	Middle to Upper Cretaceous	II	6
22	Northwest Arabian (Syria)	>	Triassic and Upper Cretaceous	II	5
23	Plato (Colombia)	<	Oligocene–Miocene	II-III to III	5
24	Northwest Arabian (Turkey)	<	Upper Silurian–Lower Devonian	II	4
25	Celtic Sea (Ireland)	<	Lower Jurassic	II to II-III	4
26	Malvinas (Argentina)	0	Lower Cretaceous	II to II-III	3
27	Williston (U.S.A.)	>	Upper Devonian–Lower Carboniferous	II	3
28	Senegal (Senegal)	0	Paleocene–Eocene	II-III	2
29	Cantabrian (Spain)	0	Lower Jurassic	II	2
30	Ogaden (Ethiopia)	0	Upper Jurassic	II to II-III	2
31	Magallanes-Austral (Chile)	<	Lower Cretaceous	II-III	1
32	Metan (Argentina)	<	Upper Cretaceous	II	1
33	Parana (Brazil)	0	Lower Permian	II	1
34	Palawan (Philippines)	<	Eocene	II	1[c]
35	Pelagian (Tunisia)	<	Middle Cretaceous	II	1[c]
36	Tres Cruces (Argentina)	0	Upper Cretaceous	II	<1
35	Pelagian (Tunisia)	<	Eocene	II	<1[c]

[a]Map number locations on Figure 4.3.

[b]>, oil or gas field size > 0.5 billion BOE; <, oil or gas field size < 0.5 billion BOE; 0, no known oil or gas fields.

[c]Estimated.

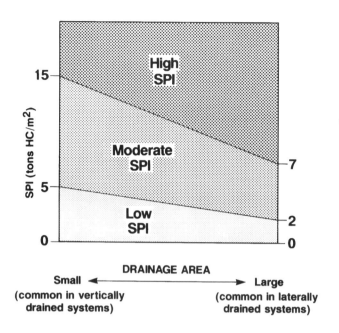

Figure 4.4. Preliminary source potential index (SPI) classification.

as possible, within or adjacent to the pod of mature source rock, and averaging these values. Although these averaged results are tabulated in numerical order from highest to lowest, only substantial relative differences are considered important in the SPI comparison of two or more source rocks. Some provinces contain more than one source rock, which are listed separately in Table 4.1 (e.g., the Miocene and Eocene–Oligocene source rocks of the San Joaquin basin), or some may not all appear due to lack of data (see Talukdar and Marcano, Chapter 29, this volume).

In the appraisal of a petroleum system, the source rock must be evaluated in the context of the overall structural and stratigraphic framework, which determines the migration style. We have developed a preliminary SPI classification (Figure 4.4), which has been empirically derived from worldwide measurements of SPI and a general knowledge of the discovered hydrocarbon reserves that are likely to be derived from these specific source rocks. In vertically drained petroleum systems, SPIs are classified as low (SPI < 5), moderate (5 ≤ SPI < 15), and high (15 ≤ SPI). In contrast, laterally drained petroleum systems are significantly less demanding on the magnitude of SPI. Traps in laterally drained systems tend to focus migrating petroleum from larger drainage areas relative to those in vertically drained systems. Because areal extent is also critical in determining source rock volume, we tentatively propose lower limits to define the SPI categories in laterally drained systems: low (SPI < 2), moderate (2 ≤ SPI < 7), and high (7 ≤ SPI). So far, our database includes SPIs from only a limited number of laterally drained petroleum systems (e.g., Central Arabia, Maturin, West Siberia, Illinois, Oriente, and Williston). Thus, the SPI categories for laterally drained systems are subject to future refinement.

In extensively explored areas, a positive correlation

exists between the magnitudes of the SPIs of source rocks and the associated petroleum reserves of that petroleum system. Source rocks with high SPIs, as defined in Figure 4.4, are statistically associated with large petroleum reserves and production from giant oil and gas fields (Figure 4.3; Table 4.1). In contrast, areas containing a source rocks with low SPIs, as defined in Figure 4.4, are associated with either small petroleum reserves and production from subgiant oil and gas fields or are nonproductive (Figure 4.3; Table 4.1). Although the use of SPI categories that shift with respect to the size of drainage areas (Figure 4.4) shows great promise as an operationally viable shortcut for estimating regional charging capacity, we will continue to evaluate and refine this sliding SPI scale as more data become available.

In the genetic classification of a petroleum system, the ability of a source rock to expel hydrocarbons is described by the charge factor (Figure 4.1), which semi-quantitatively characterizes the total amount of hydrocarbons available for entrapment (i.e., regional charge). The three terms used to describe the charge factor (supercharged, normally charged, or undercharged) are provisionally assigned according to the magnitude of SPI (high, moderate, or low SPI, respectively, as defined in Figure 4.4).

After a source rock showing a favorable SPI rating is identified, it is economically important to delineate the specific areas that have the highest charging capacity. This is primarily achieved by the integration of SPI and thermal maturity maps. The evaluation of regional trends in hydrocarbon charging capacity is also enhanced with the aid of paleogeographic maps, a knowledge of source rock depositional models (Demaison et al., 1984), and a recognition of migration styles. This information will help in interpolating the charging capacity for areas occurring between locations of known SPI and possibly assist in extrapolating trends away from measured SPI data points.

QUALIFICATION OF MIGRATION–ENTRAPMENT

General Considerations

Because expulsion and migration mechanisms are relatively inefficient, the existence of petroleum accumulations requires that migrating hydrocarbons be focused from a much larger volume of mature source rock into a much smaller trap. Lateral oil movement along the carrier bed is an important migration mechanism. However, reservoir systems cannot function as efficient lateral drains unless they are continuously overlain by unbreached sealing lithologies. These beneficial reservoir–seal associations are often regionally extensive wherever marine transgressive sequences rest on marine regressive or continental clastic sedimentary rocks. Widespread evaporitic sequences overlying reservoir units in carbonate platform systems can also function in the same favorable manner.

Geologists comfortably accept lateral migration distances of hundreds of kilometers ("long-distance migration"), but are often skeptical when vertical migration distances of two orders of magnitude less (1–5 km) are proposed to explain geochemical observations. Explorationists are often surprised when oils from reservoirs of widely different ages in the same field are shown by biological markers to be derived from a single source. Yet this situation is commonly observed in extensional regimes and thrust belt plays (Price, 1980). The reluctance in accepting vertically dominated migration may be partially psychological: stratigraphic fabrics always display more vertical than lateral variability. Thus, it is intuitively assumed that vertical migration must be an unusual phenomenon. This paradigm is also reinforced by the observation that fault and fracture zones exposed at the outcrop generally appear to the naked eye to be sealed and impervious. Most significantly, the occurrence of oil accumulations in fault traps supports the widely held perception that faults always behave as barriers rather than conduits to migration in the subsurface. The point can be lost that faults do not seal fault traps; the lithologies and/or pressure regimes on the other sides of the faults do (Downey, 1984; Chapter 8, this volume). Furthermore, fault zones have a dual character, in some situations acting as a conduit for fluid flow while in other cases acting as a barrier to flow (Smith and Forster, 1989). Whether faults and fracture zones act as barriers or conduits is also controlled by the presence and positioning of deep, abnormally pressured hydraulic systems (Hunt, 1990).

The interaction of the following three physical constraints explains why vertical migration phenomena are so commonly observed in certain tectonic settings:

1. Faults and fractures that are persistently reactivated by tectonic movements may serve as highly efficient avenues for vertical migration of petroleum. Given a relatively limited time (e.g., 10 m.y.), a vertical or subvertical open fracture 1 mm across and 1 km long is capable of filling (or depleting) a large oil field. The role of faults and fractures as loci of hydrothermal fluid movement and sites of metallic ore deposition has been recognized by the mining profession for well over a century (Park and MacDiarmid, 1975). Thus, the importance of faults and fractures in the vertical transport of petroleum from a deeper source rock to significantly shallower reservoir rocks should be acceptable to petroleum geologists.
2. Low-angle lateral migration is physically less efficient than vertical migration. The buoyant force of an oil filament of fixed length and volume is several times higher for purely vertical displacement than for lateral upward transport along a gently dipping carrier bed. Consequently, lateral migration is more demanding on the amount of oil needed to create an adequate buoyant force capable of breaking through capillary pressure barriers in the carrier unit (Illing, 1939).
3. In general, the volumes of water-wet porous rock percolated through during long-distance lateral migration of petroleum are several orders of

magnitude larger than those traveled through during vertical migration. For this reason alone, lateral migration of petroleum is likely to result in substantially larger secondary migration losses than are incurred during vertical migration through faults and fractures. This is particularly the case for natural gas, which must continuously saturate the water phase in the carrier bed if it is to persist as a separate hydrocarbon phase during secondary migration (Sluijk and Nederlof, 1984).

Because of the physical constraints previously reviewed, short-range lateral migration along permeable carrier beds and vertical migration through faults and fractures are the most commonly observed mechanisms of petroleum charging into traps. Evidence for a strong vertical component to migration from a deeply buried active source rock is increasingly being recognized, thanks to modern biological marker correlations (Seifert et al., 1979; Moldowan et al., 1985). Except for unusual cases of long-distance lateral migration (e.g., peri-Andean foreland basins, Western Canada basin, Central Arabia, and Williston basin), the petroleum accumulations in most areas are commonly found over or immediately adjacent to a pod of mature source rock (Demaison, 1984). In fact, most commercial petroleum accumulations result from relatively short lateral migration distances (less than 30 km), which are constrained by the dimensions of the structural drainage cells surrounding individual traps (Sluijk and Nederlof, 1984).

Recognition of Migration Styles

For this classification, it is important to identify those secondary migration patterns that lead to concentration rather than dispersion of hydrocarbons once they have been expelled from the mature source rock. Recognition of focused secondary migration patterns, rather than dispersive mechanisms, helps to predict the location of plays and their potential petroleum richness (Pratsch, 1982). Evaluation of migration style is the critical step in recognizing whether drainage is focusing or dispersive. Migration drainage style is tectonically controlled and thus is predictable from the broad structural and stratigraphic fabrics of the basin fill. Petroleum systems can be classified as laterally drained or vertically drained (Figure 4.1), as outlined below.

Laterally Drained Petroleum Systems

Lateral drainage of petroleum requires a laterally continuous regional seal resting on a widespread, permeable reservoir unit (i.e., seal–reservoir "doublets"), a weak to moderate degree of compressive structural deformation, and uninterrupted homoclinal ramps. Foreland basins, such as the North Slope of Alaska (Figure 4.5) and the peri-Andean basins of South America, or saucer-shaped intracratonic sags, such as the Williston basin (Figure 4.6) and the Triassic salt province of eastern Algerian Sahara, are favorable settings for focused lateral drainage, provided some low-amplitude arches plunge into the pod of mature source rock. Lack

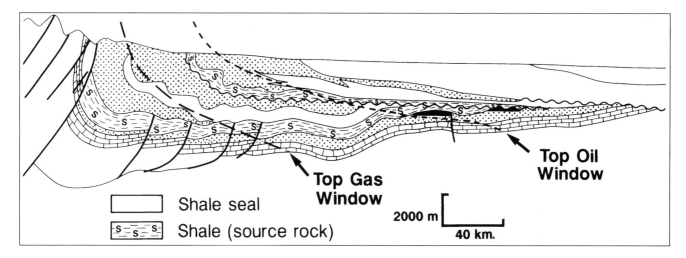

Figure 4.5. Example of a supercharged, laterally drained, high-impedance petroleum system, patterned after the North Slope of Alaska, U.S.A.

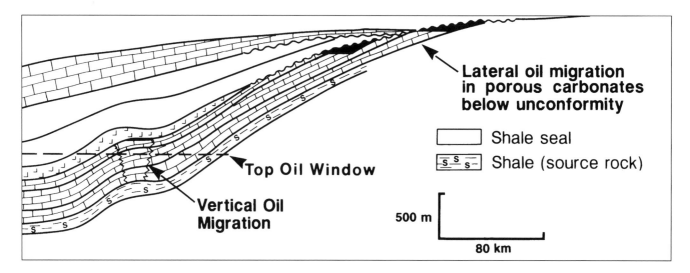

Figure 4.6. Example of a normally charged, laterally drained, low-impedance petroleum system, patterned after the Williston basin, U.S.A.

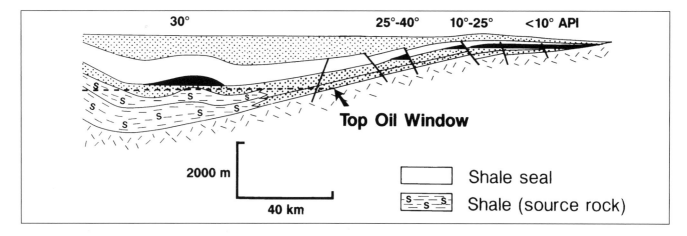

Figure 4.7. Example of a supercharged, laterally drained, low-impedance petroleum system, patterned after the eastern Venezuela foreland basin. Large accumulations of heavy oil are found near the margins of the petroleum system in the shallow immature sedimentary strata.

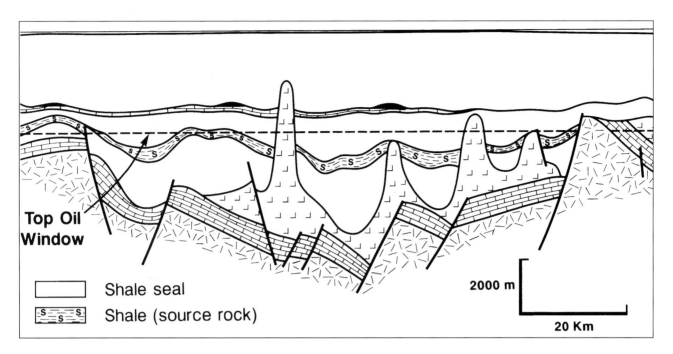

Figure 4.8. Example of a supercharged, vertically drained, high-impedance petroleum system, patterned after the Central graben of the North Sea. The basin fill of a rift basin tends to be vertically drained due to petroleum transfer along faults and fractures. (Adapted from Thomas et al., 1985.)

of tectonic activity (e.g., faulting) after the petroleum has been generated and entrapped is critical to the preservation of seal integrity.

Basin fill that contains laterally drained petroleum systems share many common features:

1. Oil accumulations tend to occur in immature sedimentary strata located far away from the pod of mature source rock. Accumulations containing long-distance migrated oil commonly account for more than 50% of the entrapped oil volume within the petroleum system. Lateral migration distances in excess of 160 km have been observed.
2. A single reservoir rock of the same age, present under the most effective regional seal, usually hosts most of the entrapped oil and gas within the petroleum system.
3. Faulting of the effective regional seal rock is minor or insignificant.
4. In supercharged, laterally drained petroleum systems, large accumulations of heavy oil are often found near the margins of the system in shallow immature sedimentary strata. Examples include the heavy oil belts of eastern Venezuela (Figure 4.7) and western Canada (Demaison, 1977; Creany and Allan, 1990; Krause and James, 1990).

Vertically Drained Petroleum Systems

Focused vertical drainage of petroleum is associated with a moderate to high degree of structural deformation capable of creating selective breaching and local petroleum leakage through stratigraphically widespread seal rocks (Price, 1980). Although continuous seals are

absolutely essential to laterally drained systems, seal continuity is also important in vertically drained systems. Deeper seals cause petroleum to converge on the faults, fractures, or other "windows" or "chimneys" through these seals, where focused vertical drainage transports the petroleum upward until effective top seals are reached, thus charging associated traps.

Extensional, wrench, and thrust tectonics produce faults and fractures that function as avenues for focused vertical migration, particularly if tectonic activity keeps them open for much of their geologic history. Petroleum-rich basin fill of a rift basin owes much of the petroleum transfer to vertical movement along faults, which are also responsible for much of the entrapment. Examples include the North Sea (Figure 4.8), Gulf of Suez, Gippsland, Reconcavo, and Sirte. Passive Atlantic-type margins affected by salt tectonics and extensional faulting, such as Campeche–Reforma (Figure 4.9), Lower Congo, and Campos, also tend to be vertically drained.

The highly productive Tertiary deltas of Nigeria and the U.S. Gulf Coast are typical vertically drained systems due to the formation of listric faults in an extensional regime (Figure 4.10). The structure may also be complicated by piercement salt domes, such as along the Gulf Coast, that facilitate vertical drainage. Multiple sandstone reservoirs containing identical oil types migrated from deep-seated, overpressured source rocks are commonplace in these deltaic settings. Similarly, hydrocarbons entrapped in more ancient deltaic sequences (e.g., the Lower Cretaceous reservoirs of the Jeanne d'Arc basin in Canada and the Barrow–Dampier basin in Australia) have migrated vertically through fault zones from an underlying source rock (Upper Jurassic source rock in both examples).

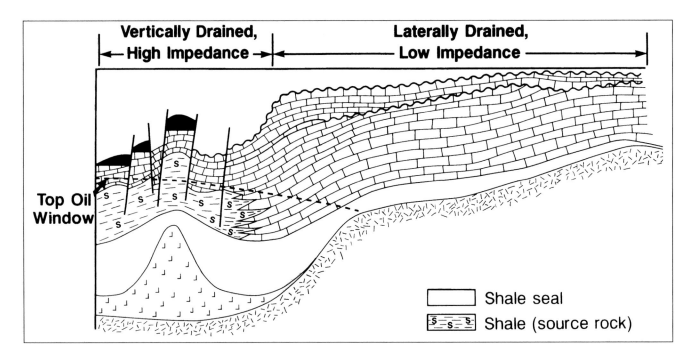

Figure 4.9. Example of a supercharged, vertically drained, high-impedance petroleum system, patterned after the Campeche–Reforma area, Mexico). The petroliferous part of the basin fill is vertically drained and has high impedance (left side). In contrast, the right side of the basin fill is laterally drained and shows low impedance but is petroleum poor.

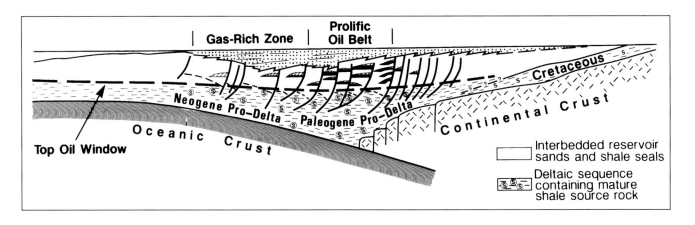

Figure 4.10. Example of a normally charged, vertically drained, high-impedance petroleum system, patterned after the Niger delta, Nigeria. Sedimentary rocks in Tertiary deltas are usually vertically drained, due primarily to the presence of listric faults.

Petroliferous basin fill in wrench-fault basins is also characterized by multiple reservoir rocks charged by deeply buried source rocks, with vertical redistribution of the same type of petroleum through faults, as occurs in the Los Angeles and Ventura basins of California (Figure 4.11).

Thrust belt provinces are also typical habitats for petroleum transfer by mostly vertical migration through breached seals, until a seal capable of containing the accumulation is encountered (Figure 4.12). Most of the world's prolific thrust belt plays are charged by a source rock that is significantly older and/or deeper than the reservoir rocks (e.g., Zagros fold belt, eastern Venezuela thrust belt, overthrust belt of Wyoming, middle

Magdalena Valley of Colombia, and the Carpathians). Prolific thrust belt plays are typically constrained by effective top seals, such as the Fars salt in the Zagros fold belt, the highly overpressured shales in the eastern Venezuela thrust belt, and several thin evaporites in the overthrust belt of Wyoming.

In summary, vertically drained petroleum systems share several common features:

1. Nearly all of the petroleum accumulations occur over the pod of mature source rock or in close proximity to it. Lateral migration distances are short (generally less than 30 km) (Sluijk and Nederlof, 1984).

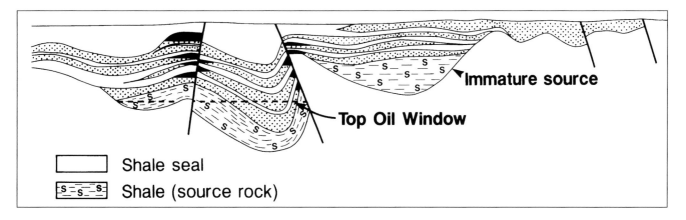

Figure 4.11. Example of a supercharged, vertically drained, high-impedance petroleum system, patterned after the Los Angeles basin, U.S.A. Basin fill in wrench-fault basins typically shows vertical migration of petroleum through faults.

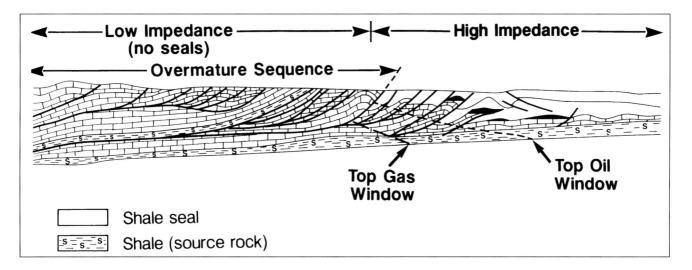

Figure 4.12. Example of a vertically drained fold and thrust belt. The presence of an effective top seal causes part of the petroleum system to show high impedance (right side), whereas the lack of seal rock results in a low-impedance sector of the fold and thrust belt (left side).

2. Multiple, vertically stacked reservoir rocks, sometimes of grossly different ages, often contain the same genetic type of oil, such as the Lower Cretaceous–Tertiary reservoirs of the Campos basin (Mohriak et al., 1990). The oils may show varying degrees of postentrapment alteration (e.g., biodegradation and water washing). Biological markers can distinguish between compositional variations caused by secondary alteration processes and those resulting from source rock and thermal maturity differences.
3. Faulting remains active until the last effective regional seal has been laid down.
4. In supercharged, vertically drained petroleum systems, surface seepages are abundant wherever tectonic activity, persisting to the present day, has breached the regional top seal in places (e.g., San Joaquin basin of California, salt domes in the U.S. Gulf Coast, Zagros fold belt, and Magdalena Valley of Colombia).

Entrapment Style

Traps are subsurface loci where petroleum can no longer continue its migration toward the surface because the buoyant movement of oil and gas has been arrested. The foremost scientific basis for finding petroleum is the identification of traps by geophysical methods. Convex-upward structural traps are physically the most efficient in retaining petroleum because any layer serving as a top seal is also a lateral seal (Downey, 1984). That is why the bulk of the world's oil reserves has been found in four-way closures. Although structural traps are the most efficient on the whole, a structural trap reliant on a fault for closure carries substantial seal risks (Downey, 1984). Structural–stratigraphic traps, featuring three-way structural closures in combination with reservoir wedge-outs, account for a few of the world's supergiant oil accumulations, including Prudhoe Bay (Figure 4.5), Venezuela's Bolivar Coastal fields, and the East Texas field, as well as many other accumulations of substantial economic merit.

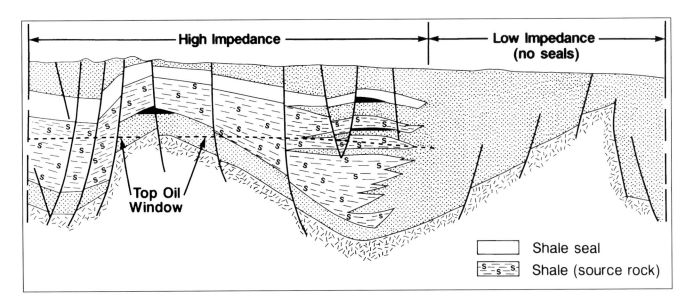

Figure 4.13. Example of a normally charged, vertically drained, high-impedance petroleum system, patterned after the Reconcavo basin, Brazil. The petroliferous portion of the basin fill (left side) contains the petroleum system, which is best characterized by high impedance. However, the basin fill also contains a low-impedance sector (right side) that lacks effective seals, resulting in vertical dispersion and loss of petroleum, regardless of structure. The boundary between the high and low impedance defines the geographic extent of this petroleum system.

In contrast, purely stratigraphic traps that lack any partial structural control tend to be imperfectly sealed and, consequently, are generally small in size.

In a natural system, any change or transfer of energy brings about a statistically increasing degree of randomness in that system. Therefore, it is compatible with thermodynamic principles that, given geologic time, the ultimate fate of petroleum in sedimentary rocks is dispersion and destruction by thermal or bacterial processes. Each petroleum accumulation, regardless of size, corresponds to a local, temporary entropy reversal requiring an improbable set of geologic circumstances. The larger the accumulation, the exponentially higher the degree of geologic improbability, resulting in the well-known log normal distribution of field sizes observed in most petroleum basins (Klemme, 1983; North, 1985). A critical geologic factor responsible for lowering entropy is the degree of physical resistance working against wholesale dispersion of petroleum as it tends to migrate toward the surface. This physical factor is called *impedance.*

The degree of structural deformation and the seal integrity are the two key factors used to qualify entrapment styles. Together, these factors control the degree of impedance working against the natural tendency for petroleum to become randomly dispersed and lost in sedimentary rocks. Entrapment style can be classified as high impedance or low impedance (Figure 4.1).

High-impedance entrapment style is characterized by laterally continuous seals coupled with a moderate to high degree of structural deformation. Regional seal continuity is essential to the integrity and retention characteristics of traps and to the collecting efficiency of drainage areas surrounding the traps. However, local breaching of seals in faulted regimes results in combined vertical migration focusing and entrapment. This is a commonly encountered situation in Tertiary deltas, rift systems, and other extensional regimes.

Low-impedance entrapment style is characterized by either a high degree of regional seal continuity and a low degree of structural deformation, or a low degree of regional seal effectiveness coupled with a high or low degree of structural deformation. In the latter case, the degree of structural deformation is irrelevant to defining the impedance because a deficiency in seals results in vertical dispersion and loss of petroleum, regardless of structure (Figure 4.13).

CONCLUSIONS AND IMPLICATIONS FOR EXPLORATION

The genetic classification of petroleum systems consists of applying the following three geologic factors: (1) charge factor (supercharged, normally charged, or undercharged), (2) migration drainage style (vertically drained or laterally drained), and (3) entrapment style (high impedance or low impedance). A petroleum system can be classified by using a combination of qualifiers, selected from each of these three categories (Figure 4.1). Provinces containing known petroleum systems have been classified to illustrate the use of this scheme (Figure 4.14).

This genetic classification scheme describes petroleum systems in terms of their process-driven attributes. Discrimination between petroleum systems is based on differences in regional charging capacity and in the geologic styles controlling hydrocarbon concentration and retention. This classification provides explorationists

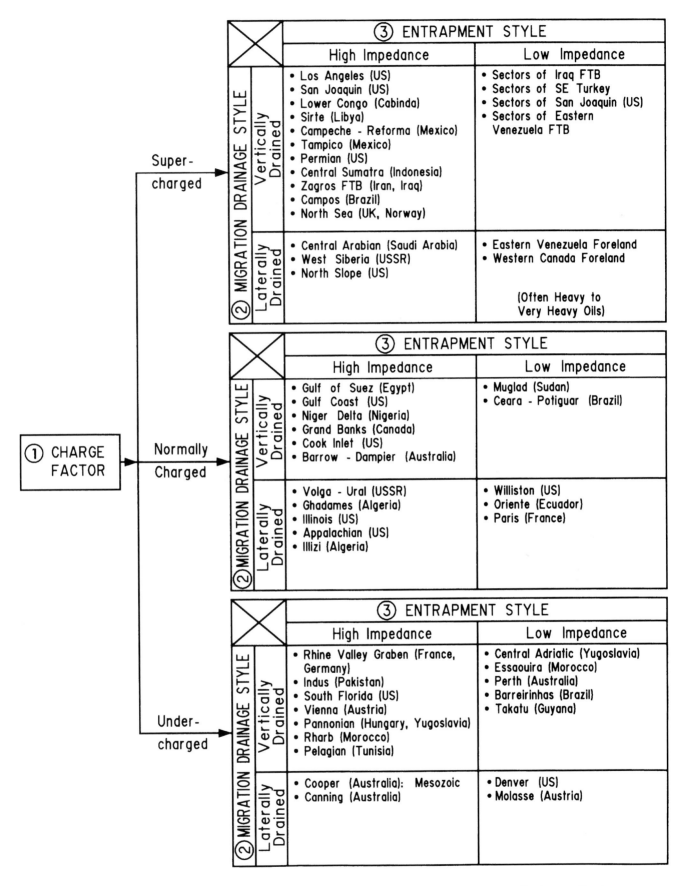

Figure 4.14. Examples of petroleum provinces that contain at least one petroleum system described according to our genetic classification. FTB, fold and thrust belt.

with a methodology reaching beyond the conventional evaluation of the static geologic framework. For instance, the use of analogs can be expanded from that of comparing descriptive "look-alike" sedimentary basins to that of comparing genetic "work-alike" petroleum systems. Furthermore, the forced integration of regional charging capacity of the pod of mature source rock into the conventional evaluation of traps will lead to significantly improved accuracy in ranking worldwide exploration opportunities.

Qualitative approaches still underpin the migration–entrapment subsystem of this genetic classification because it is not yet feasible to quantify all of the processes at work in the subsurface. Whether uncalibrated deterministic models can ever quantify migration and expulsion phenomena in an operationally useful manner remains in doubt. In the meantime, descriptive tectonic classifications provide useful qualitative support to predict migration, entrapment, and retention characteristics. Thus, the genetic classification of petroleum systems needs to be used together with descriptive sedimentary basin classifications.

The most important control determining the ultimate petroleum richness of a petroleum system is regional charging, which primarily relates to the hydrocarbon yield and volume of a mature source rock, or the charge factor. The use of the empirical–statistical source potential index (SPI) approach as a short cut to evaluate the charge factor is still in its early developmental phase. However, it shows promise of being a valuable tool for the rapid evaluation of the charging capacity of a petroleum system. The critical observation is that, in extensively explored regions, a positive correlation exists between the magnitude of SPI and the associated petroleum reserves. Another important statistical observation, derived from our SPI ranking, is that vertically drained systems, such as those found in basin fill of rift basins, deltas, wrench-fault basins, and thrust belts, are more demanding on the magnitude of SPI because traps generally fetch from smaller drainage areas than those occurring in laterally drained systems.

Acknowledgments   *The writers wish to acknowledge W. Dow and A. Perrodon for the initial concept of the petroleum system, B. Tissot for first introducing the idea of integrating thickness and yield into a single numerical expression, G. Ulmishek for his early critical review of our manuscript, and N. Schneidermann whose support and encouragement resulted in this paper being written and presented. We are especially indebted to L. Magoon, who has refined the concept of the petroleum system over recent years and has also spent considerable effort in improving our original manuscript. In addition, the authors gratefully acknowledge the constructive views of Chevron's management, namely M. W. Boyce, E. L. Couch, and R. E. Kropschot.*

References Cited

Bacoccoli, G., I. Garcia da Costa, and J. A. S. Brandão, 1989, Account of hydrocarbon discovery process in Brazil (abs.): AAPG Bulletin, v. 73, p. 330.

Bally, A. W., and S. Snelson, 1980, Realms of subsidence, in A. D. Miall, ed., Facts and principles of world petroleum occurrence: Canadian Society of Petroleum Geologists Memoir 6, p. 9–94.

Bois, C., 1975, Petroleum-zone concept and the similarity analysis—contribution to resource appraisal, in J. D. Haun, ed., Methods of estimating the volume of undiscovered oil and gas resources: AAPG Studies in Geology 1, p. 87–89.

Bois, C., P. Bouche, and R. Pelet, 1982, Global geologic history and distribution of hydrocarbon reserves: AAPG Bulletin, v. 66, p. 1248–1270.

Carmalt, S. W., and B. St. John, 1986, Giant oil and gas fields, in M. T. Halbouty, ed., Future petroleum provinces of the world: AAPG Memoir 40, p. 11–53.

Creany, S., and J. Allan, 1990, Hydrocarbon generation and migration in the Western Canada sedimentary basin, in J. Brooks, ed., Classic petroleum provinces: Geological Society Special Publication 50, p. 189–202.

Demaison, G., 1977, Tar sands and supergiant oil fields: AAPG Bulletin, v. 61, p. 1950–1961.

Demaison, G., 1984, The generative basin concept, in G. Demaison and R. J. Murris, eds., Petroleum geochemistry and basin evaluation: AAPG Memoir 35, p. 1–14.

Demaison, G., 1988, Genetic classification of petroleum basins (abs.), in C. Masters and N. Schneidermann, eds., AAPG Research Conference on Petroleum Potential of Sedimentary Basins, Leesburg, VA.

Demaison, G., A. J. J. Holck, R. W. Jones, and G. T. Moore, 1984, Predictive source bed stratigraphy: a guide to regional petroleum occurrence: Proceedings of the Eleventh World Petroleum Congress, v. 2, p. 17–29.

Demaison, G., and B. J. Huizinga, 1989, Genetic classification of petroleum basins (abs.): AAPG Bulletin, v. 73, p. 349.

Dembicki, H., and F. L. Pirkle, 1985, Regional source rock mapping using a source potential rating index: AAPG Bulletin, v. 69, p. 567–581.

Dow, W. G., 1974, Application of oil-correlation and source rock data to exploration in Williston basin: AAPG Bulletin, v. 58, p. 1253–1262.

Downey, M. W., 1984, Evaluating seals for hydrocarbon accumulations: AAPG Bulletin, v. 68, p. 1752–1763.

Durand, B., 1988, Understanding of hydrocarbon migration in sedimentary basins (present state of knowledge), in L. Mattavelli and L. Novelli, eds., Advances in organic geochemistry, 1987: Organic Geochemistry, v. 13, n. 1–3, p. 445–459.

Espitalié, J., M. Madec, B. Tissot, J. J. Mennig, and P. Leplat, 1977, Source rock characterization method for petroleum exploration, in Proceedings of the Ninth Annual Offshore Technology Conference, v. 3, p. 439–448.

Gonzalez, R., and I. N. Holguin, 1992, Geology of the source rocks of Mexico: Proceedings of the 13th World Petroleum Congress, Buenos Aires, v. 2, p. 95–104.

Grunau, H. R., 1987, A worldwide look at the cap-rock problem: Journal of Petroleum Geology, v. 10, p. 245–266.

Helwig, J. A., 1985, Origin and classification of sedimentary basins: Proceedings of the Seventeenth Annual Offshore Technology Conference, v. 1, p. 21–32.

Hunt, J. M., 1990, Generation and migration of petroleum from abnormally pressured fluid compartments: AAPG Bulletin, v. 74, p. 1–12.

Illing, V. C., 1939, Some factors in oil accumulation: Journal of the Institute of Petroleum, v. 25, n. 186, p. 201–255.

Jones, R. W., 1987, Organic facies: Advances in Petroleum Geochemistry, v. 2, p. 1–90.

Kingston, D. R., C. P. Dishroon, and P. A. Williams, 1983, Global basin classification system: AAPG Bulletin, v. 67, p. 2175–2193.

Klemme, H. D., 1975, Giant oil fields related to their geologic setting: a possible guide to exploration: Bulletin of Canadian Petroleum Geology, v. 23, p. 30–66.

Klemme, H. D., 1980, Types of petroliferous basins, *in* J. F. Mason, ed., Petroleum Geology in China: Tulsa, OK, PennWell Books.

Klemme, H. D., 1983, Field size distribution related to basin characteristics: Oil & Gas Journal, December, p. 168–176.

Krause, H. H., and K. H. James, 1990, Hydrocarbon resources of Venezuela, their source rocks and structural habitat: Circum-Pacific Council for Energy and Mineral Resources Earth Science Series, v. 11, p. 405–414.

Magoon, L. B., 1987, The petroleum system—a classification scheme for research, resource assessment, and exploration (abs.): AAPG Bulletin, v. 71, p. 587.

Magoon, L. B., 1988, The petroleum system—a classification scheme for research, exploration and resource assessment, *in* L. B. Magoon, ed., Petroleum systems of the United States: U.S.G.S. Bulletin 1870, p. 2–15.

Meissner, F. F., J. Woodward, and J. L. Clayton, 1984, Stratigraphic relationships and distribution of source rocks in the greater Rocky Mountain region, *in* J. Woodward et al., eds., Hydrocarbon source rocks of the greater Rocky Mountain region: Rocky Mountain Association of Geologists, p. 1–34.

Mohriak, W. V., M. R. Mello, J. F. Dewey, and J. R. Maxwell, 1990, Petroleum geology of the Campos basin, offshore Brazil, *in* J. Brooks, ed., Classic petroleum provinces: The Geological Society Special Publication 50, p. 119–141.

Moldowan, J. M., W. K. Seifert, and E. J. Gallegos, 1985, Relationship between petroleum composition and depositional environment of petroleum source rocks: AAPG Bulletin, v. 69, p. 1255–1268.

Nederlof, M. H., 1979, The use of habitat of oil models in exploration prospect appraisal: Proceedings of the 10th World Petroleum Congress, Bucharest, Romania, p. 13–21.

Nederlof, M. H., 1981, Calibrated computer simulation as a tool for exploration prospect assessment: United Nations ESCAP CCOP Technical Publication 10, p. 122–138.

Nijhuis, H. J., and A. B. Baak, 1990, A calibrated prospect appraisal system: Proceedings of the Indonesian Petroleum Association, 19th Annual Convention, p. 69–83.

North, F. K., 1985, Petroleum Geology: Boston, Allen and Unwin, 607 p.

Park, C. F., and R. A. MacDiarmid, 1975, Ore Deposits, 3rd ed.: San Francisco, W. H. Freeman, 530 p.

Perrodon, A., 1972, Essai de classification des bassins sedimentaires: Science de la Terre, v. 16, p. 197–227.

Perrodon, A., 1980, Geodynamique petroliere: genese et repartition des gisements d'hydrocarbures: Paris, Masson–Elf-Aquitaine, 381 p.

Perrodon, A., 1983, Geodynamique des bassins sedimentaires et systems petroliers: Bulletin des Centres de Recherches Exploration-Production Elf-Aquitaine, v. 7, p. 645–676.

Perrodon, A., and P. Masse, 1984, Subsidence, sedimentation, and petroleum systems: Journal of Petroleum Geology, v. 7, p. 5–26.

Peters, K. E., 1986, Guidelines for evaluating petroleum source rock using programmed pyrolysis: AAPG Bulletin, v. 70, p. 318–329.

Pratsch, J.-C., 1982, Focused gas migration and concentration of deep-gas accumulations: Erdoel und Kohle, Erdgas, Petrochemie, v. 35, p. 59–65.

Price, L. C., 1980, Utilization and documentation of vertical oil migration in deep basins: Journal of Petroleum Geology, v. 2, p. 353–387.

St. John, B., A. W. Bally, and H. D. Klemme, 1984, Sedimentary provinces of the world—hydrocarbon productive and nonproductive: AAPG map, scale 1:31,368,000.

Schowalter, T. T., 1979, Mechanics of secondary hydrocarbon migration and entrapment: AAPG Bulletin, v. 63, p. 723–760.

Schowalter, T. T., 1989, Migration and entrapment efficiency (abs.): Technical Program of the Geological Society of London Migration Symposium, September.

Seifert, W. K., J. M. Moldowan, and R. W. Jones, 1979, Application of biological-marker chemistry to petroleum exploration: Proceedings of the 10th World Petroleum Congress, Bucharest, Romania, Paper SP8, p. 425–440.

Sluijk, D., and M. H. Nederlof, 1984, Worldwide geological experience as a systematic basis for prospect appraisal, *in* G. Demaison and R. J. Murris, eds., Petroleum geochemistry and basin evaluation: AAPG Memoir 35, p. 15–26.

Smith, L., and C. Forster, 1989, Interaction between fault zones, fluid flow, and heat transfer at basin scale (abs.): 28th International Geological Congress, Washington, D.C., v. 3, p. 104.

Thomas, B. M., P. Moller-Pedersen, M. F. Whitaker, and N. D. Shaw, 1985, Organic facies and hydrocarbon distributions in the Norwegian North Sea, *in* B. M. Thomas et al., eds., Petroleum geochemistry in exploration of the Norwegian Shelf: Proceedings of the Norwegian Petroleum Society (NPF), 1984, p. 19.

Tissot, B. P., G. Demaison, P. Masson, J. R. Delteil, and A. Combaz, 1980, Paleoenvironment and petroleum potential of middle Cretaceous black shales in Atlantic basins: AAPG Bulletin, v. 64, p. 2051–2063.

Tissot, B. P., R. Pelet, and P. Ungerer, 1987, Thermal history of sedimentary basins, maturation indices, and kinetics of oil and gas generation: AAPG Bulletin, v. 71, p. 1445–1466.

Ulmishek, G., 1986, Stratigraphic aspects of petroleum resource assessment, *in* D. D. Rice, ed., Oil and gas assessment—methods and applications: AAPG Studies in Geology 21, p. 59–68.

Ulmishek, G. F., and H. D. Klemme, 1990, Depositional controls, distribution, and effectiveness of world's petroleum source rocks: U.S.G.S. Bulletin 1931, p. 1–59.

Vann, I. R., 1989, Critical factors in exploration of Mesozoic and Cenozoic thrust belts (abs.): William Smith Lectures Program, Geological Society of London, April.

Weeks, L. G., 1952, Factors of sedimentary basin development that control oil occurrence: AAPG Bulletin, v. 36, p. 2071–2124.

Part II

Essential Elements

Magoon, L. B, and W. G. Dow, eds., 1994, The petroleum
system—from source to trap: AAPG Memoir 60.

Chapter **5**

Applied Source Rock Geochemistry

Kenneth E. Peters*

Chevron Overseas Petroleum Inc.
San Ramon, California, U.S.A.

Mary Rose Cassa

California Environmental Protection Agency
Department of Toxic Substances Control
Berkeley, California, U.S.A.

Abstract

Applied organic geochemistry provides the information needed to make maps of the richness, type, and thermal maturity of a source rock. These maps are a necessary step toward determining the stratigraphic and geographic extent of a pod of active source rock in a petroleum system, and they are based on geochemical analyses of rock samples from outcrops and wells that are displayed on logs. These geochemical well logs are based on Rock-Eval pyrolysis, total organic carbon, vitrinite reflectance, and other rapid, inexpensive "screening" methods. The logs define (1) potential, effective, and spent petroleum source rock; (2) the thermal maturation gradient, including immature, mature, and postmature zones, and (3) *in situ* and migrated petroleum shows. Useful geochemical logs require proper sample selection, preparation, analysis, and interpretation. Detailed studies, including oil–source rock correlations by biomarker and supporting techniques, are undertaken on selected samples only after the screening methods are completed.

INTRODUCTION

The goal of this chapter is to show how geochemical "screening" technology is applied to petroleum exploration. This chapter provides a conceptual framework for later discussions in this book by defining key terms used to describe source rock characteristics and reviewing principles and recent developments in source rock geochemistry. Major emphasis is placed on (1) criteria for sampling, preparation, and analysis of rocks and oils; (2) geochemical logs; and (3) geochemical maps.

The main contribution of organic geochemistry to sedimentary basin analysis is to provide analytical data to identify and map source rocks. These maps include the richness, type, and thermal maturity of a source rock and are a necessary step toward determining the stratigraphic and geographic extent of a pod of active source rock in a petroleum system. The volume, richness, and thermal maturity of this pod of active source rock determines the amount of oil and gas available for traps. Because of this, maps that show the pod of active source rock reduce exploration risk (e.g., Demaison, 1984).

Geochemical well logs are essential for mapping active source rocks. These logs plot various geochemical parameters versus depth and can be made from surface sections and during or after drilling. Certain criteria that are largely omitted from the literature must be met to ensure useful geochemical logs. These criteria include well site sampling, type of samples (core, sidewall, cuttings), sample spacing, sample preparation procedures, and methods of analysis and interpretation.

SOURCE ROCK PROPERTIES AND TERMS

Sedimentary rocks commonly contain minerals and organic matter with the pore space occupied by water, bitumen, oil, and/or gas. *Kerogen* is the particulate fraction of organic matter remaining after extraction of pulverized rock with organic solvents. Kerogen can be isolated from carbonate- and silicate-bearing rocks by treatment with inorganic acids, such as HCl and HF (e.g., Durand, 1980). This is only an operational definition because the amount and composition of insoluble organic matter or kerogen remaining after extraction depends on the types and polarities of the organic solvents. Kerogen is a mixture of macerals and reconstituted degradation products of organic matter. *Macerals* are the remains of various types of plant and animal matter that can be distinguished by their chemistry and by their morphology and reflectance using a petrographic microscope (Stach et al., 1982). This term was originally applied to components in coal but has been extended to sedimentary rocks. *Palynomorphs* are resistant, organic-walled microfossils such as spores, pollen, dinoflagellate cysts, and chitinozoa.

*Present address: Mobil Exploration and Producing Technical Center, Dallas, Texas, U.S.A.

Bitumen in rocks is that fraction of the organic matter that is soluble in organic solvents. Small amounts of bitumen originate from lipid components in once-living organisms, but most is generated by *cracking* (thermal dissociation) of the kerogen. *Lipids* are oil-soluble, water-insoluble organic compounds, including fats, waxes, pigments, steroids, and terpenoids, that are major precursors for petroleum (Peters and Moldowan, 1993).

Petroleum is a complex mixture of gas, liquid, and solid hydrocarbons and nonhydrocarbons occurring naturally in the earth (Magoon and Dow, Chapter 1, this volume). The term *hydrocarbon* is commonly used in the petroleum industry to indicate crude oil or natural gas. In the chemical sense, hydrocarbons are compounds containing only carbon and hydrogen. *Nonhydrocarbons* contain elements in addition to hydrogen and carbon. For example, NSO compounds contain nitrogen, sulfur, or oxygen, and porphyrins contain metals such as vanadium or nickel. For this volume, petroleum, oil and gas, and hydrocarbons, used without modifiers, have similar meanings.

Depositional Environment

Descriptions of oils or source rocks using the terms *marine* or *terrigenous* are unclear without specifying whether these terms refer to provenance (origin) or depositional environment. Geochemists commonly use these terms to refer to organic matter derived from marine and land plants, respectively, whereas geologists usually refer to marine or terrigenous depositional environments. For example, when geologists refer to a "marine" sedimentary rock, they are discussing depositional environment, not provenance of the mineral grains. Likewise, a geologist might equate a marine source rock with marine depositional conditions, although the included organic matter or kerogen might be of marine, terrigenous, or mixed origin. For similar reasons, the meaning of the terms *marine oil, lacustrine oil,* or *terrigenous oil* is unclear without further explanation. Misunderstandings can occur because a marine oil might be (1) generated from land plant organic matter deposited in a marine environment, (2) generated from marine organic matter, or (3) produced from a reservoir rock deposited in a marine environment. Rather than just "marine" oil, it must be specified whether the oil is derived from a source rock deposited under marine conditions or from marine organic matter.

Various factors play a role in the preservation of organic matter, notably the oxygen content of the water column and sediment (oxic versus anoxic), primary productivity of new organic matter by plants, water circulation, and sedimentation rate (Demaison and Moore, 1980; Emerson, 1985).

For ancient sediments, the oxygen content of the overlying water column is unknown, but it can be interpreted from the presence or absence of laminated or bioturbated sediments and organic matter content in the sediment (Demaison and Moore, 1980). The oxygen content of water is determined by availability and solubility of oxygen (which depends upon the temperature,

pressure, and salinity). *Oxic* water (saturated with oxygen) contains 8.0–2.0 mL O_2/L H_2O (Tyson and Pearson, 1991). *Dysoxic* water contains 2.0–0.2 mL O_2/ H_2O, *suboxic,* 0.2–0.0 mL O_2/L H_2O, and *anoxic* water lacks oxygen. When referring to biofacies, the corresponding terms are *aerobic, dysaerobic, quasi-anaerobic,* and *anaerobic.*

Below the 0.5 mL O_2/L H_2O threshold, the activity of multicellular organisms as agents in the oxidative destruction of organic matter is severely limited (Demaison and Moore, 1980). Anoxic sediments are typically thinly laminated (distinct alternating layers <2 mm thick) because of the lack of bioturbation by burrowing, deposit-feeding organisms. Pederson and Calvert (1990) contend that anoxia is less important than primary productivity in determining quantities of organic matter preserved. However, Peters and Moldowan (1993) stress the effect of anoxia on the quality rather than quantity of organic matter preserved, that is, anoxia favors preservation of all organic matter, including hydrogen-rich, oil-prone organic matter. This may explain the positive relationship between petroleum source rocks and the faunal, sedimentologic, and geochemical parameters indicating anoxia.

Alteration of Organic Matter

Diagenesis refers to all chemical, biological, and physical changes to organic matter during and after deposition of sediments but prior to reaching burial temperatures greater than about 60°–80°C. The quantity and quality of organic matter preserved and modified during diagenesis of a sediment ultimately determine the petroleum potential of the rock (Horsfield and Rullkötter, Chapter 10, this volume).

Catagenesis can be divided into the *oil zone,* which corresponds to the *oil window,* where liquid oil generation is accompanied by gas formation, and the more mature *wet gas zone,* where light hydrocarbons are generated through cracking and their proportion increases rapidly (Tissot and Welte, 1984). *Wet gas* (<98% methane) contains methane and significant amounts of ethane, propane, and heavier hydrocarbons. The *gas window* corresponds to the interval from the top of the wet gas zone to the base of the dry gas zone.

Metagenesis corresponds to the *dry gas zone* where dry gas is generated (2.0–4.0% R_o). *Dry gas* consists of 98% or more of methane (Tissot and Welte, 1984). Dry gas is also found as deposits of bacteriogenic (microbial) gas generated during diagenesis of organic matter by methanogenic bacteria under anoxic conditions (Rice and Claypool, 1981).

Thermal maturity refers to the extent of temperature–time driven reactions that convert sedimentary organic matter (source rock) to oil, wet gas, and finally to dry gas and pyrobitumen. Thermally *immature* source rocks have been affected by diagenesis without a pronounced effect of temperature (<0.6% R_o) and are where microbial gas is produced. Thermally *mature* organic matter is (or was) in the *oil window* and has been affected by thermal processes covering the temperature range that generates

Table 5.1. Geochemical Parameters Describing the Petroleum Potential (Quantity) of an Immature Source Rock

| Petroleum Potential | Organic Matter | | | Bitumen[c] | | Hydrocarbons (ppm) |
| | TOC (wt. %) | Rock-Eval Pyrolysis | | (wt. %) | (ppm) | |
		S_1[a]	S_2[b]			
Poor	0–0.5	0–0.5	0–2.5	0–0.05	0–500	0–300
Fair	0.5–1	0.5–1	2.5–5	0.05–0.10	500–1000	300–600
Good	1–2	1–2	5–10	0.10–0.20	1000–2000	600–1200
Very Good	2–4	2–4	10–20	0.20–0.40	2000–4000	1200–2400
Excellent	>4	>4	>20	>0.40	>4000	>2400

[a]mg HC/g dry rock distilled by pyrolysis.

[b]mg HC/g dry rock cracked from kerogen by pyrolysis.

[c]Evaporation of the solvent used to extract bitumen from a source rock or oil from a reservoir rock causes loss of the volatile hydrocarbons below about $n\text{-}C_{15}$. Thus, most extracts are described as "C_{15+} hydrocarbons." Lighter hydrocarbons can be at least partially retained by avoiding complete evaporation of the solvent (e.g., C_{10+}).

Table 5.2. Geochemical Parameters Describing Kerogen Type (Quality) and the Character of Expelled Products[a]

Kerogen Type	HI (mg HC/g TOC)	S_2/S_3	Atomic H/C	Main Expelled Product at Peak Maturity
I	>600	>15	>1.5	Oil
II	300–600	10–15	1.2–1.5	Oil
II/III[b]	200–300	5–10	1.0–1.2	Mixed oil and gas
III	50–200	1–5	0.7–1.0	Gas
IV	<50	<1	<0.7	None

[a]Based on a thermally immature source rock. Ranges are approximate.

[b]Type II/III designates kerogens with compositions between type II and III pathways (e.g., Figure 5.1) that show intermediate HI (see Figures 5.4–5.11).

oil (~0.6–1.35% R_o) or about 60°–150°C. Thermally *post-mature* organic matter is in the wet and dry gas zones (gas window) and has been heated to such high temperatures (about 150°–200° C, prior to greenschist metamorphism) that it has been reduced to a hydrogen-poor residue capable of generating only small amounts of hydrocarbon gases.

It is generally accepted that oil is unstable at higher temperatures and progressively decomposes to gases and *pyrobitumen*, a thermally-altered, solidified bitumen that is insoluble in organic solvents (e.g., Hunt, 1979; Tissot and Welte, 1984). Mango (1991) shows evidence that hydrocarbons in oil are more thermally stable than their kerogenous precursors. He believes that oil and gas are generated by direct thermal decomposition of kerogen, but that hydrocarbons in oils show no evidence of decomposing to gas in the earth. This scenario does not exclude some oxidative decomposition of hydrocarbons during thermochemical sulfate reduction (e.g., Krouse et al., 1988).

Source Rock Terms

Sedimentary rocks that are, or may become, or have been able to generate petroleum are *source rocks* (Tissot and Welte, 1984). An *effective source rock* is generating or has generated and expelled petroleum. This definition excludes the requirement that the accumulations be "commercially significant," because (1) the terms *significant* and *commercial* are difficult to quantify and change depending on economic factors, and (2) oil–source rock

relationships are never proven because some level of uncertainty always exists depending on the available data. Nonetheless, effective source rocks satisfy three geochemical requirements that are more easily defined (Tables 5.1–5.3):

- Quantity, or amount of organic matter (Table 5.1)
- Quality, or type of organic matter (Table 5.2)
- Thermal maturity, or extent of burial heating (Table 5.3).

A *potential source rock* contains adequate quantities of organic matter to generate petroleum, but only becomes an effective source rock when it generates bacterial gas at low temperatures or it reaches the proper level of thermal maturity to generate petroleum. An *active source rock* is generating and expelling petroleum at the critical moment, most commonly because it is within the oil window (Dow, 1977a). An *inactive source rock* has stopped generating petroleum, although it still shows petroleum potential (Barker, 1979). For example, an inactive source rock might be uplifted to a position where temperatures are insufficient to allow further petroleum generation. A *spent oil source rock* has reached the postmature stage of maturity and is incapable of further oil generation, but may still be capable of generating wet and dry gas.

Active source rocks include rocks or sediments that are generating petroleum without thermal maturation. For example, a peat bog might produce microbially generated gas (*marsh gas* consisting mostly of bacterio-

Table 5.3. Geochemical Parameters Describing Level of Thermal Maturation

Stage of Thermal Maturity for Oil	Maturation			Generation		
	R_o (%)	T_{max} (°C)	TAI[a]	Bitumen/ TOC[b]	Bitumen (mg/g rock)	PI[c] $[S_1/(S_1 + S_2)]$
Immature	0.2–0.6	<435	1.5–2.6	<0.05	<50	<0.10
Mature						
Early	0.6–0.65	435–445	2.6–2.7	0.05–0.10	50–100	0.10–0.15
Peak	0.65–0.9	445–450	2.7–2.9	0.15–0.25	150–250	0.25–0.40
Late	0.9–1.35	450–470	2.9–3.3	—	—	>0.40
Postmature	>1.35	>470	>3.3	—	—	—

[a]TAI, thermal alteration index.

[b]Mature oil–prone source rocks with type I or II kerogen commonly show bitumen/TOC ratios in the range 0.05–0.25. Caution should be applied when interpreting extract yields from coals. For example, many gas–prone coals show high extract yields suggesting oil–prone character, but extract yield normalized to TOC is low (<30 mg HC/g TOC). Bitumen/TOC ratios over 0.25 can indicate contamination or migrated oil or can be artifacts caused by ratios of small, inaccurate numbers.

[c]PI, production index.

genic methane) without significant heating due to shallow burial. By this definition, trapped methane and nearby unconsolidated swamp muds from which it was derived represent a petroleum system.

Criteria for describing the quantities of extractable organic matter in source rocks (Tables 5.1 and 5.3) can be used to map the pod of active source rock where data are available from several wells. For example, source rock bitumen yields normalized by weight of rock or by total organic carbon (TOC) generally increase from immature to peak thermal maturity (Table 5.3). The principal regions of oil accumulation in many petroleum provinces are confined to areas showing the greatest normalized bitumen yields (e.g., figure 21 in Kontorovich, 1984).

Organic Matter Classifications

Kerogen Type

The amount and maceral composition of kerogen determine petroleum potential and can differ vertically or laterally within a source rock. No universally accepted classification for kerogen types exists in the literature. In this chapter, we use types I, II, III (Tissot et al., 1974), and IV (Demaison et al., 1983) to describe kerogens (see Chapter Appendix A).

Kerogen types are distinguished using the atomic H/C versus O/C or *van Krevelen diagram* (Figure 5.1A), originally developed to characterize coals (van Krevelen, 1961; Stach et al., 1982). Tissot et al. (1974) extended the use of the van Krevelen diagram from coals to include kerogen dispersed in sedimentary rocks. Modified van Krevelen diagrams (Figure 5.1B) consist of hydrogen index (HI) versus oxygen index (OI) plots generated from Rock-Eval pyrolysis and TOC analysis of whole rock. HI versus OI data can be generated more rapidly and at less expense than atomic H/C versus O/C data for van Krevelen diagrams.

Higher relative hydrogen content in kerogen (atomic H/C, HI) generally corresponds to higher oil-generative potential. Gas (methane, or CH_4) and oil are enriched in hydrogen compared to kerogen. During thermal maturation, generation of these products causes the kerogen to become depleted in hydrogen and relatively enriched in

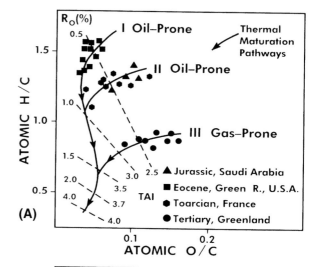

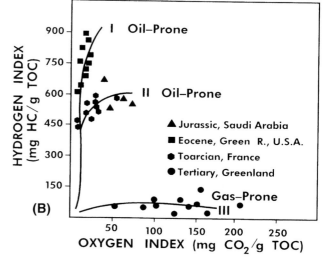

Figure 5.1. (A) Atomic H/C versus O/C or van Krevelen diagram based on elemental analysis of kerogen and (B) HI versus OI diagram based on Rock-Eval pyrolysis of whole rock can be used to describe the type of organic matter in source rocks . TAI, thermal alteration index (Jones and Edison, 1978). The type IV (inertinite) pathway is not shown. (From Peters, 1986.)

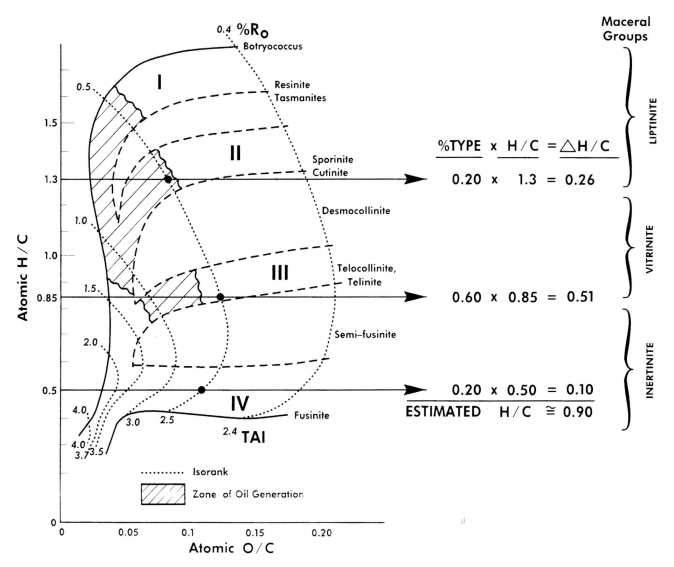

Figure 5.2. Combined use of organic petrography, elemental analysis, and Rock-Eval pyrolysis and TOC improves confidence in assessment of the quality and maturity of kerogen in rock samples. A sample analyzed by Rock-Eval pyrolysis was characterized as being marginally mature (T_{max} = 435°C) and gas prone (HI = 150 mg HC/g TOC). Organic petrography shows a TAI of 2.5, an R_o of 0.5% (supporting the maturity assessment from pyrolysis), and the following maceral composition: type II 20%, type III 60%, and type IV 20%. The calculated atomic H/C (0.90) corresponds with that determined by elemental analysis, supporting a dominantly gas-prone character. (Concept for figure courtesy of T. A. Edison.)

carbon. During catagenesis and metagenesis, all kerogens approach graphite in composition (nearly pure carbon) near the lower left portion of both diagrams (Figure 5.1).

Maceral Groups

The three principal maceral groups in coal and sedimentary rocks are *liptinite (exinite), vitrinite,* and *inertinite* (Stach et al., 1982). Liptinite macerals, such as alginite, sporinite, cutinite, and resinite, generally mature along the type I or II kerogen pathways on the van Krevelen diagram (Figure 5.2). Preserved remains of the algae *Botryococcus* and *Tasmanites* are examples of structured alginite. Vitrinite macerals originate from land plants and mature along the type III kerogen pathway. *Collinite*

is the structureless constituent of vitrinite, whereas *telinite* is the remains of cell walls of land plants. Figure 5.2 shows two types of collinite: *telocollinite* contains no inclusions and is the maceral recommended for vitrinite reflectance measurements, whereas *desmocollinite* shows submicroscopic inclusions of liptinite and other materials. Because of the inclusions, desmocollinite shows a higher atomic H/C, has a lower reflectance (Figure 5.3), and commonly fluoresces under ultraviolet light, unlike telocollinite. Inertinitic macerals, such as semi-fusinite and fusinite, mature along the type IV kerogen pathway. Because of the combined effects of diagenesis, thermal maturity, and differing organic matter input, a kerogen can plot anywhere on the van Krevelen diagram and need not fall on any of the indicated maturation curves.

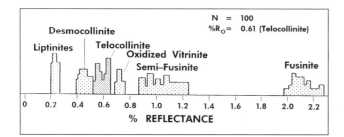

Figure 5.3. A complete reflectogram showing the reflectance of all macerals in a kerogen sample. In cases where selection of the "true" vitrinite population (telocollinite) is difficult, the trend of R_o versus depth established by many samples is useful for selecting the correct population. Here, telecollinite (hatchured) has a mean % R_o of 0.61. This sample contains significant amounts of oxidized vitrinite and semi-fusinite that could be mistaken for vitrinite. (Courtesy of S. C. Teerman.)

Petrography alone is too imprecise to evaluate the petroleum potential of a source rock, primarily because hydrogen-rich and hydrogen-poor kerogen is difficult to distinguish. "Amorphous" kerogen is commonly presumed to be hydrogen rich and oil prone, but not all amorphous kerogens can generate oil. Ultraviolet-induced fluorescence microscopy of samples of low thermal maturity distinguishes hydrogen-rich, oil-prone amorphous (fluorescent) from hydrogen-poor, non-generative amorphous (nonfluorescent) kerogen, suggesting that petrographic methods might be further refined to better predict generative potential (Senftle et al., 1987).

Organic Facies

Various workers have used the term *organic facies* as a synonym for kerogen facies (based on chemical data) or palynofacies or maceral assemblage facies (based on petrographic data). Jones (1984, 1987) propose a concise definition:

> An *organic facies* is a mappable subdivision of a designated stratigraphic unit, distinguished from the adjacent subdivisions on the basis of the character of its organic constituents, without regard to the inorganic aspects of the sediment.

Jones (1984, 1987) has defined organic facies using a combination of three types of kerogen analyses: atomic H/C ratios, Rock-Eval pyrolysis and TOC, and transmitted–reflected light microscopy. He showed that all organic facies can exist in either carbonates or shales and that there is little evidence that TOC requirements are lower for carbonate than for shale source rocks. Integration of organic facies studies with the concepts of sequence stratigraphy is a step toward improving our ability to predict the occurrence of a source rock (e.g., Pasley et al., 1991).

When used together, elemental analysis, Rock-Eval pyrolysis and TOC, and organic petrography are powerful tools for describing the richness, type, and thermal maturity of organic matter. Jones and Edison (1978) and Jones (1984) have shown how maceral compo-

sition and thermal maturity from microscopy can be used to estimate the atomic H/C ratio of a kerogen (Figure 5.2). If the measured atomic H/C differs by more than 0.1 from the estimated value, both analyses are suspect and are repeated. These maturity and atomic H/C results are commonly supported by T_{max} and HI data obtained from each whole rock sample using Rock-Eval pyrolysis and TOC.

Coal

Coal is a rock containing more than 50% organic matter by weight. Both coals and sedimentary rocks can contain any combination of macerals. Various classifications of these organic-rich rocks are found in the literature (e.g., Cook and Sherwood, 1991). Not all coals are composed of humic organic matter (higher plant, type III kerogen). *Humic* and *sapropelic coals* contain less than 10% and more than 10% liptinite, respectively. Humic coal has long been recognized as a source for gas, primarily methane and carbon dioxide. However, *boghead* and *cannel coals* are dominated by type I and II kerogens, respectively, are oil prone, and thus show high oil potential.

Coals can generate oil, as exemplified by major accumulations in Indonesia and Australia. Two principal limitations for coals as effective source rocks are (1) expulsion efficiency and (2) organic matter type (sufficient hydrogen). Because of the physical properties of thick coal seams, generated liquid products are usually adsorbed and generally escape only when cracked to gas and condensate (Snowdon, 1991; Teerman and Hwang, 1991). Coals that can generate and release oil must contain at least 15–20% by volume of liptinite macerals prior to catagenesis, corresponding to an HI of at least 200 mg HC/g TOC and an atomic H/C ratio of 0.9 (Hunt, 1991).

Kerogen and Bitumen Composition

Detailed structural information on kerogen is limited because of its heterogeneous composition and difficulties associated with the chemical analysis of solid organic matter. Kerogen has been described as a *geopolymer*, which has been "polymerized" from a random mixture of monomers. These monomers are derived from the diagenetic decomposition of *biopolymers*, including proteins and polysaccharides (e.g., Tissot and Welte, 1984). This view has led to many publications showing generalized chemical structures for kerogen, none of which are particularly informative.

The discovery of insoluble biopolymers in living organisms, sediments, and sedimentary rocks has led to a reappraisal of the structure of kerogen (Rullkötter and Michaelis, 1990). In the modified scheme, more emphasis is placed on selective preservation of biopolymers and less on reconstitution of monomers. Progress has been achieved by the application of specific chemical degradation (Mycke et al., 1987), pyrolysis (Larter and Senftle, 1985), and spectroscopic techniques (Mann et al., 1991). Structural elucidation techniques are beyond the scope of this chapter, although the reader should be aware that these studies are likely to impact our understanding of kerogen.

Asphaltenes in bitumen are lower molecular weight fragments of kerogen and may be intermediates between kerogen and bitumen. For example, although asphaltenes are soluble in polar solvents, they show elemental compositions similar to associated kerogens (Orr, 1986) and similar distributions of hydrocarbons (Bandurski, 1982; Pelet et al., 1985), including steranes and triterpanes (Cassani and Eglinton, 1986).

Lipids can be incorporated into kerogen during diagenesis, but many survive as free constituents in the bitumen and are known as molecular fossils, biological markers, or biomarkers. *Biological markers* are complex organic compounds composed of carbon, hydrogen, and other elements which show little or no change in structure from their parent organic molecules in living organisms (Peters and Moldowan, 1993).

Expelled Products

Petroleum expelled from an active source rock, *(primary migration)* (Lewan, Chapter 11, this volume) can migrate along a fault plane or permeable *carrier bed (secondary migration)* (England, Chapter 12, this volume) to a porous *reservoir rock* (Morse, Chapter 6; Jordan and Wilson, Chapter 7, this volume) capped or surrounded by a comparatively impermeable *seal* (Downey, Chapter 8, this volume) that together form a *trap* (Biddle and Wielchowsky, Chapter 13, this volume). Examples of how this happens are described in the case studies in this volume. Factors controlling the quantities of petroleum needed to saturate the pore space in a source rock prior to expulsion and the efficiency of expulsion are poorly understood and represent active research topics (e.g., Wilhelms et al., 1990; Mackenzie and Quigley, 1988). Accurate estimates of these quantities will improve mass balance calculations.

Shows of petroleum are proof of a petroleum system and when encountered during drilling are useful exploration clues, particularly when they can be quantified and regionally mapped. Cuttings or cores that bubble or bleed oil and gas during removal from the well are called "live" shows, in contrast to the asphaltic staining of "dead" shows. The quality of shows can be evaluated by their fluorescence under ultraviolet light, by the color of organic solvent extracts, or by the geochemical screening methods described later. Quantitative bitumen or hydrocarbon yields from reservoir rocks assist in distinguishing between commercial and noncommercial subsurface petroleum occurrences (Swanson, 1981).

Oils inherit biomarker distributions similar to those in the bitumen from the source rock, thus allowing oil–oil and oil–source correlation or "fingerprinting" and paleoreconstruction of source rock depositional conditions (Peters and Moldowan, 1993). An advantage of biomarkers is their resistance to biodegradation by aerobic bacteria in the reservoir. For heavily biodegraded oils where biomarkers have been partially altered, correlation sometimes requires sealed tube pyrolysis of asphaltenes, followed by biomarker analysis of the generated bitumen (e.g., Cassani and Eglinton, 1986). Biomarker and other correlation technologies, such as stable carbon isotope analysis and pyrolysis–gas chromatography, are among the most powerful tools for mapping petroleum systems to reduce exploration risk, particularly when oils migrate large distances from their pod of active source rock or when more than one source rock pod exists in the basin fill. Based on these fingerprinting techniques, the level of certainty for a petroleum system is determined. This level of certainty indicates the confidence that the petroleum from a particular accumulation came from a specific pod of active source rock.

SCREENING METHODS

Sedimentary basin analysis (Magoon and Dow, Chapter 1, this volume) of frontier areas begins with geologic and geophysical reconnaissance. Early evaluations focus on sample and data collection to assess the presence of thick sedimentary sequences, regional hydrocarbon seals, and appropriate reservoir lithologies. Maps using well control, outcrop, and geophysical data must be prepared or revised.

Geochemical *screening analyses* are practical exploration tools for rapid and inexpensive evaluation of large numbers of rock samples from outcrops and wells. Outcrop samples from measured stratigraphic sections are better than random outcrop samples because they can easily be made into a geochemical log that can be compared to nearby geochemical logs of wells. Rock samples from wells include drill cuttings, sidewall cores, and conventional cores, in order of decreasing abundance. Large numbers of analyses of these rock samples are used to make geochemical logs to evaluate the thickness, distribution, richness, type, and thermal maturity of source rocks in the basin fill. Evaluating the source rock in the basin fill is an important part of sedimentary basin analysis. The next step is to identify the pod of active source rock, which is the first step in evaluating a petroleum system.

The most effective screening method for large numbers of rock samples from wells and outcrops combines Rock-Eval pyrolysis and TOC measurements. These data are usually supplemented by vitrinite reflectance and spore coloration results to construct detailed geochemical logs (see Figures 5.4–5.11).

Chapter Appendix B describes key criteria for useful geochemical logs. These include proper (1) sample spacing, (2) sample quality and storage, and (3) sample preparation.

Rock-Eval Pyrolysis and Total Organic Carbon

Total organic carbon (TOC, wt. %) describes the quantity of organic carbon in a rock sample and includes both kerogen and bitumen. TOC can be determined in several ways, and geologists should be familiar with the advantages and disadvantages of each (Chapter

Appendix C). TOC is *not* a clear indicator of petroleum potential. For example, graphite is essentially 100% carbon, but it will not generate petroleum. Some Tertiary deltaic marine shales contain up to 5 wt. % TOC but generate little if any petroleum because the organic matter is gas prone or inert. The theory and pitfalls of Rock-Eval pyrolysis interpretation are discussed by Peters (1986) and are not repeated here. Key parameters are defined in Chapter Appendix D.

Gas Analysis

Residual gas (C_1–C_5) and heavier hydrocarbons in drill cuttings and mud arriving at the shaker table can be liberated with a blender and analyzed by *gas chromatography* (GC) at the well site as part of a process called *hydrocarbon mud logging*. Some systems use a simple hot wire detector to make only two measurements, methane and ethane-plus hydrocarbons. Hydrocarbon mud log gas curves are commonly available from wildcat wells and provide useful information on hydrocarbon shows (e.g., see Figure 5.7).

Alternately, gaseous hydrocarbons can be detected at the well site or in the laboratory using an oil show analyzer (Espitalié et al., 1984) or by hydrogen stripping GC (Schaefer, et al., 1978). In GC, an inert carrier gas (mobile phase) passes through a column coated with a nonvolatile, high molecular weight liquid (stationary phase). The temperature of the column is gradually raised using a temperature-programmed oven. Petroleum components are separated depending on their volatility and affinity for the mobile versus stationary phases as they pass through the column. A plot of detector response versus time shows separated peaks representing single or multiple components and is called a *chromatogram*.

Headspace gas analysis is sometimes used as a screening tool because it assists in quantitative show detection (Tissot and Welte, 1984). For this method, cuttings are frozen or canned with water and a bactericide. Agitation and/or heating releases some of the hydrocarbons from the cuttings into the headspace over the water, which can be sampled through a septum with a syringe and analyzed by GC (e.g., Bernard, 1978; Whelan, 1984). Many choose not to use this technique because it is costly and time consuming and metal cans rust or leak in storage. Furthermore, this method is not particularly useful for establishing maturity profiles because gas readily migrates. Vitrinite reflectance and Rock-Eval pyrolysis are more reliable methods for establishing thermal maturity profiles than gas analysis.

Light hydrocarbon gas distributions combined with isotopic compositions can be used to describe the origin and level of thermal maturity of the gas (e.g., Rice and Claypool, 1981; James, 1983; Schoell, 1984). Reliable sampling methods are important because sample handling can alter these gas compositions. For example, drill cuttings used for headspace gas analyses should be kept in gas-tight containers at deep freeze temperatures to avoid evaporative loss of components. Examples of procedures for sampling gases in drilling muds and cuttings are given in Schaefer et al. (1978), Reitsema et al. (1981), and Whelan (1984). Other procedures are used for sampling gases under pressure (Gas Processors Association, 1986). The more advanced aspects of gas geochemistry are beyond the scope of this chapter, which deals primarily with rapid screening methods for evaluating oils and source rocks. However, readers should be aware that analysis of gases is likely to become increasingly important as future exploration shifts from oil to gas.

Organic Petrography

Thermal Alteration Index

Thermal alteration index (TAI) is a numerical scale based on thermally induced color changes in spores and pollen. Strew-mount slides of kerogen are examined in transmitted light, typically using a split-stage comparison microscope. The analyst matches the color of the specimen under one ocular with that of a standard under the other ocular of the microscope. Several TAI scales have been published (e.g., Staplin, 1969; Jones and Edison, 1978). An advantage of TAI is that the greatest color changes occur in the oil window. TAI measurements are imprecise because description of color is subjective, palynomorph thickness and type affect results, and many samples contain few palynomorphs. Quantitative spore color measurements (Marshall, 1991) offer the possibility of more precise assessment of thermal maturity. Despite limitations, TAI commonly provides useful data, even when other maturity parameters fail.

Vitrinite Reflectance

Vitrinite reflectance (R_o) increases during thermal maturation due to complex, irreversible aromatization reactions. Approximate R_o, TAI, and T_{max} values have been assigned for the beginning and end of oil generation (Table 5.3). R_o versus depth plots generally show linear trends on semi-log paper. Dow (1977b) showed how these plots can be used to support the existence of faults, intrusions, and changes in geothermal gradient and how to estimate the thickness of a section lost at an unconformity. This information provides valuable calibration for reconstructing burial histories.

For vitrinite reflectance, kerogen isolated from sedimentary rocks is embedded in epoxy on a slide or in an epoxy plug and polished to a flat, shiny surface (Bostick and Alpern, 1977; Baskin, 1979). Measurements are made of the percentage of incident light (usually at a wavelength of 546 nm) reflected from vitrinite particles (preferably telocollinite) under oil immersion (Stach et al., 1982). The subscript "o" in R_o refers to oil immersion. Some old papers refer to R_a and R_w, reflectance in air and water, respectively. Vitrinite becomes anisotropic at high levels of maturity (above about 1% R_o), resulting in the terms R_{min} and R_{max} for the minimum and maximum reflectance values obtained upon rotation of each particle. Most kerogen studies report random mean R_o rather than R_{min} or R_{max} because rotation of the microscope stage is not required.

Several factors based on the experience of the analyst are weighed in the process of selecting vitrinite particles. R_o trends established above and below the sample can be used to eliminate certain populations of macerals from consideration. Because TAI and R_o are related (Jones and Edison, 1978), a measured TAI can be used to estimate the R_o of the vitrinite population. This process is not always reliable, however, because TAI is commonly measured on less than a dozen palynomorphs and these might represent recycled organic matter or contamination from drilling mud.

Reliability of R_o measurements from single samples increases when supported by independent maturity parameters (e.g., TAI and T_{max}) and R_o versus depth trends established by multiple samples in a well. For example, T_{max} can be used to support R_o, particularly in the thermally mature stage. In situ vitrinite in some samples can be overwhelmed by recycled (high maturity) or caved (low maturity) particles. Selection of these particles as the "true" vitrinite might result in anomalous values compared to the R_o trend established by samples from other depths. As an extreme example, some Alaskan wells show little change or even a decrease in R_o with increasing depth at shallow well depth due to shedding of recycled (high R_o) organic matter from Mesozoic highlands into thermally "cool" Tertiary basins.

R_o cannot be measured in rocks that lack vitrinite. Vitrinite is derived from land plants and is not common in rocks older than Devonian because abundant land plants had not yet evolved. Reflectance can be measured on graptolites in lower Paleozoic rocks (Link et al., 1990). Some oil-prone source rocks that formed on broad marine carbonate shelves (e.g., Jurassic of Saudi Arabia) or in large lakes (e.g., Lower Cretaceous of West Africa) contain only small amounts of vitrinite due to limited terrigenous organic matter input. The reflectance of solid bitumen has been calibrated to R_o and is particularly useful in vitrinite-poor carbonate rocks (Jacob, 1989). Evidence suggests that large amounts of bitumen (Hutton et al., 1980) and oil-prone macerals (Price and Barker, 1985) retard the normal increase of vitrinite reflectance with maturity. Low R_o values can result from poor polishing, whereas high values are typical of oxidized vitrinite.

R_o Histograms

R_o histograms show the frequency distribution of reflectance measurements determined on about 50–100 vitrinite particles in each polished kerogen preparation. The random mean R_o is determined from these histograms. R_o versus depth plots use the random mean value and refer *only* to the population of organic particles identified by the analyst as vitrinite. Likewise, the standard deviation for these R_o values represents the repeatability by which the analyst can select these particles. Because R_o values based on fewer than 50 particles can be unreliable, we recommend that R_o histograms be examined for all samples.

Reflectograms

Reflectograms (Figure 5.3) are frequency plots of the reflectance of all macerals measured in the polished kerogen slide. Unlike R_o histograms, reflectograms may provide an idea of the difficulty in selecting vitrinite particles for measurement. Selection of the correct particles for measurement may be difficult when there is no clearly predominant population of telocollinite (Figure 5.3). R_o must be determined using vitrinite because other macerals mature at different rates (e.g., Dow, 1977b). However, R_o can be extrapolated from reflectance measurements of some macerals other than telocollinite, such as exinite (Alpern, 1970).

INTERPRETIVE TECHNIQUES
Source Potential Index

During the source rock assessment phase of sedimentary basin evaluation, geologists commonly rely on the quantity, type, and thermal maturity of organic matter as criteria to indicate favorable risk for significant petroleum charge. However, source rock volumetrics (thickness and lateral extent) must not be ignored. An oil-prone source rock dominated by type I or II kerogen and showing excellent *genetic potential* (e.g., $S_1 + S_2 > 10$ mg HC/g rock) may be too thin to charge economically significant oil accumulations. *Source potential index* (SPI) (Demaison and Huizinga, 1991) is defined as the quantity of hydrocarbons (metric tons) that can be generated in a column of source rock under one square meter of surface area (Demaison and Huizinga, Chapter 4, this volume). SPI (or "cumulative hydrocarbon potential," according to Tissot et al., 1980) is a simple method for ranking source rock productivity because it integrates both source rock richness and thickness. A relative source rock ranking system has been developed by compiling the average SPI values for source rock units from around the world.

The SPI is relevant only where a pod of active source rock has been established. The entire source rock interval must be sampled and systematically logged at closely spaced intervals using Rock-Eval pyrolysis. Samples that were positively picked (Chapter Appendix B) or affected by substantial caving should be avoided. Gross thickness of the source rock must be corrected for well deviation, structural complexities, and nonsource units lacking significant hydrocarbon generative potential ($S_1 + S_2 < 2$ mg HC/g rock) to get net source rock thickness. The samples should be representative of the organic facies in the area of interest. Samples should show no evidence of contamination or migrated oil (Chapter Appendix B) and should be from thermally immature or early mature portions of the source rock. SPI values determined from thermally mature or postmature sections can be low because of petroleum expulsion. Although specific source rock densities should be used, a density of 2.5 t/m³ is used for most SPI calculations.

Laterally drained petroleum systems tend to accumulate petroleum from larger drainage areas compared to vertically drained systems. For this reason, lower limits are used to define SPI categories for laterally drained systems (low, SPI < 2; moderate, 2 ≤ SPI < 7; high, SPI ≥ 7) than for vertically drained petroleum systems (low, SPI < 5; moderate, 5 ≤ SPI < 15; high, SPI ≥ 15) (see figure 4.4 of Lewan, Chapter 4, this volume).

SPI is a measure of the petroleum potential of a source rock and ideally is determined from thermally immature rock. After a source rock shows a favorable SPI rating, maps of SPI and thermal maturity are used to evaluate which areas of a basin have the highest petroleum charge. Areas with the highest charge are most likely to be nearest the source rock where it is the most thermally mature, or nearest the pod of active source rock. Conversely, areas most likely to have the lowest charge are farthest from the mature source rock, or farthest from the pod of active source rock. Whether this charge is mostly gas or mostly oil is determined from the kerogen type and maturity. Demaison and Huizinga (1991; Chapter 4, this volume) provide a complete discussion of migration drainage and entrapment styles for different petroleum systems and show how to estimate the SPI for source rocks, even when they have undergone thermal maturation beyond the immature stage.

Mass Balance Calculations

Mass balance calculations, either by accumulation (or prospect) or petroleum system, can be used to provide another comparison of the amount of petroleum generated with the amount that has accumulated. The geochemical data for screening can also be used for SPI calculations (Demaison and Huizinga, Chapter 4, this volume) and for mass balance calculations as suggested by Schmoker (Chapter 19, this volume), whose technique is used in many of the case studies in this volume.

EXAMPLES
Geochemical Logs

Geochemical logs are among the most valuable tools for basin analysis, yet few examples are given in the literature (e.g., Clementz et al., 1979; Espitalié et al., 1977, 1984, 1987; Peters, 1986; Magoon et al., 1987, 1988). Proper use of geochemical logs allows identification of the following features in penetrated intervals:

- Occurrence of potential, effective, and spent as well as active and inactive source rocks
- Main stages of thermal evolution: diagenesis (immature), catagenesis (mature), and metagenesis (postmature) zones
- Occurrence of varying amounts of *in situ* and migrated petroleum

When geochemical logs are unavailable, geophysical wireline logs and interpretive techniques can be used as qualitative indicators of organic content (e.g., Passey et al., 1990; Schmoker and Hester, 1983; Stocks and

Lawrence, 1990; Hester et al., 1990). These methods are most reliable within small areas where wireline response has been calibrated to geochemical data.

Geochemical logs for eight exploratory wells are included to show their usefulness for detecting free hydrocarbons and identifying source rocks. The first three geochemical logs (Figures 5.4–5.6) are from three wells (I, II, and III) that are in the same area and demonstrate the lateral continuity of two different source rocks. The last five geochemical logs (Figures 5.7–5.11) are from wells that are in different areas, but are used as examples of different ways to identify and evaluate a source rock.

Wells I through III

The high-quality geochemical log for well I is based on closely spaced Rock-Eval pyrolysis and TOC data supplemented by vitrinite reflectance (Figure 5.4). Closely spaced samples allow a critical evaluation of source and reservoir rock intervals (note the wider sample spacing in the C formation, a Lower Cretaceous reservoir rock). The penetrated section contains two source rocks. The Upper Cretaceous B formation source rock interval at 780–1540 m is a potential source rock that has the capacity to generate significant quantities of oil (SPI = 42 t HC/m^2). The T_{max} versus depth trend is slightly depressed through this interval, probably because this sulfur-rich kerogen undergoes thermal degradation at lower temperatures than many type II kerogens. Because the Lower Cretaceous is at maximum burial depth, the F formation source rock at 3120–3620 m is an active source rock that is presently generating oil (SPI ≥ 8 t HC/m^2). The production or productivity index (PI) gradually increases below about 3200 m, reflecting the onset of generation, which is also indicated by T_{max} and R_o data. Vitrinite is generally absent in the carbonate section and in the strata containing particularly hydrogen-rich kerogen. PI anomalies (e.g., at 100–600 m and 1600–3050 m) are "mathematical artifacts" caused by relatively low S_2 yields where S_1 yields may be slightly elevated by small quantities of organic drilling additives or minor shows. The F formation penetrated in well I is presently an active source rock.

The geochemical log for well II, which is located in the same basin about 120 km southeast of well I (Figure 5.5), shows that the Upper Cretaceous potential source rock is thicker than in well I. This potential source rock is still immature and shows a similar source potential index (SPI = 40 t HC/m^2) to that in well I. The Lower Cretaceous source rock in well II is thicker and shows more discrete zones of higher and lower source potential than in well I. The total thickness of the Lower Cretaceous interval in well II is 700 m, but the net source rock thickness is only about 550 m and shows an SPI of 25 t HC/m^2. Only the deeper portions of the Lower Cretaceous source rock are actively generating petroleum (because the onset of petroleum generation for this source rock occurs at 0.6% R_o). Stratigraphically equivalent Lower Cretaceous source rocks buried more deeply adjacent to this trap are the probable source for hydrocarbon shows in the Lower Cretaceous sandstone in well

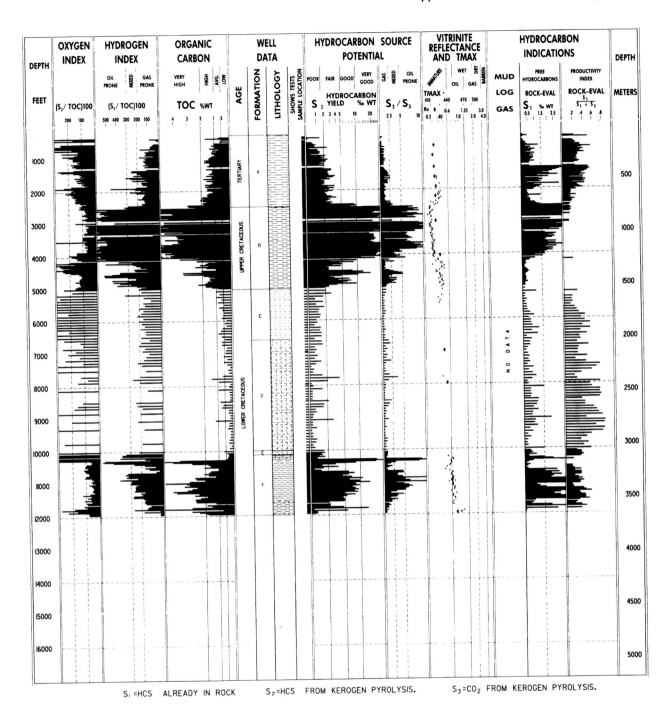

Figure 5.4. Geochemical log for well I, showing immature and mature source rocks in the Upper and Lower Cretaceous (see Tables 5.1–5.3). Mud gas data were unavailable for this well.

II. High productivity indices (at 100–600 m and 1820–2600 m) are an artifact of low S_1 and S_2 values in rocks containing highly oxidized organic matter.

Well III is located about 80 km northwest of well I (Figure 5.6). Sidewall cores are indicated by dotted bars, while ditch cuttings are indicated by solid bars. Only the Upper Cretaceous potential source rock was penetrated in this well. This unit is less oil prone than in wells I and II, but it is approaching the onset of oil generation (R_o

equivalent 0.5% for this unit). Because it is very thick, the Upper Cretaceous source rock still shows a high SPI of 15 t HC/m². Variations in TOC and HI in the Upper Cretaceous source rock in this well are more obvious than in wells I and II and can be explained by local sea level fluctuations. Geochemical parameters on the logs in Figures 5.4–5.6 allow individual units to be correlated among these three wells, similar to conventional correlations using wireline logs and paleontology.

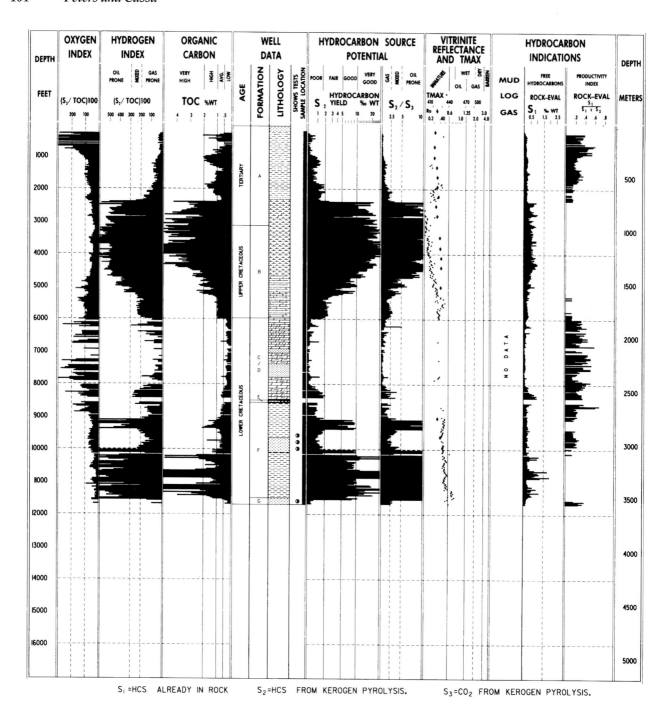

Figure 5.5. Geochemical log for well II, located about 120 km southeast of well I (Figure 5.4). The Upper Cretaceous potential source rock in well II is thicker than in well I but is still immature. The Lower Cretaceous section in well II is thicker and comprises more discrete zones of organic-rich and -lean rock compared to well I.

Wells IV through VIII

The geochemical log for well IV shows a largely poor source section above 3500 m (Figure 5.7). Tick marks in the sample location column to the left of the hydrocarbon yield column (S_2) in the figure show locations of samples. The hydrocarbon yield column shows that most samples above 3500 m contain kerogen with little or no petroleum potential. PI data indicate the presence of hydrocarbon

shows in the sandstone and siltstone interval between 2400 and 3500 m. Deeply buried shale below 3500 m represents an active source rock that is presently generating oil (SPI $\geq$ 8 t HC/m²). T_{max} values increase with depth in this shale, establishing a thermal maturity trend that is consistent with that in the poor source shale above about 2400 m. The thermal maturity of the sandstone and siltstone interval between 2400 and 3500 m can be extrapolated from the T_{max} trend established by the overlying

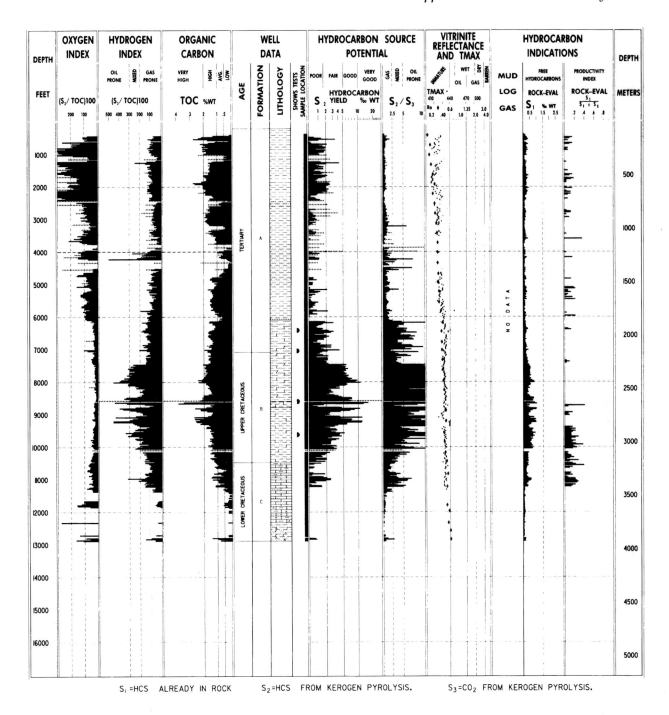

S_1 = HCS ALREADY IN ROCK S_2 = HCS FROM KEROGEN PYROLYSIS. S_3 = CO_2 FROM KEROGEN PYROLYSIS.

Figure 5.6. Geochemical log for well III, located about 80 km northwest of well I (Figure 5.4). The Upper Cretaceous section in well III is not as oil prone as in wells I or II and is more thermally mature, approaching the onset of oil generation. Geochemical parameters on the logs in Figures 5.4 to 5.6 allow individual units to be correlated among the wells. Sidewall cores indicated by dotted bars, drill cuttings by solid bars.

and underlying shales. Measured T_{max} values are either anomalously high or low in the sandstone and siltstone interval compared to the established trend based on T_{max} in the shales. The anomalously high T_{max} values result from dominance of recycled organic matter in these coarse-grained, organic-poor rocks. The low T_{max} values correspond to zones impregnated by migrated oil or where S_2 peaks are too small (<0.2 mg HC/g rock) to

yield reliable T_{max} values. High molecular weight components in oil commonly generate a spurious S_2 peak with a corresponding low T_{max} (e.g., Peters, 1986). Note the good correlation in the deeper shale between free hydrocarbon indications (S_1) and the mud log gas.

Well V penetrates Mesozoic marine shale and sandstone and Tertiary carbonate rocks (Figure 5.8). Some fine-grained marine rocks are relatively lean in

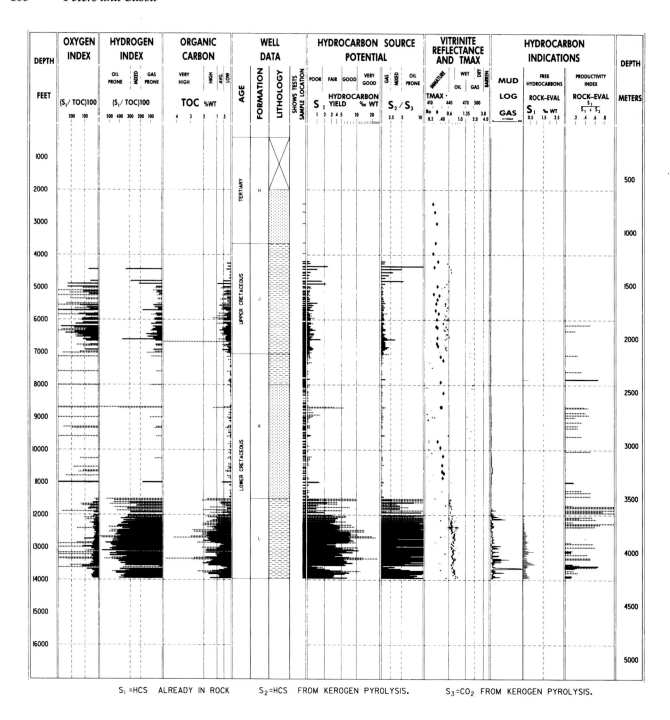

Figure 5.7. Geochemical log for well IV shows a clear thermal maturity trend established by T_{max} for shales above 2400 m (poor source) and below 3500 m (presently active source rock). The intermediate zone consists of sandstones and siltstones where T_{max} values are either anomalously high or low compared to the above trend. The high T_{max} values result from a dominance of recycled kerogen in coarse-grained, organic-poor rocks. The low T_{max} values correspond to zones impregnated by migrated oil. Heavy ends in the oil generate a spurious S_2 peak with an anomalously low T_{max} (Peters, 1986). Sidewall cores indicated by dotted bars, drill cuttings by solid bars.

organic matter, but still may be source rocks for petroleum accumulations because they are thick and/or widespread. The geochemical log for well V shows organic-lean Jurassic source rock from 2880 m to total depth. *In situ* bitumen in this presently active source rock has been geochemically correlated with oils in the area.

An SPI of 2 t HC/m² has been calculated for this Jurassic source rock using samples that have a genetic potential $(S_1 + S_2) \geq 1$ mg HC/g rock.

The geochemical log for well VI shows a depressed trend in T_{max} in the Lower Cretaceous lacustrine rocks below 2500 m (Figure 5.9). Organic petrography data

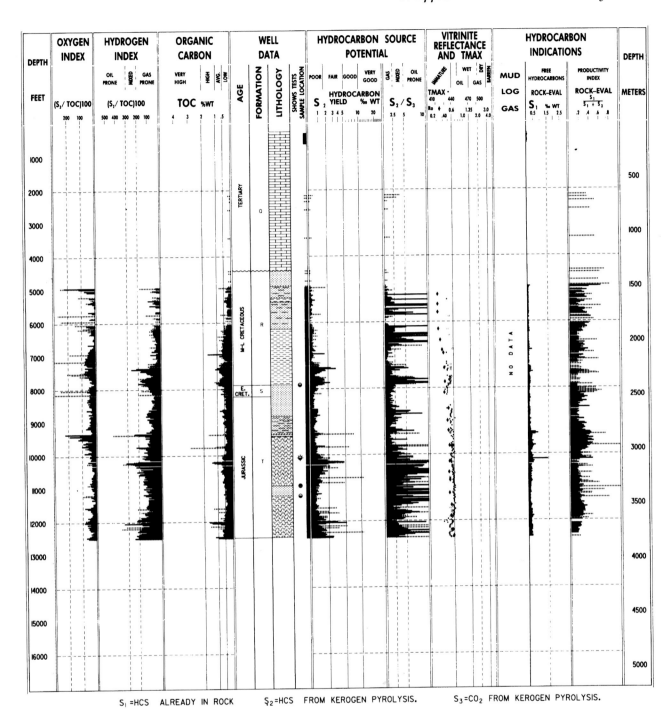

Figure 5.8. Geochemical log for well V showing organic-lean, marginally mature Jurassic source rock. In situ bitumen from this source rock has been geochemically correlated with oils in the area. An SPI of 2 t HC/m² has been calculated from the Jurassic source rock (see text). Sidewall cores indicated by dotted bars, drill cuttings by solid bars.

indicates a significant alginite component in the kerogen from these rocks. Espitalié et al. (1985) and Huizinga et al. (1988) have shown that T_{max} is seldom useful as a maturation parameter for oil-prone algal kerogens because, unlike other kerogens, it shows little to no increase throughout the oil window. Facies effects on T_{max} are discussed in Peters (1986). In this case, vitrinite reflectance represents a more useful thermal maturity parameter than T_{max}.

Well VII penetrates Mesozoic and Tertiary marine shales and sandstones, reaching Precambrian basement at total depth (Figure 5.10). The geochemical log shows the results for sidewall cores (dotted bars) and drill cuttings (solid bars). Thin shale beds sampled by sidewall cores are more organic-rich than nearby samples, but are too thin to generate significant quantities of petroleum. When mixed with adjacent lithologies in drill cuttings composited over 10–20 m intervals, these

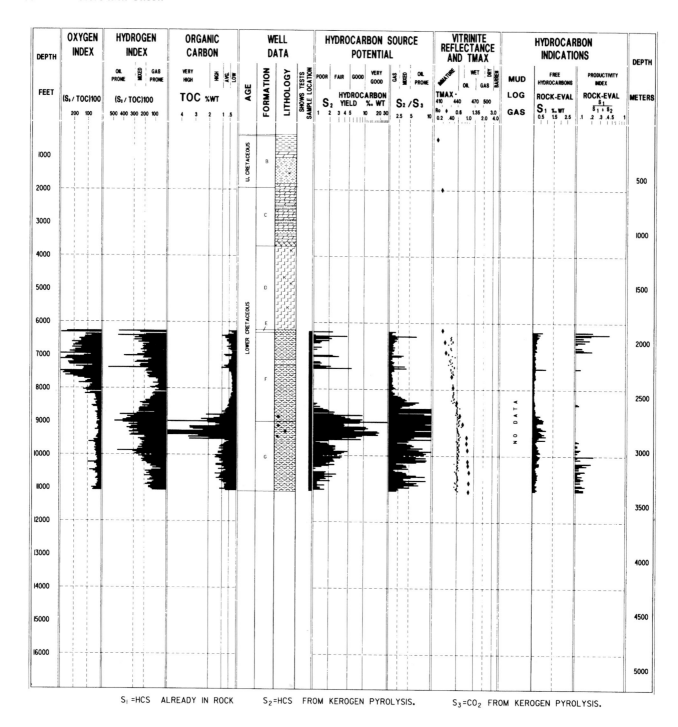

Figure 5.9. Geochemical log for well VI showing a depressed T_{max} trend compared to R_o in Lower Cretaceous lacustrine rock. Type I kerogen, commonly associated with lacustrine source rock, shows little change in T_{max} during maturation throughout the oil window. For example, Espitalié et al. (1985) show that T_{max} for type I kerogen does not exceed 440°–445°C throughout the maturity range defined by R_o = 0.4–1.5%.

thin organic-rich shales are difficult to recognize. If the drill cuttings samples had been used alone, these source rocks would have been overlooked in the penetrated section. These thin beds could represent the feather-edge of a source rock that thickens and is more deeply buried somewhere else in the basin fill. Based on the results in this well, more of these types of geochemical analyses in nearby wells could be obtained to determine if this

source rock does thicken and become more mature where it is more deeply buried. If these thin shale beds do not increase in thickness and maturity, there is little chance they could charge nearby traps. In this case, other source rocks must be identified if this area is to remain prospective for oil exploration.

Well VIII penetrates a thick Cretaceous marine sequence dominated by gas-prone organic matter

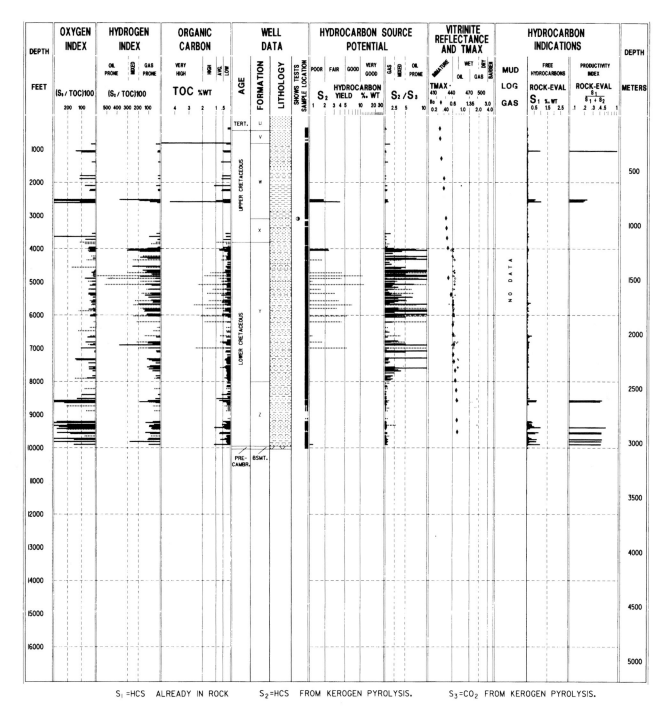

S₁ =HCS ALREADY IN ROCK   S₂=HCS FROM KEROGEN PYROLYSIS.   S₃=CO₂ FROM KEROGEN PYROLYSIS.

Figure 5.10. Geochemical log for well VII. The thin shale beds sampled by the sidewall cores are organic-rich, but are too thin to generate commercial quantities of petroleum. When mixed with adjacent lithologies as in cuttings samples, these organic-rich shales can be overlooked. If drill cuttings had been used alone, no source rock intervals would have been recognized in this well. Sidewall cores indicated by dotted bars, drill cuttings by solid bars.

(Figure 5.11). The geochemical log shows the effects of a major thrust fault on T_{max}, PI, and vitrinite reflectance trends. Thrusting of more thermally mature over less mature rocks results in an offset in the maturity trend, with higher maturity values above the fault plane than below. The rocks above the thrust fault are postmature (>1.35% R_o). If a source rock had been present in this zone, it would now be described as a spent source rock.

Geochemical Maps

Geochemical maps are made from geochemical logs. The properly designed and implemented geochemical log allows the geologist and geochemist to evaluate a source rock in one dimension. The power of the geochemical log is obvious when several logs in the same area are used to make source rock maps and cross sections. An example is a series of maps and a cross

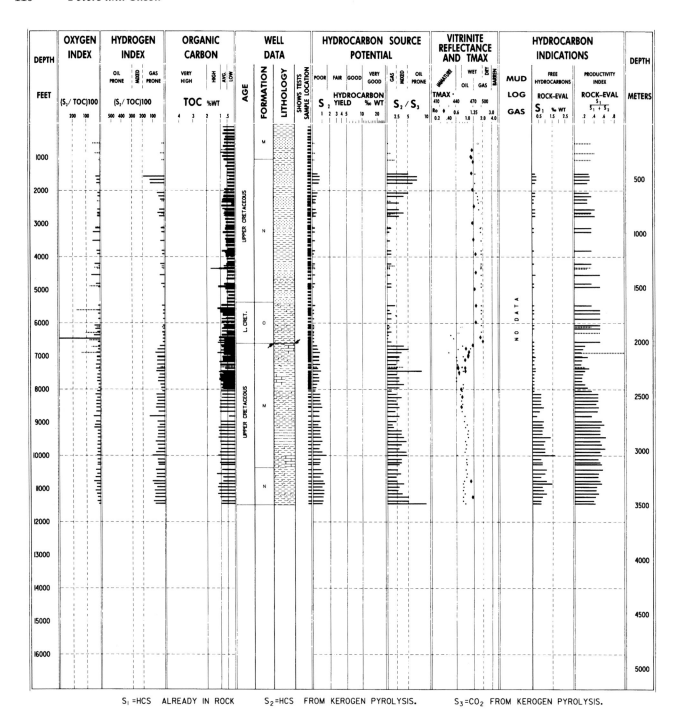

Figure 5.11. Geochemical log for well VIII shows the effects of a major thrust fault at about 2000 m in this well on T_{max}, R_o, and PI. The footwall shows good quantities of mature, gas-prone to inert organic matter, while the hanging wall contains postmature organic matter. Sidewall cores indicated by dotted bars, drill cuttings by solid bars.

section for the fictitious Deer Shale source rock.

The fictitious Deer–Boar(.) petroleum system was introduced by Magoon and Dow (Chapter 1, this volume) through four figures and a table (Figures 1.2–1.5 and Table 1.4). The map and cross section were drawn to show the essential elements of the petroleum system at the critical moment, or at the end of the Paleozoic. At that time, the Deer Shale was an active source rock, whereas now, because of uplift, it is inactive. In addition, a rift

graben formed on the right (east) side of the cross section during the Tertiary. To elaborate on this example, four source rock maps and one cross section (Figure 5.12) that represent the present-day geology show how a source rock is evaluated and placed into the context of a petroleum system that was operating in late Paleozoic time. Sedimentary basin analysis techniques are used to evaluate the source rock, whereas the petroleum system is used to evaluate the hydrocarbons.

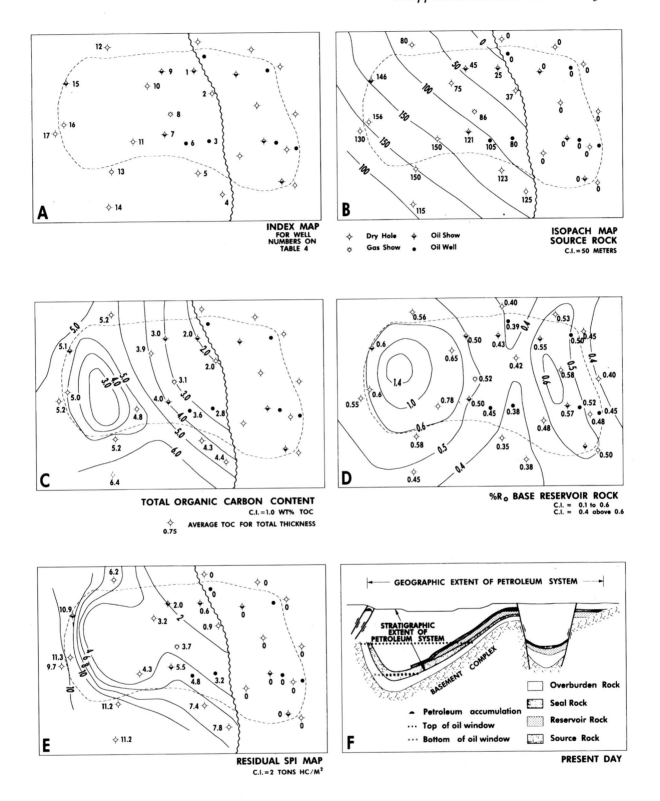

Figure 5.12. Source rock maps and cross section used in sedimentary basin analysis showing thickness, richness, and thermal maturity of the fictitious Deer Shale. (A) Index map. (B) Isopach map. (C) TOC content map. (D) % R_o base reservoir rock map. (E) Source potential index (SPI) map, which is used in studies of petroleum systems to classify a system and to determine its petroleum potential. (F) Cross section showing extent of petroleum system.

Table 5.4. Geochemical Information on the Fictitious Deer Shale[a]

Well No.	R_o (%)	h (m)	S_1[b]	S_2[b]	$S_1 + S_2$[b]	ρ (g/cm3)	SPI (t HC/m2)	TOC (wt. %)	HI (mg HC/g TOC)
1	0.43	25	1.7	8	9.7	2.4	0.6	2.0	400
2	0.42	37	1.8	8	9.8	2.4	0.9	2.0	400
3	0.38	80	2.8	14	16.8	2.4	3.2	2.8	500
4	0.38	125	4.1	22	26.1	2.4	7.8	4.4	500
5	0.35	123	4.0	21	25.0	2.4	7.4	4.3	488
6	0.45	105	3.1	16	19.1	2.4	4.8	3.6	444
7	0.50	121	1.9	17	18.9	2.4	5.5	4.0	425
8	0.52	86	3.1	15	18.1	2.4	3.7	3.1	484
9	0.50	45	2.9	16	18.9	2.4	2.0	3.0	533
10	0.65	75	3.0	15	18.0	2.4	3.2	3.9	384
11	0.78	150	2.0	10	12.0	2.4	4.3	4.8	208
12	0.56	80	5.3	27	32.3	2.4	6.2	5.2	519
13	0.58	150	5.1	26	31.1	2.4	11.2	5.2	500
14	0.45	115	6.4	34	40.4	2.4	11.2	6.4	531
15	0.60	146	5.1	26	31.1	2.4	10.9	5.1	510
16	0.60	156	5.1	25	30.1	2.4	11.3	5.0	500
17	0.55	130	5.2	26	31.2	2.4	9.7	5.2	500

[a]See equation 1 in text for definition of terms.

[b]mg HC/g dry rock.

Sedimentary Basin Analysis

The data used to construct this hypothetical example might include geochemical logs for the 32 exploratory wells, as well as other types of geologic and geophysical information that are not shown (Figure 5.12A). Information from geochemical logs is summarized for 17 of these wells in Table 5.4. The symbols in Figure 5.12A indicate that the exploratory well is a dry hole, encountered gas or oil shows, or is an oil well. A dry hole indicates that from well site drill cuttings examination, mud log, Rock-Eval pyrolysis, or other geochemical analyses, there is a lack of petroleum. Oil and gas shows indicate that some petroleum was encountered. The oil wells correlate with the fields shown on the Deer–Boar petroleum system map and table (Figure 1.3 and Table 1.3, Chapter 1). The dashed line represents the geographic extent of the same petroleum system, and the wavy unconformity line represents the erosional edge of the source rock.

The isopach map of the Deer Shale indicates that it thickens from 25 to 150 m (Figure 5.12B). Because of essentially uniform lithology vertically through the shale, this is both a gross and net source rock thickness. The contours trend in a northwesterly direction and indicate that before or during the deposition of the overlying reservoir rock erosion stripped away the source rock east of the unconformity line.

The TOC contour map of the Deer Shale source rock ranges from 2.0 to >6.0 wt. % (Figure 5.12C and Table 5.4). The average TOC contoured is derived from the net source rock thickness, that is, TOC data is first averaged over 20 m intervals then these 20 m intervals are averaged. This procedure is used to average TOC because the frequency with which each 20 m interval is sampled and analyzed is different. For example, a 10-m core may be sampled and analyzed every 1 m, whereas drill cuttings samples may be sampled every 10 m. The lowest TOC values are nearest the unconformity at the top of the map, and the highest TOC values are where the source rock is immature at the bottom of the map. From right to left, TOC values increase to 5.0 wt. %, but then decrease with burial depth to about 3.0 wt. % because of thermal maturity. This TOC map suggests that the Deer Shale is a very good to excellent source rock (Table 5.1).

To determine the present-day thermal maturity of the Deer Shale source rock, a vitrinite reflectance value was determined for the base of the overlying Boar Sandstone reservoir rock, and this value was contoured (Figure 5.12D). The isoreflectance map indicates that the base of the reservoir rock was buried enough to be in the oil window (>0.6 % R_o) in two areas and has reached the gas window (>1.35 %R_o) on the left. Because the source rock is only present in the west (left) and is thermally mature, it is logical to conclude that the oil and gas shows and oil accumulations originated from this pod of mature source rock. When the thermal maturity pattern is compared with the TOC map, the TOC is interpreted to decrease where the thermal maturity is highest.

Rock-Eval pyrolysis data are summarized for 17 of the 32 wells (Table 5.4) to determine the hydrogen index (HI) and (SPI). The HI shows the present-day amount of hydrogen in the source rock organic matter and indicates the kerogen type or quality (Table 5.2). HI is the S_2 peak (mg HC/g rock) divided by the TOC (mg TOC/g rock) times 100. The average HI values were determined in the same way as the average TOC values, that is, over 20-m intervals. The average HI contours range from 400 to 583 mg HC/g TOC, indicating type II kerogen.

The source potential index requires Rock-Eval pyrolysis data as well as the thickness and density of the source rock unit, as discussed by Demaison and Huizinga (Chapter 4, this volume). If the density, net thickness, and quality of a source rock remain constant, SPI decreases as thermal maturity increases. Because these SPI values indicate remaining potential, they are called "residual SPI" (Figure 5.12E). Residual SPI values for the Deer Shale increase to the southwest (lower left), but are interpreted to be less than 4 where the source rock is buried deepest. The source rock density is constant (Table 5.4). If prior to increased thermal maturity, the SPI values all increased to the southwest from 2 to 10, then along strike there is a decrease of up to 8 SPI units caused by thermal maturity. These are moderate to high SPIs (Figure 4.4).

These maps indicate that the Deer Shale is a very good to excellent source rock that contains type II kerogen and that there is a pod of thermally mature source rock in the west-central part of the map. Additional information, such as paleontology, indicates that the Deer Shale was deposited in a marine environment, and organic petrography indicates that the kerogen macerals are in part waxy pollen (terrigenous), but mostly marine algal debris.

The cross section that represents present-day geology indicates that the overburden rock to the east in the rifted graben is Tertiary in age, whereas the overburden rock in the foreland basin to the west is late Paleozoic (Figure 5.12F). Because the source rock is absent from either side of the graben, and the graben is filled with nonmarine siliciclastics, the conclusion is that the hydrocarbons originated from the west side of the cross section from the pod of mature source rock mapped earlier.

The maps and interpretations outlined here are part of sedimentary basin analysis because organic and rock matter are investigated. The thickness, TOC content, % R_o, and SPI are all mappable properties of the source rock. However, the well control shown on the base map indicates that hydrocarbons have been detected in the area (Figure 5.13). These hydrocarbons are proof that in this area a petroleum system exists. To determine the origin and economic significance of these hydrocarbons, a petroleum system study is carried out.

Petroleum System Study

The presence of hydrocarbons in such close proximity to a pod of mature source rock strongly suggests that the two are genetically related, that is, the oil came from the Deer Shale source rock. This makes the Deer Shale an effective source rock.

Oil has been discovered to the east of the graben, whereas the pod of mature source rock is on the west side of the graben. Unless the oil came from the east, south, or north of the rift graben, it had to migrate before the rift graben formed in Tertiary time. This observation

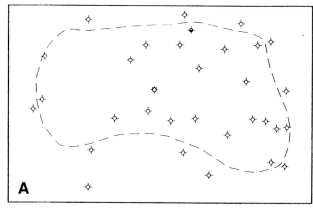

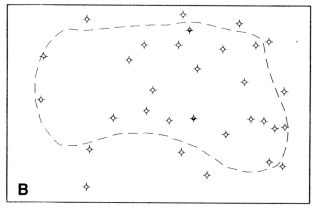

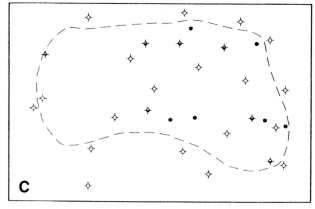

Figure 5.13. Maps indicating the oil and gas shows encountered in exploratory wells penetrating the Deer Shale and Boar sandstone. Few shows were detected in (A) the overburden rock and (B) the seal rock, whereas numerous shows were detected in (C) the reservoir rock horizon, indicating that this is the interval through which the oil migrated.

indicates that the Deer Shale was an active source rock sometime in pre-Tertiary time. Burial history charts (Figure 1.2, Chapter 1) in several places in the area confirm that the source rock was active in late Paleozoic time.

Because the hydrocarbon shows in the wells are proof of the petroleum system, an understanding of the distribution of these shows is important to determine the geographic and stratigraphic extent of the system. Most of the wells were drilled to basement. Where the basement rock, underburden rock, and source rock intervals were penetrated, shows were not detected. Hydrocarbon shows were detected in the overburden rock and seal rock intervals.

Slight oil shows (streaming cut-fluorescence) were detected near the base of the overburden rock in the north-central part of the area, and gas shows were detected at a depth of 350 m in the central part of the area (Figure 5.13A). Well site evaluation of the gas shows indicated substantial gas on the hot wire that was 99.7% methane on the GC (dry gas). Laboratory analyses of headspace gas from canned cuttings collected through this interval indicate a carbon isotope value of −71.6‰, or biogenic gas. The conclusion is that this gas is part of a separate petroleum system probably related to Carboniferous coals in the overburden rock.

Within the seal rock, two shows were detected near the base of the unit (Figure 5.13B). The show in the north-central part of the area underlies the oil show in the overburden rock. Both shows are interpreted to be vertically migrating oil from the reservoir rock below. South of this show is another show in the seal rock, which is also interpreted to be oil that migrated from the reservoir rock below.

The reservoir rock interval, the Boar Sandstone, has the most abundant oil shows of any interval investigated (Figure 5.13C). Of the 32 wells that penetrated the reservoir horizon, 7 have oil shows and 6 recovered oil when drill-stem tested. Based on the distribution of these oil shows and their proximity to the pod of mature source rock, there is little doubt that the oil originated from this source rock. If this is true, the pattern of oil shows should give some indication as to the migration path of the oil. Two east-west bands of shows are shown, one at the top and one in the middle of the map with five wells in between that lack shows. These bands are good circumstantial evidence that the oil migrated from the mature source rock on the west through the reservoir rocks along two corridors to the east (Figure 1.3, Chapter 1). The distribution of these oil shows and the pod of mature source rock provide a basis for the geographic extent of the petroleum system.

Gas chromatography of the Deer Shale source rock extract shows that the pristane–phytane ratio is above 1.5 and the carbon preference index (CPI) is 1.2. Organic petrography indicates that the organic matter is mostly marine amorphous material with up to 35% terrigenous material.

The API gravity of the oil ranges from 32° to 43° and sulfur content is less than 0.3%. The pristane–phytane ratio is 1.6 and the CPI is 1.1. A more definitive oil–source rock correlation using biomarkers was not completed. Based on the rock extract and oil geochemistry, the oil probably originated from the Deer Shale, therefore the level of certainty for the Deer–Boar petroleum system is hypothetical.

The maps and cross sections in Figures 1.2–1.5 (Chapter 1) and in Figures 5.12 and 5.13 indicate the stratigraphic and geographic extent of the Deer–Boar petroleum system. Based on the burial history chart, the Deer Shale was an active source rock in late Paleozoic time. The oil show map of the Boar Sandstone reservoir rock interval indicates the oil migrated along two corridors into anticlinal and stratigraphic traps. In Tertiary time, a rift graben formed, isolating the oil accumulations on the east from those on the west side of the graben and the pod of inactive source rock. Oil samples from the shows and accumulations were used in an oil–oil correlation. Results showed that all these oils originated from the same source rock. The confidence that this oil originated from the Deer Shale is based on the similarity of certain geochemical parameters for both the oil and rock extract even though a detailed oil–source rock correlation was not completed.

After the source rock is demonstrated to be effective, that is, it generated and expelled hydrocarbons, then the question remains as to how effective. Decreased TOC and pyrolysis yields of source rocks resulting from thermal maturation must be taken into account to assess their original generative potential accurately and to make volumetric estimates of petroleum generated (Dow, 1977b; Schmoker, Chapter 19, this volume). For example, TOC is little affected by maturation of rocks containing type IV kerogen, but TOC can be reduced by 12–20 wt. % for type III and by as much as 50 and 70 wt. % for types II and I, respectively (Daly and Edman, 1987). Failure to account for these effects on mature or spent source rocks can cause source intervals to be overlooked on geochemical logs and can result in underestimates of original source rock potential or oil generated.

The volume of hydrocarbons generated and accumulated can be demonstrated in many ways. The case studies in this volume use a mass balance method (Schmoker, Chapter 19), and Demaison and Huizinga (1991; Chapter 4) use the SPI. Because the case studies adequately explain the mass balance method, only the SPI method is outlined here.

The residual SPI map is constructed from the net source rock thickness map and the genetic potential ($S_1 + S_2$) (Table 5.4) of the source rock from Rock-Eval pyrolysis (Figure 5.12E). The SPI ranges from 0.6 to 11.3. The residual SPI where the source was buried deepest suggests that up to 8 SPI units were lost as the source rock generated oil. Based on the preliminary SPI classification (Figure 4.4), the burial of this source rock indicates a large drainage area with moderate to high potential. Using regional geology and SPI, this petroleum system can be classified as a supercharged, low impedance, laterally drained petroleum system.

SUMMARY

Source rock characterization using geochemical logs and maps is an exercise in sedimentary basin analysis with the objective of identifying the pod of active source rock. The pod of active source rock contributes hydrocarbons to the petroleum system.

This chapter emphasizes (1) terms used to describe source rocks; (2) sampling, preparation, and analysis criteria; (3) geochemical logs and their use to describe source rocks and petroleum shows in one dimension; and (4) geochemical maps and their use for interpolating between one-dimensional control points for a three-dimensional understanding of the petroleum system.

Proper use of terms is critical for clearly describing petroleum systems. Some examples of source rock terms include richness, kerogen type, thermal maturity, product generated, time generated, and provenance or depositional environment. Source rock organic richness can be poor, fair, good, very good, or excellent (Table 5.1). Kerogen can be described as type I, II, III, or IV based on elemental analysis (Table 5.2). Organic petrography provides information on organic matter type and thermal maturity, but is currently too imprecise to describe generative potential. Thermal maturity is divided into immature, mature, and postmature based on such parameters as vitrinite reflectance, T_{max}, and thermal alteration index (Table 5.3). A source rock can be described as potential (could generate oil), effective (generated or currently generating oil), or spent (generated oil). A spent source rock can still generate gas. An inactive source rock is not generating oil today, but in the past it was an active source rock. The term "marine source rock" implies marine deposition, while the terms "marine organic matter" and "marine kerogen" could imply an origin from marine organisms. A marine source rock might contain dominantly land plant organic matter.

Geochemical logs of closely spaced Rock-Eval pyrolysis and TOC, vitrinite reflectance, lithology, mud log gas, and related data are indispensable tools in the sedimentary basin evaluation process. Useful geochemical logs require adherence to proper procedures for sample selection, preparation, analysis, and interpretation. These logs identify petroleum source rocks (as potential, effective, or spent), the thermal maturation gradient (including immature, mature, and postmature zones), and *in situ* and migrated petroleum shows.

Because of the rapid and inexpensive screening methods used, it is practical to generate libraries of geochemical logs that progressively reduce the risk associated with petroleum exploration as a petroleum province becomes more thoroughly sampled. Logs from various locations can be used to map the pod of active source rock, regional variations in organic facies, and the volume of generated petroleum. This information can be used as input to refine mathematical basin models. Finally, the two-step procedure consisting of screening followed by detailed geochemical analyses on selected samples reduces cost and simplifies interpretation.

Acknowledgments We thank L. B. Magoon and W. G. Dow for their invitation to prepare this paper and G. J. Demaison for his suggestion that it be written. The following people contributed timely reviews that improved the manuscript: L. B. Magoon, S. C. Teerman, D. K. Baskin, T. A. Edison, G.J. Demaison, J.T. Smith, and W.G. Dow. Tables 5.1, 5.2, and 5.3 were improved by input from D. K. Baskin, L. B. Magoon, and J. Miles. Concepts for Figures 5.2 and 5.3 were provided by T. A. Edison and S. C. Teerman, respectively. S. D. Northam and B. R. Barden coordinated the production of figures and text. We thank E. L. Couch and N. Schneidermann for their support and the management of Chevron Overseas Petroleum Inc. for permission to publish this work.

References Cited

Alpern, B., 1970, Classification pétrographique des constituants organiques fossiles des roches sédimentaires: Revue Institut Francais du Pétrole et Annual Combustion Liquid, Paris, v. 25, p. 1233–1266.

Bandurski, E., 1982, Structural similarities between oil-generating kerogens and petroleum asphaltenes: Energy Sources, v. 6, p. 47–66.

Barker, C., 1979, Organic geochemistry in petroleum exploration: AAPG Continuing Education Course Note Series 10, 159 p.

Baskin, D. K., 1979, A method of preparing phytoclasts for vitrinite reflectance analysis: Journal of Sedimentary Petrology, v. 49, p. 633–635.

Baskin, D. K., and K. E. Peters, 1992, Early generation characteristics of a sulfur-rich Monterey kerogen: AAPG Bulletin, v. 76, p. 1–13.

Bernard, B. B., 1978, Light hydrocarbons in marine sediments: Ph.D. dissertation, Texas A&M University, College Station, TX, p. 53–62.

Bostick, N. H., and B. Alpern, 1977, Principles of sampling, preparation, and constituent selection for microphotometry in measurement of maturation of sedimentary organic matter: Journal of Microscopy, v. 109, p. 41–47.

Cassani, F., and G. Eglinton, 1986, Organic geochemistry of Venezuelan extra-heavy oils, 1. Pyrolysis of asphaltenes: a technique for the correlation and maturity evaluation of crude oils: Chemical Geology, v. 56, p. 167–183.

Clementz, D. M., G. J. Demaison, and A. R. Daly, 1979, Well site geochemistry by programmed pyrolysis: Proceedings of the 11th Annual Offshore Technology Conference, Houston, OTC 3410, v. 1, p. 465–470.

Cook, A. C., and N. R. Sherwood, 1991, Classification of oil shales, coals and other organic-rich rocks: Organic Geochemistry, v. 17, p. 211–222.

Daly, A. R., and J. D. Edman, 1987, Loss of organic carbon from source rocks during thermal maturation (abs.): AAPG Bulletin, v. 71, p. 546.

Demaison, G. J., 1984, The generative basin concept, in G.J. Demaison and R. J. Murris, eds., Petroleum Geochemistry and Basin Evaluation: AAPG Memoir 35, p. 1–14.

Demaison, G. J., A. J. J. Holck, R. W. Jones, and G. T. Moore, 1983, Predictive source bed stratigraphy; a guide to regional petroleum occurrence: Proceedings of the 11th World Petroleum Congress, London, v. 2, p. 17–29.

Demaison, G. J., and B. J. Huizinga, 1991, Genetic classification of petroleum systems: AAPG Bulletin, v. 75, p. 1626–1643.

Demaison, G. J., and G. T. Moore, 1980, Anoxic environments and oil source bed genesis: AAPG Bulletin, v. 64, p. 1179–1209.

Dow, W. G., 1977a, Petroleum source beds on continental slopes and rises: AAPG Continuing Education Course Notes Series 5, p. D1–D37.

Dow, W. G., 1977b, Kerogen studies and geological interpretations: Journal of Geochemical Exploration, v. 7, p. 79–99.

Durand, B., 1980, Kerogen, Insoluble Organic Matter from Sedimentary Rocks: Paris, Éditions Technip, 519 p.

Emerson, S., 1985, Organic carbon preservation in marine sediments, in E. T. Sundquist and W. S. Broecker, eds., The carbon cycle and atmospheric CO_2: natural variations from Archean to Present: American Geophysical Union, Geophysical Monograph 32, p. 78–86.

Espitalié, J., M. Madec, B. Tissot, J. J. Mennig, and P. Leplat, 1977, Source rock characterization method for petroleum exploration: Proceedings of the Ninth Offshore Technology Conference, Houston, p. 439–442.

Espitalié, J., F. Marquis, and I. Barsony, 1984, Geochemical logging, in K. J. Voorhees, ed., Analytical Pyrolysis—Techniques and Applications: Boston, Butterworth, p. 276–304.

Espitalié, J., G. Deroo, and F. Marquis, 1985, La pyrolyse Rock-Eval et ses applications (deuxième partie): Revue Institut Francais du Pétrole, v. 40, p. 755–784.

Espitalié, J., F. Marquis, and L. Sage, 1987, Organic geochemistry of the Paris basin, in J. Brooks and K. Glennie, eds., Petroleum Geology of North-West Europe: London, Graham and Trotman, p. 71–86.

Gas Processors Association, 1986, Obtaining natural gas samples for analysis by gas chromatography: GPA Standard 2166-86, p. 4–14.

Hester, T. C., J. W. Schmoker, and H. L. Sahl, 1990, Log-derived regional source rock characteristics of the Woodford Shale, Anadarko basin, Oklahoma: U.S.G.S. Bulletin 1866-D, 38 p.

Huizinga, B. J., Z. A. Aizenshtat, and K. E. Peters, 1988, Programmed pyrolysis–gas chromatography of artificially matured Green River kerogen: Journal of Energy and Fuels, v. 74, p. 74–81.

Hunt, J. M., 1979, Petroleum Geochemistry and Geology: San Francisco, W. H. Freeman, 617 p.

Hunt, J. M., 1991, Generation of gas and oil from coal and other terrestrial organic matter: Organic Geochemistry, v. 17, p. 673–680.

Hutton, A. C., A. J. Kantsler, A. C. Cook, and D. M. McKirdy, 1980, Organic matter in oil shales: Journal of the Australian Petroleum Exploration Association, v. 20, p. 44–67.

Jacob, H., 1989, Classification, structure, genesis and practical importance of natural solid oil bitumen ("migrabitumen"): International Journal of Coal Geology, v. 11, p. 65–79.

James, A. T., 1983, Correlation of natural gas by use of carbon isotopic distribution between hydrocarbon components: AAPG Bulletin, v. 67, 1176–1191.

Jones, R. W., 1984, Comparison of carbonate and shale source rocks, in J. G. Palacas, ed., Petroleum geochemistry and source rock potential of carbonate rocks: AAPG Studies in Geology 18, p. 163–180.

Jones, R. W., 1987, Organic facies, in J. Brooks and D. Welte, eds., Advances in Petroleum Geochemistry: New York, Academic Press, p. 1–90.

Jones, R. W., and G. J. Demaison, 1982, Organic facies-stratigraphic concept and exploration tool, in A. Salvidar-Sali, ed., Proceedings of the Second ASCOPE Conference and Exhibition: ASCOPE Asean Council on Petroleum, October 1981, Manila, Philippines, p. 51–68.

Jones, R. W., and T. A. Edison, 1978, Microscopic observations of kerogen related to geochemical parameters with emphasis on thermal maturation, in D. F. Oltz, ed., Low temperature metamorphism of kerogen and clay minerals: SEPM Pacific Section, Los Angeles, October, p. 1–12.

Kontorovich, A. E., 1984, Geochemical methods for the quantitative evaluation of the petroleum potential of sedimentary basins, in G. J. Demaison and R. J. Murris, Petroleum geochemistry and basin evaluation: AAPG Memoir 35, p. 79–109.

Krouse, H. R., C. A. Viau, L. S. Eliuk, A. Ueda, and S. Halas, 1988, Chemical and isotopic evidence of thermochemical sulphate reduction by light hydrocarbon gases in deep carbonate reservoirs: Nature, v. 333, p. 415–419.

Langford, F. F., and M. M. Blanc-Valleron, 1990, Interpreting Rock-Eval pyrolysis data using graphs of pyrolyzable hydrocarbons versus total organic carbon: AAPG Bulletin, v. 74, p. 799–804.

Larter, S. R., and J. T. Senftle, 1985, Improved kerogen typing for petroleum source rock analysis: Nature, v. 318, p. 277–280.

Link, C. M., R. M. Bustin, and F. Goodarzi, 1990, Petrology of graptolites and their utility as indices of thermal maturity in lower Paleozoic strata in northern Yukon, Canada: International Journal of Coal Geology, v. 15, p. 113–135.

Mackenzie, A. S., and T. M. Quigley, 1988, Principles of geochemical prospect appraisal: AAPG Bulletin, v. 72, p. 399–415.

Magoon, L. B., P. V. Woodward, A. C. Banet, Jr., S. B. Griscom, and T. A. Daws, 1987, Thermal maturity, richness, and type of organic matter of source rock units, in K. J. Bird and L. B. Magoon, eds., Petroleum geology of the northern part of the Arctic National Wildlife Refuge, northeastern Alaska: U.S.G.S. Bulletin 1778, p. 127–179.

Magoon, L. B., K. J. Bird, G. E. Claypool, D. E. Weitzman, and R. H. Thompson, 1988, Organic geochemistry, hydrocarbon occurrence, and stratigraphy of government drilled wells, North Slope, Alaska, in G. Gryc, ed., Geology and exploration of the National Petroleum Reserve in Alaska, 1974 to 1982: U.S. Geological Survey Professional Paper 1399, p. 483–487.

Mango, F.D., 1991, The stability of hydrocarbons under the time-temperature conditions of petroleum genesis: Nature, v. 352, p. 146–148.

Mann, A. L., R. L. Patience, and I. J. F. Poplett, 1991, Determination of molecular structure of kerogens using ^{13}C NMR spectroscopy: I. The effects of variation in kerogen type: Geochimica Cosmochimica Acta, v. 55, p. 2259–2268.

Marshall, J. E. A., 1991, Quantitative spore colour: Journal of the Geological Society, London, v. 148, p. 223–233.

Mycke, B., F. Narjes, and W. Michaelis, 1987, Bacteriohopanetetrol from chemical degradation of an oil shale kerogen: Nature, v. 326, p. 179–181.

Orr, W. L., 1986, Kerogen/asphaltene/sulfur relationships in sulfur-rich Monterey oils: Organic Geochemistry, v. 10, p. 499–516.

Pasley, M. R., W. A. Gregory, and G. F. Hart, 1991, Organic matter variations in transgressive and regressive shales: Organic Geochemistry, v. 17, p. 483–509.

Passey, Q. R., S. Creaney, J. B. Kulla, F. J. Moretti, and J. D. Stroud, 1990, A practical model for organic richness from porosity and resistivity logs: AAPG Bulletin, v. 74, p. 1777–1794.

Pederson, T. F., and S. E. Calvert, 1990, Anoxia versus productivity: what controls the formation of organic-carbon-rich sediments and sedimentary rocks?: AAPG Bulletin, v. 74, p. 454–466.

Pelet, R., F. Behar, and J. C. Monin, 1985, Resins and asphaltenes in the generation and migration of petroleum: Organic Geochemistry, v. 10, p. 481–498.

Peters, K. E., 1986, Guidelines for evaluating petroleum source rock using programmed pyrolysis: AAPG Bulletin, v. 70, p. 329.

Peters, K. E., and J. M. Moldowan, 1993, The Biomarker Guide: Englewood Cliffs, NJ, Prentice Hall, 363 p.

Peters, K. E., and B. R. T. Simoneit, 1982, Rock-Eval pyrolysis of Quaternary sediments from Leg 64, Sites 479 and 480, Gulf of California: Initial Reports of the Deep Sea Drilling Project, v. 64, p. 925–931.

Price, L. C., and C. E. Barker, 1985, Suppression of vitrinite reflectance in amorphous rich kerogen—a major unrecognized problem: Journal of Petroleum Geology, v. 8, p. 59–84.

Reitsema, R. H., A. J. Kaltenback, and F. A. Lindberg, 1981, Source and migration of light hydrocarbons indicated by carbon isotopic ratios: AAPG Bulletin, v. 65, p. 1536–1542.

Rice, D. D., and G. E. Claypool, 1981, Generation, accumulation, and resource potential of biogenic gas: AAPG Bulletin, v. 65, p. 5–25.

Roberts, A. A., J. G. Palacas, and I. C. Frost, 1973, Determination of organic carbon in modern carbonate sediments: Journal of Sedimentary Petrology, v. 43, p. 1157–1159.

Rullkötter, J., and W. Michaelis, 1990, The structure of kerogen and related materials: a review of recent progress and future needs: Organic Geochemistry, v. 16, p. 829–852.

Schaefer, R. G., B. Weiner, and D. Leythaeuser, 1978, Determination of sub-nanogram quantities of light hydrocarbons (C_2–C_9) in rock samples by hydrogen stripping in the flow system of a capillary gas chromatograph: Analytical Chemistry, v. 50, p. 1848–1854.

Schmoker, J. W., and T. C. Hester, 1983, Organic carbon in Bakken Formation, United States portion of Williston basin: AAPG Bulletin, v. 67, p. 2165–2174.

Schoell, M., 1984, Stable isotopes in petroleum research, *in* J. Brooks and D. Welte, eds., Advances in Organic Geochemistry: San Diego, Academic Press, p. 215–245.

Senftle, J. T., J. H. Brown, and S. R. Larter, 1987, Refinement of organic petrographic methods for kerogen characterization: International Journal of Coal Geology, v. 7, p. 105–117.

Snowdon, L. R., 1991, Oil from type III organic matter: resinite revisited: Organic Geochemistry, v. 17, p. 743–747.

Stach, E., M.-Th. Mackowsky, M. Teichmüller, G. H. Taylor, D. Chandra, and R. Teichmüller, 1982, Coal Petrology: Gebrüder Borntraeger, Berlin, 535 p.

Staplin, F. L., 1969, Sedimentary organic matter, organic metamorphism, and oil and gas occurrence: Canadian Petroleum Geologists Bulletin, v. 17, p. 47–66.

Stocks, A. E., and S. R. Lawrence, 1990, Identification of source rocks from wireline logs, *in* A. Hurst, M. A. Lovell, and A. Morton, eds., Geological applications of wireline logs: The Geological Society Special Publication, n. 48, p. 241–252.

Swanson, R. G., 1981, Sample Examination Manual: AAPG Methods in Exploration Series, n. 1, 103 p.

Teerman, S. C., and R. J. Hwang, 1991, Evaluation of the liquid hydrocarbon potential of coal by artificial maturation techniques: Organic Geochemistry, v. 17, p. 749–764.

Tissot, B. P., G. Demaison, P. Masson, J. R. Delteil, and A. Combaz, 1980, Paleoenvironment and petroleum potential of middle Cretaceous black shales in Atlantic basins: AAPG Bulletin, v. 64, p. 2051–2063.

Tissot, B. P., B. Durand, J. Espitalié, and A. Combaz, 1974, Influence of the nature and diagenesis of organic matter in formation of petroleum: AAPG Bulletin, v. 58, p. 499–506.

Tissot, B. P., and D. H. Welte, 1984, Petroleum formation and occurrence: New York, Springer-Verlag, 699 p.

Tyson, R. V., and T. H. Pearson, eds., 1991, Modern and ancient continental shelf anoxia: Geological Society of London Special Publication, n. 58, p. 1–24.

van Krevelen, D. W., 1961, Coal: New York, Elsevier, 514 p.

Whelan, J. K., 1984, Volatile C_1–C_8 compounds in marine sediments, *in* G. Odham, L. Larsson, and P. A. Mardh, eds., Gas chromatography/mass spectrometry applications in microbiology: New York, Plenum Press, p. 381–414.

Wilhelms, A., S. R. Larter, D. Leythaeuser, and H. Dypvik, 1990, Recognition and quantification of the effects of primary migration in a Jurassic clastic source rock from the Norwegian continental shelf: Organic Geochemistry, v. 16, p. 103–113.

CHAPTER APPENDIX A:
Kerogen Types

There are four principal types of kerogens found in coals and sedimentary rocks which are defined using atomic H/C versus O/C or Rock-Eval HI versus OI diagrams (see Figures 5.1 and 5.2.)

Type I

Immature type I kerogens are oil prone, show high atomic H/C (≥ 1.5), low O/C (<0.1) (Figures 5.1 and 5.2), and generally have low sulfur content. These kerogens are dominated by liptinite macerals, but vitrinites and inertinites can be present in lesser amounts. Type I kerogens appear to be derived from extensive bacterial reworking of lipid-rich algal organic matter, commonly, but not always, in lacustrine settings (e.g., Eocene Green River Formation). *Botryococcus* and similar lacustrine algae and their marine equivalents, such as *Tasmanites,* can be major contributors to type I kerogens.

Type II

Immature type II kerogens are oil-prone (e.g., Jurassic of Saudi Arabia) and show high atomic H/C (1.2–1.5) and low O/C compared to types III and IV. Sulfur is generally higher in type II compared to other kerogens. Type II S kerogens (e.g., Miocene Monterey Formation) show high sulfur (e.g., 8–14 wt. %; atomic S/C ≥ 0.04) and appear to generate petroleum at lower thermal maturity than other type II kerogens (Orr, 1986; Baskin and Peters, 1992). Type II kerogens are also dominated by liptinite macerals.

Type III

Immature type III kerogens show low atomic H/C (<1.0) and high O/C (≤ 0.3). Type III kerogen is called gas-prone because it yields some hydrocarbon gas but little oil during maturation. This term is misleading because type III kerogens actually yield less gas than types I and II. Some thick deltaic deposits dominated by type III kerogen have generated substantial oil (e.g., Mahakam Delta in Indonesia, U.S. Gulf Coast, and offshore West Africa), primarily from liptinite macerals that may represent only a small portion of the kerogen.

Type IV

Type IV kerogen is "dead carbon" showing very low atomic H/C (about 0.5–0.6) and low to high O/C (≤ 0.3). These kerogens are dominated by inertinite macerals that generate little or no hydrocarbons during maturation. Type IV kerogens can be derived from other kerogen types that have been reworked or oxidized.

CHAPTER APPENDIX B:
Key Factors Affecting Accuracy of Geochemical Logs

We recommend Rock-Eval pyrolysis and TOC analyses every 10–20 m and vitrinite reflectance data every 100–200 m *throughout each well.* Closer sample spacing results in better geochemical logs. The strength of the pyrolysis and TOC screening approach lies in sheer numbers of analyses. Trends are established by statistically significant amounts of data, and occasional anomalies become obvious (e.g., Figure 5.6). Incomplete geochemical logs based on isolated measurements are of little exploration value.

Because screening analyses are inexpensive, it is practical to generate libraries of detailed geochemical logs. As provinces become better explored, libraries of logs progressively reduce exploration risk by clarifying the three-dimensional distributions of organic facies, thermal maturity, and prospective reservoirs. Consistent scales for geochemical logs simplify comparisons of source rock intervals between wells.

Rock Sample Preparation

Rock sample quality generally decreases in the following order: conventional whole core, sidewall core, drill cuttings, and outcrops. Cuttings can be contaminated by particulate or fluid (e.g., oil-based mud) drilling additives or can contain rock chips "caved" from higher in the section during drilling. Cuttings polluted with diesel can be cleaned with a solvent, but the residue lacks useful volatile compounds and only the kerogen can be analyzed reliably. Samples stored for long periods are generally reliable, provided they are clean and were stored under conditions restricting the growth of fungus. Core, sidewall, and outcrop samples can be brushed or scraped to remove mudcake, residues from marking pens, or weathered surfaces.

Outcrops are commonly weathered, resulting in altered organic matter. Outcrops should be systematically collected (e.g., every 2 m vertically) from fresh cuts, such as cliffs, roadcuts, or river banks. In general, outcropping rocks with high dips are more deeply weathered than those with low dips. Fist-sized samples ($5 \times 5 \times 8$ cm) are sufficient for most source rock analyses. Accurate positioning (within about 10 m) can be obtained using a commercially available hand-held satellite positioning system. Sample locations should be recorded on a measured section, outcrop sketch, or photograph.

Samples can be screened in the field by sedimentologic features or using a commercially available portable pyrolysis system. Shales or dense, fine-grained micritic carbonates are the best candidates for source rocks. Good source rocks containing type I or II kerogen are commonly thinly laminated and range from yellowish brown to grayish brown or brownish black (GSA Rock Color Chart, 1979). However, good source rocks can be light-colored on weathered surfaces. Burrows and abundant benthic macrofossils indicate poor conditions for preservation of organic matter. When in doubt, it is better to sample a candidate source rock for laboratory confirmation.

Most geochemical logs are based on cuttings, complemented by sidewall cores and conventional cores. The following discussion is directed toward cuttings, although the same general criteria for preparation and interpretation apply to cores and outcrop samples. Each sample should weigh about 50 g. Cuttings are best washed at the well site prior to shipment and storage because mudcake can become more difficult to remove with time. Cuttings are washed of mudcake using fresh or salt water, and in the process, wet-sieved with a 2-mm top sieve and a 180-μm bottom sieve. Cuttings must not be washed with organic solvents, which remove soluble components. Many particulate additives can be floated off by panning in an evaporating basin. Samples are air-dried at about 40°C.

After arrival in the geochemical laboratory, cuttings are rewashed and described for lithology. Washed and air-dried cuttings are examined using a binocular microscope, and contaminants, such as walnut hulls, woodchips, metal, and obvious caved material, are removed by "negative picking." We do not recommend "positive picking," where an inferred representative lithology is selected for analysis from a mixture of lithologies in a sample. Positive picking generally results in nonrepresentative samples. We do not recommend composite samples of cuttings from several intervals. Natural mixing of cuttings in the mudstream during drilling is a form of compositing that need not be compounded in the laboratory. When severe, caving or bypass of lithologies on the shaker table can cause problems in interpretation. We have found that natural mixing is reasonably representative of significant rock lithologies. For example, thin, organic-rich beds that might be sampled by sidewall cores are "averaged" and do not appear as organic-rich spikes on geochemical logs (Figure 5.10).

A small portion of the dried cuttings is crushed to fine sand particle size (0.125–0.25 mm). Grinding to a smaller size is not recommended because powdered samples can result in anomalous Rock-Eval results, including poor S_2 peak definition, low S_2 yield, and erroneous T_{max} values. The crushed samples (100 mg) are analyzed using Rock-Eval pyrolysis where every twentieth sample is a rock standard. If very rich in organic matter (>10 wt. % TOC), sample size is reduced and the sample is rerun to ensure linearity of response. Sample size also affects Rock-Eval pyrolysis response (Peters, 1986). Another approach that avoids this problem is to dilute an organic-rich sample with pure carbonate, followed by pyrolysis of 100 mg of the mixture (Peters, 1986).

Samples showing high S_1 values result from (1) potential or effective source rocks or (2) rocks containing migrated oil or contaminated by drilling additives. Samples containing migrated oil or drilling additives are readily distinguished from source rocks by anomalously high production indices for their level of thermal maturity. Samples that do not meet the following criteria (Table 5.3) are assumed to be contaminated by drilling additives or migrated oil:

- If T_{max} is in the range 390°–435°C, then PI must be ≤0.1.
- If T_{max} is in the range 436°–445°C, then PI must be ≤0.3.
- If T_{max} is in the range 445°–460°C, then PI must be ≤0.4.

These criteria must be applied with caution because the relationship between T_{max} and PI vary with kerogen type, thus, some highly oil-prone lacustrine kerogens show little change in T_{max} during maturation (Espitalié et al., 1985; Huizinga et al., 1988).

All samples containing migrated oil or contamination that show $S_1 \geq 1.0$ mg/g rock are solvent extracted in an ultrasonic bath for 30 min using dichloromethane:methanol (9:1). This step is intended to reduce interference by migrated oil or contaminants in the measurement of T_{max}, S_2, and other Rock-Eval parameters. Not all samples show reduced S_2 and altered T_{max} after extraction of contaminants. For example, some diesel cuts commonly affect only S_1 and not S_2. The extracted sample is transferred onto microfiber filter paper using additional solvent, placed on a watch glass, and oven dried at 40°C for 2 hr prior to pyrolysis. If the S_1 peak is still ≥1.0 mg/g rock, then the sample is Soxhlet extracted for 24 hr with dichloromethane:methanol (9:1), dried for 2–3 hr, and pyrolyzed.

We recommend that both pyrolysis and TOC be completed on every sample. Rock-Eval pyrolysis is more expensive than TOC, so many prefer to complete Rock-Eval pyrolysis only on samples exceeding 0.3% TOC. Alternately, TOC can be performed only on samples with $S_2 \geq 0.05$ mg HC/g rock.

Sidewall and conventional cores are better than cuttings or outcrop samples for both screening and detailed geochemical analyses. However, caution must be applied where these samples represent organic-rich beds of insufficient thickness to serve as regionally significant source rocks. Sidewall or core samples for source rock analysis should be taken at 15–30 m intervals in fine-grained lithologies. Although not recommended for cuttings, composites of sidewalls or cores at 15–30 m intervals may be a useful supplement for analyses of isolated samples, particularly where organic matter in the source rock varies nonsystematically with depth (Figure 5.10).

Critical information that should be included with rock samples includes well name, operator, location, formation, age, depth, and type of sample. Good quality paper or zip-lock plastic sample bags are recommended. Paraffin coatings are not recommended for storing rock samples. Maps and lithology logs assist in evaluating sample quality and geologic relations. If additives or migrated oil could represent contaminants, samples of these materials are helpful.

Oil Sample Preparation

Oils are best collected in quart-sized or smaller glass containers with teflon cap liners. Oil can leach contaminants, such as phthalates, from plastic containers or rubber-lined caps. Fill only to the shoulder of the container to minimize contact of oil with the cap. Each sample container should be carefully labeled using waterproof ink. Bottled oils do not appear to undergo biodegradation for several years in storage. However, metal containers react with emulsified water and can leak.

Care must be taken in collecting production oils because they may represent mixtures from several zones. Surface exposure diminishes the information content of seeps due to evaporation, biodegradation, and possible contamination. It may be necessary to dig into seeping rock exposures to obtain the freshest possible samples.

APPENDIX C:
Methods for Measuring TOC

Direct Combustion

Weighed, pulverized rock (1–2 g) is treated with hydrochloric acid (6 N HCl) in Leco filtering crucibles. Spent acid and wash water are removed by vacuum filtration. The dried residue (100°C, 30 min. is mixed with metal accelerator (elemental iron and copper), combusted using a high-frequency induction furnace (1200°C), and measured as carbon dioxide. Direct combustion is the most commonly used method for TOC. However, certain samples that contain immature oil-prone organic matter can lose from 10% (Peters and Simoneit, 1982) to 44% (Roberts et al., 1973) TOC as hydrolyzate with the acid filtrate prior to combustion.

Modified (Nonfiltering) Direct Combustion

Pulverized rock is weighed into Leco nonfiltering crucibles and treated dropwise with HCl until all CO_2 evolution ceases, followed by reaction overnight. Spent acid and wash water are decanted, the residue is dried, mixed with accelerator, and analyzed as described for direct combustion. Although prohibiting loss of hydrolyzate, this method is laborious, and difficulties in removing all acid can result in corrosion of the drying oven.

Indirect (by Difference)

Two weighed aliquots of a pulverized, homogeneous sample are treated separately. One aliquot is mixed with accelerator and combusted to yield total carbon (TC = organic plus carbonate carbon). Another aliquot is treated dropwise with HCl and the evolved CO_2 is measured. Total organic carbon is the difference between TC and carbonate carbon. Indirect TOC is generally more accurate for organic-poor (<0.5 wt. % TOC), carbonate-rich samples than direct TOC. However, for samples with TOC values over about 0.5 wt. %, cumulative errors resulting from measurements for two aliquots make this approach less satisfactory than other methods.

Pyrolysis plus Combustion Products

Some pyrolysis systems allow determination of TOC by summing the carbon in the pyrolyzate with that obtained by oxidizing the residual organic matter at 600°C. For small samples (100 mg), this method provides more reliable TOC data than conventional combustion methods, which require about 1–2 g of ground rock. However, mature samples, in which vitrinite reflectance (R_o) exceeds about 1%, yield poor TOC data because the temperature is insufficient for complete combustion.

CHAPTER APPENDIX D:
Key Rock-Eval Pyrolysis and TOC Parameters

S_1 measures hydrocarbon shows as the amount of free hydrocarbons that can be volatilized out of the rock without cracking the kerogen (mg HC/g rock). S_1 increases at the expense of S_2 with maturity.

S_2 measures the hydrocarbon yield from cracking of kerogen (mg HC/g rock) and heavy hydrocarbons and represents the existing potential of a rock to generate petroleum. S_2 is a more realistic measure of source rock potential than TOC because TOC includes "dead carbon" incapable of generating petroleum.

$S_1 + S_2$ is a measure of genetic potential (Tissot and Welte, 1984) or the total amount of petroleum that might be generated from a rock.

Production or productivity index [PI = $S_1/(S_1+S_2)$] gradually increases with depth for fine-grained rocks as thermally labile components in the kerogen (S_2) are converted to free hydrocarbons (S_1). Reservoir rocks show anomalously high PI values compared to adjacent fine-grained rocks. For T_{max} values of <435°C and T_{max} in the range 435°–445° C, PI values exceeding 0.2 and 0.3, respectively, are considered anomalous.

Hydrogen index [HI = (S_2/TOC) × 100, mg HC/g TOC] and S_2/S_3 are proportional to the amount of hydrogen in the kerogen and thus indicate the potential of the rock to generate oil. High hydrogen indices indicate greater potential to generate oil. Although HI versus OI plots are generally reliable indicators of kerogen type, gas-prone coals and coaly rocks can give anomalously high HI values that must be confirmed by elemental analysis (Peters, 1986). The average HI in a rock interval is best determined from the slope of a regression line on a graph of S_2 versus TOC (Langford and Blanc-Valleron, 1990).

Oxygen index [OI = (S_3/TOC) × 100, mg CO_2/g TOC] is related to the amount of oxygen in the kerogen. In general, the S_3 measurement is not as reliable as other Rock-Eval parameters, partially because of interference of carbonate minerals or kerogen oxidation resulting from pulverizing the sample. When S_3 results are suspected to be unreliable, HI versus T_{max} (Espitalié et al., 1984) can be substituted for the HI versus OI plot.

T_{max} measures thermal maturity and corresponds to the Rock-Eval pyrolysis oven temperature (°C) at maximum S_2 generation. T_{max} should not be confused with geologic temperatures. T_{max} is partly determined by the type of organic matter (Figure 5.9) (Peters, 1986).

Magoon, L. B., and W. G. Dow, eds., 1994, The petroleum
system—from source to trap: AAPG Memoir 60.

Chapter **6**

Siliciclastic Reservoir Rocks

David G. Morse*

Houston, Texas, U.S.A.

Abstract

Depositional environments determine the basic architecture and geometry of siliciclastic hydro-carbon reservoir rocks. In nonmarine settings, sandstone reservoirs are deposited in fluvial, eolian, and lacustrine environments, whereas in marine settings these reservoir rocks are in deltaic, shallow marine, and deep marine settings. Facies and reservoir rock properties of giant oil and gas fields in each depositional setting are tabulated and described. The most prolific sandstone reservoirs are deposited in marine deltaic distributary mouth bars and distributary channels in delta lobes. Stacking of delta lobes by channel avulsion and subsidence of inactive lobes due to compaction of the underlying prodelta silts and clays greatly increases the volume of reservoir sand. Tertiary deltaic sediments, underlying major modern deltas, offer likely places to find these reservoir rocks in rollover anticlines. Shallow marine sediments provide the next most prolific reservoir facies, which are deposited as barrier islands, beach, shoreface, and offshore bar sands. Great potential exists for siliciclastic reservoir rocks in deep marine fans, a relatively underexplored target occurring at the base of delta slopes or in rift or wrench basins. Advanced three-dimensional seismic technology and the present knowledge of seismic and sequence stratigraphy should help locate these sandstone reservoirs. Nonmarine reservoirs offer excellent targets in some basins, such as the fluvial sands of North Africa and the underexplored lacustrine-related reservoir rocks of China. Because of their high quality, areal extent, and thickness, eolian sand reservoirs must always be considered, particularly in continental interior strata with paleolatitudes in the 15°–40° range north and south of the paleoequator.

INTRODUCTION

Siliciclastic reservoir rocks owe much of their diversity and stratigraphic heterogeneity to the many different depositional environments in which they are deposited. These hydrocarbon reservoirs are formed in settings ranging from continental alluvial sands and gravels to deep marine fans. This chapter reviews a variety of these occurrences and highlights examples from around the world. Of the 266 giant hydrocarbon accumulations described by Halbouty (1970), 62% have siliciclastic reservoirs. Although most of these accumulations are structurally trapped, 10% of the giant fields with siliciclastic reservoirs found before 1970 occur as stratigraphic traps. This was during an age when papers on modern sedimentary environments were just beginning to appear in the literature (Reading, 1978).

Stratigraphic traps occur where "a variation in the stratigraphy is the chief confining element in the reservoir" (Levorson, 1936, p. 524). Today, a stratigraphic trap is considered to be a container formed by any variation in the stratigraphy that is independent of structural deformation other than regional tilting (North, 1985). The depositional environments described in this chapter are all capable of containing stratigraphic traps formed by facies or unconformity pinchouts, by buried paleotopography, erosional relief, or updip cementation. The successful, creative, and knowledgeable explorationist must be able to identify the style of the particular trap and find the way to locate it.

The petroleum system is a series of genetically related hydrocarbon accumulations whose provenance is a pod of active source rock. Even though the genetic relationship is based on the similarity of hydrocarbons in the accumulations, it is often true that the reservoir rock is also the same throughout the system because the plumbing from the source to trap shares the same seal and reservoir rock. This chapter discusses single accumulations, but one should always remember that they are part of a larger petroleum system.

The reservoir, an essential element of the petroleum system, is the storage space within a trap (Biddle and Wielchowsky, Chapter 13, this volume). The reservoir must be able to accommodate a significant volume of fluids and be capable of transferring or exchanging fluids to obtain its hydrocarbon charge and be produced (North,

---

*Present address: Environmental Quality Division, Watervliet Arsenal—PWG, Watervliet, New York, U.S.A.

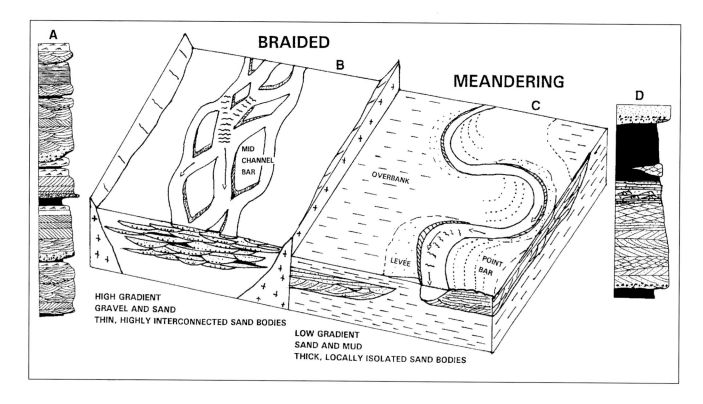

Figure 6.1. Fluvial depositional models. (A) Braided river system idealized vertical section with tabular cross beds formed by mid-channel bars and trough cross beds formed by migrating megaripples on the channel floor. (B) Block diagram of a braided river. (C) Meandering river system with laterally aggrading point bars, highly sinuous channels, and thick fine-grained overbank deposits (after LeBlanc, 1972). (D) Meandering river idealized vertical section with fining-upward, cross-bedded point bar sands, finely laminated sands and silts, and overbank silt and clay (after Cant, 1982). Lithology pattern: solid black, silt and clay size; large to small dots, conglomerate to sand size; patterned lines, bedding and cross-bedded sandstone; combs, climbing ripple deposits.

Table 6.1. Fluvial and Alluvial Reservoirs

Field	Location Country	Basin	Age[a]	Formation	Thickness of Pay (m)	Depositional Environment
Hassi R'Mel	Algeria	—	Tr	Hassi er R'mel Ss	—	Alluvial sands, anastomosing channels
Sarir	Libya	Sirte	K	Nubian equiv of Sarir Ss	—	Fluvial–alluvial
Messla	Libya	Sirte	K	Sarir Ss	300	Stacked braided channels
Hassi Messaoud	Algeria	—	Camb	Ra Ss	120	Blanket ss
Amal	Libya	Sirte	Camb–Ord	Amal Ss	—	Continental ss
October	Egypt	—	Carb–K	Nubia Ss	135	Stacked fluvial channels, blanket ss
Snorre	Norway	—	Tr	Lunde Ss Statfjord	—	Braided to meandering, wide, shifting channels, alluvial plain, blanket ss
McArthur River	U.S.A. (Alaska)	—	Olig	Hemlock Cgl– Kenai Ss	—	Alluvial–fluvial
Dom Joao	Brazil	—	LK	Sergi Ss	—	Fluvial
Carmopolis	Brazil	—	—	Muribeca	—	Alluvial fan and plains
—	Argentina	—	J	Challaco Ss	—	Alluvial fans and plains

[a]L, lower; Camb, Cambrian; Ord, Ordovician; Carb, Carboniferous; Tr, Triassic; J, Jurassic; K, Cretaceous; Olig, Oligocene.
[b]A, anticline; Up, unconformity pinchout; Bl, tilted block; St, stratigraphic; D, domal; WrA, wrench anticline.
[c]V, vertical; Lt, lateral.

1985). Migration of petroleum from a pod of active source rock to the trap requires a conduit that may involve vertical migration, such as along fractures or faults, or lateral migration within a reservoir quality carrier bed. The dynamics of migration are examined by England (Chapter 12, this volume). Rates of migration in sandstone carriers are in the range of 1–1000 km/m.y., two orders of magnitude greater than for limestones. Lateral migration requires both a continuous carrier bed and seal (Demaison and Huizinga, 1991; Chapter 4, this volume). Favorable areas for long distance migration of up to several hundred kilometers occur in foreland basins and intracratonic sags where blanket sands of transgressive, eolian, or fluvial origins are sealed by evaporites or shales.

This chapter reviews siliciclastic reservoir rocks found in hundreds of giant and supergiant oil and gas fields by depositional environment (Halbouty, 1970, 1980b, 1992). The nonmarine reservoir rocks were deposited in fluvial, eolian, and lacustrine environments, whereas the marine reservoirs were deposited in deltaic, shallow marine, and deep marine environments. The packaging of depositional facies, the distribution of principal reservoir rocks in the depositional setting, the lateral continuity or architecture of the facies, and important world examples are compiled here from the literature into tables by depositional environment.

FLUVIAL RESERVOIRS

Reservoir rocks deposited as fluvial or river deposits are formed by braided, multi-channeled rivers or by single-channeled, meandering rivers, or a combination of these "end members" (Figure 6.1). Miall (1978), Ethridge and Flores (1981), Cant (1982), and Collinson and Lewin (1983) provide comprehensive guides to fluvial deposits.

Braided rivers tend to have coarser sediment load, higher gradients, more flashy or variable flow, more easily eroded banks, and higher width–depth ratios than meandering rivers (Walker, 1979). Braided river deposits may form alluvial fans (Nilsen, 1982), cover a broad alluvial plain, or be confined to a restricted valley. Braided river deposits (Figure 6.1B) are formed by aggradation of mid-channel bars and sinuous-crested, subaqueous megaripples producing planar and trough cross-bedded strata; overbank silts and clay deposits are rarely preserved. River depth determines the thickness of an ideal fining-upward braided river sequence (Figure 6.1A), which begins with a basal lag, followed by trough cross beds, planar cross beds, and ending with a thin-bedded sandy cap. Complete sequences are commonly abbreviated by truncation from successive braid channels, resulting in highly laterally connected sands.

Meandering river deposits (Figure 6.1C) are formed by the lateral downstream accretion of point bars, filling-in of channels cut off at the narrow neck of a meander loop with silt and clay, and the vertical accretion of fine sand and mud on the flood plain during high water. The ideal point bar vertical sequence (Figure 6.1D) consists of a basal lag, trough cross-bedded sands of set amplitude and grain size, decreasing upward to rippled, fine-grained sand, and finally laminated or bioturbated silt and clay of the flood plain. Preserved mud to sand ratios are high.

Porosity and permeability of fluvial reservoirs (Table 6.1) are functions of the rock matrix, lithologic heterogeneity, compaction, and cementation. The best primary porosity is found in channel sands. Flood plain strata are poor to nonreservoir quality sediments. Fluvial sands tend to be more mineralogically and texturally immature than other sands because they occur close to the sediment source. Alluvial fans may mark the beginning of a fluvial system; with decreasing gradients, next are

Table 6.1 (*continued*)

| Reserves (BOE) | | Gas | | Migration | | | | | |
Recoverable ($\times 10^9$)	In place ($\times 10^9$)	or Oil Produced	Trap Type[b]	Style[c]	Distance (km)	Depth (m)	Porosity (%)	Permeability (md)	References
5.8	11.7	O	A–Up	Lt, V	—	2100	—	—	Magloire, 1970; Hamouda, 1980–A
8.0	21.2	O	Bl–A	—	—	2590	—	—	Sanford, 1970; Halbouty et al., 1970
1.5	3.0	O	St–UpBl	Lt	80	2644	17	500	Clifford et al., 1980
9.0	25	O	D–Up	—	—	3350	2–12	—	Balducchi & Pommier, 1970
0.8	3.2	O	A	—	—	3950	—	—	Roberts, 1970
—	—	O	Bl	V	—	3350	17	236	Lelek et al., 1992
0.77	3.1	O	Bl–Up	Lt	—	2526	23	380	Jorde and Diesen, 1992
0.57	—	O	WrA	—	—	2560	17	80	Halbouty, 1980; Chapter 22
0.25	—	O	Bl–Up	V, Lt	—	690–2400	—	—	Ghignone & Andrade, 1980
—	1.2	O	D	—	40	—	—	—	Chapter 31
—	—	O	—	—	—	—	5–26	10–150	Chapter 32

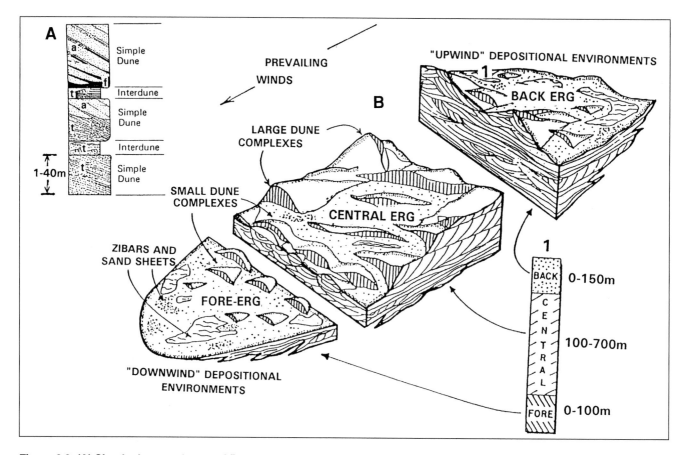

Figure 6.2. (A) Simple dune packages of fine to medium sand are composed of translatent strata (t) formed by migrating wind ripples with grain flow or avalanche strata (a) and/or grain fall strata (f). Interdune sands are formed largely by translatent strata (t). **(B)** Eolian depositional block diagram of a migrating erg system with (1) an idealized vertical facies sequence of fore-erg, central-erg, and back-erg facies divisions based on types and scale of eolian strata and the nature of intra- and extradunal facies (after Porter, 1986).

braided rivers, then meandering rivers. The fluvial system commonly ends at a lake or at the sea where it may form a delta.

Fluvial reservoirs consist of clean (lack silt and clay), poorly sorted, boulder to fine-grained sand porous bodies. Thick, stacked braided stream deposits form widespread reservoirs that are more common in the giant and supergiant fluvial reservoir fields (Table 6.1). These sands are thicker than meandering river deposits and typically occur in structural traps because they lack the lateral seals required for stratigraphic traps. Depending on the curvature or size of the meander loops and the thickness of the point bar sands, meandering river deposits form "shoe-string sands" that in an updip

Table 6.2. Eolian Reservoirs

Field	Location	Age[a]	Formation	Pay Thickness (m)	Depositional Environment
Gronigen	Netherlands and Germany	L Perm	Rotliegendes	—	Eolian with fluvial intradunal strata
Viking	United Kingdom	L Perm	Leman Ss	244	Eolian with sabkha and alluvial interbeds
Urucu	Brazil	—	C Itaituba	—	Eolian
Rangely	U.S.A. (Colorado)	L Perm	Weber Ss	—	Eolian with fluvial interbeds
Mary Ann	U.S.A. (Alabama)	J	Norphlet Ss	240	Eolian
Elk Basin	U.S.A. (Wyoming)	Penn	Tensleep Ss	—	Transverse and oblique dunes
Painter Reservoir	U.S.A. (Wyoming)	L J	Nugget Ss	260	Eolian

[a]L, lower; Penn, Pennsylvanian; Perm, Permian; J, Jurassic.

[b]A, anticline; Bl, tilted block; St, stratigraphic; WrA, wrench anticline; Th, thrust anticline.

[c]V, vertical; Lt, lateral.

meander form stratigraphic traps that can contain up to 50 million bbl of oil reserves.

Provided there is an adequate regional seal to confine migration, alluvial sands that are closely associated or interbedded with lacustrine source rocks can provide natural carrier beds for lateral drainage of expelled hydrocarbons (Demaison and Huizinga, 1991; Chapter 4, this volume). Migration of hydrocarbons in the fluvial Cretaceous Sarir Sandstone in Libya for at least 80 km was required to charge the 1.5 billion bbl (recoverable) Messla field (Clifford et al., 1980). A 40-km migration in the fluvial Muribeca Sandstone was required in the giant Carmopolis field of Argentina (Mello et al., Chapter 31, this volume). Oil recoveries in the predominantly braided reservoirs of the large or giant fields noted in Table 6.1 range from 25 to 50%. One of the most prolific areas for oil and gas fields with fluvial reservoirs occurs in North Africa where the Cretaceous Nubian Sandstone extends from Egypt to Algeria. Other foreland basins around the world have comparable deposits of fluvial sediment.

EOLIAN RESERVOIRS

Eolian reservoirs are formed by wind-blown sand deposited along sea coasts or in vast desert areas, called *sand seas* or *ergs* (McKee, 1979). Deposition of extremely well sorted, predominantly fine- to medium-sized sand occurs in dunes and sand sheets. Less well sorted sand and other lithologies are found in interdunal areas. Adjacent to these eolian environments are other continental environments, such as alluvial fans, streams, lakes, sabkhas, or nearshore marine environments (Ahlbrandt and Fryberger, 1982). An overall model of a complete eolian sequence is illustrated in Figure 6.2. The initial marginal dune deposits are overlain by central dune field or erg deposits that migrated downwind and, in turn, are capped by back-erg sands that were deposited as the sand supply was cut off and the dune field growth stopped.

Individual strata in a dune or sand sheet are identifi-

able and unique to this environment. They are formed by grainflow (avalanching), grain fall (settling directly from the air after saltating off the crest of a dune), or by migration or translation of wind ripples on the dune surface (Hunter, 1977; Kocurek and Dott, 1981). Most conspicuous in eolian strata are large (up to 40 m thick) cross-bed sets formed by successive deposits on the lee side of sand dunes. Sets of dune cross strata may be separated by nearly horizontal interdunal or toeset strata. The cross-bed sets and interdune strata aggrade vertically by bed form climbing at a low angle as long as there is sufficient sand and strength of prevailing wind.

Interdunes form flat areas between dunes in which sand sheets, intermittent streams, salt pans, or ponds may form. In dry interdunes, a simple, nearly horizontal erosional boundary surface is formed at the junction of the highly dipping, wind-eroded top of the underlying dune and the low-dipping toeset strata of the succeeding dune (Kocurek, 1981). In wet interdunes, poorly sorted sand, fine silt, clay, evaporite minerals, or limestone may be deposited. Interdune bedding may be disrupted by animals, roots, or salt.

The clean, well-sorted sand in a dune deposit commonly forms an excellent reservoir and regional carrier bed. The extensive blanket sands of the Pennsylvanian Tensleep Sandstone in Wyoming, for example, are thought to have carried oil up to 400 km across most of Wyoming from a pod of Permian Phosphoria Formation source rock in eastern Idaho (Sheldon, 1967). Porosity and permeability are the greatest in the steeply dipping dune strata, whereas interdune strata have poor reservoir characteristics. The cross-bedded sands have up to one order of magnitude higher permeability locally in the horizontal direction parallel to the strike of the cross bed than in the horizontal direction in which the cross beds are dipping or in the vertical direction (Lindquist, 1988). Preserved paleotopographic or erosional relief can form stratigraphic traps in eolian formations (Fryberger, 1984; Eschner and Kocurek, 1988).

Fields listed in Table 6.2 illustrate many of the prominent eolian reservoirs of the world. The fields generally occur in the same 15°–40° north and south

Table 6.2 *(continued)*

Reserves (BOE)		Gas		Migration					
Recoverable (×10^9)	In place (×10^9)	or Oil Produced	Trap Type[b]	Style[c]	Distance (km)	Depth (m)	Porosity (%)	Permeability (md)	References
10.9	—	G	Bl	V	—	914–1981	—	—	Stauble & Milius, 1970; Halbouty, 1980
0.6	—	G	Bl	V	—	2850–2877	14	30–80	Gage, 1980
—	0.07	O	WrA	V	—	—	10–30	10–1200	Chapter 31
0.9	—	O	A–St	Lt	300	—	—	—	Koelmel, 1986; Fryberger, 1979
0.1	—	G	St	V	—	—	—	—	Mancini et al., 1988; Pense, 1988
0.58	1.43	O	A	Lt	150	—	—	—	Carmalt & St. John, 1986¶
0.91	—	O, G	Th	V	—	2918	14	23	Lamb, 1980

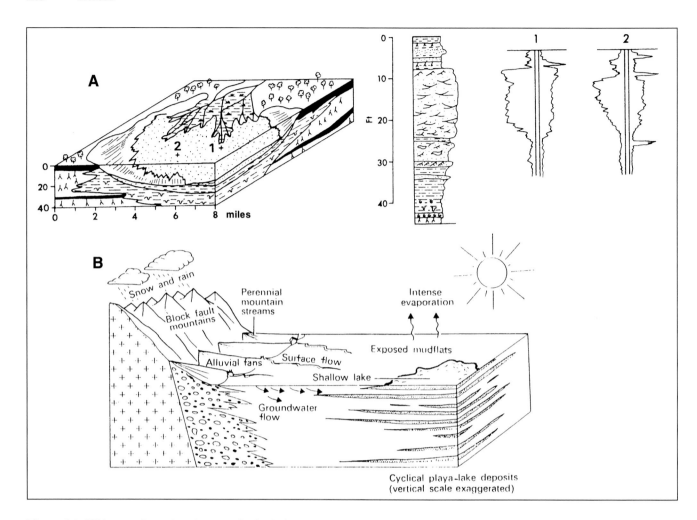

Figure 6.3. (A) Lacustrine-related reservoirs include coarsening-upward deltaic fill packages (after Coleman and Prior, 1982) and fluvial and shoreface strata. (B) Shallow water playa lakes with highly fluctuating shorelines produce cyclical deposits of potential reservoir sands and lake-deposited mud and clay (after Eugster and Hardie, 1975). See Figure 6.1 for explanation of lithologic patterns.

Table 6.3. Lacustrine-Related Reservoirs

Field	Location Country	Basin	Age[a]	Formation	Thickness of Pay (m)	Depositional Environment
Gudao	China	Zhanhua	Mio	Guantao	—	Lakeshore beaches, fan deltas, fluvial channels
Daqing	China	Taching Plateau	L K	—	—	Lacustrine and fluvial
Schuanghe	China	Binyang	Olig	Hetaoyhan	—	Lacustrine/alluvial, fan delta, braided channels, delta front bars
Red Wash	U.S.A. (Utah)	Uinta	Pal–Eoc	Wasatch, Green River	—	Lakeshore sands, fan deltas, alluvial channels, distributary mouth bars
Bluebell–Altmont	U.S.A. (Utah)	Uinta	Pal–Eoc	Wasatch, Green River	—	
Sunnyside	U.S.A. (Utah)	Uinta	Pal–Eoc	Wasatch, Green River	—	—
Moreni–Gura Ocnitei	Rumania	—	Plio	Dacian Ss	—	Shallow lacustrine to lake shore
—	Hungary	Eastern	U Mio	Szolnok Ss	400	Lacustrine turbidites

[a]U, upper; L, lower; Pal, Paleocene; Eoc, Eocene; Olig, Oligocene; Mio, Miocene.

[b]A, anticline; Up, unconformity pinchout; Bl, tilted block; St, stratigraphic; D, domal; R/O, rollover anticline or growth fault; ; WrA, wrench anticline.

[c]V, vertical; Lt, lateral.

paleolatitudinal belts as the many modern deserts of the world (McKee, 1979). When overlain by transgressive marine black shales, eolian sands can form both carrier beds along regional dip and reservoir rocks in structural trap, such as the Rotliegendes of the North Sea (Glennie, 1972, 1982, 1987) and the Tensleep Sandstone of Wyoming (Moore, 1984; Kocurek, 1988). Some very thick eolian sands, such as the Jurassic Navajo and Wingate sandstones do not appear to have been regional carriers, in spite of their 1600-km lateral extent, because they were isolated in largely continental sequences of rocks without regional seals or source rock connections. Only in the Wyoming thrust belt where the lateral equivalent of the Navajo Sandstone, the Nugget Sandstone, lies in thrust contact with a mature source rock do hydrocarbon accumulations occur. In summary, although eolian sands represent a small percentage of the world's sedimentary record, where present they form important, thick reservoirs of clean, laterally extensive sandstone.

LACUSTRINE-RELATED RESERVOIRS

The reservoir strata in or adjacent to a lacustrine setting are deposited by processes that occur in a deltaic or shallow water setting and include delta mouth bars, fluvial channels, shoreface sands, offshore bars, and even lacustrine turbidites (Fouch and Dean, 1982). Descriptions of these kinds of deposits are found in the other sections of this chapter. Sandy siliciclastics are concentrated around the margins of most lakes. However, as lake levels rise and fall, the shoreline facies extend landward or prograde into the lake forming cyclic packages that coarsen upward (Figure 6.3). Deeper water lacustrine strata, particularly in saline lakes, contain large amounts of both siliciclastic and carbonate fine-grained

sediment and organic matter (Eugster and Surdam, 1973; Eugster and Hardie, 1975; Hardie et al., 1978). Nearly all lakes are ephemeral features that are ultimately converted to fluvial plains as the lake basin fills with sediment (Picard and High, 1981).

The lacustrine-related sandstones of the Uinta basin of Utah, and particularly of basins in China, are prolific hydrocarbon reservoirs (Table 6.3). These reservoirs are associated with lakes in which large amounts of lipid-rich organic matter were preserved that commonly form oil shales (surface) and generate waxy oils (subsurface). In the Uinta basin, the marginal lacustrine facies contain the principal reservoirs for hydrocarbons (Fouch and Dean, 1982; Fouch et al., Chapter 25, this volume). At Red Wash field in the eastern Uinta basin, the reservoir sandstones are formed in lacustrine delta front bars, fluvial channels, and shoreface strata that are interstratified with impermeable lacustrine and overbank claystones. This results in poor vertical and lateral connectivity of reservoirs and requires close well spacing to maximize oil recovery.

Information on the Chinese lake deposits and the associated hydrocarbon accumulations has become more available in the past two decades (Chen et al., 1980; Li et al., 1988). Reservoirs in the Chinese deposits include turbidites, lacustrine bar, deltaic sediments (Meyerhoff and Willums, 1976), and alluvial fans (Cheng, 1981).

In summary, thick lacustrine deposits are relatively rare in the stratigraphic record. They occur in continental basins that are commonly internally drained and flanked with alluvial sediments. The reservoir strata are formed by lake-marginal facies, such as deltas, bars, or channels, and turbidites. Their proximity to deeper water source facies and to interbedded sealing shales makes them a good target for hydrocarbon exploration in large structures.

Table 6.3 (continued)

| Reserves (BOE) | | Gas | | Migration | | | | | |
Recoverable (×10⁹)	In place (×10⁹)	or Oil Produced	Trap Type[b]	Style[c]	Distance (km)	Depth (m)	Porosity (%)	Permeability (md)	References
0.6	—	O	Bl–A	V	—	1190–1300	30–32	500–2000	Chen and Wang, 1980
8.0	—	O	Bl–A	V?	—	1097	—	—	Halbouty, 1980
—	0.6	O	R/O, Bl St, Up	—	—	—	—	—	Li et al., 1988
0.22	—	O, G	St–A	V	—	1675	—	—	Chapter 25
0.30	—	O, G	St–A	V	—	3780	—	—	Chapter 25
—	4.0	O	St–A	V	—	0–400	—	—	Roadifer, 1987
0.8	2.6	O	D, A	V	—	400–1800	—	—	Paraschiv & Olteanu, 1970
—	—	O	St–A	Lt, V	—	700–4600	5–25	—	Chapter 35

DELTAIC RESERVOIRS

Deltas occur where river-borne siliciclastic sediments meet a standing body of water and form delta plains, mouth bars, interdistributary bays, distributary channels, tidal ridges, beaches, crevasse splays, and prodelta muds (Coleman and Prior, 1982). These deposits are shaped by tidal, river, and wave forces to create a particular arrangement or architecture of reservoir sands (Figure 6.4). In all deltas, the finest material is dispersed seaward and the coarsest material is deposited at the mouth of the delta. Deltas are divided into an upper delta plain, a lower delta plain, and a subaqueous delta plain.

The upper delta plain lies upstream from any tidal influence and is dominated by migrating, braided, or meandering channel deposits, such as point bars, mid-channel bars, and nonchannel deposits. Nonchannel deposits include levee and overbank silts and muds, marsh peats, lake muds, and crevasse splays that might fill the lake with fine sand. The thickest sand bodies are the channel sands that fine upward but lack widespread continuity. In short, the upper delta plain deposits are comparable to the upstream alluvial valley. However, because of their location on the protruding bulge of a delta, they are considered to be part of it.

The lower delta plain extends from the last landward area that is affected by tides to the outermost shoreline. It contains distributary channel sands, and deposits such as crevasse splays, levees, marshes, and abandoned distributary fill deposits between channels. The main reservoir facies deposited in the lower delta plain are bay-fill deposits that form between the lobes of the active channel system when distributary channels are breached during flooding. Bay-fill deposits form coarsening-upward lobes of clean sand with radially bifurcating channels (Coleman and Prior, 1982). In a large delta such as the Mississippi, bay-fill deposits can extend for 20 km and form a reservoir quality sand body that is 5–7 m thick for its full length and width. The bay-fills are commonly composed of millimeter- to centimeter-thick mud and sand laminae at their bases, becoming progressively more sandy upward, and finally capped by a marsh deposit. Bioturbation is common, especially in the more slowly deposited muddy strata. Another reservoir facies, distributary channel sands, form the thickest sands but are not as widespread as the bay-fill deposits. These channel sands generally cut into the underlying mouth bar of the subaqueous delta plain.

The subaqueous delta plain extends from the outermost shoreline seaward to the last area actively receiving fluvial sediment, where water depths may be 50–300 m. The most distal and largest area of the subaqueous delta plain receives mud and silt, forming the prodelta. The main reservoir and coarsest sands of a delta are deposited at the mouth of the river channel and form the distributary mouth bar. When river deposition

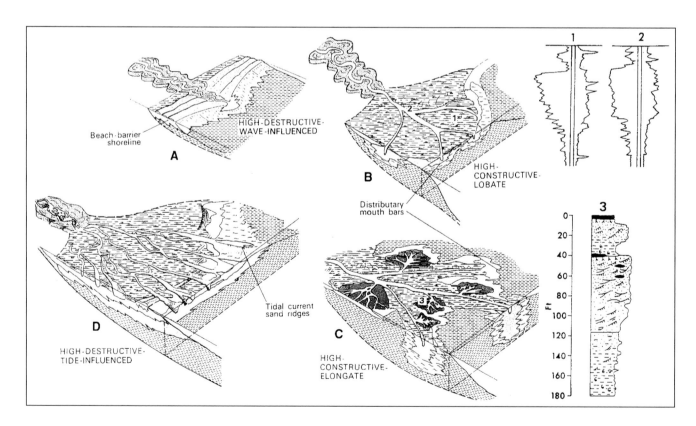

Figure 6.4. Deltaic reservoir strata electric logs (1 and 2) and lithologic log (3) consisting of distributary mouth bar and delta plain sands (after Coleman and Prior, 1982). The geometry of these sands is highly influenced by (A) wave, (B and C) river, or (D) tidal forces at the shoreline (from Fisher et al., 1969). Lithology patterns: short dashes, marine silt and clay; long dashes and combs, marsh or paludial deposits; small dots or white, channel, beach, or mouthbar sand.

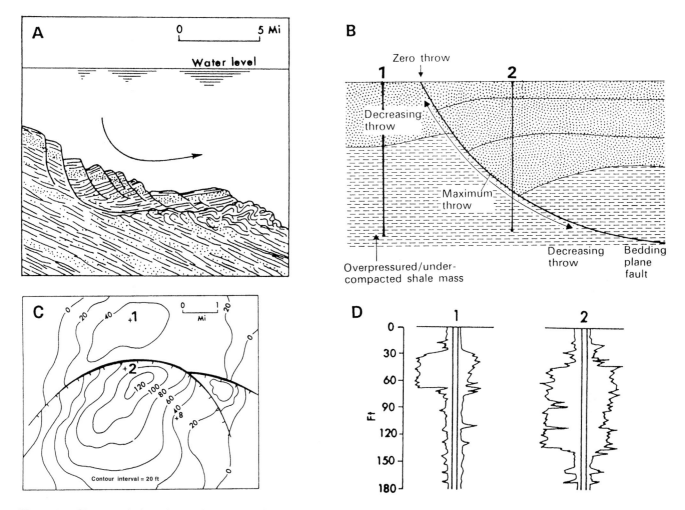

Figure 6.5. Characteristics of growth or slump features. (A) Section perpendicular to shore illustrating rollover along a listric fault. (B) Thicker sands occur on the downthrown side. (C) Idealized sand isolith map on a growth fault. (D) Idealized electric log signature comparing regular footwall sand thickness (1) with the thickened sand on the downthrown side (2) (after Reading, 1978; Coleman and Prior, 1982).

accumulates faster than waves or tidal currents can move it laterally, the delta builds seaward forming a river-dominated lobate delta. If waves move the sand back against the beach to form prograding barrier beaches or strand plains, the delta is considered to be wave dominated. Where strong tides shift sand to produce tidal current sand ridges along numerous distributary channels, the delta is considered to be tide dominated (Figure 6.4).

The distributary mouth bar of a large river, such as the Mississippi River, will form a sand body up to 40 km or more wide and up to 40–50 m thick that gradually increases in reservoir quality upward. The distal part of the distributary mouth bar forms a transition from the prodelta muds and silts to the mouth bar sands and consists of interbedded silt, mud, and fine sand. The distributary mouth bar consists of laminated, thin-bedded, cross-bedded, and massive sand of excellent reservoir potential. Rivers commonly abandon one delta lobe through channel avulsion and build another nearby. Within a short time, the initial mouth bar and lower delta plain sink below sea level as the underlying prodelta

muds compact. Then, a third delta lobe may form and overlap the first. Frazier (1967) outlined 16 lobes of the modern Mississippi delta, many of which overlap to some extent. Lobe switching such as this permits a river-dominated delta to stack successive mouth bars on top of one another to create a reservoir that can hold billions of barrels of oil, such as the Safania field in Saudi Arabia (Ayers et al., 1982).

Prodelta instability creates additional reservoir opportunities. Slumps, debris flows, and block slides are common on most modern prodeltas of the world (Bouma et al., 1982; Cook et al., 1982). These mass movements bring great quantities of shallow water deposits, such as distributary mouth bar sands, to deeper water on the shelf. Narrow gullies 50–800 m wide or chutes exceeding 8–10 km in length may extend down the surface of the <1° slope of the prodelta and terminate in lobe-shaped mounds of transported material (Coleman and Prior, 1982). Growth faults commonly form in this prodelta environment. These arcuate faults decrease in dip angle downward causing bed rotation and formation of rollover anticlines through time (Figure 6.5). Movement

Table 6.4. Deltaic Reservoirs

Field	Location Country	Location Basin	Age[a]	Formation	Thickness of Pay (m)	Depositional Environment
Burgan	Kuwait	—	K	Wasia	—	Deltaic and shallow shelf
Safaniya	Saudi Arabia	—	U K	Khafji	—	Stacked delta plain, mouth bar, and bay fill
Hibernia	Canada	—	U J	Hibernia	68	Delta plain, straight channel, fluvial delta
Badak	Indonesia	—	Mio–Plio	Balikpapan	—	Stacked delta plain, channel, mouth bar, and delta front cycles with shelf ss
Bekapai	Indonesia	—	Mio–Plio	Balikpapan	—	
Handil	Indonesia	—	Mio–Plio	Balikpapan	—	
Oseberg	Norway	—	—	Oseberg Ness	—	Delta lobes (2) stacked with delta plain
Smorbukk	Norway	—	—	Tilje, Ile, and Garn	—	Tidal influenced shoreline and braided delta complex
Beatrice	United Kingdom	—	J	Brent	110	Stacked channels, beach barrier, and deltaic
Ninian	United Kingdom	—	J	Brent	110	Fluvial–deltaic
Statfjord	U.K.–Norway	—	J	Brent and Statfjord	300	Deltaic front, mouth bar, and channels
Cano, Lemon	Colombia	—	Eoc	Mirador Ss	65–150	River-dominated delta, stacked lobes and channels
Mid-Caspian Basin System	C.I.S.	—	U J–K	—	—	Marine–deltaic
W. Siberian System	C.I.S.	—	U J–K	—	—	Deltaic
Nembe Creek	Nigeria	—	M Mio	—	—	Deltaic ss (ancestral Niger Delta)
TiaJuana,	Venezuela	—	Eoc	Misoa Ss	—	Fluvial–deltaic
Lagunnillas	Venezuela	—	Eoc	Misoa Ss	—	Fluvial–deltaic
Cambay–Hazad (!) System	India	—	M Eoc	Hazad Fm	—	Prograding deltaic ss
Prudhoe Bay	U.S.A. (Alaska)	—	L Tr	Sadlerochit	—	Deltaic, fluvial and marginal marine
Salt Creek	U.S.A. (Wyoming)	—	U K	Frontier Ss	—	Wave-dominated delta and offshore bars
Eugene Island Block 300	U.S.A. (Gulf of Mexico)	—	Plio–Pleist	—	330	Delta front ss on marine shelf

[a]U, upper; L, lower; M, middle; Tr, Triassic; J, Jurassic; K, Cretaceous; Eoc, Eocene; Mio, Miocene; Plio, Pliocene; Pleist, Pleistocene.
[b]A, anticline; Up, unconformity pinchout; Bl, tilted block; St, stratigraphic; D, domal; R/O, rollover anticline or growth fault; ; WrA, wrench anticline.
[c]V, vertical; Lt, lateral.

is contemporaneous with deposition, causing the hanging wall sands to thicken with accumulation of gravity remobilized distributary mouth bar sands. Thus, not only are trapping structures formed by listric growth faults but the reservoir rocks are thickened as well.

The biggest siliciclastic oil fields in the world are formed by stacked deltaic sands (Table 6.4). The Burgan field in Kuwait (Halbouty, 1980a) contains 66 billion bbl of recoverable oil reserves. Its neighbor, the Safaniya–Khafji field, a broad anticlinal trap in northern offshore Saudi Arabia, can produce over 32 billion bbl of oil from stacked deltaic sandstones (Ayers et al., 1982). Because distributary mouth bar sands can extend for considerable distances offshore, they can be overlain by sealing shales and underlain by deep marine muds that are commonly a good source rock. The mouth bars can capture and direct great amounts of hydrocarbons to structural

culminations like these supergiants. Modern deltas, particularly river- or tide-dominated ones such as the Mississippi (Holland et al., 1980), the Niger (Nelson, 1980), and the Mahakam (Huffington and Helmig, 1980), are commonly the site of large accumulations because thick reservoir rocks and seals are stacked adjacent to growth faults that form rollover anticlines. These traps are commonly charged with hydrocarbons by a more distal or underlying mature source rock.

SHALLOW MARINE RESERVOIRS

Coastal areas with potential reservoir sand that are not associated with active deltas include barrier islands, ebb and flood tidal deltas, shallow shelf sands, and offshore bars or ridges. A prograding sequence of these

Table 6.4 *(continued)*

Reserves (BOE)		Gas or Oil Produced	Trap Type[b]	Migration		Depth (m)	Porosity (%)	Permeability (md)	References
Recoverable (× 10⁹)	In place (× 10⁹)			Style[c]	Distance (km)				
66	—	O	A	Lt, V	—	300–2500	20–35	250–8000	Halbouty, 1980
32.3	88	O	A	Lt, V	—	1500	20–35	250–8000	Kamen–Kay, 1970; Ayers et al., 1982
2.1	—	O	R/O–Bl	V	—	3720	16	500	Kurley et al., 1992; Carmalt & St. John, 1986
3.16	—	G, O	R/O	V	—	1372	22	200	Huffington & Helmig,1980
—	—	—	—	V, Lt	—	1300	25–35	1000	DeMatharel et al., 1980
0.80	—	—	—	V, Lt	—	450–2900	—	—	Verdier et al., 1980
0.77	1.42	O,G	Bl–Up	V, Lt	—	2120–2700	24	2000	Hagen and Kvalheim, 1992
—	1.18	O, G	Bl–Up	V	—	3800–4400	11	10–1000	Ehrenberg et al., 1992
0.16	—	O	Bl–Up	V, Lt	—	1829	—	—	Linsley et al., 1980
1.2	—	O	Bl–Up	V	—	2779	29	1000	Albright et al., 1980
3.4	5.6	O	Bl–Up	V, Lt	—	2585	29	250–1500	Kirk, 1980
1.0	—	O	Wr–A	V	—	2286–2500	25	5000	McCollough and Carver, 1992
14	—	O	Bl–St	V, Lt	—	—	—	—	Chapter 3
200	—	O	Bl–St	V, Lt	—	—	—	—	Chapter 3
0.65	—	O	R/O	V	—	2134–3658	—	—	Nelson, 1980
5.0	—	O	Bl	V	—	750–4850	12–28	240	Chapter 29
5.1	—	O	—	—	—	—	—	—	Chapter 29
—	2.7	O	Bl, Wr–A	V	—	2750–3020	12–22	250	Chapter 37
14.9	—	O, G	Bl–A, Up	V	—	2438	20	500	Halbouty, 1980
>0.62	1.5	O	A–St	Lt	—	—	—	—	Barlow and Haun, 1970
0.4	—	O, G	R/O	V, Lt	—	1290–3600	30	1000	Holland et al., 1980

sediments might superficially resemble that of a delta in that a coarsening-upward sequence is formed from the deep shelf up through a barrier island. However, the geologic setting and depositional processes are different. These coastal deposits are shaped and sourced by marine processes, such as tides and storm waves, rather than river processes. Sediment is transported by long shore and tidal currents and by oblique waves hitting the beach. Detailed description of barrier and shallow marine strata can be found in Walker (1979), Reineck and Singh (1980), and McCubbin (1982).

Barrier islands (Figure 6.6) form reservoir quality sand bodies 5–15 m thick that coarsen upward. They may extend along the shore for tens of kilometers before being interrupted by tidal channel inlets. These inlets have thick sand accumulations just inside and outside the barrier called flood and ebb tidal deltas. Some barrier islands such as Galveston Island on the Texas coast have recently prograded seaward at the geologically active rate of about 1 km/1000 yr (Bernard et al., 1962). Barriers may become stacked when sea level fluctuates.

Shelf sands may form sets of parallel, linear sand ridges up to 10 m high and tens of kilometers in length (Swift et al., 1973). These are shaped and winnowed by major storm waves. Tidal ridges 10–40 m high, 1–2 km wide, and up to 60 km long have been described from the North Sea shelf (Houbolt, 1968). Thus, wave or tidal processes can form a significant sand body many kilometers from the shoreline and in water depths of up to several tens of meters. Walker (1979) examines these facies and compares them to similar Cretaceous deposits formed along the shores of the Late Cretaceous seaway in Canada and Wyoming.

Major fields with reservoirs in shallow marine sandstones are shown in Table 6.5. High wave or tidal energy is indicated in many of these examples. Stacked sequences such as barrier islands, channels, or bars are important in producing a large volume of reservoir rock.

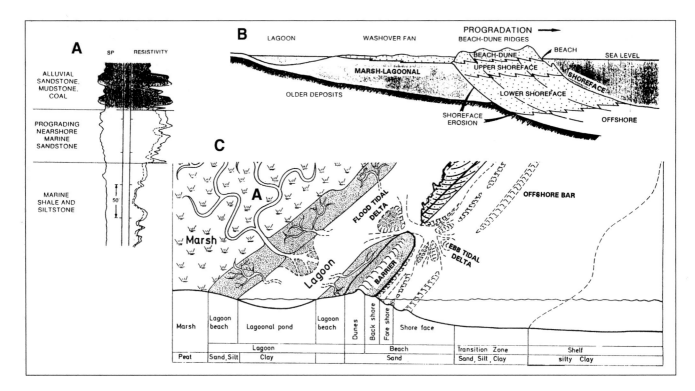

Figure 6.6. Shallow marine reservoirs include shoreface sands associated with barrier islands and tidal channel deltaic and offshore bar sands. With fluctuating sea levels, these sands may form laterally extensive blanket sands that can become stacked (after McCubbin, 1982; Reineck and Singh, 1980). (A) Electric log of prograding shallow marine to coastal marsh sequence. (B) Cross section of a barrier island with prograding shoreface and beach–dune facies. (C) Block diagram of marginal to shallow marine depositional facies.

Both transgressive and regressive sequences are identified in these stacked sequences. Although stratigraphic traps are particularly common for offshore bars, such as in the Cretaceous fields of northeastern Wyoming, few fields of this facies are listed on this table. Most fields in Table 6.5 were formed by either tilted blocks and unconformity pinchouts or by rollover anticlines. Few sedimentologic details have been published about the shallow marine reservoirs in the supergiant fields of eastern Europe (Halbouty, 1980b; Klemme, Chapter 3, this volume), but this should change when oil and gas companies from outside eastern Europe become more active in developing the larger fields.

DEEP MARINE RESERVOIRS

Deep water (marine) reservoir rocks are deposited in subaqueous fans that occur in both marine and lacustrine settings and include many gravity-driven depositional processes. Deep water fans receive shallow water or shelf sediment from feeders on the slope, such as an old river canyon inherited from a lowstand of sea level. These feeders are relatively steep and downcutting and act as conduits for all reworked sediment that is deposited on the fan. Depositional mechanisms include turbidity flow, debris flow, free fall or cascade, and traction flow. The first three can occur very quickly and with enough energy to transport silt up to 100 km from the base of the

canyon onto a basin plain. Walker (1979) and Howell and Normark (1982) have described these processes and the deposits that are formed. The upper fan (Figure 6.7) contains the coarsest grained sediments, including large blocks from the shelf or that have broken loose from the canyon walls; these are grain-supported conglomerates, matrix-supported debris flow conglomerates, and coarse-grained turbidites. This coarse-grained material, deposited primarily in the upper channel valley, is thick and does not extend laterally for more than a few kilometers. Finer suspended material may be carried to the laterally extensive levees or interchannel areas.

Deposits on the mid-fan or suprafan lobe are composed of turbidites, channelized distributary sands, and increasingly larger deposits of interchannel, finer grained sediments. The turbidites are normally graded and are likely to contain sand beds 0.25–2.5 m thick that are organized into subdivisions of the Bouma sequence (Bouma, 1962) and that extend laterally with little change in thickness. The channels shift by avulsion and ultimately cover much of the fan lobe and form a series of fining-upward sandstone beds with sand aggregates of up to 80 m. Sand bed thickness and relative amount of sand decreases with increasing distance outward from the head of the fan.

The outer fan begins where channels no longer form, yet lobe building continues by deposition of silts and clays from suspension in waning turbidity currents. Sandstone beds are thin and rare here, being transported by only the largest turbidity flows. Because fans prograde into the basal plain as they receive more and more sediment, an overall coarsening and thickening of potential reservoir strata occurs upward in the subaqueous fan sequence (Figure 6.7). With lobe switching, multiple coarsening and thickening-upward packages are likely to be stacked in the suprafan areas (Normark, 1978). Thus, reservoir quality sands are likely to form in the upper and middle fan channels and as turbidite sands deposited on the middle fan lobes. Berg (1982) and Mitchum (1988) have described the prograding sequences of fans in seismic sections.

Proximal subaqueous fan deposits contain sizeable reserves of hydrocarbons. The middle and outer fan deposits, athough not reservoirs, are interbedded with very fine grained pelagic shales that are commonly rich in organic matter. These shales act as both a source for hydrocarbons and as a seal. Because of the lateral continuity of middle and lower fan turbidite sandstones, these strata serve as natural carrier beds to bring hydrocarbons to the main reservoir sands in the middle and upper fan. Stratigraphic traps are common in subaqueous fans and may be detected with sequence stratigraphy. Examples include the Jurassic Brae Formation of the Miller field (McClure and Brown, 1992) and the Eocene Alba Formation of the Alba field (Mattingly and Bretthauer, 1992), both occurring in the North Sea area. The Wilmington field in the Los Angeles basin, with about 2.5 billion bbl of recoverable oil (Mayuga, 1970), is one of the largest subaqueous fan reservoirs. Table 6.6 identifies prominent fields with fan reservoirs in the United Kingdom, Brazil, and the United States. The fans form in rapidly subsiding basins produced by wrench faulting or rifting with deep water adjacent to a shelf. Submarine canyons commonly also form at the shelf edge in association with major rivers entering the sea. Because of the instability of the prodelta slope, turbidity flows, mass flows, and slope creep sediments are often funneled to the canyons and hence to subaqueous fans building on the basal plain. The huge Green Canyon Block discoveries in the Gulf of Mexico off the Mississippi delta are interpreted as having subaqueous fan sandstone reservoirs (Brannon et al., 1993).

CONCLUSIONS

Depositional environments of siliciclastic sandstone reservoirs were reviewed here to characterize the distribution of reservoir facies. The main reservoir facies in nonmarine sandstones include point bar or braid bar sands in fluvial environments; dune sands in eolian settings; and shoreface, mouth bar, fluvial channel, and subaqueous fans in lacustrine settings. In deltas, the main reservoirs are distributary mouth bars and channel sands. Primary shallow marine reservoirs include barrier beach and shoreface sands and offshore bars. Petroleum production in subaqueous fans is mainly from upper and middle fan channel and proximal turbidite sands. Examples of prominent oil and gas fields with reservoirs in each type of depositional environment are given in Tables 6.1–6.6.

The most prolific sandstone reservoirs of the world are deltaic distributary mouth bar and channel sands. Thick, laterally extensive reservoir sands can be deposited by one lobe of a delta. Because of delta lobe switching and subsidence of inactive lobes by compaction of prodelta silts and clays, multiple lobes can be vertically stacked, which can greatly increase the amount of reservoir sand. Tertiary deltaic sediments underlying present-day major deltas of the world account for significant petroleum reserves.

The second most productive sandstone reservoirs are from shallow marine sediments. Stacking of reservoir facies due to fluctuations in sea level adds significantly to their reservoir volume. Subaqueous fans are a relatively underexplored reservoir type that holds great promise because of the amount of sand that is present, the potential for stacking fan lobes, and the likely proximity to deep basinal source rocks.

Although nonmarine reservoirs have not produced as many giant hydrocarbon accumulations as deltaic or shallow marine sands, they do offer significant targets. Many lacustrine-related fields in China have yet to be carefully documented and published outside China. Eolian sands must always be considered because of their high quality and thick reservoirs. Fluvial sands, particularly in north Africa, have great potential when they can be tied to a source rock and a regional seal.

Acknowledgments *Preparation of this paper was encouraged by Wallace G. Dow of DGSI and Leslie B. Magoon of the USGS. Their subsequent reviews and that of Peter van de Kamp significantly improved its presentation. Linda Rausch helped to prepare this chapter.*

References Cited

Ahlbrandt, T. S., and S. G. Fryberger, 1982, Eolian deposits, *in* P. A. Scholle and D. Spearing, eds., Sandstone depositional environments: AAPG Memoir 31, p. 11–48.

Albright, W. A., W. L. Turner, and K. R. Williamson, 1980, Ninian field, UK sector, North Sea, *in* M. T. Halbouty, ed., Giant oil and gas fields of the decade: 1968–1978: AAPG Memoir 30, p. 173–193.

Ayers, M. G., M. Bilal, R. W. Jones, L. W. Slentz, M. Tartir, and A. O. Wilson, 1982, Hydrocarbon habitat in main producing areas, Saudi Arabia: AAPG Bulletin, v. 66, n. 1, p. 1–9.

Bacoccoli, G., R. G. Morales, and O. A. J. Campos, 1980, the Namorado oil field: a major oil discovery in the Campos basin, Brazil, *in* M. T. Halbouty, ed., Giant oil and gas fields of the decade: 1968–1978: AAPG Memoir 30, p. 328–338.

Balducchi, A., and G. Pommier, 1970, Cambrian oil field of Hassi Messaoud, Algeria, *in* M. T. Halbouty, ed., Geology of giant petroleum fields: AAPG Memoir 14, p. 477–488.

Barlow, J. A., and J. D. Haun, 1970, Regional stratigraphy of Frontier Formation and relation to Salt Creek field, Wyoming, *in* M. T. Halbouty, ed., Geology of giant petroleum fields: AAPG Memoir 14, p. 147–157.

Table 6.5. Shallow Marine Reservoirs

Field	Location Country	Location Basin	Age[a]	Formation	Thickness of Pay (m)	Depositional Environment
Samotlor	C.I.S.	W. Siberia	U J–L K	—	600	Shallow marine shelf
South Republics System	C.I.S.	Amu Darya–Tadjik	U J, K, Palc	Shatlyk	—	Marine shelf
Troll	Norway	—	U J	Viking Gp	—	Stacked shallow shelf, prograding shoreface.
Snohvit	Norway	—	U J	Sto and Nordmela	—	Transgressive coastal to inner shelf, coastal plain with tidal channels
Draugen	Norway	—	U J	Rogn	—	Shallow marine shelf sand bars
Piper	United Kingdom	—	U J	Piper Ss	—	High energy, marginal marine, shelf
(Northern Niger Delta System)	Nigeria	—	U Eoc–L Mio	Agbada	—	Paralic, shoreface to shelf, barrier bars and channel sands
Takula	Cabinda	—	U K	Vermelha Ss	—	Stacked nearshore to coastal sands, foreshore, tidal channels, offshore bars
Cueta–Tomporo	Venezuela	—	Eoc–Mio	Lagunillas	—	Shallow coastal bars and fluviodeltaic channels
El Furrial	Venezuela	Maturin	U Olig	Naricual Ss	—	Shallow marine, barrier bars
Iagifu/Hedinia	Papua New Guinea	—	L K	Toro Ss	90	Stacked regressive barrier bars
Fortescue	Australia	Southeast	Eoc	Latrobe Group	130	Transgressive coastal plain, upper and lower shoreface
Venture	Canada	—	U K	Venture Ss	250	Shallow marine, deltaic
Bell Creek	U.S.A. (Montana)	—	U K	Muddy Ss	—	Barrier bar, shelf bars
S. Cuyama	U.S.A. (Calif.)	—	L Mio	Vaqueros	—	Neritic sand
Tom O'Connor	U.S.A. (Texas)	—	Olig	Frio	1000	Inner–middle shelf to foreshore, beach

[a]U, upper; L, lower; Pal, Paleocene; Eoc, Eocene; Olig, Oligocene; Mio, Miocene.
[b]A, anticline; Up, unconformity pinchout; Bl, tilted block; St, stratigraphic; D, domal; R/O, rollover anticline or growth fault; WrA, wrench anticline; Th, thrust anticline.
[c]V, vertical; Lt, lateral.

Berg, O. H., 1982, Seismic detection and evaluation of delta and turbidite sequences: their application to the exploration for the subtle trap, *in* M. T. Halbouty, ed., The deliberate search for the subtle trap: AAPG Memoir 32, p. 57–75.

Bernard, H. A., R. J. Le Blanc, and C. F. Major, 1962, Recent and Pleistocene geology of southeast Texas, *in* E. H. Rainwater and R. P Zingula, eds., Geology of the Gulf Coast and central Texas, guidebook of excursions: Houston Geological Society, p. 175–224.

Bolle, L., 1992, Troll field, Norway's giant offshore gas field, *in* M. T. Halbouty, ed., Giant oil and gas fields of the decade 1978–1988: AAPG Memoir 54, p. 447–458.

Bouma, A. H., 1962, Sedimentology of Some Flysch Deposits: A Graphic Approach to Facies Interpretation: Elsevier, Amsterdam, 168 p.

Bouma, A. H., N. L. Berryhill, H. J. Knebel, and R. L. Brenner, 1982, The continental shelf *in* P. A. Scholle and D. Spearing, eds., Sandstone depositional environments: AAPG Memoir 31, p. 281–328.

Brannon, D., A. Chedburn, W. J. Schneider, and M. Sheedlo, 1993, Jolliet field revisited: producibility of upper slope

turbidites in Green Canyon 184 (abs): AAPG 1993 Annual Convention Program, April 25–28, p. 79–80.

Candido, A., and C. A. G. Cora, 1992, the Marlim and Albacora giant fields, Campos basin, offshore Brazil, *in* M. T. Halbouty, ed., Giant oil and gas fields of the decade 1978–1988: AAPG Memoir 54, p. 123–135.

Cant, D. J., 1982, Fluvial facies models and their applications, *in* P. A. Scholle and D. Spearing, eds., Sandstone depositional environments: AAPG Memoir 31, p. 115–137.

Carmalt, S. W., and B. St. John, 1986, Giant oil and gas fields, *in* M. T. Halbouty, ed., Future petroleum provinces of the world: AAPG Memoir 40, p. 11–53.

Chen, S., and Wang, P., 1980, Geology of Gudao oil field and surrounding areas, *in* M. T. Halbouty, ed., Giant oil and gas fields of the decade: 1968–1978: AAPG Memoir 30, p. 471–486.

Cheng, C., 1981, Alluvial-fan coarse clastic reservoirs in Karamay, *in* J. F. Mason, ed., Petroleum geology in China: Tulsa, OK, PennWell Books, p. 154–170.

Clifford, H. J., R. Grund, and H. Musrati, 1980, Geology of a stratigraphic giant: Messla oil field, Libya, *in* M. T.

Table 6.5 (continued)

Reserves (BOE)		Gas or Oil Produced	Trap Type[b]	Migration		Depth (m)	Porosity (%)	Permeability (md)	References
Recoverable (×10⁹)	In place (×10⁹)			Style[c]	Distance (km)				
15.1	—	O	A	—	—	1524–2134	—	—	Halbouty, 1980
16.0	—	O	Bl–A	—	—	–	—	—	Chapter 3
9.0	—	O, G	Bl–A	Lt, V	—	1300–1500	25	500–10,000	Bolle, 1992; Carmalt and St. John, 1986
—	4.5	G	Bl	Lt, V	—	2280–2418	5–15	200	Linjordet and Olsen, 1992
0.41	1.1	O	Bl–A	Lt, V	—	1600	28	700–10,000	Provan, 1992
0.6	—	O	Bl–A	V	—	2195	24	4000	Maher, 1980
—	4.5	O, G	R/O, St	V	—	1700	15–25	1000–2000	Chapter 36 Carmalt and St. John, 1986
—	2.1	O	R/O	V	—	971–1038	25	1000	Dale et al., 1992
1.4	—	O	WrA	—	—	4510–5180	12–17	10–1200	Ramirez and Marcano, 1992
0.89	4.5	O	Th–A	V	—	3962–4120	11–16	—	Prieto and Valdes, 1992
0.15	—	O	Th–A	Lt, V	—	2438	13	300	Matzke et al., 1992
0.28	0.42	O	St, Up, Bl	Lt, V	—	2300–2400	20	100–10000	Hendrich et al., 1992
0.25	—	G	R/O	V	—	4436–5800	16	10–40	Drummond, 1992; Chapter 3
0.2	—	O	St	Lt	—	1371	—	—	McGregor and Biggs, 1970
0.25	—	O, G	Bl–A, WrD	V	—	—	—	—	Chapter 27
0.67	—	O, G	R/O, A	—	—	1371–1828	31	500–2300	Mills, 1970

Halbouty, ed., Giant oil and gas fields of the decade: 1968–1978: AAPG Memoir 30, p. 507–524.

Coleman, J., and D. B. Prior, 1982, Deltaic environments, *in* P. A. Scholle and D. Spearing, eds., Sandstone depositional environments: AAPG Memoir 31, p. 139–178.

Collinson, J. D., and J. E. Lewin, eds., 1983, Modern and ancient fluvial systems: International Association of Sedimentologists Special Publication 6, 575 p.

Cook, H. E., M. E. Field, and J. V. Gardner, 1982, Continental slopes, *in* P. A. Scholle and D. Spearing, eds., Sandstone depositional environments: AAPG Memoir 31, p. 329–364.

Dale, C. T., J. R. Lopes, and S. Abilio, 1992, Takula oil field and the greater Takula area, Cabinda, Angola, *in* M. T. Halbouty, ed., Giant oil and gas fields of the decade 1978–1988: AAPG Memoir 54, p. 197–215.

Demaison, G., and B. J. Huizinga, 1991, Genetic classification of petroleum systems: AAPG Bulletin, v. 75, p. 1626–1643.

DeMatharel, M., P. Lehmann, and T. Oki, 1980, Geology of Bekapai field, *in* M. T. Halbouty, ed., Giant oil and gas fields of the decade: 1968–1978: AAPG Memoir 30, p. 459–469.

Drummond, K. J., 1992 Geology of Venture, a geopressured gas field, offshore Nova Scotia, *in* M. T. Halbouty, ed., Giant oil and gas fields of the decade 1978–1988: AAPG Memoir 54, p. 55–71.

Ehrenberg, S. N., H. M. Gjerstad, F. Hadler-Jacobson, 1992, Smorbukk field, a gas condensate fault trap in the Haltenbanken Province, offshore mid-Norway, *in* M. T. Halbouty, ed., Giant oil and gas fields of the decade 1978–1988: AAPG Memoir 54, p. 323–348.

Eschner, T. B., and Kocurek, G. A., 1988, Origins of relief along contacts between eolian sandstones and overlying marine strata: AAPG Bulletin, v. 78, p. 932–943.

Ethridge, F. G., and R. M. Flores, 1981, Recent and ancient nonmarine depositional environments: models for exploration: SEPM Special Publication 31, 349 p.

Eugster, H. P., and L. A. Hardie, 1975, Sedimentation in an ancient playa-lake complex: The Wilkins Peak Member of the Green River Formation of Wyoming: GSA Bulletin, v. 86, p. 319–334.

Eugster, H. P., and R. C. Surdam, 1973, Depositional environment of the Green River Formation of Wyoming: a preliminary report: GSA Bulletin, v. 84, p. 115–120.

Fisher, W. L., L. F. Brown, A. J. Scott, and J. H. McGowen, 1969, Delta systems in the exploration for oil and gas: The University of Texas at Austin, Bureau of Economic Geology, 78 pp.

Fouch, T. D., and W. E. Dean, 1982, Lacustrine and associated clastic depositional environments, *in* P. A. Scholle and D. Spearing, eds., Sandstone depositional environments:

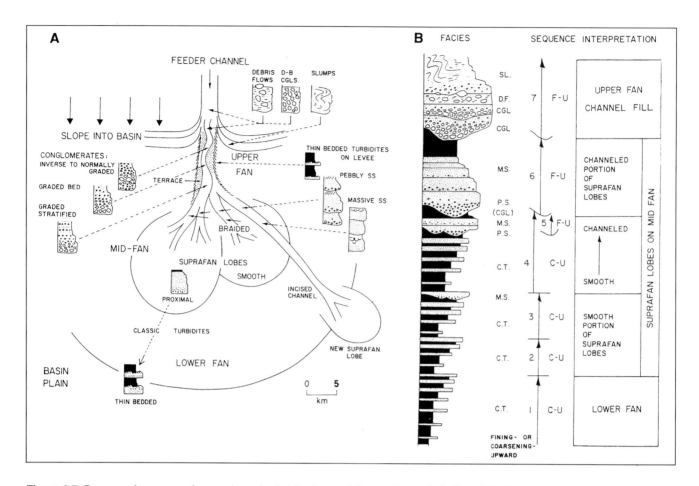

Figure 6.7. Deep marine reservoirs are deposited at the base of the continental shelf or delta front slope as submarine fans. (A) Reservoir sands are deposited on the upper fan valley and the suprafan lobes (after Normark, 1970). (B) An idealized vertical sequence through a prograding fan illustrates thickening and coarsening-upward (C-U) and thinning and fining-upward (F-U) sand bodies. Lithofacies include classic turbidites (C.T.), massive sands (M.S.), pebbly sands (P.S.), conglomerates (CGL), debris flows (D.F.), and slumps (SL.) (after Walker, 1978).

Table 6.6. Deep Marine Reservoirs

Field	Location Country	Basin	Age[a]	Formation	Thickness of Pay (m)	Depositional Environment
Alba	United Kingdom	North Sea	Eoc	Alba Fm	90	Deep sea fan, channel and levee complex
Forties	United Kingdom	North Sea	Pal	Forties Fm	110	Mid to lower prograding submarine fan, two lobes stacked, amalgamated channels
Miller	United Kingdom	North Sea	U J	Brae Fm	60	Submarine fan, sandy lobe on basin floor
Marlim	Brazil	—	U Olig	Carapebus Ss	200	Submarine fan, lobe, and channels
Albacora	Brazil	—	U K–Mio	Ss	110	Submarine fan, lobe and channels
Namorado	Brazil	—	U K	Ss	—	Submarine fan, stacked channels and lobes
Marimba	Brazil	—	U K	Ss	—	Turbidite
Wilmington	U.S.A. (Calif.)	Los Angeles	U Mio–U Plio	Puente, Repetto	>600	Turbidite

[a]U, upper; J, Jurassic; K, Cretaceous; Pal, Paleocene; Eoc, Eocene; Olig, Oligocene; Mio, Miocene; Plio, Pliocene.
[b]A, anticline; Up, unconformity pinchout; Bl, tilted block; St, stratigraphic; D, domal; R/O, rollover anticline or growth fault; ; WrA, wrench anticline.
[c]V, vertical; Lt, lateral.

Spearing, eds., Sandstone depositional environments: AAPG Memoir 31, p. 87–114.

Frazier, D. E., 1967, Recent deltaic deposits of the Mississippi River: their development and chronology: Gulf Coast Association Geological Societies, Transactions, v. 17, p. 287–315.

Fryberger, S. G., 1979, Eolian-fluviatile (continental) origin of ancient stratigraphic trap for petroleum in Weber Sandstone, Rangely oil field, Colorado: Mountain Geologist, v. 16, n. 1, p. 1–36.

Fryberger, S. G., 1984, The Permian Upper Minnelusa Formation, Wyoming: ancient example of an offshore prograding eolian sand sea with geomorphic facies, and system-boundary traps for petroleum, *in* J. Goolsby and D. Morton, eds., The Permian and Pennsylvanian: 35th Annual Field Conference, Wyoming Geological Association Guidebook, p. 241–271.

Gage, M., 1980, A review of the Viking Gas field, *in* M. T. Halbouty, ed., Giant oil and gas fields of the decade: 1968–1978: AAPG Memoir 30, p. 39–57.

Ghignone, J. I., and G. D. Andrade, 1980, General geology and major oil fields of Reconcavo basin, Brazil, *in* M. T. Halbouty, ed., Geology of giant petroleum fields: AAPG Memoir 14, p. 337–358.

Glennie, K. W., 1972, Permian Rotliegendes of northwest Europe interpreted in light of modern desert sedimentation studies: AAPG Bulletin, v. 56, n. 6, p. 1048–1071.

Glennie, K. W., 1982, Early Permian (Rotliegendes) paleo-winds of the North Sea: Sedimentary Geology, v. 34, p. 245–265.

Glennie, K. W., 1987, Desert sedimentary environments, present and past—a summary: Sedimentary Geology, v. 50, p. 135–165.

Hagen, J., and B. Kvalheim, 1992, Oseberg field, *in* M. T. Halbouty, ed., Giant oil and gas fields of the decade 1978–1988: AAPG Memoir 54, p. 417–428.

Halbouty, M. T., 1970, ed., Geology of giant petroleum fields: AAPG Memoir 14, 575 p.

Halbouty, M. T., 1980a, Geologic significance of Landsat data for 15 giant oil and gas fields, *in* M. T. Halbouty, ed., Giant oil and gas fields of the decade: 1968–1978: AAPG Memoir 30, p. 7–38.

Halbouty, M. T., 1980b, ed., Giant oil and gas fields of the decade: 1968–1978: AAPG Memoir 30, 596 p.

Halbouty, M. T., 1992, ed., Giant oil and gas fields of the decade 1978–1988: AAPG Memoir 54, 526 p.

Halbouty, M. T., A. A. Meyerhoff, R. E. King, R. H. Dott, Sr., H. D. Klemme, and T. Shabad, 1970, World's giant oil and gas fields, geological factors affecting their formation and basin classification, *in* M. T. Halbouty, ed., Geology of giant petroleum fields: AAPG Memoir 14, p. 502–575.

Hamouda, A., 1980, Petroleum potential—Ouargla region Triassic basin, Algeria, *in* M. T. Halbouty, ed., Giant oil and gas fields of the decade: 1968–1978: AAPG Memoir 30, p. 539–542.

Hardie, L. A., J. P. Smoot, and H. P. Eugster, 1978, Saline lakes and their deposits: a sedimentological approach, *in* A. Mather and M. E. Tucker, eds., Modern and ancient lake sediments: International Association of Sedimentologists Special Publication, n. 2, p. 7–42.

Hendrich, J. H., I. D. Palmer, and D. A. Schwebel, 1992, *in* M. T. Halbouty, ed., Giant oil and gas fields of the decade 1978–1988: AAPG Memoir 54, p. 483–492.

Hill, P. J., and G. V. Wood, 1980,. Geology of the Forties field, U.K. continental shelf, North Sea, *in* M. T. Halbouty, ed., Giant oil and gas fields of the decade: 1968–1978: AAPG Memoir 30, p. 81–93.

Holland, D. S., W. E. Nunan, D. R. Lammlein, and R. L. Woodhams, 1980, Eugene Island Block 330 field, offshore Louisiana, *in* M. T. Halbouty, ed., Giant oil and gas fields of the decade: 1968–1978: AAPG Memoir 30, p. 253–280.

Horschutz, P. M. C., L. C. S. de Freitas, C. V. Stank, A. da S. Barroso, and W. M. Cruz, 1992, The Linguado, Carapeba, Vermelho, and Marimba giant oil fields, Campos basin, offshore Brazil, *in* M. T. Halbouty, ed., Giant oil and gas fields of the decade 1978–1988: AAPG Memoir 54, p. 137–153.

Houbolt, J. J. H. C., 1968, Recent sediments in the southern bight of the North Sea: Geol. Mijnbouw, v. 47, p. 245–273.

Table 6.6 *(continued)*

Reserves (BOE)		Gas orOil Produced	Trap Type[b]	Migration		Depth (m)	Porosity (%)	Permeability (md)	References
Recoverable (×10⁹)	In place (×10⁹)			Style[c]	Distance (km)				
—	1.1	O	St	V	—	1860	35	2800	Mattingly and Bretthauer, 1992
1.8	4	O	A, St?	Lt	—	2090–2217	24–29	9–753	Hill and Wood, 1980
0.4	0.67	O, G	St	Lt	—	3890–4090	12–23	50–1200	McClure and Brown, 1992
—	8.2 (System 13.9)	O	St–Up Bl–A	Lt	20	2500–2700	30	1200	Chapter 31; Candido and Cora, 1992
—	4.0	O	A	V	—	2350–3260	25	1500	Candido and Cora, 1992
0.25	—	O	A–St	V	—	2980–3080	30	1000	Bacoccoli et al., 1980
0.17	0.47	O	R/O St–Up	V	—	2700	27	1700	Horschutz et al., 1992
2.5	9.6	O	WrA	V	—	610–1830	30–35	700–1500	Mayuga, 1970

Howell, D. G., and W. R. Normark, 1982, Submarine fans, *in* P. A. Scholle and D. Spearing, eds., Sandstone depositional environments: AAPG Memoir 31, p. 365–404.

Huffington, R. M., and H. M. Helmig, 1980, Discovery and development of the Badok field, East Kalimantan, Indonesia, *in* M. T. Halbouty, ed., Giant oil and gas fields of the decade: 1968–1978: AAPG Memoir 30, p. 441–458.

Hunter, R. E., 1977, Basic types of stratification in small eolian dunes: Sedimentology, v. 39, p. 361–387.

Jorde, K., and G. W. Diesen, 1992, The Snorre field, a major field in the northern North Sea, *in* M. T. Halbouty, ed., Giant oil and gas fields of the decade 1978–1988: AAPG Memoir 54, p. 407–416.

Kamen-Kay, M., 1970, Geology and productivity of Persian Gulf synclinorium: AAPG Bulletin, v. 54, n. 12, p. 2371–2394.

Kirk, R. H., 1980, Statfjord field—a North Sea giant, *in* M. T. Halbouty, ed., Giant oil and gas fields of the decade: 1968–1978: AAPG Memoir 30, p. 95–116.

Kocurek, G. A., 1981, Significance of interdune deposits and bounding surfaces in eolian dune sands: Sedimentology, v. 28, p. 753–780.

Kocurek, G. A., 1988, ed., Late Paleozoic and Mesozoic eolian deposits of the Western Interior of the United States: Sedimentary Geology, v. 56, 413 p.

Kocurek, G. A., and R. H. Dott, Jr., 1981, Distinctions and uses of stratification types in the interpretation of eolian sand: Journal Sedimentary Petrology, v. 51, p. 579–595.

Koelmel, M. H., 1986, Post–Mississippian paleotectonic, stratigraphic, and diagenetic history of the Weber Sandstone in the Rangely field area, Colorado, *in* J. A. Peterson, Paleotectonics and sedimentation: AAPG Memoir 41, p. 371–396.

Kurley, T. J., R. D. Kreisa, G. G. Taylor, and W. R. L. Yates, 1992, The reservoir geology and geophysics of the Hibernia field, offshore Newfoundland, *in* M. T. Halbouty, ed., Giant oil and gas fields of the decade 1978–1988: AAPG Memoir 54, p. 35–54.

Lamb, C. F., 1980, Painter Reservoir field—giant in the Wyoming thrustbelt, *in* M. T. Halbouty, ed., Giant oil and gas fields of the decade: 1968–1978: AAPG Memoir 30, p. 281–288.

LeBlanc, R. J., 1972, Geometry of sandstone reservoir bodies; *in* T. D. Cook, ed., Underground waste management and environmental implications: AAPG Memoir 18, p. 133–190.

Lelek, J. J., D. B. Shepherd, D. M. Stone, and A. S. Abdine, 1992, October field, the latest giant under development in Egypt's Gulf of Suez, *in* M. T. Halbouty, ed., Giant oil and gas fields of the decade 1978–1988: AAPG Memoir 54, p. 231–249.

Levorsen, A. I., 1936, Stratigraphic versus structural accumulation: AAPG Bulletin, v. 20, p. 521–530.

Li, C., S. Zha, and Z. Shaobi, 1988, Sedimentary analysis and oil-bearing structures of the Biyang basin, southern Henan Province, China, *in* H. C. Wagner, L. C. Wasner, F. F. H. Wang, and F. L. Wong, eds., Petroleum resources of China and related subjects: Circum-Pacific Council for Energy and Mineral Resources, Earth Sciences Series, v. 10, p. 297–310.

Lindquist, S. J., 1988, Practical characterization of eolian reservoirs for development: Nugget Sandstone, Utah-Wyoming thrustbelt: Journal Sedimentary Geology, v. 56, p. 315–339.

Linjordet, A., and R. G. Olsen, 1992, The Jurassic Snohvit gas field, Hammerfest basin, offshore northern Norway, *in* M. T. Halbouty, ed., Giant oil and gas fields of the decade 1978–1988: AAPG Memoir 54, p. 349–370.

Linsley, P. N., H. C. Potter, G. McNab, D. Racher, 1980, The Beatrice field, inner Moray Firth, U.K., North Sea, *in* M. T. Halbouty, ed., Giant oil and gas fields of the decade: 1968–1978: AAPG Memoir 30, p. 117–129.

Magloire, P. R., 1970, Triassic gas field of Hassi er R'Mel, Algeria, *in* M. T. Halbouty, ed., Geology of giant petroleum fields: AAPG Memoir 14, p. 489–501.

Maher, C. E., 1980, Piper oil field, *in* M. T. Halbouty, ed., Giant oil and gas fields of the decade: 1968–1978: AAPG Memoir 30, p. 131–172.

Mancini, E. A., R. M. Mink, B. L, Bearden, R. P. Hamilton, 1988, A look at recoverable gas reserves in the Jurassic Norphlet Formation off Alabama: Oil and Gas Journal, v. 86, n. 3, p. 62–64.

Mattingly, G. A., and H. H. Bretthauer, 1992, The Alba field, a Middle Eocene deep water channel system in the U.K. North Sea, *in* M. T. Halbouty, ed., Giant oil and gas fields of the decade 1978–1988: AAPG Memoir 54, p. 297–305.

Matzke, R. H., J. G. Smith, and W. K. Foo, 1992, Iagifu/Hedinia field, first oil from the Papuan fold and thrust belt, *in* M. T. Halbouty, ed., Giant oil and gas fields of the decade 1978–1988: AAPG Memoir 54, p. 471–482.

Mayuga, M. N., 1970, Geology and development of California's giant—Wilmington oil field, *in* M. T. Halbouty, ed., Geology of giant petroleum fields: AAPG Memoir 14, p. 158–184.

McClure, N. M., and A. A. Brown, 1992, Miller field, a subtle Upper Jurassic submarine fan trap in the South Viking Graben, United Kingdom sector, North Sea, *in* M. T. Halbouty, ed., Giant oil and gas fields of the decade 1978–1988: AAPG Memoir 54, p. 307–322.

McCollough, C. N., and J. A. Carver, 1992, The giant Cañon Limon field, Llanos basin, Colombia, *in* M. T. Halbouty, ed., Giant oil and gas fields of the decade 1978–1988: AAPG Memoir 54, p. 175–195.

McCubbin, D. G., 1982, Barrier island and strand-plain facies, *in* P. A. Scholle and D. Spearing, eds., Sandstone depositional environments: AAPG Memoir 31, p. 247–279.

McGregor, A. A., and C. A. Biggs, 1970, Bell Creek field: a rich stratigraphic trap, *in* M. T. Halbouty, ed., Geology of giant petroleum fields: AAPG Memoir 14, p. 128–146.

McKee, E. D., 1979, Global sand seas: U. S.G.S. Professional Paper 1052, 429 p.

Meyerhoff, A. A., and J. O. Willums, 1976, Petroleum geology and industry of the People's Republic of China: United Nations ESCAP, CCOP Technical Bulletin, v. 10, p. 103–212.

Miall, A. D., ed., 1978, Fluvial sedimentology: Canadian Society of Petroleum Geologists Memoir 5, 859 p.

Mills, H. G., 1970, Geology of Tom O'Connor field, Refugio County, Texas, *in* M. T. Halbouty, ed., Geology of giant petroleum fields: AAPG Memoir 14, p. 292–300.

Mitchum, R. M., 1988, Seismic stratigraphic criteria for recognition of submarine fans, *in* H. C. Wagner, L. C. Wasner, F. F. H. Wang, and F. L. Wong, eds., Petroleum resources of China and related subjects: Circum-Pacific Council for Energy and Mineral Resources, Earth Sciences Series, v. 10, p. 753–776.

Moore, D. A., 1984, The Tensleep Formation of the southeastern Big Horn basin, Wyoming, *in* J. Goolsby and D. Morton, eds., The Permian and Pennsylvanian geology of Wyoming: 35th field Conference Guidebook, Wyoming Geological Association, p. 273–279.

Nelson, P. H. H., 1980, Role of reflection seismic in development of Nembe Creek field, Nigeria, *in* M. T. Halbouty, ed., Giant oil and gas fields of the decade: 1968–1978: AAPG Memoir 30, p. 565–576.

Nilsen, T. H., 1982, Alluvial fan deposits, *in* P. A. Scholle and D. Spearing, eds., Sandstone depositional environments: AAPG Memoir 31, p. 49–86.

Normark, W. R., 1970, Growth patterns of deep sea fans: AAPG Bulletin, v. 54, p. 2170–2195.

Normark, W. R., 1978, Fan valleys, channels, and depositional lobes on modern submarine fans; characters for recognition of sandy turbidite environments: AAPG Bulletin, v. 62, p. 912–931.

North, F. K., 1985, Petroleum geology: Boston, Allen and Unwin, p. 5–53.

Paraschiv, D., and G. Olteanu, 1970, Oil fields in Mio-Pliocene zone of eastern Carpathians (District of Ploiesti), *in* M. T. Halbouty, ed., Geology of giant petroleum fields: AAPG Memoir 14, p. 399–427.

Pense, G. M., 1988, Depositional and diagenetic controls on reservoir quality of the Norphlet sandstone, Mary Ann field, offshore Alabama: AAPG Bulletin, v. 72, n. 9, p. 1120.

Picard, M. D., and L. R. High, Jr., 1981, Physical stratigraphy of ancient lacustrine deposits *in* F. B. Ethridge and R. M. Flores, eds., Recent and ancient nonmarine depositional environments for exploration: SEPM Special Publication 31, p. 233–259.

Porter, M. L., 1986, Sedimentary record of erg migration: Geology, v. 14, p. 497–500.

Prieto, R., and G. Valdes, 1992, El Furrial oil field, a new giant in an old basin, *in* M. T. Halbouty, ed., Giant oil and gas fields of the decade 1978–1988: AAPG Memoir 54, p. 155–161.

Provan, D. M. J., 1992, Draugen oil field, Haltenbanken Province, offshore Norway, *in* M. T. Halbouty, ed., Giant oil and gas fields of the decade 1978–1988: AAPG Memoir 54, p. 371–382.

Ramirez, E., and F. Marcano, 1992, Ceuta-Tomoporo field, Venezuela, *in* M. T. Halbouty, ed., Giant oil and gas fields of the decade 1978–1988: AAPG Memoir 54, p. 163–173.

Reading, H. G. , ed., 1978, Sedimentary Environments and Facies: New York, Elsevier, 557 p.

Reineck, H. E., and I. B. Singh, 1980, Depositional Sedimentary Environments, 2nd ed.: New York, Springer-Verlag, 549 p.

Roadifer, R. E., 1987, Size distributions of the world's largest known oil and tar accumulations, *in* R. F. Meyer, ed., Exploration for heavy crude oil and natural bitumen: AAPG Studies in Geology 25, p. 3–23.

Roberts, J. M., 1970, Amal field, Lybia, *in* M. T. Halbouty, ed., Geology of giant petroleum fields: AAPG Memoir 14, p. 438–448.

Sanford, R. M., 1970, Sarir Oil field, Libya—desert surprise, *in* M. T. Halbouty, ed., Geology of giant petroleum fields: AAPG Memoir 14, p. 449–476.

Sheldon, R. P., 1967, Long distance migration of oil in Wyoming: Mountain Geologist, v. 4, p. 53–65.

Stauble, A. J., and G. Milius, 1970, Geology of Gronigen gas field, Netherlands, *in* M. T. Halbouty, ed., Geology of giant petroleum fields: AAPG Memoir 14, p. 359–369.

Swift, D. J. P., D. B. Duane, and T. F. McKinney, 1973, Ridge and swale topography of the Middle Atlantic Bight, North America: Secular response to the Holocene hydraulic regime: Marine Geology, v. 15, p. 227–247.

Verdier, A. C., T. Oki, and A. Suardy, 1980, Geology of the Handil field (East Kalimantan–Indonesia), *in* M. T. Halbouty, ed., Giant oil and gas fields of the decade: 1968–1978: AAPG Memoir 30, p. 399–421.

Walker, R. G., 1978, Deep water sandstone facies and ancient submarine fans: Models for exploration for stratigraphic traps: AAPG Bulletin, v. 62, p. 932–966.

Walker, R. G., ed., 1979, Facies models: Geological Association of Canada, Geoscience Canada Reprint Series, n. 1, 211 p.

"The term 'petroleum geology' has come into use to describe the area of common interest between petroleum producers and geologists."

—A. I. Levorsen

Passage from Levorsen, A. I., 1956, Geology of Petroleum: W.H. Freeman, p. 5.

Magoon, L. B., and W. G. Dow, eds., 1994, The petroleum
system—from source to trap: AAPG Memoir 60.

Chapter **7**

Carbonate Reservoir Rocks

Clifton F. Jordan, Jr.
Integrated Data Services
Bonne Terre, Missouri, U.S.A.

James Lee Wilson
New Braunfels, Texas, U.S.A.

Abstract

The main factors in evaluating carbonate reservoirs are lithofacies, pore types, shelf setting, sequence stratigraphy, and diagenetic overprint. Several patterns are evident based on a review of carbonate reservoirs from around the world. First, dolomites, grainstones, and boundstones are the most common carbonate reservoir rock types, but any carbonate lithofacies can be modified by diagenesis to form porous rock. Second, secondary pore types tend to dominate carbonate reservoir facies, as opposed to primary pore types. Third, inner shelf, outer shelf, and slope lithofacies belts are prime exploration fairways that are relatively predictable, with middle shelf prospects being less so. Fourth, sequence stratigraphy describes the shelf-building and basin-filling pattern of carbonate sediments and provides useful models for exploration and production. Finally, carbonate sediments are subjected to two main types of diagenetic overprinting: steady subsidence into deep burial realms of diagenesis or subsidence interrupted by one or more periods of uplift and associated porosity-producing diagenetic reactions.

INTRODUCTION

Carbonate reservoirs with their seemingly endless variety of textures, fossil components, and diagenetic overprints present a challenge to categorize (Owen, 1964; Schmoker et al., 1985). Nonetheless, there are generalized trends and patterns that account for oil and gas production from carbonate reservoir rocks on a worldwide basis. These patterns are the subject of this review and are discussed here with regard to five considerations: lithofacies, pore type, shelf setting, sequence stratigraphy, and diagenetic overprint. This review concentrates on reservoir facies development and not on source rocks, seals, or traps involving carbonates. It was necessary to avoid the diversity of rock descriptions used in the literature by standardizing lithofacies terminology for purposes of comparison. Hence, throughout this discussion, a scheme of "symbol logic" is used to describe the texture, composition, sedimentary structures, and diagenetic overprints of carbonate rocks (Jordan, 1985). This review is directed toward two main audiences: exploration geologists, who need to understand carbonate reservoirs in a regional framework, and production geologists, who need to know details regarding the distribution of reservoir facies in a particular field.

Figure 7.1 shows the worldwide distribution of basins that produce hydrocarbons from carbonate reservoirs. A list of these basins and the ages of their carbonate reservoirs are shown in Table 7.1. The following trends emerge from this data: (1) the number of basins that produce hydrocarbons from carbonate rocks is lowest for South America, Africa, and Australia and highest for North America and Eurasia; and (2) Tertiary carbonate reservoir rocks are found mainly in Southeast Asia, whereas the rest of the world's production is primarily from Paleozoic and Mesozoic carbonate reservoirs, which includes the giant and supergiant Jurassic and Cretaceous fields of the Middle East.

LITHOFACIES

Many schemes of classifying carbonate rocks have been proposed, but that of Dunham (1962) has been used in more studies involving carbonate rocks than any other. The reasons for this are its simplicity and directness, as well as its effectiveness in accurately describing reservoir facies in carbonate rocks. The reader is referred to Dunham's (1962) classic paper in which he described grain versus matrix support, the effects of particle shape on grain packing, and the spectrum of carbonate rock types observed from mudstones through grainstones and boundstones.

Dunham's attention to grain- versus matrix-supported framework is more in accord with the principles of carbonate sedimentation than classifications that consider primarily particle size or amounts of matrix. Particulate carbonate sediment, unless winnowed completely to form a grainstone deposit, is a mixture of

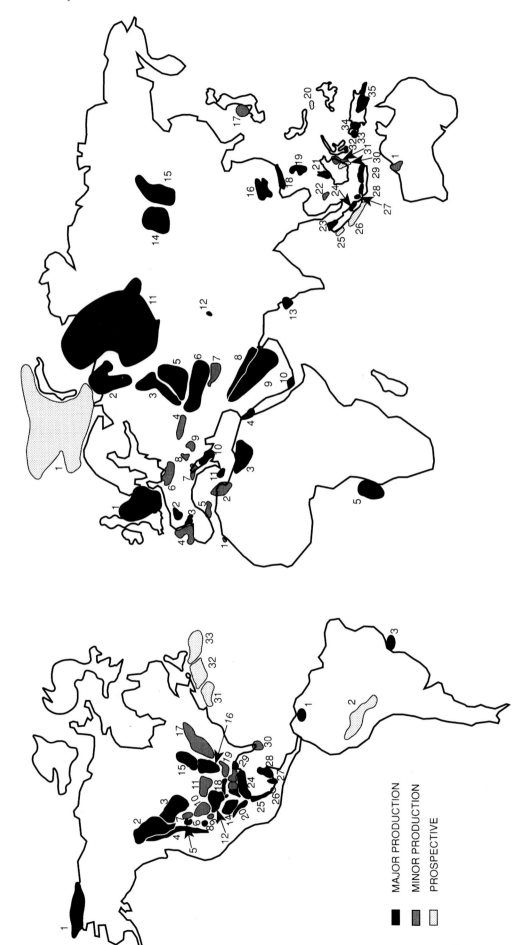

Figure 7.1. Map showing the worldwide distribution of basins that produce hydrocarbons from carbonate reservoirs. (Most basins drawn after St. John, 1980.)

MAJOR PRODUCTION

MINOR PRODUCTION

PROSPECTIVE

Table 7.1. Basins with Fields Producing from Carbonate Reservoirs.

Map No.[a]	Basin	Age[b]	Map No.[a]	Basin	Age[b]
North America			**Europe**		
1.	North Slope	**mid Pal**	1.	Southern North Sea	up Pal, **Cret–Paleoc**
2.	Alberta	**mid Pal**, Tri	2.	Paris	**Jur**
3.	Williston	**low Pal, mid Pal**	3.	Aquitaine	**Jur**, Cret
4.	Rocky Mtn. Thrust Belt	**mid Pal**, Jur	4.	Bay of Biscay	Cret
5.	Bighorn	low Pal, **mid Pal**	5.	Gulf of Valentia	Jur, Cret
6.	Wind River	**mid Pal**	6.	Polish–North German	up Pal, Jur
7.	Powder River	mid Pal, Cret	7.	Po	Tri, Jur
8.	Paradox	mid Pal, **up Pal**	8.	Pannonian	Mio
9.	Denver	low Pal, mid Pal	9.	Carpathian Foredeep	Cret
10.	Raton	Cret	10.	South Adriatic	**Cret**
11.	Salina–Forest City	low Pal	11.	Caltanesetta	**Mio**
12.	Anadarko	low, **mid,** and up Pal			
13.	Ardmore	**low Pal,** mid Pal	**Asia**		
14.	Permian	**low,** mid, and **up** Pal	1.	Barents Sea	up Pal
15.	Michigan	low Pal, **mid Pal**	2.	Pechora	**mid Pal**
16.	Illinois	low Pal, **mid Pal**	3.	Volga–Urals	**mid Pal**
17.	Appalachian	low Pal	4.	Donetz–Dneiper	mid Pal, up Pal, Jur
18.	Arkoma	low Pal, **mid Pal**	5.	North Caspian	**mid Pal**
19.	Black Warrior	low Pal	6.	Middle Caspian	**mid Pal, up Pal**
20.	Sabinas	**Jur, Cret**	7.	North Caucasus Trough	Jur, Cret
21.	East Texas Salt Dome	**Jur, Cret**	8.	Iranian Foldbelt	Cret, **Mio**
22.	Louisiana Salt Dome	Jur, Cret	9.	Arabian	**up Pal, Jur, Cret**
23.	Mississippi Salt Dome	Jur, Cret	10.	Yemen	Jur
24.	Gulf Coast	**Jur, Cret**	11.	West Siberia	**up Pal**
25.	Misantl-Tampico	Jur, **Cret**	12.	Fergana	**Cret**, Paleoc
26.	Veracruz	Cret	13.	Bombay	**Mio**
27.	Reforma	**Jur, Cret**	14.	Kansk	**up Pal**
28.	Campeche	**Cret**	15.	Angara Trough	**up Pal**
29.	NE Gulf Salt Dome	**Jur,** Cret	16.	Szechwan	**up Pal**
30.	South Florida	Cret	17.	Nigata	Mio
31.	Georges Bank	Jur	18.	South China Sea	**Mio**
32.	Scotian Shelf	Jur	19.	Northwest Palawan	**Mio**
33.	Grand Banks	Jur	20.	Visayan	Mio
			21.	South Brunei	**Mio**
South America			22.	East Natuna	Mio–Plio
1.	Maracaibo	**Cret**, Mio	23.	North Sumatra	**Mio**
2.	Madre de Dios	up Pal	24.	South Sumatra	**Mio**
3.	Campos	**Cret**	25.	Sibolga	Mio
			26.	Benkulu	Mio
Africa			27.	Sunda	**Mio**
1.	Gharb	Jur, Mio	28.	West Java	**Mio**
2.	Pelagian	Cret, Paleoc, Eoc	29.	East Java	Eoc, Olig, **Mio,** Plio
3.	Sirte	**Paleoc**	30.	Barito	Olig
4.	Gulf of Suez	**Mio**	31.	Kutei	Mio
5.	Angola South	**Cret**	32.	East Sengkang	**Mio**
			33.	Salawati	**Mio**
Australia			34.	Bintuni	**Mio**
1.	Canning	mid Pal	35.	Papuan	**Mio**

[a]Basin numbers correspond to those mapped in Figure 7.1 by continent; basin names are taken mainly from St. John (1980) and production data are from reviews such as Halbouty (1992).
[b]low Pal is Cambrian–Ordovician, mid Pal is Silurian–Mississippian, and up Pal is Pennsylvanian–Permian. **Boldface** type indicates major production.

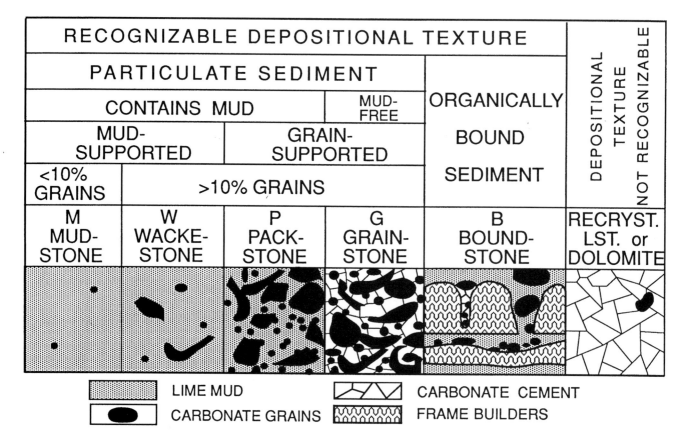

Figure 7.2. The Dunham (1962) classification of carbonate rocks, with two minor modifications: (1) mud is defined at the sedimentologic silt–sand boundary of 62.5 μm and (2) up to 5% lime mud is allowed in the category of grainstones.

various amounts of lime mud matrix with various sizes of bioclasts and peloids (with local concentrations of intraclasts or ooids). The size and shape of particles in this type of sediment are dependent on the breakdown fabric of constituent parts of calcified plants and animals and the degree of burrowing, ingesting, and reworking of the sediment. Moderate water movement and mechanical processes of sediment winnowing, so significant to siliciclastic deposition, are much less important in carbonates.

Two minor modifications of Dunham's (1962) classification scheme are recommended. First, the size of what is considered lime mud is increased from Dunham's limit of 35 μm to 62.5 μm, thus standardizing the use of the term *mud* in the sedimentologic sense. Second, the amount of lime mud allowable in a grainstone is increased from 1% to 5%, thus widening the scope of the term *grainstone* and incorporating many porous mud-lean packstones (Figure 7.2).

By using symbols to represent words (or word strings) for lithic descriptors and sedimentary structures, grain composition, remarks, and/or porosity and by adding these to the textural terms of Dunham (Jordan, 1985), the compilation and comparison of large amounts of carbonate lithofacies information becomes more manageable. This "lithofacies shorthand" is a rigorous semi-quantitative approach that normalizes facies descriptions for comparison and mapping purposes. This system is based on the lithofacies symbols in Figure

7.3, which shows the most common symbols used to describe carbonate reservoirs. (A complete listing of nearly 500 lithofacies symbols used in describing siliciclastics, carbonates, and other rocks is available from the author upon request.)

Carbonate lithofacies fall into several distinct lithologic associations, ranging from various types of lime mudstones to wackestones, packstones, grainstones, boundstones, and dolomites. These six main textural families are grouped in Figure 7.4 according to the most common types of constituent grains. This grouping shows that there is a limited number of combinations of carbonate rock textures and compositions to be dealt with in nature. By using the generalized bioclastic symbol, λ, which represents an assortment of normal marine fossils (usually fragmented) from any given geologic time period, the number of common carbonate lithofacies observed reduces to about 26 (Figure 7.4) and provides boundary conditions for the variability of carbonate lithofacies throughout geologic time. Wilson (1975) and Flugel (1982) used a typical shelf to basin profile as a framework for compiling a list of standard microfacies of commonly recurring carbonate rock types through geologic time (Table 7.2). Based on this, it is evident that the natural variation in carbonate rock textures and compositions occurring on shelves and platforms through time is limited and that, to some extent, carbonate reservoir facies are predictable in their distribution.

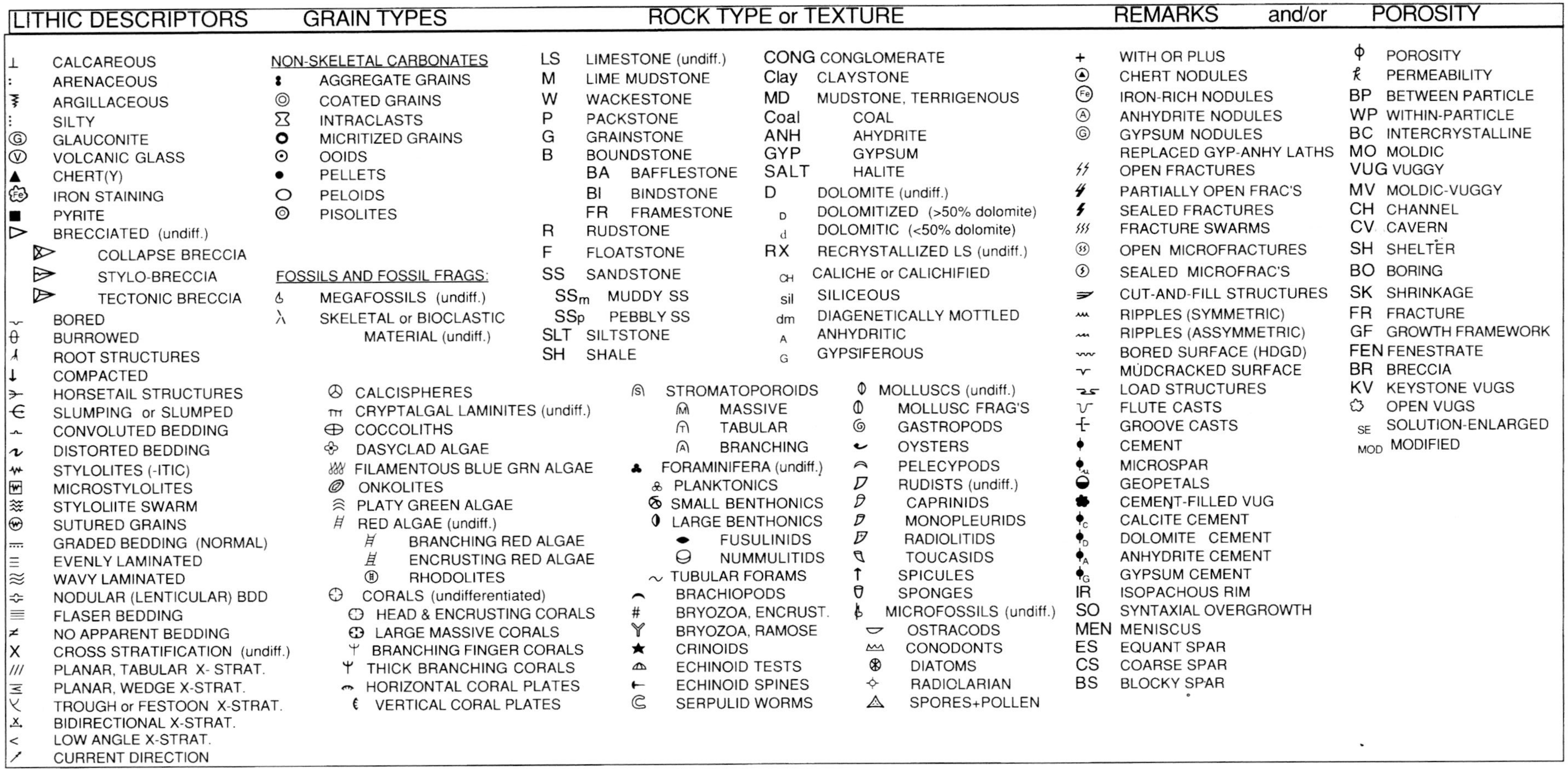

LITHIC DESCRIPTORS

- CALCAREOUS
- ARENACEOUS
- ARGILLACEOUS
- SILTY
- GLAUCONITE
- VOLCANIC GLASS
- CHERT(Y)
- IRON STAINING
- PYRITE
- BRECCIATED (undiff.)
- COLLAPSE BRECCIA
- STYLO-BRECCIA
- TECTONIC BRECCIA
- BORED
- BURROWED
- ROOT STRUCTURES
- COMPACTED
- HORSETAIL STRUCTURES
- SLUMPING or SLUMPED
- CONVOLUTED BEDDING
- DISTORTED BEDDING
- STYLOLITES (-ITIC)
- MICROSTYLOLITES
- STYLOLITE SWARM
- SUTURED GRAINS
- GRADED BEDDING (NORMAL)
- EVENLY LAMINATED
- WAVY LAMINATED
- NODULAR (LENTICULAR) BDD
- FLASER BEDDING
- NO APPARENT BEDDING
- CROSS STRATIFICATION (undiff.)
- PLANAR, TABULAR X- STRAT.
- PLANAR, WEDGE X-STRAT.
- TROUGH or FESTOON X-STRAT.
- BIDIRECTIONAL X-STRAT.
- LOW ANGLE X-STRAT.
- CURRENT DIRECTION

GRAIN TYPES

NON-SKELETAL CARBONATES
- AGGREGATE GRAINS
- COATED GRAINS
- INTRACLASTS
- MICRITIZED GRAINS
- OOIDS
- PELLETS
- PELOIDS
- PISOLITES

FOSSILS AND FOSSIL FRAGS:
- MEGAFOSSILS (undiff.)
- SKELETAL or BIOCLASTIC MATERIAL (undiff.)
- CALCISPHERES
- CRYPTALGAL LAMINITES (undiff.)
- COCCOLITHS
- DASYCLAD ALGAE
- FILAMENTOUS BLUE GRN ALGAE
- ONKOLITES
- PLATY GREEN ALGAE
- RED ALGAE (undiff.)
- BRANCHING RED ALGAE
- ENCRUSTING RED ALGAE
- RHODOLITES
- CORALS (undifferentiated)
- HEAD & ENCRUSTING CORALS
- LARGE MASSIVE CORALS
- BRANCHING FINGER CORALS
- THICK BRANCHING CORALS
- HORIZONTAL CORAL PLATES
- VERTICAL CORAL PLATES

ROCK TYPE or TEXTURE

- LS   LIMESTONE (undiff.)
- M   LIME MUDSTONE
- W   WACKESTONE
- P   PACKSTONE
- G   GRAINSTONE
- B   BOUNDSTONE
- BA   BAFFLESTONE
- BI   BINDSTONE
- FR   FRAMESTONE
- R   RUDSTONE
- F   FLOATSTONE
- SS   SANDSTONE
- SSm MUDDY SS
- SSp PEBBLY SS
- SLT SILTSTONE
- SH   SHALE
- CONG CONGLOMERATE
- Clay CLAYSTONE
- MD   MUDSTONE, TERRIGENOUS
- Coal COAL
- ANH ANHYDRITE
- GYP GYPSUM
- SALT HALITE
- D   DOLOMITE (undiff.)
- D   DOLOMITIZED (>50% dolomite)
- d   DOLOMITIC (<50% dolomite)
- RX   RECRYSTALLIZED LS (undiff.)
- cH   CALICHE or CALICHIFIED
- sil SILICEOUS
- dm   DIAGENETICALLY MOTTLED
- A   ANHYDRITIC
- G   GYPSIFEROUS

- STROMATOPOROIDS
- MASSIVE
- TABULAR
- BRANCHING
- FORAMINIFERA (undiff.)
- PLANKTONICS
- SMALL BENTHONICS
- LARGE BENTHONICS
- FUSULINIDS
- NUMMULITIDS
- TUBULAR FORAMS
- BRACHIOPODS
- BRYOZOA, ENCRUST.
- BRYOZOA, RAMOSE
- CRINOIDS
- ECHINOID TESTS
- ECHINOID SPINES
- SERPULID WORMS
- MOLLUSCS (undiff.)
- MOLLUSC FRAG'S
- GASTROPODS
- OYSTERS
- PELECYPODS
- RUDISTS (undiff.)
- CAPRINIDS
- MONOPLEURIDS
- RADIOLITIDS
- TOUCASIDS
- SPICULES
- SPONGES
- MICROFOSSILS (undiff.)
- OSTRACODS
- CONODONTS
- DIATOMS
- RADIOLARIAN
- SPORES+POLLEN

REMARKS and/or

- WITH OR PLUS
- CHERT NODULES
- IRON-RICH NODULES
- ANHYDRITE NODULES
- GYPSUM NODULES
- REPLACED GYP-ANHY LATHS
- OPEN FRACTURES
- PARTIALLY OPEN FRAC'S
- SEALED FRACTURES
- FRACTURE SWARMS
- OPEN MICROFRACTURES
- SEALED MICROFRAC'S
- CUT-AND-FILL STRUCTURES
- RIPPLES (SYMMETRIC)
- RIPPLES (ASSYMMETRIC)
- BORED SURFACE (HDGD)
- MUDCRACKED SURFACE
- LOAD STRUCTURES
- FLUTE CASTS
- GROOVE CASTS
- CEMENT
- MICROSPAR
- GEOPETALS
- CEMENT-FILLED VUG
- CALCITE CEMENT
- DOLOMITE CEMENT
- ANHYDRITE CEMENT
- GYPSUM CEMENT
- ISOPACHOUS RIM
- SYNTAXIAL OVERGROWTH
- MENISCUS
- EQUANT SPAR
- COARSE SPAR
- BLOCKY SPAR

POROSITY

- ϕ POROSITY
- k PERMEABILITY
- BP BETWEEN PARTICLE
- WP WITHIN-PARTICLE
- BC INTERCRYSTALLINE
- MO MOLDIC
- VUG VUGGY
- MV MOLDIC-VUGGY
- CH CHANNEL
- CV CAVERN
- SH SHELTER
- BO BORING
- SK SHRINKAGE
- FR FRACTURE
- GF GROWTH FRAMEWORK
- FEN FENESTRATE
- BR BRECCIA
- KV KEYSTONE VUGS
- OPEN VUGS
- SE SOLUTION-ENLARGED
- MOD MODIFIED

Figure 7.3. A chart of common lithofacies symbols used in describing carbonate reservoirs and associated rock types. (Based on Dunham, 1962; Choquette and Pray, 1970; Embry and Klovan, 1971; Swanson, 1981; Wilson and Jordan, 1983.)

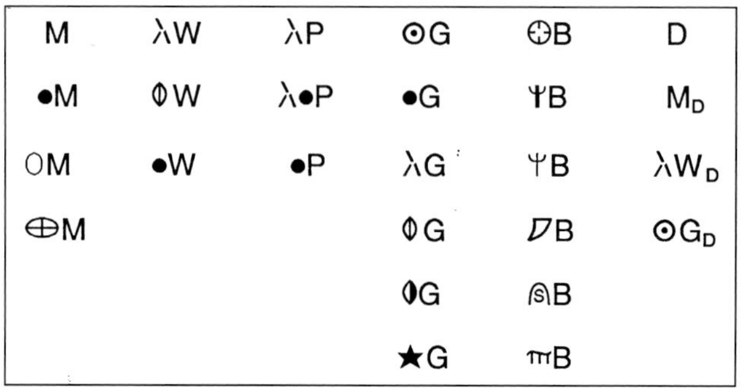

M	λW	λP	⊙G	⊕B	D
•M	⍉W	λ•P	•G	ⵟB	M_D
ⵔM	•W	•P	λG	Ψ B	λW_D
⊕M			⍉G	ⅅB	⊙G_D
			ⵔG	⍰B	
			★G	⊓B	

Figure 7.4. Common carbonate lithofacies, shown as six families of carbonate textures.

PORE TYPES

Porosity is best described by the system of Choquette and Pray (1970), which is reproduced in Figure 7.5. The only modification from the original is the addition of "keystone vugs." Certain types of porosity in carbonate rocks occur as a function of a rock's fabric (i.e., its Dunham texture); these are the eight porosity types listed as fabric selective. The terms *interparticle* and *intraparticle* are abbreviated as BP (for between particle) and WP (for within particle), respectively, to avoid confusion with the similar sounds of "inter-" and "intra-." The terms used are descriptive, although it helps to realize that *fenestra* (Latin for "window") refers to rectangular voids arranged in a rectilinear pattern and that *shelter* refers to an umbrella effect provided by shell fragments or other large platy bioclasts. *Growth-framework* porosity refers to

large voids between branching or platy elements of a colonial organism. Claims that this is a common and significant type of porosity, especially in reefal facies, are refuted by the nearly universal filling of such voids by reef-derived sediments, either coarse-grained skeletal grainstones (λG) or skeletal wackestones–mudstones (λW/M). Four additional pore types (fractures plus three types of dissolution pores) are listed as nonfabric selective, indicating that they can be produced in any carbonate rock type. Finally, there are four unusual and less important pore types listed at the bottom of Figure 7.5 that may or may not be associated with rock fabric.

From this complete listing of every possible pore type, six are recognized as being of major importance to reservoir facies development in carbonate rocks: interparticle (BP), intraparticle (WP), intercrystalline (BC), moldic (MO), fracture (FR), and vuggy (VUG). The fact that only two of these (BP and WP) are primary in origin emphasizes the role of diagenesis in porosity development in carbonate reservoirs.

A direct relationship exists between the most common pore types observed in carbonate rocks (Choquette and Pray, 1970) and carbonate textures (Figure 7.6). The strong association of BC porosity with dolomites, growth-framework (GF) porosity with boundstones, and BP and keystone vug (KV) porosity with grainstones further demonstrates that a rock's composition and texture control (or at least limit) the types of porosity that may be developed. Figure 7.7 shows the average porosity of carbonate reservoirs plotted against the environment of deposition, using as a data set all fields described in *Carbonate Petroleum Reservoirs* by Roehl and Choquette (1985). The relationship between permeability

Table 7.2 Compilation of 24 Standard Microfacies[a]

Depositional Environment	Carbonate	Facies	Remarks
BASIN and LOWER SLOPE	1. SPICULITE	ⵟ TW/M	
	2. MICROBIOCLASTIC CALCISILTITE	λ ⊙G/P	silt-sized; cross-bedded
	3. PELAGIC LIME MUDSTONE	ⵜ W/M+⍉	Halobia common; may have graptolites
MIDDLE and UPPER SLOPE	4. MICROBRECCIA of BIOCLASTIC LITHOCLASTIC PACKSTONE	▷ λⵠP	
	5. BIOCLASTIC GRAINSTONE/PACKSTONE	λ G/P	
	6. REEF RUDSTONE	⊕ R ⅅR ⵟⵒR	
REEF or OUTER SHELF	7. BOUNDSTONE	B = BA, BI, or FR e.g., ⵒB ⊕B ⍰B ⵟⵒF ⅅBI	
MIDDLE SHELF	8. WHOLE-FOSSIL WACKESTONE	δ_w W	
	9. BIOCLASTIC WACKESTONE	θ λW+●	
	10. COATED, WORN BIOCLASTS IN MICRITE (P&W'S)	◎ P/W	
SHOALS	11. COATED BIOCLASTS IN SPARITE (GRAINSTONES)	◎ ●G	
	12. COQUINA, SHELL HASH, BIOCLASTIC GRAINSTONE OR RUDSTONE	⍉ G λG/R	may have dasyclads
	13. ONKOID BIOSPARITE; GRAINSTONE	ⵔ G	
	14. LAG	● λG+ⵠ	iron-staining common
	15. OOLITE; OOID GRAINSTONE	X ⊙G	
RESTRICTED MARINE SHOALS (Inner Shelf)	16. PELSPARITE, PELOIDAL GRAINSTONE, LOFERITE	ⵔ G	may have ostracods and/or forams
	17. GRAPESTONE PELSPARITE or GRAINSTONE	! ⵔG ⵔⵠG	
	18. FORAMINIFERA or DASYCLAD GRAINSTONE	⍉ ⵔG	
RESTRICTED MARINE SHELF LAGOONS (Inner Shelf)	19. PELLETED LIME MUDSTONE/WACKESTONE or a LOFERITE (which is a PELSPARITE with FENESTRAL POROSITY)	ⵔ M/W ⵔλW	may have ostracods and gastropods
	20. ALGAL STROMATOLITE MUDSTONE	⊓ B	
	21. SPONGIOSTROME MUDSTONE	⊓ ⵔB	
	22. MICRITE WITH LARGE ONKOIDS	ⵔ W/F	
	23. UNLAMINATED HOMOGENEOUS UNFOSSILIFEROUS PURE MICRITE	M	may have selenite crystals
	24. COARSE LITHOCLASTIC BIOCLASTIC RUDSTONE or FLOATSTONE	ⵠ λR/F	ⵠ = M cross-bedded

[a]After Wilson (1980a,b).

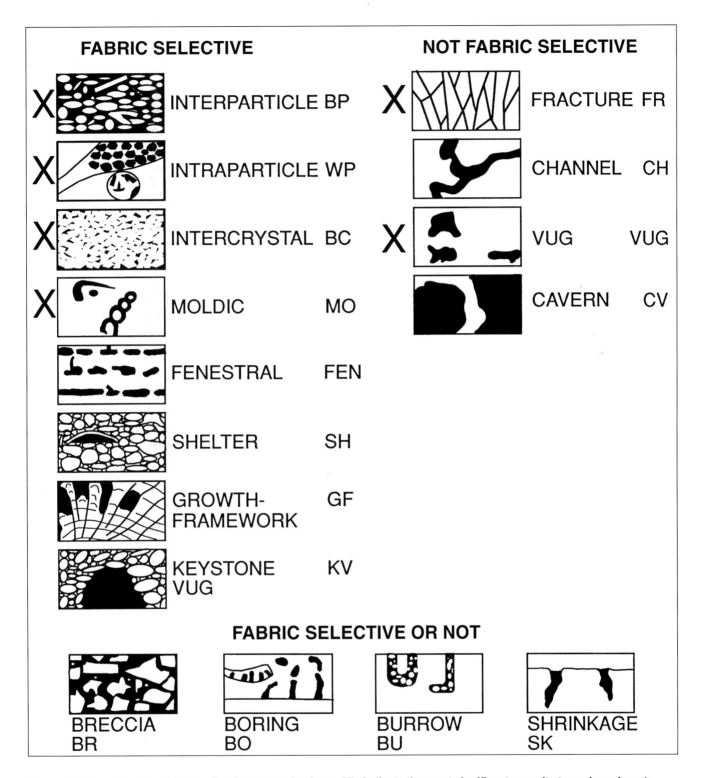

Figure 7.5. Porosity classification of carbonate rocks. Large X's indicate the most significant porosity types in carbonate reservoirs; black areas are porosity. (After Choquette and Pray, 1970).

and depositional environment is shown in Figure 7.8. These two plots together show that the highest average porosity and permeability values are in lithofacies associated with shoal environments, the second highest with reef environments, and the next highest with tidal flat environments. Granted, with only one field contributing to slope facies (i.e., Poza Rica), adequate statistical treatment is not possible.

High porosity and low permeability associated with basinal and, to a lesser extent, slope deposits can be accounted for in a number of ways: (1) ineffective but abundant WP porosity within tests of planktonic foraminifera that make up nearly 90% of certain deep water ooze deposits; (2) microcrystalline BC porosity between clay-sized coccolith fragments in true chalk deposits; or (3) microcrystalline BC porosity (also

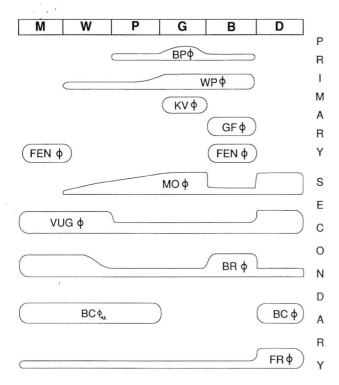

Figure 7.6. The correspondence between carbonate rock textures of Dunham (1962) and porosity types of Choquette and Pray (1970); bar heights indicate relative significance. M, mudstone; W, wackestone; P, packstone; G, grainstone; B, boundstone; D, dolomite.

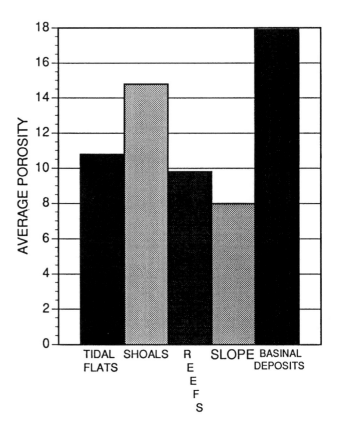

Figure 7.7. A plot of average porosity versus the depositional environment of reservoir lithofacies, based on an equal weight averaging of all fields presented in Table 7.4.

referred to as matrix porosity) between particles of lime mud matrix material of indeterminate origin.

One of the best types of secondary porosity and permeability is developed in thoroughly dolomitized packstones or grainstones in which early BP and WP pores are connected by a medium to coarsely crystalline fabric of dolomite with high intercrystalline (BC) porosity.

In general, carbonate reservoir rocks in North America and Europe, especially those of Paleozoic age, more commonly exhibit secondary types of porosity, rather than primary. This includes intercrystalline porosity (and the commonly associated moldic-vuggy porosity) observed in dolomites and some recrystallized limestones of Mesozoic and Tertiary age. In contrast, reservoir facies of many of the giant carbonate fields of the Middle East occur in Cretaceous peloidal grainstones ($\bigcirc$G), coated-grain grainstones ($\copyright$G), and peloidal bioclastic grainstones ($\bigcirc\lambda$G) of Jurassic age, and in rudist boundstones ($\triangledown$B) and rudist grainstones ($\triangledown$G).

SHELF SETTING

It has long been recognized (Wilson, 1975) that carbonate facies patterns show regular and somewhat predictable trends when lithofacies are mapped in a dip direction from the shallowest to the deepest part of a shelf or basin. These patterns depend on the shape of this profile, which varies in a spectrum between two end

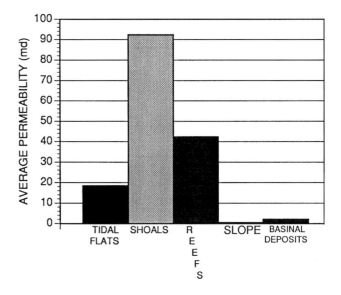

Figure 7.8. A plot of average permeability versus the depositional environment of reservoir lithofacies based on an equal weight averaging of all fields presented in Table 7.4.

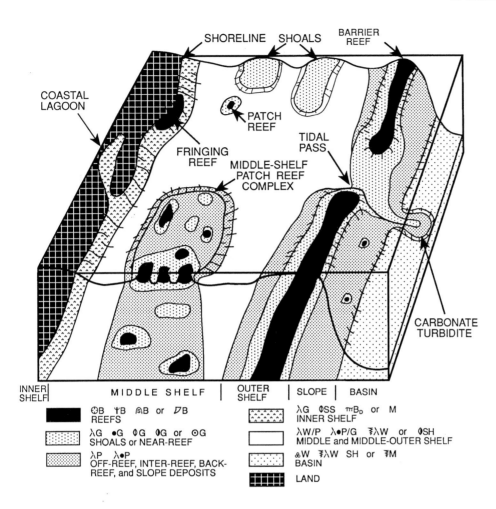

Figure 7.9. Block diagram of carbonate lithofacies patterns on a drop-off profile across an idealized carbonate shelf during dominantly progradational stages of sedimentation during the formation of highstand systems tracts (HSTs), shelf margin wedges (SMWs), and lowstand wedges (LSWs).

members: the ramp and the drop-off profiles (Read, 1982; Wilson and Jordan, 1983). The relative position of sea level on either of these profiles is important in that the width of subtidal shelf facies can vary significantly (Irwin, 1965; Shaw, 1964).

The relative position of sea level is a major point of emphasis in the development of sequence stratigraphy (van Wagoner et al., 1990; Schlager, 1992). Narrow belts of subtidal shelf facies (at most, a few tens of kilometers wide) correspond to lowstand wedges of carbonate sedimentation deposited in front of older stranded shelves, whereas wide belts (up to several hundred kilometers wide) correspond to highstand systems tracts, deposited on broad, flooded shelves (Shaw, 1964; van Wagoner et al., 1990). At any given stage of sea level, a shelf can be divided into inner, middle, and outer zones. (See Figures 7.9, 7.10, and 7.12 for block diagrams of carbonate lithofacies patterns across an idealized shelf and atoll.)

In general, the inner shelf setting is characterized by lithofacies containing euryhaline faunas (lacking organisms associated with normal marine salinity), by sedimentary structures, or by lithic sequences indicating the proximity of a shoreline. Examples include ostracod wackestones ($\triangledown$W) and algal stromatolite boundstones ($\pi\pi$B) deposited in nearshore lagoonal and intertidal environments, respectively. Low-angle accretion cross stratification and evaporite beds are also associated with inner shelf environments.

The inner shelf zone extends from shallow subtidal to high (storm) tide levels. It includes nearshore subtidal environments, coastal lagoons, tidal flats or sabkhas, and beach environments. Consequently, lithofacies variation may be considerable along strike. For example, a 10-km length of coastline may be rocky (e.g., an eroding shore that hosts fringing reefs), sandy (a typical beach), or muddy (an algal flat where stromatolites bind and trap lime mud). The term *facies mosaic* has been used to describe this high degree of variability associated with inner shelf facies patterns.

At the time of deposition, this facies belt ranges from a few kilometers wide to a maximum of about 15 km wide where the gradient of the sea floor is low. The shifting of inner shelf environments through time produces a wide fairway for exploration, best exemplified by three Permian San Andres zones of production from tidal flat deposits in a belt about 30 km wide on the northern shelf of the Delaware basin of West Texas (Meissner, 1974). Generally, if arid climates prevail, inner shelf lithofacies in the profile of Figure 7.9 would likely be modified to include dolomites (mainly dolomitized mudstones, M_D) and possibly evaporites. In addition, the zone of nearshore faunal restriction (the inner shelf zone) would extend farther out into subtidal environments.

Inner shelf deposits can also potentially form around the shoreline of any island. However, most islands, especially those in moderate- to high-energy middle shelf

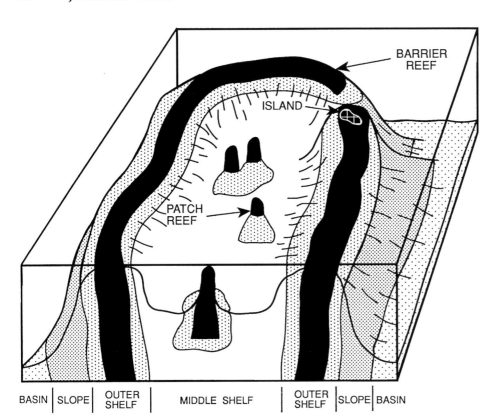

BARRIER
REEF

ISLAND

PATCH
REEF

| BASIN | SLOPE | OUTER SHELF | MIDDLE SHELF | OUTER SHELF | SLOPE | BASIN |

Figure 7.10. Block diagram of carbonate lithofacies patterns across an idealized oceanic atoll during dominantly aggradational stages of sedimentation associated with transgressive systems tracts (TSTs). (See Figure 7.9 for lithofacies legend.)

settings or those associated with open ocean atolls, show little evidence in the rock record that they were emergent. Unless tidal flat deposits formed, island deposits are difficult to distinguish from subtidal shoal deposits (Ebanks, 1975).

The middle shelf setting (Wilson and Jordan, 1983) consists of a broad band of lithofacies that separates inner and outer shelf settings. Middle shelf environments generally include vast areas of subtidal sediments dominated by lime mud (e.g., skeletal wackestones, λW) and account for the bulk of carbonate deposits on a typical shelf. Burrowing in these sediments is common; by definition, they host normal marine faunas and floras. Water depths in middle shelf environments vary from about 2–3 m to 60 m). Shelves commonly lie within normal wave base (about 10 m deep), unless subsidence exceeds the tendency to build up to sea level.

Within the regional backdrop of muddy sedimentation across the middle shelf, sand shoals (grainstone deposits), patch reefs (boundstones and related grainstones), and patch reef complexes can occur, all of which have high potential as reservoir facies. Patch reefs and shoals can reflect considerable environmental variation: some are emergent forming islands of storm-tossed detritus; some are capped with boundstone; others are sand shoals with small heads of reef framework; and still others are sand shoal deposits devoid of any frame builders (Figures 7.9, 7.10, and 7.11).

Generally, a halo of skeletal grainstone–packstone (λG–P) occurs around individual patch reefs, demonstrating the radial transport of reef-derived material away from the reef core and out into the middle shelf lagoon. Dominant paleowind directions can be inferred from asymmetric reef halos or from shoals whose spits point toward shore. Beyond the skeletal grainstone–packstone halo in deeper water off the reef, a background sedimentation of skeletal packstone (λP) occurs, deposited in interreef lagoonal settings. These packstones surround and include all the individual reefs of a typical middle shelf reef complex (Figure 7.11). Farther beyond the reef complex, the regional background of middle shelf sedimentation is generally muddier, e.g., consisting of skeletal wackestone–packstone (λW/P), argillaceous skeletal wackestone–packstone ($\bar{\mathbf{3}}\lambda$W/P), benthonic foram-rich shale (\textbf{0}SH), or benthonic-foram planktonic-foram packstone (\textbf{0}\&P).

The outer shelf setting consists of a moderately narrow facies belt (2–8 km wide) of grainstone shoals or boundstone facies, forming either a linear shelf edge shoal or a barrier reef. Outer shelf facies form consistent linear to curvilinear trends that provide remarkably reliable exploration fairways along depositional strike.

Figure 7.9 show the basic lithofacies pattern associated with progradational sedimentation characteristic of highstand systems tracts. A similar pattern can form farther downslope as lowstand systems tracts. The sea floor slopes gently from the shoreline to perhaps several tens of meters deep somewhere in the middle shelf environment, then rises toward the shoaling environments of the outer shelf, and finally drops down the steep slope (the upper part of which may be vertical) to form an apron out into the basin. There is a general trend from muddy carbonate textures nearshore, to more grain-rich textures offshore near the shelf break and slope (or near local middle shelf highs with reefs or grainstone shoal deposits), and finally to muddy textures out in the basin. The productivity of carbonate grains in the outer shelf and slope is high, rather like a well run "carbonate

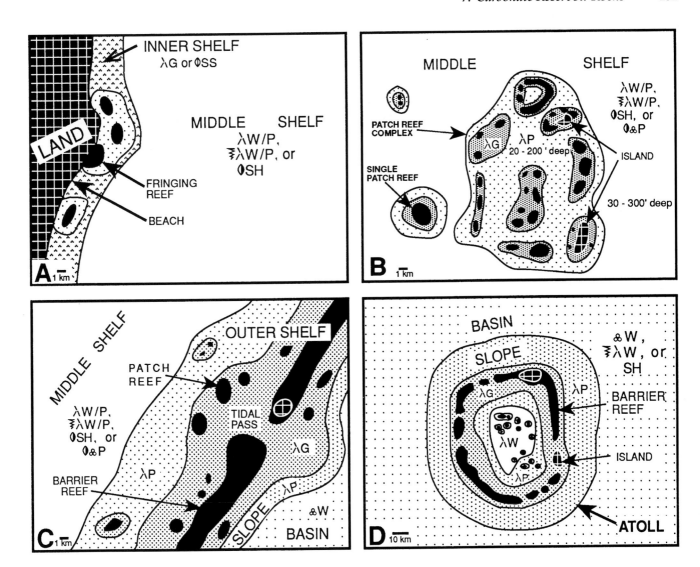

Figure 7.11. Map views of carbonate lithofacies patterns across an idealized carbonate shelf during dominantly aggradational stages of sedimentation associated with highstand systems tracts (HSTs). (A) Inner shelf, (B) middle shelf, (C) outer shelf and slope, and (D) basin. (See Figure 7.9 for lithofacies legend.)

factory" (James, 1984). These offshore areas are away from the input of clastic materials that interfere with photosynthesis, filter feeding, and the growth of colonial frame builders and are positioned near the shelf edge where open marine wave energies winnow out most of the lime mud in the sediments. At the outer shelf, either barrier reefs or grainstone shoals develop, forming long, narrow, nearly continuous lithofacies belts that rim shelves or major structural blocks, while considerable amounts of coarse-grained shallow water sediments slump and slide down the slope. Prime examples of prolific outer shelf deposits are rudist boundstones and grainstones of Cretaceous age around the Gulf of Mexico (Bebout and Loucks, 1977; Enos, 1985).

The outer shelf lithofacies belt is the focal point of Figure 7.11C. It generally forms a topographic high on the shelf to basin profile (commonly forming small islands) and is the main factor influencing facies patterns on either side of it. Facies changes occur as a broad shoal forms and dampens marine energies enough to make

relatively low energy water (the middle shelf lagoon) behind it. The outer shelf is a site of grain production, exporting sediment downslope in front of it and back onto the shelf behind it. The sediment is completely free of lime mud along the open basinward side of this facies belt, but it consists of packstones on its leeward side. Outer shelf patch reefs occur mainly in the lee of the main barrier where they may preferentially develop opposite the mouths of tidal passes. Three such reefs are shown in Figure 7.11C, portraying tidal flow onto the shelf through a pass in the barrier reef. Oceanic swells impinge on the shelf edge from the open ocean basin, piling up broken frame builders and winnowing lime mud. In front of the outer shelf reef is a belt of slope deposits which consists of a mixture of indigenous slope sediment (a rain of planktonics and settling lime mud) and allochthonous outer shelf sediments, a considerable amount of what can be coarse sand-size to boulder-size debris with good interparticle porosity. The best example of oil production from slope facies is the Cretaceous

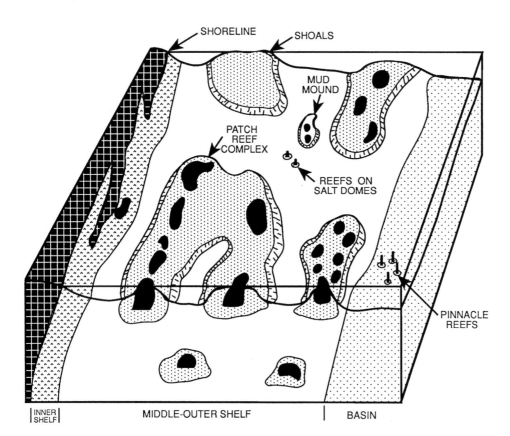

SHORELINE   SHOALS

MUD MOUND

PATCH REEF COMPLEX

REEFS ON SALT DOMES

PINNACLE REEFS

| INNER SHELF | MIDDLE-OUTER SHELF | BASIN

Figure 7.12. Block diagram of carbonate lithofacies patterns across an idealized carbonate shelf during dominantly aggradational stages of sedimentation associated with transgressive systems tracts (TSTs). (See Figure 7.9 for lithofacies legend.)

Tamabra Limestone from the Poza Rica field of eastern Mexico (Enos, 1985).

A variation of the inner middle outer shelf pattern occurs on oceanic atolls (Figures 7.10 and 7.11D). Here, the dominant facies belt is middle shelf, with a narrow rim of outer shelf deposits outlining the atoll. Only small, localized occurrences of inner shelf settings might be represented on small islands. Reef types include the main barrier reef of the outer shelf and numerous steep-sided patch reefs in the central lagoon of the atoll.

A similar diagrammatic approach is used to show aggradational lithofacies patterns (Figures 7.12 and 7.13). Here, the profile is a homoclinal ramp that gently slopes basinward (with dips commonly less than 1°–2°), with numerous reversals of water depth (or dip) occurring at localized shoals and patch reefs. In this profile, shorelines are generally not smooth but rather digitate or barred. Extensive tidal flat deposits are formed on a gently dipping coast. Grainstone shoals or reefs form above any submarine topographic expression: faults, salt or shale diapirs, paleohighs formed as erosional remnants, or older reefs. Water depth and substrate type are critical to facies development, and slight changes affect facies patterns, resulting in complex lithofacies maps. In addition, on ramp profiles, it is difficult to distinguish easily between middle and outer shelf settings. In the proximal parts of the basin and in lower slope settings, pinnacle reefs may occur in a belt subparallel to the basin margin. They are steep sided and have narrow halos of reef-derived material around them. Pinnacles are characteristically surrounded by and encased in basinal shales (or evaporites) that may provide source and seal.

SEQUENCE STRATIGRAPHY

The theoretical basis of sequence stratigraphy takes into account constructive and destructive interference among tectonic subsidence, eustatic sea level changes, and sediment accommodation space and accounts for trends in relative sea level change. The concepts of sequence stratigraphy as applied to carbonate rocks (Shaw, 1964; Irwin, 1965; Sarg, 1988; Schlager, 1992) are based on the lateral correlation of coeval lithogenetic units that are separated by one of two kinds of unconformities: type 1, extending out into the basin, and type 2, restricted mainly to inner shelf settings. Correlations are made on shelf to basin profiles across carbonate shelves and atolls that exhibit one of two main types of depositional profiles: ramps or drop-offs (Wilson, 1975).

A shelf to basin profile shows the general concepts of sequence stratigraphy in time and depth (Figure 7.14). Within this framework, time-equivalent inner , middle , and outer shelf, slope, and basinal environments of deposition can be recognized, and associated lithofacies can be predicted for various systems tracts. With this approach, it is evident that the best developed barrier reef sequences can be expected in shelf-margin wedges (SMWs), in highstand system tracts (HSTs) where reefs can "stack up," and in lowstand wedges (LSWs). Patch reefs occur across middle shelf environments in all systems tracts and in outer shelf settings in transgressive system tracts (TSTs). Empirically, it appears that ramp profiles can evolve into drop-off profiles, but not vice versa, and that they tend to be related to TSTs and to early stages of HSTs.

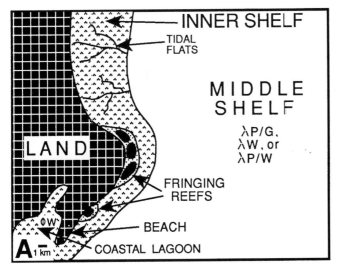

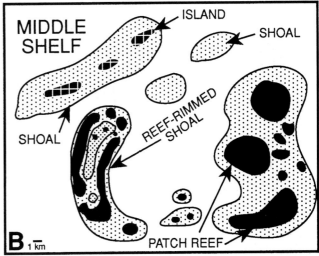

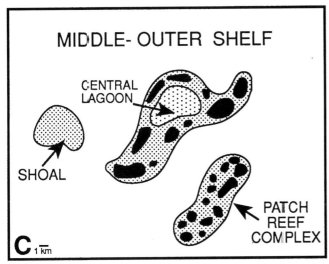

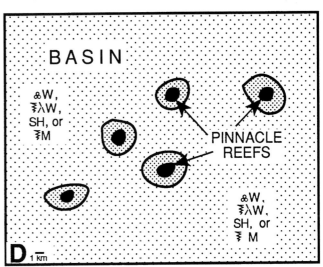

Figure 7.13. Map views of carbonate lithofacies patterns across an idealized carbonate shelf during dominantly aggradational stages of sedimentation associated with transgressive systems tracts (TSTs). (A) Inner shelf, (B) middle shelf, (C) middle outer shelf, and (D) basin. (See Figure 7.9 for lithofacies legend.)

Highstand systems tracts in clastic-dominated systems tracts are notably progradational. In contrast, wide carbonate lagoons (middle shelf deposits) may fill in with a progradational pattern building out from the shoreline or with a regular layering of cyclic sediments, as the outer shelf aggrades or possibly progrades. Clastic- and carbonate-dominated shelves respond differently to sea level lowstands. Clastic material on stranded shelves is uncemented and is easily reworked and transported across the shelf into the adjoining basin. In contrast, carbonate sediments, upon subaerial exposure, are subject to cementation and/or dissolution but not to reworking as a second-cycle sand.

Throughout the development of depositional sequences, two prime fairways of opportunity for the development of carbonate reservoir facies exist: an inner and an outer shelf fairway. Other sites of porosity development include shoals and patch reefs of the middle shelf, porous sand-rich slope and lowstand fan deposits, and pinnacle reefs in slope settings. Carbonate LSWs are

not common in shallow intracratonic basins, but are logically found downslope of thick, older, well-developed carbonate platforms. Sources for lowstand sediments are linear and not from point sources, such as deltaic systems associated with clastic-dominated shelves.

In summary, sequence stratigraphy as applied to carbonate lithofacies describes the detailed patterns of shelf building and basin filling in carbonate systems tracts. Original depositional environments favorable for primary and diagenetic (secondary) porosity can be positioned on a sequence stratigraphic model. In addition, disconformable surfaces can be easily recognized, indicating areas where more intense diagenetic processes such as meteoric dissolution, surface calichification, and dolomitization can be expected. Benefits of this approach are (1) a framework for integrating all appropriate seismic and well data, which make porosity and permeability more predictable; (2) a natural division of the sedimentary column into lithogenetic units where correla-

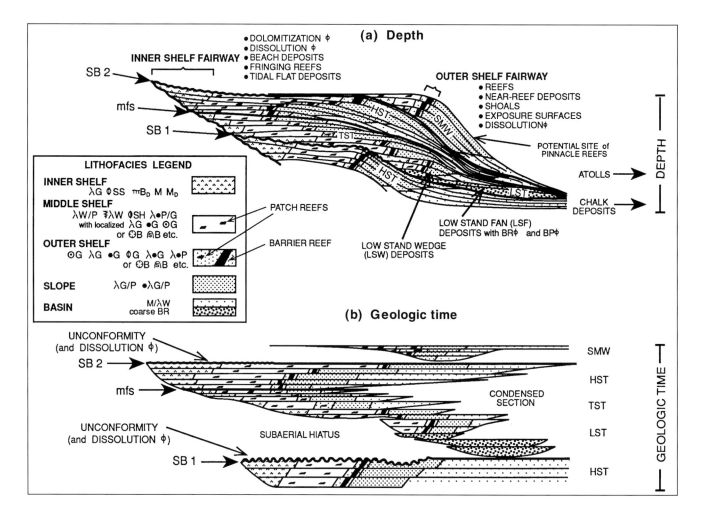

Figure 7.14. Carbonate lithofacies patterns and generalized reef distribution (a) in depth and (b) in geologic time, overlain on the sequence stratigraphic framework of Sarg (1988). SB1, sequence boundary associated with a Type 1 unconformity; SB2, sequence boundary associated with a type 2 unconformity; mfs, maximum flooding surface; HST, highstand systems tract, LST, lowstand systems tract, TST, transgressive systems tract, SMW, shelf margin wedge. Major unconformity surface at the top of SB1 is where porosity (φ) due to dissolution and/or dolomitization is most likely to occur.

tions of fossil-poor zones are treated logically; and (3) logical and somewhat predictable progradations of facies belts, useful for prospect generation involving stratigraphic traps. There is, however, the possibility of "over applying" the principles of sequence stratigraphy to situations where lateral correlations cannot be made (e.g., a single core 10 m long from a rank wildcat well), usually due to a lack of data.

DIAGENETIC OVERPRINT

Porosity in carbonate rocks results from two processes: preservation from primary conditions of deposition or creation by dissolution processes, many of which occur at relatively shallow burial depths. In general, few carbonate reservoirs—the giant Jurassic fields of Saudi Arabia being notable exceptions—display unmodified primary intergranular porosity. If primary porosity remains at all, it is commonly reduced to some degree by cementation, for example, by isopachous rim cement. More commonly, porosity in carbonate rocks is

secondary, formed by various dissolution mechanisms. One of the main debates today is how much dissolution is produced at depth (Mazzullo and Harris, 1992) by reactions involving the formation of weak organic acids, the thermal maturation of kerogen, and reactants from dewatering shales.

Because rock–water reactions mainly control carbonate cementation as well as the development of dissolution porosity, it is important to know the distribution of various pore fluids in the subsurface. The typical distribution of freshwater lenses, mixing zones, marine phreatic zones, and "subsurface brines" along a typical carbonate shelf profile is summarized in Figure 7.15. A well drilled into a middle shelf high on this profile would encounter zones of cementation, dissolution, and chemical stability or inactivity (Figure 7.16), as summarized by Longman (1980), Harris et al. (1985), and Moore (1989). Since most carbonate rocks originate as marine deposits, their diagenetic history can be plotted, using the theoretical considerations of Figure 7.16, by beginning in the marine phreatic zone and following one of two diagenetic pathways: (1) steady subsidence from the marine

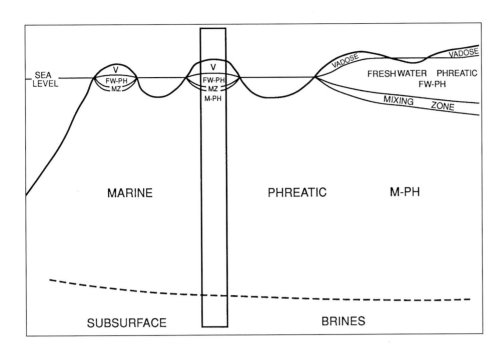

Figure 7.15. Profile of the distribution of subsurface fluids showing diagenetic environments in an idealized shelf to basin profile. The single middle shelf high through which the columnar section of Figure 7.16 is drilled is exaggerated in height to show the freshwater lens typical of most islands.

phreatic into shallow burial and finally deep burial diagenetic realms, or (2) uplift from the marine phreatic to be exposed to meteoric diagenesis, then subsidence back into the marine realm and finally into burial diagenesis. Carbonate sediments tend to build upward to sea level, thus meteoric exposure commonly affects at least inner shelf deposits. It also strongly affects emergent shoals or reefs of the middle and outer shelf. The cause of dissolution porosity remains problematic in that several modes of origin exist: (1) subaerial exposure, (2) regional freshwater aquifers extending out below the sea floor, or (3) deep burial reactions involving weak acids produced at depth from the dewatering of shales or from the formation of weak organic acids associated with the maturation of kerogen. Of these possibilities, the first two—occurring near or at the surface—appear to be most likely because fluids there are exchanged relatively rapidly and contain relatively high concentrations of unspent reactants.

Carbonate diagenesis is greatly limited by the presence of migrating hydrocarbons. As pores become filled with less reactive substances, rock–water reactions are restricted to residual water saturations that coat pore walls as thin films (Feazel and Schatzinger, 1985).

CONCLUSIONS

The lithology and types of porosity that characterize carbonate reservoirs are summarized in Figure 7.17, which also shows geographic positions favoring porosity development on shelf to basin profiles. Wilson (1980a,b) summarized the occurrence of carbonate reservoirs as seven recurrent settings. Table 7.3 lists these generically, whereas Table 7.4 presents a summary based on 39 field studies of carbonate fields by Roehl and Choquette (1985).

From these data and the basic carbonate lithofacies patterns discussed and portrayed, certain trends emerge.

First, inner shelf, outer shelf, and slope lithofacies belts are prime exploration fairways that are relatively predictable. Second, middle shelf prospects are variable in their size and distribution and present more difficult exploration problems. Third, slope facies may exist as a porous downslope extension of an outer shelf fairway, formed as debris flow deposits, and may host belts of porous pinnacle reefs. Finally, basinal or oceanic settings may produce porous chalk facies or may have shallow water carbonate facies deposited as atolls on horst blocks or volcanic pedestals, producing rimmed margins of outer shelf facies that encircle a central lagoonal area with numerous middle shelf patch reefs.

Acknowledgments   This paper was improved by reviews from William A. Morgan of Conoco, Inc., and Perry O. Roehl of Trinity University. Thanks for contributions to Figure 7.1 and Table 7.1 by Mark Longman (Consultant, Denver, Colorado), Ian Russell of Mobil Exploration and Producing, Australia, and Mateu Esteban (ERICO—Petroleum Information, London, England). Computer drafting was done by Ceth Jordan.

References Cited

Bebout, D. B., and R. G. Loucks, 1977, Cretaceous carbonates of Texas and New Mexico, applications to subsurface exploration: The University of Texas at Austin, Bureau of Economic Geology Report of Investigations 89, 332 p.

Choquette, P. W., and L. C. Pray, 1970, Geologic nomenclature and classification of porosity in sedimentary carbonates: AAPG Bulletin, v. 54, p. 207–250.

Dunham, R. J., 1962, Classification of carbonate rocks according to depositional texture, *in* W. E. Ham, ed., Classification of carbonate rocks: AAPG Memoir 1, p. 108–121.

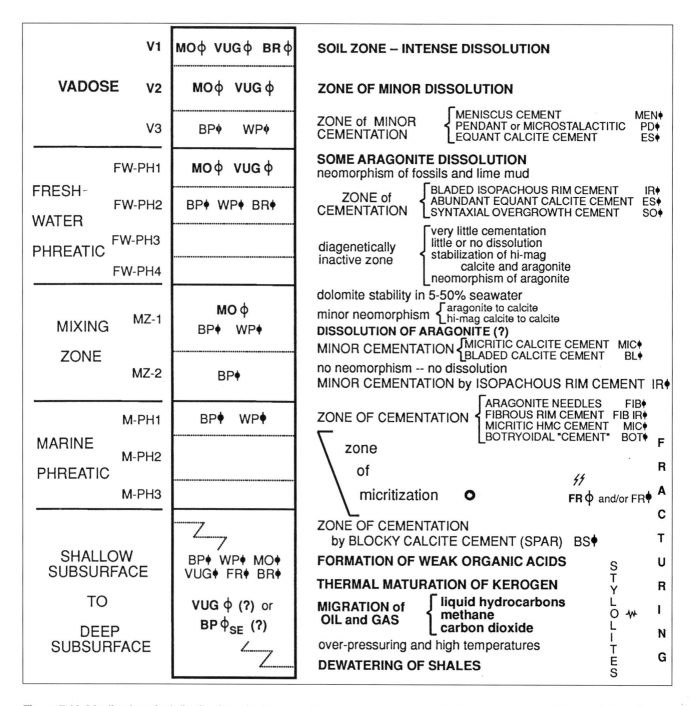

Figure 7.16. Idealized vertical distribution of primary and dissolution porosity and calcite cementation. The vertical profile showing porous and tight zones is taken through a middle shelf high on a typical shelf to basin profile (see Figure 7.15 for the position of this column). ϕ, porosity; ♦, cement. The bold type in all caps indicates phenomena associated with porosity development or preservation; normal type in all caps indicates phenomena associated with cementation.

Ebanks, W. J. Jr., 1975, Holocene carbonate sedimentation and diagenesis, Ambergris Cay, Belize, *in* K. F. Wantland and W. C. Pusey III, eds., Belize shelf–carbonate sediments, clastic sediments, and ecology: AAPG Studies in Geology 2, p. 234–296.

Embry, A. F., and Klovan, J. E., 1971, A Late Devonian reef tract on Northwestern Banks, Northwest Territories: Canadian Petroleum Geology Bulletin, v. 19, p. 730–781.

Enos, P., 1985, Cretaceous debris reservoirs, Poza Rica field, Veracruz, Mexico, *in* P. O. Roehl and P. W. Choquette,

eds., Carbonate Petroleum Reservoirs: Heidelberg, Springer–Verlag, p. 455–470.

Feazel, C. T., and R. A. Schatzinger, 1985, Prevention of carbonate cementation in petroleum reservoirs, *in* N. Schneidermann and P. M. Harris eds., SEPM Special Publication 36, p. 97–106.

Flugel, E., 1982, Microfacies Analysis of Limestones: New York, Springer–Verlag, 633 p.

Halbouty, M. T., ed., 1992, Giant oil and gas fields of the decade 1978–1988: AAPG Memoir 54, 526 p.

Lithology:	D	G	B	M-W-P

Porosity:	Primary	BP	WP	BC
	Secondary	MO	VUG	BC

Position on shelf to basin profiles:	Inner shelf fairway
	Outer shelf fairway
	Middle shelf highs
	Deep water reefs and atolls

Figure 7.17. General properties of carbonate reservoirs.

Table 7.3. Recurrent Carbonate Reservoir Types[a]

1. Middle shelf grainstone bars with primary (or modified primary) porosity (ϕ)
2. Middle and outer shelf reefs
   a. Primary ϕ in boundstones and associated grainstones
   b. BC ϕ and FR ϕ if dolomitized
3. Grainstones and breccias of slope deposits
4. Inner shelf dolomites (BC ϕ and VUG ϕ) with anhydrite seals; tidal flat deposits
5. Dissolution, paleokarst development, and dolomitization below regional unconformities
6. Fractured carbonate reservoirs
7. Chalks with BC ϕ and FR ϕ

[a]After Wilson (1980a,b).

Harris P. M., C. G. St. C. Kendall, and I. Lerche, 1985, *in* N. Schneidermann and P. M. Harris, eds., Carbonate cements: SEPM Special Publication 36, p. 79–96.

Irwin, M. L., 1965, General theory of epeiric clear water sedimentation: AAPG Bulletin, v. 49, p. 445–459.

James, N. P., 1984, Introduction to carbonate facies models, *in* R. G. Walker, ed., Facies models, 2nd ed.: Geological Association of Canada, Geoscience Canada, p. 209–211.

Jordan, C. F., Jr., 1985, A shorthand notation for carbonate facies–Dunham revisited (abs.): AAPG Bulletin, v. 69, p. 146.

Longman, M. W., 1980, Carbonate diagenetic textures from near surface diagenetic environments: AAPG Bulletin, v. 64, p. 461–487.

Mazzullo, S. J., and P. M. Harris, 1992, Mesogenetic dissolution: its role in porosity development in carbonate reservoirs, AAPG Bulletin, v. 76, p. 607–620.

Meissner, F. F., 1974, Hydrocarbon accumulation in San Andres Formation of Permian basin, southeast New Mexico and West Texas (abs.): AAPG Bulletin, v. 58, p. 909–910.

Moore, C. H., Jr., 1989, Carbonate diagenesis and porosity: Developments in Sedimentology 46, Amsterdam, Elsevier, 338 p.

Owen, E. W., 1964, Petroleum in carbonate rocks: AAPG Bulletin, v. 48, p. 1727–1730.

Read, J. F., 1982, Carbonate platforms of passive (extensional) continental margins: types, characteristics, and evolution: Tectonophysics, v. 81, p. 195–212.

Roehl, P. O., and P. W. Choquette, 1985, Carbonate Petroleum Reservoirs: New York, Springer–Verlag, 622 p.

Sarg, J. F., 1988, Carbonate sequence stratigraphy, *in* C. K. Wilgus, B. S. Hastings, C. G. St. C. Kendall, H. W. Posa-mentier, C. A. Ross, and J. C. van Wagoner, eds., Sea level changes–an integrated approach: SEPM Special Publication 42, p. 155–181.

Schlager, W., 1992, Sedimentology and sequence stratigraphy of reefs and carbonate platforms: AAPG Continuing Education Notes Series 34, 71 p.

Schmoker, J. W., K. B. Krystinik, and R. B. Halley, 1985, Selected characteristics of limestone and dolomite reservoirs in the United States: AAPG Bulletin, v. 69, p. 733–741.

Shaw, A. B., 1964, Time in Stratigraphy: New York, McGraw-Hill, 353 p.

St. John, B., 1980, Sedimentary Basins of the World (map compilation): AAPG map.

Swanson, R. G., 1981, Sample examination manual: AAPG Methods in Exploration Series, 66 p.

van Wagoner, J. C., R. M. Mitchum,. Jr., K. M. Campion, and V. D. Rahmanian, 1990, Siliciclastic sequence stratigraphy in well logs, cores, and outcrops: concepts for high-resolution correlation of time and facies: AAPG Methods in Exploration Series 7, 55 p.

Wilson, J. L., 1975, Carbonate Facies in Geologic History: New York, Springer–Verlag, 471 p.

Wilson, J. L., 1980a, A review of carbonate reservoirs, *in* A. D. Miall, ed., Facts and principles of world petroleum occurrence: Canadian Society of Petroleum Geologists Memoir 6, p. 95–115.

Wilson, J. L., 1980b, Limestone and dolomite reservoirs, *in* G. D. Hobson, ed., Developments in Petroleum Geology, v. 2: Essex, U.K., Applied Science Publishers, p. 1–52.

Wilson, J. L., and C. F. Jordan, 1983, Middle shelf, *in* P. A. Scholle; D. G. Bebout, and C. H. Moore, eds., Carbonate depositional environments: AAPG Memoir 33, p. 298–343.

Table 7.4. Summary of Lithofacies and Porosity Types from Carbonate Reservoirs Around the World[a]

Field Name	Location	Formation	Age	Type of Profile	Shelf Setting	Environment of Deposition	Producing Lithofacies[b]	Porosity Type(s)	Porosity (%) Range	Porosity (%) Avg	Permeability Range	Permeability Avg
Puckett	Texas	Ellenberger	Ord	Ramp	Inner	Tidal Flat	⁄⁄▷ D	BR BC FR	0-12	3.5	0-169	10-50
Cabin Creek	Montana	Red River	Ord	Ramp	Inner	Tidal Flat	λ●W/M$_D$	MO VUG BC BP	1-25	13	0-142	8
Killdear	N. Dakota	Red River	Ord	Ramp	Inner	Tidal Flat	πB$_D$ (B zone)	BC	7-15	12-15	na	na
Killdear	N. Dakota	Red River	Ord	Ramp	Inner	Tidal Flat	θλW$_D$ (D zone)	BC MV FR	0-25	12-25	na	na
Pennel	Montana	Red River	Ord	Ramp	Inner	Tidal Flat	λW/M$_D$ ●W/P$_D$ ≡M$_D$	BC MV FR	2-22	11	<0.1-35	9
Cabin Creek	Montana	Interlake	Sil	Ramp	Inner	Tidal Flat	πB$_D$ ≡M$_D$ D>ΣG$_D$	BC MV FR BR	6-23	15	0.1-X	5
Mt. Everette	Oklahoma	Clarita	Sil	Ramp	Middle	Shoals	★P/G$_D$ λW/P$_D$	MO	0-15	8	0-560	93
SW Reading	Oklahoma	Henryhouse	SII	Ramp	Middle	Shoals	●G	BP	0-20	7	0.1->30	na
Belle River Mills	Michigan	Guelph	SII	Ramp	Slope	Pinnacle Reef	πB$_D$ ⑤⊙B$_D$ ★#W$_D$	VUG CAV	3-30	10	5-1000	8
Rainbow A Pool	Alberta	Keg River	Dev	Drop-off	Middle	Reef	⑤B$_D$	BP WP BC MV FR	3-15	10.1	x-570	184
NW Lisbon	Utah	Leadville	Miss	Ramp	Inner	Tidal Flat	λ●W/P$_D$ ▷λ●W/P$_D$	MO BC BR FR	1-12	5.5	0.01-100	22
Little Knife	N. Dakota	Mission Canyon	Miss	Ramp	Inner	Tidal Flat	λW$_D$ ●W/P$_D$	MO BC	8.5-27	14	1.0-167	30
Glenburn	N. Dakota	Mission Canyon	Miss	Ramp	Inner	Tidal Flat	●W ●G/P	FEN VUG BP	15-20	17.3	na	23
N Bridgeport	Illinois	Ste. Genevieve	Miss	Ramp	Middle	Shoal	●G	BP WP	2-22	12	0.1-9500	115
N Bridgeport	Illinois	Ste. Genevieve	Miss	Ramp	Middle	Subtidal	λW/M$_D$	BC MO	13-40	27	0.7-130	12
Seminole SE	Texas	Strawn	Penn	Drop-off	Outer	Reef	λ (λG+●●) ≋W/P	BC VUG CH	3-18	13	0.1-80	29
Happy	Kansas	Lansing-K. City	Penn	Drop-off	Middle	Algal Mounds	≋W/P λG	MO VUG	2-12	4	0.1-900	1
Seberger	Kansas	Lansing-K. City	Penn	Drop-off	Middle	Algal Mounds	≋W/P λG	MO VUG	2-12	4	0.1-900	1
Tarchaly	Poland	Zechstein	Perm	Ramp	Inner	Tidal Flat	●G$_D$ M$_D$	BP	na	8.2	na	0.3
Rybaki	Poland	Zechstein	Perm	Ramp	Inner	Tidal Flat	●G$_D$ M$_D$	BP	na	3.5	na	na
Sulecir	Poland	Zechstein	Perm	Ramp	Inner	Tidal Flat	---	BP	na	10.6	na	5.7
N Anderson Rch	New Mexico	Bursum	Perm	Drop-off	Middle	Patch Reef	▲≋B ▲λG ▲λP/W	BP SH MV	1.2-12.5	9.6	0.1->1000	124
Morton	New Mexico	Hueco	Perm	Drop-off	Middle	Tidal Flat	≋BA λG/P	MO BP GF	3-20	7	na	67
Reeves	Texas	San Andres	Perm	Drop-off	Inner	Tidal Flat	λW/M$_D$	BC MO VUG	7.8-17.6	10.4	0.01-230	2.2
Blalock Lake E.	Texas	Wolfcamp	Perm	Drop-off	Outer	Barrier Reef	≋BA/M #▲B/G ●G	MO VUG BP	8-10	9	na	na
Qatif	Saudi Arabia	Arab C	Jur	Ramp	Mid/Inner	Shoals	✥OP/G$_D$	BP MO BC	12-25	na	12-100	na
Qatif	Saudi Arabia	Arab C	Jur	Ramp	Mid/Inner	Shoals	✥OP/G	BP MO	25-31	na	80-100	na
Qatif	Saudi Arabia	Arab C	Jur	Ramp	Mid/Inner	Shoals	●●G	BP MO	21-31	na	250-5000	na
Qatif	Saudi Arabia	Arab D	Jur	Ramp	Mid/Inner	Shoals	●G	BP	5-25	na	4-500	na
Qatif	Saudi Arabia	Arab D	Jur	Ramp	Mid/Inner	Shoals	●G$_D$	BP MO BC	15-26	na	50-500	na
Coulommes	France	CC + Dalle Nacree	Jur	Ramp	Middle	Shoals	●G/P ●λG/P OW	MO BP	5-30	15	na	na
Chatom	Arkansas	Smackover	Jur	Ramp	Inner	Shoals	●G$_D$	BC MO VUG	20-35	25	40-200	63
Mt Vernon	Arkansas	Smackover	Jur	Ramp	Inner	Shoals	●G ●λG	BC MO	13-18	13	0.01-1250	108
Hico Knowles	Louisiana	Smackover	Jur	Ramp	Mid/Outer	Reef	✥●FR λR/P	BP MO	10-18	15	1-25	3
La Paz	Venezuela	Cogollo	Cret	Drop-off	Outer	Shoals	✥λG ✦W/P	MO BP WP FR	2-12	na	0-80	2
Fateh	Dubai	Mishrif	Cret	Ramp	Outer	Reef	✦G/P ✦B	MV BP WP	1-25	19	1-102	30
Sunniland	Florida	Sunniland	Cret	Drop-off	Middle	Shoals	✦G D	BP MO BC	0-30	18	1-1000	65
Poza Rica	Mexico	Tamabra	Cret	Drop-off	Distal Slope	Debris Flow	λG ▷ΣλG	MO VUG BP	na	8	0.01-700	0.3-0.6
Garoupa & Pampo	Brazil	Macae	Cret	Drop-off	Middle	Shoal	✦P	MO VUG BP	18-30	20	50-2450	200
Fairway	Texas	James	Cret	Drop-off	Middle	Patch Reef	✦B/W λG	MO BP	na	11	3-27	na
Ekofisk	North Sea	Ekofish-Tor	Cret-Pal	Drop-off	Basinal	Pelagic Sheets	⊕M	BP FR	0-45	32	0.1-1000	1.0
Gachsaran and Hakimeh	Iran	Asmari	Oligo-Mio	Drop-off	Middle	Lagoonal muds	λW/P D	FR BC MO	na	na	na	na
West Cat Canyon	California	Monterey	Mio	Drop-off	Oceanic	Pelagic Sheets	D CHT	FR	na	12	na	186
Nido A & B	Philippines	St. Paul	Mio	Drop-off	Middle	Reef	λP/G ΣP	FR MV	1-9	3	<0.01-3.3	1
Fukubezawa	Japan	Onnagawa	Mio	Drop-off	Basinal	Pelagic Sheets	D	BC BP	0.6-30.9	9.7	0.3-8.5	3.2

[a]Based on Roehl and Choquette (1985).

[b]Lithofacies symbols (from Figure 7.3), displayed for producing carbonate reservoirs, are given in this order: lithic descriptor, grain size, and texture.

Magoon, L. B, and W. G. Dow, eds., 1994, The petroleum
system—from source to trap: AAPG Memoir 60.

Chapter 8

Hydrocarbon Seal Rocks

Marlan W. Downey

President, ARCO International Oil & Gas
Plano, Texas, U.S.A.

ABSTRACT

The geographic extent of a petroleum system is defined by the observed occurrences of genetically related hydrocarbons that emanated from a given pod of mature source rock. These related hydrocarbon occurrences and associated migration routes, in turn, are confined and limited by the presence of sealing surfaces. Where confining seals are lacking, hydrocarbons escape to the surface. Therefore, the seal rock is an essential element of the petroleum system.

In the petroleum system, there are two important classes of seals: regional seals that roof migrating hydrocarbons and local seals that confine accumulations. Major roofing seals act to confine migrating hydrocarbons to particular stratigraphic units. Any lithology can serve as a seal for a hydrocarbon accumulation. The only requirement is that minimum displacement pressure of the lithologic unit comprising the sealing surface be greater than the buoyancy pressure of the hydrocarbon column in the accumulation. In practice, however, the overwhelming majority of effective seal rocks are evaporites, fine-grained clastics, and organic-rich rocks. These lithologies are commonly evaluated as seals because they have high entry pressures, are laterally continuous, maintain uniformity of lithology over large areas, and are relatively ductile.

Regional evaluation of the exploration potential of an area should start with (1) determination of stratigraphic position and areal distribution of thermally mature source rocks, (2) identification of the regional seals for migrating hydrocarbons, (3) an analysis of trapping conditions focused on the areas under the regional seals and updip from the thermally mature source rocks, and (4) an examination of the distribution of hydrocarbon shows and production.

INTRODUCTION

The geographic extent of a petroleum system is defined by the observed occurrences of genetically related hydrocarbons that emanated from a given pod of mature source rock. These related hydrocarbon occurrences and associated migration routes, in turn, are confined and limited by the presence of sealing surfaces. A *seal rock* can be defined as one that has pore throats too small and poorly connected to allow the passage of hydrocarbons. The geographic extent of seal rocks defines the effective limits of the petroleum system. Where confining seals are lacking, hydrocarbons escape to the surface. Therefore, the seal rock is an essential element of the petroleum system.

Many stratigraphic horizons have properties of a seal; it is important to identify those that define the hydrocarbon migration and accumulation system at the critical moment. All other seals are irrelevant to the petroleum system.

Two important classes of seals occur in a petroleum system: regional seals that roof migrating hydrocarbons and local seals that confine accumulations (Ulmishek, 1988). Most quantitative seal data derive from studies of seals roofing local accumulations, but such field data are related only inferentially to the general properties of the regional seals that must roof and guide the migrating hydrocarbons in the petroleum system.

In a petroleum system investigation, seal analysis should start with a determination of the time and place where hydrocarbons are generated and expelled. Many stratigraphic horizons display properties of a seal, but only those few that are above the mature source rock(s), are regionally extensive, and have a seal–transmission (reservoir rock) couplet are important to a particular petroleum system. Making maps, cross sections, and measurements of all possible sealing rocks in a petroleum province would be an inefficient and time-consuming way to understand the distribution of hydrocarbons in a petroleum system.

Understanding seals that are part of a petroleum system involves focusing on just those impermeable surfaces that control migration and accumulation of genetically related hydrocarbon pools. Maps of the distribution, character, and structural attitude of regional seals are important in understanding the petroleum system.

Where these seal maps are combined with data on the presence (or absence) of hydrocarbon shows, they become a powerful tool in the search for new accumulations.

MICROPROPERTIES

Rocks that are seals have pore throats that are too small and poorly connected to allow passage of adjoining hydrocarbons. A typical rock-sealing surface does not behave like an impermeable plastic sheet but more like a "fine mesh" screen. A rock-sealing surface holds back hydrocarbons only until the hydrocarbons exert sufficient buoyancy pressure to pass through the water-wet rock pores, or *membrane seal* (Watts, 1987). Laboratory experiments and theory allow an exact description of the capacity of a rock to impede the flow of hydrocarbons. Fundamentally, the quality of a rock seal at any given time is determined by the minimum pressure required to displace connate water from pores or fractures in the seal, thereby allowing leakage. This minimum entry pressure (capillary entry pressure) thus describes the buoyancy pressure of the hydrocarbon phase that must be attained to allow hydrocarbons to penetrate through an adjacent surface.

Capillary entry pressure (P_d) of a water-filled rock is a function of the hydrocarbon–water interfacial tension (γ), wettability (θ), and radius of largest pore throats (R), according to the following relationship (Purcell, 1949):

$$P_d = 2\gamma \cos\theta / R$$

This equation states that capillary entry pressure (sealing capacity) of the seal rock *increases* as (1) the throat radius of the largest connected pores *decreases,* (2) the wettability *decreases,* and (3) the hydrocarbon–water interfacial tension *increases.*

Capillary forces of a seal act to confine hydrocarbons within an accumulation. The buoyancy forces of the hydrocarbon column of a static accumulation are given by the product of the hydrocarbon column height and the difference in density between the hydrocarbon and the reservoir pore water. These hydrocarbon buoyancy forces must be matched or exceeded by the resistance of the capillary entry pressure that characterizes the pore structure of the seal. When the buoyancy pressure of an underlying hydrocarbon column exceeds the hydrocarbon water displacement pressure of the seal, the hydrocarbons pass through. Of course, downward-directed hydrodynamic flow increases the entry pressure of seals, while upward-directed hydrodynamic flow decreases the effective entry pressure of the seal.

One can measure in a laboratory the displacement pressure necessary to force a given hydrocarbon through a given rock under specified conditions of temperature and pressure. Such measurements provide quantitative data about the capacity of that seal to entrap those hydrocarbons. Indeed, the displacement pressure of sandstone seals can be estimated from grain size and sorting data, using the method of Berg (1981). Quantita-

tive data are valuable and, where properly used (Schowalter, 1979), can provide an important starting point for assessment of seal capacity. Unfortunately, such "microdata" taken from a rock sample may have limited use when attempts are made to extrapolate rock sample data to the entire "macro" sealing surface that roofs or bounds an accumulation (Downey, 1984).

MICROPROPERTIES TO MACROSURFACES

The difficulty of extrapolating precise measurements made on, for example, a piece of core 4 in. (10 cm) in diameter to the entire entrapping surface can be understood by a simple example. Assuming a domal closure area of 6400 ac (2590 ha.), a core sample of the top seal would provide a ratio of areas of about 1 to 3.5 billion. What is the probability that the "microproperties" characterizing the core are invariant when extrapolated over the entire domal sealing surface? Large extrapolations of data are commonly necessary in geologic work, but it is important in assessing seal properties to remember that average values are nearly meaningless in determining the probability of a seal for a hydrocarbon accumulation. If the sealing surface is a homogeneous, very fine grained claystone or evaporite, the sealing capacity of a casually encountered rock sample is likely to be extremely high. Caution is in order, however, since a single flaw or fracture in dense rock can render the apparent seal totally ineffective. In looking at sealing surfaces, we are basically concerned with the properties of the "weakest" point of the sealing surface. The measured values from a random core sample, unfortunately, have little relevance to the problem of determining the most likely leak point of the seal.

Where the sealing surface is a homogeneous, laterally continuous, fine pore throated lithology, laboratory measurements of the capillary entry pressure of the seal can provide useful data. Such data are useful in assessing the maximum hydrocarbon buoyancy column that the seal can resist. If the capillary entry pressure of a random point on the sealing surface is measured and found to be balanced, for example, by the pressure equivalent of a 50-ft oil column, then a maximum of 50 ft of oil should be expected in the trap, no matter how excellent the sealing surface is, on average.

MACROCHARACTERISTICS
Lithology

Any lithology can serve as a seal for a hydrocarbon accumulation. The only requirement is that the minimum displacement pressure of the lithologic unit comprising the sealing surface be greater than the buoyancy pressure of the hydrocarbon column in the accumulation. In practice, however, the overwhelming majority of effective seals are evaporites, fine-grained clastics, and organic-rich rocks. These lithologies are commonly found as seals because they typically have high entry pressures, are laterally continuous, maintain a uniform lithology over large areas, are relatively ductile, and are a significant portion of the fill of sedimentary basins. Statistical analyses of the top seals of apparently unfaulted structural traps by Nederlof and Mohler (1981) indicated that lithology is the most important factor in determining a good seal rock.

Ductility

The folding and faulting that accompany the formation of many traps put significant strain on the sealing surfaces of accumulations. Brittle lithologies develop fractures, whereas ductile lithologies tend to flow plastically under deformation (Table 8.1). Carbonate mudstones may have high entry pressures, but under conditions of deformation, they fracture much more readily than salt, anhydrite, clay shale, and organic-rich rock. Ductility is a rock property that varies with pressure and temperature (burial depth) as well as with lithology. Evaporite rocks makes extraordinarily good ductile seals when overburden rocks exceed several thousand feet, but they can be quite brittle at shallow depths.

Lithologies having a very fine pore structure and a ductile matrix can retain sealing properties even under severe deformation. Organic-rich rocks contain deformable layers of kerogen; such rocks commonly have a plastic behavior during folding. The flowage of the soft kerogen layers causes high displacement pressures in the relict pores. In the overthrust provinces of the world, where deformation and fracturing are expected to be most intense, ductility becomes important when assessing sealing layers for accumulations. The presence of evaporite top seals is described as being essential for hydrocarbon entrapment in the central overthrust belt of Wyoming and Utah (McIntyre, 1988). An analysis of the characteristics of the world's 25 largest gas fields indicates that all of those in thrust provinces depend on evaporite seals. Indeed, in reviewing the world's 176 giant gas fields, almost all depended on shale or evaporite seals (Grunau, 1981).

Thickness

Several centimeters of ordinary clay shale are theoretically adequate to trap a large vertical column of hydrocarbons. For example, a clay shale with a particle size of 10^{-4} mm would be expected to have a capillary entry pressure of about 600 psi (Hubbert, 1953), theoretically capable of holding back an oil column of 3000 ft (915 m). Unfortunately, there is a low probability that a zone only a few centimeters thick could be continuous, unbroken, and unbreached and also maintain uniform lithic character over a sizable accumulation. The benefits of a thick seal are that it provides many layers of contingent sealing beds and a larger probability that a sealing surface will actually be distributed over an entire prospect. A thick seal is important and beneficial, but it does not directly influence the amount of hydrocarbon column that can be held by a top seal.

Table 8.1. Ductile Seal Lithologies Ranked Most to Least

Ductility	Lithology
Most	Salt
↓	Anhydrite
	Kerogen-rich shales
	Silty shales
	Carbonate mudstones
Least	Cherts

Where traps are created by fault offset of reservoirs, thickness of the top seal can be important. In such places, the top seal can be offset to become a lateral seal, and seal thickness can relate directly to the column height of entrapped hydrocarbons.

Uniformity

Stratigraphic layers identified as having the capillary properties of seals need to be studied to see whether those layers are lithologically uniform throughout the areal distribution of the stratigraphic unit. Identifiable stratigraphic units may vary greatly in their capillary properties with only modest changes in lithology. A stratigraphic cross section of the potential seal unit, using electric log character and lithology, is an excellent start toward establishing whether the seal unit is uniform over the geographic extent of the petroleum system.

SIGNIFICANCE OF REGIONAL SEALS

Most sedimentary sequences contain major widespread sealing layers. These regional seals are characterized by having a broad extent, significant thickness, lateral uniformity, and ductile lithologies. Where these seals are found above a mature source rock and good quality reservoirs, they largely control the regional distribution of genetically related hydrocarbons. A study of the oil fields of the Arabian Gulf (Murris, 1980) provides excellent examples of this interdependence. Two major source rocks are present in the area: the Upper Jurassic Hanifa and the Aptian Shuaiba. The Upper Jurassic Hith Anhydrite and the Albian Nahm Umr Shale are the two principal seals. Hydrocarbon accumulations are concentrated in reservoirs under these regional seals. In areas where the primary seals are absent or disrupted by faulting, the hydrocarbons have migrated upward to be trapped by secondary seals. Here, two petroleum systems exist because each pod of active source rock charges separate traps isolated by mostly regional, but some local, seals.

Major roofing seals act to confine migrating hydrocarbons within particular stratigraphic units. Regional evaluation of the exploration potential of an area should start with (1) determination of stratigraphic position and areal distribution of the mature source rock, (2) identification of the regional seal for migrating hydrocarbons, (3) an analysis of trapping conditions under the regional seal and updip from the mature source rock, and (4) an examination of the distribution and composition of hydrocarbon shows and production.

FAULTS AS SEALS OR LEAKS

An enormous body of dogma is quotable from technical literature providing opinions that particular faults "must have" leaked or "must have" sealed. Without arguing against anyone's particular prejudices, it seems worthwhile to provide some guidance as to when faulting can aid *entrapment* and when faulting *causes leakage* from traps.

Considerable efforts are commonly made by interpreters to identify and map faults; this is proper and important. It is, however, only the first step toward evaluating hydrocarbon entrapment. On an interpretative map, the black line identifying a fault trace does not seal hydrocarbons (or cause them to leak, for that matter). The fault trace is itself only a representation of the narrow discontinuity where capillary properties, fluid properties, and structural dips of the co-joined rock layers have a high probability of being altered.

The fault plane itself can behave as an open fracture in three particular circumstances: (1) a fault plane will *generally* behave as a transmissive open fracture in tensional settings at shallow depths; (2) a fault plane will *often* transmit fluids in tensional settings within geopressures; and (3) the fault plane *can be expected* to transmit hydrocarbons during fault movement (Downey, 1990). In each of these cases, the fault may behave as an open fracture and provide passage of hydrocarbons along the plane of the tensional fault (Figure 8.1). It is sometimes thought that leakage from such hairline-width openings is negligible; nothing could be farther from the truth. Transport capacity (permeability) along planar openings is enormous; a single planar opening 0.001 in. wide in the seal overlying a 500-ft oil column could cause leakage at a rate exceeding 150 million bbl per 1000 yr (see figure 7, Downey, 1984, for details of calculation).

To summarize, (1) it is unlikely that a pure fault trap for hydrocarbons would exist at very shallow depths; (2) a high level of risk exists for tensional fault seals within overpressured sections; and (3) leakage can occur during fault movements. In active compressional settings, the fault plane is rarely a pathway for hydrocarbon migration, as the fault plane itself is almost never an open fracture.

When a Fault Is a Seal

A fault plane surface is often invoked by interpreters as a seal to laterally migrating hydrocarbons; this rarely happens. Technical interpretations often stop after identifying the fault plane in the mistaken belief that the fault plane itself creates a lateral seal. A fault plane is not a magical membrane, an impervious seal instantly created by the fault. In the overwhelming predominance of cases, hydrocarbons pass readily from a permeable horizon on one side of the fault plane to a juxtaposed permeable horizon on the other side of the fault plane.

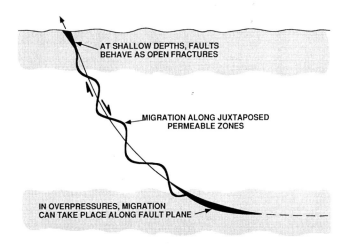

Figure 8.1. Leakage of hydrocarbons along the fault plane of tensional faults is likely at shallow depths and common in geopressures.

There are a few exceptions to this statement. Faulting in areas with abundant thick layers of plastic clays (such as the Tertiary of the Gulf of Mexico and Niger Delta) can cause plastering of clay smears across permeable horizons along considerable portions of a fault surface (Smith, 1966, 1980; Weber et al., 1978; Bouvier et al., 1989). Also, considerable granulation along the fault surface can locally alter lateral transmissibility in juxtaposed reservoirs. Finally, fluid movement through reservoirs joined by faulting can induce pore-filling diagenesis in the reservoirs near a fault (Foster et al., 1987). Such phenomena are real and create important impediments that profoundly affect reservoir production performance. It is doubtful, however, that they create absolute lateral seals to hydrocarbon movement over a geologic time scale.

A simple calculation can serve to indicate the magnitude of the difficulties in relying on an absolute in situ seal to be created along a fault plane. Assume that the area of the fault-joined reservoirs is 1 mi by 100 ft. What degree of perfection of clay smearing is necessary to ensure that the juxtaposed reservoirs will not allow leakage through the fault plane? Let's take the example of a Gulf of Mexico Tertiary sandstone of 30% porosity, 1000-md permeability, and 20-psi differential driving pressure. *If a single square foot of the entire fault-joined surface is left unaltered and the 20-psi driving pressure is dissipated over a distance of 1 ft, then leakage at a rate of about 10 billion bbl/m.y. can occur.*

Maps of Fault Planes

Faults are most commonly seen and studied in the two dimensions of a seismic section. Mapping of an entire fault plane is necessary if the interpreter wants to understand lateral seal risk on a fault-sealed prospect. A single two-dimensional cross section at right angles to the fault can serve to describe the fault seal only at those points.

Because all faults change their relative offset or "throw" along their length, a near-infinity of cross sections would be necessary to perfectly describe the characteristics of a fault-sealed prospect. Faults that greatly change offset along their length make lateral entrapment across the fault plane difficult. For many types of fault, the lateral variation in offset is theoretically predictable and systematic. Typical growth faults and thrust faults decrease their stratigraphic offset and pass into bedding planes at the fault ends. In interpreting the likelihood that a fault will offset a reservoir bed laterally against a sealing bed to provide a trap, the lateral variation in bed offset must be considered. It is easy to find two-dimensional "traps." Hydrocarbon accumulations require three-dimensional seals. Fault seal mapping requires analysis in three dimensions.

The quality of a fault-controlled prospect is best determined through the actual mapping of the structural attitude of the lithologies co-joined by the fault plane within the apparent closure. Such fault plane maps, depicting the joining of reservoir and seal units at the fault plane, are an important part of understanding hydrocarbon migration and entrapment (Allan, 1989).

Subparallel Faults as Seals

Where a fault juxtaposes a permeable reservoir against an updip impermeable layer, this lateral seal against the reservoir rock may form a hydrocarbon trap. In a sedimentary section composed of alternating layers of reservoirs and seals, the probability that a trap is formed by juxtaposing a reservoir and seal is dependent on the relative proportions of reservoir to seal within the fault-affected section. If two or more subparallel faults affect the sedimentary section, the probability of a reservoir eventually being laterally sealed is greatly increased.

As a generalization, if an interbedded series of layered reservoirs and seals contains 25% reservoirs, a single fault offset provides about a 50% chance that a reservoir might be completely trapped across the fault. A second paralleling fault would increase the probability of trapping to about 75%, a third to 88%, a fourth to 94%, and a fifth to 97%. This example is graphed for one, two, and five faults in Figure 8.2. Careful mapping with high-resolution reflection seismic data may reveal the presence of multiple subparallel faults that can strongly increase the probability of eventual updip lateral seals that would form hydrocarbon traps.

SUMMARY

Hydrocarbon seals are an essential element of the petroleum system. Regional and local seal rocks act to confine and limit the distribution of genetically related hydrocarbons within the petroleum system by the source rock. Understanding the structural form and the areal distribution of the regional seals is a vital part of the analysis of a petroleum system. The local sealing surfaces for hydrocarbon accumulations are often more complex

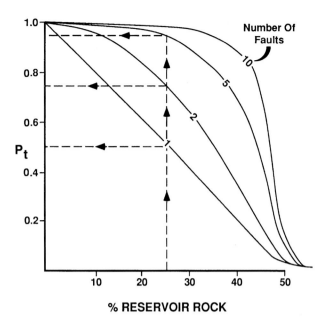

Figure 8.2. Probability of a reservoir eventually being trapped (*P*$_t$) is dependent on the proportion of reservoir to seal rocks in the section and the number of affecting faults. The dashed line shows the example discussed in the text.

than the regional seals and require a detailed understanding of the petrophysical properties of the sealing surfaces. Faulting causes a redistribution of sealing surfaces and needs to be carefully analyzed to determine the three-dimensional sealing surface of an accumulation of hydrocarbons.

References Cited

Allan, U. S., 1989, A model for the migration and entrapment of hydrocarbons within faulted structures: AAPG Bulletin, v. 73, p. 803–812.

Berg, R. R., 1981, Calculation of seal capacity from porosity and permeability data (abs.): AAPG Bulletin, v. 65, p. 900.

Bouvier, J. D., C. H. Kaars-Sijpesteijn, D. F. Kluesner, C. C. Onyejekwe, and R. C. van der Pal, 1989, Three-dimensional seismic interpretation and fault sealing investigations, Nun River field, Nigeria: AAPG Bulletin, v. 73, p. 1397–1414.

Downey, M. W., 1984, Evaluating seals for hydrocarbon accumulations: AAPG Bulletin, v. 68, p. 1752–1763.

Downey, M. W. 1990, Faulting and hydrocarbon entrapment: Geophysics, Leading Edge, January, p. 20–22.

Foster, N. H., H. K. Veal, and C. Bortz, 1987, Fault seals in oil fields in Nevada (abs.): AAPG Bulletin, v. 71, p. 1006.

Grunau, H. R., 1981, Worldwide review of seals for major accumulations of natural gas (abs.): AAPG Bulletin, v. 65, p. 933.

Hubbert, M. K., 1953, Entrapment of petroleum under hydrodynamic conditions: AAPG Bulletin, v. 37, p. 1954–2026.

McIntyre, J. F., 1988, Presence and control of evaporite top seals on occurrence and distribution of hydrocarbon traps: main fairway, central overthurst belt, Wyoming and Utah (abs.): AAPG Bulletin, v. 72, p. 221.

Murris, R. J., 1980, Middle East: stratigraphic evolution and oil habitat: AAPG Bulletin, v. 64, p. 597–618.

Nederlof, M. H., and H. P. Mohler, 1981, Quantitative investigation of trapping effect of unfaulted caprock: (abs.): AAPG Bulletin, v. 65, p. 964.

Purcell, W. R., 1949, Capillary pressures—their measurement using mercury and the calculation of permeability there from: Petroleum Transactions, American Institute of Mining Engineers, v. 186, p. 39–48.

Schowalter, T. T., 1979, Mechanics of secondary hydrocarbon migration and entrapment: AAPG Bulletin, v. 63, p. 723–760.

Smith, D. A., 1966, Theoretical considerations of sealing and nonsealing faults: AAPG Bulletin, v. 50, p. 363–374.

Smith, D. A., 1980, Sealing and nonsealing faults in Louisiana Gulf Coast Salt basin: AAPG Bulletin, v. 64, p. 145–172.

Ulmishek, G. F., 1988, Types of seals as related to migration and entrapment of hydrocarbons, *in* L. B. Magoon, ed., Petroleum systems of the United States: U.S.G.S. Bulletin 1870, p. 39–40.

Watts, N. L., 1987, Theoretical aspects of cap-rock and fault seals for single- and two-phase hydrocarbon columns: Marine and Petroleum Geology, v. 4, p. 274–307.

Weber, K. S., G. Mandl, W. F. Pilaar, F. Lehner, and R. G. Precious, 1978, Growth fault structures: 10th Offshore Technology Conference, Paper 3356, p. 2643–2653.

Magoon, L. B, and W. G. Dow, eds., 1994, The petroleum
system—from source to trap: AAPG Memoir 60.

Chapter **9**

Overburden Rock, Temperature, and Heat flow

David Deming

School of Geology and Geophysics
University of Oklahoma
Norman, Oklahoma, U.S.A.

ABSTRACT

Overburden rock, an essential element of the petroleum system, is that series of mostly sedimentary rock that overlies the source rock, seal rock, and reservoir rock. Generation of hydrocarbons from thermal degradation of organic matter in the source rock is determined by thickness of the overburden rock in conjunction with the physical properties and processes that determine temperature in sedimentary basins. Thickness of the overburden rock is a by-product of the fundamental forces and processes that control the structural development of the sedimentary basin in which the overburden rock is found. Source rock temperature is largely determined by thickness and thermal conductivity of the overburden rock, heat flow, and ground surface temperature. Processes such as groundwater flow and sedimentation may also have significant effects on the thermal regime.

INTRODUCTION

Overburden rock is one of four essential elements of the petroleum system, but on the basis of volume, it is usually the largest part of the basin fill. *Overburden rock* is that series of mostly sedimentary rock that overlies the source rock, seal rock, and reservoir rock, the three other essential elements. In some situations, these other elements may also be part of the overburden rock. The remainder of the basin fill is the *underburden rock*, that portion of mostly sedimentary rock that lies between the basement rock and the essential elements of the petroleum system. The sedimentary basin is the geometric form defined by the interface of the basin fill and basement rock (Figure 1.4 in Magoon and Dow, Chapter 1, this volume).

The overburden rock affects a number of physical processes important to the petroleum system. Because of burial, a source rock generates petroleum, a reservoir rock experiences a loss of porosity through compaction, a seal rock becomes a better barrier to petroleum migration, and if oil and gas are kept in a trap at an optimum temperature, biodegradation is prevented. The time sequence in which the overburden rock is deposited affects the geometry of the interface of the source rock and overburden rock, and of the seal rock and reservoir rock. In turn, the geometry of the source–overburden horizon influences the timing and direction of petroleum migration, and the seal–reservoir horizon dictates the timing and effectiveness of trap formation. In this way,

the overburden rock is important to the generation, migration, and accumulation of petroleum and to the formation of traps that contain petroleum.

Although the role of the overburden rock in the petroleum system is multifaceted, this chapter discusses only the key role of the overburden rock in determining the thermal evolution of the source rock. Oil and/or gas is generated from organic matter (kerogen) in the source rock through one or more chemical reactions that have an exponential dependence on temperature. For a normal range of geologic heating rates (1°–10°C/m.y.), the main zone of oil generation occurs between 100° and 150°C (Quigley et al., 1987). For these temperatures to be reached, a source rock must be buried by overburden rock through the process of sedimentation. The extent, depth, and timing of hydrocarbon generation from the source rock thus depend on the sedimentation rate and the geothermal gradient. For a typical geothermal gradient of 25°C/km, most oil generation takes place at depths of about 3–6 km. However, there is a tremendous range of natural variability associated with both sedimentation rates and geothermal gradients in sedimentary basins.

Sedimentation rates can vary by as much as three orders of magnitude, from 1 to 1000 m/m.y.(Figure 9.1). Rates below and above these values can be important locally, but burial histories between these limits are most common. The sedimentation rate for a passive margin (e.g., Cordilleran miogeosyncline, Atlantic margin, and Gulf of Lion) changes as it evolves from a rift basin

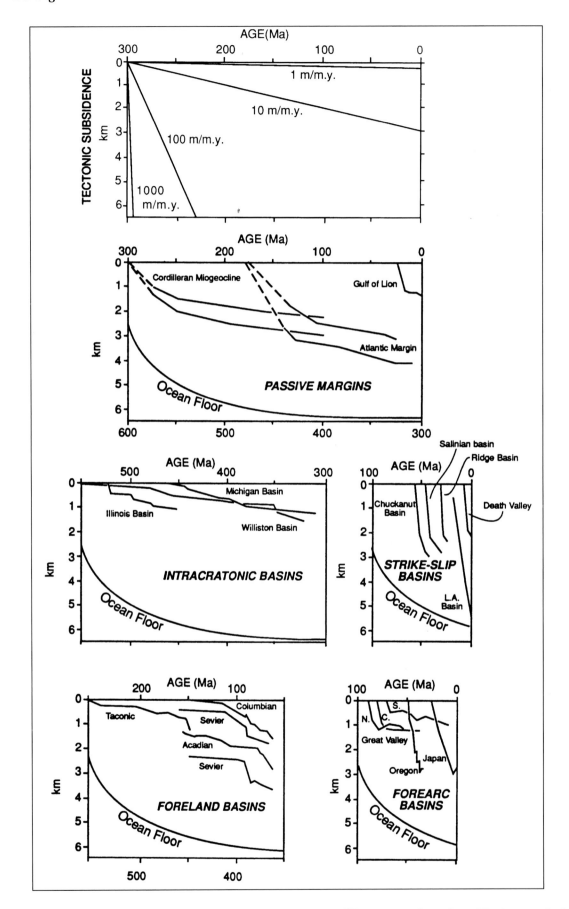

Figure 9.1. Representative tectonic subsidence histories for basins from different tectonic settings. The top graph shows the slopes of a range of sedimentation rates after compaction and is provided for reference. (After Angevine et al., 1990.)

(100–50 m/m.y.) to a passive margin basin (20–10 m/m.y.). The lowest sedimentation rates (~10 m/m.y.) are found in intracratonic basins such as the Michigan, Illinois, and Williston basins in North America (Sleep, 1971; Schwab, 1976; Sleep et al., 1980). Strike-slip and forearc basins are characterized by much higher rates (1000–100 m/m.y.). Foreland basins experience the most varied sedimentation rates, but generally occupy the middle ground. The highest sedimentation rates are found in areas of rapidly prograding river deltas (e.g., U.S. Gulf Coast basin), where sediment deposition can be as much as 1000–5000 m/m.y. (Sharp and Domenico, 1976; Bethke, 1986; Bredehoeft et al., 1988).

Geothermal gradients in sedimentary basins also vary widely, from as low as 10°–15°C/km to as high as 50°–60°C/km. Part of this variation can be attributed to differences in the background thermal state of the crust on which the basin rests. However, the thermal properties of sediments (e.g., thermal conductivity) and physical processes acting within basins (e.g., sedimentation and groundwater flow) are also important determinants.

Why do some basins accumulate sediment much faster than others? What controls temperature in sedimentary basins and its variation between and within basins? How does sedimentation itself affect the thermal regime? The purpose of this chapter is to address these questions by describing why and how sedimentary basins form and the physical properties and processes that control temperature within them.

FORMATION OF SEDIMENTARY BASINS

Sedimentation and Subsidence

A *sedimentary basin* is any downwarped area of the continental or oceanic crust where sediments accumulate and compact with burial into sedimentary rock. The accumulation and removal of these rocks defines the life cycle of a basin, from the initial event that creates the basin through senescence, culminating in eventual uplift and destruction.

A sedimentary basin forms when a topographic low is created in the basement rock through either tectonic subsidence or sedimentation subsidence, or both. *Sedimentation subsidence* can be defined as the downward movement of the basement rock–sedimentary rock contact in response to sediment loading (e.g., a major river delta), while *tectonic subsidence* is the subsidence of basement rock that occurs, or would occur, in the absence of sedimentation (e.g., the deep ocean basins).

In general, both tectonic subsidence and sedimentation are necessary for the creation of a sedimentary basin. Sediments accumulate only in topographic lows, thus a basin must generally exist before the fill. Conversely, sedimentation reinforces the tectonic subsidence that was initiated by a basin-forming event. The load due to accumulated sediments is capable of increasing total basin depth by a factor of two or three (Turcotte, 1980). The

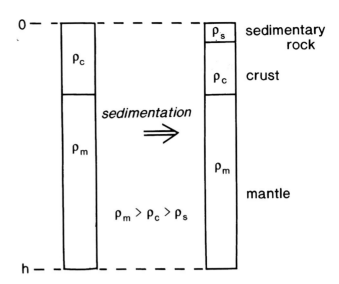

Figure 9.2. Schematic illustration of isostatic subsidence following crustal thinning and sedimentation. Terms are as follows: ρ_c = crustal density; ρ_s = sediment density; ρ_m = mantle; h = depth of compensation.

relative importance of tectonic subsidence and sedimentation as driving forces for the creation of sedimentary basins varies according to the circumstances involved. Major river deltas (e.g., Mississippi, Amazon, and Niger) are primary examples in which sedimentation itself plays a major role in forcing subsidence and increasing the depth of a basin. On the opposite extreme, the abyssal plains of the oceanic basins are relatively sediment starved. They owe their existence to the cooling and subsidence of oceanic lithosphere as it moves away from the site of its creation at a mid-oceanic spreading ridge; sedimentation is limited and plays an insignificant role in determining total subsidence.

Isostasy and Flexure

What controls the subsidence of a sedimentary basin? If we assume that the lithosphere has no lateral strength, the principle of isostasy applies. Isostasy is the fundamental principle governing the development and evolution of topography on the earth's surface. A succinct mathematical statement of isostasy is that density (ρ) integrated over an imaginary column extending from the surface to the depth of compensation remains constant:

$$\int_0^h \rho \, dz = \text{constant} \qquad (1)$$

where z is depth and h the depth of compensation, commonly taken as near the base of the lithosphere, or about 100 km (Figure 9.2). More simply stated, equation 1 is a mass balance equation. The total mass of material in a column between the surface and the depth of compensation must be constant. If the mass (or weight) of the column increases, the column must sink, or isostatically subside. As the column sinks, relatively high density (~3300 kg/m³) mantle material moves below the depth of compensation. Simultaneously, relatively low density air, water, or sediment fills the void created at the top of the column. This process is termed *isostatic compensation*, and it continues until equilibrium is restored.

Isostatic subsidence may be inhibited by the bending rigidity of the lithosphere. Flexural rigidity is determined by temperature and composition; the lithosphere tends to be weaker in areas of higher heat flow, and the quartz-rich crust tends to be weaker than the olivine-rich mantle. The degree to which the rigidity of the lithosphere can successfully resist isostatic subsidence also depends on the width of the load. For typical continental lithosphere, the critical value is about 80 km (Turcotte, 1980). Sedimentary basins with lateral dimensions much larger than this number subside isostatically; the subsidence of smaller basins is resisted by the flexural strength of the lithosphere. If the lithosphere is loaded by horizontal mass transport (e.g., a migrating fold–thrust belt), the tendency of the lithosphere to flex elastically in response to the imposed load can itself lead to the formation of a sediment-filled depression, a foreland basin (Beaumont, 1981).

TYPES OF SEDIMENTARY BASINS

Rift and Passive Margin Basins

The largest set of sedimentary basins on earth are the oceanic basins, covering approximately two-thirds of the earth's surface area. The formation of these basins is well understood in the context of plate tectonic theory. New oceanic crust is formed by the upwelling of mantle material at mid-oceanic spreading ridges where the effective lithospheric thickness is essentially zero. As the newly formed lithosphere moves away from the ridge through the process of seafloor spreading, it cools and thickens, becomes more dense, and subsides through a process of isostatic compensation (Figure 9.1).

A relatively simple thermal model of a cooling half-space can be used to derive expressions for surface heat flow and subsidence of the oceanic lithosphere as functions of time. The theoretical model predicts both heat flow and tectonic subsidence to be proportional to the square root of time elapsed since basin formation. With few exceptions, the agreement of these theoretical predictions with heat flow and bathymetry data is extremely good. There is little doubt that the thermal model of cooling and subsidence is an essentially accurate description of reality (Sclater and Francheteau, 1970; Sclater and Parsons, 1981).

At passive continental margins (e.g., the Atlantic margin of North America), the ocean basin (basement rock) is heavily loaded with sedimentary rock (basin fill), leading to further subsidence as the lithosphere isostatically compensates for the added load. The total sediment thickness in this setting can reach 20 km (Turcotte, 1980). Thus, the thermal and structural evolution of oceanic basins from the initial rift basin to the final passive

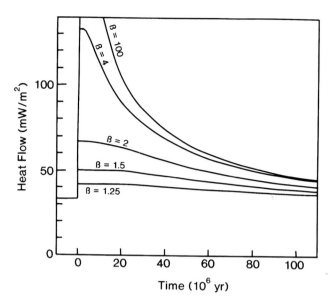

Figure 9.3. Surface heat flow as function of time and stretching factor β. (After McKenzie, 1978.)

margin basin is well understood in the framework of plate tectonic theory. An initial thermal event leads to cooling, thermal contraction, and tectonic subsidence. The tectonic subsidence is then increased by loading from erosional products washed off adjacent continents. In its final stage, an oceanic basin is destroyed through subduction or continental collision. The entire process from formation to eventual destruction typically takes a few hundred million years.

The success of the plate tectonic model in explaining the thermal and structural evolution of ocean basins suggests that similar mechanisms may be involved in the formation of rift basins on continents. McKenzie (1978) derived a simple and elegant model of continental extension as a mode of rift basin formation. In McKenzie's model, the lithosphere is instantaneously stretched by a factor β and the thickness of the lithosphere decreased by a factor $1/\beta$. In the context of the McKenzie model, ocean basins are rift basins for which $\beta = \infty$ and continental rift basins are basins in which the rifting process stopped before completely eroding and splitting the lithosphere.

The formation of a rift basin is characterized by two phases of subsidence. During the initial extensional event, relatively low density crustal material (~2800 kg/m³) is thinned and replaced by higher density mantle (~3200 kg/m³) upwelling from below and isostatic subsidence occurs. The hot mantle material then cools, and its density increases through thermal contraction, leading to a second phase of slower tectonic subsidence. A time constant for thermal events in the lithosphere of about 50 m.y. governs the rate of cooling and tectonic subsidence. Relatively simple expressions for surface heat flow (Figure 9.3) and tectonic subsidence as functions of elapsed time and stretching factor β can be derived (McKenzie, 1978).

McKenzie's model is often applied (and misapplied) to estimate the timing of hydrocarbon generation. The usual procedure is to "backstrip" sedimentary basin fill for the purpose of separating tectonic subsidence from the total subsidence. This is done by applying the principle of isostasy and compensating for factors such as sediment compaction and changes in sea level (Steckler and Watts, 1978; Sclater and Christie, 1980; Sclater et al., 1980). The estimated tectonic subsidence curve is then compared to McKenzie's theoretical predictions and a "best" value for the stretching factor β found. Once β is known, heat flow can be estimated, temperature calculated, and source rock maturity predicted (provided that the location of the source rock in the basin fill is known). This is a straightforward approach, but there are many ancillary determinants that must also be taken into consideration if meaningful estimates of the thermal history are to be made. These include the depression of heat flow by sedimentation (De Bremaecker, 1983), the thermal conductivity of rocks within the basin (Blackwell and Steele, 1989), the surface temperature, and the possible influence of groundwater flow. The relative importance of these intrabasin factors grows with passing time as the influence of the initial basin-forming event wanes.

Intracratonic Basins

Intracratonic, or platform, basins form on continental interiors (e.g., the Michigan, Illinois, and Williston basins of North America; Figure 9.1). They are typically a few hundred kilometers wide and contain a few kilometers of flat-lying sedimentary rocks recording continuous subsidence and sediment deposition over periods of time greater than 100 m.y. (Sleep et al., 1980). Sleep (1971) was the first to note that the subsidence of these basins was, like oceanic basins, proportional to the square root of time, with a time constant of about 50 m.y. This led to speculation that the formation of these basins, like rift basins, was controlled by some type of heating or thermal event followed by thermal contraction (Sleep, 1971; Sleep and Snell, 1976; Ahern and Mrkvicka, 1984; Nunn et al., 1984; Klein and Hsui, 1987).

For an intracratonic basin to be formed by thermal contraction, isostasy requires that a considerable amount of crustal erosion occur during the initial heating, uplift, and thermal expansion phase. For example, if the basin fill is 3 km deep, it would be necessary to first remove about 1 km of the continental crust through erosion. However, in many instances, there is little evidence that this type of dramatic erosion ever occurred (Sleep et al., 1980). Recognition of this problem has led to the proposal of several alternative hypotheses. These include (1) an increase in density of the crust due to one or more phase transitions, (2) rifting, (3) mechanical subsidence caused by an isostatically uncompensated excess mass of igneous intrusions, (4) tectonic reactivation along older structures, or (5) some combination of these or other theories (see review by Klein, 1991). For example, Klein (1991) suggests that intracratonic basins in North America initially underwent fault-controlled mechanical subsidence in response to rifting. The initial phase of basin formation was followed by thermal subsidence and subsidence due to the isostatically uncompensated mass of a cooled igneous intrusion.

Although the subsidence history of intracratonic basins is apparently consistent with some type of thermal mechanism, the exact nature of the initial thermal event, its subsequent evolution, and the role of other factors in basin genesis and development are apparently not well understood at the present time.

Foreland Basins

Foreland basins (Beaumont, 1981) are asymmetric, wedge-shaped accumulations of sedimentary rock that form adjacent to fold–thrust belts. Migration of the fold–thrust sheet loads the lithosphere, causing isostatic subsidence underneath the core of the orogen and flexural downwarping in the adjacent foreland. The foredeep that forms next to the orogenic belt rapidly fills with sediment eroded from the adjacent mountains. Sedimentation amplifies flexural subsidence, and a foreland basin is formed (Figure 9.1).

The foreland basin process continues until the forces driving uplift and orogeny cease. Erosion then dominates, reducing the weight of the mountain chain, leading to uplift and further erosion. The life cycle of a foreland basin is thus typically one of fairly rapid burial and subsidence followed by a much longer period of uplift and erosion. Most source rocks buried by the foreland basin fill probably go through a relatively short heating and maturation phase, followed by a longer cooling phase.

Thermal events play a minor role in the formation of foreland basins. However, the thermal state of the lithosphere influences its flexural strength, thereby exerting an indirect control on the structural evolution of foreland basins (Watts et al., 1982).

Other Types of Basins

Many other types of basins can be defined; these types are potentially as numerous as the heterogeneous crust of the earth. Some of these include strike-slip, forearc, and backarc (Figure 9.1). Strike-slip or pull-apart basins are formed by lateral movement along transform faults, literally pulling the crust apart and creating a void that fills with sediment (e.g., the Los Angeles basin) (Turcotte and Ahern, 1977; Turcotte and McAdoo, 1979). Backarc and forearc basins form in back of and in front of volcanic arcs, respectively, near subduction zones. Backarc basins may form from active seafloor spreading and rifting, in which case they exhibit high heat flow. In other cases, backarc basins are apparently passive features that may merely represent trapped segments of old oceanic crust. Forearc basins are the result of sediments filling the topographic low created by subduction.

STRUCTURAL AND THERMAL EVOLUTION OF SEDIMENTARY BASINS

Are the structural and thermal evolution of sedimentary basins linked? In some cases the answer is yes, but on the scale of a petroleum system, this fact may have little utility in attempts to understand the temperature history of the basin fill. For example, the formation of rift basins is well understood through relatively simple theoretical models that invoke an initial extensional event. In these cases, it is possible to demonstrate with a fair amount of confidence a link between the thermal and structural evolution of these basins. However, this may be of limited relevance in estimating temperature of the basin fill at a time when hydrocarbons are being thermally generated. The magnitude of the initial thermal event associated with the creation of a rift basin decays with passing time (Figure 9.3). Thus, by the time sufficient overburden accumulates for hydrocarbon maturation to begin, the influence of the initial basin-forming thermal event may be relatively small in comparison to other factors.

An example of a rift basin in which the initial thermal event had little influence on the maturation of hydrocarbons is the Gulf Coast basin of the southeastern United States. This basin formed by rifting in Late Triassic–Early Jurassic time (~180 Ma), but it was relatively sediment starved up to about 40 Ma. Rapid accumulation of sediments since that time has increased the burial depth and temperature of the source rocks. Cretaceous and early Tertiary age source rocks are estimated to presently be in the oil generation window (Nunn and Sassen, 1986). Because the thermal anomaly associated with the rifting of the Gulf Coast basin has been decaying for the last 180 m.y., the degree to which the lithosphere was extended or rifted has a negligible influence on the present-day thermal state (Figure 9.3). Factors such as lateral variations in overburden thickness and the depression of heat flow by sedimentation have a greater influence on source rock temperature. For example, Nunn and Sassen (1986) estimate that present-day heat flow in the Gulf Coast basin is depressed ~30% below its equilibrium value by high rates of sedimentation.

On the scale of the petroleum system, the influence of initial basin-forming thermal events is thus of indirect or limited importance in determining temperature of the basin fill at the time hydrocarbons are generated. Temperature of the sedimentary basin fill is more likely to be sensitive to intrabasin factors such as thermal conductivity, groundwater flow, sedimentation, and surface temperature (Table 9.1). The following sections discuss the importance of these four factors in more detail.

MATHEMATICAL DESCRIPTION OF HEAT TRANSPORT

Sedimentary basins are never in complete thermal equilibrium, and groundwater flow may drastically change the distribution of thermal energy within a basin.

Table 9.1. Factors Determining Temperature in Sedimentary Basin Fill

Factor	Importance (Order)	Qualifications
Overburden thickness	1st	Always important
Heat flow	1st	Always important
Thermal conductivity	1st	Always important
Surface temperature	2nd	Always important
Sedimentation	1st	>100 m/m.y.
	2nd	100 m/m.y.
	3rd	<10 m/m.y.
Groundwater flow		
Gravity driven	1st–2nd	Foreland basins
Compaction driven	3rd	Unless focused
Free convection	Unknown	
Initial thermal event	1st (0–20 Ma)	Rift basins only
	2nd (20–60 Ma)	
	3rd (>60 Ma)	

Nevertheless, steady-state conductive heat transport is a useful first order approximation that provides a starting point from which one may later consider departures. Fourier's law of heat conduction is

$$q = kg \qquad (2)$$

where q is heat flow, k is thermal conductivity, and g is the thermal gradient. Applying this to the analysis of temperature within sedimentary basins, we obtain

$$T = T_o + (q/k)\,\Delta z \qquad (3)$$

where T is subsurface temperature, T_o is the mean annual surface temperature, and Δz is thickness of the overburden. Thus, heat flow, thermal conductivity, and overburden thickness are of equal importance in determining subsurface temperature. However, heat flow is generally a more useful measure of the thermal state of sedimentary basins than temperature gradient alone because the geothermal gradient, $g = (q/k)$, varies according to thermal conductivity, which can change by as much as factor of three or four among common rock types.

A more generalized description of heat transport can be obtained by considering departures from steady-state conditions and including advection of heat by moving fluids. The change of temperature with respect to time $(\partial T/\partial t)$ is then described by

$$\rho C(\partial T/\partial t) = \partial/\partial z[k_z\,(\partial T/\partial z)] - v_z \rho_w C_w\,(\partial T/\partial z) + A^* \qquad (4)$$

where z is depth, ρ and C are the bulk density and heat capacity, respectively, of a porous rock, ρ_w is fluid density, C_w is fluid heat capacity, v_z is the Darcy velocity of a fluid moving through a porous medium, k_z is thermal conductivity, and A^* is radioactive heat generation per unit volume per unit time. The extension of equation 4 to two or three dimensions is straightforward. In most geologic settings, however, the variation of temperature with respect to depth ($\partial T/\partial z$) is much greater than lateral variations, and a one-dimensional approximation is justified.

SOURCES OF HEAT

Roughly 40% of surface heat flow on the continents comes from a superficial layer of radioactively enriched crystalline rocks about 10 km thick (Pollack and Chapman, 1977). The remaining 60%, or reduced heat flow, comes from a combination of radioactive sources in the lower crust and upper mantle, as well as a convective flux into the base of the thermal lithosphere. The half-life of common heat-generating elements (K, U, and Th) is on the order of 10^9 yr or greater; thus, the radioactive component of heat flow has not changed appreciably since the Precambrian (assuming no loss or gain of mass). In contrast, heat flow into the base of the lithosphere can vary markedly, as shown by the passage of the lithosphere over hot spots with resultant isostatic uplift, enhanced heat flow, and volcanism (Crough, 1979).

How long do thermal transients in the lithosphere persist? A useful rule of thumb is that the time (t) taken for a thermal disturbance to propagate a distance (y) through a material of thermal diffusivity (α) is (Lachenbruch and Sass, 1977)

$$t = y^2/4\alpha \qquad (5)$$

For the lithosphere, α is approximately 32 km²/m.y., and for an average lithospheric thickness of 100 km, transient thermal events typically have lifetimes on the order of 50–100 m.y. Thus, the lithosphere has a relatively high thermal inertia; background thermal states tend to persist for periods of time that are comparable to the lifetime of a petroleum system. In our studies of temperature-dependent source rock maturation, it is therefore usually relevant to determine the present-day thermal state as a starting point for extrapolation back to the likely thermal state at the time oil and/or gas were formed.

ESTIMATING TEMPERATURE AND HEAT FLOW IN SEDIMENTARY BASINS

Temperature

Traditionally, geothermal studies have been concerned with estimating heat flow, although temperature is the actual quantity of interest. The utility of heat flow studies lies in the ability to infer thermal conditions at great depth from measurements in shallow boreholes. Measuring the geothermal gradient alone is not nearly as revealing because the geothermal gradient may change markedly with depth due to changes in thermal conductivity.

Heat flow is never measured but instead estimated from equation 2 by making measurements of tempera-

ture and thermal conductivity. The quantity that is estimated is the conductive heat flow; there is usually an implicit assumption that advective heat transport by groundwater flow is absent. Because the holes used in traditional heat flow studies tend to be relatively shallow (~100–600 m), it is necessary to obtain continuous, high-precision temperature logs to derive accurate estimates of thermal gradients. However, opportunities to log boreholes in sedimentary basins are scarce. Most wells are drilled for the purpose of petroleum exploration and are either producing or cemented shut. The temperature data usually available for analysis are bottom-hole temperatures (BHTs) measured during the geophysical logging of oil and gas wells. BHTs represent direct measurements of temperature at depths (1–6 km) much greater than those normally associated with traditional heat flow studies in shallow (100–600 m) holes. In this sense, use of BHTs obviates the need to infer temperatures at depth indirectly from shallow measurements and avoids the complications due to near-surface effects (terrain corrections) that plague traditional heat flow studies (Birch, 1950; Jaeger, 1965; Lachenbruch, 1968; 1969; Blackwell et al., 1980; Powell et al., 1988; Lee, 1991).

Unfortunately, BHTs are noisy. They tend to be lower than true formation temperatures due to the cooling effect of drilling fluid circulating at the bottom of boreholes. Corrections can be made for drilling disturbances, but the information needed to make accurate corrections is usually not available (Deming, 1989). It is therefore necessary to take the presence of noise into account when working with BHTs. The process of reconstructing basin temperature from analysis of BHT data can be generalized into three steps. First, raw data are extracted from well log headers and screened. Inconsistent or implausible data are excluded at this stage. Second, raw BHTs are corrected for drilling disturbances. A number of correction schemes are available (e.g., Bullard, 1947; Lachenbruch and Brewer, 1959; Luheshi, 1983; Shen and Beck, 1986); these are reviewed by Deming (1989), who offers practical recommendations. Rarely, however, does sufficient information exist to allow accurate corrections to be made; the best that can usually be hoped for is to reduce the systematic bias introduced by the drilling disturbance. A third stage of interpretation is essential. In the third stage, the corrected data are averaged through some interpretive model that reduces the random error in individual measurements. By necessity, when the data are averaged, resolution suffers, although noise is reduced.

Some aspects of interpreting BHT data can be illustrated through the following examples. Figure 9.4 shows BHTs collected from a small area a few kilometers square near the Iberia salt dome in south Louisiana. These data were collected from original well log headers and corrected for drilling disturbances using the AAPG depth-based correction (Kehle, 1971, 1972; Deming, 1989). Following correction, an average geothermal gradient of 21.6°C/km was derived by a least-squares regression. The implicit supposition is that the regression line (Figure 9.4) is a more accurate description of temperature than the corrected BHTs from which it was derived

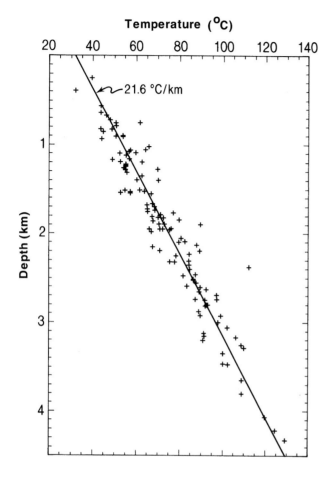

Figure 9.4. Corrected bottom-hole temperatures (BHTs) from Iberia oil field in south Louisiana.

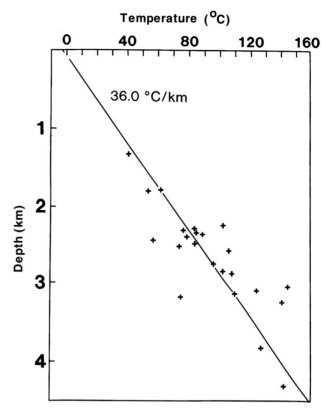

Figure 9.5. Corrected bottom-hole temperatures (BHTs) from North Slope basin, Alaska.

because the corrected BHTs contain random noise that is averaged and reduced by the least-squares regression.

How noisy are the corrected data? Most of the corrected BHTs fall within ±10°C of the regression line (Figure 9.4); the rms residual is about 5°C. Scatter about the regression line thus defines the maximum magnitude of random noise in the data. Departures from the average gradient of 21.6°C/km may also be due to lateral and vertical variations in thermal conductivity, as well as refraction of heat into the Iberia salt dome, to name just two of the possible reasons. If we attribute about 2°C of the scatter to actual physical variations in the thermal gradient, then the average error in these corrected BHTs is probably about ±5°C. Note, however, that this is an average, not an upper limit. There is one outlier near 2.4 km depth that is probably in error by about 30°C. It is dangerous to place confidence in single BHTs, corrected or uncorrected.

A second BHT data set was collected (Blanchard and Tailleur, 1982; Deming et al., 1992) from the North Slope basin in Alaska (Figure 9.5). In contrast to the data set from Louisiana, these data span an area covering approximately 10^4–10^5 km^2. The temperatures shown in Figure 9.5 are formation temperatures estimated from extrapolation of sets of BHTs measured at the same depths in the same wells, but at different times. The

extrapolation procedure is commonly known as a Horner plot (Dowdle and Cobb, 1975), although it was originally derived by Bullard (1947) and Lachenbruch and Brewer (1959).

Because this correction scheme is based on multiple temperature measurements in each well, it should yield corrected temperatures that have less error than those corrected with empirical schemes, such as the AAPG depth-based correction. However, in contrast to the Louisiana data set (Figure 9.4), the scatter about the regression line is much greater. The root mean square residual is about 16°C—more than three times as high as for the Louisiana data. Because the Alaskan data are expected to have less error than the Louisiana temperatures, one can conclude that the scatter shown in Figure 9.5 largely reflects real variation in thermal state throughout the North Slope basin and that this variation is significantly greater than the noise level in the data. The corollary to this observation is that a single average gradient model is insufficient to model temperature in the North Slope basin because there is no accommodation for lateral variation throughout the basin.

Methods of estimating subsurface temperature from BHTs that can accommodate lateral and vertical variations in thermal gradients include kriging (Bodner and Sharp, 1988), inversion for thermal gradients in individual geologic formations (Speece et al., 1985; Deming and Chapman, 1988), stochastic inversion (Willett, 1990), and the method of variable bias (Deming et al., 1990a). Each of these methods has its advantages and limitations.

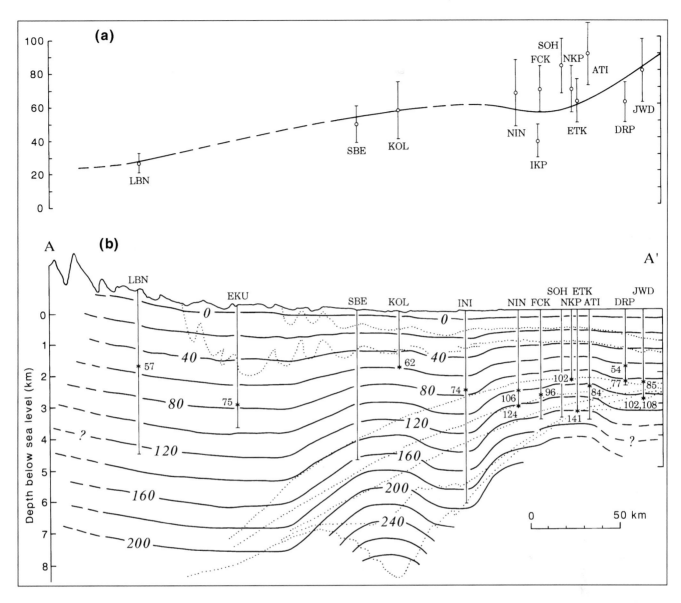

Figure 9.6. Estimated (a) shallow heat flow (in mW/m²)and (b) subsurface temperature (in °C) from the North Slope basin, Alaska . Dotted lines are stratigraphic units of cross section; solid lines are isotherms. Numbers on trace of well bore are corrected bottom-hole temperatures. Abbreviations for wells: ATI, Atigaru Point #1; DRP, Drew Point #1; EKU, East Kurupa #1; ETK, East Topagoruk #1; FCK, Fish Creek #1; IKP, Ikpikpuk #1; INI, Inigok #1; JWD, J. W. Dalton #1; KOL, Koluktak #1; LBN, Lisburne #1; NIN, North Inigok #1; NKP, North Kalikpik #1; SBE, Seabee #1; and SOH, South Harrison Bay #1. (After Deming et al., 1992.)

For the North Slope basin, Deming et al. (1992) used the method of *variable bias*, a conceptually simple algorithm designed to extract the maximum amount of information from the data while simultaneously averaging the noise. The method involves the sequential estimation of temperature at different spatial locations through a series of weighted least-squares regressions. Based on an estimate of the magnitude of error in the data, a decision is made that *n* BHTs are to be averaged through an interpretive model. For each point at which temperature is to be estimated, the algorithm searches through three-dimensional space until it locates the closest *n* BHTs. These are given substantial weighting in the regression analysis; distant data are given much

lower weightings. Instead of all of the data from a basin being averaged simultaneously, only data in the immediate vicinity of the estimation point are averaged. If data density is locally high, local features of the temperature field are thus resolved. If data density is low, it is impossible to resolve detailed features of the temperature field, and the data are averaged over a wider area. Thus, the balance between the need to resolve the temperature field and the need to reduce noise by averaging is largely determined by the data themselves. A complete description of this method is given by Deming et al. (1990a).

Figure 9.6 shows temperature in the North Slope basin estimated from the method of variable bias along a south-north cross-section. Heat flow estimates are also shown, along with error bars. The heat flow estimates were derived from thermal conductivity measurements along with high-resolution temperature logs made in the upper few hundred meters of the same boreholes in which the BHTs were measured (Deming et al., 1992). To obtain accurate measurements of temperature in this manner, it was necessary to compensate for drilling disturbances by making repeated temperature logs over a period of about 7 years and extrapolating to equilibrium conditions (Lachenbruch et al., 1987, 1988). The temperature field estimated from BHTs and heat flow estimates were thus derived from independent data sets. However, both show a dramatic change in thermal state across the basin; heat flow and thermal gradients are both much higher in the north than in the south. The utility of heat flow estimates is the demonstration that the change in thermal gradients cannot be ascribed merely to changes in thermal conductivity related to changes in lithology. Deming et al. (1992) considered a number of hypotheses to explain the observed variation in thermal state, but they concluded the only reasonable explanation involved a basin-wide groundwater flow system driven by topography in the Brooks Range and its foothills. Further speculation suggested that this same flow system may have been the mechanism by which hydrocarbons migrated to Prudhoe Bay. The North Slope basin is thus an outstanding example of integrating information from traditional heat flow studies with analysis of BHTs measured in oil and gas wells. The resulting estimates of temperature and heat flow allow important inferences to be made concerning the mechanism of oil migration in the basin and also constitute a present-day boundary condition on thermal history and maturation studies.

Thermal Conductivity

The thermal conductivity of rocks and sediments is an intrinsic physical property that is determined by mineralogy, porosity, and temperature. Most sedimentary rocks are an aggregate of minerals with pore spaces saturated with saline water. Their bulk thermal conductivity depends on both the solid rock component and the pore fluid. A number of different mixing models have been proposed to relate the thermal conductivity of an aggregate to its individual components (Woodside and Messmer, 1961). The most common of these is the geometric mean model:

$$k_{pr} = k_m^{(1-\phi)} k_w^{\phi} \qquad (6)$$

where ϕ is the fractional porosity, k_{pr} is the thermal conductivity of a porous rock, k_m is the thermal conductivity of the matrix, and k_w is the thermal conductivity of the pore fluid (usually water).

Over the range of temperatures found in sedimentary basins, matrix thermal conductivity tends to decrease with increasing temperature. Most measurements are made in the laboratory at ~25°C and then corrected for estimated in situ temperatures. Sass et al. (1992) suggest

the following empirical correction, calibrated from the data of Birch and Clark (1940):

$$k(0) = k(25)[1.007 + 25(0.0037 - 0.0074/k(25))] \qquad (7)$$

$$k(T) = k(0)/[1.007 + T(0.0036 - 0.0072/k(0))] \qquad (8)$$

where $k(25)$ is the thermal conductivity measured in the laboratory at 25°C, $k(0)$ is the inferred thermal conductivity at 0°C, and $k(T)$ is the estimated thermal conductivity at in situ temperature T. The thermal conductivity of water can be calculated as a known function of temperature (Touloukian et al., 1970):

$$k_w = a + bT + cT^2 \qquad (9)$$

where k_w is the thermal conductivity of pure water in W/m K (watts per meter degrees Kelvin). For $0 \leq T \leq 137°C$, $a = 5.65 \times 10^{-1}$, $b = 1.88 \times 10^{-3}$, $c = -7.23 \times 10^{-6}$; for $137 \leq T \leq 300°C$, $a = 6.02 \times 10^{-1}$, $b = 1.31 \times 10^{-3}$, and $c = -5.14 \times 10^{-6}$. Compared to the rock matrix, the thermal conductivity of water is relatively low. At 0°C, $k_w = 0.56$ W/m K, at 100°C, $k_w = 0.68$ W/m K. Thus, the bulk thermal conductivity of a porous rock is inversely correlated to porosity and temperature.

Comprehensive compendia of thermal conductivity data are given by Clark (1966), Kappelmeyer and Haenel (1974), and Roy et al. (1981). The in situ thermal conductivity of most sedimentary rocks is in the range of about 1.0 –4.5 W/m K, although some lithologies fall outside of this range. Most coals are probably less than 1.0 W/m K and can be as low as 0.25 W/m K. In contrast, halite and quartzite are about 5–7 W/m K. In general, the thermal conductivity of most clastic sedimentary rocks is inversely correlated to their clay content. Most shales are probably less than 1.5 W/m K (Blackwell and Steele, 1989), while clean sandstones commonly have thermal conductivities of about 3–4.5 W/m K. Carbonates tend to mostly fall in the range of 2–3 W/m K. These are all rough approximates that have common exceptions. It is therefore risky to estimate (guess) thermal conductivity on the basis of lithology alone. The average error in such estimates is usually at least ±30–40%, and the maximum error may exceed 100% (e.g., see Issler and Beaumont, 1986).

Due to the unacceptably large error involved in estimates based on lithology, it is necessary to measure the thermal conductivity of representative samples in the laboratory if accuracy levels greater than ±30–40% are desired. Measurements are commonly made on cores or drill chips using a divided bar apparatus (Sass et al., 1971, 1984b; Galson et al., 1987) or a needle probe (line source) (Von Herzen and Maxwell, 1959; Sass et al., 1984a; Lee, 1989). The absolute error of most measuring devices is usually about ±5%; however, the corrections needed for in situ porosity and temperature commonly raise this number to about ±10%. Additional uncertainties concerning anisotropy and sample bias, particularly important when working with drill chips, can lead to uncertainties of ±10–20% (e.g., Sass et al., 1992).

Figure 9.7 shows a profile of thermal conductivity

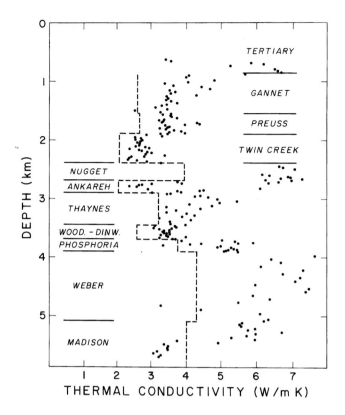

Figure 9.7. Thermal conductivity data, Anschutz Ranch well 34-02, Utah–Wyoming thrust belt. Dots are matrix conductivities measured at 20°C in the laboratory; dashed lines are estimated *in situ* thermal conductivity. (After Deming and Chapman, 1988.)

data measured on samples from the Anschutz Ranch 34-02 well in the Utah–Wyoming thrust belt (Deming and Chapman, 1988). The discrete points represent matrix conductivities measured in the laboratory on drill chips; the dashed lines show estimated in situ thermal conductivities. The in situ estimates are lower than the laboratory measurements due to the effects of porosity and temperature, and range from about 2 to 4 W/m K. The wide scatter of measurements for any formation is partially due to errors in measurement, but most of the scatter can be attributed to changes in lithology and mineralogy.

The number of measurements needed to determine the average thermal conductivity of a geologic unit to an acceptable level of precision depends on its lithologic heterogeneity. For some marine Paleozoic units that are lithologically uniform over hundreds of kilometers, it may be possible to make only 10–20 measurements for an entire basin. However, large spatial variations in thermal conductivity are more typical because most sedimentary rocks tend to have facies changes that occur both vertically and laterally. It is therefore difficult in most cases to collect enough data to estimate how the thermal conductivity of a geologic unit changes throughout a basin.

To overcome this difficulty, concerted efforts have been made to estimate thermal conductivity from geophysical well logs. In many instances, strong correlations have been found between thermal conductivity and one or more log parameters such as resistivity, seismic velocity, and density (Houbolt and Wells, 1980; Reiter et al., 1980; Vacquier et al., 1988; Blackwell and Steele, 1989). In other cases, mineralogy has been estimated from well logs, and the thermal conductivity of the bulk rock estimated from laboratory-derived values for different mineralogies (Brigaud and Vasseur, 1989; Brigaud et al., 1990; Demongodin et al., 1991). The limitation of all of these methods is the lack of an accurate mineralogy log. Matrix thermal conductivity is determined by mineralogic composition; correlations and inferences found to be valid in specific instances cannot be generalized. Thus, at the present time, there is no simple algorithm for estimating thermal conductivity from well logs that is demonstrably accurate. However, well logs may prove useful in interpolating between measurement sites when log parameters can be calibrated by laboratory measurements.

CONTROLS ON TEMPERATURE IN SEDIMENTARY BASINS

Heat Flow and Thermal Conductivity

Because the primary mode of heat transport in the crust is conduction, both heat flow (determined from equation 2) and thermal conductivity (measured directly) are of first-order and equal importance in determining temperature in sedimentary basin fill.

Heat flow is inversely correlated to tectonic age (Vitorello and Pollack, 1980; Morgan, 1984) and is depressed by sedimentation (see later discussion). Heat flow in young (<25 Ma) rift basins can be as high as 90–120 mW/m² or higher, but it decreases with increasing age. Foreland basins are typically associated with post-Precambrian orogenic belts and therefore tend to have heat flows in the range of 50–70 mW/m². Intracratonic basins generally have modest heat flows in the range of 30–50 mW/m², reflecting their location on old, stable cratons. Other types of basins, such as pull-apart or backarc basins (e.g., the Salton trough; Lachenbruch et al., 1985) may have young tectonic ages and can have high heat flows. Heat flow in basins subject to sedimentation rates higher than 100 m/m.y. (e.g., passive margins) can be extremely depressed.

Thermal conductivity varies by as much as a factor of three or four among common lithologies. However, any relatively thick stratigraphic section tends to be composed of a variety of different lithologies. Some of these may have thermal conductivities that are relatively high and some relatively low. A useful rule of thumb is that the average thermal conductivity of a section containing diverse lithologies is about 2.5 W/m K. It is unusual to find a lithologically diverse section of sedimentary rocks with an average thermal conductivity lower than 1.5 W/m K or higher than 3.0 W/m K. However, a variation of 100% is of first-order importance.

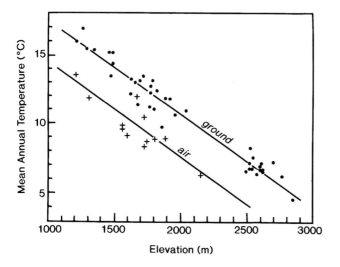

Figure 9.8. Mean annual air temperatures (+) from metero-
logic data (collected by author), and mean annual ground
temperatures (•) estimated from extrapolation of borehole
temperature logs from the north-central Colorado Plateau.
(Made by Bodell and Chapman, 1982.)

Surface Temperature

Although it is often ignored, surface temperature (T_o)
is an important boundary condition on geothermal
conditions. The temperature at the earth's surface is
determined by climate and has diurnal and annual cycles
that rapidly attenuate in the subsurface. By applying
equation 5, it can be seen that the annual variation of
temperature propagates no deeper than about 10 m into
the subsurface. Thus, the quantity of interest in geothermal studies (T_o) is a long term mean, a fictional
quantity that is usually estimated by the linear extrapolation of a borehole temperature log to the surface. Observations have shown that extrapolated borehole temperatures are closely related to mean annual air temperatures,
but that ground temperatures are always higher by
about 2°–3°C (Figure 9.8). This discrepancy is commonly
attributed to the insulating effect of snow cover in
winter. However, the offset between mean annual
ground and air temperatures is also found at low latitude
sites (e.g., Howard and Sass, 1964). Mean annual air
temperature on the earth's surface is ~16°C, varying
from ~25°C at the equator, to ~–22°C at the poles (Gross,
1993). Air temperatures also decrease with elevation;
lapse rates typically range from –4 to –10°C/km.

Air and ground temperatures vary not only spatially
but also have short and long term temporal trends. From
about 1400 to 1900, air temperatures were about 0.5°C
colder than present day (the "little ice age"). Before that,
from about 1000 to 1400 A.D., there was a Medieval
warm period when air temperatures were about 0.5°C
higher than present day. . Over the past 1 m.y., temperatures have fluctuated about 5–6°C as the glaciers
retreated and advanced in a series of ice ages. The last
such ice age ended about 10,000 yr ago as temperatures
rose 5–6°C, coincident with the emergence of civilization
(Folland et al., 1990). Since Late Cretaceous time (70 Ma),

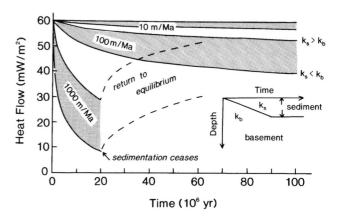

Figure 9.9. Effect of sedimentation on surface heat flow.

studies of oxygen isotope ratios have shown that the
temperature of seawater has systematically decreased by
about 10°–15°C (Savin, 1984). If this decrease is interpreted to indicate a global cooling with concomitant
lower air and ground temperatures, then it is probably
reasonable to take this effect into account when modeling
the thermal evolution of sedimentary basins. The degree
to which shorter term variations in climate (e.g., ice ages)
have effected subsurface temperature profiles can be
estimated by application of equation 5 (Birch, 1948).

Sedimentation

Sedimentation depresses heat flow, and the depression persists long after sedimentation ceases (assuming
no erosion). The magnitude of depression depends on
the thermal conductivity of the sediments deposited and
the rate and duration of sedimentation. A one-dimensional numerical model (Deming and Chapman, 1989)
can be used to estimate the effect of sedimentation on
near-surface heat flow for sediments of different thermal
conductivities (Figure 9.9). The initial background heat
flow in the model is 60 mW/m², the thermal conductivity of the basement is 2.5 W/m K, and the sedimentation rate varies from 10 to 1000 m/m.y. The thermal
conductivity of the sediments deposited varies from 1.0
to 4.0 W/m K.

Heat flow is significantly depressed by sedimentation
rates on the order of 100 m/m.y. or greater. The lower
the thermal conductivity of the sediments, the greater the
reduction in heat flow. Once sedimentation ceases, it
may take tens of millions of years or more for the heat
flow deficit at the surface to be alleviated. For example, if
sedimentation proceeds at 1000 m/m.y. for 20 m.y. and
then stops, it takes 40 m.y. for the heat flow deficit to be
reduced to half of its maximum value (Figure 9.9).

Some interesting and unexpected conclusions can be
drawn from this example. Because the depression of heat
flow by sedimentation tends to persist long after sedimentation ceases, underburden rock deposited before a
source rock may affect the eventual maturation of
organic material in the source rock. Also, if sedimentation proceeds at a constant rate, but the thermal conductivity of the sediments deposited increases, heat flow

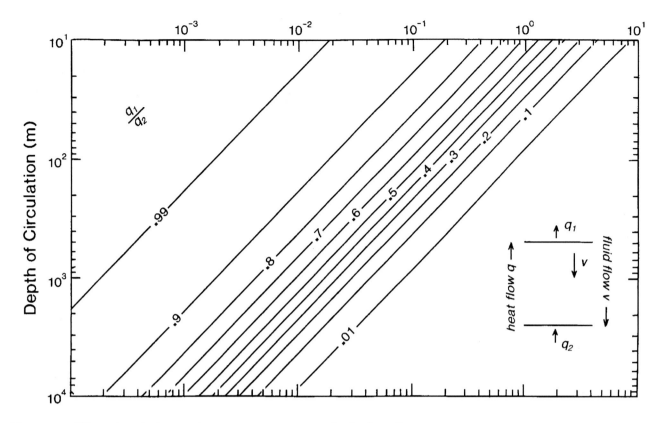

Figure 9.10. Effect of vertical groundwater movement on conductive heat flow.

must also increase. Heat flow is still depressed compared to the initial state of no sedimentation, but the magnitude of the depression is smaller.

Groundwater Flow

Groundwater flow has the potential to be an effective agent for redistributing heat in sedimentary basins. The heat capacity of water (~4200 J/kg K) is more than four times as high as the average matrix component of sedimentary rocks (~1000 J/kg K). Significant perturbations to the background thermal regime can be obtained in the presence of Darcy velocities as low as a millimeter per year, depending upon the depth of circulation (see later discussion).

Vertical fluid movement is usually required to perturb the thermal regime. Little or no heat is transported by the horizontal movement of groundwater because isotherms are almost always parallel to the ground surface. The extent to which heat flow (or the geothermal gradient) is enhanced or reduced by upward or downward movement of groundwater depends on the Darcy (volumetric) velocity and depth of fluid circulation. Lachenbruch and Sass (1977) have shown that under steady-state conditions,

$$q(z_1)/q(z_2) = e^{\Delta z/s} \tag{10}$$

where $q(z_1)$ is the conductive heat flow at the top of a layer of thickness Δz, $q(z_2)$ is the conductive heat flow at the bottom of the layer, and

$$s = k/\rho_w C_w v \tag{11}$$

where k is the bulk thermal conductivity of the fluid–rock aggregate, ρ_w and C_w are the density and heat capacity, respectively, of the fluid moving with Darcy velocity v, and v is negative for downward flow. Assuming typical values of $k = 2.5$ W/m K, $\rho_w = 1000$ kg/m³, and $C_w = 4200$ J/kg K, the reduction of surface heat flow (and geothermal gradient) can be calculated as a function of groundwater velocity and depth of circulation (Figure 9.10). For downward percolation through 1000 m at a Darcy velocity of 1 cm/yr, the conductive surface heat flow (and geothermal gradient) is reduced by 41% (0.59 on Figure 9.10). If the extent of fluid movement reaches a depth of 5 km, then the conductive heat flow at the surface is reduced by 23% (0.77) even if the Darcy velocity is only 1 mm/yr. As a consequence of the relatively low fluid velocities needed to appreciably perturb the thermal regime, hydrologic disturbances are possible even in basins composed primarily of aquitards (permeability of ~10^{-14}–10^{-17} m²). High-permeability (>10^{-14} m²) aquifers and conspicuous signs of underground flow (e.g., artesian wells) are not a prerequisite. In areas of high relief and rugged topography, the presence of groundwater flow is nearly ubiquitous, making it difficult to obtain accurate estimates of background thermal conditions in these locations.

Groundwater moves (1) in response to potential

gradients (Hubbert, 1940) or (2) as a result of free convection. Strictly speaking, it is impossible to define a hydraulic potential for a fluid whose density is variable. However, the use of a hydraulic potential or pseudopotential is a useful concept that can be used to obtain insight into geologic problems for which an exact answer is unobtainable.

Common geologic mechanisms for creating potential gradients are sediment compaction and elevation gradients. Groundwater flow driven by sediment compaction and pore collapse, however, is a relatively inefficient mechanism for heat and mass transport unless pore fluids are focused spatially or temporally (Cathles and Smith, 1983; Bethke, 1985; Deming et al., 1990b). Flow velocities tend to be very low, and the total amount of water is limited to the water contained in the original sediments. Few direct observations of thermal anomalies have been ascribed to compaction-driven flow. Bodner and Sharp (1988) speculated that relatively high geothermal gradients associated with fault zones in the Gulf Coast basin in south Texas may be due to the upward flow of pore water along the faults. However, they were unable to rule out alternative explanations for the high thermal gradients, such as changes in thermal conductivity.

In contrast to compaction-driven flow, regional groundwater flow over distances of 100–1000 km due to potential gradients arising from elevation differences has been documented for several sedimentary basins. There is virtually no doubt that such flow systems exist (e.g., Bredehoeft et al., 1982). Correspondingly, the thermal regime must be disturbed, with the nature of the thermal disturbance depending upon the depth and velocity of groundwater flow. In foreland basins, the following pattern is typical. In the foothills of the mountain range where water infiltrates at high elevations, the geothermal gradient and surface heat flow are depressed as heat is advected downward by moving groundwater. Near the midpoint of the basin (axis of the basin fill), flow is largely horizontal and the effect on basin temperature is minimal. At the distal edge of the basin, flow is forced upward by the basin geometry, leading to a high geothermal gradient and high surface heat flow. This pattern has been observed in the Western Canadian basin (Majorowicz and Jessop, 1981; Hitchon, 1984; Majorowicz, 1989); the Kennedy, Denver, and Williston basins of the Great Plains province of the central United States (Gosnold, 1985, 1990); the Uinta basin in western United States (Chapman et al., 1984); the Great Artesian basin in Australia (Cull and Conley, 1983); and the North Slope basin in Alaska (Deming et al., 1992). The thermal anomalies associated with these flow systems can dramatically influence the temperature-dependent generation of oil and gas, and the flow systems themselves may play a role in oil and gas migration (Toth, 1988; Garven, 1989; Bethke et al., 1991; Meissner, 1991).

Free convection in sedimentary basins may conceivably arise from density gradients due to thermal expansion or the presence of solutes. For free convection to occur, the permeability of the porous medium must be sufficiently high and a density inversion must exist, with

higher density fluid overlying less dense. In most sedimentary basins, however, free convection is probably inhibited because the increase of salinity (and density) with depth overshadows the decrease in density due to increased temperature and concomitant thermal expansion.

Relatively little is known about the occurrence or significance of free convection in sedimentary basins; there are no direct observations of the process. However, the presence of extensive quartz cementation in sandstones found in the geopressured zone of the Gulf Coast basin of the southeastern United States requires much higher fluid volumes than could possibly be supplied by pore water alone (Land, 1991). One solution to this discrepancy would be to invoke free convection within compartmentalized cells in the geopressured zone. Within each cell, the pressure gradient would be hydrostatic and fluid would be free to circulate (Cathles, 1990). An interesting new hypothesis by Nunn (1992) attributes episodic subsidence in the Michigan basin to the catastrophic release of heat by periodic episodes of free convection in the upper 10 km of the continental crust, as originally envisaged by Deming (1992). At the present time, however, the possible occurrence of free convection in sedimentary basins and the continental crust remains speculative. For example, little is known about the extent to which fracture permeability exists in the crust and what stress states and tectonic processes could create sufficient permeability to allow for free convection.

THERMAL HISTORY OF A WELL FROM NORTH SLOPE BASIN, ALASKA

The importance of some of the factors that determine temperature in sedimentary basins (and thus source rock maturation in the petroleum system) can be illustrated by considering an example from the North Slope basin, Alaska.

During the years 1977–1984, the U.S. Geological Survey drilled 28 deep (1–6 km) petroleum exploration wells in the North Slope basin. (See Gryc, 1988; Tailleur and Weimer, 1987; and Bird, Chapter 21, this volume, for comprehensive discussions of the exploration history and regional geology.) A large amount of geologic and geophysical data were collected as part of this drilling program. Thermal data include thermal conductivity measurements on core and drill chip samples (Deming et al., 1992), equilibrium ($\pm0.1°C$) temperature logs in the upper sections (0–600 m, average) of 21 of 28 boreholes (Lachenbruch et al., 1987, 1988), and 23 reliable ($\pm3°C$) estimates of formation temperatures at depths of about 1–4.5 km obtained from extrapolation of series of BHTs measured during geophysical logging runs (Blanchard and Tailleur, 1982; Deming et al., 1992). Vitrinite reflectance measurements were also made on core and drill chip samples (Magoon and Bird, 1988).

One of the wells from which temperature, thermal conductivity, and vitrinite reflectance data are available is the Ikpikpuk well (latitude 70.46°N, longitude 154.33°W) (Figure 9.11). The history of burial and

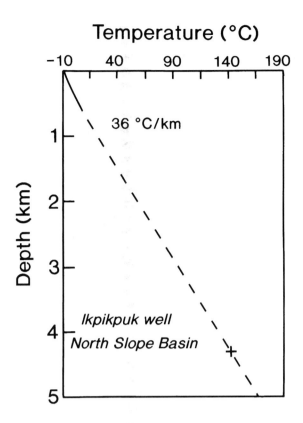

Temperature (°C)

Figure 9. 11. Equilibrium temperature log (solid line from 0 to 600 m), and equilibrium temperature estimated from extrapolation of bottom-hole temperature (142°C, 4316 m), Ikpikpuk well, North Slope basin, Alaska.

sediment deposition at the Ikpikpuk well reflects two stages in the evolution of the North Slope basin. The basin originally formed as a passive margin in the Paleozoic (350 Ma) with average sedimentation rates of about 10 m/m.y. (Table 9.2). Starting with deposition of the Torok formation (116–106 Ma), however, there was a transition to a foreland basin setting as orogeny, over-thrusting, and erosion in the ancestral Brooks Range to the south led to sedimentation rates of about 100 m/m.y. Maximum overburden thickness occurred about 55 Ma with deposition of the Colville Group and/or Saga-vanirktok Formation. From 55 Ma to the present, erosion has dominated, with the exception of deposition of 10 m of surficial deposits in the last 1 m.y. or so.

Vitrinite reflectance data from the Ikpikpuk well include 41 measurements on drill cuttings and 15 measurements on core samples. The samples are spaced to provide good coverage through nearly the entire sedimentary section, from the top of the Nanushuk Group to the bottom of the Endicott Group. Average values for the top and bottom of each formation were determined by a piecewise linear regression on log % R_o versus depth (Figure 9.12); the actual data are tabulated and plotted by Magoon and Bird (1988).

Many different models have been suggested for relating vitrinite reflectance (R_o) to temperature or to time and temperature (e.g., Middleton, 1982; Waples, 1980 and Chapter 17, this volume; Barker and

Pawlewicz, 1986; Wood, 1988; Sweeney and Burnham, 1990). This example uses the model of Barker and Pawlewicz (1986), which relates vitrinite reflectance to maximum temperature, T_{max}:

$$R_o (\%) = \exp[(0.0096\ T_{max}) - 1.4] \qquad (12)$$

where T_{max} is in degrees Celsius. Barker and Pawle-wicz's model is empirically based and is calibrated from modern temperature measurements in which the tectonic setting allows a reasonable supposition that the present-day temperature is the maximum temperature to which the vitrinite has been exposed.

Because vitrinite reflectance is most sensitive to the maximum temperature to which it has been exposed, present-day values at the Ikpikpuk well were most probably frozen in near the time of uplift, erosion, and cooling, estimated to be about 55 Ma, and have not changed since that time (Table 9.2). The vitrinite reflectance data (Figure 9.12) thus record a snapshot in time of the thermal conditions existing at the Ikpikpuk well about 55 Ma.

An examination of the vitrinite reflectance data and maximum paleotemperatures estimated from equation 11 verifies that substantial erosion has occurred at the Ikpikpuk well (Figure 9.12). Vitrinite reflectance at the top of the Nanushuk formation near the ground surface is 0.40 %R_o, which is equivalent to a maximum paleo-temperature of 50°C. The present-day mean annual ground temperature determined from extrapolation of a temperature log is about –11°C (Lachenbruch et al., 1987, 1988). For an average geothermal gradient of 36°C/km (Figure 9.11), erosion of about 1.7 km is implied. However, air and ground temperatures during much of the Cenozoic were probably at least 10–15°C warmer than today (Savin, 1984). Similarly, heat flow may have been lower or higher 55 Ma, or the thermal conductivity of the eroded Colville Group and/or Sagavanirktok Formation may have been lower or higher than the average thermal conductivity of other geologic units at the Ikpikpuk site. Thus, although it is apparent there has been considerable erosion at the Ikpikpuk well, it is not possible to make a precise estimate of the total amount with any certainty.

Thermal maturation of potential source rocks (Shublik Formation, Kingak Shale, pebble shale unit) may have occurred before, during, or after the time of maximum burial. However, most thermal maturation probably took place from about 100–50 Ma, when source rocks were being buried by deposition of the Nanushuk Group, Torok Formation, Colville Group, and/or Sagavanirktok Formation, together representing a combined thickness of more than 3 km. If one assumes that the kinetic properties of organic matter in source rocks are understood, the problem of estimating the timing and extent of hydrocarbon generation reduces to reconstructing the thermal history of the Ikpikpuk well from two control points: the present-day thermal state (constrained by present-day temperature measurements) and the thermal state about 55 Ma (constrained by vitrinite reflectance data).

Table 9.2. Depositional History, Ikpikpuk Well, North Slope of Alaska

Geologic Unit(s) or Event	Thickness (m)	Age of Deposition or Event (Ma)	Sedimentation Rate (m/m.y.)
Basement at surface		350 and older	
Endicott Group	235	350–335	16
Lisburne Group	946	335–258	12
Sadlerochit Group	320	258–235	14
Shublik Formation/			
Sag River Sandstone	168	235–208	6
Kingak Shale	721	208–133	10
Nondeposition/erosion (?)	0	133–122	
Pebble shale unit	76	122–116	13
Torok Formation	1304	116–106	130
Nanushuk Group	869	106–95	79
Colville Group/			
Sagavanirktok Formation	~1000	95–55 (?)	25
Erosion	~1000	55–1 (?)	
Gubik Formation	10	1–0	10

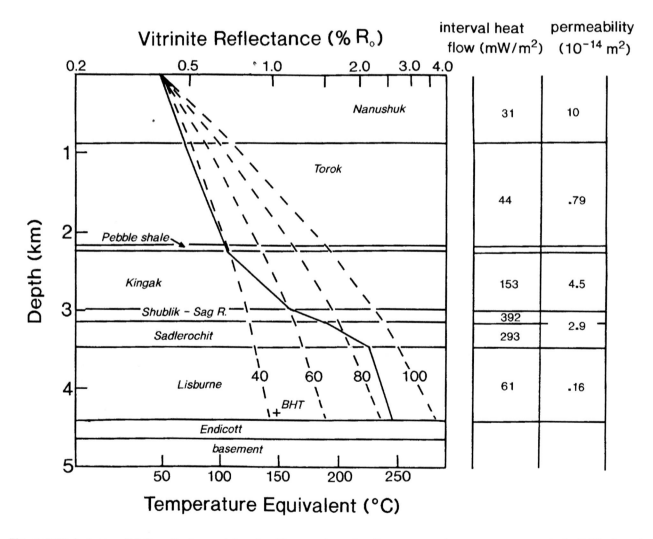

Figure 9.12. Average vitrinite reflectance determined from a piecewise linear regression on measurements (solid line), and predicted for steady-state conductive heat flows of 40, 60, 80, and 100 mW/m² (dashed lines), Ikpikpuk well, North Slope basin, Alaska. Also shown are interval heat flows calculated from vitrinite reflectance and thermal conductivity data along with average permeabilites measured parallel to bedding.

Table 9.3. Vitrinite Reflectance and Thermal Conductivity Data, Ikpikpuk Well

Geologic Unit(s)	Thickness (m)	Estimated Thermal Conductivity (W/m K)	Vitrinite Reflectance Top–Bottom (% R_o)
Nanushuk Group	869	1.4	0.40–0.48
Torok Formation	1304	1.7	0.48–0.67
Pebble shale unit	76	1.6	0.67–0.68
Kingak Shale	721	2.0	0.68–1.15
Shublik Formation/Sag River Sandstone	168	2.4	1.15–1.50
Sadlerochit Shale	320	2.5	1.50–2.15
Lisburne Shale	946	2.9	2.15–2.60
Endicott Shale	235	3.4	≥2.60

The simplest approach to estimating the temperature history of potential source rocks at the Ikpikpuk well would be to start with present-day heat flow and temperature and work backward, assuming conductive heat transport and making some allowance for changing surface temperature and the depression of heat flow by sedimentation. However, two different types of temperature data from the Ikpikpuk yield very different heat flow estimates. Near-surface heat flow determined from a shallow (0–600 m) equilibrium temperature log and 11 thermal conductivity measurements on drill chip samples is estimated to be 38 ± 10 mW/m^2. In contrast, heat flow estimated from extrapolation of BHT measurements at 4316 m depth (142°C) and average formation thermal conductivities (Table 9.3) is 71 ± 21 mW/m^2 (Deming et al., 1992). The discrepancy between these two heat flow estimates would usually be attributed to spurious BHT measurements or error in thermal conductivity estimates (Deming et al., 1992). However, information about paleotemperatures and paleotemperature gradients gleaned from interpretation of vitrinite reflectance data suggests that a similar discrepancy between shallow and deep heat flow may have existed in the Ikpikpuk well at the time that vitrinite reflectance was frozen in, about 55 Ma (Figure 9.12).

From equation 11 it follows that a plot of $\log_e R_o$ versus depth should be linear if the geothermal gradient that determined T_{max} at the time of maximum heating was linear. However, a plot of $\log_e R_o$ versus depth for the Ikpikpuk well implies low paleothermal gradients in the top section of the well, with much higher paleothermal gradients lower in the same section. If we fix the estimated paleotemperature at the top of the well, thermal conductivity data (Table 9.3) can be used in conjunction with equation 11 to calculate theoretical vitrinite reflectance profiles for constant heat flows of 40, 60, 80, and 100 mW/m^2 (Figure 9.12). A comparison of the theoretical predictions with the observed data indicates that the observed vitrinite reflectance data cannot be explained by steady-state heat conduction. Interval heat flows calculated from the vitrinite reflectance and thermal conductivity data are in the range of 30–40 mW/m^2 for the top of the well, while those near the bottom are about 200–300 mW/m^2 (Figure 9.12). If the vitrinite reflectance and thermal conductivity

data are used to estimate average heat flow over the entire section, an estimate of 84 mW/m^2 is derived, close to the present-day estimate of 71 mW/m^2 obtained from extrapolation of BHTs. Thus, heat flow estimates obtained from both modern-day temperature measurements and interpretation of vitrinite reflectance data indicate the same apparent discrepancy: low heat flow (~30–40 mW/m^2) in intervals near the top of the well, while heat flow averaged from the surface to a depth of about 4300 m is much higher (~70–85 mW/m^2).

Several hypotheses can possibly explain the apparent discrepancy between deep and shallow heat estimates:

1. Both modern and ancient heat flow estimates are wrong due to such factors as error in estimates of in situ thermal conductivity, error in interpretation of paleotemperature from vitrinite reflectance, error in temperature measurements, or contamination of vitrinite from well bore cavings (Feazel and Aram, 1990). Both methods may give similar results that are apparently anomalous because they both rely on the same thermal conductivity estimates, or the similar results may be a coincidence.
2. Both the ancient thermal state recorded in the vitrinite reflectance data at the time of maximum burial and the modern thermal state are temporary conditions of thermal disequilibrium resulting from some unknown geologic process; their simultaneous presence at these specific times is a coincidence.
3. Both the ancient thermal state recorded in the vitrinite reflectance data at the time of maximum burial and the modern thermal state are in approximately steady-state thermal equilibrium. The apparent discrepancy in conductive heat flows is due to downward transport of heat by some process such as groundwater flow such that the total heat flow through the well is constant.
4. Energy is not conserved.

Hypothesis (4) is contrary to all observations of physical science and thus not a possibility. Hypotheses (1) and (2) cannot be ruled out, but are unsatisfactory in that they do not explain the observations but rather attribute the observations to statistical flukes. An attractive feature of hypothesis (1) is the possibility that both modern and ancient heat flow estimates are similarly in error simply because both rely on the same flawed thermal conductivity estimates. However, for thermal conductivity errors to explain the high interval heat flows (200–300 mW/m^2) inferred from vitrinite reflectance data (Figure 9.12), the error in thermal conductivity estimates would have to be 500–1000%. Another plausible explanation for the low reflectance gradient in the top part of the well and high gradient in the bottom is contamination of drill cuttings from caving, where vitrinite from higher levels in the well drops to lower levels, resulting in anomalously low maturity levels that may suddenly increase at a casing point. However, measurements on core samples from the Ikpikpuk well are in good agreement with those on cuttings samples and are sufficient in number to validate the dramatic increase in reflectance gradient in the lower levels of the well (Magoon and Bird, 1988).

Hypothesis (3), downward groundwater flow, is a viable theory that could explain the apparent difference in shallow and deep heat flow through a physical mechanism. This hypothesis can be tested by fixing estimated paleotemperatures at the top of the Nanushuk Group and bottom of the Sadlerochit Group and then calculating the temperature distribution between these two points for different groundwater velocities (Figure 9.13). Bredehoeft and Papadopolous (1965) showed that if temperature at the top and bottom of a zone of vertical groundwater circulation is fixed, then the steady-state temperature as a function of depth $T(z)$ between these points can be given by

$$T(z) = T_{top} + (T_{bot} - Tt_{op}) [exp(\beta z/L) - 1]/[exp(\beta) - 1]$$

(13)

where T_{top} is the temperature at the top of an interval of length L, T_{bot} is the temperature at the bottom of the interval, z is depth (positive downward), and

$$\beta = C_o \rho_o V_z L/k$$

(14)

where C_o is the specific heat of the circulating fluid, ρ_o is the fluid density, V_z is the Darcy or volumetric fluid velocity, and k is the thermal conductivity of the fluid–rock aggregate. Taking $C_o = 4200$ J/kg K, $\rho_o = 1000$ kg/m^3, $k = 1.9$ W/m K (harmonic mean from measurements), and $L = 3458$ m, $T(z)$ can be calculated for $V_z = 0.001$, 0.01, and 0.1 m/yr (Figure 9.13). A comparison of temperature calculated from equation 12 with temperature estimated from vitrinite reflectance data (Figure 9.13) shows that the paleotemperatures and thermal gradients inferred from the vitrinite reflectance data can be explained by a temperature distribution resulting from a downward Darcy velocity of 0.01 m/yr.

If groundwater is (and was) moving downward through the Ikpikpuk well, how far down does the circulation extend? When fluid reaches the Sadlerochit Group, it is probably diverted laterally. Permeability data (Deming, 1993) reveal that the Sadlerochit Group is

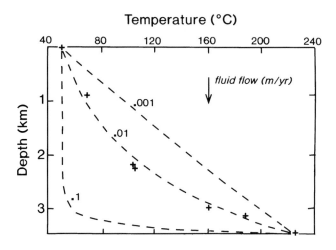

Figure 9.13. Maximum paleotemperatures calculated from vitrinite reflectance data (+) and temperature profiles predicted from steady-state fluid flow vertically downward at Darcy (volumetric) velocities of 0. 001, 0. 01, and 0. 1 m/yr. Theoretical profiles (dashed lines) are fixed by estimated paleotemperatures at top and bottom of interval.

about 20 times more permeable than the underlying Lisburne Group (Figure 9.12). The interval heat flow inferred from vitrinite reflectance data in the Lisburne Group, below the zone of postulated circulation, is estimated to be 61 mW/m^2, the average background heat flow in the North Slope basin (Deming et al., 1992).

What force could drive groundwater down through the sedimentary section at the Ikpikpuk well? Deming et al. (1992) found that heat flow in general is disturbed throughout the North Slope basin by the probable existence of a regional (~300–400 km) groundwater flow system that transports heat by advection from areas of high elevation in the Brooks Range and its foothills to the coastal plain (see Figure 9.6). However, the Ikpikpuk well (elevation 8 m) is not located in the Brooks Range (elevations >1–2 km) or its foothills (elevations ~50–500 m), but on the coastal plain where near-surface heat flow determined at neighboring wells is in the range of 60–90 mW/m^2 (Deming et al., 1992).

Downward flow at the Ikpikpuk well may result from local focusing as groundwater moves downward into the relatively thick section of highly permeable Endicott sandstones that lies near the basement in the vicinity of the Ikpikpuk well (see isopach maps by Bird, 1988). For example, modeling studies by Freeze and Witherspoon (1967) have shown that topographically driven groundwater will flow into a high-permeability lens of material at the base of a sedimentary basin, even if such a layer occurs in what would otherwise be a discharge area. However, this would also apparently require flow through the relatively impermeable Lisburne Group at the Ikpikpuk well site, and this is not supported by the analysis above. It may be that groundwater flow moves parallel to bedding through the Sadlerochit, with sporadic fracture permeability in the Lisburne allowing downward movement into the Endicott sandstones.

Another significant driving force for fluid flow in

sedimentary basins that could be responsible for fluid circulation at the Ikpikpuk well is free convection. Free convection is normally inhibited in sedimentary basins because increasing salinity with depth more than offsets the decrease of fluid density due to thermal expansion. However, original brines in the North Slope basin have apparently been flushed out by the regional groundwater flow system (see analyses of formation waters by Kharaka and Carothers, 1988; Woodward, 1987). It may therefore be conceivable that the Ikpikpuk well is located in the descending section of one or more convection cells. If so, other wells in the North Slope basin may be located in upwelling sections of the same or other convection cells. Vitrinite reflectance data from these wells should show the opposite pattern to that found in the Ikpikpuk well—high paleothermal gradients near the top of the well and low paleothermal gradients near the bottom.

Although it is possible to demonstrate that a particular hypothesis (groundwater flow) is consistent with data from the Ikpikpuk well, the proposed hypothesis (3) cannot be shown to be the only one that satisfies the observations. At our current level of understanding, the estimation of any thermal history is a complex problem that usually cannot be brought to a unique conclusion. Data errors and the difficulties inherent in inferring paleotemperatures from geothermometers such as vitrinite reflectance make it difficult to reconstruct the temperature history of potential source rocks accurately. Similarly, the potential of different mechanisms (e.g., sedimentation, groundwater flow, and conductive heat refraction) to lead to identical thermal anomalies makes it difficult to uniquely designate specific physical processes as important factors in specific instances.

Acknowledgments *I would like to thank my colleagues and friends at the Branch of Petroleum Geology in the U.S. Geological Survey at Menlo Park, California. Ken Bird provided the estimated burial history for the Ikpikpuk well, and Les Magoon made substantial contributions that improved the manuscript. Jud Ahern, George Klein, Dan McKenzie, Jeffrey Nunn, Gerard Demaison, Peter van de Kamp, and John T. Smith reviewed the manuscript and made suggestions for its improvement.*

References Cited

Ahern, J. L., and S. R. Mrkvicka, 1984, A mechanical and thermal model for the evolution of the Williston basin: Tectonics, v. 3, p. 79–102.

Angevine, C. L., P. C. Heller, and C. Paola, 1990, Quantitative sedimentary basin modeling: AAPG Continuing Education Course Notes Series 32, 133 p.

Barker, C. E., and M. J. Pawlewicz, 1986, The correlation of vitrinite reflectance with maximum temperature in humic organic matter, *in* G. Buntebarth and L. Stegna, eds., Paleogeothermics: evaluation of geothermal conditions in the geological past, Lecture Notes in Earth Sciences: Berlin, Springer-Verlag, p. 79–93.

Beaumont, C., 1981, Foreland basins: Geophysical Journal of the Royal Astronomical Society, v. 65, p. 291–329.

Bethke, C. M., 1985, A numerical model of compaction-driven groundwater flow and heat transfer and its application to the paleohydrology of intracratonic basins: Journal of Geophysical Research, v. 90, p. 6817–6828.

Bethke, C. M., 1986, Inverse hydrologic analysis of the distribution and origin of Gulf Coast-type geopressured zones: Journal of Geophysical Research, v. 91, p. 6535–6545.

Bethke, C. M., J. D. Reed, and D. F. Oltz, 1991, Long-range petroleum migration in the Illinois basin: AAPG Bulletin, v. 75, p. 925–945.

Birch, F., 1948, The effects of Pleistocene climatic variations upon geothermal gradients: American Journal of Science, v. 246, p. 729–760.

Birch, F., 1950, Flow of heat in the Front Range, Colorado: GSA Bulletin, v. 61, p. 567–620.

Birch, F., and H. Clark, 1940, The thermal conductivity of rocks and its dependence upon temperature and composition: American Journal of Science, v. 238, p. 529–558, 613–635.

Bird, K. J., 1988, Structure-contour and isopach maps of the National Petroleum Reserve in Alaska, *in* G. Gryc, ed., Geology and exploration of the National Petroleum Reserve in Alaska, 1974 to 1982: U.S.G.S. Professional Paper 1399, p. 355–377.

Blackwell, D. D., and J. L. Steele, 1989, Thermal conductivity of rocks: measurement and significance, *in* N. D. Naeser and T. H. McCulloh, eds., Thermal history of sedimentary basins: methods and case histories: New York, Springer-Verlag, p. 13–36.

Blackwell, D. D., J. L. Steele, and C. A. Brott, 1980, The terrain effect on terrestrial heat flow: Journal of Geophysical Research, v. 85, p. 4757–4772.

Blanchard, D. C., and I. L. Tailleur, 1982, Temperatures and interval geothermal gradients determinations from wells in National Petroleum Reserve in Alaska: U.S.G.S. Open-File Report 82-391, 79 p.

Bodell, J. M., and D. S. Chapman, 1982, Heat flow in the north-central Colorado Plateau: Journal of Geophysical Research, v. 87, p. 2869–2884.

Bodner, D. P., and J. M Sharp, Jr., 1988, Temperature variations in South Texas subsurface: AAPG Bulletin, v. 72, p. 21–32.

Bredehoeft, J. D., W. Back, and B. B. Hanshaw, 1982, Regional ground-water flow concepts in the United States: historical perspective, *in* T. N. Narasimhan, ed., Recent trends in hydrogeology: GSA Special Paper 189, p. 297–316.

Bredehoeft, J. D., and I. S. Papadopulos, 1965, Rates of vertical groundwater movement estimated from the earth's thermal profile: Water Resources Research, v. 1, p. 325–328.

Bredehoeft, J. D., R. D. Djevanshir, and K. R. Belitz, 1988, Lateral fluid flow in a compacting sand–shale sequence: South Caspian basin: AAPG Bulletin, v. 72, p. 416–424.

Brigaud, F., and G. Vasseur, 1989, Mineralogy, porosity and fluid control on thermal conductivity of sedimentary rocks: Geophysical Journal, v. 98, p. 525–542.

Brigaud, F., D. S. Chapman, and S. Le Douaran, 1990, Estimating thermal conductivity in sedimentary basins using lithologic data and geophysical well logs: AAPG Bulletin, v. 74, p. 1459–1477.

Bullard, E. C., 1947, The time necessary for a borehole to attain temperature equilibrium: Monthly Notes of the Royal Astronomical Society, v. 5, p. 127–130.

Cathles, L. M. III, 1990, Scales and effects of fluid flow in the upper crust: Science, v. 248, p. 323–329.

Cathles, L. M., and A. T. Smith, 1983, Thermal constraints on the formation of Mississippi Valley type lead-zinc deposits and their implications for episodic basin dewatering and deposit genesis: Economic Geology, v. 78, p. 983–1002.

Chapman, D. S., T. H. Kehom, S. Bauer, and M. D. Picard, 1984, Heat flow in the Uinta basin determined from bottom hole temperature (BHT) data: Geophysics, v. 49, p. 453–466.

Clark, S. P. Jr., 1966, Thermal conductivity, in S. P. Clark, ed., Handbook of physical constants: GSA Memoir 97, p. 459–482.

Crough, T., 1979, Hotspot epeirogeny: Tectonophysics, v. 61, p. 321–333.

Cull, J. P., and D. Conley, 1983, Geothermal gradients and heat flow in Australian sedimentary basins: BMR Journal of Australian Geology and Geophysics, v. 8, p. 329–337.

De Bremaecker, J.-Cl., 1983, Temperature, subsidence, and hydrocarbon maturation in extensional basins: a finite element model: AAPG Bulletin, v. 67, p. 1410–1414.

Deming, D., 1989, Application of bottom-hole temperature corrections in geothermal studies: Geothermics, v. 18, p. 775–786.

Deming, D., 1992, Catastrophic release of heat and fluid flow in the continental crust: Geology, v. 20, p. 83–86.

Deming, D., 1993, Regional permeability estimates from investigations of coupled heat and groundwater flow, North Slope of Alaska: Journal of Geophysical Research, in press.

Deming, D., and D. S. Chapman, 1988, Heat flow in the Utah–Wyoming thrust belt from analysis of bottom-hole temperature data measured in oil and gas wells: Journal of Geophysical Research, v. 93, p. 13657–13672.

Deming, D., and D. S. Chapman, 1989, Thermal histories and hydrocarbon generation: example from Utah–Wyoming thrust belt: AAPG Bulletin, v. 73, p. 1455–1471.

Deming, D., J. S. Hanor, and J. A. Nunn, 1990a, Method of variable bias and its application to estimating subsurface temperature: Geophysical Research Letters, v. 17, p. 1949–1952.

Deming, D., J. A. Nunn, and D. G. Evans, 1990b, Thermal effects of compaction driven groundwater flow from overthrust belts: Journal of Geophysical Research, v. 95, p. 6669–6683.

Deming, D., J. H. Sass, A. H. Lachenbruch, and R. F. De Rito, 1992, Heat flow and subsurface temperature as evidence for basin-scale groundwater flow, North Slope of Alaska: GSA Bulletin, v. 104, p. 528–542.

Demongodin, L., B. Pinoteau, G. Vasseur, and R. Gable, 1991, Thermal conductivity and well logs: a case study in the Paris basin: Geophysical Journal, v. 105, p. 675–691.

Dowdle, W. L., and W. M. Cobb, 1975, Static formation temperature from well logs—an empirical approach: Journal of Petroleum Technology, v. 27, p. 1326–1330.

Feazel, C. T., and R. B. Aram, 1990, Interpretation of discontinuous vitrinite reflectance profiles: discussion: AAPG Bulletin, v. 74, p. 91–93.

Folland, C. K., Karl, T. R., and Vinnikov, K. Y. A., 1990, Observed climate variations and change, in J. T. Houghton, G. J. Jenkins, and J. J. Ephraums, eds., Climate Change, the IPCC Scientific Assessment: Cambridge, U.K., Cambridge University Press, p. 195–238.

Freeze, R. A., and P. A. Witherspoon, 1967, Theoretical analysis of regional groundwater flow, 2. Effect of water-table configuration and subsurface permeability variation: Water Resources Research, v. 3, p. 623–634.

Galson, D. A., N. P. Wilson, U. Scharli, and L. Rybach, 1987, A comparison of the divided-bar and QTM methods of measuring thermal conductivity: Geothermics, v. 16, p. 215–226.

Garven, G. 1989, A hydrogeologic model for the formation of the giant oil sands deposits of the western Canada sedimentary basin: American Journal of Science, v. 289, p. 105–166.

Gosnold, W. D., Jr., 1985, Heat flow and groundwater flow in the Great Plains of the United States: Journal of Geodynamics, v. 4, p. 247–264.

Gosnold, W. D., Jr., 1990, Heat flow in the Great Plains of the United States: Journal of Geophysical Research, v. 95, p. 353–374.

Gross, M. G., 1993, Oceanography, a view of Earth: Englewood Cliffs, NJ, Prentice Hall, 446 p.

Gryc, G., ed., 1988, Geology and exploration of the National Petroleum Reserve in Alaska, 1974 to 1982: U.S.G.S. Professional Paper 1399, 940 p.

Hitchon, B., 1984, Geothermal gradients, hydrodynamics, and hydrocarbon occurrences, Alberta, Canada: AAPG Bulletin, v. 68, p. 713–743.

Houbolt, J. J. H. C., and P. R. A. Wells, 1980, Estimation of heat flow in oil wells based on a relation between heat conductivity and sound velocity: Geologie en Mijnbouw, v. 59, p. 215–224.

Howard, L. E., and J. H. Sass, 1964, Terrestrial heat flow in Australia: Journal of Geophysical Research, v. 69, p. 1617–1626.

Hubbert, M. K., 1940, The theory of ground-water motion: Journal of Geology, v. 48, p. 785–944.

Issler, D. R., and C. Beaumont, 1986, Estimates of terrestrial heat flow in offshore eastern Canada (discussion): Canadian Journal of Earth Science, v. 23, p. 2083–2085.

Jaeger, J. C., 1965, Application of the theory of heat conduction to geothermal measurements, in W. H. K. Lee, ed., Terrestrial heat flow: Geophysical Monographs, v. 8, American Geophysical Union, Washington, D.C., p. 7–23.

Kappelmeyer, O., and Haenel, R., 1974, Geothermics with special reference to application: Berlin, Gebruder Borntraeger, 238 p.

Kehle, R. O., 1971, Geothermal survey of North America, annual progress report (unpublished): Tulsa, OK, AAPG.

Kehle, R. O., 1972, Geothermal survey of North America, annual progress report (unpublished): Tulsa, OK, AAPG.

Kharaka, Y. K., and W. W. Carothers, 1988, Geochemistry of oil field water from the North Slope, in G. Gryc, ed., Geology and exploration of the National Petroleum Reserve in Alaska, 1974 to 1982: U.S.G.S. Professional Paper 1399, p. 551–561.

Klein, G. deV., 1991, Origin and evolution of North American cratonic basins: South African Journal of Geology, v. 94, p. 3–18.

Klein, G. deV., and A. T. Hsui, 1987, Origin of cratonic basins: Geology, v. 15, p. 1094–1098.

Lachenbruch, A. H., 1968, Rapid estimation of the topographic disturbance to superficial thermal gradients: Reviews of Geophysics and Space Physics, v. 6, p. 365–400.

Lachenbruch, A. H., 1969, The effect of two-dimensional topography on superficial thermal gradients: U.S.G.S. Bulletin 1203-E, 86 p.

Lachenbruch, A. H., and M. C. Brewer, 1959, Dissipation of the temperature effect of drilling a well in Arctic Alaska: U.S.G.S. Bulletin 1083C, p. 73–109.

Lachenbruch, A. H., and J. H. Sass, 1977, Heat flow in the United States and the thermal regime of the crust, in J. G. Heacock, ed., The earth's crust, its nature and physical properties: American Geophysical Union, Geophysical Monograph 20, p. 626–675.

Lachenbruch, A. H., J. H. Sass, and S. P. Galanis, Jr., 1985, Heat flow in southernmost California and the origin of the Salton trough: Journal of Geophysical Research, v. 90, p. 6709–6736.

Lachenbruch, A. H., J. H. Sass, L. A. Lawver, M. C. Brewer, B. V. Marshall, R. J. Munroe, J. P. Kennelly, Jr., S. P. Galanis, Jr., and T. H. Moses, Jr., 1987, Temperature and depth of permafrost on the Alaskan Arctic slope, *in* I. Tailleur and P. Weimer, eds., Alaskan North Slope geology: SEPM Pacific section, v. 2, p. 545–558.

Lachenbruch, A. H., J. H. Sass, L. A. Lawver, M. C. Brewer, B. V. Marshall, R. J. Munroe, J. P. Kennelly, Jr., S. P. Galanis, Jr., and T. H. Moses, Jr., 1988, Temperature and depth of permafrost on the Alaskan arctic slope, *in* G. Gryc, ed., Geology and exploration of the National Petroleum Reserve in Alaska, 1974 to 1982: U.S.G.S. Professional Paper 1399, p. 645–656.

Land, L. S., 1991, Evidence for vertical movement of fluids, Gulf Coast sedimentary basin: Geophysical Research Letters, v. 18, p. 919–922.

Lee, T. C., 1989, Thermal conductivity measured with a line source between two dissimilar media equals their mean conductivity: Journal of Geophysical Research, v. 94, p. 12443–12447.

Lee, T. C., 1991, On terrain corrections in terrestrial heat flow: Pure and Applied Geophysics, v. 135, p. 1–13.

Luheshi, M. N., 1983, Estimation of formation temperatures from borehole measurements: Geophysical Journal of the Royal Astronomical Society, v. 74, p. 747–776.

Magoon, L. B., and K. J. Bird, 1988, Evaluation of petroleum source rocks in the National Petroleum Reserve in Alaska, using organic carbon content, hydrocarbon content, visual kerogen, and vitrinite reflectance, *in* G. Gryc, ed., Geology and exploration of the National Petroleum Reserve in Alaska, 1974 to 1982: U.S.G.S. Professional Paper 1399, p. 381–450.

Majorowicz, J. A., 1989, The controversy over the significance of the hydrodynamic effect on heat flow in the Prairies basin, *in* A. E. Beck, G. Garven, and L. Stegena, eds., Hydrological regimes and their subsurface thermal effects: American Geophysical Union, Geophysical Monograph 47, p. 101–105.

Majorowicz, J. A., and A. M. Jessop, 1981, Regional heat flow patterns in the western Canadian sedimentary basin: Tectonophysics, v. 74, p. 209–238.

McKenzie, D., 1978, Some remarks on the development of sedimentary basins: Earth and Planetary Science Letters, v. 40, p. 25–32.

Meissner, F. F., 1991, Origin and migration of oil and gas, *in* H. J. Gluskoter, D. D. Rice, and R. B. Taylor, eds., The geology of North America: Geological Society of America, Economic Geology, v. P–2, p. 225–240.

Middleton, M. F., 1982, Tectonic history from vitrinite reflectance: Geophysical Journal of the Royal Astronomical Society, v. 68, p. 121–132.

Morgan, P., 1984, The thermal structure and thermal evolution of the continental lithosphere: Physics and Chemistry of the Earth, v. 15, p. 107–193.

Nunn, J. A., 1992, Free thermal convection beneath the Michigan basin: thermal and subsidence effects (abs.): Abstract Volume Supplement to EOS, v. 73, n. 43, p. 547.

Nunn, J. A., and R. Sassen, 1986, The framework of hydrocarbon generation and migration, Gulf of Mexico continental slope: Transactions, Gulf Coast Association of Geological Societies, v. 36, p. 257–262.

Nunn, J. A., N. H. Sleep, and W. E. Moore, 1984, Thermal subsidence and generation of hydrocarbons in Michigan basin: AAPG Bulletin, v. 68, p. 296–315.

Pollack, H. N., and D. S. Chapman, 1977, On the regional variation of heat flow, geotherms, and the thickness of the lithosphere: Tectonophysics, v. 38, p. 279–296.

Powell, W. G., D. S. Chapman, N. Balling, and A. E. Beck, 1988, Continental heat-flow density, *in* R. Haenel, L. Rybach, and L. Stegna, eds., Handbook of Terrestrial Heat-Flow Density Determination: Dordrecht, Holland, D. Reidel Publishing, p. 167–222.

Quigley, T. M., A. S. Mackenzie, and J. R. Gray, 1987, Kinetic theory of petroleum generation, *in* B. Doligez, ed., Migration of hydrocarbons in sedimentary basins: Paris, Editions Technip, p. 649–665.

Reiter, M., A. J. Mansure, and B. K. Peterson, 1980, Precision continuous temperature logging and comparison with other types of logs: Geophysics, v. 45, p. 1857–1868.

Roy, R. F., Jr., A. E. Beck, and Y. S. Touloukian, 1981, Thermophysical properties of rocks, *in* Touloukian, Y. S., Judd, W. R., and Roy, R. F., eds., Physical properties of rocks and minerals: McGraw–Hill CINDAS Data Series on Material Properties, v. II–2, p. 409–502.

Sass, J. H., A. H. Lachenbruch, and R. J. Munroe, 1971, Thermal conductivity of rocks from measurements on fragments and its application to heat-flow determinations: Journal of Geophysical Research, v. 76, p. 3391–3401.

Sass, J. H., J. P. Kennelly, Jr., E. P. Smith, and W. E. Wendt, 1984a, Laboratory line-source methods for the measurement of thermal conductivity of rocks near room temperature: U.S.G.S. Open-File Report 84-91, 21 p.

Sass, J. H., C. Stone, and R. J. Munroe, 1984b, Thermal conductivity determinations on solid rock– a comparison between a steady-state divided bar apparatus and a commercial transient line-source device: Journal of Volcanology and Geothermal Research, v. 20, p. 145–153.

Sass, J. H., A. H. Lachenbruch, T. H. Moses, Jr., and P. Morgan, 1992, Heat flow from a scientific research well at Cajon Pass, California: Journal of Geophysical Research, v. 97, p. 5017–5030.

Savin, S. M., 1984, The history of the earth's surface temperature, *in* B. Durand, ed., Thermal Phenomena in Sedimentary Basins: Paris, Editions Technip, p. 11–20.

Schwab, F. L., 1976, Modern and ancient sedimentary basins: comparative accumulation rates: Geology, v. 4, p. 723–727.

Sclater, J. G., and P. A. F. Christie, 1980, Continental stretching: an explanation of the post–mid-Cretaceous subsidence of the central North Sea basin: Journal of Geophysical Research, v. 85, p. 3711–3739.

Sclater, J. G., and J. Francheteau, 1970, The implications of terrestrial heat flow observations on current tectonic and geochemical models of the crust and upper mantle of the earth: Geophysical Journal of the Royal Astronomical Society, v. 20, p. 509–542.

Sclater, J. G., and B. Parsons, 1981, Oceans and continents: similarities and differences in the mechanisms of heat loss: Journal of Geophysical Research, v. 86, p. 11535–11552.

Sclater, J. G., L. Royden, F. Horvath, B. C. Burchfiel, S. Semken, and L. Stegna, 1980, The formation of the intra-Carpathian basins as determined from subsidence data: Earth and Planetary Science Letters, v. 51, p. 139–162.

Sharp, J. M., and P. A. Domenico, 1976, Energy transport in thick sequences of compacting sediment: GSA- Bulletin, v. 87, p. 390–400.

Shen, P. Y., and A. E. Beck, 1986, Stabilization of bottom hole temperature with finite circulation time and fluid flow:

Geophysical Journal of the Royal Astronomical Society, v. 86, p. 63–90.

Sleep, N. H., 1971, Thermal effects of the formation of Atlantic continental margins by continental break up: Geophysical Journal of the Royal Astronomical Society, v. 24, p. 325–350.

Sleep, N. H., and N. S. Snell, 1976, Thermal contraction and flexure of mid-continent and Atlantic marginal basins: Geophysical Journal of the Royal Astronomical Society, v. 45, p. 125–154.

Sleep, N. H., J. A. Nunn, and L. Chou, 1980, Platform Basins: Annual Review of Earth and Planetary Science, v. 8, p. 17–34.

Speece, M. A., T. D. Bowen, J. L. Folcik, and H. N. Pollack, 1985, Analysis of temperatures in sedimentary basins: the Michigan basin: Geophysics, v. 15, p. 1048–1051.

Steckler, M. S., and A. B. Watts, 1978, Subsidence of the Atlantic-type continental margin off New York: Earth and Planetary Science Letters, v. 41, p. 1–13.

Sweeney, J. J., and A. K. Burnham, 1990, Evaluation of a simple model of vitrinite reflectance based on chemical kinetics: AAPG Bulletin, v. 74, p. 1559–1570.

Tailleur, I., and P. Weimer, eds., 1987, Alaskan North Slope geology: SEPM Pacific Section, Book 50, 874 p.

Toth, J., 1988, Ground water and hydrocarbon migration, in W. Back, J. S. Rosenhein, and P. R. Seaber, eds., The geology of North America: GSA, Hydrogeology, v. O-2, p. 485–502.

Touloukian, Y. S., D. E. Liley, and S. L. Saxena, 1970, Thermophysical properties of matter, v. 3, Thermal conductivity: nonmetallic liquids and gases: New York, Plenum Press, p. 120.

Turcotte, D. L., 1980, Models for the evolution of sedimentary basins, in A. W. Bally, ed., Dynamics of plate interiors: American Geophysical Union, Geodynamic Series, v. 1, p. 21–26.

Turcotte, D. L., and J. L. Ahern, 1977, On the thermal and subsidence history of sedimentary basins: Journal of Geophysical Research, v. 82, p. 3762–3766.

Turcotte, D. L., and D. C. McAdoo, 1979, Thermal subsidence and petroleum generation in the southwestern block of the Los Angeles basin, California: Journal of Geophysical Research, v. 84, p. 3460–3464.

Vacquier, V., Y. Mathieu, E. Legendre, and E. Blondin, 1988, Experiment on estimating thermal conductivity of sedimentary rocks from oil well logging: AAPG Bulletin, v. 72, p. 758–764.

Vitorello, I., and H. N. Pollack, 1980, On the variation of continental heat flow with age and the thermal evolution of continents: Journal of Geophysical Research, v. 85, p. 983–995.

Von Herzen, R. P., and A. E. Maxwell, 1959, The measurement of thermal conductivity of deep-sea sediments by a needle probe method: Journal of Geophysical Research, v. 64, p. 1557–1563.

Waples, D. W., 1980, Time and temperature in petroleum exploration: application of Lopatin's method to petroleum exploration: AAPG Bulletin, v. 64, p. 916–926.

Watts, A. B., G. D. Karner, and M. S. Steckler, 1982, Lithospheric flexure and the evolution of sedimentary basins: Philosophical Transactions of the Royal Society of London, Series A, v. 305, p. 249–281.

Willet, S. D., 1990, Stochastic inversion of thermal data in a sedimentary basin: resolving spatial variability: Geophysical Journal, v. 103, p. 321–339.

Wood, D. A., 1988, Relationships between thermal maturity indices calculated using Arrhenius equation and Lopatin method: implications for petroleum exploration: AAPG Bulletin, v. 72, p. 115–134.

Woodside, W., and J. H. Messmer, 1961, Thermal conductivity of porous media: Journal of Applied Physics, v. 32, p. 1688–1706.

Woodward, P. V., 1987, Regional evaluation of formation fluid salinity by SP log, Ivishak Sandstone, North Slope, Alaska (abs.): AAPG Bulletin, v. 71, p. 629.

Part III

Processes

Magoon, L. B, and W. G. Dow, eds., 1994, The petroleum
system—from source to trap: AAPG Memoir 60.

Chapter **10**

Diagenesis, Catagenesis, and Metagenesis of Organic Matter

Brian Horsfield
Forschungszentrum Jülich
Jülich, Germany

Jürgen Rullkötter
Universität Oldenburg
Oldenburg, Germany

ABSTRACT

Upon burial, organic matter in sedimentary rock undergoes numerous compositional changes that are dictated initially by microbial agencies and later mainly by thermal stress. This continuum of processes is termed *thermal maturation* and is divided into three consecutive stages: *diagenesis* (R_o < 0.5%), *catagenesis* (0.5% < R_o < 2.0%), and *metagenesis* (2.0% < R_o < 4.0%). Kerogen, the major global precursor of petroleum, consists of selectively preserved, resistant, cellular organic materials (algal, pollen, spores, and leaf cuticle) and the degraded residues of less resistant biological organic matter (amorphous material) in variable proportions. Kerogen formation is complete by the end of diagenesis. The mode of kerogen formation exerts a strong influence on its structure and bulk composition, and hence on oil- and gas-generating characteristics, during catagenesis. Sulfur-rich type II kerogen, occurring in carbonate–evaporite source rocks, can generate oil at low levels of thermal stress. Low sulfur type II kerogen requires more thermal energy to generate oil, and type I and type III kerogens still more. High-wax oils appear to be generated from both wax ester and biopolymeric precursors, the first of which generates at an early stage of catagenesis and the other throughout catagenesis. The base of the oil window (occurring at R_o < 1.3%) appears to be controlled by the depletion of long chain components in the case of some terrigenous kerogens and by oil stability in the case of marine kerogens. In the latter part of catagenesis, all source rocks contain strongly enhanced proportions of hydrocarbon gases (wet gas). Throughout metagenesis, source rock kerogens are strongly depleted in hydrogen and generated gases consist of methane (dry gas) and sometimes hydrogen sulfide or nitrogen. Nevertheless, original oil potential can sometimes be recognized. Thermal maturity level can be monitored using a wide array of parameters. Steranes, hopanes, and other biological markers respond sensitively to thermal stress. Because their pseudokinetic parameters are known, these reactions are frequently used in numerical simulation to calibrate thermal history.

INTRODUCTION

Diagenesis, catagenesis, and metagenesis are three consecutive alteration stages within the carbon cycle that irreversibly effect progressive changes in the composition of sedimentary organic matter. Collectively, they make up what is commonly termed the *process of maturation*. Each stage is characterized by different types of chemical processes, although the boundaries between adjacent stages are gradational. Diagenetic processes occur early in sediment history and form the link between the biosphere and geosphere. Because kerogen plays a major role as a petroleum progenitor, its formation can be considered as the most important feature of this zone. Nevertheless, defunctionalization and structural rearrangement of biologically inherited

compounds are valuable means for registering the subtle progress of diagenetic change. The succeeding stage of catagenesis corresponds to the main stage of oil formation from kerogen and is characterized by the occurrence of (assumed) first order thermal cracking reactions whose overall rate is governed by kerogen structure and the extent of thermal stress over geologic time. Substantial transformation of oil into gas also occurs later in catagenesis. Metagenesis falls between catagenesis and rock (inorganic) metamorphism and is characterized by dry gas generation. Being able to recognize these zones and determine their occurrence in time and space is now accepted as a key consideration in petroleum exploration strategy.

The subject of thermal maturation of source rocks has been thoroughly reviewed many times, and most

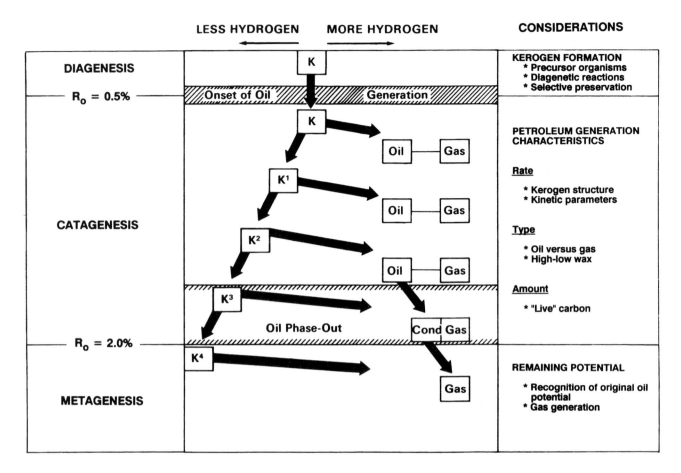

Figure 10.1. The zonation of thermal maturation into diagenesis, catagenesis, and metagenesis, a simplified representation of the bulk resultant processes involved, and highlighted elements indicating the scope of this chapter.

petroleum geoscientists are familiar with its most fundamental aspects. The reader is referred to the reviews of Hunt (1979) and Tissot and Welte (1984) for concise descriptions of the fundamental processes involved in thermal maturation and to Héroux et al. (1979) for a compilation and generalized correlation of inorganic and organic thermal maturity parameters. This review sets out to describe the phenomena characterizing each stage with balanced reference to both historical milestones and the latest available literature to May, 1991. Contrary to the popular view of 10 years ago that petroleum geochemistry must be stripped to its bare bones to be of any practical use to the explorationist, we have chosen to discuss selected aspects of diagenesis, catagenesis, and metagenesis in some geochemical detail because, far from being of only academic interest, these subtleties impinge upon everyday decision-making in petroleum exploration. The scope of this chapter is summarized in Figure 10.1.

DIAGENESIS

The term *diagenesis,* as applied to organic matter, refers to its earliest stage of alteration whereby the remains of aquatic and/or terrestrial organisms are altered and/or degraded by biological and low temperature chemical transformation processes. This alteration begins in the water column and extends via unconsolidated sediments to include some compacted sedimentary rocks (typically $R_o < 0.5\%$; $T < 50°C$).

Kerogen Precursors

Microbial activity is highest at the sediment–water interface and at shallow burial depths. This activity is responsible for the degradation of a high proportion of the originally deposited organic matter into simple molecules such as CO_2, N_2, and H_2O (aerobic conditions), then NH_3, H_2S, and CH_4 (anaerobic conditions) and causes the concomitant mobilization of mineral species (Curtis, 1978). The rate of degradation of biologically derived organic matter varies, with a selective fractionation in favor of nonhydrolyzable substances. The major survivors of microbial degradation consist of three chemically ill-defined macromolecular materials called *fulvic acids, humic acids,* or *humin* depending on their solubilities in acids and bases. All three are considered to be potential precursors of kerogens (insoluble in nonoxidizing acids, bases, and common organic solvents), which are the major petroleum precursors in fine-grained sedimentary rocks. Only a small proportion of the surviving organic matter is in the form of monomolecular species such as polar lipids or the hydrocarbons that result from their defunctionalization.

Fulvic and humic acids are thought to form via the random "repolymerization" or "condensation" of amino acids, sugars, and phenols that originate from the microbial breakdown of proteins, polysaccharides, and lignins (Stevenson, 1974). These processes have been simulated in the laboratory (Maillard, 1913; Hoering, 1973; Hedges, 1978; Rubinsztain et al., 1984). Polyunsaturated lipids such as those found in certain algae (Knights et al., 1970; Blumer et al., 1971) may polymerize directly (Cane and Albian, 1973; Saxby, 1981) or via sulfur atoms (Sinninghe-Damsté and de Leeuw, 1990; Adam et al., 1993) to form macromolecular organic matter in a similar way. Fulvic and humic acids occur in the water column (Stuermer and Harvey, 1974) and in sediments (e.g., Rashid and King, 1969; Orem et al., 1986), and they act as a geochemical sink for all types of functionalized compounds such as wax acids and wax alcohols from plant cuticles (Larter et al., 1983), isoprenoid moieties from chlorophyll *a* (Larter et al., 1979), membrane constituents of archaebacteria (Michaelis and Albrecht, 1979), and tocopherols (Goossens et al., 1984). Decreases in the concentrations first of fulvic acids and then of humic acids occur as a result of progressive combination reactions with increasing diagenesis. There is a concurrent elimination of heteroatomic moieties, such as N_2, H_2O, and notably CO_2 (Huc and Durand, 1977), as kerogen gradually forms (Nissenbaum and Kaplan, 1972; Huc and Durand, 1977). Kerogen formation is considered complete by the end of diagenesis because fulvic and humic acid abundances are very low.

Investigations have shown that some kerogens consist largely of preserved resistant cell wall material rather than being newly formed during diagenesis (Philp and Calvin, 1976; Largeau et al., 1986, 1990; Mycke and Michaelis, 1986; Nip et al., 1986; Tegelaar et al., 1989b) and occur in the humin fraction. Included in this category are morphologically structured phytoclasts, such as spores and pollen that are readily identifiable by means of transmitted and reflected light microscopy, and extremely fine cell wall debris with morphology that is discernible only under the electron microscope.

The proportion of kerogen resulting from either diagenetic reactions or direct preservation depends on the nature of the starting material and the depositional environment. This is exemplified by variations in humic acid versus kerogen concentrations in different Australian coal lithotypes of equal rank (Verheyen and Johns, 1981; Verheyen et al., 1983). Because the ratio of resistant biopolymer to other cellular components varies according to plant species and climate (Tegelaar et al., 1989b), original biota composition may impart a bias on one mode of kerogen formation versus the other, although the final proportions of surviving materials is strongly dependent on the anoxic versus oxic nature of the sediment–water interface. Differences in biodegradability of the organic matter usually leads to a selective preservation of nonhydrolyzable components. However, under strongly reducing conditions, even those plant components with only a relatively weak resistance to degradation (e.g., cellulose) may contribute significantly to kerogen formation if they are present in sufficient concentration to form fulvic and humic acids upon partial degradation. In contrast, the same starting mixture may yield a kerogen richer in resistant biopolymers in more oxygenated waters. This process may be operative during the sedimentation and early diagenesis of both siliciclastic and carbonate source rocks (Gehman, 1962; Horsfield, 1978; Jones, 1984).

The mode of kerogen formation, and hence the type of kerogen that results, is important because it can exert a strong influence on the oil- versus gas-generating potential of a source rock. This is particularly true in deltaic depositional environments where, because changing river courses are commonplace and tidal influences may be strong, humic substances can be flushed from peats to flocculate elsewhere or be fully degraded, leading to the formation of a residue rich in oil-prone biopolymeric debris (Thompson et al., 1985). Kerogen formed under these conditions is very different from that formed from the same starting material but which was deposited and preserved in a stable peat bog where condensation products were more abundant (Karweil, 1966) and the coal was typically gas prone.

Kerogen Types

Molecular structural models are derived through elemental analysis, spectroscopic methods (such as infrared, ^{13}C nuclear magnetic resonance, and X-ray), solvent extract data, and the results of oxidation and pyrolysis experiments (Burlingame et al., 1969; Yen, 1974; Oberlin et al., 1980; Béhar and Vandenbroucke, 1986). These models give some valuable insights into the chemical constituents and variable complexity of kerogen, especially when morphologic habit and optical properties (e.g., Stach et al., 1982) are also considered. Nevertheless, the detailed chemistry of kerogens is broadly viewed within the petroleum industry as being of only academic interest and of little practical value, especially as far as petroleum exploration is concerned. Indeed, kerogens are most often considered to fall into one of only three basic types (I, II, or III) based either on atomic H/C and O/C ratios from elemental analysis or on the correlated hydrogen index (HI) and oxygen index (OI) from Rock-Eval pyrolysis yields (Tissot et al., 1974; Espitalié et al., 1977). While this simple scheme is practical because it is directly linked to potential petroleum yields and because parameters are easily mappable (e.g., organic facies definitions of Jones, 1987), its limitations should not be overlooked, especially with respect to predictive geochemistry. Namely, the types and thermal stabilities of petroleum precursors vary significantly within any single elementally defined kerogen type (Horsfield et al., 1993). Hence, the type of petroleum and the timing of its generation vary accordingly.

This point can be briefly illustrated here by the cases of sulfur-rich kerogens and certain types of land plant organic matter that may generate petroleum at low levels of thermal maturation. For the vast majority of marine kerogens containing degraded algal and bacterial remains and nonmarine kerogens containing sporinite, vitrinite, and cutinite, it can be said that the zone of diagenesis corresponds to the immature zone. Heavier early oil generation, starting at a late stage of diagenesis, appears to be common in carbonates, evaporites, phosphorites, and siliceous rocks (diatomites). Cross-linking sulfur bridges, incorporated during early diagenesis, are broken before carbon–carbon bond cleavage starts. This leads to asphaltene- and resin-rich heavy bitumens and eventually to a mobile oil phase. Similarly, early generation has been invoked for condensate formation from organic matter rich in resinite (Snowdon and Powell, 1982; Nissenbaum et al., 1985), although this has also been questioned (Lewan and Williams, 1987). Likewise, suberinite, formed from the corky tissue of land plants, has been found to undergo major structural transformations during diagenesis, ostensibly to generate oil (Khorasani and Murchison, 1988).

Practically oriented molecular characterization of kerogens can give some insight into these additional source rock attributes and is therefore discussed in the section Catagenesis and Metagenesis.

Biological Markers

A small portion of sedimentary organic matter is soluble in organic solvents and contains lipid compounds that are either directly inherited from the biological precursor organisms or cleaved by hydrolysis from larger cellular units such as cell walls or membranes. Most are functionalized polar lipids that undergo decarboxylation and dehydration reactions during early diagenesis to produce saturated and olefinic hydrocarbons, of which the latter are progressively hydrogenated into their saturated analogs during diagenesis. These hydrocarbons essentially have the same carbon skeletons and steric configurations as their functionalized biogenic precursors, although structural rearrangements of carbon skeletons, catalyzed by clay minerals, may also occur as side reactions. These carbon skeletons that retain their biogenic characteristics are biological markers and are useful for conducting oil–source rock correlations. Their progressively changing stereochemistry is also a valuable means of calibrating thermal histories.

The strong preference for *n*-alkanes with odd numbers of carbon atoms falls dramatically during diagenesis (e.g., decrease of carbon preference index, CPI) from the high values seen in higher plant waxes (Eglinton and Hamilton, 1963) because of reactions involving the reduction of even carbon numbered alcohols and fatty acids with retention of their carbon skeletons (Bray and Evans, 1961; Brooks and Smith, 1967). Also, the central magnesium ion of chlorophyll *a* is lost during earliest diagenesis to form phaeophorbides or to be replaced by other metal ions, particularly Ni^{2+} or VO^{2+} (Baker and Louda, 1986). Dehydrogenation of the chlorins to porphyrins, accompanied by loss or reduction of the oxygen functionalities, are the next steps (Barwise

and Roberts, 1984), until Ni- or VO-desoxophylloerythroetioporphyrins (DPEP) are the dominant species at the end of diagenesis. Phytane (C_{20}), pristane (C_{19}), and some lower carbon number isoprenoids are formed as saturated hydrocarbons fairly early during diagenesis. The pristane/phytane ratio is often referred to as an indicator of depositional conditions (redox potential). This assumes that carbon skeleton is preserved during anoxic transformation of phytol (C_{20}, from chlorophyll *a* side chain) and that pristane is formed by oxidative alteration involving loss of one carbon atom by decarboxylation (Powell and McKirdy, 1975; Didyk et al., 1978). The scheme may not apply to hypersaline environments because alternative sources of phytane, such as archaebacterial lipids, must be considered (ten Haven et al., 1987).

Much is known about the reactions, intermediates, and products of the diagenesis of steroids and hopanoids, of which many hundreds of compounds are documented (Mackenzie et al., 1982; Ourisson et al., 1979; Ourisson, 1990). During diagenesis, steroids undergo a series of defunctionalization, isomerization, and aromatization reactions (Brassell et al., 1984; de Leeuw and Baas, 1986; de Leeuw et al., 1989; Peakman and Maxwell, 1988a, b; Peakman et al., 1988, 1989; Rechka et al., 1992). While most of these reactions involve unsaturated sterenes, their saturated hydrocarbon analogs dominate in sediments at the end of diagenesis. Where not directly involved in double bond isomerization reactions, the chiral centers in the steranes still have the steric configuration of the biogenic precursor molecules. In the aromatic hydrocarbon fraction, monoaromatic steroid hydrocarbons are predominant.

As in the case of steroids, defunctionalization of oxygen-bearing precursors in hopanoids leads to hopenes that are then hydrogenated to saturated hopanes. Important stereochemical reactions of hopanoids occur earlier than those of steroids during diagenesis (Seifert and Moldowan, 1980).

CATAGENESIS AND METAGENESIS

Catagenesis follows diagenesis and constitutes the principal stage of oil formation. *Catagenesis* is defined by vitrinite reflectance values of $0.5\% < R_o < 2.0\%$ and is characterized by thermal degradation of kerogen and the accompanying formation of petroleum. The zone of metagenesis is one of even higher thermal stress, extending up to the onset of greenschist metamorphism. Only methane, hydrogen, and highly carbonized solid organic matter are stable ($2.0\% < R_o < 4.0\%$). The oil window is often generalized as $0.5\% < R_o < 1.3\%$ and the gas window as $1.3\% < R_o < 4.0$, with the threshold from wet to dry gas being $2.0\% R_o$. The ensuing chemical and physical changes involving kerogen have been studied using numerous chemical, microscopic, and spectroscopic approaches, and indices of maturation have been formulated (e.g., Héroux et al., 1979; Durand, 1980). The abundance and composition of generated compounds and compound classes may also be used for this purpose, but this has been deemphasized more recently because yields are more strongly influenced by migration than was thought earlier (Larter, 1988).

Kerogen Evolution

During catagenesis, kerogen aliphaticity decreases and its aromaticity increases, with the absolute values being dependent on the kerogen type. Coals of increasing rank (thermal maturity) yield pyrolysates that are progressively enriched in total and low molecular weight aromatic compounds (Romovacek and Kubat, 1968; McHugh et al., 1976; Larter and Douglas, 1980), reflecting the aromatization of the coal macromolecule. Increasing aromaticity is manifested physically as an increase in vitrinite reflectance. The contemporaneous decrease in phenolic structures associated with the loss of oxygenated species during catagenesis (van Graas et al., 1980; Senftle et al., 1986) has been used to build a kinetic model for vitrinite reflectance prediction (Larter, 1989). The loss of H_2O, CO_2, $(CH_2)_n$, and CH_4 from vitrinite form the basis of an alternative model (Sweeney and Burnham, 1990). Other changes taking place during catagenesis include the loss of aliphatic groups and an increase in the ratio of CH_3/CH_2, as revealed by ^{13}C-NMR and IR spectroscopy (Witte et al., 1988). Stable radicals formed in the kerogen during bond rupture increase in concentration as petroleum generation takes place (Pusey, 1973; Durand, 1980). Free radical concentrations are both dependent on kerogen type and maturity. During metagenesis, aromatic stacks aggregate and a decrease occures in aromatic C-H infrared spectral vibrations (Rouxhet and Robin, 1978). Stabilized free radicals formed during catagenesis pair up, bringing about a reversal in their concentration (Retkofsky et al., 1968).

As catagenesis proceeds, the three kerogen types (I, II, and III) become progressively more hydrogen deficient and depleted in volatilizable components (Dormans et al., 1957; McIver, 1967; Tissot et al., 1974). The proportion of residual or "dead" carbon increases from its original value, low for type I to high for type III kerogens, to overall higher values as thermally labile, volatilizable carbon species are generated and released from macromolecular structures (Gransch and Eisma 1970; Connan et al., 1975). Masses of generated and expelled petroleum can be calculated using such data, provided that thermally mature samples and their immature equivalents can be confidently identified (Goff, 1984; Larter, 1985; Cooles et al., 1986; Rullkötter et al., 1988).

The progressive loss of components from the kerogen structure proceeds according to bond strengths, with weaker bonds breaking before stronger bonds. For type II and type III kerogens, there is a progressive increase in Rock-Eval pyrolysis T_{max} values with increasing thermal maturity (Barker, 1974; Espitalié et al., 1977) as a result of petroleum generation and a switch to higher mean values of activation energy for residual kerogens (Tissot et al., 1987; Schaefer et al., 1990). The distribution of petroleum potentials for immature sulfur-rich type II kerogen has a lower mean activation energy than does normal type II kerogen of the same maturity (Tissot et al., 1987) because of the presence of weak carbon–sulfur linkages. Sulfur is therefore lost from kerogen mainly during early catagenesis as these bonds rupture (see Sinninghe-Damsté and de Leeuw, 1990, for review). The petroleum potential of type I kerogen is distributed across a narrow range of activation energies and has a higher generation threshold than do commonly occurring type II kerogens. Type III kerogens also have a relatively high overall stability.

While the onset of thermal maturity varies according to kerogen type, it is important to note that there is no single "magic R_o value" at which the onset of thermal maturity occurs for any given kerogen type. This is because the kinetics of kerogen decomposition differ from that of vitrinite reflectance change, a fact that is manifested in a rapidly subsiding source rock where the overburden rock is of Tertiary age. Here R_o may underestimate the extent of petroleum generation.

Gross Petroleum Composition Inherited from Kerogen

Natural unaltered oils vary in bulk composition because of broad differences in paraffinic, naphthenic, aromatic, and asphaltic components (Tissot and Welte, 1984). These variations are largely governed by the types of parent structures in the kerogen (Larter and Senftle, 1985; Horsfield, 1984, 1989). Empirical compositional relationships therefore exist between oils and kerogen pyrolysates (Horsfield, 1989), making it possible to assess the potential to generate condensate, high- and low-wax varieties of mixed base (paraffinic-naphthenic-aromatic) crude oil, and high- and low-wax varieties of paraffinic crude oil. These relationships may be substantially modified by displacement phenomena and phase behavior (England and Mackenzie, 1989). Indeed, because the composition of petroleum in the subsurface is dependent on phase behavior (England and Mackenzie, 1989), it is desirable to go one stage further and quantify these relationships in terms of gas–oil ratio, for example, so as to serve as input parameters for migration models (England and Mackenzie, 1989). It is, however, difficult to assess gas–oil ratios of petroleums directly in the subsurface using pyrolysis methods because of the abundance of high molecular weight, polar reaction intermediates in laboratory experiments (Larter et al., in press).

Interestingly, average carbon chain lengths for many *algal* kerogens appear to remain essentially constant over a broad range of thermal maturation, suggesting that this homogeneous pool of precursor structures in the kerogen and other macromolecular components is a potentially powerful oil–source rock and oil–oil correlation tool (Horsfield et al., 1989; Düppenbecker and Horsfield, 1990; Muscio et al., 1991). A shortening of average chain length was found to take place only during the very early stages of thermal maturation of Green River Shale and Posidonia Shale kerogens (Horsfield and Düppenbecker, 1991). Furthermore, based on the pyrolysis results of Dungworth and Schwartz

(1972), McKirdy et al. (1980), and Jackson et al. (1984) for highly mature Proterozoic and lower Paleozoic source rocks, it appears that long chain substituents inherited from biological organisms may be preserved even into metagenesis. This means that original oil potential can be recognized in some instances, even where levels of thermal maturity have been exceedingly high.

Because no preferred depletion of long alkyl chains occurs during the main phase of petroleum generation, it can be speculated that the base of their oil window is likely to be defined by oil stability. It should be noted, however, that significant changes in chain length distribution may occur during the maturation of heterogeneous and algal kerogens such as oil-prone coals as they readily lose long alkyl chains from their apparently nucleated structure (Horsfield, 1989). In this case, the base of the oil window is likely to be brought about by depletion of the kerogen's long chain components. Depletion would appear to occur far in advance of the generalized oil phase ($R_o = 1.3\%$). A distinctly separate phase of gas and condensate generation may occur at elevated thermal maturities, this being quantitatively significant in the case of coals.

Late in catagenesis and within metagenesis, either hydrogen sulfide or nitrogen may be generated from heterocyclic kerogen moieties in carbonates and coals, respectively (Le Tran et al., 1974; Jüntgen and Klein, 1975).

The *n*-alkanes in many paraffinic oils exhibit an odd–even carbon number predominance, typically between 1.2 and 1.5. This periodicity is inherited from biologically derived molecular structures in the source rock (van de Meent et al., 1980; Reed et al., 1986; Douglas et al., 1991). Precursors in the case of high-wax oils were previously thought to be wax esters or free hydrocarbons derived from leaf cuticles (Brooks and Smith, 1967). Because carbon number preferences approach unity in most thermally mature source rocks and "marine" oils (Bray and Evans, 1961; Brooks and Smith, 1967; Leythaeuser and Welte, 1969), it was logical to conclude that high-wax crude oils were generated at a low level of thermal maturity. This may still be the case for some coals (see below). However, the discovery that aliphatic biopolymers of plant cuticular membranes yield *n*-alkanes with a pronounced odd carbon number predominance, even at high degrees of thermal conversion (Tegelaar et al., 1989a), indicates that there is more than one type of high-wax oil precursor and that the latter may be generated late in catagenesis.

Molecular Maturation Parameters

The progress of thermal maturation can be monitored in the bitumen fraction by the use of so-called molecular maturation parameters ranging from the relatively simple CPI of *n*-alkanes (Bray and Evans, 1961) to sophisticated geochemical reactions of biological markers (see Mackenzie, 1984, for overview). While these are most useful in the early to peak oil generation range, aromatic hydrocarbon parameters can also be applied at higher levels of thermal maturity (see Radke, 1987, and Alexander et al., 1988, for overviews).

Random thermal cracking in most cases generates *n*-alkanes without odd–even carbon number predominance (for exceptions, see earlier discussion). Because of the high abundance of these newly formed compounds, this dilutes the biologically inherited odd carbon number preference maintained through diagenesis. Kerogen cracking also favors the formation of pristane, thus increasing the pristane/phytane ratio as thermal maturity increases. In a similar fashion, pristane/*n*-C_{17} and phytane/*n*-C_{18} ratios decrease with thermal maturity due to the preferential generation of *n*-alkanes. These parameters can only be applied to rock sequences with nearly identical starting organic material because changes in kerogen facies influence the mechanisms of the maturity-dependent alterations.

Steroid hydrocarbon isomer ratios are the most widely applied biological marker thermal maturation parameters. When these parameters were first established (Mackenzie et al., 1980), steranes were thought to undergo an epimerization reaction at C_{20} in the side chain, thus transforming the biogenic 20*R* configuration into the geologically occurring 20*S* configuration. This reaction continued until an equilibrium ratio of 0.54 was reached (van Graas et al., 1982). In a similar way, the biogenic configuration of steranes at C_{14} and C_{17} in the ring system is apparently altered, resulting in the formation of the thermodynamically most stable sterane isomers, 5α(H),14β(H),17β(H)-steranes (20*S* + 20*R*) (Mackenzie et al., 1980). Later it was shown that sterane isomer ratios are not always related to thermal maturity but are dependent on kerogen facies (ten Haven et al., 1986; Moldowan et al., 1986; Rullkötter and Marzi, 1988) because specific precursor molecules lead to the early formation of the geologic epimers. This effect is particularly important in carbonate and evaporite source rocks (ten Haven et al., 1986; Rullkötter et al., 1985) where sterane isomer ratios usually fail as thermal maturation indicators. In contrast to this, steroid aromatization, i.e., the transformation of monoaromatic to triaromatic steroid hydrocarbons (Mackenzie et al., 1981), appears to be kerogen facies independent and has been successfully used as a thermal maturity indicator for carbonate source rocks and genetically related crude oils (Rullkötter et al., 1985).

For both sterane isomerization and aromatization reactions, however, recent studies have shown that our understanding of the reaction mechanisms involved is far from adequate and that the chemical basis for some of the systematic changes observed is more complex than previously thought (Rullkötter and Marzi, 1989; Abbott et al., 1990; Peters et al., 1990; Marzi and Rullkötter, 1992). While, the related thermal maturity parameters should be applied with the necessary caution, it is clear that they constitute an important means for calibrating thermal history.

Changes of hopane composition in source rocks during catagenesis involve an increase in the 17α(H)-hopane/moretane ratio (Seifert and Moldowan, 1980) and in the amount of 22,29,30-trisnorneohopane relative to its C_{27} 17α(H)-hopane counterpart (Seifert and Moldowan, 1978). Both parameters, however, show significant variations with organic facies in addition to the dependence on thermal maturity. On the other hand, because epimerization of extended hopanes (C_{31}–C_{35}) is complete before catagenesis starts, they are of little use as thermal maturity parameters (Mackenzie et al., 1980).

Porphyrins respond to increasing thermal stress by the loss of the five-membered isocyclic ring, so that DPEP porphyrins are progressively transformed into etioporphyrins (Barwise and Roberts, 1984; Sundararaman et al., 1988). This parameter has been shown to be useful beyond the peak of oil generation.

Aromatic hydrocarbon maturity parameters monitor the thermally induced changes in the isomer distributions of methylated biphenyls, naphthalenes, and phenanthrenes (Radke, 1987; Alexander et al., 1988). These parameters have been calibrated using coals or sedimentary rocks containing mainly terrigenous organic matter. The application range extends up to 1.5% R_o or higher. The correlation with vitrinite reflectance is excellent for coaly organic matter such that the molecular parameters are often used to calculate vitrinite reflectance equivalents. Application to marine organic matter, although successful in some cases, appears to be more problematic.

SUMMARY

The subject of thermal maturation is familiar to the vast majority of petroleum explorationists because it is the most important criterion for delineating the occurrence of active source rocks. Maturation parameters such as vitrinite reflectance continue to be routinely used to assess present-day maturity zonation, and the terms *diagenesis, catagenesis,* and *metagenesis,* along with *oil window* and *gas window,* are widely used to describe the extent of thermal alteration. The importance of kerogen typing is also appreciated, at least to the extent that kerogen types II and III are known to have gross differences in oil versus gas potential.

While these fundamental concepts have stood the test of time to a large degree, it is clear that our ideas on maturation are constantly being refined, as is the application of the ideas to help reduce the risk of exploration. Regarding application, quantitative assessments using kinetic and mass balance models are now used by most of the major oil companies, whereas not long ago they were the exception. Rather than relying on present-day maturation levels, maturation histories are now determinable, with biomarker reaction kinetics continuing to play a crucial role in thermal history calibration. Identifying more precursor–product relationships will further assist these efforts.

Regarding conceptual advances, the dangers of using fixed vitrinite reflectance limits to define the onset and end of oil generation have become clearer as we have gained a better appreciation of how variable the kinetic parameters of petroleum generation are (both between and within kerogen types II and III). The need for molecular kerogen typing has recently been rekindled because mass balance models, relying on matching pairs of immature and mature source rock equivalents, and

secondary migration models, utilizing compositional information on generated petroleums, require information that kerogen types I, II, and III are unable to provide. On a more fundamental note, there is still a need to clarify the degree to which pressure and mineral catalysts affect the rates of petroleum-forming chemical reactions in the subsurface. This will best be acheived by using the combined approach of regional studies, process simulation, and numerical modeling.

Acknowledgments   *We would like to express our gratitude to A. G. Douglas for critically reviewing an earlier draft of the manuscript.*

References Cited

Abbott, G. D., G. Y. Wang, T. I. Eglinton, A. K. Home, and G. S. Petch, 1990, The kinetics of biological marker release during the hydrous pyrolysis of vitrinite kerogen: Geochimica et Cosmochimica Acta, v. 54, p. 2451–2461.

Adam, P., C. Schmid, B. Mycke, C. Strazielle, J. Connan, A. Huc, A. Riva, and P. Albrecht, 1993, Structural investigation of non-polar sulfur cross-linked macromolecules in petroleum: Geochimica et Cosmochimica Acta, v. 57, p. 3395–3419.

Alexander, R., R. I. Kagi, E. Tok, and W. van Bronswijk, 1988, The use of aromatic hydrocarbons for assessment of thermal histories in sediments, *in* P. G. Purcell and R. R. Purcell, eds., Proceedings of the Northwest Shelf Symposium: Perth, Petroleum Exploration Society of Australia, p. 559–562.

Baker, E. W, and J. W. Louda, 1986, Porphyrins in the sedimentary record, *in* R. B. Johns, ed., Biological markers in the sedimentary record: Amsterdam, Elsevier, p. 125–225.

Barker, C, 1974, Pyrolysis techniques for source rock evaluation: AAPG Bulletin, v. 58, p. 2349–2361.

Barwise, A. J. G, and I. Roberts, 1984, Diagenetic and catagenetic pathways for porphyrins in sediments, *in* P. A. Schenk, J. W. de Leeuw, and G. W. M. Lijmbach, eds., Advances in Organic Geochemistry 1983: Oxford, Pergamon Press, p. 167–176.

Béhar, F., and M. Vandenbroucke, 1986, Représentation chimique de la structure des kérogènes et des asphaltènes en fonction de leur origine et de leur degré d'Evolution: Revue of the Institut Français du Pétrole, v. 41, p. 173–188.

Blumer, M., R. R. L. Guillard, and T. Chase, 1971, Hydrocarbons of marine phytoplankton: Marine Biology, International Journal on Life in Oceans and Coastal Waters, v. 8, n. 4, p. 183–189.

Brassell, S. C., J. McEvoy, C. F. Hoffmann, N. A. Lamb, T. M. Peakman, and J. R. Maxwell, 1984, Isomerisation—rearrangement and aromatisation of steroids in distinguishing early stages of diagenesis, *in* P. A. Schenk, J. W. de Leeuw, and G. W. M. Lijmbach, eds., Advances in Organic Geochemistry1983: Oxford, Pergamon Press, p. 11–23.

Bray, E. E, and E. D. Evans, 1961, Distribution of *n*-paraffins as a clue to recognition of source beds: Geochimica et Cosmochimica Acta, v. 22, p. 2–15.

Brooks, J. D, and J. W. Smith, 1967, The diagenesis of plant lipids during the formation of petroleum, coal and natural gas, I: Geochimica et Cosmochimica Acta, v. 31, p. 2389–2397.

Burlingame, A. L., P. A. Haug, H. K. Schnoes, and B. R. Simoneit, 1969, Fatty acids derived from the Green River Formation oil shale by extractions and oxidations—a review, *in* P. A. Schenck and I. Havenaar, eds., Advances in Organic Geochemistry 1968: Oxford, Pergamon Press, p. 85–129.

Cane, R. F, and P. R. Albian, 1973, The organic geochemistry of torbanite precursors: Geochimica et Cosmochimica Acta, v. 37, p. 1543–1549.

Connan, J., K. LeTran, and B. M. van der Weide, 1975, Alteration of petroleum in reservoirs: Proceedings from the Eighth World Petroleum Congress, p. 171–178.

Cooles, G. P., A. S. Mackenzie, and T. M. Quigley, 1986, Calculation of petroleum masses generated and expelled from source rocks, *in* D. Leythaeuser and J. Rullkötter, eds., Advances in Organic Geochemistry 1985: Oxford, Pergamon Press, p. 235–245.

Curtis, C. D., 1978, Possible links between sandstone diagenesis and depth-related geochemical reactions occurring in enclosing mudstones: Journal of the Geologic Society of London, v. 135, p. 107–117.

de Leeuw, J. W, and M. Baas, 1986, Early-stage diagenesis of steroids, *in* R. B. Johns, ed., Biological markers in the sedimentary record: Amsterdam, Elsevier, p. 101–123.

de Leeuw, J. W., H. C. Cox, G. van Graas, F. W. van de Meer, T. M. Peakman, J. M. A. Baas, and B. van de Graaf, 1989, Limited double bond isomerisation and selective hydrogenation of sterenes during early diagenesis: Geochimica et Cosmochimica Acta, v. 53, p. 903–909.

Didyk, B. M., B. R. T. Simoneit, S. C. Brassell, and G. Eglinton, 1978, Organic geochemical indicators of paleoenvironmental conditions of sedimentation: Nature, v. 272, p. 216–222.

Dormans, H. N. M., F. J. Huntgens, and D. W. van Krevelen, 1957, Chemical structure and properties of coal XX—composition of the individual macerals: Fuel, v. 36, p. 321.

Douglas, A. G., J. S. Sinninghe-Damsté, M. G. Fowler, T. I. Eglinton, and J. W. de Leeuw, 1991, Unique distributions of hydrocarbons and sulfur compounds released by flash pyrolysis from the fossilised alga *Gloeocapsomorpha prisca*, a major constituent in one of four Ordovician kerogens: Geochemica et Cosmochimica Acta, v. 55, p. 275–291.

Dungworth, G., and A. W. Schwartz, 1972, Kerogen isolates from the Precambrian of South Africa and Australia, *in* H. R. V. Gaertner and H. Wehner, eds., Advances in Organic Geochemistry 1971: Oxford, Pergamon Press, p. 699–706.

Düppenbecker, S., and B. Horsfield, 1990, Compositional information for kinetic modelling and petroleum type prediction, *in* B. Durand, and F. Béhar, eds., Advances in Organic Geochemistry 1989: Oxford, Pergamon Press, p. 259–266.

Durand, B., 1980, Kerogen: Paris, Editions Technip, 519 p.

Eglinton, G., and R. J. Hamilton, 1963, The distribution of alkanes, *in* T. Swain, ed., Chemical plant taxonomy: London, Academic Press, p. 187–217.

England, W. A., and A. S. Mackenzie, 1989, Some aspects of the organic geochemistry of petroleum fluids: Geologische Rundschau, v. 78, p. 291–303.

Espitalié, J., J. L. Laporte, M. Madec, F. Marquis, P. Leplat, J. Paulet, and A. Boutefeu, 1977, Méthode rapide de caractérisation des roches mères de leur potential petrolier et de leur degré d'evolution: Revue of the Institute Français du Pétrole, v. 32, p. 23–42.

Gehman, H. M., Jr., 1962, Organic matter in limestones: Geochimica et Cosmochimica Acta, v. 26, p. 885–897.

Goff, J. C., 1984, Hydrocarbon generation and migration from Jurassic source rocks in the East Shetland Basin and Viking Graben of the northern North Sea, *in* G. Demaison and R. J. Murris, eds., Petroleum geochemistry and basin evaluation: AAPG Memoir #35, p. 273–302.

Goossens, H., J. W. de Leeuw, P. A. Schenck, and S. C. Brassell, 1984, Tocopherols as likely precursors of pristane in ancient sediments and crude oils: Nature, v. 312, p. 440–442.

Gransch, J. A., and E. Eisma, 1970, Characterisation of the insoluble organic matter of sediments by pyrolysis, *in* G. D. Hobson and G. C. Speers, eds., Advances in Organic Geochemistry 1966: New York, Pergamon Press, p. 407–426.

Hedges, J. I., 1978, The formation and clay mineral reactions of melanoidins: Geochimica et Cosmochimica Acta, v. 42, p. 69–76.

Héroux, Y., A. Chagnon, and R. Bertrand, 1979, Compilation and correlation of major thermal maturation indicators: AAPG Bulletin, v. 63, p. 2128–2144.

Hoering, T. C., 1973, A comparison of melanoidin and humic acid: Carnegie Institute Washington Yearbook, v. 72, p. 682–690.

Horsfield, B., 1978, Influence of type, maturation, and environment on the organic chemical composition of sedimentary organic matter: Ph.D. dissertation, University of Newcastle-upon-Tyne, U.K.

Horsfield, B., 1984, Pyrolysis studies and petroleum exploration, *in* J. Brooks and D. H. Welte, eds., Advances in Petroleum Geochemistry: London, Academic Press, v. 1, p. 247–292.

Horsfield, B., 1989, Practical criteria for classifying kerogens: some observations from pyrolysis–gas chromatography: Geochimica et Cosmochimica Acta, v. 53, p. 891–901.

Horsfield, B., and S. J. Düppenbecker, 1991, The decomposition of Posidonia Shale and Green River Shale kerogens using microscale sealed vessel (MSSV) pyrolysis: Journal of Analytical and Applied Pyrolysis, v. 20, p. 107–123.

Horsfield, B., U. Disko, and F. Leistner, 1989, The microscale simulation of maturation: outline of a new technique and its potential applications: Geologische Rundschau, v. 78, p. 361–374.

Horsfield, B., S. J. Düppenbecker, H. J. Schenk, and R. G. Schäfer, 1993, Kerogen typing concepts designed for the quantitative geochemical evaluation of petroleum potential, *in* A. G. Doré, J. H. Augustson, C. Hermanrud, D. J. Steward, O. Sylta, eds., Basin modelling, advances and applications: Norwegian Petroleum Society Special Publication 243, 249 p.

Huc, A. Y, and B. M. Durand, 1977, Occurrence and significance of humic acids in ancient sediments: Fuel, v. 56, p. 73–80.

Hunt, J. M., 1979, Petroleum geochemistry and geology: San Francisco, W. H, Freeman and Company, 617 p.

Jackson, K. S., D. M. McKirdy, and J. A. Deckelmann, 1984, Hydrocarbon generation in the Amadeus basin, Central Australia: APEA Journal, v. 24, p. 43–65.

Jones, R. W., 1984, Comparison of carbonate and shale source rocks, *in* J. G. Palacas, ed., Petroleum geochemistry and source rock potential of carbonate rocks: AAPG Studies in Geology, n. 18, p. 163–180.

Jones, R. W., 1987, Organic facies, *in* J. Brooks and D. H. Welte, eds., Advances in Petroleum Geochemistry, v. 2, p. 1–89.

Jüntgen, H., and J. Klein, 1975, Entstehung von Erdgas aus Kohligen Sedimenten. Erdöl and Kohle, Erdgas: Petrochemie, v. 1, p. 52–69.

Karweil, J., 1966, Inkohlung, pyrolyse und primaire Migration des Erdöls: Brennstoff-Chem, v. 47, p. 161–169.

Khorasani, G. K, and D. G. Murchison, 1988, Order of generation of petroleum hydrocarbons from liptinitic macerals with increasing thermal maturity: Fuel, v. 67, p. 1160–1162.

Knights, B. A., A. C. Brown, E. Conway, and B. S. Middleditch, 1970, Hydrocarbons from the green form of the freshwater alga *Botryococcus braunii*: Phytochemistry, v. 9, n. 6, p. 1317–1324.

Largeau, C., S. Derenne, E. Casadevall, A. Kadouri, and N. Sellier, 1986, Pyrolysis of immature Torbanite and of the resistant biopolymer, PRBA, isolated from extant alga *Botryococcus braunii*, Mechanism of formation and structure of Torbanite, *in* D. Leythaeuser and J. Rullkötter, eds., Advances in Organic Geochemistry 1985: Oxford, Pergamon Press, p. 1023–1032.

Largeau, C., S. Derenne, E. Casadevall, C. Berkaloff, M. Corolleur, B. Lugardon, J.F. Raynaud, and J. Connan, 1990, Occurrence and origin of "ultralaminar" structures in "amorphous" kerogens of various source rocks and oil shales, *in* B. Durand and F. Béhar, eds., Advances in Organic Geochemistry 1989: Oxford, Pergamon Press, p. 889–895.

Larter, S. R., 1985, Integrated kerogen typing and the quantitative evaluation of petroleum source rocks, *in* B.M. Thomas et al., eds., Petroleum geochemistry in exploration of the Norwegian shelf: London, Graham and Trotman, p. 269–286.

Larter, S. R., 1988, Some pragmatic perspectives in source rock geochemistry: Marine and Petroleum Geology, v. 5, p. 194–204.

Larter, S. R., 1989, Chemical models of vitrinite reflectance evolution: Geologische Rundschau, v. 78, p. 349–359.

Larter, S. R., and A. G. Douglas, 1980, A pyrolysis–gas chromatographic method for kerogen typing, *in* A. G. Douglas and J. R. Maxwell, eds., Advances in Organic Geochemistry 1979: Oxford, Pergamon Press, p. 579–584.

Larter, S. R, and J. Senftle, 1985, Quantitative typing of kerogens: Nature, v. 318, p. 277–280.

Larter, S. R., H. Solli, A. G. Douglas, F. de Lange, and J. W. de Leeuw, 1979, Occurrence and significance of prist-1-ene in kerogen pyrolysates: Nature, v. 279, p. 405–408.

Larter, S. R., H. Solli, and A. G. Douglas, 1983, Phytol-containing melanoidins and their bearing on the fate of isoprenoid structures in sediments, *in* M. Bjorøy et al., eds., Organic Geochemistry 1981: Chichester, John Wiley, p. 513–523.

Larter, S. R., T. I. Eglinton, and B. Horsfield, in press, Kerogen, kinetics and pyrolysate composition—an absence of theoretical justification for "global" maturation models: Organic Geochemistry.

Le Tran, K., J. Connan, and B. van der Weide, 1974, Diagenesis of organic matter and occurrence of hydrocarbons and hydrogen sulphide in the S.W. Aquitaine basin (France): Bulletin of the Pau Research Centre (SNPA), v. 8, p. 111–137.

Lewan, M. D., and J. A. Williams, 1987, Evaluation of petroleum generation from resinites by hydrous pyrolysis: AAPG Bulletin, v. 71, p. 207–214.

Leythaeuser, D., and D. H. Welte, 1969, Relation between distribution of heavy *n*-paraffins and coalification in Carboniferous coals from the Saar district, Germany, *in* P. A. Schenck and I. Havenaar, eds., Advances in Organic Geochemistry 1968: New York, Pergamon Press, p. 429–442.

Mackenzie, A. S., 1984, Applications of biological markers in petroleum geochemistry, *in* J. Brooks, and D. H. Welte, Advances in Petroleum Geochemistry: London, Academic Press, v. 1, p. 115–214.

Mackenzie, A. S., R. L. Patience, J. R. Maxwell, M. Vandenbroucke, and B. Durand, 1980, Molecular parameters of maturation in the Toarcian shales, Paris basin, France, I: Changes in the configuration of acyclic isoprenoid alkanes, steranes and triterpanes: Geochimica et Cosmochimica Acta, v. 44, p. 1709–1721.

Mackenzie, A. S., C. F. Hoffmann, and J. R. Maxwell, 1981, Molecular parameters of maturation in the Toarcian shales, Paris basin, France, III: Changes in aromatic steroid hydrocarbons: Geochimica et Cosmochimica Acta, v. 45, p. 1345–1355.

Mackenzie, A. S., S. C. Brassell, G. Eglinton, and J. R. Maxwell, 1982, Chemical fossils—the geologic fate of steroids: Science, v. 217, p. 481–505.

Maillard, L. C., 1913, Formation de matières humique par l'action de polypeptides sur sucres: C.R., Acad. Sci, v. 156, p. 148–149.

Marzi, R., and J. Rullkötter, 1992, Qualitative and quantitative evolution and kinetics of biological marker transformations—laboratory experiments and application to the Michigan basin, *in* J. M. Moldowan, P. Albrecht, and R. P. Philp, Biological markers in sediments and petroleum: Englewood Cliffs, Prentice-Hall, p. 18–41.

McHugh, D. J., J. D. Saxby, and J. W. Tardif, 1976, Pyrolysis–hydrogenation–gas chromatography of carbonaceous material from Australian sediments, Part I, some Australian coals: Chemical Geology, v. 17, p. 243–259.

McIver, R. D., 1967, Composition of kerogen—clue to its role in the origin of petroleum: Mexico City, Proceedings of Seventh World Petroleum Congress, v. 2, p. 26–36.

McKirdy, D. M., D. J. McHugh, and J. W. Tardif, 1980, Comparative analysis of stromatolitic and other microbial kerogens by pyrolysis–hydrogenation–gas chromatography (PHGC), *in* P. A. Trudinger, M. R. Walter, and B. J. Ralph, eds., Biogeochemistry of ancient and modern environments: Australian Academy of Science, and Berlin, Springer-Verlag, p. 187–200.

Michaelis, W., and P. Albrecht, 1979, Molecular fossils of Archaebacteria in kerogen: Nature, v. 66, p. 420–421.

Moldowan, J. M., P. Sundararaman, and M. Schoell, 1986, Sensitivity of biomarker properties to depositional environment and/or source input in the lower Toarcian of SW-Germany, *in* D. Leythaeuser and J. Rullkötter, eds., Advances in Organic Geochemistry 1985: Oxford, Pergamon Press, p. 915–926.

Muscio, G. P. A., B. Horsfield, and D. H. Welte, 1991, Compositional changes in the macromolecular organic matter (kerogens, asphaltenes and resins) of a naturally matured source rock sequence from northern Germany as revealed by pyrolysis methods, *in* D. Manning, ed., Organic geochemistry advances and applications in energy and the natural environment: Manchester, U.K., Manchester University Press, p. 447–449.

Mycke, B., and W. Michaelis, 1986, Molecular fossils from chemical degradation of macromolecular organic matter, *in* D. Leythaeuser, and J. Rullkötter, eds., Advances in Organic Geochemistry 1985: Oxford, Pergamon Press, p. 847–858.

Nip, M., E. W. Tegelaar, H. Brinkhuis, J. W. de Leeuw, P. A. Schenck, and P. J. Holloway, 1986, Analysis of modern and fossil plant cuticles by Curie point Py-GC and Curie point

Py-GC-MS: recognition of a new, highly aliphatic and resistant biopolymer, *in* D. Leythaeuser and J. Rullkötter, eds., Advances in Organic Geochemistry 1985: Oxford, Pergamon Press, p. 769-778.

Nissenbaum, A., and I. R. Kaplan, 1972, Chemical and isotopic evidence for the in situ origin of marine humic substances: Limnology and Oceanography, v. 17, p. 570–582.

Nissenbaum, A., M. Goldberg, and Z. Aizenshtat, 1985, Immature condensate from southeastern Mediterranean coastal plain, Israel: AAPG Bulletin, v. 69, p. 946–949.

Oberlin, A., J. L. Boulmier, and M. Villey, 1980, Electron microscopic study of kerogen microtexture, selected criteria for determining the evolution path and evolution stage of kerogen, *in* B. Durand, ed., Kerogen, insoluble organic matter from sedimentary rocks: Paris, Editions Technip, p. 191–241.

Orem, W. H., P. G. Harcher, E. C. Spiker, N. M. Szeverenyi, and G. E. Maciel, 1986, Dissolved organic matter in anoxic pore waters from Mangrove Lake, Bermuda: Geochimica et Cosmochimica Acta, v. 50, p. 609–618.

Ourisson, G., 1990, Frontiers of organic geochemistry: Some unresolved problems, *in* B. Durand and F. A. Behar, eds., Advances in Organic Geochemistry 1989: Oxford, Pergamon Press, p. 21–24.

Ourisson, G., P. Albrecht, and M. Rohmer, 1979, The hopanoids, paleochemistry and biochemistry of a group of natural products: Pure Applied Chemistry, v. 51, p. 709–729.

Peakman, T. M., and J. R. Maxwell, 1988a, Acid-catalysed rearrangements of steroid alkenes, Part 1, rearrangement of 5α-cholest-7-ene: Journal of Chemistry, Perkin Society Transactions, v. 1, p. 1065–1070.

Peakman, T. M, and J. R. Maxwell, 1988b, Early diagenetic pathways of steroid alkenes, *in* L. Mattavelli and L. Novelli, eds., Advances in Organic Geochemistry 1987: Oxford, Pergamon Press, p. 583–592.

Peakman, T. M., K. Ellis, and J. R. Maxwell, 1988, Acid-catalysed rearrangements of steroid alkenes, Part 2, a re-investigation of the backbone rearrangement of 5α-cholest-7-ene: Journal of Chemistry, Perkin Society Transactions, v. 1, p. 1071–1075.

Peakman, T. M., H. L. ten Haven, J. A. Rechka, J. W. de Leeuw, and J. R. Maxwell, 1989, Occurrence of 20R and 20S Δ$^{8(14)}$ and Δ^{14} 5α(H)-sterenes and the origin of 5α(H),14β(H),17β(H)-steranes in an immature sediment: Geochimica et Cosmochimica Acta, v. 53, p. 2001–2009.

Peters, K. E., J. M. Moldowan, and P. Sundararaman, 1990, Effects of hydrous pyrolysis on biomarker thermal maturity parameters: Monterey phosphatic and siliceous members: Organic Geochemistry, v. 15, p. 249–265.

Philp, R. P., and M. Calvin, 1976, Possible origin for insoluble kerogen, debris in sediments from insoluble cell-wall materials of algae and bacteria: Nature, v. 262, p. 134–136.

Powell, T. G., and D. M. McKirdy, 1975, Geologic factors controlling crude oil composition in Australia and Papua, New Guinea: AAPG Bulletin, v. 59, p. 1176–1197.

Pusey, W. C. III, 1973, The ESR-kerogen method: a new technique of estimating the organic maturity of sedimentary rocks: Petroleum Times, v. 77, p. 21–26.

Radke, M., 1987, Organic geochemistry of aromatic hydrocarbons, *in* J. Brooks and D. H. Welte, eds., Advances in Petroleum Geochemistry: London, Academic Press, v. 2, p. 141–207.

Rashid, M. A., and L. H. King, 1969, Molecular weight distribution measurements on humic and fulvic acid fractions from marine clays on the Scotian Shelf: Geochimica et Cosmochimica Acta, v. 33, p. 147–151.

Rechka J. A., H. C. Cox, T. M. Peakman, J. W. de Leeuw, and J. R. Maxwell, 1992, A reinvestigation of aspects of early diagenetic pathways of 4-methylsterenes bases on molecular mechanics calculations and the acid catalysed isomerisation of 4-methylcholest-4-ene, *in* J. M. Moldowan, P. Albrecht, and R. P. Philp, eds., Biological markers in sediments and petroleum: Englewood Cliffs, Prentice-Hall, p. 42–57.

Reed, J., H. A. Illich, and B. Horsfield, 1986, Biochemical evolutionary significance of Ordovician oils and their source, *in* D. Leythaeuser and J. Rullkötter, eds., Advances in Organic Geochemistry 1985: Oxford, Pergamon Press, p. 347–358.

Retkofsky, A. L., J. M. Stark, and R. A. Friedal, 1968, Electron spin resonance in American coals: Analytical Chemistry, v. 40, p. 1699–1704.

Romovacek, J., and J. Kubat, 1968, Characterisation of coal substances by pyrolysis–gas chromatography: Analytical Chemistry, v. 40, p. 1119–1124.

Rouxhet, P. G, and P. L. Robin, 1978, Infrared study of the evolution of kerogens of different origins during catagenesis and pyrolysis: Fuel, v. 57, p. 533–540.

Rubinsztain, Y., P. Ioselis, R. Ikan, and Z. Aizenschtat, 1984, Investigations of the structural units of melanoidins: Organic Geochemistry, v. 6, p. 791–804.

Rullkötter, J., and R. Marzi, 1988, Natural and artificial maturation of biological markers in Toarcian shale from northern Germany, *in* L. Mattavelli and L. Novelli, eds., Advances in Organic Geochemistry 1987: Oxford, Pergamon Press, p. 639–645.

Rullkötter, J., and R. Marzi, 1989, New aspects of the application of sterane isomerization and steroid aromatization to petroleum exploration and the reconstruction of geothermal histories of sedimentary basins: Reprint Division of Petroleum Chemistry, American Chemical Society, v. 34, p. 126–131.

Rullkötter, J., B. Spiro, and A. Nissenbaum, 1985, Biological marker characteristics of oils and asphalts from carbonate source rocks in a rapidly subsiding graben, Dead Sea, Israel: Geochimica et Cosmochimica Acta, v. 49, p. 1357–1370.

Rullkötter, J., et al., 1988, Organic matter maturation under the influence of a deep intrusive body: a natural experiment for quantitation of hydrocarbon generation and expulsion from a petroleum source rock, Toarcian shale, northern Germany, *in* L. Mattavelli, and L. Novelli, eds., Advances in Organic Geochemistry 1987: Oxford, Pergamon Press, v. 13, p. 847–856.

Saxby, J. D., 1981, Kerogen genesis and structure—Similarities to rubber: Fuel, v. 60, p. 994–996.

Schaefer, R. G., H. J. Schenk, H. Hardelauf, and R. Harms, 1990, Determination of gross kinetic parameters for petroleum formation from Jurassic source rocks of different maturity levels by means of laboratory experiments, *in* B. Durand and F. Béhar, eds., Advances in Organic Geochemistry 1989: Oxford, Pergamon Press, v. 16, p. 115–120.

Seifert, W. K, and J. M. Moldowan, 1978, Application of steranes, terpanes and monoaromatics to the maturation, migration and source of crude oils: Geochimica et Cosmochimica Acta, v. 42, p. 77–95.

Seifert, W. K, and J. M. Moldowan, 1980, The effect of thermal stress on source rock quality as measured by hopane stereochemistry, *in* A. G. Douglas, and J. R. Maxwell, eds., Advances in Organic Geochemistry 1979: Oxford,

Advances in Organic Geochemistry 1979: Oxford, Pergamon Press, p. 229–237.

Senftle, J. T., S. R. Larter, B. W. Bromley, and J. H. Brown, 1986, Quantitative chemical characterization of vitrinite concentrates using pyrolysis–gas chromatography: rank variation of pyrolysis products: Organic Geochemistry, v. 9, p. 345–350.

Sinninghe-Damsté, J. S., and J. W. de Leeuw, 1990, Analysis, structure and geochemical significance of organically bound sulfur in the geosphere: state of the art and future research, *in* B. Durand and F., Béhar, eds., Advances in Organic Geochemistry 1989: Oxford, Pergamon Press, p. 1077–1101.

Snowdon, L. R., and T. G. Powell, 1982, Immature oil and condensate-modification of hydrocarbon generation model for terrestrial organic matter: AAPG Bulletin, v. 66, p. 775–788.

Stach, E., M. T. Mackowsky, M. Teichmüller, G. H. Taylor, D. Chandra, and R. Teichmüller, 1982, Stach's textbook of coal petrology, 3rd ed: Berlin, Gebrüder Borntraeger, 428 p.

Stevenson, F. J., 1974, Nonbiological transformations of amino acids in soils and sediments, *in* B. Tissot and F. Bienner, eds., Advances in Organic Geochemistry 1973: Paris, Editions Technip, p. 701–714.

Stuermer, D. H., and G. R. Harvey, 1974, Humic substances from seawater: Nature, v. 250, p. 480–481.

Sundararaman, P., W. R. Biggs, J. R. Reynolds, and J. C. Fetzer, 1988, Vanadylporphyrins, indicators of kerogen breakdown and generation of petroleum: Geochimica et Cosmochimica Acta, v. 52, p. 2337–2341.

Sweeney, J., and A. K. Burnham, 1990, Evaluation of a simple model of vitrinite reflectance based on chemical kinetics: AAPG Bulletin, v. 74, p. 1559–1570.

Tegelaar, E. W., R. M. Matthezing, B. H. Jansen, B. Horsfield, and J. W. de Leeuw, 1989a, Possible origin of *n*-alkanes in high-wax crude oils: Nature, v. 342, n. 6249, p. 529–531 .

Tegelaar, E. W., J. W. de Leeuw, S. Derenne, and C. Largeau, 1989b, A reappraisal of kerogen formation: Geochimica et Cosmochimica Acta, v. 53, p. 3103–3106.

ten Haven, H. L., J. W. de Leeuw, T. M. Peakman, and J. R. Maxwell, 1986, Anomalies in steroid and hopanoid maturity indices: Geochimica et Cosmochimica Acta, v. 50, p. 853–855.

ten Haven, H. L., J. W. de Leeuw, J. Rullkötter, and J. S. Sinninghe-Damsté, 1987, Restricted utility of the pristane/phytane ratio as a palaeoenvironmental indicator: Nature, v. 330, p. 641–643.

Thompson, S., B. S. Cooper, R. J. Morley, and P. Barnard, 1985, Oil-generating coals, *in* B.M. Thomas et al., eds., Petroleum geochemistry in exploration of the Norwegian Shelf: London, Graham and Trotman, p. 59–73.

Tissot, B. P., and D. H. Welte, 1984, Petroleum formation and occurrence, 2d ed.: Berlin, Springer-Verlag, 699 p.

Tissot, B. P., B. Durand, J. Espitalié, and A. Combaz, 1974, Influence of nature and diagenesis of organic matter in formation of petroleum: AAPG Bulletin, v. 58, p. 499–506.

Tissot, B. P., R. Pelet, and P. Ungerer, 1987, Thermal history of sedimentary basins, maturation indices, and kinetics of oil and gas generation: AAPG Bulletin, v. 71, p. 1445–1466.

van de Meent, D., S. C. Brown, R. P. Philp, and B. R. T. Simoneit, 1980, Pyrolysis–high resolution gas chromatography and pyrolysis gas chromatography–mass spectrometry of kerogen precursors: Geochimica et Cosmochimica Acta, v. 44, p. 999–1014.

van Graas, G., J. W. de Leeuw, and P. A. Schenck, 1980, Analysis of coals of different rank by Curie-point pyrolysis–mass spectrometry and Curie-point pyrolysis–gas chromatography–mass spectrometry, *in* A. G. Douglas and J. R. Maxwell, eds., Advances in Organic Geochemistry 1979: Oxford, Pergamon Press, p. 485–494.

van Graas, G., J. M. A. Baas, B. van de Graaf, and J. W. de Leeuw, 1982, Theoretical organic geochemistry I, The thermodynamic stability of several cholestane isomers calculated by molecular mechanics: Geochimica et Cosmochimica Acta, v. 46, p. 2399–2402.

Verheyen, T. V., and R. B. Johns, 1981, Structural investigations of Australian coals—I, a characterization of Victorian brown coal lithotypes and their kerogen and humic acid fractions by IR spectroscopy: Geochimica et Cosmochimica Acta, v. 45, p. 1899–1908.

Verheyen, T. V., R. B. Johns, and R. J. Esdaile, 1983, Structural investigations of Australian coals—IV, a characterization of the variation in rank of bituminous coal fractions by elemental analysis and IR spectroscopy: Geochimica et Cosmochimica Acta, v. 47, p. 1579–1587.

Witte, E. G., H. J. Schenk, P. J. Müller, and K. Schwochau, 1988, Structural modifications of kerogen during natural evolution as derived from ^{13}C CP/MAS NMR, IR spectroscopy and Rock-Eval pyrolysis of Toarcian shales, *in* L. Mattavelli and L. Novelli, eds., Advances in Organic Geochemistry 1987: Oxford, Pergamon Press, p. 1039–1044.

Yen, T. F., 1974, A new structural model of oil shale kerogen: preparation/division, *in* Fuel chemistry: American Chemistry Society, v. 19, p. 109–114.

"The essential elements of a pool are simple. A porous and permeable body of rock, called the reservoir rock, which is overlain by an impervious rock, called the roof rock, contains oil or gas or both, and is deformed or obstructed in such a manner that they are trapped."

—A. I. Levorsen

Passage from Levorsen, A. I., 1956, Geology of Petroleum: W.H. Freeman, p. 5-6.

Magoon, L. B, and W. G. Dow, eds., 1994, The petroleum
system—from source to trap: AAPG Memoir 60.

Chapter 11

Assessing Natural Oil Expulsion from Source Rocks by Laboratory Pyrolysis

Michael D. Lewan

U.S. Geological Survey
Denver, Colorado, U.S.A

Abstract

The amount of oil a pod of active source rock is capable of expelling is an important parameter in determining the ultimate oil potential of a petroleum system. Laboratory pyrolysis methods available for determining this parameter can be grouped into three categories: (1) *hydrous pyrolysis*, (2) *closed anhydrous pyrolysis*, and (3) *open anhydrous pyrolysis*. The processes responsible for expulsion of oil in nature are best simulated by hydrous pyrolysis. The presence of water in both nature and hydrous pyrolysis ensures the occurrence of a water-saturated bitumen within a source rock. This dissolved water reduces cleavage of bitumen molecules by terminating free radicals with water-derived hydrogen and allows the cleavages that do occur to form an immiscible oil. The importance of water is best demonstrated by its absence in closed anhydrous pyrolysis, which generates a bitumen that ultimately decomposes into an insoluble pyrobitumen rather than an expelled oil. As a result, this method is not useful in evaluating oil expulsion. Conversely, a vaporized oil may be generated in open anhydrous pyrolysis, but the amount of oil generated is dependent on experimental conditions, and the processes responsible for this evolved oil are not operative in nature.

INTRODUCTION

Determining the amount of oil that may be expelled from a pod of active source rock is an important consideration in assessing and ranking the hydrocarbon potential of a petroleum system. Once a source rock has been identified and its mature and overmature volume determined, reliable expulsion efficiencies may be used to determine the ultimate petroleum charge. Although economic accumulations from this charge will be determined by secondary migration and trapping, the ultimate charge is critical in evaluating the efficiencies of these processes within a petroleum system. Determining this ultimate petroleum charge is not only essential in ranking frontier systems but also necessary in assessing when drilling budgets should shift from exploration to exploitation strategies in extensively drilled systems. The success of these applications depends on accurately determining the amount of oil that may be expelled from a pod of active source rock for a given petroleum system. Laboratory pyrolysis methods offer a feasible approach in understanding primary oil migration and determining expulsion efficiencies of source rocks, but the type of pyrolysis method used is an important consideration in extrapolating experimental results to a petroleum system. The objective of this paper is to examine the utility of various pyrolysis methods in determining the amount of oil expelled from a source rock. The pyrolysis methods are discussed under three general headings: (1) hydrous pyrolysis, (2) closed anhydrous pyrolysis, and (3) open anhydrous pyrolysis.

HYDROUS PYROLYSIS

Hydrous pyrolysis involves heating a rock or kerogen sample in liquid water at subcritical temperatures in a closed reactor (Lewan et al., 1979; Lewan, 1985). If the proper time and temperature conditions are employed, a generated oil is expelled from the sample and accumulates on the water surface within the reactor. This generated and expelled oil is compositionally similar to natural crude oils and is typically a free-flowing liquid oil (Winters et al., 1983). Although the amounts of expelled oil generated in hydrous pyrolysis may be exaggerated, the processes responsible for the expulsion of oil are conceivably the same as those in nature (Lewan, 1991). Petroleum formation as determined by hydrous pyrolysis consists of two overall reactions: (1) partial decomposition of kerogen to bitumen and (2) partial decomposition of bitumen to oil (Lewan, 1985). This reaction series has long been recognized in oil shale

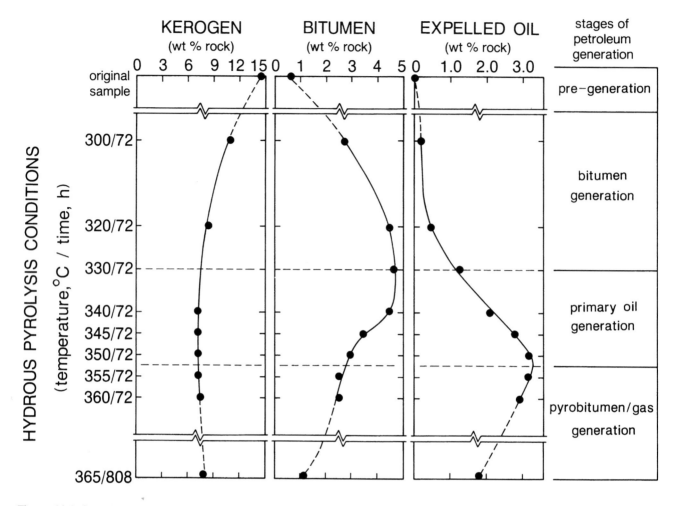

Figure 11.1. Amounts of kerogen, bitumen, and expelled oil collected after conducting isothermal hydrous pyrolysis experiments on aliquots of a Woodford Shale sample (WD-5) at temperatures ranging from 300° to 360°C for 72 hr, and at 365°C for 808 hr. Each experiment consists of heating 500 g of a separate aliquot of the original sample with 260 g of distilled water in a 1-L reactor at the temperature and time specified along the vertical axis. The bitumen generation stage represents the partial decomposition of kerogen to bitumen through the cleavage of weak noncovalent bonds. The primary oil generation stage represents the partial decomposition of bitumen to an immiscible expelled oil through cleavage of covalent bonds. The pyrobitumen/gas generation stage represents the decomposition of expelled oil and bitumen to insoluble organic matter (pyrobitumen) and gas.

retorting (Hershkowitz et al., 1983) and has also been suggested in natural petroleum formation (Louis and Tissot, 1967). Figure 11.1 illustrates these two overall reactions with a series of isothermal hydrous pyrolysis experiments conducted on aliquots of a sample of Woodford Shale (WD-5) at temperatures from 300° to 365°C.

The original rock used in this experimental maturation sequence contains insoluble oil-prone kerogen (type II), which constitutes more than 95 wt. % of the total organic matter (Figure 11.1). As thermal stress is applied in the experiments, part of the kerogen decomposes to a bitumen, which can be extracted from the rock with organic solvents (e.g., benzene and dichloromethane). This extracted bitumen is a tarry substance that consists mainly of high molecular weight components. Low activation energies ranging from 10 to 20 kcal/mol for this overall reaction (Connan, 1974; Barth et al., 1989) indicate that kerogen decomposition to bitumen involves

cleavage of weak noncovalent bonds. Bonds of this type are not well defined, but they may include hydrogen bonds or electron donor–acceptor complexes as suggested in structural models for coals (Larsen and Mohammadi, 1990; Kirchko and Gagarin, 1990). Petrographic studies of rocks subjected to hydrous pyrolysis and natural maturation show that continuous organic networks may be established by expansion of bitumen into the rock matrix during kerogen decomposition to bitumen (Lewan, 1987). This bitumen network impregnates the micropores and bedding plane partings as a result of a net volume increase in the organic matter within a confining mineral matrix. Petrophysical (Meissner, 1978) and petrographic data (Lewan, 1987) suggest that the development of a continuous bitumen network is essential for oil migration within and oil expulsion from effective source rocks. As denoted in Figure 11.1, this stage in which kerogen partially decomposes is referred to as *bitumen generation*.

As thermal stress increases, the subsequent overall reaction commences with the partial decomposition of bitumen to oil. Kerogen content does not change during this overall reaction, but the bitumen content decreases in proportion to the amount of expelled oil generated (Figure 11.1). This overall reaction does involve cleavage of covalent bonds with activation energies ranging from 34 to 67 kcal/mol (Lewan, 1985, 1989; Huizinga et al., 1988). In addition to the distinctly different activation energies between bitumen and oil generation, the concept of bitumen and oil being two different organic phases from two different overall reactions is also supported by their distinct compositional differences and their occurrence in hydrous pyrolysis experiments with only isolated kerogen (Lewan, 1991, 1993). An important prerequisite for differentiation of these two organic phases is the presence of dissolved water in the bitumen network. Although the solubility of hydrocarbons in water is low, the solubility of water in hydrocarbons is two orders of magnitude greater (Griswold and Kasch, 1942; Guerrant, 1964; Brady et al., 1982). As a result, sufficient quantities of water may be dissolved within the bitumen to participate in the partial decomposition of bitumen to oil. Water surrounding a bitumen-impregnated rock sample during hydrous pyrolysis is therefore only important in maintaining a bitumen network that is fully saturated with dissolved water (Lewan, 1991).

A generalized reaction pathway for thermal maturation of bitumen under hydrous pyrolysis conditions is proposed in Figure 11.2. The hypothetical bitumen molecule at the beginning of the reaction pathway is considered to be only one of many different molecular motifs that are produced from the breaking of noncovalent bonds during the thermal decomposition of kerogen (Figure 11.2a). These high molecular weight molecules make up the soluble bitumen phase, which under hydrous pyrolysis conditions is saturated with dissolved water derived from the original pores, parting planes, and fractures in a rock. As thermal maturation increases, encounters with extraneous free radicals from the decomposing kerogen or other bitumen molecules generate free radical sites on the bitumen molecule. At this point in the reaction pathway, Lewan (1991) suggests that hydrogen derived from dissolved water in the bitumen frequently terminates these free radical sites (Figure 11.2b, open circles), which prevents the cleavage of covalent carbon–carbon bonds in the β-position from the terminated free radical site (i.e., β-scission). Those free radical sites that are not terminated subsequently initiate β-scission in the bitumen molecule (Figure 11.2c). The cleaved free radical fragments may at this time be terminated by water-derived hydrogen or continue to undergo β-scission until termination occurs. Highly aliphatic fragments generated by β-scissions are hydrophobic in character and separate from the water-saturated bitumen as an immiscible oil phase (Figure 11.2c, dotted area).

The lower density of the immiscible oil relative to the water-saturated bitumen generates a buoyancy force, but the presence of an opposing capillary force within a source rock requires an additional force for oil expulsion.

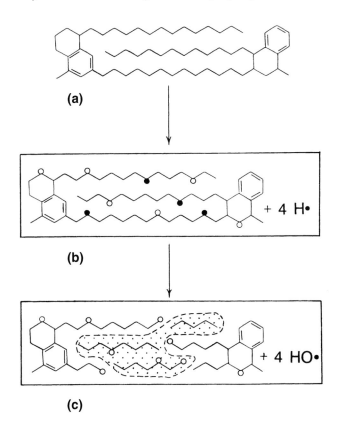

(a)

(b) + 4 H•

(c) + 4 HO•

Figure 11.2. Generalized reaction pathway proposed for thermal maturation of bitumen in a closed system under hydrous pyrolysis conditions. (a) Hypothetical bitumen molecule generated from the partial decomposition of kerogen by the breaking of weak noncovalent bonds. (b) Bitumen molecule in water-saturated bitumen phase (denoted by enclosing rectangle) after encountering free radicals generated from other bitumen molecules and decomposing kerogen. Some of the free radical sites imposed on the bitumen molecule are terminated by water-derived hydrogen (open circles) from dissolved water in the bitumen. (c) The remaining unterminated free radical sites (solid circles) initiate cleavage of covalent bonds in the bitumen molecule by β-scission. The cleaved free radical fragments are subsequently terminated by water-derived hydrogen from dissolved water in the bitumen. The hydrophobic character of the cleaved products results in their separation from the water-saturated bitumen as an immiscible oil phase (dotted area).

This additional force is most likely an internal pressure resulting from a net volume increase of the organic components within the confining inorganic matrix of a source rock. Evidence of this volume increase associated with oil generation during hydrous pyrolysis is the development of en echelon parting separations in the rock that are parallel to the bedding fabric and filled with oil (Lewan, 1987). This oil is included with the expelled oil by rinsing the rock sample with an organic solvent at room temperature after the water is decanted at the end of an experiment (Lewan, 1987).

At least three causes of this volume increase can be envisaged. The first involves the chemical volume increase that accompanies thermal cracking, as observed in petroleum refining (Egloff and Davis, 1954; Nelson, 1958). The second involves the physical volume increases resulting from thermal expansion of the generated oil (Lewan, 1987). The third involves a physicochemical volume increase due to the uptake of more dissolved water in the bitumen as it becomes more hydrophilic with increasing maturity (Lewan, 1991). The individual importance of each of these causes remains to be evaluated quantitatively, but their cumulative effect is the generation of an internal pressure as the water-saturated bitumen network partially decomposes to an immiscible oil. As denoted in Figure 11.1, this stage of petroleum generation is called *primary oil generation.*

The processes and mechanisms responsible for generation and expulsion of oil in hydrous pyrolysis experiments are conceivably the same as those in nature. However, the degree to which they are operative in nature remains to be determined. Overburden and confining pressures may have some influence on these processes and mechanisms (Takeda et al., 1990), but as a first approximation, the higher temperatures used in hydrous pyrolysis are likely to have the greatest influence. The effect of this higher temperature is most obvious in the decrease in solubility of water in bitumen with decreasing temperatures (Lewan, 1991). A reduction in the amount of water dissolved in the bitumen may cause a corresponding reduction in the amount of immiscible oil generated. In addition, the internal pressure resulting from the physical volume increase associated with oil generation is expected to be reduced at the lower temperatures in nature due to a reduction in thermal expansion of the generated oil. Therefore, the same processes and mechanisms may be operative in both hydrous pyrolysis and nature, but the amount of oil generated and expelled by hydrous pyrolysis is exaggerated relative to nature. An implication of this qualitative assessment is that thermally immature rocks that do not generate and expel oil in hydrous pyrolysis experiments will definitely not be effective source rocks in nature.

CLOSED ANHYDROUS PYROLYSIS

Anhydrous pyrolysis is defined here as experiments in which samples are pyrolyzed in the absence of liquid water. Anhydrous pyrolysis experiments reported in the literature can be described as either closed or open. These two types are distinguished on the basis of whether the generated products are maintained in the same thermal regime as the pyrolyzed samples. Pyrolyzing samples in a sealed reactor that is uniformly heated at a given temperature constitutes closed pyrolysis. The previously described hydrous pyrolysis experiments are also conducted in a closed system, and similar experiments without liquid water in a sealed reactor are referred to as *closed anhydrous pyrolysis.* Comet et al. (1986) reported pyrolysate yields from kerogens at 330°C after 72 hr to be 16–41% lower in closed anhydrous pyrolysis than in hydrous pyrolysis. Similarly, Tannenbaum et al. (1986) reported pyrolysate yields from kerogen–mineral mixtures at 300°C after 10 and 100 hr to be 9% and 44%

lower, respectively, in closed anhydrous pyrolysis than in hydrous pyrolysis.

Pyrolysate yield in both of these comparative studies is defined as the total solvent–soluble organic matter within the sample and reactor, with no distinction made between expelled oil and bitumen in their hydrous pyrolysis yields. To better assess the amount of oil expelled in closed anhydrous pyrolysis relative to hydrous pyrolysis, a series of 72-hr experiments at 300°, 330°, and 350°C were conducted on aliquots of an immature sample of Woodford Shale (WD-26) under anhydrous and hydrous conditions. All of these experiments were conducted in 1-L stainless steel-316 reactors with 400 g of crushed rock ranging in size from 0.5 to 2.0 cm. Hydrous pyrolysis experiments at the three temperatures were conducted with 320 g of deionized water and an initial helium pressure of 241 kPa. The comparable closed anhydrous pyrolysis experiments were conducted in the same type of reactor with the same amount of rock, but without water and with an initially evacuated gas space.

Pyrolysate yields from these comparative experiments in Table 11.1 (experiments 1–6) show the most obvious difference to be the total lack of expelled oil in the closed anhydrous experiments. Surfaces of the rock chips removed from the anhydrous experiments are devoid of oil droplets and oily films. At 300°C for 72 hr (experiments 1 and 2), only a small amount of expelled oil is generated in the hydrous experiment and the amount of oil plus bitumen is essentially the same under hydrous and anhydrous conditions. Partial decomposition of kerogen to bitumen predominates at this time–temperature condition (Figure 11.1), and the presence of water appears to have no significant effect on this overall reaction. However, significant differences are evident at the higher temperature experiments (330°C/72 hr, experiments 3 and 4, and 350°C/72 hr, experiments 5 and 6), which represent conditions under which bitumen partially decomposes to an expelled oil (Figure 11.1). The large decrease in bitumen and lack of an expelled oil through the anhydrous experimental sequence indicates that the decomposition of bitumen ultimately forms an insoluble pyrobitumen and gas under closed anhydrous conditions. Conversely, bitumen decomposes to an expellable oil under hydrous conditions. Lewan (1991) suggests this difference between closed anhydrous and hydrous reaction pathways is the result of water-derived hydrogen being available for free radical terminations and the immiscibility of generated oil in a water-saturated bitumen under hydrous conditions. The lack of dissolved water in bitumen under closed anhydrous conditions results in cross-linking polymerization and aromatization through free radical recombinations and disproportionations, respectively.

Table 11.1 shows the final pressures at the experimental temperatures to be significantly lower in the closed anhydrous experiments than in the hydrous experiments. The higher pressures in the hydrous experiments are a result of water vapor, generated gases, and helium, and the lower pressure in the closed anhydrous experiments are only a result of the generated gases.

Table 11.1. Experimental Conditions and Pyrolysate Yields from Hydrous and Anhydrous Pyrolysis Experiments on Aliquots of Woodford Shale Sample WD-26[a]

Experiment Reference Number	Experimental Temperatures (°C)	Final Pressure at Experimental Temperature (MPa)	Experimental Conditions	Expelled Oil (wt. % rock)	Bitumen Extract (wt. % rock)	Oil Plus Bitumen (wt. % rock)
1	300.1	2.17	Anhydrous	0.00	8.66	8.66
2	300.4	9.76	Hydrous	0.65	8.35	9.00
3	330.0	4.24	Anhydrous	0.00	6.62	6.62
4	329.7	15.89	Hydrous	2.79	8.19	10.98
5	350.6	5.69	Anhydrous	0.00	3.30	3.30
6	350.3	21.13	Hydrous	4.15	5.71	9.86

[a]Duration of all experiments was 72 hr. Details on experiments and collection procedures are given by Lewan (1993).

Monthioux et al. (1985) have concluded on the basis of a comparative experimental study on coals that pyrolysate yields from closed anhydrous pyrolysis at high confining gas pressures are similar to those obtained from hydrous pyrolysis. Pyrolysate yields from aliquots of the Woodford Shale (sample WD-26) in Table 11.2 for closed anhydrous pyrolysis with high confining pressures of helium (experiment 7) and generated gases (experiment 8) at 350°C for 72 hr do not support their conclusion. The high helium pressure (experiment 7) was attained in the one anhydrous experiment by loading the reactor at room temperature with 7.72 MPa of helium. The final pressure of 23.48 MPa at 350°C in this experiment consists of mostly helium and lesser amounts of generated gas. The high generated gas pressure was attained in the other anhydrous experiment (experiment 8) by mechanically pressing an excess of rock sample into a reactor to reduce the available gas space. The final pressure of 21.76 MPa at 350°C in this experiment consists only of generated gases. No expelled oil was generated in either of these experiments (experiments 7 and 8). Similar to the lower pressure anhydrous experiment (experiment 5), the amount of bitumen generated was significantly lower than that in hydrous pyrolysis. This discrepancy with Monthioux et al. (1985) is attributed by Lewan (1991b) to be their use of coals that are not capable of generating oil.

A generalized reaction pathway for thermal maturation of bitumen in a closed system under low- and high-pressure anhydrous conditions is proposed in Figure 11.3 for comparison with the hydrous pyrolysis pathway proposed in Figure 11.2. The bitumen generated by the breaking of weak noncovalent bonds in the kerogen is not apparently influenced by the presence of water, and therefore the hypothetical bitumen molecule at the beginning of the reaction pathway is considered the same under anhydrous- and hydrous conditions (Figures 11.3a and 11.2a, respectively). As thermal maturation increases, encounters with extraneous free radicals from the decomposing kerogen or other bitumen molecules generate free radical sites on the bitumen molecule. These free radical sites under anhydrous conditions are infrequently terminated by hydrogen atoms due to the lack of dissolved water in the bitumen (Figure 11.3b). Consequently, more free radical sites and subsequent β-

scissions occur in closed anhydrous pyrolysis (Figures 11.3b and c) than in hydrous pyrolysis (Figures 11.2b and c). The resulting free radical fragments under anhydrous conditions are also deprived of terminations by water-derived hydrogen and alternatively resort to terminations by recombination with other free radical sites on the bitumen molecule or neighboring free radical fragments (Figure 11.3d). These carbon–carbon bond terminations form a highly cross-linked bitumen molecule, which develops into an insoluble pyrobitumen. The inability of this method to generate an expelled oil renders it useless in assessing oil expulsion.

OPEN ANHYDROUS PYROLYSIS

Open anhydrous pyrolysis involves moving pyrolysate products out of the thermal regime in which they are generated. This movement of products is typically accomplished with a carrier gas that sweeps the volatile products into an external detector or with a cooling gradient that concentrates the condensable volatile products in an external cold trap. Neither of these transport methods are operative in subsiding sedimentary basins, but their adaptation to subjecting small amounts of sample to high-temperature heating ramps (300°–550°C) over short durations (15–60 min) makes them useful in providing a rapid screening method for assessing relative hydrocarbon potential of a rock. Rock-Eval is one of the most commonly used open anhydrous pyrolysis methods and employs a carrier gas and a flame ionization detector (Espitalié et al., 1977). Table 11.3 compares samples of Woodford Shale and Phosphoria Retort Shale with their hydrous pyrolysis yields at maximum oil generation. The total pyrolysate yield for both methods is similar, but the Rock-Eval makes no distinction among bitumen, oil, and gas. As a result, the generated hydrocarbon yields from Rock-Eval are greater than the expelled oil yields from hydrous pyrolysis by a factor greater than two.

The other open anhydrous pyrolysis method distinguishes gas and oil pyrolysate products by using a cold trap to collect the condensable volatile products. There are many variations on the conditions under which this method is done, but they can be collectively referred to

Table 11.2. Experimental Conditions and Pyrolysate Yields from Hydrous Pyrolysis and Closed Anhydrous Pyrolysis With and Without High Confining Pressures[a]

Experiment Reference Number	Final Pressure at 350°C (MPa)	Major Source of Pressure[b]	Experimental Conditions	Expelled Oil (wt. % rock)	Bitumen Extract (wt. % rock)	Oil Plus Bitumen (wt. % rock)
6	21.13	H₂O, He, gen. gases	Hydrous	4.15	5.71	9.86
5	5.69	Gen. gases	Anhydrous	0.00	3.30	3.30
7	23.48	He, gen. gases	Anhydrous	0.00	2.99	2.99
8	21.76	Gen. gases	Anhydrous	0.00	2.27	2.27

[a]All experiments were conducted at 350°C for 72 hr. Experimental details on procedures are given by Lewan (1993).
[b]Gen. gases = gases generated during the experiment; He = helium initially added to the gas space at the beginning of the experiment; H₂O = water vapor from water added at the beginning of experiments.

as *modified Fischer assays.* In its simplest form, a rock sample is heated from room temperature to 500°C at a specified heating rate and then held at 500°C for a specified duration referred to as a *soak period* (Smith, 1962). The volatile pyrolysate products are usually self-purged through an external cold trap where condensable liquid products are collected. Although this method provides what is referred to as a modified Fischer assay oil yield, this yield is dependent on the heating rate, soak period, temperature, and physical state of the rock (Stanfield and Frost, 1949; Heistand, 1976; Wildeman, 1977).

Oil yields from aliquots of the same rock sample subjected to a Fischer assay and hydrous pyrolysis are currently not available for comparison. However, pyrolysate yields from aliquots of the same rock sample subjected to a modified Fischer assay and Rock-Eval pyrolysis are available for comparison, as shown in Figure 11.4 (solid dots). The pyrolysate yields from the Toarcian oil shales done by the modified Fischer assay and Rock-Eval pyrolysis are essentially the same despite the inclusion of pyrolysate gases in the latter. The modified Fischer assay used to generate these data are presumed to have involved heating samples from room temperature to 500°C at a heating rate of 12°C/min with a soak period of 20 min and a cold trap temperature of 0°–100°C (Stanfield and Frost, 1949).

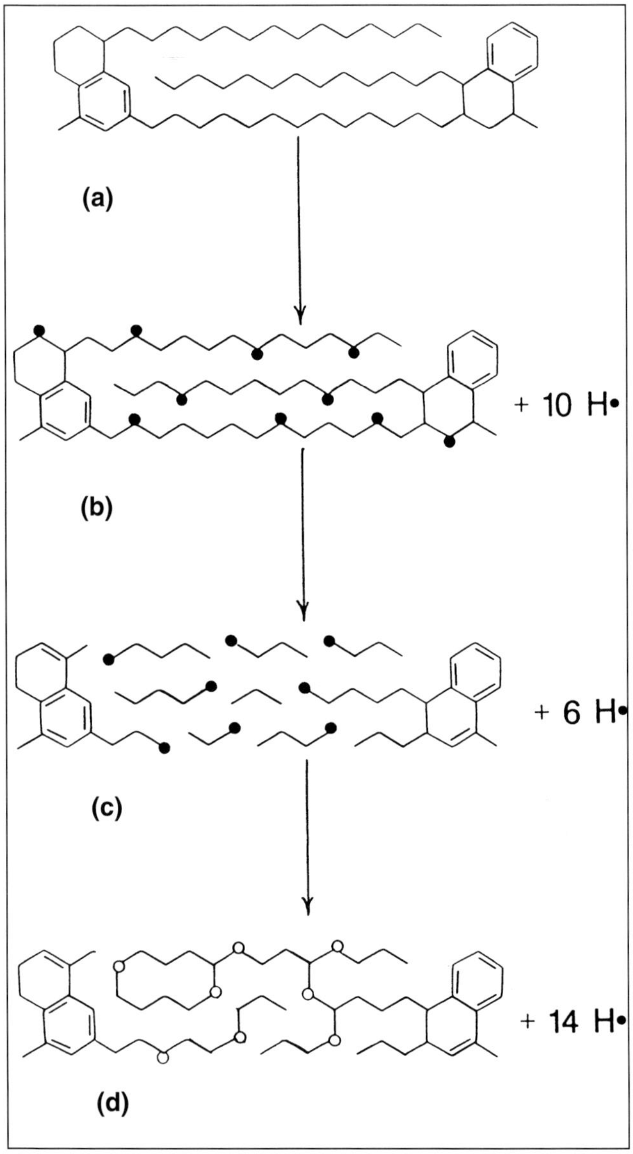

Figure 11.3. Generalized reaction pathway proposed for thermal maturation of bitumen in a closed system under anhydrous pyrolysis conditions. (a) Hypothetical bitumen molecule generated from the partial decomposition of kerogen by the breaking of weak noncovalent bonds. (b) Free radical sites (solid circles) are generated on the bitumen molecule through encounters with extraneous free radicals generated from other bitumen molecules and decomposing kerogen. (c) Lack of water-derived hydrogen for free radical terminations results in frequent covalent bond cleavage by β-scission. The resulting free radical fragments remain miscible due to the lack of a water-saturated bitumen, and an oil phase does not occur. (d) Termination of the free radical fragments (open circles) occurs by recombination, which results in carbon–carbon bond cross-linking and the development of an insoluble pyrobitumen.

Table 11.3. Comparison of Rock-Eval Pyrolysis and Hydrous Pyrolysis Yields (wt. % of rock) from the Same Samples of Woodford Shale (WD-5) and Phosphoria Retort Shale (P-64)[a]

Pyrolysis Method	Type of Pyrolysate	Woodford Shale	Phosphoria Retort Shale
Rock-Eval II (Cycle 1) on original sample	Volatile hydrocarbons (S_1)	0.25	0.50
	Generated hydrocarbons (S_2)	7.11	13.45
	Total pyrolysate ($S_1 + S_2$)	7.36	13.95
Hydrous pyrolysis at maximum oil generation	Bitumen extract	2.56	6.52
	Expelled oil	3.14	6.52
	Hydrocarbon gas	0.63	0.94
	Total pyrolysate	6.33	13.98

[a]From Lewan (1985).

Different conditions for a modified Fischer assay were used by Burnham (1991) on a variety of petroleum source rocks, which were also subjected to Rock-Eval pyrolysis. The modified Fischer assay in this study involved heating compressed rock samples from 100°C up to 450°–500°C at a heating rate of either 2°C/min or 0.033°C/min (2°C/hr) with the collection tube at room temperature. As shown in Figure 11.4, the oil yields from this modified Fischer assay (open triangles) are significantly lower than their corresponding hydrocarbon yields from Rock-Eval pyrolysis (solid triangles) compared to the relationship for the Toarcian oil shales. This difference between the relationships is a function of differences in heating rates, with slower heating rates giving lower oil yields by modified Fischer assays. This effect of heating rate on oil yields from modified Fischer assays has been reported previously (Campbell et al., 1978; Burnham and Singleton, 1983) and is evident in Figure 11.4 by the consistently lower oil yields from aliquots of the same samples at the slower heating rate of 0.033°C/min.

A generalized reaction pathway for thermal maturation of bitumen under open anhydrous conditions is proposed in Figure 11.5. Similar to closed anhydrous and hydrous pyrolysis, bitumen generation from the breaking of weak noncovalent bonds in the kerogen can be observed in open anhydrous pyrolysis when conducted isothermally at lower temperatures (Hubbard and Robinson, 1950). The generation of free radical sites on the hypothetical bitumen molecule (Figure 11.5b) with increasing thermal maturation leads to the same frequency of β-scissions and subsequent free radical fragments in open anhydrous pyrolysis (Figure 11.5c) as in closed anhydrous pyrolysis (Figure 11.3c). The critical difference between the open and closed anhydrous system depends on the rate at which the free radical fragments are vaporized in and removed from the pyrolysis chamber.

Pyrolysis conditions that promote rapid vaporization and removal of pyrolysate products with rapid heating and flow rates result in essentially all of the bitumen decomposing into a volatile product (Figure 11.5d). Scarcity of hydrogen atoms or donors and lack of contact between free radical fragments in the vapor state causes terminations by disproportionation to dominate under these conditions. Terminations of this type produce pyrolysate products enriched in alkenes, which are rarely found in natural crude oils. Examples of this extreme condition include Rock-Eval pyrolysis (Table 11.3), which uses rapid heating rates (25°C/min) with a carrier gas, and the modified Fischer assay, which typically uses a rapid heating rate (12°C/min).

Conversely, pyrolysis conditions that promote slow vaporization and removal of pyrolysate products from the pyrolysis chamber result in more bitumen decomposing into pyrobitumen (Figure 11.5e) rather than vaporized oil (Figure 11.5d). The ultimate extreme results in all of the bitumen converting to a pyrobitumen by recombination of free radical fragments to form carbon–carbon bond cross-linking, as described for the reaction pathways of closed anhydrous pyrolysis (Figure 11.3d). It has been well documented that the proportionality between generation of vaporized oil (Figure 11.5d) and generation of pyrobitumen (Figure 11.5d) in open anhydrous pyrolysis is dependent on heating rates (Campbell et al., 1978), which control the rate at which free radical fragments in a vapor state are removed from a rock. As heating rates decrease below about 12°C/min, pyrobitumen yields increase at the expense of decreasing vaporized oil yields. Accompanying the increase in pyrobitumen formation is an increase in hydrogen generation (Figure 11.5e), which may be active in free radical terminations and may reduce the frequency of disproportionations in the vaporized oil (Figure 11.5d). Therefore, as the vaporized oil yield decreases with decreasing heating rates, its alkene content decreases because of the increased availability of hydrogen generated by pyrobitumen formation. Alkene contents of vaporized oils from open anhydrous pyrolysis have been shown to decrease as heating rates decrease and oil yields decrease (Evans and Campbell, 1979).

Although the conditions under which open anhydrous pyrolysis is conducted can be manipulated to give vaporized oil yields and compositions comparable to those from hydrous pyrolysis, the unnatural processes involved in obtaining these vaporized oils makes their use in determining amounts of oil expelled in nature highly speculative and tenuous. Specifically, removal of

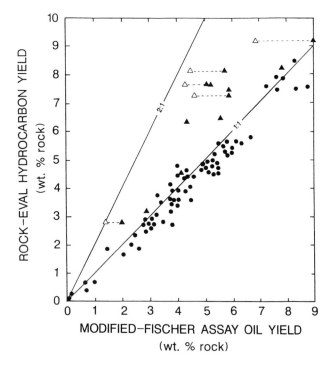

Figure 11.4. Plot of Rock-Eval pyrolysis hydrocarbon yields versus modified Fischer assay oil yields determined on the same samples of Toarcian oil shales from the Paris basin, presumably using a 12°C/min heating rate in the modified Fischer assay (solid circles) (Madec and Espitalié, 1984), and a variety of petroleum source rocks using 2°C/min (solid triangles) and 0.033°C/min (open triangles) heating rates in a modified Fischer assay (Burnham, 1991). Dashed lines connect samples that were subjected to the modified Fischer Assay at both heating rates. The 1:1 and 2:1 lines are included as reference lines.

Figure 11.5. Generalized reaction pathways proposed for →
thermal maturation of bitumen in an open system under anhydrous pyrolysis conditions. (a) Hypothetical bitumen molecule generated from the partial decomposition of kerogen by the breaking of weak noncovalent bonds. (b) Free radical sites (solid circles) are generated on the bitumen molecule through encounters with extraneous free radicals generated from other bitumen molecules and decomposing kerogen. (c) Lack of water-derived hydrogen for free radical terminations results in covalent bond cleavage by β-scission. The subsequent pathways followed by the resulting free radical fragments depends on the conditions under which the open anhydrous pyrolysis is conducted. (d) If the pyrolysis conditions promote rapid vaporization and removal of the free radical fragments from the thermally maturing bitumen, then essentially all of the bitumen will decompose into a volatile product. The volatilized free radical fragments are terminated by disproportionation resulting in alkenes or by available hydrogen donors (open circles) resulting in alkanes. (e) If the pyrolysis conditions promote slow vaporization and removal of the free radical fragments from the thermally maturing bitumen, then more of the bitumen will decompose into nonvolatile pyrobitumen as a result of free radical terminations by recombination.

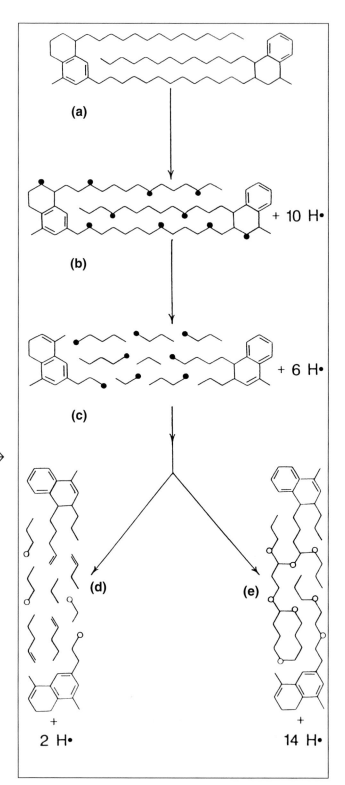

generated oil in a vapor state from a source rock is critical to determining evolved oil yields from open anhydrous pyrolysis (Stout et al., 1976; Campbell et al., 1978). This required vaporization of generated oil is not operative under the pressure–temperature conditions of subsiding sedimentary rocks, which are also water saturated.

The unlikelihood of oil yields from open anhydrous pyrolysis being applicable to nature is also evident by the decrease in oil yields with decreasing heating rates. A linear extrapolation of this experimental relationship (Evans and Campbell, 1979) (Figure 11.2) to heating rates typical for subsiding sedimentary basins (1°–10°C/m.y.) indicates that only pyrobitumen formation will occur (Figure 11.5e) by this process. It is therefore not feasible to use open anhydrous pyrolysis directly to determine the amount of oil expelled from a source rock in nature. However, indirect determinations may be feasible on the basis of well-established correlations between expelled oil yields from hydrous pyrolysis and vaporized oil yields from open anhydrous pyrolysis.

CONCLUSIONS

Hydrous pyrolysis is the most useful laboratory method for understanding expulsion of oil in nature. The liquid water used in this method ensures the presence of a water-saturated bitumen within a heated source rock. This dissolved water within a bitumen network reduces the frequency of carbon–carbon bond cross-linking in the bitumen and allows the occurrence of an immiscible oil to form from the partial decomposition of the bitumen. In addition to the buoyancy force generated by the density difference between immiscible oil and water-saturated bitumen, a net volume increase associated with the partial decomposition of bitumen to oil generates an internal pressure within the confining mineral matrix of a rock. As a result, the immiscible oil is expelled from the rock as it is being generated.

These processes are also considered operative in nature, but they may be exaggerated to some degree under hydrous pyrolysis conditions due to its use of higher temperatures. The possibility of some degree of exaggeration suggests that rocks incapable of expelling a generated oil under hydrous pyrolysis conditions are definitely not effective source rocks for oil expulsion in nature. Although hydrous pyrolysis gives the most realistic expulsion efficiencies for petroleum source rocks, additional research to determine the degree to which it exaggerates nature is needed.

Closed anhydrous pyrolysis is the least useful laboratory method for understanding primary migration or expulsion of oil because an expelled oil is not generated. The lack of dissolved water in the bitumen prevents frequent terminations of free radical sites on bitumen molecules with water-derived hydrogen. Consequently, frequent carbon–carbon bond cleavages occur and terminations of the resulting free radical fragments are accomplished by recombination to form carbon–carbon cross-linking bonds due to the lack of water-derived hydrogen. No internal pressure nor immiscible oil is generated by this process, and only a pyrobitumen is formed. Excluding the gases generated, the recoverable pyrolysate yield from hydrous pyrolysis at maximum expelled oil generation is three times greater than that from closed anhydrous pyrolysis with or without a confining pressure. The total lack of an expelled oil by this method renders it useless in determining expulsion efficiencies for source rocks.

Similarly, open anhydrous pyrolysis is not a useful method in determining expulsion efficiencies of source rocks unless it is calibrated against expelled oil yields generated by hydrous pyrolysis. Although open anhydrous pyrolysis is capable of generating a vaporized oil, the amount of oil varies considerably with experimental conditions (e.g., heating rate), and the processes responsible for its vaporized oil (e.g., vaporization) are not operative in natural systems.

Acknowledgments The experimental data presented in this study were collected by the author while employed by Amoco Production Company at their Research Center in Tulsa, Oklahoma. The author is indebted to Amoco Production Company for supporting this experimental work and for releasing the data presented in this publication. The Department of Geosciences at the University of Tulsa is acknowledged for providing office space and library facilities, which were most helpful in interpreting these experimental data and in writing this paper.

References Cited

Barth, T., A. E. Borgund, and A. L. Hopland, 1989, Generation of organic compounds by hydrous pyrolysis of Kimmeridge oil shale—bulk results and activation energy calculations: Organic Geochemistry, v. 14, p. 69–76.

Brady, C. J., J. R. Cunningham, and G. M. Wilson, 1982, Water-hydrocarbon liquid-liquid-vapor equilibrium measurements to 500°F: Gas Processors Association Research Report 62, 66 p.

Burnham, A. K., 1991, Oil evolution from a self-purging reactor: Kinetics and composition at 2°C/min and 2°: Energy & Fuels, v. 5, p. 205–214.

Burnham, A. K., and M. F. Singleton, 1983, High-pressure pyrolysis of Green River oil shale, *in* F. P. Miknis and J. F. McKay, eds., Geochemistry and chemistry of oil shales: American Chemical Society Symposium Series 230, p. 335–351.

Campbell, J. H., G. H. Koskinas, N. D. Stout, and T. T. Coburn, 1978, Oil shale retorting: effects of particle size and heating rate on oil evolution and intraparticle oil degradation: In Situ, v. 2, p. 1–47.

Comet, P. A., J. McEvoy, W. Giger, and A. G. Douglas, 1986, Hydrous and anhydrous pyrolysis of DSDP Leg 75 kerogens—a comparative study using a biological marker approach: Organic Geochemistry, v. 9, p. 171–182.

Connan, J., 1974, Time–temperature relation in oil genesis: AAPG Bulletin, v. 58, p. 2516–2521.

Egloff, G., and R. F. Davis, 1954, Cracking, *in* Modern petroleum technology: London, The Institute of Petroleum,

Egloff, G., and R. F. Davis, 1954, Cracking, *in* Modern petroleum technology: London, The Institute of Petroleum, p. 215.

Espitalié, J., J. L. Laporte, M. Madec, F. Marquis, P. Leplat, J. Paulet, and A. Boutefeu, 1977, Méthode rapide de characterisation des roches méres de leur potential pétrolier et de Leur degré d' Évolution: Revue Institute Français du Petrole, v. 32, p. 23–42.

Evans, R. A., and J. H. Campbell, 1979, Oil shale retorting: a correlation of selected infrared absorbance bands with process heating rates and oil yield: In Situ, v. 3, p. 33–51.

Griswold, J., and J. E. Kasch, 1942, Hydrocarbon–water solubilities at elevated temperatures and pressures: Industrial Engineering Chemistry, v. 34, p. 804–806.

Guerrant, R. P., 1964, Hydrocarbon–water solubilities at high temperatures under vapor-liquid-liquid equilibrium conditions: Ph.D. dissertation, Pennsylvania State University, University Park, PA, 124 p.

Heistand, R. N., 1976, The Fischer assay, a standard method?: American Chemical Society Division of Fuel Chemistry Papers, v. 21, p. 40–54.

Hershkowitz, F., W. N. Olmstead, R. P. Rhodes, and K. D. Rose, 1983, Molecular mechanism of oil shale pyrolysis in nitrogen and hydrogen atmospheres, *in* F. P. Miknis and J. F. McKay, eds., Geochemistry and chemistry of oil shales: American Chemical Society Symposium Series 230, p. 301–316.

Hubbard, A. B., and W. E. Robinson, 1950, A thermal decomposition study of Colorado oil shale: U.S. Bureau of Mines Report of Investigations 4744, 25 p.

Huizinga, B. J., Z. A. Aizenshtat, and K. E. Peters, 1988, Programmed pyrolysis–gas chromatography of artificially matured Green River kerogen: Energy & Fuel, v. 2, p. 74–81.

Kirchko, A. A., and S. G. Gagarin, 1990, New ideas of coal organic matter chemical structure and mechanism of hydrogenation processes: Fuel, v. 69, p. 885–891.

Larsen, J. W., and M. Mohammadi, 1990, Structural changes in coals due to pyridine extraction: Energy & Fuel, v. 4, p. 107–110.

Lewan, M. D., 1985, Evaluation of petroleum generation by hydrous pyrolysis experimentation: Philosophical Transactions of the Royal Society, v. 315A, p. 123–134.

Lewan, M. D., 1987, Petrographic study of primary petroleum migration in the Woodford Shale and related rock units, *in* B. Doligez, ed., Migration of hydrocarbons in sedimentary basins: Paris, Editions Technip, p. 113–130.

Lewan, M. D., 1989, Hydrous pyrolysis study of oil and tar generation from Monterey Shale containing high sulfur kerogen (abs.): American Chemical Society National Meeting Symposium on Geochemistry, abs. n. 46.

Lewan, M. D., 1991, Primary oil migration and expulsion as determined by hydrous pyrolysis: Proceedings of the 13th World Petroleum Congress, n. 2, 215–223.

Lewan, M. D., 1993, Laboratory simulation of petroleum formation: hydrous pyrolysis, *in* M. H. Engel and S. A. Macko, eds., Organic Geochemistry: New York, Plenum Press, p. 419–442.

Lewan, M. D., J. C. Winters, and J. H. McDonald, 1979, Generation of oil-like pyrolyzates from organic rich shale: Science, v. 203, p. 897–899.

Louis, M., and B. Tissot, 1967, Influence de la temperature et de la pression sur la formation des hydrocarbures dans les argiles a kerogene: Proceedings of the 7th World Petroleum Congress, n. 2, p. 47–60.

Madec, M., and J. Espitalié, 1984, Application of pyrolysis to the characterization and the upgrading of the Toarcian oil shales from the Paris basin: Fuel, v. 63, p. 1720–1725.

Meissner, F. F., 1978, Petroleum geology of the Bakken Formation, Williston basin, North Dakota and Montana, *in* D. Estelle and R. Miller, eds., Economic geology of the Williston basin: Billings, Montana Geological Society 1978 Symposium, p. 207–227.

Monthioux, M., P. Landais, and J.-C. Monin, 1985, Comparison between natural and artificial maturation series of humic coals from the Mahakam Delta, Indonesia: Organic Geochemistry, v. 8, p. 275–292.

Nelson, W. L., 1958, Petroleum refinery engineering, 4th ed.: New York, McGraw-Hill, p. 668.

Smith, J. W., 1962, Analytical method for study of thermal degradation of oil shale: Bureau of Mines Report of Investigation 5932, 17 p.

Stanfield, K. E., and I. C. Frost, 1949, Method of assaying oil shale by a modified Fischer retort: Bureau of Mines Report of Investigation 4477, 10 p.

Stout, N. D., G. J. Koskinas, J. H. Raley, S. D. Santor, R. L. Opila, and A. J. Rothman, 1976, Pyrolysis of oil shale: Effects of thermal history on oil yield: Quarterly of the Colorado School of Mines, v. 71, p. 153–172.

Takeda, N., S. Sato, and T. Machihara, 1990, Study of petroleum generation by compaction pyrolysis—I: Construction of a novel pyrolysis system with compaction and expulsion of pyrolyzate from source rock: Organic Geochemistry, v. 16, p. 143–153.

Tannenbaum, E., B. J. Huizinga, and I. R. Kaplan, 1986, Role of minerals in thermal alteration of organic matter—II. A material balance: AAPG Bulletin, v. 70, p. 1156–1165.

Wildeman, T. R., 1977, Preparation and Fischer assay of a standard oil shale: American Chemical Society, Division of Petroleum Chemistry Preprints, v. 22, p. 760–764.

Winters, J. C., J. A. Williams, and M. D. Lewan, 1983, A laboratory study of petroleum generation by hydrous pyrolysis, *in* M. Bjorøy, ed., Advances in Organic Geochemistry 1981: New York, John Wiley, p. 524–533.

Magoon, L. B, and W. G. Dow, eds., 1994, The petroleum
system—from source to trap: AAPG Memoir 60.

Chapter **12**

Secondary Migration and Accumulation of Hydrocarbons

William A. England

BP Research Centre
Sunbury-on-Thames, Middlesex, U.K.

Abstract

Secondary migration is the process by which petroleum is transported from the pod of active source rock to the trap. Most petroleum migrates as a separate, immiscible phase through water-saturated rock. The driving force for migration is the vertical buoyancy force due to the lower density of petroleum compared to that of formation water. The capillary pressure difference between the oil and water phases opposes the buoyancy force, discouraging the entry of petroleum into smaller water-wet pores. The interaction of these two forces causes petroleum to migrate along coarser parts of the "carrier bed," often by a tortuous pathway that is disrupted by the presence of heterogeneities. Subsurface water potential gradients due to active aquifers or rapid sedimentation (such as in the Gulf Coast) can alter the direction of secondary migration. Secondary migration by aqueous solution is not expected to be a significant process due to the low solubilities of most components of petroleum.

Secondary migration efficiency is an important parameter when estimating the degree of fill of a prospect or the location of dry hole belts. It can be estimated by a statistical analysis of past exploration results or by assuming that a certain fraction of the migration pathway's pore space must be saturated by petroleum before a prospect can fill with oil or gas.

Once petroleum starts to fill a trap, the tortuous migration pathway tend to fill from one side. Because petroleum composition changes with time as the source rock becomes more mature, compositional differences (e.g., in GOR, API gravity) may be "inherited" from the filling process. In the presence of barriers, diffusional and convective mixing may be too slow, even on geologic time scales, to eliminate all compositional differences. By examining present-day compositional differences from a set of wells in a field under appraisal or development, it is possible to identify the presence of flow barriers and the direction from which the field filled.

INTRODUCTION

Secondary migration is the movement of petroleum beyond the point where the hydrocarbon exits the active source rock. The fate of this migrating hydrocarbon is dependent on the efficiency of the conduit within which it is moving and the nature and efficiency of a trap it may encounter. A *trap* includes a reservoir rock and a seal rock that are in a three-dimensional configuration capable of impeding or storing petroleum in the subsurface. Reservoired petroleums are classified into three types according to their subsurface phase behavior: *gas reservoirs, gas condensate reservoirs,* and *oil reservoirs.*

Gas reservoirs contain mostly methane (C_1) and some ethane through pentane (C_2–C_5) in diminishing concentrations. Gas condensate reservoirs are entirely gas phase in the subsurface, but produce a liquid (or *condensate*) at

the surface that is usually rich in hexane through decane (C_6–C_{10}). Some condensates contain significant quantities of higher molecular weight material in the C_{30} range. Oil reservoirs are liquid in the subsurface. When taken to the surface, the liquid produced (stock tank oil or *crude oil*) is rich in heavier hydrocarbons (C_{15+}). Substantial quantities of gas (rich in C_1–C_5 and possibly N_2, CO_2, and H_2S originally dissolved in the subsurface) are usually produced with the oil.

Using an extensive database of case studies, Sluijk and Nederlof (1984), showed that the modal lateral migration distance for petroleum was about 10 km, with a significant number of cases that exceed 80 km. Vertical distances range up to 1200 m. The purpose of this chapter is to provide a short review of the current theories of secondary migration, particularly with respect to its place in the evaluation of a trap within a petroleum system. Comprehensive reviews of this topic are given by Durand (1983), Schowalter (1979), Welte (1988), and two conference proceedings edited by Doliguez (1988) and England and Fleet (1991).

MIGRATION MECHANISMS

Solution in Water

The theory that petroleum migrates by aqueous solution in formation water has been proposed by several authors, for example, Toth (1987). After the expelled petroleum near the source rock is dissolved, secondary migration is postulated to occur by bulk flow of water prior to exsolution of the petroleum in the trap. Most authors have rejected this as a major mechanism due to the low solubilities of most components of petroleum in water (McAuliffe, 1980). To account for the large size of known accumulations, unrealistically large volumes of water would be required to migrate updip from a deeply buried thermally mature source rock. Furthermore, the petroleum in this aqueous solution would have to experience a drastic compositional change during migration, which in practice is undetected (England et al., 1991).

Two-Phase Migration

Presently, there is a consensus that secondary migration occurs by a mechanism involving two phases: petroleum and water (Durand, 1983; England et al., 1987; Welte, 1988). Petroleum, expelled from the mature source rock gradually accumulates as a separate phase (since its solubility in water is so low). Because petroleum in gas or liquid phase is less dense than surrounding pore water, a net upward buoyant force is experienced by the growing globule or *stringer* of petroleum. As the stringer grows, the pressure at its upper surface (or seal rock) increases so it moves laterally updip, provided it can overcome the local capillary pressure barrier, such as the pore throat of a coarse-grained sandstone. Here, the coarse-grained rock is defined as the carrier bed. Any capillary pressure heterogeneities in the carrier bed are expected to lead to a tortuous migration pathway involving much of the carrier bed, as shown in Figure 12.1. Presumably in a lithologically homogeneous carrier bed, the migration pathway would be more restricted along the upper contact with the overlying seal. However, in either case, only a small fraction of the total carrier pore volume is exploited by the migrating petroleum (England et al., 1987). Because the migrating petroleum phase uses a small fraction of the water phase of the carrier bed, this two-phase migration process is extremely efficient, considering that the petroleum must pass through an enormous volume of water-saturated rock.

The final step of migration occurs when hydrocarbon passing through a carrier bed reaches a trap and the process of accumulation starts. The trap may be defined by the capillary barrier presented by the top seal, as well

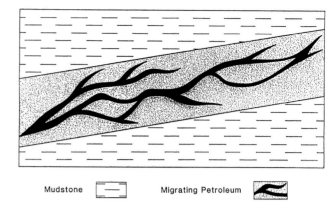

Mudstone   ⊡   Migrating Petroleum

Figure 12.1. Dendritic migration pathway. The petroleum moves generally updip, but contrasts in capillary entry pressures in different parts of the pathway may lead the migrating petroleum to follow the coarsest beds preferentially. In uniform units, the capillary effects are small and the petroleum tends to move along the upper part of the carrier bed.

as by the perturbation brought about by hydrodynamic flow (Hubbert, 1953). By mapping the depth from sea level to the top surface of the carrier bed at the time of migration, it is possible to determine the directions of petroleum migration for the region. This map can be modified to include the effect of hydrodynamics (see Dahlberg, 1982, for details). This map is an invaluable aid to exploration because it provides a basis for determining which direction to go to find additional accumulations; from a full trap, move updip, or from a partially filled trap, move downdip.

To use the two-phase migration scheme in petroleum exploration, one should map the interface between the seal and carrier beds, look for any residual hydrocarbons or shows within the carrier bed, and map the geometry of traps to determine how they filled with petroleum.

Pressure and Temperature Reduction

Gas (C_1–C_5) and condensate/oil (C_{6+}) are not mutually soluble in any given proportion. As gas and condensate/oil migrate to shallower depths, formation pressure and temperature drop. This drop causes gas to exsolve from the subsurface liquid phase, creating increasing volumes of gas compared to the liquid phase (England and Mackenzie, 1988). These phase changes will also lead to alteration of petroleum composition (Mills and Larter, 1991) and engineering parameters, such as the condensate–gas ratio (CGR) and gas–oil ratio (GOR) which are measured at the well head.

Price et al. (1983) and Zhuze et al. (1963) have considered the solubility of C_{6+} in subsurface gases. For example, if a mature source rock expels a gas condensate at a depth of 4 km (12,000 ft) with a CGR of 175 bbl/MMscf (barrels per million standard cubic ft), this composition might be stable as a single gas phase. However, when the gas migrates to a shallower trap at 2

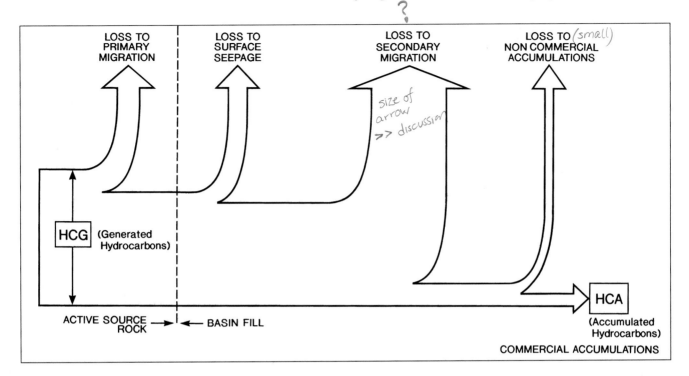

Figure 12.2. Hydrocarbon loss during migration from an active source rock through basin fill. Only a portion of the hydrocarbons generated (HCG) form commercial accumulations (HCA), of which only some is recoverable. The relative magnitudes of hydrocarbon loss change greatly from case to case.

km (6000 ft), the lower pressure and temperature might reduce the amount of condensate dissolved in the gas to a CGR of 50 bbl/MMscf. This reduction in the condensate content occurs because some of the gas phase condenses to a C_{6+}-rich liquid that is then lost along the migration pathway. This results in a loss of migration efficiency for C_{6+} hydrocarbons. *strange phrasing*

In practice, when a phase separation is expected during migration, it may be unclear which of the liquid or gaseous phases will continue to move toward the trap and which will remain immobilized in the carrier bed. Each case should be evaluated individually.

Speed of Migration

nope.

A simple order of magnitude calculation (England et al., 1991) suggests that the two-phase secondary migration in geologic time is a fast process. By using Darcy's law, an estimate of carrier bed permeability up to 1 d (Darcy), and the buoyant forces that drive migration, one calculates rates as high as 1000 km/m.y. (1 cm/1000 yr) in siliciclastic sandstone. This depends, however, on the starting assumptions. ~~Therefore~~ in most geologic settings, secondary migration is fast compared to the deposition of overburden rock needed to initiate the process of hydrocarbon generation.

SECONDARY MIGRATION EFFICIENCY

Migration efficiency is an important unknown in any attempt to estimate the amount of petroleum reaching a trap. This can sometimes be a crucial factor when

assessing the likelihood of petroleum reaching a particular trap when its reservoir rock is different than the carrier bed immediately in contact with a mature source rock. If drilling is carried out too far from the pod of active source rock, petroleum will be absent; this line, beyond the range of migration, defines the geographic extent of the petroleum system.

Assuming that the mature source rock that charged a particular trap or series of traps has been correctly identified and delimited, the quantity of hydrocarbon generated (HCG) can be calculated using the methods described by Schmoker (Chapter 19, this volume). If the total amount of trapped petroleum (hydrocarbon accumulated, or HCA) in a petroleum system can be correctly estimated, then the overall efficiency (PS_{EFF}) of the system can be calculated as follows:

$$PS_{EFF} (\%) = 100(HCA/HCG) \qquad (1)$$

In other words, PS_{EFF} represents the percentage of generated hydrocarbons that accumulates in identifiable traps. In practice, if the petroleum system has been adequately explored, the value of PS_{EFF} is a combination of the efficiencies of petroleum migration along valid pathways, as well as the loss of petroleum to the surface along unsealed carrier beds. It also includes losses to subeconomic accumulations that may contain many millions of barrels, but are unlisted in conventional reserve data (especially offshore). Figure 12.2 shows a diagrammatic representation of these losses in a well-explored system.

The following sections describe methods for estimating the efficiency of secondary migration, particularly in petroleum exploration.

Statistically Based Method

Sluijk and Nederlof (1984) presented a statistically based method for evaluating the probability that a trap contains hydrocarbons. As well as involving conventional source rock information such as thickness and richness, the method included an assessment of secondary migration efficiency.

Based on a database of approximately 300 traps for which the drilling outcomes were known, a statistical analysis was used to identify the main controls on migration efficiency. The possible controlling parameters included lateral and vertical *migration distance* as well as lateral and vertical *migration factors*. Migration factors include an estimate of the migration resistivity based on the lithology and the degree and orientation of fractures.

Unexpectedly, the efficiency of secondary migration appeared to be unrelated to the migration distances. Instead, the lithology and faulting of the carrier system appeared to be the most important factor. This analysis implies that secondary migration in a continuous unfaulted carrier bed is very efficient, whereas migration through a discontinuous faulted carrier bed is less efficient.

The advantage of this type of statistical approach is that it represents an encapsulation of past successes and failures; however, this approach would probably not work as well in areas with radically different geology and lithologies compared to the calibration areas. Nevertheless, Sluijk and Nederlof's (1984) database contained data from 37 different areas representing many different structural and stratigraphic conditions.

Threshold Method

England et al. (1987) presented a model for secondary migration in which a certain critical saturation level has to be reached in the carrier bed before hydrocarbons can start to accumulate in the trap. Mackenzie and Quigley (1988) showed how this concept can be incorporated into a rapid geochemical prospect evaluation method. In effect, the secondary migration pathway is assumed to operate like a petroleum pipeline: nothing flows out of the exit until the volume of the pipe itself is filled. Mackenzie and Quigley represented this so-called pipeline volume by V_L (the volume lost). Thus, the volume of the charge, V_C (reaching the trap) is given by

$$V_C = V_E - V_L \qquad (2)$$

where V_E is the volume of petroleum expelled from the mature source rock into the migration pathway. It can be calculated from HCG by allowing for the expulsion efficiency and converting mass to volume:

$$V_E \ (m^3) = HCG \ (kg) \times PS_{EFF} \ (\%) / density \ (kg/m^3) \qquad (3)$$

[handwritten annotations:] frac

PS$_{EXP}$, PS$_{EFF}$ is overall efficiency

The volume of petroleum lost in the carrier bed, V_L, (of porosity ϕ) is estimated as a fraction of the carrier bed volume (V_D):

$$V_L = f\phi V_D \qquad (4)$$

where f is the migration loss factor and varies from 1 to 3% in the cases described by Mackenzie and Quigley (1988). Until more case histories are available, the range of loss factors will not be known with any certainty. For any given carrier bed, a fixed volume fraction of the total carrier pore space (ϕV_D) is "lost" during secondary migration. This model can be used to estimate migration efficiency. In a particular trap or prospect appraisal, the charge volume is estimated from equation 2. If the calculated charge volume, V_C, is positive, the trap is predicted to be filled with hydrocarbons. If V_C is negative, it implies that the migration losses are sufficient to prevent trap filling.

The practical problems that arise in applying the method stem from the uncertainties in V_E and V_L; since both quantities have significant errors attached to them, V_C (the amount reaching the trap) has even greater errors associated with it. However, the relative error associated with two items (A, B) is greatly magnified if A and B are of a similar size. In other words if V_E and V_L are similar in size for a particular prospect, V_C is hard to estimate; this corresponds to a trap near to but within the petroleum system boundary. But only some traps are near the system boundary; other traps are closer to the mature source rock, in which case $V_E \gg V_L$, and the difficulty in estimating the charge volume is reduced. This question of propagation of errors and uncertainties in prospect evaluation has been discussed in considerable detail by Fang and Chen (1990).

Computer Models

Despite their sophistication in applying numerical modeling to complex processes such as compaction, heat flow, and water–petroleum movement, geochemical "basin" models treat secondary migration relatively simply. This is due to their use of the relative permeability concept to describe the flow of oil and water in the subsurface. Reservoir engineering models, designed to simulate viscous flows on a 10-yr time scale, use a similar approach. Secondary migration losses are handled by adjusting the assumed relative permeability curves so that a low residual oil saturation of a few percent is left by migrating petroleum (e.g., Ungerer et al., 1988). This value is analogous to the migration loss factor in equation 4, and it is interesting that similar results are obtained by the computer modeling and threshold method used by Mackenzie and Quigley (1988).

The ability of a geochemical basin model to estimate migration efficiency is therefore limited by its user's skill in estimating the relative permeability curves, especially the residual saturation. In practice, the best approach is probably to make use of analogy and calibration in similar geologic settings to establish migration efficiency.

Discussion

Several ways of estimating secondary migration losses have been described. All of them have some critical factors that must be provided by the users to describe secondary migration efficiency. Migration loss is a valuable aid in prospect or trap evaluation and is most powerful when combined with case histories of analogous systems, as well as a good geologic understanding of the petroleum system involved.

ACCUMULATION

Filling Mechanisms

Petroleum migrates through water-wet rock as a separate phase along a pathway (Figure 12.1). When petroleum reaches a trap, the accumulation process starts (Figure 12.3) (England et al. 1987). The geochemical composition of this migrating petroleum is constantly changing because the thermal maturity of the source rock is increasing from mature to overmature. As maturity increases over time, gas–oil ratios increase, as do other geochemical measures of maturity. However, because most reservoirs fill from one side, there is a compositional gradient inherited from the filling process.

For the petroleum system near the end of its duration time, the most recently arrived petroleum will tend to be found nearest to the actively generating source rock. The situation is more complicated when two or more petroleum systems charge the same trap (see Chapter 1, Figure 1.8b, this volume). Alternatively during the preservation time, processes such as biodegradation may affect the hydrocarbons in some parts of a reservoir more than others. A good example is in the Gullfaks oil field in the Norwegian North Sea (Horstad et al., 1990).

Mixing Mechanisms

During the actual filling process, which is usually fast on a geologic time scale, the degree of connectivity across the growing accumulation is too small to permit wide-scale mixing, as suggested in Figure 12.3. Over time, however, diffusion and convection can eliminate much of the inherited compositional gradients.

Estimates of the rate of hydrocarbon mixing within a trap (England and Mackenzie, 1988; England, 1990) show that molecular diffusion is a geologically rapid process over a few hundred meters. However, diffusion over distances greater than a few kilometers is usually too slow to cause lateral mixing across an oil field. Diffusion is more likely to mix the oil column at a single location,

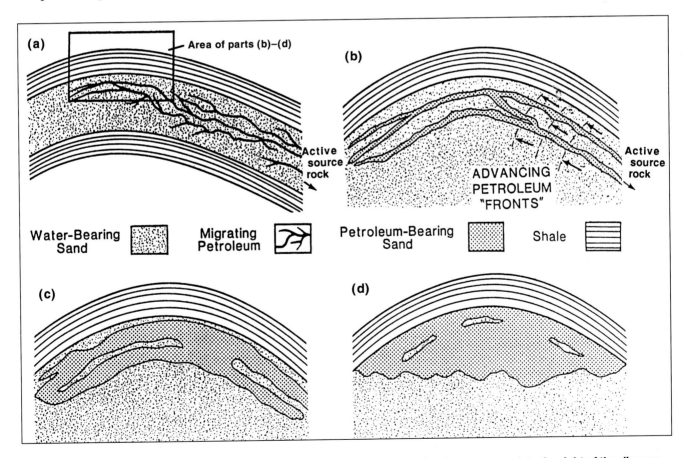

Figure 12.3. Reservoir filling. (a) Petroleum migrating into a trap from a pod of active source rock to the right of the diagram. (b) During the initial filling process, the coarsest beds are filled first with petroleum. Widespread mixing is impossible due to poor reservoir-wide connectivity. (c) and (d) The increasing column height causes other (but not all) parts of the reservoir rock to become saturated with petroleum.

but less likely to mix oil over a distance of several kilometers.

Convection, driven by differences in the densities of the oils on different sides of a reservoir, is usually fast on a geologic time scale, but may be slowed down by the presence of barriers to mixing such as a partially sealing fault or a discontinuous sealing rock within the reservoir. In these cases, a proportion of the inherited compositional differences will persist throughout the preservation time and may yield important information for further exploration or production activities (England, 1990).

Thermal convection is an ineffective mixing mechanism in oil accumulations without gas caps, but it is important in accumulations with large gas caps, particularly those with lateral thermal gradients (Jacqmin, 1990).

Establishing Migration Direction

A study of the geochemical properties of oils and gases in accumulations within a petroleum system can add useful information about the direction from which a field is filled. In many situations, this is not immediately obvious from the geologic information, in which case the geochemical information can be useful in planning future exploration in the area and in predicting how GORs and CGRs are likely to vary in future development wells.

The method is based on the filling model previously described for a trap, but expanded to include two or more fields. In a field that contains some barriers to mixing, or a series of accumulations within a petroleum system, the distribution of parameters such as GOR or geochemical maturity will reflect the way the field filled. If, for example, a field was found to have higher GOR oil in the north, this suggests that the most mature source rock lay in that direction. Geochemical measurements on the source rock would hopefully confirm this interpretation. Five examples of this type of investigation are given in Table 12.1. This same principle applies to a set of fields within the same petroleum system; the more mature the geochemical parameter is for the hydrocarbon, the closer the hydrocarbon is to the pod of active source rock.

CONCLUSIONS

An understanding of secondary migration is important in any exploration and production program. At present, all models of secondary migration efficiency rely on a set of empirically derived parameters obtained by analogy or analysis of statistical databases of past data. A direct method to predict secondary migration efficiencies from fundamental measurements of rock properties or larger scale sedimentologic data is as yet unavailable. However, the indirect method, which compares the summed up in-place hydrocarbons of all accumulations to an estimate of the expelled hydrocarbons from mature source rock within the same petroleum system, is acceptable if carried out in enough systems.

Table 12.1. North Sea Oil and Gas Fields for Which Migration Studies Have Been Done

Oil Field Name	Reference
Unnamed	England and MacKenzie (1988)
Tor and Draugen	Karlsen and Larter (1989)
Forties and Magnus	England (1990)
Gullfaks	Horstad et al. (1990)
Ula	Larter et al. (1990)

Once the petroleum reaches an accumulation, a detailed geochemical analysis of the reservoired hydrocarbons and their variation across the field can supply useful information about filling directions and the possible location of barriers to efficient production.

Acknowledgments   *I acknowledge the help and encouragement of my colleagues, and BP for permission to publish.*

References Cited

Dahlberg, E. C., 1982, Applied Hydrodynamics in Petroleum Exploration: New York, Springer-Verlag, p. 75–82.

Doliguez, B., ed., 1988, Migration of Hydrocarbons in Sedimentary Basins: Paris, Editions Technip, 681 p.

Durand, B., 1983, Present trends in organic geochemistry in research on migration of hydrocarbons, in M. Bjorøy et al., eds., Advances in Organic Geochemistry 1981: Chichester, John Wiley, pp. 117–128.

England, W. A., 1990, The organic geochemistry of petroleum reservoirs, in E. Durand and F. Behar, eds., Advances in Organic Geochemistry 1989: Oxford, Pergamon Press, v. 16, p. 415–425.

England, W. A., and A. J. Fleet, eds., 1991, Petroleum migration: Geological Society of London Special Publication 59, 280 p.

England, W. A., and A. S. Mackenzie, 1988, Some aspects of the geochemistry of petroleum fluids, in Evolution of sedimentary basins: Geologische Rundschau, Special Volume, v. 78, n. 1, p. 291–303.

England, W. A., A. S. Mackenzie, D. M. Mann, and T. M. Quigley, 1987, The movement of entrapment of petroleum in the subsurface: Journal of the Geological Society (London), v. 144, p. 327–347.

England, W. A., A. L. Mann, and D. M. Mann, 1991, Migration from source to trap, in Merrill, R. K., ed., Source and migration processes and evaluation techniques: AAPG Treatise of Petroleum Geology, p. 23–46.

Fang, J. H., and H. C. Chen, 1990, Uncertainties are better handled by fuzzy arithmetic: AAPG Bulletin, v. 74, p. 1228–1233.

Horstad, I., S. R. Larter, D. Dypvik, P. Aagaard, A. M. Bjornvik, P. E. Johansen, and S. Eriksen, 1990, Degradation and maturity controls on oilfield petroleum column heterogeneity in the Gullfaks field, Norwegian North Sea, in E. Durand and F. Behar, eds., Advances in Organic Geochemistry 1989: Oxford, Pergamon Press, v. 16, p. 497–510.

Hubbert, M. K., 1953, Entrapment of petroleum under hydrodynamic conditions: AAPG Bulletin, v. 37, p. 1954–2026.

Jacqmin, D., 1990, Interaction of natural convection and gravity segregation in oil/gas reservoirs: SPE Reservoir Engineering, p. 233–238.

Karlsen, D. A., and S. Larter, 1989, A rapid correlation for petroleum population mapping within individual petroleum reservoirs: applications to petroleum reservoir description, *in* J. D. Colliason, ed., Correlation in Hydrocarbon Exploration NPF: London, Graham & Trokman, p. 77–85.

Larter, S. R., Bjorlykke, K. O., Karlsen, D. A., Nedkvitne, T., Eglinton, T., Johansen, P. E., and Leythaeuser, D., 1990, Determination of petroleum accumulation histories: examples from the Ula field, Central graben, Norwegian North Sea, *in* Buller, A. T., et al., eds., North Sea Oil and Gas Reservoirs–II: The Norwegian Institute of Technology, London, Graham & Trotman, p. 319–330.

Mackenzie, A. S., and T. M. Quigley, 1988, Principles of geochemical prospect appraisal: AAPG Bulletin, v. 72, n. 4, p. 399–415.

McAuliffe, C. D., 1980, Oil and gas migration, *in* W. H. Roberts III and R. J. Cordell, eds., Chemical and physical constraints: AAPG Studies in Geology 10, p. 89–108.

Mills, N., and S. Larter, 1991, Phase controlled molecular fractionations in migrating petroleum charges, *in* W. A. England and A. J. Fleet, eds., Petroleum migration: Geological Society of London Special Publication , p. 137–148.

Price, L. C., L. M. Wenger, T. Ging, and C. W. Blount, 1983 Solubility of crude oil in methane as a function of pressure and temperature: Organic Geochemistry, v. 4, p. 201–21.

Schowalter, T. T., 1979, Mechanics of secondary hydrocarbon migration and entrapment: AAPG Bulletin, v. 63, p. 723–760.

Sluijk, D., and M. H. Nederlof, 1984, A worldwide geological experience as a systematic basis for prospect appraisal, *in* G. Demaison and J. R. Morris, eds., Petroleum geochemistry and basin analysis: AAPG Memoir #35, p. 15–26.

Toth, J., 1987, Petroleum hydrogeology: a potential application of groundwater science: Journal of the Geological Society of India, v. 29, n. 1, p. 172–179.

Ungerer, P., B. Doligez, P. Y. Chenet, J. Burrus, F. Bessis, E. Lafargre, G. Giroir, O. Heum, and S. Eggen, 1988, A 2-D model of basin-scale petroleum migration by two-phase fluid flow: application to some case studies, *in* B. Doliguez, ed., Migration of Hydrocarbons in Sedimentary Basins: Paris, Editions Technip, p. 415.

Welte, D. H., 1988, Migration of hydrocarbons, facts and theory, *in* B. Doliguez, ed., Migration of Hydrocarbons in Sedimentary Basins: Paris, Editions Technip, p. 393.

Zhuze, T. P., G. N. Yushkevich, G. S. Ushakova and K. K. Tumarev, 1963, Use of phase composition data in the system oil–gas at high pressures for ascertaining the genesis of some pools: Petroleum Geology, v. 7, n. 4, p. 186–191.

"We usually find oil in new places with old ideas. Sometimes, also, we find oil in an old place with a new idea, but we seldom find much oil in an old place with an old idea."

—Parke A. Dickey

Passage from Dickey, P. A., 1958, Oil is found with ideas: Tulsa Geological Society Digest, v. 26, p. 84.

Magoon, L. B, and W. G. Dow, eds., 1994, The petroleum
system—from source to trap: AAPG Memoir 60.

Chapter **13**

Hydrocarbon Traps

Kevin T. Biddle

Charles C. Wielchowsky

Exxon Exploration Company
Houston, Texas, U.S.A.

Abstract

Trap identification is a first step in prospect evaluation and an important part of any exploration or assessment program. Future success in exploration will depend increasingly on an improved understanding of how traps are formed and an appreciation of the numerous varieties of trap types that exist. We define a trap as any geometric arrangement of rock that permits significant accumulation of hydrocarbons in the subsurface. A trap must include a reservoir rock in which to store hydrocarbons, and a seal or set of seals that impede or stop migration out of the reservoir. Although it is the geometric arrangement of reservoirs and seals that determines if a trap is present, both reservoir and seal analysis should be an integral part of trap evaluation.

Traps can be divided into three broad categories: structural traps, stratigraphic traps, and combination traps, which exhibit both structural and stratigraphic elements. We have subdivided structural traps into fold traps, traps associated with faults, traps associated with piercement features, and combination traps that require elements of both faults and folds for effectiveness. Stratigraphic traps can be grouped into primary or depositional traps, traps associated with unconformities (either above or beneath the unconformity), and secondary or diagenetic stratigraphic traps. We note that although each trap has unique characteristics, early recognition of trap type will aid in mapping and evaluating a prospect.

INTRODUCTION

Trap evaluation is fundamental in the analysis of a prospect and an important part in any successful oil and gas exploration or resource assessment program. A *trap* can be defined as any geometric arrangement of rock, regardless of origin, that permits significant accumulation of oil or gas, or both, in the subsurface (modified from North, 1985). Although we define a trap as the geometric configuration that retains hydrocarbons, several critical components must be in place for a trap to be effective, including adequate reservoir rocks and seals, and each of these must be addressed during trap evaluation.

The oil and gas within a trap is part of a petroleum system, whereas the trap itself is part of one or more sedimentary basins and is evaluated as part of a prospect or play (see Chapter 1, Figure 1.1, this volume). The hydrocarbon-forming process and the trap-forming process occur as independent events and commonly at different times. The timing of the trap-forming process,

as shown on the events chart (Chapter 1, Figure 1.5), is important in a petroleum system study because if the trap forms before the hydrocarbon-forming process, the evidence (oil and gas) that a petroleum system exists is preserved. The volume of oil and gas preserved depends on the type and size of the trap, which is important in the evaluation of the prospect.

The critical components of a trap (the reservoir, seal, and their geometric arrangement with each other) can be combined in a variety of ways by a number of separate processes. This variability has led to many different trap classifications (e.g., Clapp, 1929; Wilson, 1934; Heroy, 1941; Wilhelm, 1945; Levorsen, 1967; Perrodon, 1983; North, 1985; Milton and Bertram, 1992). Different authors have focused on various trap attributes as the key element or elements of their classification. Some have emphasized trap geometry, while others have concentrated on the mechanisms of trap formation. Others have considered reservoir or seal characteristics as the major parts of their classification. Space limitations preclude a thorough review of the various classifications

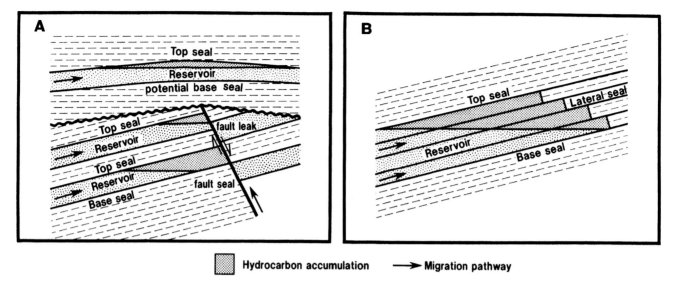

Figure 13.1. Key elements for (A) structural and (B) stratigraphic hydrocarbon traps.

here, but we note a general consensus on three broad categories of traps (Levorsen, 1967): those created by structural deformation, those formed by stratigraphic phenomena, and those that combine aspects of both. In addition, dynamic fluid conditions in the subsurface can modify the capacity of some structural and stratigraphic traps, or perhaps lead to hydrocarbon accumulations in unexpected locations. This chapter covers what we consider to be two critical components of a trap. It also describes the major structural and stratigraphic types of traps and provides suggestions for trap evaluation.

TWO CRITICAL COMPONENTS OF A TRAP

To be a viable trap, a subsurface feature must be capable of receiving hydrocarbons and storing them for some significant length of time. This requires two fundamental components: a *reservoir rock* in which to store the hydrocarbons, and a *seal* (or set of seals) to keep the hydrocarbons from migrating out of the trap (Figure 13.1). Both seal and reservoir are discussed in more detail elsewhere in this volume (see Morse, Chapter 6; Jordan and Wilson, Chapter 7; Downey, Chapter 8), but these are such basic parts of a trap that some of their aspects must also be covered here.

We do not consider the presence of hydrocarbons to be a critical component of a trap, although this is certainly a requirement for economic success. The absence of hydrocarbons may be the result of failure of other play or prospect parameters, such as the lack of a pod of active source rock or migration conduits, and it may have nothing to do with the ability of an individual feature to act as a trap. After all, "a trap is a trap, whether or not it has a mouse in it" (attributed to W. C. Finch, in Rittenhouse, 1972, p. 16).

Reservoir Rock

The reservoir within a trap provides the storage space for the hydrocarbons. This requires adequate porosity within the reservoir interval. The porosity can be primary (depositional), secondary (diagenetic), or fractures, but it must supply enough volume to accommodate a significant amount of fluids.

The reservoir must also be capable of transmitting and exchanging fluids. This requires sufficient effective permeability within the reservoir interval and also along the migration conduit that connects the reservoir with a pod of active source rock. Because most traps are initially water filled, the reservoir rock must be capable of exchanging fluids as the original formation water is displaced by hydrocarbons. As North (1985, p. 254) noted, "Traps are not passive receivers of fluid into otherwise empty space; they are focal points of active fluid exchange."

A trap that contains only one homogeneous reservoir rock is rare. Individual reservoirs commonly include lateral and/or vertical variations in porosity and permeability. Such variations can be caused either by primary depositional processes or by secondary diagenetic or deformational effects and can lead to hydrocarbon-saturated but nonproductive waste zones within a trap (Figure 13.2A). Variations in porosity and, more importantly, permeability can also create transitions that occur over some distance between the reservoirs and the major seals of a trap (Figure 13.2C and D). These intervals may contain a significant amount of hydrocarbons that are difficult to produce effectively. Such intervals should be viewed as uneconomic parts of the reservoir and not part of the seal. Otherwise, trap spill points may be mis-identified. Many traps contain several discrete reservoir rocks with interbedded impermeable units that form internal seals and segment hydrocarbon accumulations into separate compartments with separate gas–oil–water

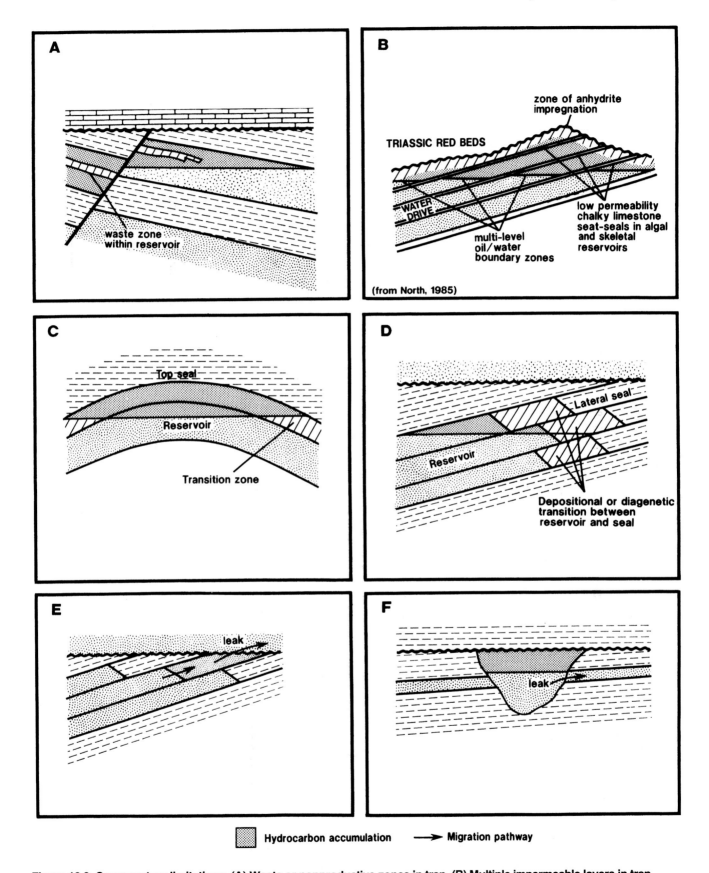

Hydrocarbon accumulation   ⟶ Migration pathway

Figure 13.2. Common trap limitations. (A) Waste or nonproductive zones in trap. (B) Multiple impermeable layers in trap creating several individual oil–water contacts. (C) Non- to poorly productive transition zone (from reservoir to seal) rock above productive reservoir. (D) Lateral transition from reservoir to seal. (E) Lateral, stratigraphically controlled leak point. (F) Lateral leak point or thief bed.

contacts and different pressure distributions (Figure 13.2B). As illustrated, these are complications of a single trap and are not multiple traps.

Seal

The seal is an equally critical component of a trap (Milton and Bertram, 1992; Downey, Chapter 8, this volume). Without effective seals, hydrocarbons will migrate out of the reservoir rock with time and the trap will lack viability. Most effective seals for hydrocarbon accumulations are formed by relatively thick, laterally continuous, ductile rocks with high capillary entry pressures (Downey, 1984 and Chapter 8, this volume), but other types of seals may be important parts of individual traps (e.g., fault zone material, volcanic rock, asphalt, and permafrost).

All traps require some form of top seal (Figure 13.1). When the base of the top seal is convex upward in three dimensions, the contours drawn to represent this surface (called the *sealing surface* by Downey, 1984) close in map view. If this is the case, no other seal is necessary to form an adequate trap. In fact, some authors (e.g., Wilhelm, 1945; North, 1985) have used the basic convex or nonconvex geometry of the sealing surface as a way of classifying traps.

Many traps are more complicated and require that, in addition to a top seal, other effective seals must be present (Figure 13.1). These are the poly-seal traps of Milton and Bertram (1992). Lateral seals impede hydrocarbon movement from the sides of a trap (Figure 13.1B) and are a common element of successful stratigraphic traps. Facies changes from porous and permeable rocks to rocks with higher capillary entry pressures (Figures 13.1B and 13.2D) can form lateral seals, as can lateral diagenetic changes from reservoir to tight rocks. Other lateral seals are created by the juxtaposition of dissimilar rock types across erosional or depositional boundaries. Traps in incised valley complexes commonly rely on this type of lateral seal (Figure 13.2F). Stratigraphic variability in lateral seals poses a risk of leakage and trap limitation. Even thinly interbedded intervals of porous and permeable rock (thief beds) (Figures 13.2E and F) in a potential lateral seal can destroy an otherwise viable trap.

Base seals (Figure 13.1) are present in many traps and are most commonly stratigraphic in nature. The presence or absence of an adequate base seal is not a general trap requirement, but it can play an important role in deciding how a field will be developed.

Faults can be important in providing seals for a trap, and fault leak is a common trap limitation (Smith, 1966, 1980; Downey, 1984; Allan, 1989). Faults can create or modify seals by juxtaposing dissimilar rock types across the fault (Figure 13.1A), by smearing or dragging less permeable material into the fault zone, by forming a less permeable gouge because of differential sorting and/or cataclasis, or by preferential diagenesis along the fault. Fault-induced leakage may result from juxtaposition of porous and permeable rocks across the fault (Figure 13.1A) or by formation of a fracture network along the fault itself.

STRUCTURAL TRAPS

Structural traps are created by the syn- to postdepositional deformation of strata into a geometry (a structure) that permits the accumulation of hydrocarbons in the subsurface. The resulting structures involving the reservoir, and usually the seal intervals, are dominated by either folds, faults, piercements, or any combination of the foregoing (Figures 13.3A–D). Traps formed by gently dipping strata beneath an erosional unconformity are commonly excluded from the structural category (North, 1985) (Figure 13.3E), although as subunconformity deformation increases, this distinction becomes ambiguous (Figure 13.3F). Superposed multiple deformation may also blur the foregoing distinctions (e.g., Lowell, 1985).

Subdivisions of structural traps have been proposed by many authors based on a variety of schemes. For example, in his general trap classification, Clapp (1929) distinguished between anticlinal, synclinal, homoclinal, quaquaversal, and fault-dominated traps. Harding and Lowell (1979) based their classification of structural traps on the concept of structural styles, which emphasizes basement involvement or noninvolvement, inferred deformational force, and mode of tectonic transport. Levorsen (1967) divided structural traps into those caused by folding, faulting, fracturing, intrusion, and combinations of these processes. North (1985), under the category of convex traps, distinguished between buckle- or thrust-fold, bending fold, and immobile convexity traps. North (1985) appropriately pointed out that many convex traps are caused by faults (i.e., the folding is a response to the faulting rather than the other way around). However, the reverse is true under certain conditions in which prospect-scale faulting results from the folding process, such as in the development of chevron folds (Ramsey, 1974) or in keystone normal faulting above a rising salt diapir (Harding and Lowell, 1979).

The following sections discuss in more detail the two most important structural trap types: fold dominated versus fault dominated. In our experience, fold-dominated traps are by far the most important structural traps. We agree with North (1985) that purely fault-dominated traps (those on which the fault itself creates the trap without the presence of a fold) are relatively uncommon. Traps dominated by piercements (in which the reservoir is sealed by intrusion of salt or shale) and those resulting from combinations of faulting, folding, and piercement are treated by Harding and Lowell (1979), Lowell (1985), and North (1985).

Fold-Dominated Traps

Structural traps that are dominated by folds at the reservoir–seal level exhibit a wide variety of geometries and are formed or modified by a number of significantly different syn- and postdepositional deformation mechanisms. Although usually considered to result from tectonically induced deformation, the term *fold* is purely descriptive and refers to a curved or nonplanar arrange-

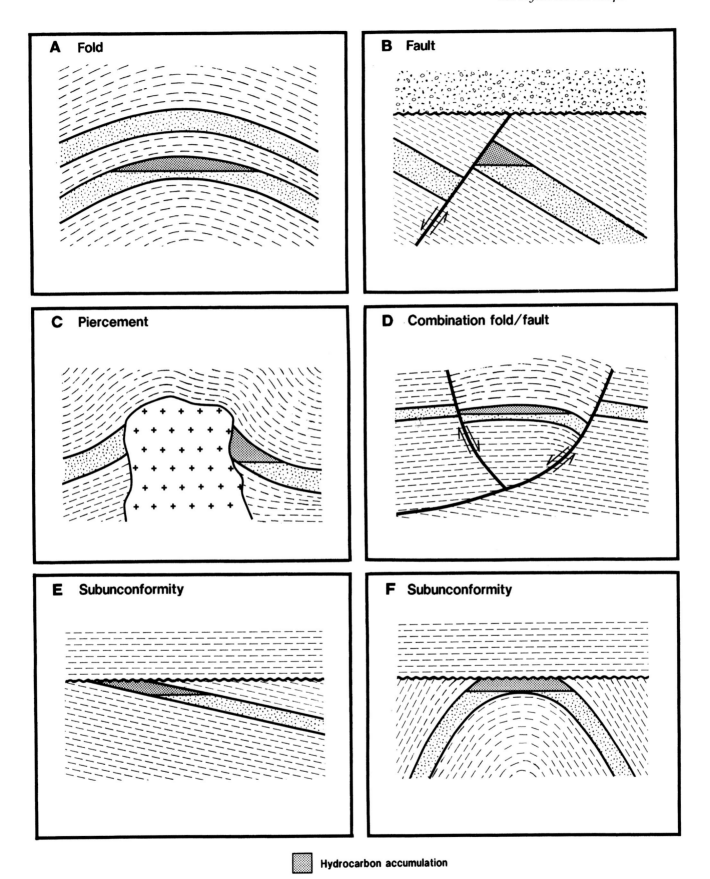

Figure 13.3. Major categories of structural traps: (A) fold, (B) fault, (C) piercement, (D) combination fold–fault, (E) and (F) subunconformities. The situation in (E) is commonly excluded from the structural category.

ment of geologic (usually bedding) surfaces (after Dennis, 1967). Therefore, folds include not only tectonically induced phenomena but also primary depositional features, gravity-induced slumping, compaction effects, and so on. It is convenient to divide prospect-scale folds into two categories—those that are directly fault related and those that are largely fault free.

Most fault-related folds result from bending above a nonplanar fault surface (Figures 13.4A and B). Crystalline basement may or may not be involved, and stratal shortening, extension, or transcurrent movements may have occurred. Common examples are *fault bend folds* (Figure 13.4A) (Suppe, 1983) and *fault propagation folds* (Figure 13.4B) (Suppe and Medwedeff, 1984) in detached fold and thrust belts. Fault bend folds are also common in extensional terranes. Other fault-related folds include *drag folds*, or folds formed by frictional forces acting across a fault (Figure 13.4C) (Suppe, 1985), and *drape folds*, those formed by flexure above a buried fault along which there has been renewed movement Figure 13.4D) (Suppe, 1985). These latter folds, however, are not caused by slip over a nonplanar fault surface. Also, drape folds do not involve significant stratal shortening or extension at the reservoir–seal level.

Fault-free, décollement, or *lift-off folds* (Figure 13.4E) (e.g., Namson, 1981) result from buckling caused by stratal shortening above a décollement, usually within a thick or very efficient (i.e., weak and ductile) sequence of evaporites or shale. Kink bands and chevron folds are special types of fault-free folds (Figure 13.4F). Other types of fault-free folds may form by bending above material that moves vertically or horizontally by flow without significant stratal shortening or extension at the reservoir–seal interval (Figure 13.4G). This would usually include folding related to flow and diapirism of salt and shale, although some prospect-scale folds are related to intrusive igneous activity. Drape folding can be caused not only by faulting, as previously mentioned, but also by differential compaction above buried topography, reefs, or other relatively immobile subsurface masses (Figure 13.4H). Initial depositional dips may also produce a drape fold geometry, but we would classify such features as a type of stratigraphic trap. Broad folding or warping of unknown genesis above basement arches and domes would fall into this latter category as well.

The distinction between fault-related and fault-free folds is somewhat artificial because the dominant fold generation mechanism may vary with time. For example, a fold may nucleate above a thick detachment horizon as a fault-free fold that is subsequently modified by fault propagation out of the detachment zone. Also, fold geometry may result from the action of more than one of the preceding mechanisms, such as extensional fault bend folding above a rising salt diapir.

In hydrocarbon exploration, it can be important to distinguish among the mechanisms of fold formation for a variety of reasons. These include predicting trap geometry where the subsurface is incompletely imaged by seismic data and untested by the drill bit, mapping migration pathways, and analyzing fracture distribution.

In addition, the mechanism of fold generation in part controls secondary faulting, which can play a major role in trap segmentation and disruption even though the secondary faults are not integral to fold genesis.

Fold traps tend to change significantly in their geometry with depth. For example, detachments in fold and thrust belts, angular unconformities, primary stratigraphic convergence of reservoir units, and the tendency of parallel folds to die upward in synclines and downward in anticlines cause major vertical changes in trap capacity. In addition, regional tilting affects trap capacity because structural relief (the height that a reservoir unit rises above the regional slope) can become ineffective as a fold's crest in profile drops below the horizontal (Levorsen, 1967).

Fault-Dominated Traps

As already pointed out, faults can be extremely important to the viability of a trap by providing either seals or leak points. They are capable of acting as top, lateral, or base seals by juxtaposing relatively impermeable rock units against more permeable reservoir units (Figure 13.5), or by acting as sealing surfaces due to the impermeable nature of the material along the fault. In addition, they may act as leak points by juxtaposition of permeable units or by creation of a fracture network. The term *fault* is descriptive in that it refers to a surface across which there has been displacement without reference to the cause of that displacement (i.e., whether it is tectonically, gravitationally, diagenetically, or otherwise induced). Structural traps that are dominated by faults at the reservoir–seal level (the fault itself makes the trap by sealing the reservoir without an ancillary fold) can be divided into three categories based on the type of separation, or slip if it is known, that geologic surfaces exhibit across the fault (Dennis, 1967). These are normal, reverse, and strike separation or slip fault traps.

Normal fault traps are the most common fault-dominated structural traps. They are of two fundamentally different geometries and are most common in two different tectonostratigraphic settings. Normal faults involving the basement occur in areas of significant crustal extension, such as the Gulf of Suez and North Sea, and are characterized by tilted fault blocks that exhibit a zig-zag map pattern (Harding and Lowell, 1979). Probably the most important trap geometry is the trap door closure at fault intersections (Figure 13.6A). Syn- and postdepositional normal faults that are detached from the basement occur in areas of rapid subsidence and sedimentation, commonly on passive continental margins, such as the U.S. Gulf Coast or Niger Delta (Weber et al., 1978), and are characterized by a listric profile and a cuspate map pattern that is usually concave basinward (Figure 13.6B). On the downthrown side of major displacement normal faults in this setting, smaller synthetic and antithetic fault-dominated traps are typical. Keystone normal fault-dominated traps above deep-seated salt intrusions are also common (North, 1985).

Reverse fault traps may be associated with detached or basement-involved thrust (low angle) or high-angle

FAULT RELATED

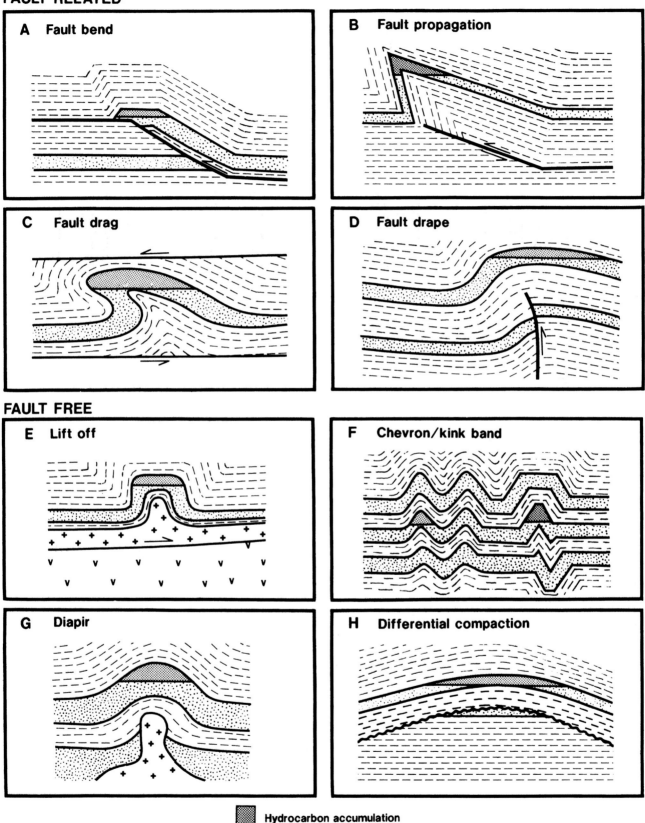

Hydrocarbon accumulation

Figure 13.4. Types of traps in which folding dominates the reservoir–seal interval. Fault-related types include (A) fault bend, (B) fault propagation, (C) fault drag, and (D) fault drape. Fault-free types include (E) lift off, (F) chevron/kink band, (G) diapir, and (H) differential compaction.

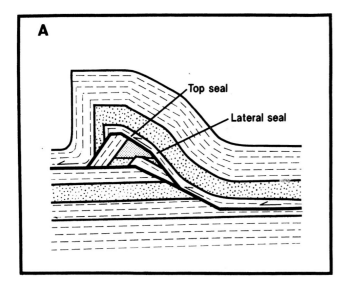
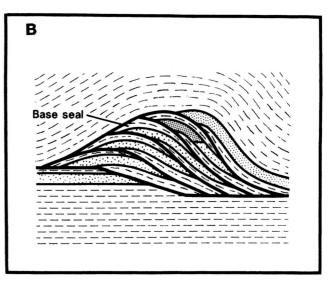

Hydrocarbon accumulation

Figure 13.5. Combination fold and fault traps in which both are critical to trap viability. (A) Complex fault-bend fold showing associated sealing fault. (B) A duplex structure with a thrust fault forming an element of the base seal. Selected fault sealing properties are also illustrated.

reverse faults. These structures tend not to produce pure fault-dominated traps because of attendant folding. However, Figure 13.6C shows how regional dip plus thrusting can produce a viable reverse fault-dominated trap without folding at the relevant reservoir–seal interval and how minor footwall drag can provide a viable trap sealed by an overlying thrust fault.

Figure 13.6D is an example of a *strike-slip fault* trap in the Los Angeles basin of the United States (Harding, 1974). Folding and a tar seal also play a significant role in this trap.

STRATIGRAPHIC TRAPS

In 1936 (p. 524), Levorsen proposed the term *stratigraphic trap* for features "in which a variation in stratigraphy is the chief confining element in the reservoir which traps the oil." The existence of such nonstructural traps has been recognized since at least the late 1800s (Carll, 1880). Today, we would define a stratigraphic trap as one in which the requisite geometry and reservoir–seal(s) combination were formed by any variation in the stratigraphy that is independent of structural deformation, except for regional tilting (modified from North, 1985).

Many attempts have been made to classify types of stratigraphic traps. Early efforts, while not specifically using the term *stratigraphic*, led to broad categories of traps that were "closed" because of varying porosity within rock (e.g., Wilson, 1934). Later work recognized that considerable variability exists among such traps (e.g., Levorsen, 1967), and subdivisions became more numerous. A number of treatments of stratigraphic traps provide information on different approaches to classifi-

cation and supply abundant examples of types of stratigraphic traps (e.g, Levorsen, 1936; Dott and Reynolds, 1969; King, 1972; Busch, 1974; Halbouty, 1982; Foster and Beaumont, 1988, 1991). Here, we generally follow Rittenhouse (1972) and divide stratigraphic traps into primary or depositional stratigraphic traps, stratigraphic traps associated with unconformities, and secondary stratigraphic traps.

Primary or Depositional Stratigraphic Traps

Primary or *depositional stratigraphic traps* (Figure 13.7) are created by changes in contemporaneous deposition (see MacKenzie, 1972). As described here, such traps are not associated with significant unconformities. Two general classes of primary stratigraphic traps can be recognized: those formed by lateral depositional changes, such as facies changes and depositional pinchouts (Figure 13.7A), and those created by buried depositional relief (Figure 13.7B).

Facies changes (Figure 13.7A) may juxtapose potential reservoir rocks and impermeable seal rocks over relatively short lateral distances in either siliciclastic or carbonate settings. The lateral transition from reservoir to seal is generally gradational, leading to possible noneconomic segments within the reservoir. Particular care must be taken to identify strike closure in this type of trap. *Depositional pinchouts* (Figure 13.7A) may lead to reservoir and seal combinations that can trap hydrocarbons. The transition from reservoir to lateral seal may be abrupt, in contrast to facies change traps. Strike closure is also a risk for pinchout traps.

Both lateral facies change and depositional pinchout traps generally require a component of regional dip to be effective. Both types are common elements of combina-

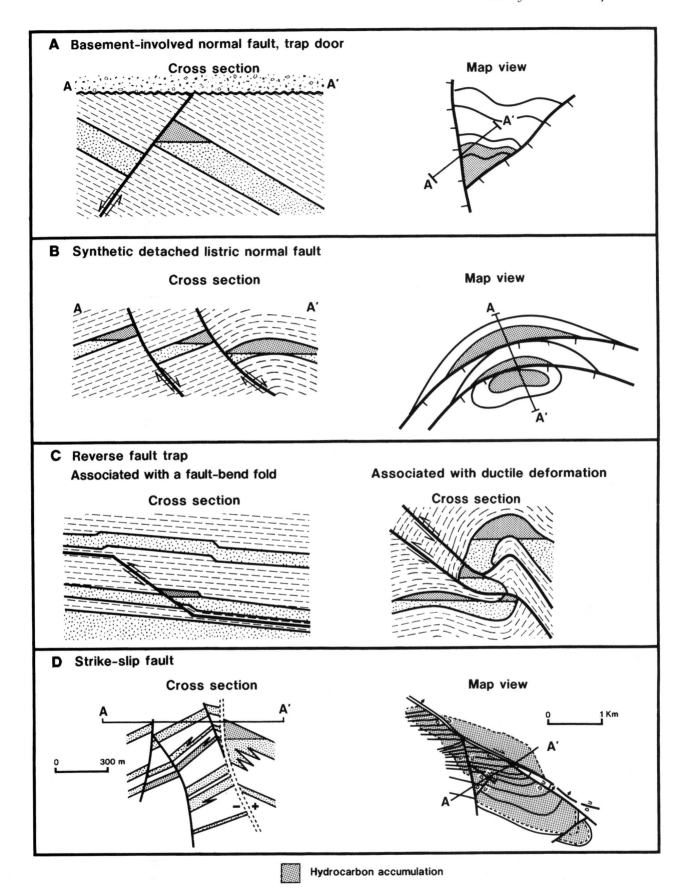

A Basement-involved normal fault, trap door

Cross section

Map view

B Synthetic detached listric normal fault

Cross section

Map view

C Reverse fault trap
Associated with a fault-bend fold

Cross section

Associated with ductile deformation

Cross section

D Strike-slip fault

Cross section

0   300 m

Map view

0   1 Km

Hydrocarbon accumulation

Figure 13.6. Types of traps in which faulting dominates the reservoir–seal interval. (A) Basement-involved normal fault trap and trap door. (B) Synthetic detached listric normal fault traps. (C) Two types of reverse fault traps. (D) Strike-slip fault traps.

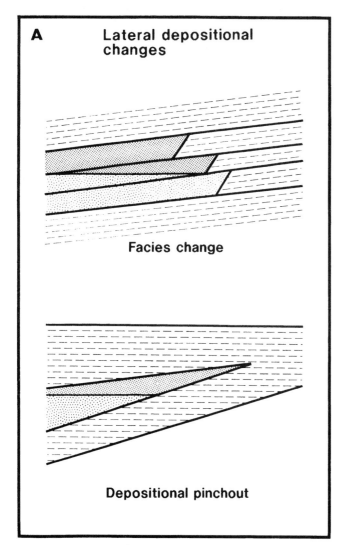

A   **Lateral depositional changes**

Facies change

Depositional pinchout

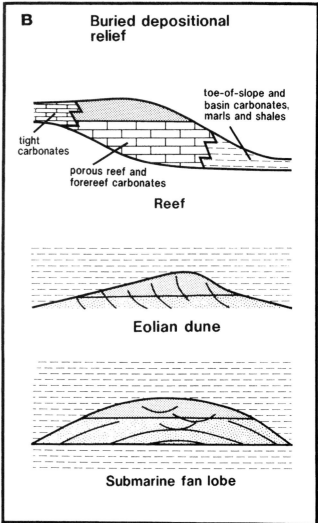

B   **Buried depositional relief**

toe-of-slope and basin carbonates, marls and shales

tight carbonates

porous reef and forereef carbonates

Reef

Eolian dune

Submarine fan lobe

Hydrocarbon accumulation

Figure 13.7. Primary or depositional stratigraphic traps. (A) Traps created by lateral changes in sedimentary rock type during deposition. Top: juxtaposition of reservoir and seal caused by lateral facies changes. Bottom: reservoir termination due to the depositional pinchout of porous and permeable rock units. (B) Traps formed by buried depositional relief. In each example, sedimentary processes form a potential trapping geometry, but require burial by younger impermeable section to create the required top seal.

tion structural–stratigraphic traps, particularly if the structure was growing during deposition of the reservoir and seal rocks.

The second general class of primary stratigraphic traps is associated with *buried depositional relief*. These traps are equivalent to the constructive paleogeomorphic traps of Martin (1966). There are many different types of such traps, a few of which are illustrated in Figure 13.7B. Each of these has distinct characteristics and attendant trap risks.

Carbonate reefs provide a classic example of potential traps associated with buried depositional relief. Reef growth with time enhances depositional relief, and the transition from tight lagoonal rocks to porous and permeable backreef–reef–forereef rocks may provide a good reservoir–lateral seal combination. The relationship

between the forereef rocks and adjacent basinal deposits (potential source rocks) can create excellent migration pathways. Formation of a top seal requires that reef growth is terminated and that the reef is buried beneath a cap of low-permeability material. A key risk for this type of trap is accurate prediction of porosity and permeability within the reef complex. The Devonian reef fields of the Western Canada sedimentary basin are excellent examples of this type of trap (Hemphill et al., 1970; Barss et al, 1970).

Another type of buried depositional relief is associated with some submarine fan deposits (Figure 13.7B). In such depositional settings, sand-rich depositional lobes may be encased in shale. The Balder oil field in the Norwegian section of the North Sea is an example of this type of trap (Sarg and Skjold, 1982).

Other types of buried depositional relief exist (e.g., the eolian dune example in Figure 13.7B), and most of these are capable of producing potential traps for hydrocarbons. Exploration for these traps requires good knowledge of depositional models and careful attention to potential reservoir and seal limitations.

Stratigraphic Traps Associated with Unconformities

The important relationship between many types of stratigraphic traps and unconformities has been recognized for a long time (e.g., Clapp, 1917; Levorsen, 1954; Chenoweth, 1972; Rittenhouse, 1972). In 1972, Rittenhouse proposed that traps associated with unconformities can be grouped into two major categories: those occurring *beneath* an unconformity and those located *above* an unconformity (Figure 13.8).

Truncation of tilted strata beneath an unconformity (Figure 13.8A) can lead to the formation of a classic type of subunconformity stratigraphic trap. Rocks immediately above the unconformity provide the top seal and subunconformity units stratigraphically above and below the reservoir provide elements of lateral seal. Lateral seal in the strike direction can be created by variations in the subcrop pattern beneath the unconformity. The presence of permeable material just above the unconformity surface may seriously degrade the top seal and is a risk for this type of trap. Some of the largest stratigraphic traps discovered to date are of this type, such as the super giant East Texas field (Halbouty, 1991). Loma de la Lata, a super giant gas–condensate field in the Neuquen basin of Argentina is another giant field that produces from a subunconformity truncation trap. There, however, the truncation is on the flank of a large structure in the basin, and trap formation is clearly tied to the evolution of the structure. This trap is best viewed as a combination structural–stratigraphic trap.

Another type of subunconformity trap is set up by the truncation of reservoir-quality strata along the flanks of *incised valleys* or canyons (Figure 13.8A). These traps require that the fill of the incised valley forms part of the necessary lateral seal. Sinuosity of the incised valley along its strike can complete the lateral seal. Rittenhouse (1972) further subdivided this type of trap into valley-flank traps and valley-shoulder traps, depending on the position of the reservoir beds and the erosional surface of the valley.

A third type of subunconformity trap is created by *buried landforms* or erosional relief (Figure 13.8A). Many of Martin's (1966) paleogeomorphologic traps are of this type. There are numerous different subtypes of potential traps associated with buried erosional relief (Martin, 1966; Rittenhouse, 1972). The geometry of such traps depends on the geometry of the erosional surface and of the underlying beds. Key risks are the identification and distribution of reservoir beneath the unconformity and the effectiveness of seal above the unconformity. The buried hills oil and gas fields in the North China basin provide a broad spectrum of examples from buried erosional features, such as the Rengin field, to combina-

tion normal fault–eroded structures, such as the Xinlungai field (Zhai and Zha, 1982).

Deposition above unconformities can also form trapping configurations, several of which are illustrated in Figure 8B. *Onlap* onto an unconformable surface may lead to the areally widespread deposition of reservoir and seal rocks. Strike closure can be provided by the geometry of the underlying unconformity, but may be hard to define.

A common type of stratigraphic trap above an unconformity is created by deposition within incised valleys or canyons (Figure 13.8B). The incised feature itself defines much of the geometry of the potential trap, although pinchouts and facies changes within the valley fill can greatly complicate trap geometry. In fact, many incised valleys are relatively easy to map, but predicting reservoir and seal rock distribution within the incised valley fill is a significant challenge. Many of the fields in the Powder River basin of Wyoming that produce from the Muddy Formation are examples of traps within the fill of incised valleys.

Onlap of erosional relief (Figure 13.8B) is the last illustrated example of possible stratigraphic traps above an unconformity. This type of trap forms rims or halos around the buried erosional feature and may be associated with so-called bald-headed highs.

Secondary Stratigraphic Traps

Another major category of stratigraphic traps results from *postdepositional alteration* of strata. Such alteration may either create reservoir-quality rocks from nonreservoirs or create seals from former reservoirs. Two examples are shown in Figure 13.9. The first (Figure 13.9A) shows updip porosity loss caused by cementation in previously porous and permeable carbonate rocks. Although the example used is taken from a carbonate setting, similar diagenetic plugging can occur in just about any rock type under the proper circumstances. Porosity occlusion is not limited to only diagenetic mineral cements. Asphalt, permafrost, and gas hydrates are other possible agents that may form seals for this type of stratigraphic trap. Unfortunately, it is often difficult to predict the position of cementation boundaries in the subsurface before drilling, and this type of trap can be a challenging exploration target.

The second type of secondary stratigraphic trap is associated with *porosity enhancement* that improves reservoir quality in otherwise tight sections. Dolomitization of limited-permeability limestones is a good example (Figure 13.9B). Dissolution of framework or matrix material is another porosity- and permeability-enhancement mechanism. Porosity enhancement associated with dolomitization and dissolution potentially can create traps on its own. Commonly, though, porosity enhancement is associated with other types of traps as a modifying element. The dolomitized reservoirs of the Scipio–Albion trend in Michigan are a good example of porosity and permeability enhancement along a structural trend (Harding, 1974).

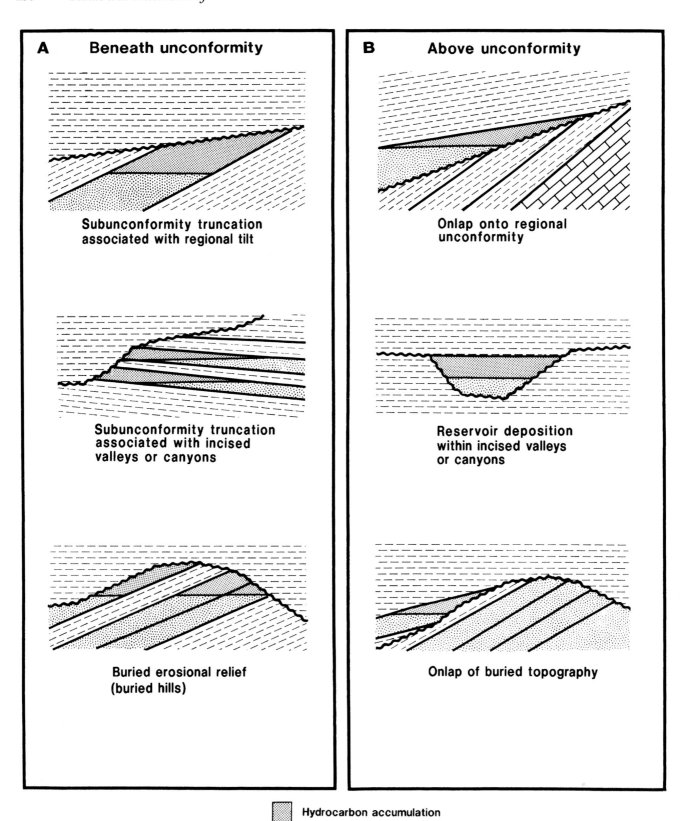

Figure 13.8. Stratigraphic traps associated with unconformities. (A) Traps beneath an unconformity. (B) Traps above an unconformity.

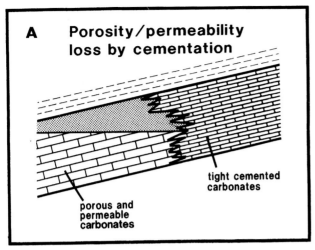
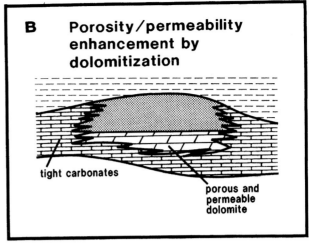

Hydrocarbon accumulation

Figure 13.9. Secondary diagenetic stratigraphic traps. (A) Traps created by postdepositional updip porosity occlusion. (B) Traps created by postdepositional porosity and permeability enhancement.

COMBINATION TRAPS

Many of the world's hydrocarbon traps are not simple features but instead combine both structural and stratigraphic elements. Levorsen recognized this in his 1967 classification of traps. He noted that almost a complete gradation exists between structural and stratigraphic end-members and that discovered traps "illustrate almost every imaginable combination of structure and stratigraphy" (Levorsen, 1967, p. 143). Levorsen restricted the use of the term *combination trap* to features in which neither the structural nor the stratigraphic element alone forms the trap but both are essential to it (Levorsen, 1967). Two examples of combination structural–stratigraphic traps are illustrated in Figure 13.10. In both cases, part of the trap is formed by an updip depositional pinchout of porous and permeable rock. Fault seal forms a required part of the trap in Figure 13.10A, while folding of the permeability pinchout creates the required strike closure in Figure 13.10B.

Many people now use the term *combination trap* in a less rigorous way and apply it to any trap that has both structural and stratigraphic elements, regardless of whether both are required for the trap to be viable. Strict adherence to definitions does not necessarily find hydrocarbons, but early recognition of stratigraphic complications associated with structural traps or structural modification of dominantly stratigraphic traps can help eliminate exploration or development surprises.

HYDRODYNAMIC TRAPS

Explorationists have known since about mid-century that oil–water contacts in many hydrocarbon-bearing traps are tilted (see Levorsen, 1967; North, 1985). In other cases, traps that have no static closure contain hydrocarbons, and traps that do have static closure and should reasonably contain hydrocarbons do not (North, 1985).

An explanation that is commonly proposed for these observations is that reservoir conditions are hydrodynamic rather than hydrostatic. In general, dips of oil–water contacts seldom exceed a few degrees, but higher dips have been reported (up to 10°) (North, 1985). If the dip (or tilt) of the oil–water contact exceeds the dip of the trap flanks, the trap will be flushed (generally, if trap flank dips exceed 5°, there is little risk of flushing). Therefore, in the evaluation of structural traps with relatively gently dipping flanks, consideration should be given to hydrodynamic conditions (see Dahlberg, 1982). It is important to note that tilted oil–water contacts may be related to phenomena other than hydrodynamics (e.g., variations in reservoir characteristics and neotectonics), and that present-day hydrodynamic conditions may not reflect those in the past.

It is possible to calculate the theoretical change in trap capacity and therefore the risk associated with trap flushing in a strongly hydrodynamic situation. Hubbert (1953) showed that the tilt of the oil–water contact in the direction of flow is a function of the hydraulic gradient and the densities of both hydrocarbons and water. The lower the oil density and greater the water flow, the more easily the oil is displaced. Figure 13.11A illustrates one type of hydrostatic trap, and Figure 13.11B demonstrates the qualitative effect of a hydrodynamic situation. If water flow rate is increased with a constant oil density, or oil density is increased with a constant water flow rate, the situation in Figure 13.11C will arise. In Figure 13.11D, a trap is created in a flexure without static closure due to downdip water movement. Figure 13.11E illustrates the effect of updip water movement for static conditions under the same structural situation. Figures 13.11F and G show the qualitative effect of downdip and updip water movement on the capacity of a fold-dominated trap to store hydrocarbons. As can be seen, downdip water flow tends to promote hydrocarbon entrapment and updip flow tends to impede it.

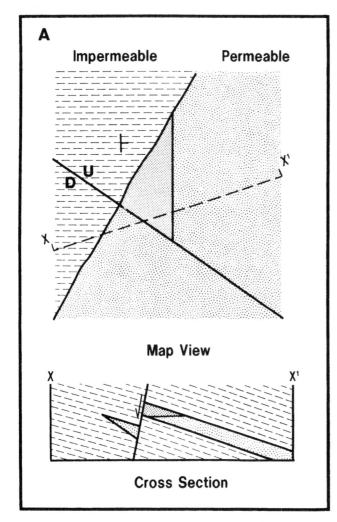

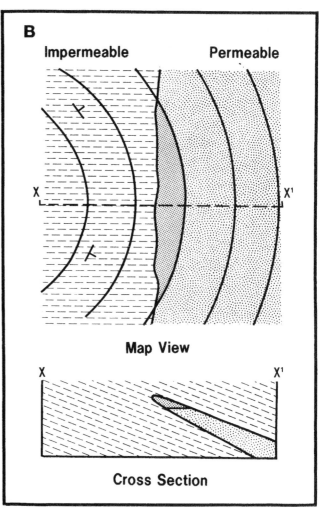

Hydrocarbon accumulation

Figure 13.10. Combination traps. (A) Intersection of a fault with an updip depositional edge of porous and permeable section. (B) Folding of an updip depositional pinchout of reservoir section. In these examples, both the structural and stratigraphic elements are required to form a viable trap. (After Levorsen, 1967.)

TRAP EVALUATION

In this chapter, our illustration of various trap types has focused on cross-sectional views. This is because cross sections provide diagnostic images of many of the various trap types. Map views of traps are equally important, although sometimes not as visually distinctive of trap type. Those involved in trap evaluation should develop a detailed understanding of the various map patterns associated with different styles of traps. This can guide mapping during the early stages of evaluation or in cases where only limited data are available. Examples of map patterns for the types of traps discussed here can be found in many of the references that we have cited (e.g., King, 1972; North, 1985; Foster and Beaumont, 1991). Useful mapping techniques are described by Tearpock and Bischke (1991).

Regional trap evaluation should concentrate on placing potential traps in the context of the operating petroleum system. Plate tectonic setting, basin type, and structural evolution (sedimentary basin study) can be used at this stage to predict the possible styles of structural and stratigraphic traps that should be expected in an area (Harding and Lowell, 1979). Regional seals and their relation to potential traps should be established early in the evaluation. Particular attention should be paid to the timing of trap formation and its relation to the timing of generation, migration, and accumulation of hydrocarbon. Traps that form after hydrocarbon migration has ceased are not attractive targets unless remigration out of earlier formed traps has occurred.

Detailed evaluation of individual traps, once identified, should begin with the selection of the mapping surface. Ideally, this would be the sealing surface of the trap. Identification of the actual sealing surface requires that both seal and reservoir characterization are integral

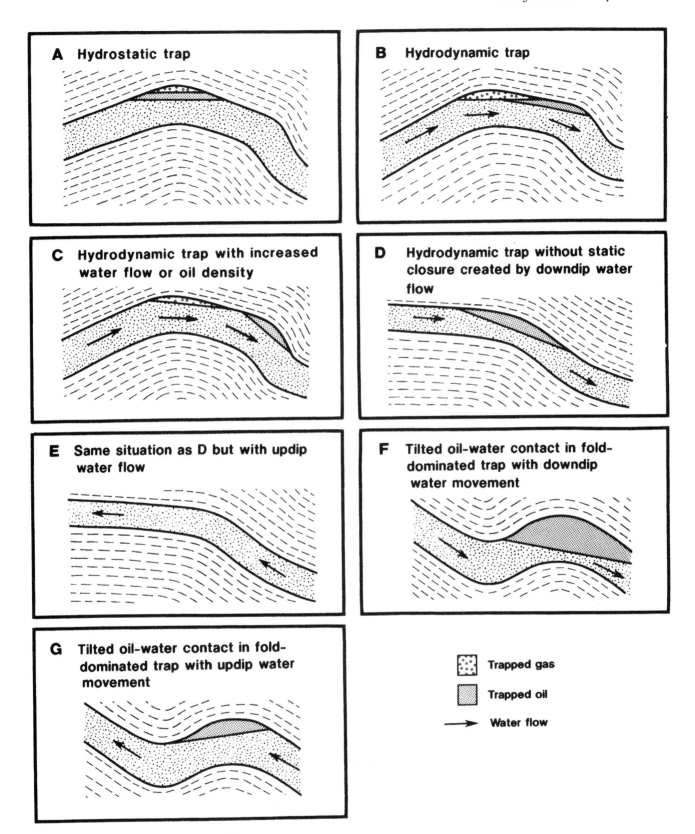

Figure 13.11. Illustrations of the qualitative effect of the amount and direction of water flow and oil density on hydrocarbon trap configuration. (A) Generalized hydrostatic trap. (B) Generalized hydrodynamic trap. (After Hubbert, 1953; North, 1985.) (C) Hydrodynamic trap with increased water flow or oil density. (D) Hydrodynamic trap without static closure created by downdip water flow. (E) Same situation as in (D) but with updip water flow. (F) Tilted oil–water contact in fold-dominated trap with downdip water movement. (G) Tilted oil–water contact in fold-dominated trap with updip water movement.

parts of the trap evaluation. Also, if the sealing surface of the trap is not correctly identified, trap leak points may be missed. A common flaw in trap evaluation results from ignoring the transition (or waste) zone, if present, between an economic reservoir and its ultimate seal.

Before drilling, reservoir and seal characteristics can be predicted by combining regional and local paleogeographic information, sequence stratigraphic concepts, and detailed analyses of seismic facies and interval velocities. If well data are available, detailed log analysis and incorporation of pertinent drill-stem test data will greatly improve predictions. Petrophysical measurements from downhole samples are also useful, but because of small sample sizes, such information may not characterize either reservoir or seal properties throughout the trap and should be extrapolated with caution.

We have defined a trap as any geometric arrangement of rock that permits significant accumulation of hydrocarbons in the subsurface. We do not consider the presence of hydrocarbons in economic amounts to be a critical element of a trap. The absence of oil or gas in a subsurface feature can be the result of failure or absence of other essential elements or processes of a petroleum system and may have nothing to do with the viability of the trap.

Although we use the geometric arrangement of key elements to define a trap, trap evaluation must include much more than just mapping the configuration of those elements. Reservoir and seal characteristics are so important to trap viability that their evaluation must be an integral part of any trap study. Timing of trap formation is also critical. No trap should be viewed out of context but rather should be evaluated in concert with all of the other elements of a petroleum system.

Traps can be classified as structural, stratigraphic, or combination traps. In addition, hydrodynamic flow can modify traps and perhaps lead to hydrocarbon accumulations where no conventional traps exist. The trap classification discussed here is a useful way to consider traps during the early stages of prospect evaluation. An understanding of end-member trap types can help guide data acquisition strategy and mapping efforts, but there is an almost bewildering array of documented and potential hydrocarbon traps, many of which may be subtle or unconventional. As more and more of the world's hydrocarbon provinces reach mature stages of exploration, such traps may provide some of the best opportunities for future discoveries.

Acknowledgments   *Reviews by T. L. Bush, T. P. Harding, T. A. Hauge, K. O. Stanley, and book reviewers J. T. Smith and P. C. van de Kamp have improved this manuscript. We thank Exxon Exploration for permission to participate in this project and for permission to publish. Finally, we thank Les Magoon for his forbearance and assistance during the preparation of this contribution.*

References Cited

Allan, U. S., 1989, Model for hydrocarbon migration and entrapment within faulted structures: AAPG Bulletin, v. 73, p. 803–811.

Barss, D. L., A. B. Copland, and W. D. Ritchie, 1970, Geology of Middle Devonian reefs, Ranbow area, Alberta, Canada, *in* M. T. Halbouty, ed., Geology of giant petroleum fields: AAPG Memoir 14, p. 19–49.

Busch, D. A., 1974, Stratigraphic traps in sandstones—exploration techniques: AAPG Memoir 21, 174 p.

Carll, J. F., 1880, The geology of the oil regions of Warren, Venango, Clarion, and Butler counties: Second Pennsylvania Geological Survey, v. 3, 482 p.

Chenoweth, P. A., 1972, Unconformity traps, *in* R. E. King, ed., Stratigraphic oil and gas fields—classification, exploration methods, and case histories: AAPG Memoir 16, p. 42–46.

Clapp, F. G., 1917, Revision of the structural classification of the petroleum and natural gas fields: Geological Society of America Bulletin, v. 28, p. 553–602.

Clapp, F. G., 1929, Role of geologic structure in accumulations of petroleum, structure of typical American oil fields: AAPG Bulletin, v. 2, p. 667–716.

Dahlberg, E. C., 1982, Applied hydrodynamics in petroleum exploration: New York, Springer-Verlag, 161 p.

Dennis, J. G., 1967, International tectonic dictionary: AAPG Memoir 7, 196 p.

Dott, R. H., Sr., and M. J. Reynolds, 1969, The trap, *in* R. H. Dott, Sr., and M. J. Reynolds, compilers, Source book for petroleum geology: AAPG Memoir 5, p. 395–440.

Downey, N. W., 1984, Evaluating seals for hydrocarbon accumulations: AAPG Bulletin, v. 68, p. 1752–1763.

Foster, N. H., and E. A. Beaumont, compilers, 1988, Traps and seals, II: stratigraphic and capillary traps: AAPG Treatise of Petroleum Geology Reprint Series 7, 410 p.

Foster, N. H., and E. A. Beaumont, compilers, 1991, Stratigraphic traps, II: AAPG Treatise of Petroleum Geology, Atlas of Oil and Gas Fields, 360 p.

Halbouty, M. T., ed., 1982, The deliberate search for the subtle trap: AAPG Memoir 32, 351 p.

Halbouty, M. T., 1991, East Texas field—U.S.A., East Texas basin, Texas, *in* N. H. Foster and E. A. Beaumont, compilers, Stratigraphic traps, II: AAPG Treatise of Petroleum Geology, Atlas of Oil and Gas Fields, p. 189–206.

Harding, T. P., 1974, Petroleum traps associated with wrench faults: AAPG Bulletin, v. 58, p. 1290–1304.

Harding, T. P., and J. D. Lowell, 1979, Structural styles, their plate tectonic habitats, and hydrocarbon traps in petroleum provinces: AAPG Bulletin, v. 63, p. 1016–1058.

Hemphill, C. R., R. I. Smith, and F. Szabo, 1970, Geology of Beaverhill Lake reefs, Swan Hills area, Alberta, *in* M. T. Halbouty, ed., Geology of giant petroleum fields: AAPG Memoir 14, p. 50–90.

Heroy, W. B., 1941, Petroleum geology, in 1888–1938: Geological Society of America 50th Anniversary Volume, p. 535–536.

Hubbert, M. K., 1953, Entrapment of petroleum under hydrodynamic conditions: AAPG Bulletin, v. 37, p. 1954.

King, R. E., ed., 1972, Stratigraphic oil and gas fields—classification, exploration methods, and case histories: AAPG Memoir 16, 687 p.

Levorsen, A. I., 1936, Stratigraphic versus structural accumulation: AAPG Bulletin, v. 20, p. 521–530.

Levorsen, A. I., 1954, Geology of Petroleum, 1st ed.: San Francisco, W.H. Freeman and Co., 724 p.

Levorsen, A. I., 1967, Geology of Petroleum, 2nd ed.: San Francisco, W.H. Freeman and Co., 724 p.

Lowell, J. D., 1985, Structural styles in petroleum exploration: Tulsa, Oklahoma DCGI, 477 p.

MacKenzie, D. B., 1972, Primary stratigraphic traps in sandstones, *in* R. E. King, ed., Stratigraphic oil and gas fields—classification, exploration methods, and case histories: AAPG Memoir 16, p. 47–63.

Martin, R., 1966, Paleogeomorphology and its application to exploration for oil and gas (with examples from western Canada): AAPG Bulletin, v. 50, p. 2277–2311.

Milton, N. J., and G. T. Bertram, 1992, Trap styles: a new classification based on sealing surfaces: AAPG Bulletin, v. 76, p. 983–999.

Namson, J., 1981, Detailed structural analysis of the western foothills belt in the Miaoli–Hsinchu area, Taiwan, I: southern part: Petroleum Geology of Taiwan, v. 18, p. 31–51.

North, F. K. , 1985, Petroleum geology: Boston, Allen and Unwin, 553 p.

Perrodon, A., 1983, Dynamics of oil and gas accumulations: Bulletin des Centres de Recherches Exploration–Production Elf-Aquitaine, Memoir 5, 368 p.

Ramsay, J. G., 1974, Development of chevron folds: Geological Society of America Bulletin, v. 85, p. 1741–1754.

Rittenhouse, G., 1972, Stratigraphic trap classification, *in* R.E. King, ed., Stratigraphic oil and gas fields—classification, exploration methods, and case histories: AAPG Memoir 16, p. 14–28.

Sarg, J. F., and L. J. Skjold, 1982, Stratigraphic traps in Paleocene sands in the Balder area, North Sea, *in* M. T. Halbouty, ed., The deliberate search for the subtle trap: AAPG Memoir 32, p. 197–206.

Smith, D. A., 1966, Theoretical considerations of sealing and nonsealing faults: AAPG Bulletin, v. 50, p. 363–379.

Smith, D. A., 1980, Sealing and nonsealing faults in Louisiana Gulf Coast Salt basin: AAPG Bulletin, v. 64, p. 145–172.

Suppe, J., 1983, Geometry and kinematics of belt-bend folding: American Journal of Science, v. 253, p. 648–721.

Suppe, J., 1985, Principles of structural geology: Englewood Cliffs, NJ, Prentice-Hall, 533 p.

Suppe, J., and D. A. Medwedeff, 1984, Fault-propagation folding: Geological Society of America Abstracts with Programs, v. 16, p. 670.

Tearpock, D. J., and R. E. Bischke, 1991, Applied subsurface geological mapping: Englewood Cliffs, NJ, Prentice-Hall, 648 p.

Weber, J. K., G. Mandl, W. F. Pilaar, F. Lehner, and R. G. Precious, 1978, The role of faults in hydrocarbon migration and trapping in Nigerian growth structures: Offshore Technology Conference, Paper 33356, p. 2643–2652.

Wilhelm, O., 1945, Classification of petroleum reservoirs: AAPG Bulletin, v. 29, p. 1537–1579.

Wilson, W. B., 1934, Proposed classification of oil and gas reservoirs, *in* W. E. Wrather and F. M. Lahee, eds., Problems of petroleum geology: AAPG Sidney Powers Volume, p. 433–445.

Zhai, G., and Q. Zha, 1982, Buried-hill oil and gas pools in the North China basin, *in* M. T. Halbouty, The deliberate search for the subtle trap: AAPG Memoir 32, p. 317–335.

"A trap is a trap, whether or not it has a mouse in it."

—W. C. Finch

Passage attributed to W. C. Finch, in Rittenhouse, G., 1972, Stratigraphic trap classification: AAPG Memoir 16, p. 16.

Magoon, L. B, and W. G. Dow, eds., 1994, The petroleum
system—from source to trap: AAPG Memoir 60.

Chapter **14**

Preservation, Degradation, and Destruction of Trapped Oil

Philippe Blanc

Jacques Connan

Elf Aquitaine
Pau Cedex, France

Abstract

Petroleum is a fragile fluid, a part of which is likely to be destroyed or lost to the atmosphere. The moment crude oil separates from bitumen in the source rock, it begins to undergo compositional changes that continue throughout migration and accumulation. The processes and factors influencing oil composition in an accumulation take effect before, during, and after entrapment. The primary factors influencing oil composition before entrapment are source rock characteristics, primary migration, and secondary migration. The main factors influencing oil composition during entrapment are pressure and temperature, as they establish the conditions under which secondary alteration processes take place. After entrapment, secondary alteration processes influencing oil composition are the effect of thermal maturation, physical and biological degradation, gravity segregation, dysmigration (separation–migration), and deasphalting. These alteration processes can increase the API gravity and gas–oil ratio of the oil, but generally decrease the API gravity.

Knowledge of the conditions and mechanisms of degradation are needed to understand the nature and distribution of oil shows and to carry out oil–oil and oil–source rock correlations. Considerable progress has been made in understanding secondary alteration processes, but more is expected as the more poorly understood macromolecular and polar fractions are investigated. Presently, molecular chemistry is a useful tool that can recognize incipient biodegradation, detect oil gravity segregation, and discriminate a pyrobitumen from a precipitated asphaltene, whereas bulk analyses are currently inaccurate.

INTRODUCTION

Petroleum is a fragile mixture of oil and gas that is difficult to preserve. It is easily degradable by destruction or loss to the atmosphere of an unknown amount of it. The critical moment oil separates from bitumen in the source rock, it undergoes compositional changes during migration and accumulation. Except for changes in the oil and gas mix that occurs in response to pressure and temperature variations during petroleum migration, most degradation and destructive processes occur in the reservoir rock within the trap. Generally, oil and gas that first comes to the trap is defined as *normal*. By this we mean a petroleum accumulation whose composition is commonly associated with a particular kerogen type and whose chemical composition at a molecular level shows little sign of alteration. The API gravity for such oil accumulations can range from 25 to 40° API, while the gas–oil ratio (GOR) is generally 100–200 m³/m³ (500–1000 ft³/bbl). This oil is generally considered to be the

preserved petroleum. The longer a petroleum accumulation exists in nature, the more likely the original chemical composition should be altered or degraded by physico-chemical or biological processes. These processes include increase or decrease in burial depth (temperature change), flushing by meteoric water, and bacterial activity. The complete destruction of a petroleum accumulation is usually caused by erosion.

Petroleum is a complex mixture of liquid and gaseous fluids of mainly organic compounds whose proportions may depend on the PVT conditions in the trap. These fluids are usually described by bulk properties, such as API gravity, percent sulfur, GOR, and viscosity. Although these bulk properties are of limited interpretive value in shallower reservoirs, they do provide guidelines for fluids in deeper reservoirs. For instance, the API gravity of a series of oils tends to increase with burial depth. However, the composition of petroleum depends upon such complex phenomena that bulk parameters (physical and chemical) are unable to describe adequately the subtle shift in molecular composition that occurs when an oil passes through various levels of degradation.

Generally, oil in reservoir rocks and bitumen from source rocks have many similarities in their composition. Both are composed of hydrocarbons (including naphtheno-aromatics and organo-sulfur species) and polar compounds (rich in nitrogen, sulfur, and oxygen atoms), the latter being divided into asphaltenes (macromolecular fraction insoluble in light alkanes) and resins (more soluble but very polar). The main differences between accumulated oil and bitumen are created during primary migration (expulsion) and secondary migration. For instance, polar compounds are depleted in accumulated oil because these components are strongly sorbed within the source rock matrix and within the kerogen. Such a phenomenon is well documented from natural cases as well as from experimental studies (Connan et al., 1991; Lewan, Chapter 11, this volume).

The molecular composition of oil is much less affected during migration than are the bulk parameters, even though previous studies have shown that different molecules could exhibit differences in "retention times" during migration within a petroleum system (Seifert and Moldowan, 1981; Zhao-An and Philp, 1987). In general, the original biological marker fingerprint of a source rock is preserved sufficiently in migrated oils to allow its use as a tool to assess oil–source rock correlations (Curiale, Chapter 15, this volume), unless (1) the oil is a mixture from more than one source rock, (2) the migrating oil becomes contaminated by extracting biological markers from thermally immature organic matter before accumulating, or (3) the oil undergoes secondary alteration, such as biodegradation.

Hence, depending on the analytical approach, the preservation or degradation of petroleum can be demonstrated using different parameters, either physical or chemical, bulk or molecular. Some of these parameters are modified during petroleum degradation. This chapter provides a review of the major processes likely to influence oil composition after it is trapped. Diagnostic tools developed to detect this degradation are emphasized.

OIL PRESERVATION OR DEGRADATION

Assuming that a given accumulated oil will be "preserved" indefinitely makes little sense, for petroleum is a mixture of compounds that is not in a state of equilibrium. It is likely that, over geologic time, this mixture will undergo significant physical and chemical changes. The longer the time, the more likely the changes. Here again, assessment of preservation depends upon the criteria adopted. From an economic point of view, petroleum quality deteriorates if it is affected greatly by alteration processes: *preserved petroleum* is an appropriate term for a fluid that is of economic interest when a prospect evaluation is carried out. However, investigations of the petroleum system are done without regard to economics,

that is, an accumulated oil is worth studying regardless of its economic worth because of the information it may contain. Therefore, the preserved oil is synonymous with the *normal oil*, which in itself is difficult to define. The normal oil shows no signs of being degraded or altered. Normal oils are different depending on the composition of their source rock. The GOR also varies for the same reason. From a molecular point of view, this oil will never be completely preserved or remain normal since minor modifications are always occurring. At a molecular level, cases are encountered in which some of the biological markers are degraded whereas others are preserved. The challenge to the investigator is to determine the nature and extent of this oil degradation so as to carry out better oil–source rock correlations and more accurately reconstruct the accumulation history of the petroleum system.

The main factors influencing oil composition before, during, and after being trapped in the reservoir rock are outlined in Figure 14.1 (Blanc and Connan, 1993). The primary factors influencing oil composition before trapping are source rock characteristics and primary and secondary migration conditions. Oil composition is influenced to some extent by the nature of the source (organic) material and by the paleoenvironmental conditions in which it was deposited. Both factors lead to different types of kerogen that behave differently during catagenesis. In addition, several other agents (geologic, physical, and chemical) are at work to affect oil composition significantly during primary and secondary migration. These three primary factors affect oil composition before it enters the trap.

The main factors influencing oil composition in the reservoir rock are pressure and temperature. Both pressure and temperature, which increase or decrease with an increase or decrease in burial depth, affect the GOR at the time of accumulation. Otherwise, the PVT conditions in the reservoir establish the conditions under which secondary alteration processes take place.

Secondary alterations influencing oil composition after it accumulates in the trap are discussed relative to five different processes (Figure 14.1). These processes are thermal maturation, physical and biological degradation, gravity segregation, dysmigration, and deasphalting. They are discussed relative to the main agent causing them as well as the products, API gravity, and relative change in depth of the fluids. Their alteration effects, though clearly identified, are sometimes difficult to recognize unequivocally because they can lead to similar kinds of degradation products.

Thermal Maturation

Thermal maturation of oil, or *oil cracking*, is a process that sometimes occurs in the trap because temperature increases when the trapped oil is buried deeper. Hence, oil cracking reactions within the reservoir rock favor the formation of light hydrocarbons, the depletion of polycyclic biomarkers, an increase in GOR, a decrease in specific gravity (increase in API gravity), and a decrease in sulfur content. An oil expelled from a source rock that

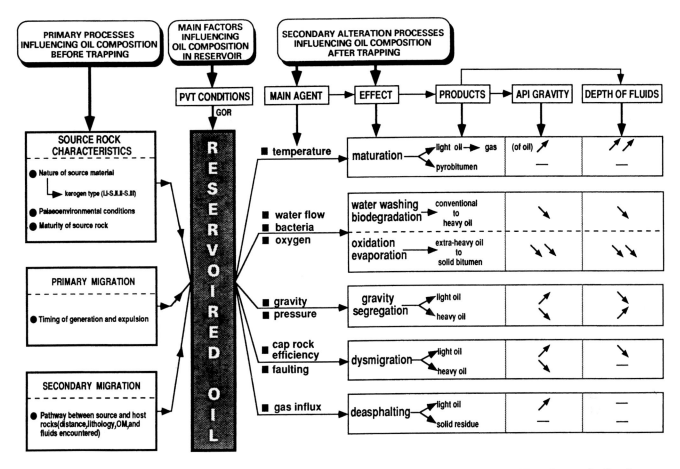

Figure 14.1. Schematic representation of the main factors and processes influencing oil composition. Arrows inclined upward indicate an increase; arrows inclined downward, a decrease.

is experiencing increasing levels of thermal maturity also shows similar compositional changes. Consequently, it often becomes difficult to separate the thermally cracked oil in the reservoir rock from the high API gravity oil caused by expulsion from a mature source rock. However, the thermal evolution of oil in a reservoir rock induces a disproportionation reaction that leads to the formation of gaseous and light hydrocarbons on one side and a black solid residue on the other side. This solid residue, often called *pyrobitumen*, is therefore a diagnostic indicator enabling the recognition of thermal cracking of the original oil. A well-known example illustrating that feature occurs in Rainbow reefs, Canada, where gas and high API gravity oil are associated with pyrobitumen (Evans et al., 1971; Bailey et al., 1974; Rogers et al., 1974).

Pyrobitumens are highly dehydrogenated structures that show a low hydrogen index (HI is ~80 mg HC/g TOC) and a very high T_{max} (>460°C) with a reflectivity that ranges between 1.5 and 2.5% R_o (J. Connan, personal communication, 1991). Their dehydrogenated character, coupled with their insolubility in $CHCl_3$, allow their easy differentiation from asphaltene-like material that may have been precipitated in the reservoir rock through a different process (e.g., gas injection resulting in natural deasphalting).

The upper temperature limits for oil occurrence before

it is thermally cracked have been reviewed by Horsfield et al. (1991): a mean value of 150°C is often given, but regional studies have produced values ranging from about 93–104°C in western Canada, 138°C in Powder basin, 150°C in Niger delta and Norway, 158°C in Italy, and up to 175–204°C in California. Closed-system pyrolysis and kinetic modeling by Horsfield et al. (1991) showed that the onset of gas generation from an oil acquired from the Norwegian North Sea Central Graben might occur between 160° and 190°C. These conclusions agree with the observation that liquid hydrocarbons can occur in fields where reservoir rocks are hot (165°C). However, the existence of liquid fluids in deep hot rocks can also be accounted for by a retardation effect of high pressure on the evolution of organic matter or overpressuring within a reservoir (Price, 1982; Goffé and Villey, 1984; Dominé, 1991; Connan et al., 1991; Blanc and Connan, 1992a).

Although well accepted on the basis of various observations in oil systems, it should be mentioned that the process of thermal decomposition of petroleum ultimately yielding methane and pyrobitumen has recently been disputed on the basis of both kinetic (Mango, 1991) and thermodynamic (Helgeson et al., 1991) considerations.

Water Washing–Biodegradation and Oxidation–Evaporation

Biodegradation is the microbial oxidation of crude oil, and it usually takes place at a shallow depth where the oil is in contact with flowing water, whereas *water washing* applies to the removal of the more water-soluble compounds. Although these phenomena are unrelated, they frequently occur simultaneously because both processes require contact with flowing meteoric water. However, petroleum geochemistry techniques are currently unable to selectively recognize the diagnostic effects of each type of alteration whenever they are extensive or even modest.

The process of water washing alone is poorly documented since bacterial degradation generally obscures its effects. Based on solubilities of hydrocarbons, simulation experiments, and field examples, water washing has been shown to be particularly effective in the low boiling range of hydrocarbons, thus causing a decrease in API gravity. Aromatics (especially benzene and toluene) are the most soluble compounds, followed by light alkanes and then naphthenes (Connan, 1984; Palmer, 1984; Lafargue and Barker, 1988). However, one should remember that benzene, toluene, and xylene concentrations are also source rock dependent. Molecular changes due to water washing without biodegradation have been tentatively proposed. They are (1) a decrease in the amount of aromatics and *n*-alkanes while naphthenes are unaltered, (2) a partial removal of C_{15+} aromatics while C_{15+} alkanes are unaffected, and (3) a decrease in sulfur-bearing aromatics (especially dibenzothiophene) while the C_{15}–C_{20} saturate fraction remains unchanged (Lafargue and Barker, 1988). Recently, phenols have been proposed as sensitive indicators for water washing (Ioppolo et al., 1991).

A review of the conditions under which biodegradation occurs and the important changes in the physical and chemical properties of crude oil has been given by Connan (1984). Generally, biodegradation affects both physical and chemical parameters. In particular, biodegradation induces a decrease in the GOR, light hydrocarbon content, and API gravity, whereas it increases the viscosity, optical activity, and heteroatomic (especially sulfur) content of the oil. These features are due to the consumption of specific molecules by aerobic bacteria, which results in the formation of oxidized compounds (the latter likely to be attacked subsequently by anaerobic strains). Because of the depletion in alkanes and aromatics, there is a relative increase in concentration of polar compounds, which is why bulk chemical composition of the oil fraction is affected by biodegradation.

The effects of biodegradation are also recorded at a molecular level. Both field observations and laboratory experiments have contributed information about the sequence in which alkanes and aromatics have been removed. Among saturated hydrocarbons, for instance, normal alkanes are consumed by bacteria first, followed by isoprenoids, regular steranes, diasteranes, hopanes, and neohopanes, in order. Moreover, bacterial consumption of hydrocarbons also depends on the oxic–anoxic conditions of the active water adjacent to the oil and on the nutrients in the water. When nutrients (nitrogen and phosphorus) are depleted, biodegradation preferentially starts with aromatics, and alkanes are unchanged. Under more favorable conditions (i.e., a medium rich in oxygen and nutrients), both alkanes and aromatics are attacked simultaneously (Fedorak et al., 1983). In addition, it has been demonstrated conclusively that anaerobic biodegradation of alkanes is possible with a strain of sulfur-reducing bacteria (Bailey et al., 1973; ZoBell, 1973; Connan and Orgeval, 1976; Aeckersberg et al., 1991). However, this form of biodegradation has limited effects on oil properties as a whole. The most effective biodegradation proceeds through aerobic pathways.

A more extreme form of degradation occurs through evaporation (inspissation) and oxidation of oil at the surface (Figure 14.1). Usually the oil degrades from an extra-heavy oil to solid bitumen (Connan, 1988). If oxidation and erosion continues, all remnants of the oil field are removed or destroyed.

Gravity Segregation

Although API gravity of oils should increase step by step with greater burial depth, a reverse situation has been observed in some reservoirs (Evans et al., 1971; Price, 1980; Ungerer et al., 1984) which cannot be attributed to thermal maturity differences of the oil or source rock. In fact, this reverse phenomenon is poorly understood, and two explanations can be proposed: (1) either a gravity segregation is occurring, with oil becoming heavier with increasing depth by a simple gravity process (larger molecules settling toward the bottom of the oil column), or (2) an "inverted gravity" phenomenon is occurring that involves lower pressure and a higher quantity of gas at the top of the reservoir than at the bottom. Silverman (1965) had previously described a similar phenomenon called a *retrograde condensation* process (see also Tissot, 1988), in which a liquid phase separates from a single phase system of gas when the pressure is reduced.

This decrease in API gravity with depth in a continous oil column should be ascribed to gravity segregation if other possible causes can be definitively ruled out. For instance, the more deeply buried oil fields should be checked for incipient biodegradation to show that a definite interaction with bacteria-containing waters does not increase with depth of burial. If all molecular properties are similar in both the conventional oils and the heavy oils, then the downward compositional changes that generate heavier and heavier oils should be explained by gravity segregation within the oil column.

Gravity segregation explains the increase in specific gravity (decrease in API gravity) in the Vic Bilh oil field in the Aquitaine basin (Figure 14.2). A vertical sequence of oil samples was obtained from two wells drilled through upper Kimmeridgian–Portlandian (Upper Jurassic) and Barremian (Lower Cretaceous) reservoir rocks. Six oil samples were recovered from well 1: three

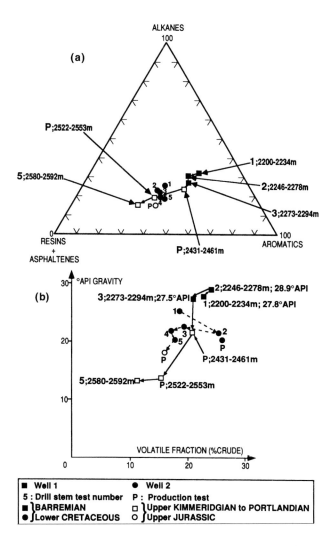

Figure 14.2. Occurrence of a possible gravity segregation phenomenon in two wells of the Vic Bilh oil field (southwestern France) on the basis of the evolution of bulk parameters with depth: (a) oil composition and (b) API gravity and volatile content. Biological marker data are needed to provide an adequate explanation for this change in bulk parameters (see Blanc and Connan, 1992a).

drill-stem test samples from the Barremian (solid squares) and two production samples and one drill-stem test sample from the Upper Jurassic (open squares). Although the relative proportion of alkanes and aromatics remained constant, the API gravity decreased with depth, coincident with a corresponding increase in polar compounds (resins and asphaltenes) for these six oil samples (Figure 14.2A). In addition, the volatile fraction of the crude oil also decreased with a decrease in API gravity (Figure 14.2B). On the basis of the molecular chemistry of these oils, it is concluded that they were expelled from the same source rock at the same level of thermal maturity. Therefore, this progressive enrichment in polar compounds associated with a decrease in API gravity with depth leads to the conclusion that this phenomenon is most likely related to gravity segregation (see Blanc and Connan, 1993).

Dysmigration

Some compositional changes within accumulated oil can be related to the efficiency of the seal rock. A seal rock over an accumulation that provides a perfect seal will prevent any compositional change in the trapped oil due to leakage. However, most hydrocarbon traps leak to some extent. This leakage is linked to the geologic conditions that formed the trap. Sometimes these conditions are related to tectonic events that cause movement along a major fault that traps hydrocarbons. In this case, a *dysmigration* phenomenon may occur where significant losses of the lightest hydrocarbons from oil can take place in a two-step process (described by Silverman, 1965, as a "separation-migration" process). First, the pressure release due to faulting converts the single phase fluid system to a two-phase system where a gas cap forms above the oil. Second, this gas is lost through the leak along with light oil and migrates to shallower traps where temperature or pressure drops can induce the previously discussed retrograde condensation. A new pool can be formed that contains a fluid with a high API gravity. This is in contrast to the low API gravity oil left behind in the original pool which, based on its molecular composition, will have a level of thermal maturity that is similar to the high API gravity oil. Therefore, significant differences in chemical composition and distinctive physical characteristics of the two respective oil accumulations will be recorded.

An example of dysmigration has been found in the Lagrave area in the Aquitaine basin. Here, an oil field that has an Upper Cretaceous reservoir rock contains a fairly light crude oil (45° API), whereas the heavy residual oil corresponding to the original oil accumulation has been found much deeper in a Barremian (Lower Cretaceous) reservoir rock of a nearby field. These upward-migrating hydrocarbon fluids accumulated in a shallower trap; the result is a shallow accumulation of high quality oil.

When no trap exists at a shallower depth above a deeper accumulation that leaks, oil shows are found within the sedimentary rock column above the deeper accumulation. In the Emeraude area offshore of the Congo in Africa, there is a good example of intense leakage through the seal rock of deeper accumulations. Oil shows have been detected in the sedimentary rock far above the oil accumulation. Studies reveal that the degree of biodegradation of these oil shows increases as the shows approach the sea floor. Large amounts of gas bubbles are recorded on the sea floor just above the Emeraude oil field (Connan and Coustau, 1987).

Deasphalting

Oils and condensates in traps are usually associated with gas. This gas can originate from the thermal maturity of a source rock as well as from secondary alteration processes affecting oil already in the reservoir rock. Gas content depends on numerous parameters, such as kerogen type, hydrocarbon availability (oil or gas) at the time of pool formation, reservoir pressure, reservoir temperature, trap efficiency, and secondary alteration processes.

The postaccumulation introduction of gas into an oil field can lead to chemical changes because the influx of gaseous hydrocarbons decreases the average molecular weight of the pooled mixture. Hence, what the organic chemist does in the laboratory when precipitating asphaltenes from an oil by adjunction of *n*-heptane, for instance, is also naturally undertaken in the oil field when gas moves up through the oil column. This natural *deasphalting* can be triggered by external gas injection, as a result of secondary migration, or by oil cracking within the reservoir rock (Evans, et al., 1971; Bailey et al., 1974; Rogers et al., 1974). This process therefore leads to the formation of a light oil on one hand and a solid residue containing asphaltenes on the other (Speight, 1984; Speight et al., 1985). This process of deasphalting is thought by Dahl and Speers (1986) to explain the occurrence of a tar mat in the Oseberg oil field in the Norwegian North Sea.

RECOGNIZING PALEODEGRADATION

The preservation, degradation, and destruction of petroleum is usually viewed from present-day. However, the petroleum system study requires the investigator to describe oil and gas accumulations at the time they formed. Whenever a degraded oil is encountered at the surface or in the subsurface, one must ask at what time this degradation process commenced and what type of paleodegradation occurred. Figure 14.1 emphasizes that most degradation processes lead to the formation of heavy or extra-heavy oils up to solid bitumens. Therefore, these various processes are difficult to disentangle, especially because they are interrelated and continuous and take place successively. Most of the time, examination of bulk parameters of the degraded oil only leads to conflicting interpretations. An increase in the API gravity, for instance, is usually thought to correlate positively with an increase in depth since pooled fluids become lighter, that is, the average hydrocarbon molecule becomes smaller with increasing thermal maturity. However, other phenomena are likely to interfere, especially at shallow depths. For example, when oil migrates updip a long distance from the source rock, it may become heavier because lighter hydrocarbons can be lost before the oil accumulates. In addition, secondary alteration processes can act on the oil within the reservoir rock to lower its API gravity. This influence of various phenomena on the API gravity of oils is illustrated in Figure 14.3. This figure shows the evolution of API gravity of oils from the North Sea as a function of depth. Although a general trend is observed (oils increase in API gravity when the reservoir rock depth increases), the correlation is not perfect due to the existence of other processes than simply a lightening of oils under increasing temperature.

To better understand the degradation of oil, a multidisciplinary approach should be undertaken (Blanc et al.,

1982; Connan and Coustau, 1987). This approach includes tools such as molecular and isotopic geochemistry, both of which provide complementary information that shows more potential for investigating degradation than do the bulk properties of oil. For instance, it would be impossible to evaluate a biodegraded oil occurrence exclusively by considering bulk properties because a heavy oil, for example, can result from various factors or phenomena, including kerogen type, level of thermal maturity, water washing, gravity segregation, and dysmigration. In contrast, since biological markers are sensitive to bacterial consumption, they are likely to give key indications, not only on the occurrence of the biodegradation itself but also on the extent of the alteration processes. Hence, classifications of biodegraded oils are proposed in relation to their level of biodegradation: *incipient, minor, moderate, extensive,* and *severe* or *extreme* (Seifert and Moldowan, 1979; Goodwin et al., 1983; Volkman et al., 1983; Connan, 1984; Peters and Moldowan, 1991; Cassani and Eglinton, 1991).

The criteria used to determine this level of biodegradation is based on the presence or absence of compound classes. Moreover, while severe biodegradation is usually relatively easy to recognize because aromatics and alkanes are strongly altered, incipient biodegradation may be questionable. *Incipient biodegradation* can be defined as degradation of *n*-alkyl chain–containing structures (*n*-alkanes, *iso-* and *anteiso*-alkanes, alkylbenzenes, and methylalkylbenzenes). In such a case, this degradation is likely to be mistaken for a token of immaturity since some *n*-alkanes can still remain. The identification of incipient biodegradation will depend on the ability of the geochemist to find suitable diagnostic information for appraisal. This significant information, which is hidden in the gas chromatograms of the saturated and aromatic hydrocarbon fractions, may be obvious in the isolated monoaromatic fraction.

Such an approach has been adopted to identify incipient biodegradation in the Pécorade oil field from the Aquitaine basin (southwestern France). The heavy (low API gravity) oil recovered from the Albian reservoir rock in the Pécorade field is a normal oil with respect to alkanes and aromatics, as the *n*-alkanes are still present and the aromatics still contain naphthalenes and benzo- and dibenzothiophenes (Figure 14.4A). Comparison of the monoaromatic fraction from the normal (medium API gravity) oil and the heavy oil recovered from the Pécorade well enables us to reach a definitive conclusion about the extent of the degradation (Figure 14.4B). Alkylbenzenes, well represented in the normal oils from the Pécorade field, have been completely removed from the heavy oil. The lack of alkylbenzenes that are readily degradable structures in this oil provides proof that this heavy oil is a residual fluid that resulted from attack by bacteria (Blanc and Connan, 1993).

Specific biological markers are also resistant to bacterial activity and are therefore of great help in assessing the level of biodegradation. Examples are gammacerane, 18α(H),21β(H)-30-norneohopane or 17α(H),21β(H)-25-norhopane (Blanc and Connan, 1992b). The use of gammacerane in this manner has been docu-

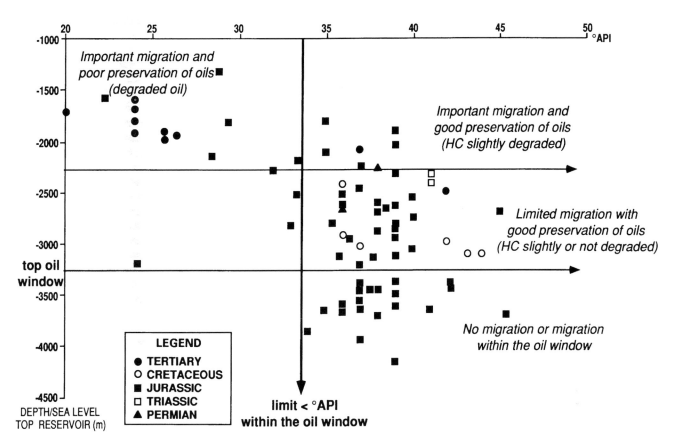

Figure 14.3. The change in API gravity of oils with reservoir depth for samples from the North Sea. (After F. Issard, personal communication, 1991.)

mented in the case of Syrian oil seepages. In this series of surface samples, different levels of biodegradation can be assessed using the gammacerane–hopane ratio because gammacerane is more resistant than hopane to biodegradation (Blanc and Connan, 1992b). This ratio is calculated easily on the *m/z* 191 mass fragmentogram. This example is illustrated in Figure 14.5, which shows the following sequence of biodegradation: sample 170 > sample 169 > sample 168. This result is confirmed by the prominence of diasteranes (rearranged steranes) among the steranes in sample 170 (*m/z* 217 mass fragmentogram on Figure 14.5). Diasteranes are in fact believed to be more bacterially resistant than the regular steranes (e.g., Seifert et al., 1984).

Particular attention should be paid to 25-norhopanes (usually called demethylated hopanes and easily observed on the *m/z* 177 mass fragmentogram) because they are particularly useful in biodegradation studies. First detected by Reed (1977) in a weathered, oil-impregnated sandstone from Utah, their presence in an oil has been subsequently regarded as indicative of extensive biodegradation (e.g., Seifert and Moldowan, 1979). Although some controversy still exists concerning their origin, geochemists now consider them as key indicators of paleobiodegradation in instances where the oil does not otherwise appear biodegraded (Philp, 1983; Volkman et al., 1983; Blanc and Connan, 1991, 1992b). Therefore, 25-norhopanes provide the geochemist with a possible tool for an oil–source rock correlation even in the case of

(paleo)biodegraded oils. Paleobiodegradation indicators are not restricted to 25-norhopanes, and other biological marker compounds should be considered. For instance, secohopanes and hexahydrobenzohopanes can be used as paleobiodegradation indicators in evaporitic carbonates (Chosson et al., 1992).

Oil–oil correlations among oils that show levels of biodegradation from incipient to severe can also be evaluated by probing the macromolecular entities (geopolymers) such as the asphaltenes and resins to find the unaltered biological markers. Indeed, these geopolymers can offer an efficient protection for covalently bound molecular structures from secondary alterations such as biodegradation. These unaltered biological markers are most likely released by pyrolytic degradation (Cassani and Eglinton, 1986; Jones et al., 1987; Connan, 1993) or chemical degradation (Chappe et al., 1980; Blanc and Albrecht, 1990; Trifilieff et al., 1992).

A more systematic investigation of the molecular content of geopolymers and solid bitumens (Curiale, 1986) seems to possess considerable geochemical potential for the future. These types of analyses will provide information making it possible to differentiate, for example, pyrobitumen resulting from intense thermal cracking of oil and precipitated asphaltene formed through natural deasphalting by gas migration. Selective chemical degradations appear to be the key techniques to document this problem (see Rullkötter and Michaelis, 1990, for a review).

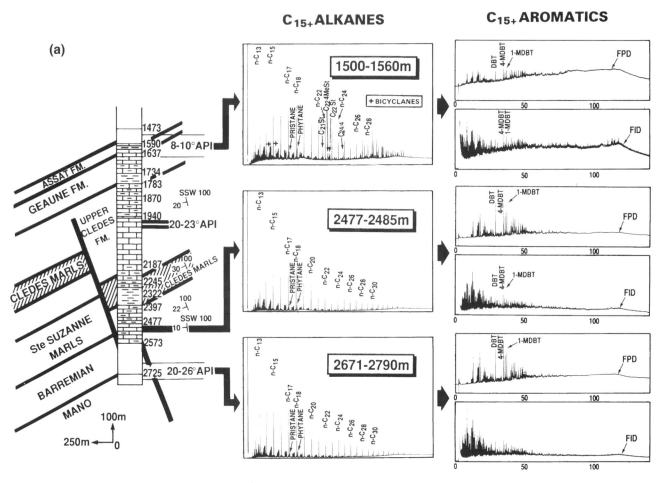

Figure 14.4. Gas chromatograms of (a) C_{15+} alkanes and C_{15+} aromatics and (b) C_{15+} mono-, di-, and polyaromatics of heavy and conventional oils from the Pécorade 26 well (Aquitaine basin, southwestern France). C_{15+} aromatics have been analyzed using a dual detector (FID for carbon, FPD for sulfur). In part (b), incipient biodegradation has been diagnosed from the lack of alkylbenzenes in monoaromatics of the heavy oil.

As already mentioned, such techniques have been successfully applied to identify coal, kerogen, or asphaltene moieties. The released molecular entities could provide information complementary to that provided by the "free" molecular components. Unlike the free components, the "bound" components are likely to avoid (or undergo to a less extent) secondary alteration, migration, and thermal maturation processes. These bound biological markers or structural subunits of the macromolecular entities (Blanc and Albrecht, 1991) could therefore be used for oil correlation or thermal maturation studies. They may also be more discriminant than "mobile" compounds in characterizing and differentiating particular geopolymers at a molecular level (Blanc et al., 1991).

Finally, this type of analysis could prove useful in understanding how oxygen is incorporated into degraded oil samples on the surface. The preferential quenching of particular classes of molecules could even be highlighted, as has been observed recently for higher plant triterpenes in high-sulfur crudes (Adam et al., 1991). It is therefore likely that geochemical interpretations based only on the free and apolar biological markers are incomplete or erroneous (Kohnen et al., 1991).

CONCLUSIONS

Among the factors influencing petroleum composition, secondary alteration processes that occur after oil entrapment are most important, as they can lead to considerable changes in both the composition and quality of the oil. Knowledge of conditions and mechanisms of degradation processes are needed for petroleum exploration, not only for economic reasons but also because multidisciplinary approaches must be developed to improve already established techniques and to create new techniques. The investigation of the detailed molecular pattern of organic natural substances (gaseous, liquid, and solid) has great potential. Research to date indicates that information relevant to oil exploration and exploitation is hidden in oil fractions presently not routinely studied. These fractions generally consist of polar compounds and macromolecular entities. Presently, molecular chemistry is a useful tool that is able to recognize incipient biodegradation, to detect oil gravity segregation, and likely to discriminate a pyrobitumen from a precipitated asphaltene, whereas bulk analyses are currently inaccurate.

(b)

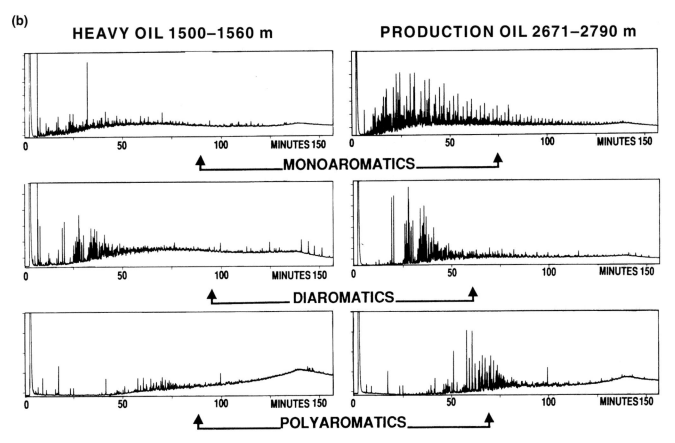

Figure 14.4 *(continued)*

Acknowledgments *We are indebted to L. B. Magoon, J. A. Curiale, J. T. Smith, and P. van de Kamp, who greatly improved our manuscript.*

References Cited

Adam, P., J. M. Trendel, P. Albrecht, and J. Connan, 1991, Novel thiophene derived from higher plant triterpenes in sediments: Tetrahedron Letters, v. 32, p. 4179–4182.

Aeckersberg, F., F. Bak, and F. Widdel, 1991, Anaerobic oxidation of saturated hydrocarbons to CO_2 by a new type of sulfate-reducing bacterium: Archives of Microbiology, v. 156, p. 5–14.

Bailey, N. J. L., A. M. Jobson, and M. A. Rogers, 1973, Bacterial degradation of crude oil: comparison of field and experimental data: Chemical Geology, v. 11, p. 203–221

Bailey, N. J. L., C. R. Evans, and C. W. D. Milner, 1974, Applying petroleum geochemistry to search for oil: examples from Western Canada basin: AAPG Bulletin, v. 58, p. 2284–2294.

Blanc, Ph., and P. Albrecht, 1990, Molecular parameters in bitumen and macromolecular matrix of coals: their evaluation as rank parameters, *in* H. Charcosset, ed., Advanced methodologies in coal characterization, Coal Science & Technology, v. 15: Amsterdam, Elsevier, p. 53–82.

Blanc, Ph., and P. Albrecht, 1991, Parameters of "macromaturity" (PMM): novel rank and type related indices from chemical degradation of macromolecular network of coals: Organic Geochemistry, v. 17, p. 913–918.

Blanc, Ph., and J. Connan, 1991, Paleobiodegradation and paleoenvironmental assessments using demethylated hopanes, *in* D. A. C. Manning, ed., Organic geochemistry, Advances and applications in energy and the natural environment: Manchester and New York, Manchester University Press, p. 346–348.

Blanc, Ph., and J. Connan, 1992a, Generation and expulsion of hydrocarbons from a Paris basin Toarcian source rock: an experimental study by confined-system pyrolysis: Energy and Fuels, v. 6, p. 666–677.

Blanc, Ph., and J. Connan, 1992b, Origin and occurrence of 25-norhopanes: a statistical study: Organic Geochemistry, v. 18, p. 813–828.

Blanc, Ph., and J. Connan, 1993, Crude oils in reservoirs: the factors influencing their composition, *in* M. L. Bordenave, ed., Applied petroleum geochemistry: Paris, Technip, p. 151–174.

Blanc, R., H. Coustau, J. Connan, W. J. Ebanks, and C. Roux, 1982, A multidisciplinary approach to the characterization of heavy oil deposits from the tri-state area (U.S.A.): Proceedings of the Second International Conference on Heavy Crudes and Tar Sands, Caracas, Venezuela, February 7–17, p. 633–657.

Blanc, Ph., J. Valisolalao, P. Albrecht, J. P. Kohut, J. F. Muller, and J. M. Duchene, 1991, Comparative geochemical study of the three maceral groups from a high volatile bituminous coal: Energy and Fuels, v. 5, p. 875–884.

Cassani, F., and G. Eglinton, 1986, Organic geochemistry of Venezuelan extra-heavy crude oils, 1. Pyrolysis of asphaltenes: a technique for the correlation and maturity evaluation of crude oils: Chemical Geology, v. 55, p. 157–183.

Terpanes

168 HAWIYYET ABOU JIR

169 HAWIYYET ABOU JIR

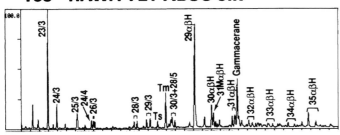

170 EL BICHRI

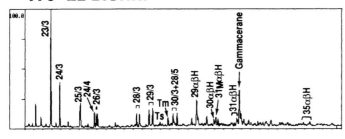

Steranes

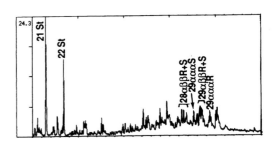

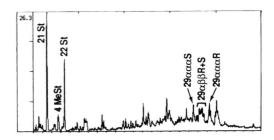

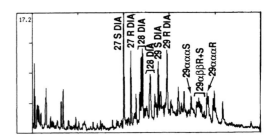

Figure 14.5. Mass fragmentograms showing the terpane (*m/z* 191) and sterane (*m/z* 217) distributions for oil from three Syrian seeps. A molecular ratio using gammacerane shows the level of biodegradation.

Cassani, F., and G. Eglinton, 1991, Organic geochemistry of Venezuelan extra-heavy crude oils, 2. Molecular assesment of biodegradation: Chemical Geology, v. 91, p. 315–333.

Chappe, B., W. Michaelis, and P. Albrecht, 1980, Molecular fossils of Archaebacteria as selective degradation products of kerogen, *in* A. G. Douglas and J. R. Maxwell, eds., Advances in Organic Geochemistry 1979: Oxford, Pergamon Press, p. 265–273.

Chosson, P., J. Connan, D. Dessort, and C. Lanau, 1992, *In vitro* degradation of steranes and terpanes: a clue to understanding geological situations, *in* J. M. Moldowan, P. Albrecht, and R. P. Philp, eds., Biological Markers in Sediments and Petroleum : Englewood Cliffs, NJ, Prentice-Hall, p. 320–349.

Connan, J., 1984, Biodegradation of crude oils in reservoirs, *in* J. Brooks and D. H. Welte, eds., Advances in Petroleum Geochemistry: London, Academic Press, v. 1, p. 299–335.

Connan, J., 1988, Quelques secrets des bitumes archéologiques de Mésopotamie révélés par les analyses de géochimie organique pétrolière: Bulletin des Centres de Recherches Exploration-Production Elf-Aquitaine, v. 12, p. 759–787.

Connan, J., 1993, Origin of severely biodegraded oils: a new approach using biomarker pattern of asphaltene pyrolysates, *in* M. L. Bordenave, ed., Applied Petroleum Geochemistry: Paris, Technip, p. 457–463.

Connan, J., and H. Coustau, 1987, Influence of the geological and geochemical characteristics of heavy oils on their recovery, *in* R. F. Meyer, ed., Exploration for heavy crude oil and natural bitumen: AAPG Studies in Geology, v. 25, p. 261–279.

Connan J., and J. J. Orgeval, 1976, Relationship between hydrocarbons and mineralizations: the Saint-Privat barite deposit (Lodéve basin, France): Bulletin du Centre de Rechercres de Pau-SNPA, v. 10, p. 359–374.

Connan, J., F. Montel, Ph. Blanc, B. Sahuquet, and R. Jouhannel, 1991, Experimental study of expulsion of hydrocarbons from shaly source rocks: importance of pressure on expulsion efficiencies, (abs.): European Association of Organic Geochemists, 15th International Meeting on Organic Geochemistry, Manchester, England, September 16–20, p. 14–15.

Curiale, J. A., 1986, Origin of solid bitumens, with emphasis on biological marker results, *in* D. Leythaeuser and J.

Rullkötter, eds., Advances in Organic Geochemistry 1985: Oxford, Pergamon, p. 559–580.

Dahl, B., and G. C. Speers, 1986, Geochemical characterization of a tar mat in the Oseberg field, Norwegian sector, North Sea, *in* D. Leythaeuser and J. Rullkötter, eds., Advances in Organic Geochemistry 1985: Oxford, Pergamon, p. 547–558.

Dominé, F., 1991, High pressure pyrolysis of *n*-hexane, 2,4-dimethylpentane, and 1-phenylbutane: is pressure an important geochemical parameter?: Organic Geochemistry, v. 17, p. 619–634.

Evans, C. R., M. A. Rogers, and N. J. L. Bailey, 1971, Evolution and alteration of petroleum in Western Canada: Chemical Geology, v. 8, p. 147–170.

Fedorak, P. M., J. M. Foght, and D. W. S. Westlake, 1983, Comparative studies on microbial degradation of aromatics and saturates in crude oil, *in* J. E. Zajic, D. G., Cooper, T. R. Jack, and N. Kosaric, eds., Microbial enhanced oil recovery: Tulsa, PennWell Books, p. 162–172.

Goffé, B., and M. Villey, 1984, Texture d'un matériel carboné impliqué dans un métamorphisme haute pression-basse température (Alpes françaises): les hautes pressions influencent-elles la carbonification?: Bulletin de Minéralogie, v. 107, p. 81–91.

Goodwin, N. S., P. J. D. Park, and A. P. Rawlinson, 1983, Crude oil biodegradation under simulated and natural conditions, *in* M. Bjorøy, ed., Advances in Organic Geochemistry 1981: Chichester, John Wiley, p. 650–658.

Helgeson, H. C., A. M. Knox, and E. L. Shock, 1991, Petroleum, oil field brines, and authigenic mineral assemblages: are they in metastable equilibrium in hydrocarbon reservoirs? (abs.): European Association of Organic Geochemists, 15th International Meeting on Organic Geochemistry, Manchester, England, September 16-20, p. 39–40.

Horsfield, B., H. J. Schenk, N. Mills, and D. H. Welte, 1991, Closed-system programmed-temperature pyrolysis for simulating the conversion of oil to gas in a deep petroleum reservoir: compositional and kinetic findings (abs.): European Association of Organic Geochemists, 15th International Meeting on Organic Geochemistry, Manchester, England, September 16–20, p. 56.

Ioppolo, M., R. Alexander, and R. I. Kagi, 1991, Phenols in crude oils (abs.): European Association of Organic Geochemists, 15th International Meeting on Organic Geochemistry, Manchester, England, September, 16–20, p. 56.

Jones, D. M., A. G. Douglas, and J. Connan, 1987, Hydrocarbon distribution in crude oil asphaltene pyrolysates, 1. Aliphatic compounds: Energy and Fuels, v. 1, p. 468–476.

Kohnen, M. E. L., J. S. Sinninghe Damsté, and J. W. de Leeuw, 1991, Biases from natural sulphurization in paleoenvironmental reconstruction based on hydrocarbon biomarker distributions : Nature, v. 349, p. 775–778.

Lafargue, E., and C. Barker, 1988, Effect of water washing on crude oil compositions: AAPG Bulletin, v. 72, p. 263–276.

Mango, F. D., 1991, The stability of hydrocarbons under the time-temperature conditions of petroleum genesis: Nature, v. 352, p. 146–148.

Palmer, S. E., 1984, Effect of water washing on C_{15+} hydrocarbon fraction of crude oils from northwest Palawan, Philippines: AAPG Bulletin, v. 68, p. 137–149.

Peters, K. E., and J. M. Moldowan, 1991, Effects of source, thermal maturity, and biodegradation on the distribution and isomerization of homohopanes in petroleum: Organic Geochemistry, v. 17, p. 57–61.

Philp, R. P., 1983, Correlation of crude oils from the San Jorge basin, Argentina: Geochimica et Cosmoschimica Acta, v. 47, p. 267–275.

Price, L. C., 1980, Crude oil degradation as an explanation of the depth rule: Chemical Geology, v. 28, p. 1–30.

Price, L. C., 1982, Organic geochemistry of core samples from an ultra-deep hot well (300 °C, 7 km): Chemical Geology, v. 37, p. 215–228.

Reed, W. E., 1977, Molecular compositions of weathered petroleum and comparison with its possible source: Geochimica et Cosmochimica Acta, v. 41, p. 237–247.

Rogers, M. A., J. D. McAlary, and N. J. L. Bailey, 1974, Significance of reservoir bitumens to thermal-maturation studies, Western Canada basin: AAPG Bulletin, v. 58, p. 1806–1824.

Rullkötter, J., and W. Michaelis, 1990, The structure of kerogen and related materials: a review of recent progress and future trends, *in* B. Durand and F. Behar, eds., Advances in Organic Geochemistry 1987: Oxford, Pergamon Press, p. 829–852.

Seifert, W. K., and J. M. Moldowan, 1979, The effect of biodegradation on steranes and terpanes in crude oils: Geochimica et Cosmochimica Acta, v. 43, p. 111–126.

Seifert, W. K., and J. M. Moldowan, 1981, Paleoreconstruction by biological markers: Geochimica et Cosmochimica Acta, v. 45, p. 783–794.

Seifert, W. K., J. M. Moldowan, and G. J. Demaison, 1984, Source correlation of biodegraded oils: Organic Geochemistry, v. 6, p. 633–643.

Silverman, S. R., 1965, Migration and segregation of oil and gas, *in* A. Young and J. E. Galley, eds., Fluids in subsurface environments: AAPG Memoir #4, p. 53–65.

Speight, J. G., 1984, The chemical nature of petroleum asphaltenes, *in* B. Tissot, ed., Characterization of heavy crude oils and petroleum residues: Paris, Technip, p. 32–61.

Speight, J. G., D. L. Wernick, K. A. Gould, R. E. Overfield, B. M. L. Rao, and D. W. Savage, 1985, Molecular weight and association of asphaltenes: a critical review: Revue de l'Institut Français du Pétrole, v. 40, p. 51–61.

Tissot, B. P., 1988, La migration des hydrocarbures dans les bassins sédimentaires: aspects géologiques et géochimiques: Revue de l'Institut Français du Pétrole, v. 43, p. 143–153.

Trifilieff, S., O. Sieskind, and P. Albrecht, 1992, Biological markers in petroleum asphaltenes: possible mode of incorporation, *in* J. M. Moldowan, P. Albrecht, and R. P. Philp, eds., Biological Markers in Sediments and Petroleum: Englewood Cliffs, Prentice-Hall, p. 350–369.

Ungerer, P., F. Bessis, P. Y. Chenet, B. Durand, E. Nogaret, A. Chiarelli, J. L. Oudin, and J. F. Perrin, 1984, Geological and geochemical models in oil exploration: principles and practical examples, *in* G. Demaison and R. J. Murris, eds., Petroleum geochemistry and basin evaluation: AAPG Memoir 35, p. 53–77.

Volkman, J. K., R. Alexander, R. I. Kagi, and G. W. Woodhouse, 1983, Demethylated hopanes in crude oils and their applications in petroleum geochemistry: Geochimica et Cosmochimica Acta, v. 47, p. 785–794.

Zhao-An, F., and R. P. Philp, 1987, Laboratory biomarker fractionations and implications for migration studies: Organic Geochemistry, v. 11, p. 169–175.

ZoBell, C. E., 1973, Microbial degradation of oil: present status, problems and perspectives, *in* D. G. Ahearn and S. P. Meyers, eds., The microbial degradation of oil pollutants: Baton Rouge, LA, Center for Wetland Resources, p. 3–16.

"In the degree to which we understand the habitat of oil, and thus make short cuts to its discovery and reductions in its cost, we add to the resources or reserves that can be produced economically for the benefit of mankind."

—Lewis G. Weeks

Passage from Weeks, L. G., 1958, Habitat of oil and some factors that control it: Habitat of Oil, AAPG, p. 60.

Part IV

Identification and Characterization

Magoon, L. B, and W. G. Dow, eds., 1994, The petroleum
system—from source to trap: AAPG Memoir 60.

Chapter 15

Correlation of Oils and Source Rocks—
A Conceptual and Historical Perspective

Joseph A. Curiale

Unocal Inc.
Brea, California, U.S.A.

Abstract

Techniques and concepts of oil–source rock correlations have developed considerably over the past four decades, with work by Hunt in the Uinta basin (1950s) and Williams and Dow in the Williston basin (1970s) shaping our present-day approach. An *oil–source rock correlation* is a causal relationship between an oil and its mature source rock(s) that is required by the constraints of the petroleum system, which are both chemical (distinctive organic facies) and geologic (lithology, subsidence rate, time of generation, structure). Correlation techniques include bulk methods (compositional fractionation, elemental composition, and isotope ratios) and molecular analyses (biomarkers and their thermal fragments). A successful oil–source rock correlation requires a distinction between genetic and nongenetic oil composition properties. Carbon isotope ratios and specific molecular characteristics are the best correlation parameters available.

Three published oil–source rock correlations are presented as case studies. The Black Creek basin in Alberta contains oil in Middle Devonian reservoir rock that originated from underlying and overlying carbonate–evaporite sequences. Although this correlation is chemically defensible, serious migration obstacles exist. The second case addresses the origin of the Beatrice oil from Inner Moray Firth field, offshore Scotland. While analytical results partially overlap, it is apparent that philosophical differences have led to different conclusions by two research groups. The oils of the Cook Inlet basin in Alaska comprise the third case, in which it is shown that rudimentary isotope and biomarker data can help resolve a dispute about the source rock's age (Cenozoic versus Mesozoic).

Future correlation success depends on continuing developments in analytical technology. Whole-oil and whole-rock analysis, using medium- to high-resolution mass spectrometry coupled with pyrolysis, will provide rapid and detailed hydrocarbon compositional data. Available technology will be applied to the development of nonhydrocarbon correlation methods. Further development of gas chromatography–carbon isotope mass spectrometry promises to revolutionize our understanding of petroleum geochemistry and correlation science.

INTRODUCTION

A petroleum system commences when a source rock generates hydrocarbons. Frequently, these hydrocarbons migrate through a conduit to a trap or escape to the surface. In actual exploration practice, the relationship between a mature source rock and an oil accumulation is initially inferred from geologic considerations, after a trap or surface seep of petroleum is identified. However, inferences of this type should also be supported by rigorous geochemical correlation data, obtained through modern methods of oil–source rock correlation. When a chemically defensible correlation has been established, and subsequently supported by existing geologic

knowledge, a particular petroleum system can be accepted with a high degree of confidence. This chapter discusses the concept of oil–source rock correlations from the standpoint of chemical methods and geologic examples.

An *oil–source rock correlation* is defined as a causal relationship, based on integrated geologic and geochemical reasoning, between an oil and its original source facies (Jones, 1987). This causal relationship must be established on the basis of what the circumstances were at the time the original source rock expelled a particular oil, rather than on the basis of subsequent changes to the composition of the source rock and oil. These changes, due to thermal maturation, migration, and alteration, can significantly alter the chemical composition of both oil and source rock and must be accounted for in any oil–source rock correlation. Thus, the goal of the geochemist in an oil–source rock correlation is to isolate and identify the compositional changes that have occurred in both the source rock and oil after the oil has left the source rock and to compensate for these changes (Curiale, 1993).

A defensible oil–source rock correlation provides a basis on which to estimate the volume of oil generated and to define migration pathways. When maps that show the location and geochemistry of oils collected from surface indications (seep or stain), wells (shows or drill-stem tests), and commercial accumulations are compared and found to be similar, we conclude that the oils all emanated from the same source rock. When the same map shows a pod of mature source rock with the appropriate organic matter richness, type, and thermal maturity in the correct stratigraphic relationship, then the oil probably originated from that mature source rock. This situation represents a hypothetical petroleum system (Magoon and Dow, Chapter 1, this volume). If geochemical results indicate a genetic relationship between the oil and the source rock, or if the oil–source rock correlation is positive, then the system is known. The mapped distribution of this oil and this pod of mature source rock establishes the geographic and stratigraphic extent of this petroleum system. The migration pathways must be between this mature source rock and the geographic extent of the system, and the volume of oil generated can be estimated (Schmoker, Chapter 19, this volume).

The oil–source rock correlation has at least three limitations. First, only mature source rocks can provide reliable oil–source correlations. This limitation is overcome, at least in part, through the use of artificial maturation techniques that are designed to generate and expel oil during laboratory pyrolysis of an erstwhile immature rock (e.g., see Lewan, 1983, and Chapter 11, this volume). Second, the oil-like substance or bitumen from the source rock that is used to compare with the oil is usually acquired by solvent extraction of the organic matter. The similarity of this oil-like substance to the oil is equivocal, but in the future this problem may also be solved through hydrous pyrolysis (Lewan, Chapter 11, this volume). Third, the likelihood that a particular drop of oil can be correlated to the exact source rock sample that it came from is remote. Therefore, a positive or negative oil–source rock correlation must be interpreted in the context of the regional geology.

The oil–source rock correlations discussed here result from chemical comparisons, supported by geologic reasoning and tempered by an understanding of those geochemical parameters that are reliable as petroleum source rock indicators. This caveat excludes from consideration most of the "correlation" attempts in the literature (particularly those published prior to 1980). This is because many of these efforts relied entirely on geologic relationships, without supporting geochemical data. A different approach is taken here. The discussion begins with the historical development of geochemical

oil–source rock correlations, then continues with the techniques of geochemical analysis pertinent to the genetic component of source rock and oil chemistry. Examples of successful integrated correlation efforts are then described. Finally, comments are made on new methods of oil–source rock correlation now in development. Concepts of correlation as well as historical developments and perspectives are emphasized.

HISTORY OF GEOCHEMICAL CORRELATION

The development of geochemical correlation as a tool in petroleum exploration was controlled initially by our conceptual understanding of the origin of oil (Welte, 1965). As drilling activity increased early in this century, it became evident that oil originates from rocks that are geographically and geologically distinct from those in which it accumulates. This distinction indicated the existence of a migration pathway, and eventually suggested that oil could become modified chemically after it left the mature source rock. The present-day paradigm of oil generation, migration, and accumulation further indicates that these chemical modifications can drastically alter the chemical composition of (1) organic matter in the source rock after the oil has been expelled, and (2) oil after it leaves the mature source rock. Finally, concepts of thermal and basin modeling have led to a consideration of the timing of generation, fluid migration, and postexpulsion burial of the source rock (England et al., 1987; Welte and Yalcin, 1988). These concepts further emphasize the chemical changes that source rock organic matter undergoes after oil is expelled.

As the understanding of petroleum's origin crystallized over the past three decades, concepts of oil–source rock correlation were revolutionized by the introduction of sophisticated molecular identification technology. In particular, the use of computer-processed data collected from on-line gas chromatograph–mass spectrometers (GC-MS) is now commonplace in the petroleum industry. GC-MS data that contain the distribution of biomarkers have become the dominant oil–source rock correlation tool. These data, along with carbon isotope data, provide diagnostic characteristics of each fraction or compound class (e.g., aromatic hydrocarbons) and are now recommended pieces of information for every reliable oil–source rock correlation. The marriage of these two technologies, in the form of on-line gas chromatography–isotope ratio mass spectrometry, promises to be the next evolutionary stage in chemical correlation.

Access to biomarker and isotopic methods in oil–source rock correlation is a relatively recent development; the first significant published correlation used more rudimentary methods. John Hunt and co-workers (Hunt et al., 1954), using compound class distributions, elemental analyses, and infrared spectroscopy, successfully correlated several oils and solid bitumens to their lacustrine source rocks collected from the Uinta basin, Utah. Furthermore, these workers incorporated then-current geologic understanding of the sedimentary basin dynamics into their conclusions, providing a conceptual framework for future oil–source rock correlations.

Twenty years passed before isotopic and molecular methods became dominant in correlation efforts (Welte et al., 1975; Leythaeuser et al., 1977; Seifert, 1977). The archetypal studies in this time period, and indeed the first to incorporate molecular–isotopic understanding into a complete geologic framework, were those by Williams (1974) and Dow (1974) in the Williston basin, North Dakota. Their approach of combining geologic requirements with modern molecular and isotopic geochemical technology has withstood the test of time and remains in use today. Indeed, later studies of the oil sources in the Williston basin (e.g., Leenheer and Zumberge, 1987) fully support the early work of Williams and Dow. By the mid- to late 1970s, biomarkers had been introduced as a correlation tool, and biological marker geochemistry continues to be the most dynamic aspect of oil–source rock correlation technology today. However, despite the introduction of new isotopic correlation methods (Burwood et al., 1988, 1990) and the identification of many new molecular suites as correlation tools (Sinninghe Damste and de Leeuw, 1990), the basic conceptual approach of Hunt et al. (1954), Williams (1974), and Dow (1974) remains intact—successful oil–source rock correlations arise by identifying those aspects of an oil that are source defined and by understanding how those source-defined aspects can change with subsequent maturation, migration, and alteration.

GEOCHEMICAL CORRELATION TECHNIQUES

Although molecular and isotopic methods provide us with the most consistent correlation results, other correlation techniques are also available. Geochemical methods of relating an oil to its source rock can be classified as either *bulk* or *molecular*. The most common methods currently available are presented in Table 15.1. This section briefly reviews the bulk and molecular techniques.

Bulk Correlation Methods

Bulk correlation methods include (1) physical characteristics, (2) compositional fractionation, (3) elemental concentrations and ratios, and (4) isotopic ratios. Bulk correlations are useful because they characterize the entire sample and are relatively insensitive to contamination. These methods all provide composites, or weighted averages, of the molecular characteristics (including molecular isotope ratios) of an oil or the organic matter in a source rock. Their use is currently required because, despite recent advances in molecular analysis, we are unable to isotopically define and identify completely the 10^4–10^6 different compounds in a typical crude oil or rock extract.

Physical characteristics such as color, API gravity, pour point, and viscosity are still used as rudimentary

Table 15.1. Common Oil-Source Rock Correlation Methods

Parameter[a]	Utility[b]	Significant Nongenetic Effects[c]
Bulk Methods		
Physical		
Color	*	BIO, MAT, WW, MIG
API	*	BIO, MAT, WW, MIG
Viscosity	*	BIO, MAT, WW, MIG
Compositional		
SANA	**	BIO, MAT, WW, MIG
SBC	**	BIO, MAT, MIG
Elemental (oil/EOM)		
Sulfur	**	BIO, MAT, WW, MIG
Nitrogen	**	BIO
Vanadium	**	BIO
Nickel	**	BIO
V/(V + Ni)	***	MAT
Isotopic ($\delta^{13}C$)		
Whole oil	***	BIO, MAT
Aliphatic HC	**	BIO
Aromatic HC	****	WW
SANA	***	BIO, MAT
Molecular Methods		
n-Alkanes	**	BIO, MAT
Isoprenoids	***	MIG
Steranes (C_{26}–C_{30})	****	MAT?
Tricyclic terpanes	***	—
Pentacyclic triterpanes	***	BIO
Metalloporphyrins	****	MAT
Aromatic HCs, ring no.	***	WW, MIG
NSOs, Z no.	***	MIG

[a]SANA, saturate, aromatic, NSO, asphaltene, includes aliphatic/aromatic ratio; SBC, straight–branched chain and cyclic aliphatic hydrocarbons; Oil/EOM, elemental concentrations and ratios in whole oils and EOMs; NSO, organic compounds containing nitrogen, sulfur, or oxygen.

[b]Increasing number of asterisks implies increasing utility.

[c]BIO, biodegradation; MAT, thermal maturation; MIG, migration; WW, water washing.

correlation parameters for oils, although they are unreliable for such purposes. Their use in oil–source rock correlation is minimal and should remain so.

Compositional fractionation is the initial separation of oils and rock extracts into compositionally related fractions and the comparison of the distribution of these fractions in oils and their suspected source rocks. These fractions provided the geochemist with the first chemically defined correlation parameter. Although later investigations have shown clearly that such distributions are affected dramatically by nongenetic processes (Table 15.1), values such as aliphatic–aromatic hydrocarbon ratios are still in common, albeit cautious, use as variables of correlation.

Elemental concentrations and ratios are applied much more commonly as correlation parameters. These methods are typified by measurements of sulfur concentration and transition elements, such as vanadium and nickel concentrations (Barwise, 1990). Although they are used widely, the susceptibility of elemental concentrations to alteration processes (such as biodegradation and in-reservoir thermal alteration; Table 15.1) makes the use of elemental data for correlation a risky proposition. The interpreter must be aware of the nongenetic processes that can affect such data (Curiale, 1987; Barwise, 1990).

Of the bulk correlation parameters, isotope ratios are the most reliable. In particular, the stable carbon isotope ratios of oils, rock extracts, kerogens, and gas chromatographic fractions are excellent correlation tools. Such ratios are often used to match crude oils chemically to source rock kerogens. The carbon isotope ratio represents one of the few oil–kerogen correlation parameters in common use. It is often inferred (see the classic work of Seifert et al., 1979, on northern Alaska oils and rocks) that an oil should be lighter isotopically than its source kerogen by about 0.5–1.5‰ (Peters et al., 1989).

Carbon isotope ratios of soluble compound class fractions are also used widely as correlation parameters. It has been demonstrated, for example, that the carbon isotope ratio of the aromatic hydrocarbon fraction is relatively invariant during simulated increases in thermal maturation (Lewan, 1983). Because this particular fraction is relatively unaffected by migration and by light to moderate biodegradation, it can be considered an excellent genetic oil–source rock correlation parameter. In contrast, the carbon isotope ratios of certain other compound class fractions can vary significantly due to nongenetic processes (Table 15.1) and should therefore be used with caution as oil–source rock correlation parameters. An example of such variability is evident in the ratio of the aliphatic hydrocarbon fraction, which can change by 1–2‰ during biodegradation and thermal maturation (Sofer, 1984; Stahl, 1980).

Molecular Correlation Methods

As molecular analysis techniques become more rapid and precise, they may eventually replace the bulk methods just discussed. As recently as the early 1980s, oil–oil and oil–source rock correlations were considered incomplete without molecular support (Mackenzie, 1984). Such support is provided currently by GC and GC-MS data on biomarkers present in oils and rock extracts. Early investigations of biomarkers as correlation tools established that, like bulk parameters, molecular parameters can also change in nongenetic ways (Seifert and Moldowan, 1978). Several present-day efforts in biomarker geochemistry are directed toward identifying those molecular components of oils and rock extracts whose distributions reflect only the influences of original source input and early diagenesis.

Over the past decade, many molecular parameters have been proposed as oil–source rock correlation tools, all under the initial assumption that the parameter in question was insignificantly influenced by nongenetic factors (Wehner et al., 1986). Subsequent efforts have shown that this assumption is sometimes unwarranted. The best example is the use of steroid carbon number distributions as both depositional environment indica-

tors and correlation parameters. Originally introduced using sterols as a depositional setting indicator (Huang and Meinschein, 1979), these distributions were (and still are) used widely as a genetic parameter, despite evidence of failure in some instances (Volkman, 1986; Grantham and Wakefield, 1988). Repeated examination of this particular parameter has led to a series of important caveats (Volkman, 1988; Peters and Moldowan, 1993).

Many recent studies have indicated that the ideal oil–source rock correlation parameter is nonexistent. No single parameter, either bulk or molecular, can uniquely characterize freshly deposited organic matter prior to catagenesis. Rather, all such parameters vary as a function of (1) the original organic matter and (2) the three nongenetic processes: maturation, migration, and alteration (Curiale, 1993). The task of the interpreter is to unravel the present-day chemical composition of the oil (or source rock organic matter) into its antecedent at the time of migration.

SUCCESSFUL CORRELATIONS

Many examples of oil–source rock correlations are available in the geochemical literature. Three recently published correlation case studies involving large petroliferous regions are reviewed critically in this section. In each of the three cases involving oils recovered from Paleozoic, Mesozoic, and Cenozoic reservoir rocks, a reasonable geologic argument could be made for a source rock of approximately the same age as the reservoir rock. The case of a "local source" (minimal migration distance) is represented by the carbonate–evaporite derived oil in Devonian reservoir rocks of northwestern Alberta, Canada. The other two cases involve oils from the Jurassic reservoir rocks of the Beatrice field in offshore Scotland, and the Tertiary reservoir rocks of the upper Cook Inlet in southern Alaska, each of which originated from much older rocks. These examples are chosen because they typify the dual technological and conceptual approaches to the problem emphasized earlier. The reader is directed to the primary literature for further details.

Northwestern Alberta, Canada

The first case study involves oils and carbonates–evaporites acting as possible source rocks in the Black Creek basin, northwestern Alberta, Canada. Clark and Philp (1989) used bulk and molecular parameters to correlate oils from the Upper Keg River Member of the Keg River Formation to source rocks of the Upper Keg River Member and the overlying carbonate–anhydrite Muskeg Formation. The reservoir rock and source rocks are Middle Devonian in age, and the overburden rock that defines the geometry of the Black Creek sedimentary basin is younger. Four core samples and seven oils were examined.

Clark and Philp (1989) applied a comprehensive suite of analytical techniques to this problem (Figure 15.1). The

	OIL/EOM	ALIPHATIC HC				AROMATIC HC				NSO		KEROGEN	
	$\delta^{13}C$	GC-FID	GC-MS	$\delta^{13}C$	GC-MRM-MS	GC-FID	GC-FPD	$\delta^{13}C$	GC-MRM-MS	$\delta^{13}C$	METALLOPORPHYRINS-HPLC	$\delta^{13}C$	PYROLYZATE
BLACK CREEK BASIN CLARK & PHILP (1989)	●	●	●	●		●	●	●		●			
BEATRICE FIELD PETERS ET AL. (1989)	●	●	●		●				●		●	●	●
BAILEY ET AL. (1990)	●		●	●	●			●	●	●		●	●
COOK INLET, ALASKA MAGOON AND ANDERS (1991)	●	●	●	●				●					

Figure 15.1. Chart showing the major oil–source rock correlation techniques applied in the three case studies discussed in the text. Only analyses referenced in the text are listed here.

common methods were applied initially, including bulk fraction compositions, carbon isotope ratios of various fractions, conventional gas chromatographic–flame ionization detection (GC-FID) analysis of aliphatic and aromatic hydrocarbon fractions, and gas chromatographic–mass spectrometric (GC-MS) analysis of the common biomarker suites. In addition, they also used GC-FPD (gas chromatographic–flame photometric detection) for detailed study of the simple thiophenic compounds. The data were integrated into a single chemically sound and, to some extent, geologically supported oil–source rock correlation.

Prior to addressing the question of the source rock component of this Middle Devonian petroleum system, Clark and Philp (1989) first deduced the character of the source rock by examining the chemical composition of the oils. Low pristane–phytane ratios and the occurrence of squalane, perhydrated carotenes, a certain C_{24} tetracyclic terpane, and abundant C_{35+} extended hopanes all pointed to an anoxic, hypersaline, carbonate–evaporite character for the depositional setting of the source (Palacas et al., 1984). Using the molecular characteristics and carbon isotope ratios of the compositional fractions (particularly the aromatic hydrocarbons) (Figure 15.2), these workers correlated the oils to an undefined combination of the carbonate-containing Muskeg Formation and the underlying sedimentary rocks of the Upper Keg River Member. Minor differences between this source combination and the oils were attributed to unsampled anhydritic portions of the Muskeg Formation.

Although Clark and Philp (1989) addressed migration routes for the oils, this aspect remains the greatest

weakness in their argument. Oils in the Muskeg Formation are separated from co-genetic oils and sources of the Upper Keg River Member by a thick anhydrite. They have sidestepped this source–reservoir communication difficulty by invoking (1) fracturing of the anhydrite, (2) locally high permeabilities at the contact of the lower Muskeg Formation and Upper Keg River Member, or (3) dolomitization of Lower Keg River Member carbonates, providing high permeabilities. Clearly the migration question remains to be addressed in further detail.

Despite the difficulties in establishing migration scenarios in this Middle Devonian petroleum system, the local source conclusion for the Muskeg Formation and Upper Keg River Member oils requires relatively minor fluid movement, either stratigraphically or geographically. Such is not the case for the next case study.

Beatrice Oil, Offshore Scotland

The second case study addresses the question of the source(s) for the Beatrice oil and examines the effects of sample selection, analytical capability, and data interpretation in an oil–source rock correlation study. Oil from the Beatrice field of the Inner Moray Firth in offshore Scotland required major fluid movement. Here, because the conventional mature source rock of the central North Sea, the Upper Jurassic Kimmeridge Clay, and related oil accumulations are a long distance away from the oil in the Early–Middle Jurassic reservoir rocks of the Beatrice field, older source rocks in the vicinity of the Beatrice oil field must be considered.

The Beatrice oil is being produced from the Middle Jurassic sandstone at approximately 2040 m (6700 ft) subsea depth. The trap is faulted locally, with normal faults possibly serving as avenues to fluid migration from underlying thermally mature Devonian "flagstones," which were deposited in a lacustrine setting. Throughout the area, significant oil source rock potential is evident only in the Devonian and Jurassic rocks. The chemical differences between the oil from the Beatrice field and the oils from the Central and Viking grabens of the North Sea have been emphasized for years (e.g., Mackenzie et al., 1983). These differences were suspected to be genetic or source rock related. Nevertheless, the first comprehensive study was published only recently, and its results were quickly contested.

Peters et al. (1989) examined the Beatrice oil and four possible source rock samples: two from the Lower Devonian, one from the Middle Jurassic, and one from the Upper Jurassic. State of the art data collection techniques were used, including metastable reaction monitoring (MRM) GC-MS, biomarker quantification via internal standardization, and metalloporphyrin determination by high-performance liquid chromatography (HPLC). In addition, conventional carbon isotopic data and routine GC-MS methods were employed (Figure 15.1). From the molecular perspective, this study represents one of the most technologically advanced and comprehensive oil–source rock correlation efforts ever published.

The study by Peters et al. (1989) included examination of four potential source rock samples. Initial carbon isotopic results suggested that no single sample could have served as the source rock. Furthermore, molecular data indicated that the oil was much more thermally and compositionally mature than the analyzed source rock samples. Nevertheless, biomarker presence/absence criteria that are migration invariant, including the occurrence of perhydrogenated carotenes in the oil, could be used to invoke the Lower Devonian source rock samples as probable contributors. Such a result is consistent with the presumably hypersaline lacustrine character of the two Lower Devonian source rock samples, as determined by geologic reconstruction and kerogen maceral analysis.

In addition to perhydrocarotenes, Peters et al. (1989) concluded that the Beatrice oil also contains two benzopyrene isomers and minor amounts of C_{30} desmethylsteranes. These latter compounds were identified by MRM and are considered to be contributed solely by marine organic matter (Moldowan, 1984; Moldowan et al., 1985, 1986, 1990; Peters et al., 1986; Mello et al., 1988; Peters and Moldowan, 1993). The simultaneous occurrence of both lacustrine and marine indicators in the Beatrice oil necessitates input from a second (non–Lower Devonian) source rock. Detailed examination of the remaining Jurassic source rock samples resulted in the discovery of the C_{30} desmethylsteranes, along with the two benzopyrene isomers, in the Middle Jurassic sample. Thus, Peters et al. (1989) were able to propose a mixture of Middle Jurassic and Lower Devonian source rocks for the Beatrice oil. This proposal,

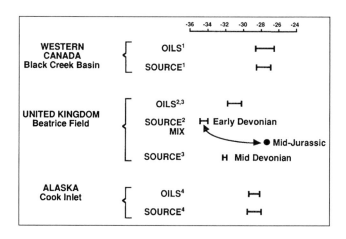

Figure 15.2. Carbon isotope comparisons for oils and proposed source rocks in the three case studies discussed in the text. Carbon isotope ratios for the aromatic hydrocarbon fractions are recorded here, except for data from Peters et al. (1989), which are from whole oil and whole EOM. Sources: [1]Clark and Philp (1989); [2]Peters et al. (1989); [3]Bailey et al. (1990); [4]Magoon and Anders (1992).

although largely derived from biomarker data, is also consistent with the carbon isotopic data. A mixture from the two sources of approximately 60:40 would provide a $\delta^{13}C$ value that is consistent with that of the Beatrice oil (Figure 15.2).

Peters et al.'s (1989) argument for a Middle Jurassic co-source depends on two factors: (1) the representative nature of their sample set and (2) the geologic importance of the low quantities of C_{30} desmethylsteranes. Both factors have been questioned by Bailey et al. (1990). These authors used a greatly expanded source rock sample set (16 Lower Devonian, 31 Middle Devonian, and 11 Middle Jurassic samples) and different methods involving source rock pyrolysis to mimic increased thermal maturation (Figure 15.1). On this basis, they contend that the Middle Devonian source rocks are solely responsible for the Beatrice oil. Their evidence includes the following:

1. Similarities between the Middle Devonian source rock $\delta^{13}C_{EOM}$ (extractable organic matter or bitumen mean of –32.0‰) and $\delta^{13}C_{oil}$ (–32.1‰) (see also aromatic hydrocarbon isotope data in Figure 15.2)
2. The occurrence of perhydrocarotenes and benzopyrenes in both oil and source rock
3. Strong similarities between carbon isotope ratios of the whole-oil and kerogen pyrolyzates
4. Sterane–hopane ratio similarities, notwithstanding considerable data suggesting that this ratio is at least partially maturity dependent (see Requejo et al., 1989; van Graas, 1990; Isaksen, 1991)
5. Sterane carbon number distribution similarities, as shown in Figure 15.3 for the Peters et al. (1989) and Bailey et al. (1990) data sets.

It is clear from Figure 15.3 that the proposed mixing of Lower Devonian and Middle Jurassic source rocks

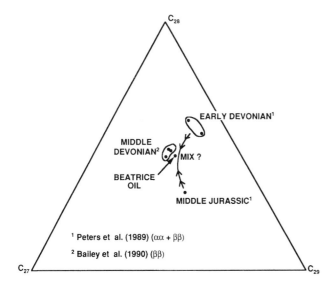

Figure 15.3. Ternary diagram showing the distribution of regular steranes by carbon number (C_{27}–C_{29}) for oil and proposed sources from Beatrice field, United Kingdom. Data from Peters et al. (1989) are derived from $\alpha\alpha$ and $\beta\beta$ 20R isomers, whereas those from Bailey et al. (1990) are derived only from $\beta\beta$ isomers (20R + 20S).

(Peters et al., 1989) and a single-source rock from the Middle Devonian (Bailey et al., 1990) both satisfy the C_{27}–C_{29} sterane results of the Beatrice oil.

The primary distinctions between these two studies are the size and age distribution of the source rock sample set and the interpretive relevance of certain biological marker data. In addition, a significant data discrepancy points out the different working philosophies of the two research groups. Peters et al. (1989) identified the presence of minor amounts of C_{30} desmethylsteranes in the Beatrice oil using metastable reaction monitoring techniques, and concluded that the presence of these compounds was both real and significant. In contrast, Bailey et al. (1990) concluded, based on their analyses, that the C_{30} desmethylsteranes in the oil "are too minor to identify with confidence and are effectively absent" (p. 1168). These workers go on to state that "as a matter of philosophy, we would suggest that it is dangerous to base hypotheses upon components which occur in petroleum only in trace amounts..." (p. 1169). The philosophical distinction is worth noting, inasmuch as it lies at the heart of all oil–source rock correlations that use biomarkers.

The reality of a Middle Jurassic source rock contribution to the Beatrice oil appears to depend on the presence of C_{30} desmethylsteranes in the oil and on the accuracy of the evidence that the provenance of these compounds is solely marine. Peters et al. (K. E. Peters, personal communication, 1992) have recently developed new evidence in support of a Middle Jurassic co-source for the Beatrice oil, so the discussion is likely to continue.

Cook Inlet, Alaska

The last example involves an oil whose origin has been in dispute for many years. Because all of the commercial oil in the upper Cook Inlet in southern Alaska is found in the thick nonmarine Tertiary section, a nonmarine source rock from this section seems geologically reasonable. However, the occurrence of organic-rich marine-dominated Jurassic shales in the pre-Tertiary section, the presence of oil possessing marine characteristics, and the thermal immaturity of most of the Tertiary section have all contributed to the Tertiary versus pre-Tertiary source rock controversy (Magoon and Claypool, 1981).

This case study reviews the work of Magoon and Anders (1992), who have examined oils, seeps, condensates, and possible source rocks from throughout the Cook Inlet. Following the application of fundamental molecular and isotopic parameters, they propose a Middle Jurassic Tuxedni Group source rock for the commercial oil in upper Cook Inlet. Their study represents an ideal application of petroleum and source rock geochemistry in resolving a long-standing geologic disagreement.

The Magoon and Anders (1992) study is comprehensive, involving 140 Cook Inlet rock samples and more than 25 oils and condensates from fields, drill-stem tests, and seeps. Our emphasis here is on oils produced from Tertiary reservoir rocks of the upper Cook Inlet; Magoon and Anders (1992) infer that these oils are part of a distinct petroleum system (Magoon, Chapter 22, this volume). This production is predominantly from Eocene and Oligocene–Miocene reservoir rocks at depths of 1220–3350 m (4000–11,000 ft). Carbon isotope ratios of whole oils and their aliphatic and aromatic hydrocarbon fractions were collected and used as the preliminary correlation parameters (Figure 15.1). Conventional sterane and terpane distributions, obtained from GC-MS analyses, were utilized to confirm their preliminary conclusions.

Carbon isotope ratios of the aromatic hydrocarbon fractions of the Middle Jurassic source rock samples in upper Cook Inlet are almost identical to those of the oils in the Tertiary reservoir rocks (Figure 15.2). This correlation is supported by tricyclic terpane, hopane, and sterane distributions for Middle Jurassic rock extracts and upper Cook Inlet oils. The occurrence of unidentified C_{30} pentacyclic compounds in both rocks and oils provides further confirmation of this oil–source rock correlation. Numerous molecular ratios are proposed to support the authors' conclusions.

The migration aspect of Magoon and Anders' (1992) conclusion appears geologically reasonable, inasmuch as Jurassic source rocks are known to be present at depth under many of the upper Cook Inlet traps. Furthermore, oil migrating updip and up section from beneath the thickest overburden rock needs to travel laterally less than 50 km to charge all of the oil fields in question.

It should be considered that the work by Magoon and Anders (1992), supported by the previous study of Magoon and Claypool (1981), has resolved a long-standing controversy by using relatively mundane geochemical tools. Only carbon isotope ratios of compositional fractions and molecular distributions of selected tri-, tetra-, and pentacyclic aliphatic hydrocarbons were necessary to confirm a pre-Tertiary source rock for these oils in Tertiary reservoir rocks. It is also clear that rudimentary isotopic and molecular data were the basis for the correlation conclusions of the case studies of northwestern Alberta and Beatrice oil field. While it continues to be true that multiple techniques of correlation must be used to obtain valid conclusions, the power of fundamental isotopic and biomarker data should not be overlooked.

DEVELOPING POSSIBILITIES

Just as past advances in oil–source rock correlation efforts have been both conceptual and technological, so too will future approaches depend on new ways of thinking and new analytical methods. Because these correlations are critical to oil exploration and development efforts conducted by the petroleum industry (and can often resolve oil genesis controversies; see Vlierboom et al., 1986), these new approaches must be both accurate and rapid.

Two such approaches are undergoing development in various laboratories: whole-sample GC-MS analysis and isotopic molecular analysis. Whole-sample analysis is already in use in some laboratories (Curiale, 1989, 1992). The approach involves whole-oil injection into a gas chromatograph interfaced to a mass spectrometer operating at medium to high resolution. GC-MS analysis of whole oils eliminates concerns of sample alteration during laboratory preparation and the time and expense of biomarker concentration prior to analysis.

Almost all current oil–source rock correlations involve the (presumably indigenous) solvent-extractable fraction of the proposed source rock. Accuracy and information yields could be improved considerably by examining the remaining 80–90% of the organic matter in the rock, namely, the kerogen. Such an examination is conducted accurately and rapidly using whole-rock analysis. The whole-rock method involves both thermal extraction and in situ kerogen cracking (on-line anhydrous pyrolysis) (Bjorøy et al., 1991a). This approach parallels that for whole-oil GC-MS analysis, having an upstream pyrolysis system at the front of the configuration. Although such systems are not yet in common use, recent development of fully contained, flow-through pyrolysis injection interfaces (Bjorøy et al., 1991a), as well as growing use of GC-high resolution-MS systems, indicate that this type of whole-rock analysis could become widespread before the end of the century. When used in an integrated manner, whole-sample analysis of a proposed oil–source rock pair could be completed in less than 3 hr.

In addition to this whole-sample approach, the isotopic molecular approach promises to revolutionize our understanding of oil generation, migration, and alteration. The advent of the on-line gas chromatograph–isotope ratio mass spectrometer (Hayes et al., 1990; Bjorøy et al., 1991b) has opened the possibility of isotopic molecular analyses, whereby carbon isotope ratios of individual compounds are determined. Eventually, this technology will provide another dimension to conventional sterane and terpane biological marker distributions by establishing the isotope ratios of these and other molecular markers in oils, source rock extracts, and pyrolyzates. Future oil–source rock correlations will then be able to use isotopic as well as molecular fingerprints in establishing chemical relationships.

CONCLUSIONS

Accurate oil–source rock correlations are a necessary component of oil exploration efforts and are required in the accurate identification of petroleum systems (Magoon and Dow, Chapter 1, this volume). In establishing a causal connection between an organic facies of a mature source rock and a crude oil within the stratigraphic and geographic extent of that petroleum system, we also implicitly identify a set of potential migration pathways and therefore provide information on the time of generation, migration, and accumulation. In addition, the knowledge that an oil originates from a particular pod of mature source rock provides us with input data for use in volumetric calculations and may help to predict the occurrence of oil accumulations that have not yet been discovered.

Our three case studies, taken from published data from northwestern Alberta in Canada, Beatrice oil field in offshore Scotland, and the Cook Inlet area of Alaska, utilized several bulk and molecular correlation techniques. In each case, the existence of the source–reservoir link was made, both chemically and geologically, and conclusions about the existence of definitive petroleum systems were possible. However, the existence of geochemically correct "matches" does not indicate that our correlations are conclusive. Geologically problematic migration routes were encountered in northwestern Alberta, and philosophical differences were shown to result in different interpretations and conflicting conclusions on the origin of the oil in Beatrice field. Nevertheless, through the fusing of the disciplines of analytical chemistry and petroleum geology, the determination of an oil–source rock correlation represents the culmination of petroleum geochemical applications. This is because correlation efforts, to be successful, must be preceded by a full complement of geochemical analyses and must be integrated into all known geologic features of an area. Thus, correlations represent end products of our combined geochemical and geologic knowledge.

Acknowledgments *The ideas in this chapter are the result of numerous discussions with many colleagues at the Science & Technology (now Energy Resources) Division of Unocal, and I thank them all for their input. I am particularly grateful to those geologists and geochemists who took the time and made the effort to publish the results of their oil–source rock correlations. I also thank Unocal for permission to publish. Last, and most important, this manuscript has been improved significantly as a result of comments by J. R. Castaño, S. A. Stout, B. W. Bromley, K. E. Peters, L. B. Magoon, P. C. van de Kamp, J. T. Smith, and G. Demaison.*

References Cited

Bailey, N. J. L., R. Burwood, and G. E. Harriman, 1990, Application of pyrolysate carbon isotope and biomarker technology to organofacies definition and oil correlation problems in North Sea basins: Organic Geochemistry, v. 16, p. 1157–1172.

Barwise, A. J. G., 1990, Role of nickel and vanadium in petroleum classification: Energy & Fuels, v. 4, p. 647–652.

Bjorøy, M., K. Hall, P. B. Hall, P. Leplat, and R. Loberg, 1991a, Biomarker analysis of oils and source rocks using a thermal extraction GC-MS: Chemical Geology, v. 93, p. 13–20.

Bjorøy, M., K. Hall, P. Gillyon, and J. Jumeau, 1991b, Carbon isotope variations in *n*–alkanes and isoprenoids in whole oils: Chemical Geology, v. 93, p. 1–12.

Burwood, R., R. J. Drozd, H. I. Halpern, and R. A. Sedivy, 1988, Carbon isotopic variations of kerogen pyrolyzates: Organic Geochemistry, v. 12, p. 195–205.

Burwood, R., L. Jacobs, and J. Paulet, 1990, Kerogen pyrolysis–carbon isotope technology: Application to source–oil correlation problems: Review of Paleobotany and Palynology, v. 65, p. 367–377.

Clark, J. P., and R. P. Philp, 1989, Geochemical characterization of evaporite and carbonate depositional environments and correlation of associated crude oils in the Black Creek basin, Alberta: Bulletin of Canadian Petroleum Geology, v. 37, p. 401–416.

Curiale, J. A., 1987, Distribution of transition metals in north Alaskan oils, *in* R. H. Filby and J. F. Branthaver, eds., Metal Complexes in Fossil Fuels: Geochemistry, Characterization, and Processing: New York, American Chemical Society, p. 135–145.

Curiale, J. A., 1989, Integrated biological marker correlations among mature oils of the Sverdrup basin, *in* Division of Petroleum Chemistry Preprints: New York, American Chemical Society, v. 34, p. 122–125.

Curiale, J. A., 1992, Molecular maturity parameters within a single oil family—a case study from the Sverdrup basin, Arctic Canada, *in* J. M. Moldowan, P. Albrecht, R. P. Philp, eds., Biological Markers in Sediments and Petroleum: Englewood Cliffs, NJ, Prentice Hall, p. 295–300.

Curiale, J. A., 1993, Oil to source rock correlation—concepts and case studies, *in* M. Engel and S. Macko, eds., Organic Geochemistry: New York, Plenum Press, p. 473–490.

Dow, W. G., 1974, Application of oil correlation and source rock data to exploration in Williston basin: AAPG Bulletin, v. 58, p. 1253–1262.

England, W. A., A. S. Mackenzie, D. M. Mann, and T. M. Quigley, 1987, The movement and entrapment of petroleum fluids in the subsurface: Journal of the Geologic Society, v. 144, p. 327–347.

Grantham, P. J., and L. L. Wakefield, 1988, Variations in the sterane carbon number distributions of marine source rock derived crude oils through geologic time: Organic Geochemistry, v. 12, p. 61–73.

Hayes, J. M., K. H. Freeman, B. N. Popp, and C. H. Hoham, 1990, Compound-specific isotopic analyses: a novel tool for reconstruction of ancient biogeochemical processes: Organic Geochemistry, v. 16, p. 1115–1128.

Huang, W. Y., and W. G. Meinschein, 1979, Sterols as ecological indicators: Geochimica et Cosmochimica Acta, v. 43, p. 739–745.

Hunt, J. M., F. Stewart, and P. A. Dickey, 1954, Origin of hydrocarbons of Uinta basin, Utah: AAPG Bulletin, v. 38, p. 1671–1698.

Isaksen, G. H., 1991, Molecular indicators of lacustrine freshwater depositional environments, *in* D. Manning, ed., Advances in Applications in Energy and the Natural Environment: Manchester, U.K.,Manchester University Press, p. 361–364.

Jones, R. W., 1987, Organic facies, *in* Advances in Petroleum Geochemistry, v. 2: London, Academic Press, p. 1–90.

Leenheer, M. J., and J. E. Zumberge, 1987, Correlation and thermal maturity of Williston basin crude oils and Bakken source rocks using terpane biomarkers, *in* J. A. Peterson, D. M. Kent, S. B. Anderson, R. H. Pilatzke, and M. W. Longman, eds., Williston basin: anatomy of a cratonic oil province: Rocky Mountain Association of Geologists Symposium, Denver, p. 287–298.

Lewan, M. D., 1983, Effects of thermal maturation in stable organic carbon isotopes as determined by hydrous pyrolysis of Woodford Shale: Geochimica et Cosmochimica Acta, v. 47, p. 1471–1479.

Leythaeuser, D., A. Hollerbach, and H. W. Hagemann, 1977, Source rock–crude oil correlation based on distribution of C_{27+} cyclic hydrocarbons, *in* R. Campos and J. Goni, eds., Advances in Organic Geochemistry 1975: Madrid, Empresa Nacional Adaro de Investigaciones Mineras, p. 3–20.

Mackenzie, A. S., 1984, Applications of biological markers in petroleum geochemistry, *in* J. Brooks and D. Welte, eds., Advances in Petroleum Geochemistry, v. 1: London, Academic Press, p. 115–214.

Mackenzie, A. S., J. R. Maxwell, M. L. Coleman, and C. E. Deegan, 1983, Biological marker and isotope studies of North Sea crude oils and sediments: Proceedings of the Eleventh World Petroleum Congress, PD1(4), p. 1–12.

Magoon, L. B., and G. E. Claypool, 1981, Petroleum geology of Cook Inlet Basin, Alaska—An exploration model: AAPG Bulletin, v. 65, p. 1043–1061.

Magoon, L. B., and D. E. Anders, 1992, Oil-to-source rock correlation using carbon-isotopic data and biological marker compounds, Cook Inlet–Alaska Peninsula, Alaska, *in* J. M. Moldowan et al., eds, Biological Markers in Sediments and Petroleum: Englewood Cliffs, NJ, Prentice Hall, p. 241–274.

Mello, M. R., P. C. Gaglianone, S. C. Brassell, and J. R. Maxwell, 1988, Geochemical and biological marker assessment of depositional environments using Brazilian offshore oils: Marine and Petroleum Geology, v. 5, p. 205–224.

Moldowan, J. M., 1984, C_{30}-steranes, novel markers for marine petroleums and sedimentary rocks: Geochimica et Cosmochimica Acta, v. 48, p. 2767–2768.

Moldowan, J. M., W. K. Seifert, and E. J. Gallegos, 1985, The relationship between petroleum composition and the environment of deposition of petroleum source rocks: AAPG Bulletin, v. 69, p. 1255–1268.

Moldowan, J. M., P. Sundararaman, and M. Schoell, 1986, Sensitivity of biomarker properties to depositional environment and–or source input in the Lower Toarcian of SW Germany: Organic Geochemistry, v. 10, p. 915–926.

Moldowan, J. M., J. F. Fago, C. Y. Lee, S. R. Jacobson, D. S. Watt, N.-E. Slougui, A. Jeganathan, and D. C. Young, 1990, Sedimentary 24-*n*-Propylcholestanes, molecular fossils diagnostic of marine algae: Science, v. 247, p. 309–312.

Palacas, J. G., D. E. Anders, and J. D. King, 1984, South Florida basin—prime example of carbonate source rocks of petroleum, *in* J. G. Palacas, ed., Petroleum geochemistry and source rock potential of carbonate rocks: AAPG Studies in Geology 18, pp. 71–96.

Peters, K. E., and J. M. Moldowan, 1993, The Biomarker Guide: Englewood Cliffs, NJ, Prentice Hall, 363 p.

Peters, K. E., J. M. Moldowan, M. Schoell, and W. B. Hempkins, 1986, Petroleum isotopic and biomarker composition related to source rock organic matter and depositional environment: Organic Geochemistry, v. 10, p. 17–27.

Peters, K. E., J. M. Moldowan, A. R. Driscole, and G. J. Demaison, 1989, Origin of Beatrice oil by co-sourcing from Devonian and middle Jurassic source rocks, Inner Moray Firth, United Kingdom: AAPG Bulletin, v. 73, p. 454–471.

Requejo, A. G., J. Hollywood, and H. I. Halpern, 1989, Recognition and source correlation of migrated hydrocarbons in upper Jurassic Hareelv Formation, Jameson Land, East Greenland: AAPG Bulletin, v. 73, p. 1065–1088.

Seifert, W. K., 1977, Source rock–oil correlations by C_{27}–C_{30} biological marker hydrocarbons, *in* R. Campos and J. Goni, eds., Advances in Organic Geochemistry 1975: Madrid, Empresa Nacional Adaro de Investigaciones Mineras, p. 21–44.

Seifert, W. K., and J. M. Moldowan, 1978, Applications of steranes, terpanes, and monoaromatics to the maturation, migration and source of crude oils: Geochimica et Cosmochimica Acta, v. 42, p. 77–95.

Seifert, W. K., J. M. Moldowan, and R. W. Jones, 1979, Application of biological marker chemistry to petroleum exploration, *in* Proceedings, Tenth World Petroleum Congress: London, Heyden & Son, p. 425–440.

Sinninghe Damste, J. S., and J. W. de Leeuw, 1990, Analysis, structure and geochemical significance of organically bound sulfur in the geosphere: state of the art and future research: Organic Geochemistry, v. 16, p. 1077–1101.

Sofer, Z., 1984, Stable carbon isotope compositions of crude oils: application to source depositional environments and petroleum alteration: AAPG Bulletin, v. 68, p. 31–49.

Stahl, W. J., 1980, Compositional changes and ^{13}C–^{12}C fractionations during the degradation of hydrocarbons by bacteria: Geochimica et Cosmochimica Acta, v. 44, p. 1903–1907.

van Graas, G. W., 1990, Biomarker maturity parameters for high maturities: calibration of the working range up to the oil–condensate threshold: Organic Geochemistry, v. 16, p. 1025–1032.

Vlierboom, F. W., B. Collini, and J. E. Zumberge, 1986, The occurrence of petroleum in sedimentary rocks of the meteor impact crater at Lake Siljan, Sweden: Organic Geochemistry, v. 10, p. 153–161.

Volkman, J. K., 1986, A review of sterol markers for marine and terrigenous organic matter: Organic Geochemistry, v. 9, p. 83–99.

Volkman, J. K., 1988, Biological marker compounds as indicators of the depositional environments of petroleum source rocks, *in* A. J. Fleet, K. Kelts, and M. R. Talbot, eds., Lacustrine petroleum source rocks: Geologic Society Special Publication 40, p. 103–122.

Wehner, H., M. Teschner, and K. Bosecker, 1986, Chemical reactions and stability of biomarkers and stable isotope ratios during in vitro biodegradation of petroleum: Organic Geochemistry, v. 10, p. 463–471.

Welte, D. H., 1965, Relationship between oil and source rock: AAPG Bulletin, v. 49, p. 2246–2268.

Welte, D. H., and M. N. Yalcin, 1988, Basin modelling—a new comprehensive method in petroleum geology: Organic Geochemistry, v. 13, p. 141–151.

Welte, D. H., H. W. Hagemann, A. Hollerbach, D. Leythaeuser, and W. Stahl, 1975, Correlation between petroleum and source rock, *in* Proceedings, Ninth World Petroleum Congress: Applied Science Publishers, v. 2, p. 179–191.

Williams, J. A., 1974, Characterization of oil types in Williston basin: AAPG Bulletin, v. 58, p. 1243–1252.

Magoon, L. B, and W. G. Dow, eds., 1994, The petroleum
system—from source to trap: AAPG Memoir 60.

Chapter **16**

Correlation of Natural Gases with Their Sources

Michael J. Whiticar

Centre for Earth and Ocean Studies
University of Victoria
Victoria, British Columbia, Canada

Abstract

Natural gases are derived from biogenic and nonbiogenic sources through diverse processes, including bacterial formation, catagenesis, hydrothermal/geothermal activity, and to an unknown degree, primordial or mantle emissions. Exploration for natural gas is aimed principally at accumulations of fossil fuel hydrocarbons, but other gas accumulations, notably those of noble gases, can also be economic targets. Investigators use the chemical and physical properties of these natural gases to identify and characterize the petroleum system using geochemical tools. Three categories of geochemical tools are commonly used to correlate natural gases to their sources and to others gases: (1) gas concentration, (2) molecular composition, and (3) stable isotope ratios. Analytical routines are frequently applied to samples from near-surface sediments/soils and seepages, drill cuttings and cores, and oil and gas accumulations, all of which can be used to demonstrate the stratigraphic and geographic extent of a petroleum system.

Light hydrocarbons are the predominant compounds used to classify natural gases. Associated and co-genetic nonhydrocarbons, such as CO_2, N_2, H_2S, He, and Rn, however, can also provide ancillary information that can help identify the appropriate source of active source rock. Interpretative schemes, combining concentration and composition, are founded extensively on empirical observations of natural gas occurrences. Significant, measurable, and predictable differences among the various gas types provide the basis for these geochemical tools to identify and characterize primary gases, which are the original, unaltered gases from a single source of active source rock. These tools can also differentiate them from secondary gases, which are mixtures of different gas types or are primary gases with altered signatures due to oxidation or migration. In addition, natural gas fingerprints can be used to estimate the type and thermal maturity of the organic matter or kerogen sourcing the hydrocarbons. For fingerprinting gases, stable isotope ratios of the light hydrocarbons are key diagnostic parameters.

INTRODUCTION

Low molecular weight hydrocarbons, or natural gases, pervade the earth's atmosphere, biosphere, hydrosphere, and geosphere and significantly impact on societal energy needs and environmental concerns. Natural gas supplies about 20% of the primary external energy requirements of humans, following the consumption of oil (38%) and coal (30%). Worldwide natural gas production is currently about 1.8×10^{12} m³/yr (65 tcf/yr) or roughly 2%/yr of the proven geosphere gas reserves (estimated total geosphere gas reserves are $>200 \times 10^{12}$ m³, or $>7 \times 10^3$ tcf) (Table 16.1). Global climate change is a consequence of increasing atmospheric loading of CO_2

and NO_x resulting from the world population's voracious consumption of fossil fuels. It is also a consequence of increasing hydrocarbon emissions directly into the atmosphere from a variety of natural and anthropogenic sources. For example, the global mean methane concentration for the lower troposphere has risen from 1.1 to 1.8 ppmv, a rate of 1%/yr over the past 50 years (Blake and Rowland, 1988).

Today, our energy resource security and environmental acuity require us to address questions of natural gas–source relationships. The availability and cost of natural gas (as well as other fossil fuels) as both a fuel and a raw material for manufacturing has an impact on how future societies will look and work.

Table 16.1. Global Natural Gas Reservoirs

Reservoir Type	Size of Natural Gas Reservoir				Residence Time (Years, approx.)
	Teragrams HC (10^{12} g)	Gigatons C (10^{15} g C)	tcf HC (10^{12} ft^3)	HC (10^{12} m^3)	
Atmosphere	4.8×10^3	3.6	240	7	8–10
Biosphere					
Wetlands and landfill	80	6×10^{-2}	4	0.1	$0.1–10^2$
Rice paddies and soils	30	2×10^{-2}	1.5	0.04	$0.1–10^2$
Hydrosphere					
Marine water column	20	1.5×10^{-2}	1.0	0.03	10^3
Geosphere					
Hydrates					
Marine clathrates	$3–11 \times 10^6$	$2–8 \times 10^3$	$1.5–5 \times 10^5$	$4–15 \times 10^3$	10^4
Terrestrial clathrates	4×10^3	3	200	6	$10^3–10^4$
Conventional accumulations					
Bacterial gas reservoirs	3×10^4	20	1.5×10^3	40	$10^2–10^7$
Thermogenic gas reservoirs	10^5	75	5×10^3	140	$10^7–10^8$
Coal gas reservoirs	$10^4–10^5$?	7.5–75	$500 –5 \times 10^3$?	14 – 140	$10^7–10^8$
Deep and ultradeep reservoirs	$10^4–10^5$?	7.5–75	$500 –5 \times 10^3$?	14 –140	$10^8–10^9$

After Whiticar (1990).

The size of most global natural gas reservoirs can generally be constrained to within one order of magnitude (Table 16.1). Conventional subsurface natural gas accumulations (thermogenic, bacterial, and coal gases) together are estimated to comprise over 8000 tcf of hydrocarbons, which is equivalent to 1.6×10^5 Tg of hydrocarbons (teragram = 10^{12} g) or 120 Gt C (gigaton of carbon = 10^{15} g C). This is far more than the mass of atmospheric methane (3.6 Gt C) and the methane held in terrestrial gas hydrates (3 Gt C) (Table 16.1). Bacterial gas (also called biogas) accumulations from anthropogenic sources, including landfills, wetlands (0.06 Gt C), and rice paddies (0.025 Gt C), are the next largest reservoirs to conventional natural gas accumulations. But all of these natural gas reservoirs are minute compared to the amount of hydrocarbons bound up as gas hydrates (clathrates) on continental margins (Table 16.1). Conservative estimates for ocean hydrates range from 2000 to 8000 Gt C ($1.5–5 \times 10^5$ tcf), and projections of up to 4×10^6 Gt C (2×10^8 tcf) have been made (Kvenvolden, 1988). The large uncertainty in the extent of gas hydrates precludes any firm estimation of the total budget for global natural gas. Furthermore, our lack of knowledge about the amounts of hydrocarbons in geothermal, crystalline, and mantle systems complicates this budget estimation, but these sources are not considered here.

This chapter focuses primarily on conventional subsurface natural gas accumulations sought by the petroleum explorationist, but the discussion also serves our understanding of the hydrocarbon fluxes between the geosphere and the atmosphere. It identifies the basic natural gas types encountered, and describes their geochemical characteristics. The natural gas signatures are related to the conditions of the sources from which the gases are derived and to secondary effects such as migration, mixing, or oxidation.

In comparison with bitumens and oils (see Curiale, Chapter 15, this volume), natural gases contain fewer compounds and therefore have a smaller chemical diversity, yet their molecular and isotope compositions are sufficiently (1) large in range, (2) specific, and (3) predictable to provide diagnostic information on their sources. In contrast to bitumens or liquid hydrocarbons, natural gases also have physical and chemical properties as volatile reduced carbon species that assist in their detection and application to the identification and mapping of petroleum systems. For example, because they migrate more readily and therefore are more widely distributed in sedimentary rocks, natural gases can be used to detect and classify hydrocarbon occurrences in near-surface sedimentary rock, alluvium, and seepages (Philp and Crisp, 1982; Hovland and Judd, 1988). Those encountered during drilling (mud gas, headspace gas, or cuttings gas) can locate reservoirs or predict (ahead-of-the-bit) the presence of deeper seated hydrocarbons and possibly characterize their source rock by estimating kerogen type and thermal maturity. In addition, the compositional signatures of natural gases are often sufficiently unique to act as a gas–gas correlation tool. It is among these reasons that geochemical exploration for petroleum relies heavily on the characterization of natural gases.

Gas–gas correlation, determination of hydrocarbon source potential and migration pathways, input into burial (geohistory) diagrams, and near-surface hydrocarbon exploration for petroleum system investigations are among the immediate applications of geochemical information obtained from natural gases. All these applications are based on the fact that there are significant and systematic compositional variations among the various gas types. Table 16.2 is a listing of some of the terms and units used in this chapter.

Table 16.2. Terminology and Units

Term or Unit	Explanation
Concentration and Composition	
C_1, C_2, C_3, i-C_4, n-C_4	Methane, ethane, propane, iso-butane, normal butane
TOC	Total organic carbon, (wt. organic carbon/wt. sediment) $\times$ 100
R_o	Mean vitrinite reflectance measured under oil in percent
Tg	Teragram, 10^{12} g hydrocarbons
Gt C	Gigaton carbon, 10^3 Tg C = 0.75×10^{15} g methane
1 m^3	35.3 ft^3;
1 tcf	28.3×10^9 m^3
ppb	Parts per billion hydrocarbon concentration = wt. gas/10^9 wt. sediment
dL	Deciliter, 0.1 L
Molecular Expressions	
95% CH_4, 5% C_2H_6 + C_3H_8 + C_4H_{10}	Average natural gas composition
540 gC/m^3	Average weight of natural gas
ΣC_{2+}	Vol. % C_2 + C_3 + i-C_4 + n-C_4
ΣC_n	C_1 + C_2 + C_3 + i-C_4 + n-C_4
$C_1/(C_2 + C_3)$	Bernard parameter, or vol. % C_1/(vol. % C_2 + vol. % C_3)
% HC	$C_x/\Sigma(C_1$–$C_4) \times 100$ by wt. (including undersaturated hydrocarbons)
Isotope Expressions	
$\delta^{13}C_{CH_4}$, $\delta^{13}C_{C_2H_6}$, $\delta^{13}C_{C_3H_8}$, $\delta^{13}C_{CO_2}$	Carbon isotope ratios ($^{13}C/^{12}C$) of methane, ethane, propane, carbon dioxide relative to PDB standard
δD_{CH_4}	Hydrogen isotope ratios ($^2H/^1H$) of methane relative to SMOW standard
$\delta^{15}N$	Nitrogen isotope ratios ($^{15}N/^{14}N$) relative to atmospheric nitrogen standard
$\alpha_{A\text{-}B}$	Isotope separation or fractionation factor

TYPES AND SOURCES OF NATURAL GASES

Natural gases can be grouped into primary and secondary types, as shown in Table 16.3. Primary gases are those generated directly by a *sole* source of organic matter, whereas secondary gases are those that no longer represent a single, *original* gas type but rather have been mixed or altered. Examples of secondary gases include the mixing of gases from different sources or thermal maturities or the microbial oxidation of hydrocarbons. Although it is generally more simple and reliable to relate primary gases to their sources or to one another, it is also possible to do so with secondary gas types. Foremost, it is important that one can recognize the influence of secondary effects and avoid misinterpretation of a natural gas.

For the purposes of this chapter, the discussion is restricted to bacterial and thermogenic primary gas types and to the secondary effects acting on them. For more detailed discussions of geothermal, hydrothermal, crystalline, abiogenic, or juvenile gases, the reader is referred to the articles and references in Whiticar et al. (1985), Schoell (1988), Simoneit et al. (1988), and Whiticar (1990).

Diagenetic and Background Gases

During 25 years of sampling and analyses, the investigations conducted by the Federal Institute for Geosciences and Natural Resources (BGR, Bundesanstalt

Table 16.3. Natural Gas Types

Type	Comments
Primary	
Diagenetic	Low temperature
Bacterial:	
CO_2 reduction	Marine
Methyl-type fermentation	Freshwater
Thermogenic:	Associated and nonassociated
Hydrogen-rich source rocks	Sapropelic, type I and II kerogen
Early mature	
Mature	Hydrocarbon window
Late mature	Condensate
Overmature	
Hydrogen-poor source rocks	Humic, type III kerogen
Geothermal or hydrothermal	
Crystalline	
Abiogenic or juvenile	Mantle
Secondary	
Mixed gases	
Altered or bacterial oxidized	
Weathered or water washed	
Migration fractionation	
Artificial	Bit metamorphic

für Geowissenschaften und Rohstoffe) have not encountered a soil or sediment totally devoid of hydrocarbons, although in deep sea red clays and sandy desert regions the concentrations can be extremely low (<1 ppb CH_4 by weight). The source of these trace or *background* hydrocarbons is often varied and unclear. They are either allochthonous, that is, deposited and buried in the sediments as included or sorbed gases (Faber and Stahl, 1984; Gerling 1985; Whiticar and Faber, 1989), or carried in by migration. They can also be produced autochthonously by low temperature diagenetic reactions (Hunt et al., 1980; Whelan et al., 1982). The formation and occurrence of these diagenetic gases is not necessarily mediated by microbial processes as compared to gases formed by bacterial generation processes. In many instances, background gases are not primary gas types; instead they represent a mixture of residual, allochthonous, and diagenetic gases. Because of this and because "background gases" are present in only low or trace concentrations in soils and sediments, it is usually not possible to assign a specific source or history to background gases.

Bacterial Gases

Roughly 20% of conventional natural gas reserves are estimated to be of bacterial origin (Rice and Claypool, 1981; Rice, 1992). These deposits are almost exclusively methane (usually <1% ΣC_{2+}) (Figure 16.1) and have been formed mostly by near-surface fermentation reactions by methanogenic bacteria as one of the final diagenetic remineralization stages. Bacterial gases have also been referred to in the literature as biogenic gas, but this term is ambiguous because most if not all thermogenic gases are derived from biogenic carbon, that is, carbon that has passed through the biosphere.

Methanogens are a broad consortium of obligate anaerobic microorganisms that use a limited suite of precursor compounds to form methane. These substrates include (1) acetate and formate or (2) bicarbonate, CO_2 + H_2. The carbonate reduction pathway, which predominates in marine environments (Whiticar et al., 1986), can be represented by this general reaction:

$$CO_2 + 8 H^+ + 8 e^- \rightarrow CH_4 + 2 H_2O \qquad (1)$$

More common in freshwater settings is the methanogenic pathway by methyl type fermentation. The net reaction for methyl type fermentation using acetate as an example is

$$^*CH_3COOH \rightarrow {^*CH_4} + CO_2 \qquad (2)$$

where the asterisk (*) indicates the intact transfer of the methyl position to CH_4. In addition to these so-called competitive substrates, there are noncompetitive substrates for methanogenesis, including methanol, mono-, di- and tri-methylamines, and certain organic sulfur compounds, such as dimethylsulfide. The relative importance of these substrates as sources for bacterial methane is uncertain. The microbiology and ecology of

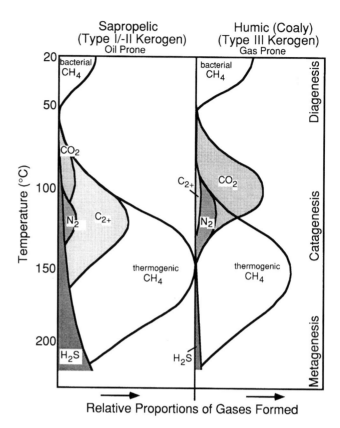

Figure 16.1. Relative proportions of natural gases types generated from sapropelic (type I and II kerogens) and humic (type III kerogen) source rocks with increasing thermal maturity. (Adapted from Hunt, 1979.)

the various methanogenic pathways have been reviewed in several monographs (Zehnder, 1988).

Methanogenesis is usually restricted to shallow, anoxic, moderate temperature sediments and soils, but it can also occur under extreme conditions of temperature (–1.2° to 110°C) (Whiticar, 1992), salinity (0–30%), depth (>1 kbar), and microaerophilia (Whiticar, 1990). In addition to surface environments, methanogenesis can also occur in oil reservoirs, and it is a common component of oil field gas.

Ethanogenesis, the bacterial formation of ethane, is also known (Oremland et al., 1988), but the amount of C_2 hydrocarbons generated by this process is generally much less than 1% of the bacterial methane formed in the same setting (Figure 16.1). Similarly, other hydrocarbons are synthesized by microbial processes, but their contribution to a sediment hydrocarbon budget is minimal. The presence of unsaturated light hydrocarbons can be instructive because they are seldom stable over geologic time and thus represent more recent activity such as bacterial generation. Olefins can also be artifacts, such as gases generated by the drilling process (see later).

Thermogenic Natural Gas

During the catagenic transformation and reorganization of organic matter, various short-chained hydrocarbons such as methyl groups are cleaved off higher molecular weight organic compounds and subsequently saturated to form the light hydrocarbons of conventional natural gas. The degree and type of product formed is dependent on several key factors, including kerogen type (sapropelic versus humic), kerogen richness (TOC and molar H/C ratio), thermal maturity, expulsion efficiency, and the presence of catalysts such as clays.

Sapropelic, type I and type II kerogens generate, over suitable time periods, significant quantities of thermogenic hydrocarbon gases at temperatures over 70°C (Figure 16.1). The initial gases generated at a low thermal maturity (<0.5% R_o) is relatively dry (<5% ΣC_{2+}) (Hunt, 1979), but the proportion of higher hydrocarbons increases with further maturation into and through the oil window (peak natural gas generation at 150–160°C). Oil-associated natural gases can have more than 80% ΣC_{2+} (Evans and Staplin, 1971). As maturation proceeds into the late mature (1.3–2.0% R_o) or condensate range (>45° API), subsequent kerogen transformation and cracking of hydrocarbons leads to a greater proportion of shorter chained hydrocarbons and essentially a methane-rich gas at the base of the catagenic stage, roughly about 200°C (Hunt, 1979) (Figure 16.1).

It is predicted that methane can remain stable at temperatures of 300°C and depths of 12 km or >4 kbar (for realistic oxidation states and expected mineral assemblages, see Holloway, 1977; Jakobsson and Holloway, 1986; Saxena and Fei, 1988; Luth, 1989). Currently, the No. 1 Bertha Rogers (31,441 ft, or 9583 m) and No. 1 Baden (30,050 ft, or 9165 m) wells in the Anadarko basin, United States, are the deepest exploration wells. The Tuscaloosa trend, Rocky Mountain overthrust belt, Appalachian basin, and Baltimore Canyon trough are examples in the United States of recent, active exploration areas with target depths of >15,000 ft (4570 m).

Natural gas generation profiles from humic type III kerogens and coals are quite different from type I and II kerogens (Figure 16.1). Significant hydrocarbon generation is traditionally thought to occur at higher levels of thermal maturity (>0.7% R_o) for humic kerogens than for sapropelic kerogens (Karweil, 1969; Tissot and Welte, 1978; Chung and Sackett, 1979). In contrast, Galimov (1988) suggested that the large quantities of methane that fill the West Siberian supergiant gas fields were produced by thermogenic processes at lower thermal maturities (0.45–0.7% R_o) based on the geology and $\delta^{13}C_{CH_4}$ values (see later discussion). However, the influence of a major bacterial contribution (as a mixed gas) and migration could not be ruled out.

Throughout their maturation history, humic kerogens generate less C_{2+} hydrocarbons, so the total methane potential, including the cracking of oil and condensates to methane, is about one or two times lower than for a sapropelic kerogen (Figure 16.1). Reliable characterization of humic kerogens is complicated by the high retention capacity of humic organic matter, especially coals, that partitions gases and results in a time- or maturity-dependent compositional fractionation of the gases that are released. These interpretative difficulties

are compounded by the high retention in humic organic matter of bacterial gases that were formed and stored while the peat or fen deposit was at or near the surface.

Artificial or Bit Metamorphic Gases

Increasing formation hardness, temperature, and pressure create technological difficulties that accompany conventional drilling, but these become particularly acute in ultradeep gas exploration. The generation of artificial hydrocarbons, often termed *bit metamorphism* (Meincke, 1967; Taylor, 1983), is a special problem during drilling and one that is commonly encountered in hard, crystalline rocks in both shallow and deeper wells (Gerling, 1985; Faber et al., 1987; Jeffrey and Kaplan, 1988; Faber and Whiticar, 1989).

The gas signature of bit metamorphic gas is most distinctive, that is, the presence of abnormally great amounts of olefins and strong isotope depletions in ^2H and enrichments in ^{13}C of methane. However, in many instances, this artificial or bit metamorphic gas is present in only trace amounts (<100 ppb by wt.) is a small component of the total natural gas encountered. This small proportion or amount of bit metamorphic gas makes it difficult to measure by conventional techniques, and it is easily masked in mixtures of natural gas from conventional (bacterial or thermogenic) source rocks.

GEOCHEMICAL PARAMETERS IN CHARACTERIZING NATURAL GASES

Three parameters are used to characterize natural gases:

1. Concentration
2. Molecular composition and ratios
3. Stable isotopic composition

In specific instances, a single parameter may be sufficient to classify the type of a particular natural gas occurrence confidently. For example, methane in a shallow section (500 m) of a drilled well with a carbon isotope ratio ($\delta^{13}C_{CH_4}$) of –90 ‰ would clearly signify a bacterial gas, probably formed by carbonate reduction. Likewise, elevated concentrations of higher hydrocarbons deeper in the same well (2000 m) would point to the presence of a thermogenic gas. Unfortunately, such clear instances of source typing are more often the exception, and all three parameter classes are frequently needed to define unambiguously the character of the gas or gases present and to identify the possible influences of secondary effects. Commonly, a suite of samples, that is, a continuum of cuttings samples in a well or a series of related reservoir gases, is required to delineate the gas types and influences. In addition to information on the type of gas present, natural gases also carry significant details concerning the source of the gas, such as kerogen type, thermal maturity of the organic matter, and the possibility of multiple kerogen/maturity source rocks. Abbreviated analytical programs may have an insufficient

Table 16.4. Guideline Ranges in Natural Gas Concentration and Composition Values in Soils, Sediments, and Drill Hole Cuttings

Natural Gas Type	Concentration ΣC_n ppb (wt./wt.) min/max	Composition		
		Molecular $C_1/(C_2 + C_3)$	Stable Isotope	
			$^{13}CH_4$ δ(‰ vs. PDB)	$\delta D-CH_4$ (‰ vs. SMOW)
Diagenetic	0.1/100	10–100	−80/−20	−350/−150
Bacterial				
CO_2 reduction	100/10^5	50–>10^6	−120/−55	−250/−150
Methyl fermentation	100/10^5	50–>10^6	−65/−50	−550/−275
Thermogenic				
Kerogen type I–II				
Early mature,	>100	100–20	−52/−44	−300/−180
Mature	>10^3	1–20	−44/−40	−250/−120
Late mature	>500	5–100	−40/−38	−250/−120
Over mature	>500	20–10^3	>−38	−250/−120
Kerogen type III	>100	50/2×10^3	−45/−30	−150/−100
Geothermal/hydrothermal	?	20/>10^6	−55/−10	−300/−200
Crystalline	≤90 v% gas	10^3–>10^6	−50/−20	−320/−125
Abiogenic/juvenile	≤98 v% gas	10^3–>10^6	−20/0	−100/−150
Artificial	≤10^3	5–100	−30/−15	−500/−900

sample number or detail to reveal the presence of secondary effects or to permit such refined interpretations.

Natural gas samples can be collected in numerous ways, including drill-stem tests (DSTs), gas sample cyclinders at well heads, drill cuttings, surface sediment and soils, and gases dissolved in oils, condensates, and water. Although basic geochemical sampling procedures are now largely standardized and the problems associated with the handling of natural gas samples are broadly understood, emphasis must still be placed on sampling and storage techniques to avoid losses, fractionation, contamination, and postsampling alteration. Without this care, reliable interpretations are difficult.

Thus, the combination of gas concentration, molecular ratios, and isotope ratios can be effective parameters to characterize natural gases from various source rocks and geologic settings. A generalized summary of the major gas types and their parameters is presented in Table 16.4. It should be emphasized that in all cases of natural gas characterization, the available geologic, geophysical, and geochemical information must be integrated into the petroleum system investigation.

Concentration

Background Gas

The concentration of gas in a specific setting is typically the first factor considered in the classification of a natural gas. Gas samples from surface and subsurface sites can vary widely in concentration depending on source and mode of emplacement. In nonpetroliferous areas with minimal methanogenic activity, hydrocarbon concentrations are detected only at trace levels in the sub-parts per billion range (by wt. basis). As mentioned,

it is difficult to assign a specific source or history to background gases, and their molecular and isotope composition should not be overinterpreted. It is expedient to set concentration threshold values below which one is cautious about the integrity and reliability of the gas composition data. These thresholds must be established for each petroleum province, but experience has set levels in near-surface sediments at about 20–50 ppb for methane and 2–5 ppb for ΣC_{2+}.

Seepages

In contrast to background gases, some natural gas seepages can flow at rates of several cubic meters per minute and can be composed almost entirely of hydrocarbons. Methane is frequently the dominant component of natural gas seepages, but higher hydrocarbons are common. Submarine seepages can ebullate from lake beds and the seafloor (Hovland and Judd, 1988), and local dissolved hydrocarbon concentrations in water columns can exceed several deciliters of CH_4 per liter of water and several centiliters C_2H_6 per liter. Although some secondary alteration can influence their gas signatures, most seepages with high flow rates are probably representative of their source rock. The fact that the major petroleum provinces all have hydrocarbon seepages associated with them makes the classification of these natural gas emissions attractive.

Microseepages

Surface microseepages are the shallow geochemical expression of deeper seated hydrocarbon accumulations. Although many outstanding questions exist concerning the vertical transport of natural gases to the surface and there are problems associated with secondary effects, in certain instances it is possible to recognize hydrocarbons (thermogenic gases) at the surface that have been generated at depth (Horvitz, 1978). Much of the more recent success in hydrocarbon surface exploration is related to the phenomenon of hydrocarbon sorption on mineral and organic particles (Faber et al., 1990), which avoids the problems of mixing and the surficial bacterial production and oxidation of hydrocarbons.

Soils and sediments have hydrocarbon concentrations varying from <100 to >10^5 ppb, which is from marginally to considerably above background levels. For those samples with higher gas concentrations, the gas type can be classified confidently using compositional data. At concentrations around or below threshold levels, classification should be made more cautiously. Bacterial gases are commonly encountered in near-surface environments and values of >5×10^4 ppb are common. In many offshore areas, free gas concentrations in unconsolidated sediments can exceed the solubility limit and form bubbles, which are recognized as zones of acoustic turbidity by 3.5–15 kHz sub-bottom sediment profilers. In soils, bogs, and lacustrine environments, free gas ebullience occurs directly into the water column and atmosphere, or the gases can be transported by emergent plants to atmosphere. Thermogenic gases are also observed in soils and sediments. In most cases, hydrocarbon concentration alone is insufficient to identify them unambiguously. The concentration is generally less than 1000 ppb (Faber and Stahl, 1984; Gerling, 1985), but they can have up to 150 ppb ΣC_{2+}, which is typical for thermogenic gases.

Cuttings and Core Gases

Gases in drill cuttings have a concentration dynamic that is slightly greater than for near-surface gases. Background values of light hydrocarbons are in the range of 50–250 ppb in the subsurface. These are observed only in nonpetroliferous regions that are also devoid of bacterial gas sections. Wells that penetrate sedimentary rock containing bacterial gas (generated through methanogenesis, either active or past) can have elevated methane values of up to 10^5 ppb. Drill cuttings and mud gas logs from wells drilled in oil-prone regions, influenced by migrated, associated, and/or thermogenic gas, can have methane levels of >2000 ppb with over 90% ΣC_{2+} (Figure 16.1) (Faber et al., 1990). Cuttings gas from humic source rocks and coals is sometimes lower in concentration, dryer (<5% ΣC_{2+}) and generated at higher thermal maturation levels than sapropelic source rocks (Hunt, 1979).

Oil and Gas Fields

For oil and gas fields, knowing the concentration of natural gas can influence further exploration strategies within that petroleum system. The information is also critical for several production decisions. Gas–oil ratios, the type of drive (gas or water), and the presence of nonhydrocarbon gases (H_2S, CO_2, He, Ar, and N_2) must be considered in hydrocarbon recovery schemes.

Molecular Composition of Natural Gas

The amount of information at a molecular level contained in the hydrocarbons of natural gas is limited primarily to five saturated aliphatic compounds: methane, ethane, propane, isobutane, and normal butane. Higher carbon number hydrocarbons (C_5–C_7) can also be present in gas samples , but due to possible condensation effects at surface pressure–temperature conditions, they (and sometimes C_4) can be severely fractionated and thus be unreliable.

Unsaturated hydrocarbons, such as ethene, propene, and butene, can also be detected in certain instances. These hydrocarbons are present in trace amounts (typically <1–2 ppb by wt. in sediments and cuttings) and are unstable over geologic time. The presence of unsaturated hydrocarbons can indicate recent bacterial, diagenetic, or possibly hydrothermal activity (Whiticar et al., 1985). Alternatively, artificially generated gases through bit metamorphism can also have abnormally high amounts of ethene (>7% HC) and propene (>5% HC) (>100 ppb by wt. in sediments and cuttings), in addition to the expected suite of saturated hydrocarbons (Gerling, 1985; Faber et al., 1987; Jeffrey and Kaplan, 1988; Faber and Whiticar, 1989).

In many cases, nonhydrocarbons such as N_2, H_2, H_2S, CO_2, and noble gases are important minor and trace constituents in natural gases. Although a detailed treatment is not presented, the following examples illustrate the value of these gases in evaluating natural gas occurrences.

Nonhydrocarbons

Sulfide (HS^-, H_2S) formation is most prominent in marine diagenetic sequences resulting from bacterial sulfate reduction. In deeper, more thermally mature source rocks that are rich in sulfur, such as organic matter in evaporites or carbonates, higher temperature dissociation reactions generate chemically reduced sulfur gases. Diagenetic sulfides are significant in near-surface sediments, but because of their small amount and high reactivity, they are an insignificant contributor to natural gas accumulations. Sulfides in gas accumulations are derived from sulfate reduction and from the sulfur-containing groups in organic matter, which are released at elevated temperatures of >120°C (Figure 16.1). The amount of sulfide formed is dependent on source rock composition and temperature, but extreme values of H_2S are known, such as in the Smackover Formation (Late Jurassic limestone, >6000 m) in Texas, in which 98% of the gas accumulation is H_2S.

Similar to sulfur, CO_2 in natural gases has a variety of sources. Principally it is derived from organic matter or from the inorganic dissolution of carbonates in the catagenetic stage by the release of oxygen-bearing groups. CO_2 can be an indicator of diagenetic remineralization (e.g., decarboxylation of organic acids) or of secondary alteration such as microbial degradation or oxidation of hydrocarbons.

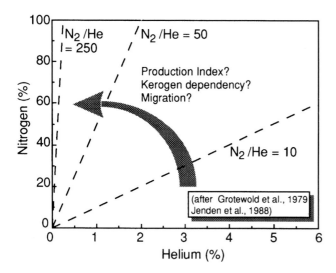

Figure 16.2. Nitrogen–helium concentration ratios of various natural gas accumulations.

The source of primordial helium and argon is the radioactive decay of uranium, thorium, and potassium and is unrelated to petroleum generation (unless the source rock is rich in uranium; Lewan and Buchardt, 1989). However, noble gases can delineate migration pathways from greater depth, and can be useful in determining the age of a natural gas reservoir (see Tissot, 1969).

Nitrogen is a common constituent in natural gases, particularly in red beds and from humic source rocks (U.S. Bureau of Mines data in Jenden et al., 1988). In the North German–Polish basin, nitrogen content can reach up to 79% of the gas accumulation in the Rotliegend reservoir rock, 19% in the upper Carboniferous (Boigk et al., 1976; Grotewold et al., 1979), and up to 90% in the eastern Zechstein Formation (Weinlich, 1991). Jenden et al. (1988) reported that of 12,000 U.S. natural gas analyses (U.S. Bureau of Mines data), the mean N_2 content was 3% and that 1% of the gases had over 90% N_2.

The genesis of nitrogen and the factors controlling its distribution in natural gases are poorly understood. Three possible sources are believed responsible for generation of the N_2 fraction: (1) release of nitrogen-bearing groups from organic matter, (2) release of ammonia from clays at elevated temperatures, and (3) influx of mantle nitrogen (Jüntgen and Klein, 1975; Lutz et al., 1975; Everlin, 1990). In some cases, atmospheric nitrogen and dissolved meteoric nitrogen may also be important sources (Coveney et al., 1987). Nitrogen contents in kerogen are often insufficient to generate the levels of N_2 found in natural gases, but kerogens do contribute to inorganic nitrogen. Pressure loss from production of natural gases can lead to the fractionation of gases, which can affect the distribution of methane and nitrogen (Weinlich, 1991).

Figure 16.2 shows the relationships observed in some natural gases between nitrogen and helium in data from Grotewold et al. (1979), Jenden et al. (1988), and the BGR (unpublished data). Nitrogen–helium ratios vary widely from 10 to 250. These variations may provide us with

information on the formation and accumulation of N_2 and He. Similar relationships in volume percent between N_2 and Ar, $\delta^{15}N$, $\delta^{13}C_{CH_4}$, or δD_{CH_4} have been observed, such as from the upper Carboniferous of northwest Germany (Boigk et al., 1976; Kettel, 1982).

Hydrocarbons

The relative proportions of C_1–C_4 *n*-alkanes in a gas sample provide an initial classification of natural gas type. Because methane is ubiquitous, it is more the relative abundance or ratios among the higher homologs that supply the interpretive information. Equations 3, 4, and 5 are examples of popular molecular ratios used to characterize natural gases. Principally, the ratios all serve the same purpose, but they emphasize different ranges in compositional variations.

$$\text{Gas wetness (vol. \%)} = (C_2 + C_3 + iC_4 + nC_4)$$
$$\div (C_1 + C_2 + C_3 + iC_4 + nC_4) \times 100 \qquad (3)$$

$$\% \textstyle\sum C_2 + (\text{vol. \% HC}) = (C_2 + C_3 + iC_4 + nC_4) \qquad (4)$$

$$\text{Bernard parameter (vol. \%)} = C_1/(C_2 + C_3) \qquad (5)$$

The literature also contains other formulations, such as C_1/C_2 (Claypool, 1974) or $1/\sum C_{2+}$ (Faber, 1987). Equations 3 and 4 are practical functions to display the wetness ratios of natural gas accumulations or lithologies with elevated amounts of higher hydrocarbons. Equation 5 is more useful in describing the compositional variations observed in seep gases, near-surface sediments and soils, and drill cuttings and mud gas logs, where extreme dynamics in composition are possible.

Hydrocarbon gas generation is neither uniform nor consistent in composition throughout its generation history. Illustrations of depth versus time hydrocarbon generation profiles can be seen in Figure 16.1 (after Hunt, 1979; Espitalié et al., 1987). For example, sapropelic source rocks of thermogenic natural gas initially release a wet gas, one with abundant higher hydrocarbons and $C_1/(C_2 + C_3) \approx 5$. As the source rocks become more thermally mature, the higher hydrocarbon content drops continually to $C_1/(C_2 + C_3)$ ratios of >20. At overmaturity, the $C_1/(C_2+C_3)$ ratio can be >50, as the previously formed higher hydrocarbons are subsequently cracked to lower molecular weight species (predominantly methane).

Using a limited data base, Berner (1989) was able to relate the relative (vol. %) amounts of methane, ethane, and propane in a thermogenic natural gas to the level of thermal maturity (% R_o) of the sapropelic source rock, according to equations 6, 7, and 8:

$$\% \text{ methane} = 9.1 \ln(\% R_o) + 93.1 \qquad (6)$$

$$\% \text{ ethane} = -6.3 \ln(\% R_o) + 4.8 \qquad (7)$$

$$\% \text{ propane} = -2.9 \ln(\% R_o) + 1.9 \qquad (8)$$

As shown in Figure 16.3, methane is the dominant hydrocarbon gas at all stages of generation, and the gas composition becomes even more methane rich with

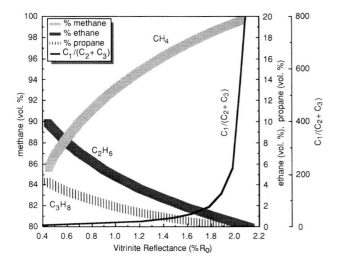

Figure 16.3. Relative amount by volume of methane, ethane, and propane compared to the thermal maturity of a sapropelic (type I and II kerogens) source rock according to equations 6, 7, and 8 in the text. (After Berner, 1989.)

increasing thermal maturity, also indicated by the $(C_1/(C_2 + C_3))$ ratio in Figure 16.3.

Composition changes related to thermal maturity were also found by Schaefer and Littke (1987), who examined the gasoline range, C_7 hydrocarbon fraction. They compared the changes in three concentration ratios as a function of maturity (square brackets indicate concentration):

1. [Paraffin]/[naphthene] ratio, *V* (after Philippi, 1975)
2. [Branched paraffin]/[cycloalkane] ratio, *J* (after Thompson, 1979)
3. [1-*cis*-2-dimethylcyclopentane]/[1-*trans*-2-dimethylcyclopentane] ratio, *R* (modified after Schaefer et al., 1984).

Schaefer and Littke (1987) found that these ratios all increase with higher thermal maturities. The maturity dependency of the molecular composition ratios *V* and *J* produce the following equations:

$$\% R_o = 1.8 \log(V) + 1.0 \qquad (9)$$

$$\% R_o = 1.1 \log(J) + 0.84 \qquad (10)$$

The relationships in equations 9 and 10 indicate a compositional shift to straight-chained alkanes over branched and cycloalkanes at higher thermal maturities.

Stable Isotope Composition

The stable isotope signatures of specific compounds are reliable parameters to characterize and distinguish different natural gas types. Concentration and molecular composition information on a natural gas is instructive and can be used to characterize broadly its gas type (bacterial versus thermogenic), but the stable isotope

ratios, such as carbon and hydrogen isotope ratios of light hydrocarbons, provide much more specific and distinctive classification information.

The carbon and hydrogen isotope signature of a reservoired natural gas can often provide more detailed information about its source rocks, in addition to identifying the natural gas type. For example, it is often possible to distinguish different kerogen types (sapropelic type I, type II, or coal/humic type III). Carbon isotopes can also be used to estimate the level of thermal maturity of the source rock. In addition to source rock typing and thermal maturity estimates, the combination of molecular and isotope compositions of a gas can serve to distinguish altered or secondary gases or delineate gas mixtures from different source rocks. Molecular composition and gas concentration by themselves are generally insufficient to provide all the answers.

For practical reasons, stable isotope data are determined as a ratio, such as $^{13}C/^{12}C$, rather than as an absolute molecular abundance and are reported as the magnitude of excursion in parts per million (‰) of the sample isotope ratio relative to a known standard isotope ratio. The usual δ notation generally used in the earth sciences is

$$\delta R_x (‰) = \left(\frac{R_a / R_b \text{ sample}}{R_a / R_b \text{ standard}} - 1 \right) \times 10^3 \qquad (11)$$

where R_x and R_a/R_b are the isotope ratios ($^{13}C/^{12}C$ or $^2H/^1H$, also referred to as D/H, deuterium/protium) referenced relative to the PDB or SMOW standards, respectively.

Numerous factors control the distribution of isotopes in natural gas components. The principal ones include the isotope ratios of the precursor material, for example, the $^{13}C/^{12}C$ or D/H ratios of the source organic compounds, and the isotope effects associated with the processes of formation, expulsion, migration, trapping, and destruction of natural gas. For isotopes to be useful to characterize gases, it is important that the isotope signatures and/or the isotope effects are distinctive and diagnostic for the various types of natural gas and the mechanisms governing them.

Equilibrium isotope effects had been proposed to explain the distribution of carbon isotopes in thermogenic hydrocarbons, most notably by Galimov and Petersil'ye (1967), Galimov and Ivlev (1973), Galimov (1974), and James (1983). Galimov (1985) modified this equilibrium effect to a "thermodynamically ordered distribution" which approaches the more accepted view that kinetic isotope effects (KIEs) control the redistribution of isotopes (for carbon, Sackett, 1968; Stahl, 1973; McCarty and Felbeck, 1986; Chung et al., 1988; for hydrogen, Frank, 1972).

Kinetic isotope theory predicts that the light hydrocarbon formed by the saturation of an alkyl group cleaved from the kerogen molecule will be depleted in the heavier isotope relative to the remaining reactive kerogen. For example, $^{12}C_{alkyl} - ^{12}C_{ker}$ bonds will break more frequently than $^{12}C_{alkyl} - ^{13}C_{ker}$, $^{13}C_{alkyl} - ^{12}C_{ker}$, or

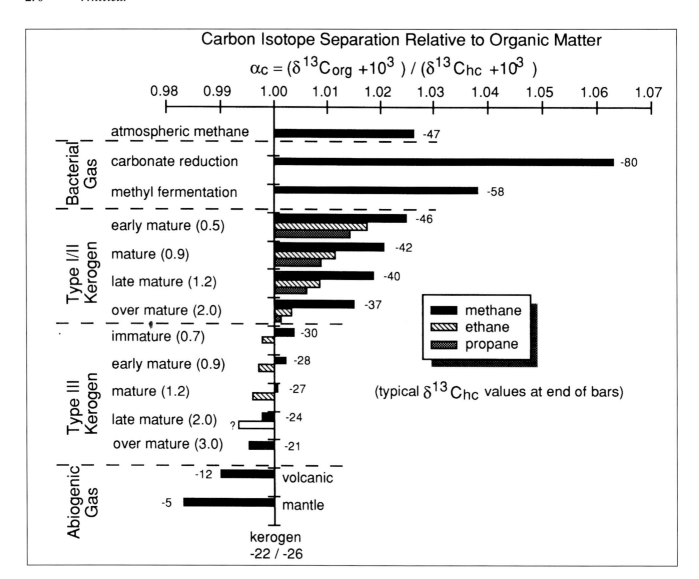

Figure 16.4. Magnitudes of isotopic offset between various generalized types of natural gas ($\delta^{13}C_{hc}$) and organic matter ($\delta^{13}C_{org}$), according to equation 13 in the text.

$^{13}C_{alkyl} - {}^{13}C_{ker}$ bonds. This leads to light hydrocarbons having lower $^{13}C/^{12}C$ ratios than the source organic matter. Similar KIE considerations apply to the microbial utilization of methanogenic substrates, whereby the methane is depleted in the heavier isotope relative to the precursor material (Whiticar, 1992).

As discussed later, the magnitudes of the KIEs related to the formation of hydrocarbon gases by bacteria are frequently larger than for thermocatalytic or cracking processes, and this is important in distinguishing gas types. Figure 16.4 illustrates the relative magnitudes of isotopic offset among various generalized types of natural gas ($\delta^{13}C_{hc}$) and organic matter ($\delta^{13}C_{org}$), according to these equations:

$$\alpha_{A,B} = R_A/R_B \tag{12}$$

$$\alpha_{org,hc} = (\delta^{13}C_{org} + 10^3)/(\delta^{13}C_{hc} + 10^3) \tag{13}$$

Typical methane carbon isotope values are also shown in

Figure 16.4 for the various natural gas types and thermal maturity stages.

The largest isotope fractionation is observed for bacterial methane formed by the carbonate reduction pathway ($\alpha_{org,hc} > 1.06$) and the methyl fermentation pathway ($\alpha_{org,hc} \approx 1.04$). In general, thermogenic hydrocarbons formed from type I or II kerogen ($\alpha_{org,hc} \approx 1.02$) have a larger KIE expressed than for type III kerogens ($\alpha_{org,hc} \approx 1.003$). In both cases, the magnitude of the isotope separation is less than for methanogenesis (Figure 16.4). It also decreases with increasing thermal maturity of the organic matter and with carbon number, thus the order for $\alpha_{org,hc}$ is methane > ethane > propane > butane (Figure 16.4). Hydrocarbons more enriched in ^{13}C than their precursor organic matter are rarely found in type I and II kerogens, but they are observed in humic or type III kerogens. In type I and II kerogens, this could signal the presence of secondary effects such as mixing of inorganic methane (volcanogenic or mantle), oxidation of hydrocarbons, or sometimes sampling and production artifacts.

Isotopic fractionation or discrimination resulting from KIEs can be described by Rayleigh distillation relationships. The isotope ratio of the remaining reactant pool (a generating kerogen) that is being depleted in the lighter isotope can be approximated by

$$R_r / R_o = f^{(1/\alpha)-1} \tag{14}$$

and the progressive isotopic shift of the cumulative product pool (accumulating hydrocarbons) by

$$R_{\Sigma} / R_o = (1 - f^{(1/\alpha)-1}) / (1 - f) \tag{15}$$

where R is the isotope ratio of the initial reactant (R_o), the residual reactant at a specified time (R_r), and the cumulative product (R_{Σ}) (Claypool and Kaplan, 1974). The fraction of the reactant remaining is f, and α is the isotope fractionation factor for the conversion of the reactant to the product. Converting to the δ notation for carbon isotopes, equations 14 and 15 become

$$\delta^{13}C_r = [(\delta^{13}C_o \times 10^3) f^{(1/\alpha_c)-1}] - 10^3 \tag{16}$$

$$\delta^{13}C_{\Sigma} = [(\delta^{13}C_o \times 10^3)(1 - f^{(1/\alpha_c)-1}) / (1 - f)] - 10^3 \tag{17}$$

There is some uncertainty in establishing the isotope value for the initial reactant (R_o) because the isotope ratio of the bulk organic matter may be unrepresentative of the actual hydrocarbon precursor molecules involved in the hydrocarbon formation. This is particularly the case for certain methanogenic substrates (Whiticar, 1992) and for type III kerogen (Berner, 1989) in which only a specific portion of the organic matter is used or reactive.

It is also important to recognize that once the hydrocarbons are formed, that is, cleaved from kerogen or released from a methanogenic bacteria, the isotopic exchange with other carbon-bearing species such as water, CO_2, or kerogen is an insignificant process at normal diagenetic and catagenetic pressure and temperature conditions and times (Galimov et al., 1972; Sackett and Chung, (1979). Rates of hydrogen isotope exchange are uncertain (Kandel, 1964; Koepp, 1979), but it appears that the isotope signatures can remain intact over geologic time, provided that secondary effects have not altered their composition.

Carbon Isotope Ratios

Carbon isotope ratios of methane are the most common isotope measurements made to classify natural gases (Colombo et al., 1965; Sackett, 1968; Silverman, 1971; Stahl, 1973; Galimov, 1974; Schoell, 1980, 1988). However, methane has many potential sources and can suffer alteration through secondary effects. Therefore, in the last decade, more emphasis has been placed on the carbon isotope ratios of (1) higher homologs such as ethane, propane, and the butanes (James 1983; Whiticar et al., 1984; Chung et al., 1988; Clayton, 1991), and (2) other coexisting species, including CO_2 or volatile organic acids (Whiticar et al., 1986). Isotope ratios of C_2–C_4 hydrocarbons are more common for associated

thermogenic gases, whereas the coexisting species are particularly valuable in distinguishing the different bacterial methane formation pathways.

Sometimes isotope pairs (e.g., $\delta^{13}C_{CO_2}$–$\delta^{13}C_{CH_4}$) can function as a geothermometer for geothermal gases (Lyon, 1974; Desmaraîs et al., 1981). However, the lower temperature limit for this equilibrium exchange is higher than that experienced in diagenetic and catagenic reactions.

Kinetic isotope effects can cause isotopic fractionation between the reactant and products pools and thus can potentially generate a considerable range in stable isotope values for hydrocarbons in natural gases. Despite this isotopic shift, the carbon isotope signatures of a natural gas often remain sufficiently unambiguous to permit their classification. Figure 16.4 provides a typical $\delta^{13}C_{CH_4}$ value for each gas type. However, this diagram can serve only as an initial orientation. For example, methanogenesis by carbonate reduction can have $\delta^{13}C_{CH_4}$ values ranging from –52 to –110‰. This range in carbon isotope ratios is due to (1) variations in the carbon isotope ratios of the methanogenic substrate, (2) the degree of substrate utilization, and/or (3) the temperature of methanogenesis (Whiticar, 1992). Fortunately for source rock correlation purposes, thermogenic hydrocarbons are more constrained in their range of isotope composition.

Natural Gas Characterization Interpretative diagrams using empirically defined molecular and isotope compositional fields have been developed by various investigators to classify natural gases. For example, Stahl (1977) compared $C_1 / \Sigma C_n$ with $\delta^{13}C_{CH_4}$ to define different thermogenic gas types. Similarly, Schoell (1980) used the combination of vol. % C_{2+} versus $\delta^{13}C_{CH_4}$ to distinguish (particularly for reservoired natural gases) thermally associated hydrocarbons from bacterial and humic sources. Bacterial gases are commonly lighter or more depleted in ^{13}C than thermogenic gases, and expelled thermogenic gases become heavier with increasing thermal maturity of the source rock.

The *Bernard diagram* (Figure 16.5), modified after Bernard et al. (1978) and Faber and Stahl (1984), compares the molecular (vol. %) ratio $C_1/(C_2 + C_3)$ of a natural gas with its $\delta^{13}C_{CH_4}$. This combination is suited to delineate gas types in sample suites, such as surface sediment gases, seepages, or conventional core. These types of samples often exhibit a large range in the relative amounts of C_{2+} hydrocarbons, which can be used to distinguish wet condensate thermogenic gas from dry bacterial gas, late mature gas, or coal (humic) gas. Secondary effects such as mixing and oxidation effects can also be recognized, again particularly on a series of samples or where primary end-member gases are known (Whiticar and Faber, 1986).

As mentioned earlier, hydrocarbon concentrations must also be considered in any interpretation. Lower hydrocarbon contents that are below the threshold (about 100 ppb CH_4) must be treated with caution. The myriad of low level hydrocarbon sources and sinks in sediments, soils, and unconsolidated lithologies can all

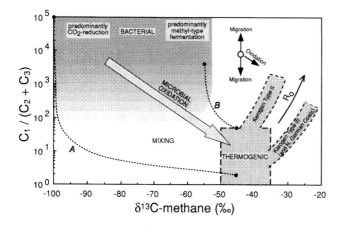

Figure 16.5. Bernard diagram to classify natural gas using the combination of its molecular ratio, $C_1/(C_2 + C_3)$ (vol. %), and its carbon isotopic ratio, $\delta^{13}C_{CH_4}$. (Modified after Bernard et al., 1978; Faber and Stahl, 1984.)

contribute to the composite sample signature and can often make a source identification unreliable, if not impossible. An attempt to convey and emphasize to the reader the importance of combining concentration, molecular, and isotope information in an interpretation is given by Figure 16.6. Superimposed on the normal Bernard diagram (Figure 16.5) is the hydrocarbon gas concentration ΣC_n. The regions in Figure 16.6 beneath the bacterial and thermogenic fields are below the threshold concentration (100 ppb C_1) and are best classified as background gases. Two extreme examples of mixing lines (A and B) have been added having the coordinates of $\delta^{13}C_{CH_4}$, $C_1/(C_2 + C_3)$, ΣC_n between the endmembers (–100, 100, 500 and –45, 20, 100) of line A and (–60, 10^3, 8×10^4 and –47, 50, 2×10^3) line B.

Despite some limitations on these natural gas characterization diagrams, preliminary gas type classification is generally possible with this basic geochemical information. However, in addition to natural gas typing, the carbon isotope ratios of methane in concert with those of CO_2 and C_2–C_4 hydrocarbons also contain significant information on the conditions of the source rock.

Thermal Maturity Estimation (Type I and II Kerogens)
Stable carbon isotope ratios of light hydrocarbons (methane–butane) can be used to estimate the thermal maturity level of the pod of active source rock from which the gases are derived. The empirical relationship between the $\delta^{13}C$ of methane, ethane, or propane in a natural gas reservoir and the vitrinite reflectance of the responsible active source rock, illustrated by Figure 16.7, was initially established by Stahl and Koch (1974) and later revised by Faber (1987). For kerogen types I and II, the calibrated relationships between the carbon isotope ratios and vitrinite reflectance (% R_o) are as follows:

$$\delta^{13}C_{CH_4} (\permil) = 15.4 \log_{(10)} \% R_o - 41.3 \qquad (18)$$

$$\delta^{13}C_{C_2H_6} (\permil) = 22.6 \log_{(10)} \% R_o - 32.2 \qquad (19)$$

$$\delta^{13}C_{C_3H_8} (\permil) = 20.9 \log_{(10)} \% R_o - 29.7 \qquad (20)$$

The magnitude of the isotope separation between the active source rock and light hydrocarbons decreases with increasing thermal maturity (Figure 16.7), and the carbon isotope ratios of the natural gas become progressively enriched in ^{13}C. Thus, an estimate of the thermal maturity of the pod of active source rock can be made from associated or nonassociated natural gases recovered in gas accumulations or from drill cuttings and seepages. Although the thermal maturity relationship for methane can be used alone, a much more reliable maturity estimate can be derived in combination with the carbon isotope ratios of ethane and propane in the same natural gas sample. Ethane and propane are never generated in significant quantities by bacterial processes (Oremland et al., 1988), and they are less susceptible to secondary effects such as oxidation (Whiticar and Faber, 1986). In many cases, it is only through the ethane and propane carbon isotope data that these secondary effects can be identified. Furthermore, type III kerogens can respond differently to thermal stress and in comparison to type I and II kerogen as it generates a dry gas. Again, a mixture of methane from type II and III kerogen would be more effectively seen by the isotopes of the higher homologs. Despite the methane values, an estimate of thermal maturity can sometimes be derived for each kerogen (Faber, 1987; Jenden et al., 1988; Berner, 1989).

Alternate models using carbon isotope data from light alkanes have been proposed to estimate natural gas palaeothermometry (Sundberg and Bennett, 1981), thermal maturity of type I and II kerogen (James, 1983; Whiticar et al., 1984), and the degree of hydrocarbon generation (Chung et al., 1988; Clayton, 1991). These techniques commonly take a theoretical approach, which relies on the differences in the isotope values between progressive alkane homologs (relative isotope separation such as between methane and ethane or ethane and propane) assuming equilibrium isotope fractionation. Figure 16.8 shows a comparison of James' (1983) and BGR carbon isotope thermal maturity models (Stahl and Koch, 1974; Whiticar et al., 1984; Faber, 1987). For this comparison, the level of organic metamorphism (LOM) values of James (1983) were converted to vitrinite reflectance equivalents after Tissot and Welte (1978). The James (1983) relationships of methane and propane were derived by equating his $\delta^{13}C_{C_2H_6}$ values to the ethane line of Faber (1987), as in equation 19. All three models agree relatively well around 1.0–1.5% R_o, although the lines diverge significantly at higher levels of thermal maturity. Some of the inconsistency between the models may be due to calibration difficulties, that is, determining the correct or *apparent* KIEs for settings with differing kerogen types and various thermal and migration histories.

Thermal Maturity Estimation (Type III Kerogen)
The relationship of carbon isotope ratios to thermal maturity is less secure for type III kerogen. This is due to several complications: (1) only a minor portion of the kerogen will react to form hydrocarbons; (2) C_2–C_4 gas generation is limited; (3) the KIEs are relatively small;

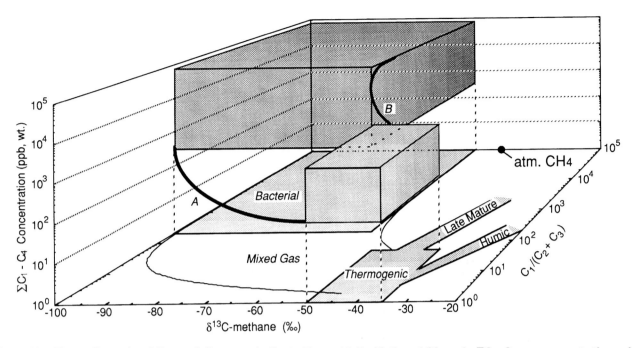

Figure 16.6. Three-dimensional Bernard diagram, similar to Figure 16. 5 with the addition of a $\sum C_1-C_4$ gas concentration axis. Although this representation of natural gas character is seldom useful as an interpretative diagram, it illustrates the importance of combining the concentration, molecular, and stable isotopic data of a natural gas in a unified approach. Two examples of mixing lines between bacterial and thermogenic gases are shown (curves A and B).

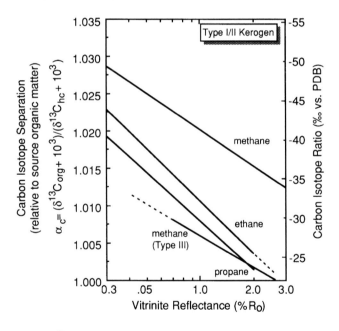

Figure 16.7. Dependence of stable carbon isotope ratios of methane, ethane, and propane in natural gas accumulations compared to the thermal maturity of the source rocks (type I and II kerogens) from which they were derived (see equations 18, 19, and 20 in the text). For comparison, the thermal maturity response of $\delta^{13}C_{CH_4}$ to a type III kerogen is also shown (see equation 22).

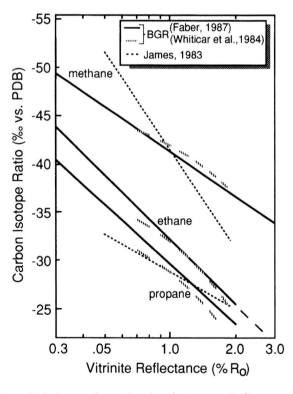

Figure 16.8. Comparison of carbon isotope maturity models of James (1983) and the BGR (text eqs. 18, 19, and 20) (Faber, 1987). The $\delta^{13}C_{CH_4}$ and $\delta^{13}C_{C_3H_8}$ values for James' (1983) relationships are based on the partition functions and are forced on this figure by equating his $\delta^{13}C_{C_2H_6}$ values to the ethane line (eq. 19) after Faber (1987). The level of organic metamorphism to vitrinite reflectance conversion is that of Tissot and Welte (1978).

(4) humic or coaly source rocks tend to retain hydrocarbons by sorption, which promotes mixed gas signatures (bacterial and coal gas) and leads to both molecular and isotopic fractionation of the hydrocarbons released; and (5) continental-scale variations in coal types, such as from Gondwana, North America, or northern Europe (Schoell, 1984). Furthermore, less emphasis had been paid to characterizing light gases from type III kerogens than for oil-associated natural gases.

The empirical relationship between the methane carbon isotope ratio and the degree of source maturity for type III kerogen (Figure 16.9) was originally established for upper Carboniferous and Rotliegend gases by Stahl and Koch (1974), Stahl et al. (1975), and Boigk et al. (1976), as reported in Stahl (1977):

$$\delta^{13}C_{CH_4} (‰) = 8.6 \log_{(10)} \% R_o - 28 \qquad (21)$$

and revised by Faber (1987):

$$\delta^{13}C_{CH_4} (‰) = 13.4 \log_{(10)} \% R_o - 27.7 \qquad (22)$$

As mentioned, this relationship is less certain, particularly in the immature ($\% R_o < 0.7$) and the overmature ($\% R_o > 3$) regions.

Using pyrolysis data of Chung and Sackett (1979) on type III kerogen, Berner (1989) modeled the isotopic effects of hydrocarbon generation and estimated the "convertible fraction" for type III kerogen according to equations 16 and 17. Berner (1989) calculated an isotopic fractionation factor of $\alpha_{org,hc} \approx 1.003$. Berner (1989), also compared the carbon isotopic ratios of methane and ethane from northwest German coal gases of Boigk et al. (1976) to the maturity of their sources and calculated the following linear functions:

$$\delta^{13}C_{CH_4} (‰) = 3.01\% R_o - 31.2 \qquad (23)$$

$$\delta^{13}C_{C_2H_6} (‰) = 3.32\% R_o - 25.9 \qquad (24)$$

The methane isotope relation of Stahl (1977) and Berner (1989) are similar in trend at maturation intervals between about 0.7 and 2% R_o (Figure 16.9) and intersect that of Faber (1987) around 0.9% R_o, but the former are about 1‰ lighter than Faber 's (1987) at maturation intervals between about 1.5 and 3% R_o. Carbon isotope ratios of ethane from humic (coal) kerogen is about 6‰ heavier than the corresponding methane, but this methane–ethane isotope separation is much less than for type I and II kerogen (~11‰). Substantially more data on the higher hydrocarbon homologs from type III kerogens are needed to test the dependence of the carbon isotope ratios of ethane on maturity.

Clayton (1991) extended the ideas of Berner (1989) by relating the $\delta^{13}C_{CH_4}$ of Boigk et al. (1976) to a production index and a thermal maturity equivalent (Figure 16.9). Clayton's (1991) $\delta^{13}C_{CH_4}$ to vitrinite reflectance relationship is also similar to those reported by Berner (1989). Shen Ping et al. (1988) reported a $\delta^{13}C_{CH_4}$–% R_o relationship from humic (coaly) kerogens of the Sychuan basin

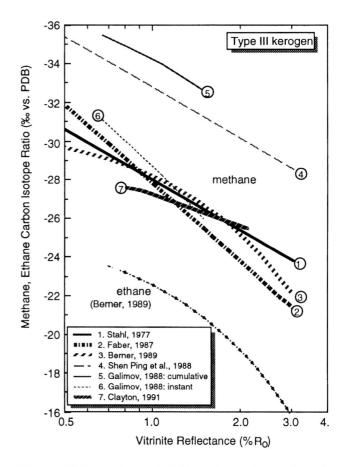

Figure 16.9. Dependence of stable carbon isotope ratios of methane in natural gases is compared to the thermal maturity of the source rock (humic, type III) from various authors and models (including equations 21, 22, 23, and 25 in the text). For comparison, the thermal maturity dependence of $\delta^{13}C_{C_2H_6}$ for type III kerogen (see equation 24) is also shown (Berner, 1989).

in China as follows:

$$\delta^{13}C_{CH_4}(‰) = 8.64 \log_{(10)} \% R_o - 32.8 \qquad (25)$$

Figure 16.9 shows that the methane carbon isotopic data from their sample set are considerably offset from those of the other authors. The explanation for this large difference is not apparent, but several possibilities have been discussed earlier.

Galimov (1988) took a slightly different approach and used the activation energies for the generation of methane from different structural positions of humic (coaly) kerogen to estimate the shift in $\delta^{13}C_{CH_4}$ as a function of the degree of reaction, or thermal maturity of the source rock. The two $\delta^{13}C_{CH_4}$–% R_o relationships generated by Galimov (1988), shown in Figure 16.9, depend on whether the methane isotopic signature is an integrated value based on the accumulation of the gas generated (cumulative) or whether the signature is only that of the latest methane generated (instantaneous). Galimov's instantaneous curve roughly follows the

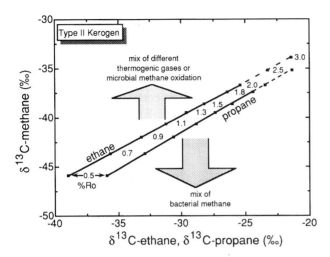

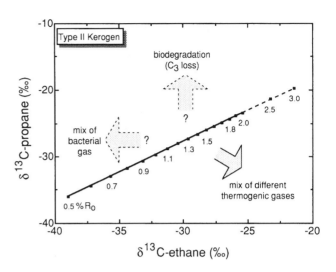

Figure 16.10. Relationship of stable carbon isotope ratios for co-genetic methane versus ethane and propane in a natural gas according to equations 26 and 27 in the text. Gases falling off the expected relation are seldom primary and may represent secondary effects such as mixing of bacterial or different thermogenic gases or microbial oxidation of methane. Vitrinite reflectance equivalents are given for reference. (After Faber, 1987; Whiticar, 1990.)

Figure 16.11. Relationship of stable carbon isotope ratios for co-genetic ethane and propane in a natural gas according to equation 28 in the text. Vitrinite reflectance equivalents are given for reference.

empirical curves of Stahl (1977), Faber (1987), and Berner (1989), but the response of $\delta^{13}C_{CH_4}$ to maturity is greater for the instantaneous curve than the calculated response by Clayton (1991). The cumulative curve of Galimov (1988) is lighter by about 5–6‰ compared to the empirical lines, but it appears to agree with the relationship of Shen Ping et al. (1988).

An approximate thermal maturity estimate is required to understand the carbon isotope–thermal maturity relationship for type III kerogen before it can be routinely applied to hydrocarbon exploration or recovery strategies.

Co-Genetic Natural Gases   Despite the predominance of methane in natural gas, devining reliable and unambiguous source rock information from this hydrocarbon alone can be complicated. Assistance is often forthcoming from other hydrocarbon gases and from co-genetic or co-existing gaseous species such as ethane, propane, carbon dioxide, and nitrogen.

Ethane and propane have been discussed earlier in the context of thermal history of a source rock. Their combination can also be useful to determine or corroborate the genesis of a natural gas (Figures 16.10 and 16.11). Using equations 18, 19, and 20 (see Figure 16.7) for type I and II kerogens and by eliminating % R_o, we can determine methane–ethane, methane–propane, and ethane–propane relationships through the following equations:

$$\delta^{13}C_{C_2H_6}(‰) = 1.47\,\delta^{13}C_{CH_4}(‰) + 28.41 \qquad (26)$$

$$\delta^{13}C_{C_3H_8}(‰) = 1.36\,\delta^{13}C_{CH_4}(‰) + 26.35 \qquad (27)$$

$$\delta^{13}C_{C_3H_8}(‰) = 0.93\,\delta^{13}C_{C_2H_6}(‰) + 0.08 \qquad (28)$$

Equation 28, derived from equations 19 and 20 and shown in Figure 16.11, is consistent with the regression fit found by Faber (1987) for the data on carbon isotope ratios of propane against ethane for natural gases from type I and II kerogens:

$$\delta^{13}C_{C_3H_8}(‰) = 0.93\,\delta^{13}C_{C_2H_6}(‰) + 0.55 \qquad (29)$$

Although the representation of these co-genetic relationships of methane, ethane, and propane in Figures 16.10 and 16.11 are repackaged versions of Figure 16.7, they are particularly useful in visualizing the single or multiple source rocks of a natural gas. Isotope ratio pairs that depart from the expected relationships indicate the influence of secondary effects, such as the mixture of bacterial gas or coal gas with thermogenic gases, as shown. Maturity levels (vitrinite reflectance equivalents) are also superimposed on Figures 16.10 and 16.11 for reference.

For natural gas data from type III kerogens, Berner (1989) calculated a methane–ethane relationship of

$$\delta^{13}C_{CH_4}(‰) = 0.76\,\delta^{13}C_{C_2H_6}(‰) - 10.8 \qquad (30)$$

which is comparable to equation 31, which is derived directly from the combination of equations 23 and 24:

$$\delta^{13}C_{CH_4}(‰) = 0.91\,\delta^{13}C_{C_2H_6}(‰) - 7.7 \qquad (31)$$

The relationship between the carbon isotopic ratios of methane and carbon dioxide at higher temperatures (>400°C) have been applied as a geothermometer. However, the success of this technique has been erratic, primarily because equilibrium isotope exchange does not always occur (Cole and Ohmoto, 1986). In contrast, under diagenetic conditions, the comparison of $\delta^{13}C_{CH_4}$ to $\delta^{13}C_{CO_2}$ is a useful method to discriminate

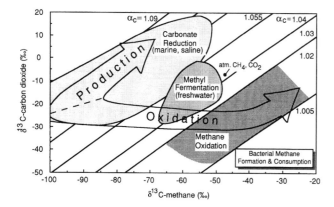

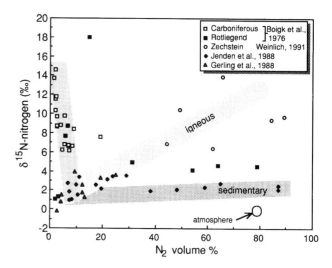

Figure 16.13. Relationship of %N₂ and δ¹⁵N of natural gases from North America and Europe. The data set differentiate into several groups, but the systematics are presently unclear.

Figure 16.12. Carbon isotope separation between co-existing methane and carbon dioxide in bacterial natural gases (see equation 13 in the text). Methanogenesis via the carbonate reduction pathway (equation 1) is associated with a larger carbon isotopic effect than the acetate fermentation pathway (equation 2), resulting in a clear separation of the various bacterial methane formation types and depositional environments. Methane oxidation also has distinctive $\delta^{13}C_{CO_2} - \delta^{13}C_{CH_4}$ separation that is less than methane formation. (After Whiticar et al., 1986.)

various bacterial methanes formed by different fermentation pathways (Figure 16.12) (after Whiticar et al., 1986). Methanogenesis by carbonate reduction operates with a carbon isotope fractionation $\alpha_{CO_2\text{-}CH_4}$ of 1.05–1.10 (Figure 16.12), where

$$\alpha_{CO_2\text{-}CH_4} = (\delta^{13}C_{CO_2} + 10^3)/(\delta^{13}C_{CH_4} + 10^3) \quad (32)$$

Use of other substrates such as acetate by methanogens involves significantly lower carbon isotopic fractionation, with $\alpha_{CO_2\text{-}CH_4}$ values equal to 1.035–1.06 (Figure 16.12). For comparison, thermogenic natural gas generally has $\alpha_{CO_2\text{-}CH_4}$ values of <1.03–1.001 (Whiticar, 1990).

Figure 16.2 showed initial compositional liaisons observed between nitrogen and helium in natural gases. Similarly, relationships between volume percent N_2 and Ar, $\delta^{15}N$, $\delta^{13}C_{CH_4}$, or δD_{CH_4} have been reported, such as from the upper Carboniferous in northwest Germany (Boigk et al., 1976; Kettel, 1982). Despite these limited efforts, our geochemical experience with nitrogen in natural gases suggests that nitrogen may be an important component to define deeply buried humic (coaly) source rock or other overmature source rocks. Figures 16.13, 16.14, and 16.15 present three preliminary sets of interpretative diagrams combining the molecular and stable isotope information from nitrogen to characterize natural gases. At this stage, we can recognize variations in composition but lack the systematics of their occurrence.

Hydrogen Isotopes

Carbon isotopes, particularly those of methane, are the most common isotopic measurement made on

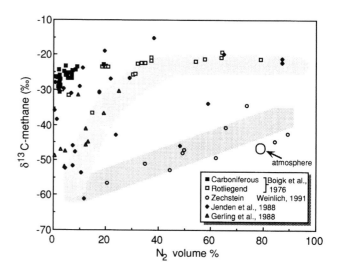

Figure 16.14. Relationship of % N₂ and δ¹³C_{CH₄} of natural gases from North America and Europe. As in Figure 16.13, a subgrouping of the various data sets is clearly seen.

natural gases, but the hydrogen isotopes of methane can also be a diagnostic parameter in classifying the type of gas and its organic source. The work by Schoell (1980) provided one of the first rigorous treatments of carbon and hydrogen isotope variations of bacterial and thermogenic hydrocarbons. This work was extended later to include information on bacterial gases, as shown in the CD diagram of Figure 16.16 (after Whiticar et al., 1986). The general zonation of carbon and hydrogen isotopic signatures occupied by the various natural gas types (outlined areas in Figure 16.16) represent a substantial data base from the BGR and other workers. The shaded regions of the diagram outside the areas of major gas

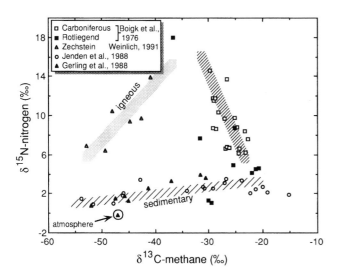

Figure 16.15. δ15N versus δ13C$_{CH_4}$ of natural gases from North America and Europe. The Carboniferous, sedimentary, and igneous sources distinguish themselves as in Figures 16.13 and 16.14, but the systematics are unclear.

types are less common or well-defined gas signatures. In contrast to carbon isotopic ratios, the hydrogen isotope data of methane never exhibits a clear thermal maturity dependency. Rather, it provides details on the depositional environment and pathway of formation. Hydrogen isotopes are particularly useful in distinguishing methane from (1) different methanogenic pathways, (2) bacterial from early mature thermogenic gas, (3) thermogenic from geothermal or hydrothermal gas, and (4) artificial or bit metamorphic sources. In these examples, methane carbon isotope ratios, if used alone, would deliver ambiguous results.

The geothermal, hydrothermal, and crystalline zone in Figure 16.16 is defined by the gas data from open boreholes in Canadian shield crystalline rocks (Sherwood et al., 1988) and from the Gravberg-1 drill well (Schmidt, 1987; Laier, 1988; Jefferey and Kaplan, 1988). Examples of geothermal and hydrothermal data include those from Yellowstone and Lassen parks (Welhan, 1988; Whiticar and Simoneit, in press), New Zealand fields (Lyon and Hulston, 1984), the Guaymas basin (Welhan and Lupton, 1987; Simoneit et al., 1988), and the Bransfield Strait (Whiticar and Suess, 1990).

Methane found at the East Pacific Rise at 21°N latitude by Welhan (1988) and from the Zambales ophiolite (Abrajano et al., 1988) are considered to be of abiogenic origin. Similarly, gas inclusions from south Greenland reported by Konnerup-Madsen et al. (1988) have ^{13}C-enriched methane (δ13C$_{CH_4}$ = –1.0 to –5.1‰). These three sample locations are used to define the region of Figure 16.16 for abiogenic or mantle methane. The free gases in dolerites from the Gravberg-1 well (Schmidt, 1987; Laier, 1988; Jefferey and Kaplan, 1988) also have carbon isotope signatures approaching those of abiogenic gas, but their origin is uncertain.

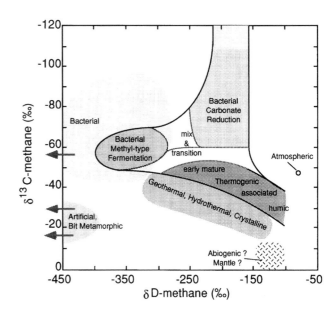

Figure 16.16. CD diagram based on δD$_{CH_4}$ and δ13C$_{CH_4}$. The various sources of methane—bacterial, thermogenic, and geothermal—can often be distinguished by the CD–isotope combination. (After Whiticar, 1990.)

Bit metamorphism hydrocarbons, formed artificially by drilling hard lithologies, have a distinctive methane isotope signature enriched in [13]C (δ13C$_{CH_4}$ ≈ –20‰) and strongly depleted in deuterium (δD$_{CH_4}$ ≈ –750‰). These gases typically have higher amounts of ethene (>7%) and propene (5%) and low ethane–ethene (1.0) and propane–propene (0.5) ratios (Gerling, 1985; Faber et al., 1987). The CD diagram (Figure 16.16) shows bit metamorphic gas data from Germany, including the Tirschenreuth and KTB pilot wells and drill wells from Bockstedt, Eldingen, and Bromberg (Gerling, 1985; Faber et al., 1987; Faber and Whiticar, 1989). Also shown in Figure 16.16 are the artificial gases found in the Gravberg-1 well (δ13C$_{CH_4}$ = –22 to –33‰; δD$_{CH_4}$ = –315 to –658‰; C$_2$H$_4$ > 100 ppb by wt. (after Schmidt, 1987; Laier, 1988; Jefferey and Kaplan, 1988).

SECONDARY EFFECTS

The emphasis of the previous sections has been on unaltered natural gases; this section treats the characterization of gases that have been subjected to some form of postgenerative change. It is common that a natural gas represents a mixture of gases from different source rocks of different thermal maturities. Furthermore, the original molecular or isotopic signatures of a natural gas can suffer minor to severe alteration, such as microbial oxidation and migration fractionation. In many cases, this alteration of the gas composition can be recognized as such, particularly if a series of samples is available with varying degrees of influence. In other cases, the effects of secondary effects may be difficult to discern or isolate.

Mixing

Mixtures of more than one gas type in a natural gas sample is a common phenomenon. Frequently this can be a contribution of bacterial gas or humic-sourced gas to a sapropelic-sourced thermogenic gas. The bacterial gas is often authochthonous, formed during diagenesis and buried with the sedimentary rock. Humic or coal gases are often allochthonous components that have migrated upward into the thermogenic section. Despite the masking of the original gas composition by gas mixtures, it is often possible (1) to recognize that the gas is a mixture and thus should be interpreted with caution, and (2) to determine the possible end-members of the mixture and their relative contributions. Mixtures on a Bernard diagram follow curved trajectories as shown by the two examples (A and B) in Figure 16.5. Unless sufficient data points are available to define the trajectory of the mixing line and one end-member is known or can be estimated, it is difficult to discern the contribution or signature of the second gas. In many cases, the general composition of the mixed gas can suggest admixtures of bacterial or humic (coal) gases to a conventional type I and II.

Carbon isotope data for ethane and propane can also be used to estimate the thermogenic $\delta^{13}C_{CH_4}$ end-members of natural gas mixtures, such as (1) bacterial and thermogenic mixtures or (2) coal gas (type III) and thermogenic mixtures. Once this is established, the amount and composition of the bacterial or coal gas component can be estimated. Mixtures of two thermogenic gases are difficult to discern using a Bernard diagram. Recognition of a mixed gas is possible if the carbon isotope ratio of ethane and/or propane is known in conjunction with methane. As shown in Figure 16.9, natural gas signatures from mixed gases fall off the expected $\delta^{13}C_{CH_4}$–$\delta^{13}C_{C_2H_6}$ or $\delta^{13}C_{CH_4}$–$\delta^{13}C_{C_3H_8}$ lines for co-genetic gases.

It is important to note that, for a natural gas sample consisting of a mixture of two different gases, the $\delta^{13}C_{CH_4}$–$\delta^{13}C_{C_2H_6}$ data pair of the mixed gas signature will occasionally plot on the relationship defined by equation 26 for a primary gas. This is also the case even if the $\delta^{13}C_{CH_4}$–$\delta^{13}C_{C_2H_6}$ data pair of the mixed natural gas sample is composed of two gases from a similar source, such as type II kerogen, but which have been generated at different levels of thermal maturity. Furthermore, a mixing line of these same two sources that can be defined by a locus of points generated for different mixing proportions will not be co-linear with equation 26, but will plot as a curve off this line. The reason for this departure from a linear relationship is that the relative rates of hydrocarbon generation throughout the maturation history of a kerogen are different for methane, ethane, and propane, as previously discussed (see Figure 16.1). For example, a type II kerogen will generate 90.0% CH₄ and 7.1% C₂H₆ at a 0.7% R₀ maturity level as compared to 94.9% CH₄ and 3.7% C₂H₆ at 1.2% R₀. Thus, the disproportionate contributions of light hydrocarbons from different stages of maturity lead to the nonlinearity.

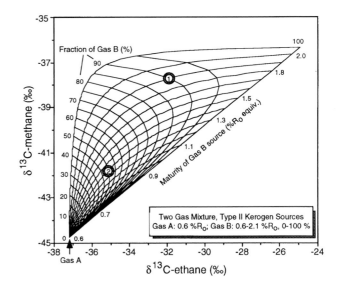

Figure 16.17. Mixing diagram for mixture of two gases that originated from type II kerogen (Berner, 1989). The mixing net is calculated by fixing or estimating the thermal maturity for one of the gases and allowing the second gas to vary in amount (0–100%) and thermal maturity. The trajectories of the mixing lines are determined by the combination of the relative generation proportions (percent methane, percent ethane) and the carbon isotope ratios ($\delta^{13}C_{CH_4}$, $\delta^{13}C_{C_2H_6}$) as a function of the thermal maturity of the source rock. These relationships are defined by equations 6, 7, 18, and 19 in the text. Two examples of mixed gases are shown (points 1 and 2). Gas A is fixed at a maturity of 0. 6% R₀. Gas B at point 1 is 1.9% R₀ and comprises 90% of the gas; at point 2 it is 1. 4% R₀ and 50% of the gas.

In a model, Berner and Faber (1988) and Berner (1989) combined the relative response of methane and ethane generation histories (equations 6 and 7) with their respective carbon isotopic ratios (equations 18 and 19) as functions of changing thermal maturities and mixing proportions. One example of the resultant mixing surface is shown in Figure 16.17. In this case, one of the gases (gas A) in a mixture is from a source rock with a fixed thermal maturity (0.6% R₀), while the source rock for the second gas (gas B) may have a maturity range of 0.6–2.1% R₀. Superimposed on this change in thermal maturity is the response of the $\delta^{13}C_{CH_4}$–$\delta^{13}C_{C_2H_6}$ data pairs on the relative proportion of each gas (A and B) in the mixture (0–100% fraction of gas B). Thus, by knowing or estimating one of the gas end-members in a mixture, it is possible to derive the amount of the second gas present, its molecular and isotopic composition, and the thermal maturity of its source rock.

Two examples (points 1 and 2) are used to illustrate this in Figure 16.17. Assume that gas A is known to have a type II kerogen source with a maturity of 0.6% R₀. Thus, the maturity of the source rock for gas B at point 1 would be 1.9% R₀ and would comprise a 90% fraction of the mixture. Correspondingly, at point 2, the source rock of gas B would have a maturity of 1.4% R₀, and gas A

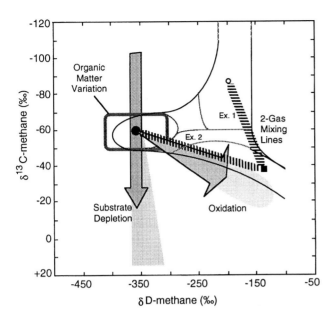

Figure 16.18. The secondary effects such as mixing, oxidation, and substrate depletion on δD_{CH_4} and $\delta^{13}C_{CH_4}$ are depicted in the CD diagram. Large isotopic offsets can potentially result, but in general, the degree of alteration and direction of the isotopic shift still permit recognition of the primary gas types. In most cases, additional information such as $C_1/(C_2 + C_3)$ (Figures 16.5 and 16.6), $\delta^{13}C_{C_2H_6}$, $\delta^{13}C_{C_3H_8}$ (Figures 16.10 and 16.17), or $\delta^{13}C_{CO_2}$ (Figure 16.12) is used in conjunction with the methane carbon and hydrogen isotopes to identify the alteration.

and B are present in equal amounts (50%). Similar models can be used with propane to confirm these results.

The combination of stable carbon and hydrogen isotope ratios of methane can also indicate a mixed gas. In the CD diagram of Figure 16.18, the $\delta^{13}C_{CH_4}$–δD_{CH_4} data pairs in a range of mixtures for two different natural gases plot as straight mixing lines between the end-member gases. Two examples of mixing lines are shown in Figure 16.18. Under unfavorable circumstances, the methane carbon and hydrogen isotope data may be unable to distinguish between the processes of mixing and oxidation, as demonstrated in Figure 16.18 (see example 2 and the oxidation trend). However, even in this case, one would still be advised that secondary effects were present and that the gas measured was not a primary gas.

Migration Fractionation

As discussed earlier, there is no substantive evidence that hydrocarbons suffer isotope fractionation during migration. Arguments for such isotopic differentiation have been suggested in earlier work by May et al. (1968), Colombo et al. (1969), and Stahl (1977), but other phenomena, such as mixtures of different gas types, could cause similar effects. Investigations by Coleman et al. (1977) and Fuex (1980) convincingly demonstrated against isotopic fractionation during gas migration.

In contrast, molecular fractionation during migration or redistribution of hydrocarbons does appear to be significant in some situations (Thompson (1979). Leythaeuser et al. (1980, 1984) pioneered our understanding of diffusion of natural gas through rocks, separating the light hydrocarbons according to their apparent diffusion coefficients. Diffusion increases with molecular geometry (*n*-alkanes < branched alkanes < cycloalkanes) (Leythaeuser and Schwarzkopf, 1986) and with decreasing carbon number (*n*-heptane < *n*-butane < methane). Karlsen et al. (1987) similarly found molecular fractionation in shallow (60-m-deep) rock cores, but this was largely attributed to differences in solubility of the various light hydrocarbons. The impact of this molecular separation or "chromatographic effect" is still uncertain, particularly for longer expulsion times and longer distance movements or migration of natural gases.

Oxidation

Bacterial oxidation in natural gas reservoirs or gassy lithologies is usually unexpressed due to the large quantity of hydrocarbons present. However, the effects of microbial alteration of a natural gas are more commonly observed in samples with lower gas contents, such as surficial sediments or cuttings from drill wells. Microbial consumption of hydrocarbons leads to changes in gas signature, whereby the altered gases have a molecular composition that is enriched in the higher homologs (ethane and propane) because microbes metabolize methane more readily. The microbes also consume isotopically lighter methane faster than ^{13}C-methane (Barker and Fritz, 1981), which leads to the enrichment of ^{13}C-methane in the residual natural gas pool, following a Rayleigh relationship (Whiticar and Faber, 1986). The fractionation factor for this process can be constrained between $\alpha_{CO_2-CH_4}$ values of 1.025 and 1.004 (Whiticar, 1992), which is distinctively less than the fractionation associated with methanogenesis (Figure 16.12). The combination of molecular and isotopic fractionations due to progressive microbial alteration of a natural gas can cause pronounced shifts in a Bernard diagram.

Figure 16.5 showed an example of the path followed by an oxidized bacterial gas. This example demonstrates that, through extensive alteration, it is possible that a bacterial gas could be shifted into the gas signature of, and be confused with, a thermogenic gas. This interpretative problem can sometimes be circumvented if the oxidation pathway can be delineated. Furthermore, the natural gas concentration levels would often tend to be beneath the interpretation threshold. It should also be pointed out that on a Bernard diagram (Figure 16.5), the pathway of an oxidized bacterial methane (straight line) is different from that of two-component mixing lines (e.g., bacterial with associated thermogenic), so that under some circumstances, mixing and oxidation can be distinguished.

Oxidation can also be recognized in the methane-ethane and methane-propane carbon isotope cross-plots as shown in Figure 16.9. Minor amounts of ethane and possibly propane can be subjected to microbial attack, but the isotopic shift is most strongly reflected in the residual methane.

There is also some indication that hydrogen isotopes are also fractionated in aerobically altered methane (Coleman et al., 1981), but the corresponding D/H isotope effects are uncertain for anaerobic conditions. Figure 16.18 shows the combined effects of carbon and hydrogen isotope shifts due to oxidation. For comparison, the carbon and hydrogen isotope (C and D) variations expected for mixtures of two gas types (mixture 1 of bacterial CO_2 reduction with thermogenic and mixture 2 of bacterial methyl fermentation with thermogenic) are shown along with the *extreme* magnitude ranges of isotopic values of kerogen and due to methanogenesis. Under specific circumstances, oxidized bacterial gas could resemble a thermogenic gas. In this case, the secondary effects of oxidation should be apparent in combination with other parameters (such as $C_1/(C_2+C_3)$, $\delta^{13}C_{C_2H_4}$, or $\delta^{13}C_{C_3H_8}$).

Although a suite of analytical parameters is a reasonable approach to interpret uncomplicated natural gas occurrences, in cases of secondary effects, it is particularly appropriate to use several geochemical indices to confirm and constrain the kerogen type and thermal maturity of different source rocks and the postformation histories of gases. In many instances, one can reconstruct much of the geochemical background of a natural gas sample even if it is a complex mixture or has suffered severe alteration. It must be emphasized that stable isotopes, especially $\delta^{13}C_{C_2H_6}$ or $\delta^{13}C_{C_3H_8}$, and δD_{CH_4} are often crucial in revealing the true character of the natural gases.

CONCLUSIONS

Natural gases contain considerable information about their origin and history. A variety of geochemical tools and techniques are available to the explorationist to characterize them. In many cases, the combination of gas concentration and molecular and isotope compositions can help to ascertain the kerogen type or thermal maturity of the source rock from which the natural gas was derived. Gas can also be correlated effectively with other gases, oils, and their source rocks. The ability to carry out gas–gas correlations allows one to map the halo of hydrocarbon that can then be related back to a pod of active source rock using gas–source rock correlations. In this way, natural gas signatures are used to map petroleum systems.

The interpretative schemes presented here have been successful for various geographic and geologic settings, but their applicability must be determined for each new situation. The schemes depend heavily on empirical observation rather than theoretical considerations, and as such are limited to our current data base and level of understanding. Furthermore, any interpretation should rely on several geochemical techniques and be integrated with the geology of the petroleum system. This intentional duplicity is essential to recognize secondary gases with mixed or altered histories.

Acknowledgments   *I wish to acknowledge my colleagues over the years at the BGR whose combined efforts have led to our geochemical understanding of the relationship between natural gases and their sources. In particular, I would like to mention Eckhard Faber, Peter Gerling, Martin Schoell, and Wolfgang Stahl. Reviews by Nick Fuex and Peter van de Kamp helped improve the manuscript. Much of this work has been funded through BMFT grants in Germany and by NSERC grant 105389 (OG) in Canada.*

References Cited

Abrajano, T. A., N. R. Sturchio, J. H. Bohlke, G. L. Lyon, R. J. Poreda, and C. M. Stevens, 1988, Methane–hydrogen gas seeps, Zambales Ophiolite, Philippines: deep or shallow origin?: Chemical Geology, v. 71, p. 211–222.

Barker, J. F., and P. Fritz, 1981, Carbon isotope fractionation during microbial methane oxidation: Nature, v. 293, p. 289–291.

Bernard, B. B., J. M. Brooks, and W. M. Sackett, 1978, Light hydrocarbons in recent Texas continental shelf and slope sediments: Journal of Geophysical Research, v. 83, p. 4053–4061.

Berner, U., 1989, Entwicklung und Anwendung empirischer Modelle für die Kohlenstoffisotopenvariationen in Mischungen thermogener Erdgase: Ph.D. dissertation, T.U. Clausthal, FRG, 160 p.

Berner, U., and E. Faber, 1988, Maturity related mixing model for methane, ethane and propane, based on carbon isotopes, *in* L. Mattavelli and L. Novelli, eds., Advances in Organic Geochemistry, v. 13, p. 67–72.

Blake, D. R., and F. S. Rowland, 1988, Continuing worldwide increase in tropospheric methane, 1978 to 1987: Science, v. 239, p. 1129–1131.

Boigk, H., H. W. Hagemann, W. Stahl, and G. Wollanke, 1976, Isotopenphysikalische Untersuchungen: Erdoel und Kohle-Erdgas-Petrochemie Vereinigt mit Brennstoff Chemie, v. 29, p. 103–112.

Chung, H. M., and W. M. Sackett, 1979, Use of stable isotope compositions of pyrolytically derived methane as a maturity indices for carbonaceous materials: Geochimica et Cosmochimica Acta, v. 43, p. 1979–1988.

Chung, H. M., J. R. Gromly, and R. M. Squires, 1988, Origin of gaseous hydrocarbons in subsurface environments: theoretical considerations of carbon isotope distribution: Chemical Geology, v. 71, p. 97–103.

Claypool, G. E., 1974, Anoxic diagenesis and bacterial methane production in deep sea sediments, Ph.D. dissertation, University of California at Los Angeles, 276 p.

Claypool, G. E., and I. R. Kaplan, 1974, The origin and distribution of methane in marine sediments, *in* I. R. Kaplan, ed., Natural Gases in Marine Sediments: New York, Plenum Press, pp. 99–139.

Clayton, C., 1991, Carbon isotope fractionation during natural gas generation from kerogen: Marine and Petroleum Geology, v. 8, p. 232–240.

Cole, D. R., and H. Ohmoto, 1986, Kinetics of isotopic exchange at elevated temperatures and pressures, *in* J. W. Valley, H. P. Taylor, and J. R. O'Neil, eds., Stable isotopes in high temperature geological processes: Reviews in Mineralogy, v. 16, p. 41–87.

Coleman, D. D., W. F. Meents, C. Lin, and R. A. Keogh, 1977, Isotopic identification of leakage gas from underground storage reservoirs—a progress report: Illinois State Geological Survey, Petroleum, v. 111, p. 1–10.

Coleman D. D., J. B. Risatti, and M. Schoell, 1981, Fractionation of carbon and hydrogen isotopes by methane-oxidizing bacteria: Geochimica et Cosmochimica Acta, v. 45, p. 1033–1037.

Colombo, U., F. Gazzarini, G. Sironi, R. Gonfiantini, and E. Tongiorni, 1965, Carbon isotope composition of individual hydrocarbons from Italian natural gases: Nature, v. 205, p. 1303–1304.

Colombo, U., E. Tongiorni, and A. M. Caflisch, 1969, Carbon isotopic study of hydrocarbons in Italian natural gases, *in* P. A. Schenk and I. Havenaar, eds., Advances in Organic Geochemistry 1968: Oxford, Pergamon Press, p. 499–516.

Coveney, R. M., E. D. Goebel, E. J. Zeller, G. A. M. Dreschhoff, and E. E. Angino, 1987, Serpentinization and the origin of hydrogen gas in Kansas: AAPG Bulletin, v. 71, p. 39–48.

DesMarais, D. J., J. H. Donchin, N. L. Nehring, and A. H. Truesdell, 1981, Molecular carbon isotopic evidence for the origin of geothermal hydrocarbons: Nature, v. 292, p. 826–828.

Espitalié J., P. Ungerer, I. Irwin, and F. Marquis, 1987, Primary cracking of kerogens, Experimenting and modeling C_1, C_2–C_5, C_6–C_{15}, and C_{15+} classes of hydrocarbons formed: Organic Geochemistry, v. 13, p. 893–899.

Evans, C. R. and F. L. Staplin, 1971, Regional facies of organic metamorphism in geochemical exploration, *in* Third International Geochemical Exploration Symposium: Proceedings of Canadian Institute of Mining and Metallurgy, Special Volume 11, p. 517–520.

Everlin, G., 1990, Das Verhalten des in Mineralen enthaltenen Stickstoffs während der Diagenese und Metamorphose von Sedimenten: Ph.D. Dissertation, T.U. Braunschweig, 154 p.

Faber, E., 1987, Zur Isotopengeochemie gasförmiger Kohlenwasserstoffe: Erdöl Erdgas und Kohle, v. 103, p. 210–218.

Faber, E., and W. Stahl, 1984, Geochemical surface exploration for hydrocarbons in the North Sea: AAPG Bulletin, v. 68, p. 363–386.

Faber, E., and M. J. Whiticar, 1989, C- und -Isotope in leichtfluchtige Kohlenwasserstoffen der KTB: Hannover, N.L.F.B., KTB Reports, 29 p.

Faber, E., P. Gerling, and I. Dumke, 1987, Gaseous hydrocarbons of unknown origin found while drilling: Organic Geochemistry, v. 13, p. 875–879.

Faber, E., W. Stahl, M. J. Whiticar, J. Lietz, and J. M. Brooks, 1990, Thermal hydrocarbons in Gulf Coast sediments: SEPM Gulf Coast Section Foundation Ninth Annual Research Conference Proceedings, October 1, p. 297–307.

Faber, E., M. J. Whiticar, and P. Gerling, 1994, Comparison of Hydrocarbons from Unconventional Sources: KTB, EPR, and bit metamorphism, *in* M. J. Whiticar, ed., The Search for Deep Gas: International Energy Agency.

Frank, D. J., 1972, Deuterium variations in the Gulf of Mexico and selected organic materials: Ph.D. do, Texas A&M University.

Fuex, A. N., 1980, Experimental evidence against an appreciable isotopic fractionation of methane during migration, *in* A. G. Douglas and J. R. Maxwell, eds., Advances in Organic Geochemistry 1979: Oxford, Pergamon Press, p. 725–732.

Galimov, E. M., 1974, Carbon isotopes in oil and gas geology Nauka, Moscow (translation): NASA TT–682, Washington, D. C., 1975, 395 p.

Galimov, E. M., 1985, The Biological Fractionation of Isotopes: New York, Academic Press, 261 p.

Galimov, E. M., 1988, Sources and mechanisms of formation of gaseous hydrocarbons in sedimentary rocks: Chemical Geology, v. 71, p. 77–96.

Galimov, E. M., and A. A. Ivlev, 1973, Thermodynamic isotope effects in organic compounds: 1. Carbon isotope effects in straight-chained alkanes: Russian Journal of Physical Chemistry, v. 47, p. 1564–1566.

Galimov, E. M., and I. A. Petersil'ye, 1967, Isotopic composition of the carbon of methane isolated in the pores and cavities of some igneous minerals: Doklady AN SSSR 176, v. 4.

Galimov, E. M., V. I. Posyagin, and V. S. Prokhorov, 1972, Experimental study of the fractionation of carbon isotopes in the system CH_4-C_2H_6-C_3H_8-C_4H_{10} at different temperatures: Geokhimiya, v. 8, p. 977–987.

Gerling, P., 1985, Isotopengeochemische Oberflächenprospektion Onshore: BGR Internal Report, n. 98576, 36 p.

Gerling, P., M. J. Whiticar, and E. Faber, 1988, Extreme isotope fractionation of hydrocarbon gases in Permian salts: Organic Geochemistry, v. 13, p. 335–341.

Grotewold, G., H. D. Fuhrberg, and W. Philipp, 1979, Production and processing of nitrogen-rich natural gases from reservoirs in the NE part of the Federal Republic of Germany: 10th World Petroleum Congress, Heyden, New York, p. 1–8.

Holloway, J. R., 1977, Fugacity and activity of molecular species in supercritical fluids, *in* D. G. Fraser, ed., Thermodynamics in Geology: Dordrecht, Holland, Reidel Publishing, p. 161–181.

Horvitz, L., 1978, Near-surface evidence of hydrocarbon movement from depth, *in* Problems of Petroleum Migration: AAPG Studies in Geology 10, p. 241–269.

Hovland, M., and A. G. Judd, 1988, Seabed pockmarks and seepages—impact on geology, *in* Biology and the Marine Environment: London, Graham and Trotman, 293 p.

Hunt, J. M., 1979, Petroleum Geochemistry and Geology: San Francisco, W. H. Freeman, 617 p.

Hunt, J. M., A. Y. Huc, and J. K. Whelan, 1980. Generation of light hydrocarbons in sedimentary rocks: Nature, v. 288, p. 688–690.

Jakobsson, S., and J. R. Holloway, 1986, Crystal-liquid experiments in the presence of a C-O-H fluid buffered by graphite + iron + wustite: experimental methods and near-liquidus relations in basanite: Journal of Volcanology and Geothermal Research, v. 29, p. 265–291.

James, A. T., 1983, Correlation of natural gas by use of carbon isotope distribution between hydrocarbon components: AAPG Bulletin, v. 67, p. 1176–1191.

Jefferey, A. W. A., and I. R. Kaplan, 1988, Hydrocarbons and inorganic gases in the Gravberg-1 well, Siljan Ring, Sweden: Chemical Geology, v. 71, p. 237–255.

Jenden, P. D., K. D. Newell, I. R. Kaplan, and W. L. Watney, 1988, Composition of stable-isotope geochemistry of natural gases from Kansas, midcontinent, U.S.A.: Chemical Geology, v. 71, p. 117–147.

Jüntgen, H., and J. Klein, 1975, Enstehung von Erdgas aus kohligen Sedimenten: Erdöl und Kohle-Erdgas-Petrochemie Vereinigt mit Brennstoff Chemie, v. 28, p. 65–73.

Kandel, R. J., 1964, Methane–tritium system III: kinetics of the exchange reaction: Journal of Chemical Physics, v. 41, p. 2435–2442.

Karlsen, D. A., D. Leythaeuser, and R. G. Schaefer, 1987, Light hydrocarbon redistribution in a shallow core from the Ravnefjeld Formation on the Wegener Halvø, East Greenland: Organic Geochemistry, v. 13, p. 393–398.

Karweil, J., 1969, Aktuelle Probleme der Geochemie der Kohle, *in* P. A. Schenk and I. Havenaar, eds., Advances in Organic Geochemistry 1968: Oxford, Pergamon Press, p. 59–84.

Kettel, D., 1982, Norddeutsche Erdgase: Erdoel und Kohle-Erdgas-Petrochemie Vereinigt mit Brennstoff Chemie, v. 35, p. 557–559.

Koepp, M., 1979. D/H-Austauschverlauf zwischen Erdöl und Wasser, *in* Energieforschungsprogramm Forschungsvorhaben ET 3003 A: D/H-Isotopenverhaeltnisse in organischen Substanzen, Erdölen und Erdgasen, Bericht III, Archiv Bundesanstalt Geowissenschaften und Rohstoffe, 83 343, Hannover, p. 105–137.

Konnerup-Madsen, J., R. Kreulen, and J. Rose-Hansen, 1988, Stable isotope characteristics of hydrocarbon gases in the alkaline Ilimaussaq complex, south Greenland: Bulletin Minéral, v. 111, p. 567–576.

Kvenvolden, K. A., 1988, Methane hydrate—a major reservoir of carbon in the shallow geosphere: Chemical Geology, v. 71, p. 41–51.

Laier, T., 1988, Hydrocarbon gases in the crystalline rocks of the Gravberg-1 well, Swedish deep gas project: Marine and Petroleum Geology, v. 5, p. 370–377.

Lewan, M. D., and B. Buchardt, 1989, Irradiation of organic matter by uranium decay in the Alum Shale, Sweden: Geochimica et Cosmochimica Acta, v. 53, p. 1307–1322.

Leythaeuser, D., and Th. Schwarzkopf, 1986, The pristane/*n*-heptadecane ratio as an indicator for recognition of hydrocarbon migration effects: Organic Geochemistry, v. 10, p. 191–197.

Leythaeuser, D., R. G. Schaefer, and A. Yükler, 1980. Diffusion of light hydrocarbons through near-surface rocks: Nature, v. 284, p. 522–525.

Leythaeuser, D., A. Mackenzie, R. G. Schaefer, and M. Bjorøy, 1984, A novel approach for recognition and quantification of hydrocarbon migration effects in shale–sandstone sequences: AAPG Bulletin, v. 68, p. 196–219.

Luth, R. W., 1989, Natural versus experimental control of oxidation state: American Mineralogist, v. 74, p. 50–57.

Lutz, M., J. P. H. Kaasschieter, and D. H. van Wijhe, 1975, Geological factors controlling Rotliegend gas accumulations in the mid-European basin: Ninth World Petroleum Congress Panel Discussion, Proceedings, v. 2, p. 93–103.

Lyon, G. L., 1974, Isotopic analysis of gas from the Caraico Trench sediments, *in* I. R. Kaplan, ed., Natural gases in marine sediments: New York, Plenum Press, p. 91–97.

Lyon, G. L., and J. R. Hulston, 1984, Carbon and hydrogen isotopic compositions of New Zealand geothermal gases: Geochimica et Cosmochima Acta, v. 48, p. 1161–1171.

May, F., W. Freund, E. P. Müller, and K. P. Dostal, 1968, Modellversuche über Isotopenfraktionierung von Erdgaskomponenten während der Migration: Zeitschrift für angewandte Geologie, v. 14, p. 376–380.

McCarty, H. B., and G. T. Felbeck, Jr., 1986, High temperature simulation of petroleum formation, IV. stable carbon isotope studies of gaseous hydrocarbons: Organic Geochemistry, v. 9, p. 183–192.

Meincke, W., 1967, Zur Herkunft des Wasserstoffs in Tiefenproben: Zeitschrift für angewandte Geologie, v. 13, p. 346–348.

Oremland, R. S., M. J. Whiticar, F. E. Strohmaier, and R. P. Kiene, 1988, Bacterial ethane formation from reduced, ethylated sulfur compounds in anoxic sediments: Geochimica et Cosmochimica Acta, v. 52, p. 1895–1904.

Philippi, G. T., 1975, The deep subsurface temperature controlled origin of the gaseous and gasoline-range hydrocarbons or petroleum: Geochimica et Cosmochimica Acta, v. 39, p. 1353–1373.

Philp, R., and P. T. Crisp, 1982, Surface geochemical methods used for oil and gas prospecting—a review: Journal of Geochemical Exploration, v. 17, p. 1–34.

Rice, D. D., 1992, Controls, habitat, and resource potential of ancient bacterial gas, *in* B. Durand, ed., Biogenic natural gas: p. 1–28.

Rice, D. D., and G. E. Claypool, 1981, Generation, accumulation and resource potential of biogenic gas: AAPG Bulletin, v. 67, p. 1199–1218.

Sackett, W. M., 1968, Carbon isotope composition of natural methane occurrences: AAPG Bulletin, v. 52, p. 853–857.

Sackett, W. M., and H. M. Chung, 1979, Experimental confirmation of the lack of carbon isotope exchange between methane and carbon oxides at high temperature: Geochimica et Cosmochimica Acta, v. 43, p. 273–276.

Saxena, S. K., and Y. Fei, 1988, Fluid mixtures in the C-O-H system at high pressure and temperature: Geochimica et Cosmochimica Acta, v. 52, p. 505–512.

Schaefer, R. G., and R. Littke, 1987, Maturity-related compositional changes in the low-molecular-weight hydrocarbon fraction of Toarcian shales: Organic Geochemistry, v. 13, p. 887–892.

Schaefer R. G., D. H. Welte, and H. Pooch, 1984. Geochemistry of low molecular weight hydrocarbons in two exploration wells of the Elmworth gas field, western Canada basin, *in* P. A. Schenck, P. A. de Leeuw, and G. W. M. Lijmbach, eds., Advances in Organic Geochemistry 1983: Oxford, Pergamon Press, p. 695–701.

Schmidt, M., 1987, Isotope-geochemical analysis of dunk tank gases, headspace gases, desorbed gases of cuttings and cores: Internal Report, Vattenfall Deep Gas Project, November, 14 p.

Schoell, M., 1980, The hydrogen and carbon isotopic composition of methane from natural gases of various origins: Geochimica et Cosmochimica Acta, v. 44, p. 649–661.

Schoell, M., 1984. Wasserstoff und kohlenstoffisotope in organischen substanzen, erdölen und erdgasen: Geologisches Jahrbuch Reihe D, v. 67, 164 p.

Schoell, M., ed., 1988, Origins of methane in the earth: Chemical Geology, v. 71, 265 p.

Shen Ping, Shen Qixiang, Wang Xiaubin and Xu Yangchang, 1988, Characteristic of the isotope composition of gas-form hydrocarbon and the identification of coal-type gas: Science Sinica Series, v. 31, n. 6.

Sherwood, B., P. Fritz, S. K. Frape, S. A. Macko, S. M. Weise, and J. A. Welhan, 1988, Methane occurrences in the Canadian shield: Chemical Geology, v. 71, p. 223–236.

Silverman, S. R., 1971, Influence of petroleum origin and transformation on its distribution and redistribution in sedimentary rocks: Proceedings of the Eighth World Petroleum Congress, v. 2, p. 47–54.

Simoneit, B. R. T., O. E. Kawka, and M. Brault, 1988, Origin of gases and condensates in the Guaymas basin hydrothermal system, Gulf of California: Chemical Geology, v. 71, p. 169–182.

Stahl, W., 1973, Carbon isotope ratios of German natural gases in comparison with isotopic data of gaseous hydrocarbons from other parts of the World, *in* B. Tissot and F. Bienner, eds., Advances in Organic Geochemistry 1972: Oxford, Pergamon Press, p. 453–462.

Stahl, W., 1977, Carbon and nitrogen isotopes in hydrocarbon research and exploration: Chemical Geology, v. 20, p. 121–149.

Stahl, W., and J. Koch, 1974, ^{13}C/^{12}C-Verhälltnis nordeutscher Erdgase-Reifemerkmal ihrer Muttersubstanzen: Erdöl und Kohle-Erdgas-Petrochemie, v. 27, p. 10.

Stahl, W., H. Boigk, and G. Wollanke, 1975, Carbon and nitrogen isotope data of Upper Carboniferous and Rotliegend natural gas from north Germany and their relationship to the maturity of the organic source material, *in* R. Campos and J. Conji, eds., Advances in Organic Geochemistry 1974: New York, John Wiley, p. 539–559.

Sundberg, K. R., and C. R. Bennett, 1981, Carbon isotope paleothermometry of natural gas, *in* M. Bjorøy, ed., Advances in Organic Geochemistry 1980: New York, John Wiley, p. 769–774.

Taylor, J. C. M., 1983, Bit metamorphism, illustrated by lithological data from German North Sea wells: Geol Mijnbouw, v. 62, p. 211–219.

Thompson K. F. M., 1979, Light hydrocarbons in subsurface sediments: Geochimica et Cosmochimica Acta, v. 43, p. 657–672.

Tissot, B. P., 1969, Premières donnéessur les mécanismes et la cinétique de la formation du pétrole dan les sédiments: simulation d'un schéma réactionnel sur ordinateur: Revue Institute Français de Petrol XXIV, v. 4, p. 470–501.

Tissot, B. P., and D. H. Welte, 1978, Petroleum Formation and Occurrence: Berlin, Springer Verlag, 538 p.

Weinlich, F. H., 1991, Genese und Verteilung der freien Gase im Stassfurt Karbonat der Lausitz: Zeitschrift fuer angewandte Geologie, v. 37, p. 14–20.

Welhan, J. A., 1988, Origins of methane in hydrothermal systems: Chemical Geology, v. 71, p. 183–198.

Welhan , J. A., and H. Craig, 1979, Methane and hydrogen in the East Rise hydrothermal fluids: Geophysical Research Letters, v. 6, p. 829–832.

Welhan , J. A., and J. E. Lupton, 1987, Light hydrocarbon gases in Guaymas basin hydrothermal fluids: Thermogenic versus abiogenic origin: AAPG Bulletin, v. 71, p. 215–223.

Whalen, M., N. Tanaka, R. Henry, and T. Yoshinari, 1987, ^{13}C, D, and ^{14}C in methane: EOS, v. 68, p. 1220–1220.

Whelan, J. K., M. E. Tarafa, and J. M. Hunt, 1982, Volatile C_1–C_8 organic compounds in macroalgae: Nature, v. 299, p. 50–52.

Whiticar, M. J., 1990, A geochemical perspective of natural gas and atmospheric methane: *in* B. Durand and F. Behar eds., Advances in Organic Geochemistry 1989: Oxford, Pergamon Press, p. 531–547.

Whiticar, M. J., 1992, Isotope Tracking of microbial methane formation and oxidation, *in* D. D. Adams, P. M. Crill, and S. P. Seitzinger, eds., Cycling of reduced gases in the hydrosphere: Mitteilung (Communications), Stuttgart, Internationalen Vereinigung für Theoretische und Angewandte Limnlogie, E. Schweizerbart'sche Verlagsbuchhandlung, v. 23.

Whiticar, M. J., and E. Faber, 1986. Methane oxidation in sediment and water column environments—isotope evidence: Organic Geochemistry, v. 10, p. 759–768.

Whiticar, M. J., and E. Faber, 1989, Molecular and stable isotope composition of headspace and total hydrocarbon gases at ODP Leg 104, Sites 642, 643, and 644, Vøring Plateau, Norwegian Sea, *in* O. Eldholm, J. Theide, et al., eds., Proceedings of the Ocean Drilling Program: Scientific Results, v. 104, p. 327–334.

Whiticar, M. J., and B. R. T. Simoneit, in press, Carbon and hydrogen isotope systematics of hydrothermal hydrocarbons at Yellowstone Park, U.S.A.: Geochimica et Cosmochimica Acta.

Whiticar, M. J., and E. Suess, 1990, Hydrothermal hydrocarbon gases in the sediments of the King George Basin, Bransfield Strait, Antarctica: Applied Geochemistry, v. 5, p. 135–147.

Whiticar, M. J., E. Faber, and M. Schoell, 1984, Carbon and hydrogen isotopes of C_1-C_5 hydrocarbons in natural gases (abs.): AAPG Research Conference on Natural Gases, San Antonio, Texas, p. 31.

Whiticar, M. J., E. Suess, and H. Wehner, 1985, Thermogenic hydrocarbons in surface sediments of the Bransfield Strait, Antarctic Peninsula: Nature, v. 314, p. 87–90.

Whiticar, M. J., E. Faber, and M. Schoell, 1986, Biogenic methane formation in marine and freshwater environments: CO_2 reduction vs. acetate fermentation—isotope evidence: Geochimica et Cosmochimica Acta, v. 50, p. 693–709.

Zehnder, A. J. B., ed., 1988, Biology of Anaerobic Microorganisms: New York, John Wiley, 318 p.

"Very large tar sands occur in geologic settings which are unconventional by accepted standards, yet they are explainable in the light of modern knowledge of generation, migration, and degradation of oil in sedimentary basins. This fact stresses the need to understand, in space and time, the origin, movements, pathways, and abundance of the oil crop in conjunction with geologic history in any given basin."

—G. J. Demaison

Passage from Demaison, G. J., 1977, Tar sands and supergiant oil fields: AAPG Bulletin v. 61, p. 1960.

Magoon, L. B, and W. G. Dow, eds., 1994, The petroleum system—from source to trap: AAPG Memoir 60.

Chapter **17**

Maturity Modeling: Thermal Indicators, Hydrocarbon Generation, and Oil Cracking

Douglas W. Waples

Consultant
Denver, Colorado, U.S.A.

Abstract

Thermal maturity modeling is now a highly developed discipline, with a number of excellent software programs available for working geologists. Maturity models are used to describe the behavior of individual thermal indicators (such as various biomarkers and vitrinite reflectance), as well as hydrocarbon generation and cracking. Maturity modeling must begin with a valid conceptual model of local geology, and should then follow a logical sequence. First, present-day heat flow and thermal conductivities are selected to predict correctly the observed present-day temperatures. Next, paleoheat flows and the magnitudes of depositional and erosional events are chosen to agree with the regional geology and concepts of basin evolution and to predict correctly the observed values for any available thermal indicators. Finally, modeling of hydrocarbon generation within a source rock and cracking of oil to gas in source or reservoir rocks is carried out once all input data are internally consistent (optimized).

Kinetic models for organic maturation are clearly superior to the time–temperature index (TTI) approach and should therefore be used in future applications. Some kinetic models now predict hydrocarbon expulsion as well as generation and thus may provide more accurate estimates of hydrocarbon composition than generation models alone. Faulting and other tectonic complexities remain problems. One-dimensional maturity modeling (z spatial dimension plus time) seems adequate for most exploration applications.

INTRODUCTION

Thermal maturity modeling has become a standard technology in petroleum exploration. When maturity modeling was first developed, the distinction between hydrocarbon generation and maturation of thermal indicators (such as vitrinite reflectance) was not consistently made. Now, however, geochemists routinely distinguish between maturation of thermal indicators and hydrocarbon generation and cracking (Table 17.1). *Maturation of thermal indicators* refers to thermally induced changes in a variety of indicators that record the thermal histories of rocks in different ways *Hydrocarbon generation* and *cracking,* in contrast, refer to two different processes: the formation and the destruction of oil and gas. Maturation of thermal indicators, hydrocarbon generation, and hydrocarbon cracking are collectively referred to as *maturation* and are now modeled under the umbrella term *maturity modeling.* It is important to be able to model all three types of phenomena, but equally important to keep them conceptually separate.

These three types of maturity modeling are important to investigations of sedimentary basins and their petroleum systems. Thermally induced changes to organic matter and other thermal indicators give important clues about the rate and extent of subsurface heating. This heat affects numerous rock properties, such as induration, porosity, and clay mineralogy. Thus, maturity modeling is important to sedimentary basin analysis. However, the moment hydrocarbons are expelled from a mature source rock, that source rock, the expelled hydrocarbons, the migration conduit, and the traps form a petroleum system. Here, the second type of maturity modeling is critical for understanding the origin and evolution of a particular petroleum system. Finally, cracking of oil to gas can take place as the petroleum system evolves, either during late generation in the source rock or in the reservoir (Blanc and Connan, Chapter 14, this volume). In either case, maturity modeling is useful for predicting the physical nature of the hydrocarbon fluids.

Neither maturity modeling (usually carried out in the z spatial dimension through time) nor its companion, basin modeling (carried out in either two or three spatial dimensions, plus time [2-D = *x, z, t;* 3-D = *x, y, z, t*]), is truly a process model (see Tetzlaff and Harbaugh, 1989) since phenomena are not modeled molecule-by-molecule, drop-by-drop, or grain-by-grain. Application of process modeling to exploration is inhibited by computer limitations, lack of data control, and imperfect knowledge of many of the processes that would have to be included. Models are therefore at best crude approximations of the general characteristics of reality, simulating the approximate sequence of events in a semiquantitative way using equations that range from highly precise to highly empirical.

We should thus recognize from the outset that our models will always contain intrinsic uncertainties and errors that limit the accuracy of their predictions. These fundamental uncertainties are further compounded by our imperfect knowledge of the history and nature of the rocks and hydrocarbon fluids being modeled. Successful application of maturity models depends largely on our ability to deal with these uncertainties. The reader who is unfamiliar with maturity modeling may find it beneficial to consult Waples (1980; 1985, chap. 9) before reading this chapter.

MATURITY MODELING

History and Present Status

The history of maturity modeling has been discussed in detail elsewhere (Waples, 1984; Ungerer, 1990) and is only summarized here. Although various maturity models had been in use in a few major oil companies since the early to mid-1970s, maturity modeling first became widely popular following Waples' (1980) application of Lopatin's (1971) time–temperature index (TTI) to petroleum generation. Many early applications of the TTI method were carried out by hand, but by the mid-1980s, commercial software became available to ease the tedium of hand calculations and to permit the use of kinetic models instead of (or in addition to) the TTI method. A large number of software programs for carrying out maturity modeling are now available to the public. A number of computer codes have also been published for independent workers (Elphick, 1989; Elphick and Reed, 1989; Sweeney, 1989, 1990; Wood, 1990), but they lack the convenient user interfaces of commercial software that greatly facilitate the modeling process.

Objectives

All maturity modeling should begin with a clear conceptual model of geologic history because modeling based on inadequate geologic concepts is likely to show serious weaknesses under close scrutiny. Regardless of the amount of attention one gives to construction of the initial geologic model, however, it will probably contain errors and incorrect assumptions. One important objective of maturity modeling, therefore, is to test the original geologic model and suggest improvements. For example, our present conceptual models are inadequate to predict from first principles such important input parameters as heat flow histories and thermal conductivities of rocks (Waples et al., 1992a,b). The second major objective is to obtain information about the status and history of hydrocarbon generation and thus help to determine whether a petroleum system exists.

In the early days of maturity modeling, these two objectives were not separated because modeling of thermal indicators and modeling of hydrocarbon generation were usually treated as the same problem. However, as the distinction between maturation of thermal indicators and hydrocarbon generation has become clear, the differences between these two objectives have also crystallized. Thermal indicators are used to check the correctness of the geologic model by comparing the modeled behavior of thermal indicators with measured values. Only after this first objective is successfully completed should an attempt be made to model hydrocarbon generation. Any modern maturity modeling study must fulfill both objectives, that is, it must model thermal indicators for basin analysis as well as hydrocarbon generation for system analysis.

Types of Thermal Maturity Modeling

Time–Temperature Index (TTI) Modeling

TTI modeling (Lopatin, 1971; Waples, 1980) assumes that (1) only time and temperature are important factors in maturation and (2) time and temperature can be substituted for each other (e.g., the lower the temperature, the longer the time required to reach a given level of thermal maturity). Pressure effects are neglected. The way in which time and temperature are interconverted depends on a gross simplification of basic principles of chemical kinetics. TTI values are calculated using equations such as those of Royden et al. (1980) or Waples (1980).

The TTI method was originally designed to predict coal rank through its calibration to vitrinite reflectance (R_o), and thus it directly models only the change in a single thermal indicator. A number of different TTI–R_o calibrations have been developed, both ignoring compaction effects (e.g., Lopatin, 1971; Waples, 1980; Goff, 1983) and including them (Dykstra, 1987). Some workers have attempted to overcome inherent weaknesses in the TTI method by providing sedimentary basin-by-basin calibration (e.g., Issler, 1984).

Because vitrinite reflectance for many years was directly correlated with hydrocarbon generation, the TTI method has also been used to predict hydrocarbon generation and cracking (e.g., Waples, 1980, 1988), although it was inappropriate for that purpose. Although the TTI method does not specify kerogen type, a crude dependence on kerogen type can be included by shifting the vitrinite reflectance value at which hydrocarbon generation begins for different types of kerogens (Waples, 1985).

Table 17.1. Division of Thermal Maturity Modeling into Thermal Indicators and Hydrocarbons

Maturation of Thermal Indicators			Hydrocarbons	
Time–Temperature	Max. Temperature	Integrated Time–Temperature	Generation	Cracking
Fission track annealing	Fluid inclusions	R_o T_{max} $20S/(20R + 20S)$ steranes $22S/(22R + 22S)$ hopanes Sterane aromatization Methylphenanthrene index (MPI) Biphenyls pollen translucency Fraction of aromatic protons (FAP or PAP)[a] C-factor (IR spectrum)[a] W_{min} (IR spectrum)[a] Fraction of aromatic protons (NMR)[a]	Oil Gas	Oil to gas

[a]Not discussed in text; see Ritter et al. (in press) for details.

Kinetic Modeling

Kinetic modeling is used both to predict hydrocarbon generation and oil cracking and to model the behavior of some thermal indicators. The theoretical foundation of kinetic modeling is much more solid than that of TTI modeling (Tissot et al., 1987), but is still imperfect. Kinetic models assume that a given process (such as hydrocarbon generation or vitrinite reflectance change) consists of one or several parallel chemical reactions. Kinetic parameters for each individual reaction are derived from laboratory experiments, empirical data from wells, or both. The maturation of different types of organic matter (including different types of kerogen) can be modeled using different kinetic parameters.

A number of weaknesses exist in kinetic models, however. First, the laboratory measurements from which kinetic parameters are derived always contain some uncertainties, such as temperature control (Espitalié et al., 1993). Second, most kinetic models are calibrated using data obtained from high-temperature laboratory experiments, but it is far from certain that the processes occurring under laboratory conditions are good analogs for those occurring in nature. Finally, even if laboratory experiments were perfect analogs for natural reactions, there would be statistical errors in extrapolating from laboratory conditions to natural situations.

Arrhenius TTI Modeling

Wood (1988) and Hunt et al. (1991) have shown that a simplified Arrhenius (kinetic) model can be used to calculate what they call TTI_{ARR} values. Hunt et al. (1991) have developed nomographs for calculating TTI_{ARR} values for a variety of different type II kerogens. This method has two advantages over standard kinetic modeling: (1) the use of nomographs eliminates the need for computers in kinetic modeling, and (2) if one does wish to use a computer, the computations are faster than standard kinetic calculations. According to these workers, loss of accuracy due to these simplifications is very small. Although these models contain the phrase "TTI" in their names, they have more in common with kinetic models than with the traditional TTI method.

Modeling of Thermal Maturity Indicators

Numerous thermal indicators exist today, and others are being developed almost continually. Curiale et al. (1989) have recently reviewed many of them, including some whose behavior can be modeled (Table 17.1). All commercially available software programs include kinetic or TTI models for one or more thermal indicators.

By far the most widely modeled thermal indicator has been vitrinite reflectance (R_o). A number of molecular transformations, including biomarkers, have become fairly popular. Apatite fission track annealing (sometimes called AFTA[R]) is also in common use. Some progress has been made in modeling T_{max} data obtained from Rock-Eval pyrolysis (e.g., Peters, 1986). In rare cases, pollen translucency (Lerche, 1988a,b, 1990), fluid inclusion homogenization temperatures (Roedder, 1984; Goldstein, 1986; Burruss, 1989; Barker and Goldstein, 1990; Leischner and Welte, 1993; Walderhaug and Fjeld-skaar, 1993), and other less common indicators (Ritter et al., 1993) have been studied.

In the past, vitrinite reflectance has usually been modeled using the TTI method (e.g., Waples, 1980), although some other approaches have been used (see Sweeney and Burnham, 1990, for review). Explanations of the details of TTI modeling are available elsewhere (e.g., Waples, 1980, 1985). However, recent development of kinetic models for vitrinite reflectance (Larter, 1988; Burnham and Sweeney, 1989; Sweeney and Burnham, 1990) now offers an alternative that is almost certainly more accurate than the TTI method (Waples et al., 1992b). Nevertheless, because current kinetic models are unable to distinguish among the different types of vitrinite, they may still predict R_o values that have an intrinsic uncertainty of as much as 0.2% R_o (Ungerer, 1993).

Biomarkers are increasing in popularity and availability as thermal indicators. The biomarker ratios most commonly used are $20S/(20R + 20S)$ for C_{29} regular steranes, $22S/(22R + 22S)$ for homohopanes, and tri- and monoaromatic steranes. The strengths and weaknesses of these parameters and our current knowledge of the kinetic parameters have been evaluated elsewhere

(Mackenzie and McKenzie, 1983; Waples and Machihara, 1991; Ritter et al., 1993). Other molecular indicators for which kinetic descriptions have been developed and used include methylphenanthrenes (Abbott and Maxwell, 1988; Tupper and Burckhardt, 1990), biphenyls (Alexander et al., 1990), esters (Alexander et al., 1991), and several indicators discussed by Ritter et al. (1993) (Table 17.1). Although all these molecular indicators are useful, their applications are fraught with more difficulties than originally anticipated. These problems stem both from uncertainties about kinetic parameters and from unexpected complexities of the chemical systems being modeled (Abbott et al., 1990; Ritter et al., 1993). Consequently, at present their accuracy and degree of application vary widely.

Apatite fission track analysis is based on the annealing of fission tracks in detrital apatite crystals as a function of time and temperature. In principle, fission track data can yield detailed information on the timing and temperature of thermal events in a rock's history below about 100°–170°C, depending on the effective heating time (e.g., Naeser et al., 1989). The technique is thus different from other thermal indicators that simply represent the total effects of heating. In practice, however, some of the mathematical framework crucial to the interpretation of fission track data is in dispute (see Crowley et al., 1991; Naeser, 1993), and unraveling thermal histories, particularly quantitative paleotemperatures, from fission track data can be tricky.

Because Rock-Eval T_{max} data are abundant, much effort has been expended trying to develop a kinetic model for T_{max} change. Although such models have now been published (e.g., Sweeney, 1989, 1990), many unsolved problems remain, largely as a result of the dependence of T_{max} on kerogen type as well as on maturity.

Modeling Hydrocarbon Generation

Kinetic modeling of hydrocarbon generation began even earlier than TTI modeling, but the initial models (Tissot, 1969; Tissot and Espitalié, 1975) were much less accurate and popular than modern ones. Today numerous kinetic models exist, some of which are in the public domain (Tissot et al., 1987; Burnham, 1989; Burnham and Sweeney, 1991). Ungerer (1990) has provided an excellent review of the technical status of kinetic models.

The public models provided by the French Petroleum Institute (IFP) and Lawrence Livermore National Laboratory (LLNL) are the most widely used. They describe the traditional type I (Green River Shale), type II (Toarcian of the Paris basin), and type III (Mahakam delta) kerogens, and they agree well with one another.

Examples of kinetic data for standard kerogen types I, II, and III are shown in Figure 17.1. Each kerogen is thought to consist of several bond types differing in activation energy by one or two kilocalories per mole. In most models, the pre-exponential factor is considered to be the same for all the bonds in the kerogen, generally on the order of 10^{13}–10^{16}/sec. If pre-exponential factors are

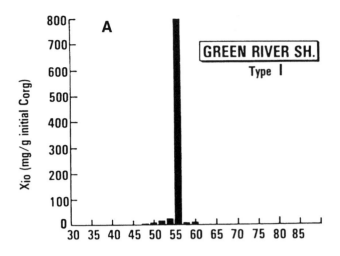

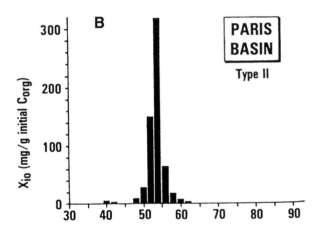

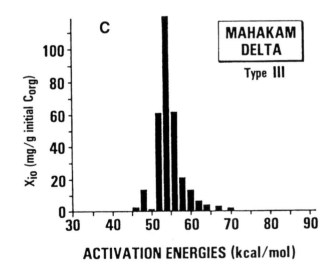

Figure 17.1. Histograms of activation energies for various bond strengths in the IFP kinetic model for (A) type I, (B) type II, and (C) type III kerogens. The *y*-axis in each histogram represents the mass of hydrocarbon formed per gram of organic carbon and thus is directly comparable among all three kerogen types. (From Tissot et al., 1987.)

Table 17.2. Comparison of Kinetic Parameters for Standard Type II and Type III Kerogens in IFP and LLNL Models

Type II Kerogen	IFP[a]	LLNL[b]
Oil potential from kerogen (mg/g TOC)	492	350
Gas potential from kerogen (mg/g TOC)	0	65
Oil to gas cracking efficiency (%)	45	50
A factor, HC generation (1/sec)	9.079×10^{13}	3.010×10^{13}
A factor, oil cracking (1/sec)	3.000×10^{14}	1.014×10^{12}
Activation energy for oil cracking (kcal/mol)	57	54
Activation energy for hydrocarbon generation (kcal/mol); fraction[c]		
40	0.014	—
48	0.010	—
49	—	0.05
50	0.057	0.20
51	—	0.50
52	0.555	0.20
53	—	0.05
54	0.293	—
56	0.045	—
58	0.012	—
60	0.008	—
62	0.006	—
Type III Kerogen		
Oil potential from kerogen (mg/g TOC)	201	50
Gas potential from kerogen (mg/g TOC)	0	110
Oil to gas cracking efficiency (%)	55	50
A factor, HC generation (1/sec)	5.460×10^{14}	1.616×10^{13}
A factor, oil cracking (1/sec)	5.501×10^{14}	1.014×10^{12}
Ea for oil cracking (kcal/mol)	62	54
Ea for hydrocarbon generation (kcal/mol); fraction[c]		
48	—	0.04
50	—	0.14
52	0.015	0.32
54	0.060	0.17
56	0.373	0.13
58	0.313	—
60	0.094	0.10
62	0.055	—
64	0.035	0.07
66	0.025	—
68	0.020	0.03
70	0.010	—

[a]IFP, French Petroleum Institute kinetics (Tissot et al., 1987).

[b]LLNL, Lawrence Livermore National Laboratory kinetics (Burnham, 1989; modified by Burnham, personal communication, 1990, as discussed in Waples et al., 1992a).

[c]Fraction of the kerogen having bonds with a particular activation energy.

the same for all bond types, changes in activation energy as small as a few kilocalories per mole can lead to major differences in the temperature and timing of hydrocarbon generation. (If pre-exponential factors vary among the bond types, it is more difficult to make general comments about sensitivity.) Thus, in comparing kinetic parameters for different models, one must look at both the pre-exponential factor and the activation energy. Different kinetic models can predict similar generation behavior over a range of geologic conditions only if both their activation energies and pre-exponential factors are similar.

Table 17.2 shows a comparison of kinetic parameters for type II and III kerogens from the IFP and LLNL models. The differences in activation energies between the two models are largely compensated by the differences in pre-exponential factors, resulting in similar predictions about oil generation for most geologic histories. The most significant difference between the two models, in fact, is that the LLNL model allows generation of gas directly from kerogen, whereas this version of the IFP model only forms gas by cracking of oil. (A later version of the IFP model [Espitalié et al., 1988] allows direct generation of gas.) Waples et al.

Table 17.3. Kerogens for Which Published Kinetic Data Are Available

Kerogen or Source Rock Name	Location	References[a]
Monterey	California, U.S.A.	A
Kirkuk	Iraq	A
La Luna	Venezuela	B
Phosphoria	Montana, U.S.A.	B, C
Woodford	Oklahoma, U.S.A.	B, C
New Albany	Illinois, U.S.A.	B
	Kentucky, U.S.A.	B
Posidonia	Germany	D
Talang Akar shales and coals	Indonesia	E
Alum Shale	Sweden	F

[a]References: A, Tissot et al. (1987); B, Burnham and Braun (1990); C, Lewan (1985); D, Burnham (1990); E, Noble et al. (1991); F, Lewan and Buchardt (1989).

(1992b) have concluded that intrinsic differences between the LLNL and IFP models are considerably smaller than most of the other uncertainties in maturity modeling. Therefore, the choice of a particular kinetic model (e.g., LLNL or IFP) for correctly identifying type I, II, or III kerogen would be unlikely to affect exploration decisions.

Identification of kerogen type, however, can present problems in modeling hydrocarbon generation. Waples et al. (1992b) have shown that normal errors in estimating the proportions of standard kerogen types II and III in a typical mixed-type kerogen can lead to important differences in modeling results. They also showed that incorrectly identifying a high-sulfur Monterey-type kerogen (type II-S) as a standard type II kerogen (or vice versa) could lead to significant errors. The same cautions probably apply to a variety of other nonstandard kerogens, such as high-wax or resin-rich types.

Kinetic parameters have now been published for a number of kerogens from source rocks other than those representing the three main kerogen types (Table 17.3). Because these data have been obtained over several years by a number of laboratories using different equipment and techniques, some discrepancies have been reported (see Burnham and Braun, 1990, for discussion). In most cases, these discrepancies are probably of little practical significance for exploration, but they might occasionally lead to different exploration decisions. One must therefore be cautious about using published kinetic data for individual kerogens.

It is now also possible to obtain "personalized" kinetic data for individual kerogen samples at a cost of about $800–$1000 (U.S. dollars) per sample. Although the cost is too high to justify routine use of this approach, a company with a strong and ongoing interest in a particular exploration area might find it worthwhile to obtain personalized kinetic data for a few samples of the suspected source rock. However, significantly different kinetic parameters have been reported for the same rock sample submitted to different laboratories (Hermanrud, 1993). It is thus still an open question whether use of

personalized kinetics really improves the accuracy of hydrocarbon generation modeling.

Two alternative types of kinetic models exist in addition to the standard IFP and LLNL types of model, which predict generation of oil and gas using a distribution of discrete activation energies (Figure 17.1 and Table 17.2). Quigley and Mackenzie (1988) and Burnham and Braun (1990) have proposed that it would be valid to assume a Gaussian (normal) distribution of activation energies for hydrocarbon formation and to express this range of activation energies using only three parameters: a mean pre-exponential factor, a mean activation energy, and a standard deviation for the distribution of activation energies. Quigley and Mackenzie (1988) allow each sample to contain two types of kerogen (called labile and refractory), each with its own set of parameters. However, this approach has yet to be embraced by builders of maturity models.

The second alternative shows more promise for widespread acceptance. It is called *compositional kinetics* because it subdivides the products of hydrocarbon generation into several groups rather than just into oil and gas. Ungerer et al. (1988b) allow formation of four products (C_{15+}, C_6–C_{14}, C_2–C_5, and methane). Forbes et al. (1991) have applied compositional kinetics in a regional analysis. Future research may subdivide the hydrocarbon groups even further. The objective of such detailed analysis is a better description of the effects of phase behavior on hydrocarbon expulsion and migration.

The kinetics of gas generation from kerogen has received less attention than that of oil generation. Most models have either ignored gas generation or have included it almost as an afterthought, assigning it the same kinetics as oil generation. The total amount of hydrocarbons generated is then simply partitioned into oil and gas according to a predefined ratio for each kerogen type (e.g., Burnham, 1989; Burnham and Braun, 1990; Burnham and Sweeney, 1991). Use of compositional kinetic models should improve our ability to predict gas generation.

Modeling Oil Cracking

In Source Rocks

The action of high temperatures over long times is responsible for the conversion of kerogen to oil and gas. However, if oil is retained in the source rock after generation, cracking will eventually convert it to gas plus carbon residue. Maturity modeling of any source rock should therefore predict how much cracking has occurred in the source rock.

This problem really has two parts: to determine expulsion efficiency and to determine whether the hydrocarbons retained in the source rock were cracked. In the past, most maturity modeling software ignored expulsion, implicitly assuming that the hydrocarbons simply remained in the source rock. Application of such models therefore often led to overly pessimistic appraisals (e.g., "overmature, burned out, worthless, gas window") for rocks that may actually have performed beautifully in the past as effective source rocks. Other models have explicitly allowed some of the hydrocarbons to be expelled and thus have treated cracking in the source rock more realistically. It is now becoming more common to calculate expulsion explicitly (e.g., Nakayama, 1987; Jabour and Nakayama, 1988; Forbes et al., 1991). Such models can distinguish between the fates of hydrocarbons that are expelled and those that remain in source rocks. Expulsion models are discussed in more detail in Chapter 18 (Waples, this volume).

In Reservoir Rocks

The application of cracking models to reservoir rocks, in contrast, has existed for a long time. To estimate the amount of cracking of oil trapped in a reservoir, we usually simply calculate the total thermal exposure of the reservoir. This method implicitly assumes that most heating of the reservoir rock occurred after the arrival of the oil. In the absence of significant erosion, such an assumption is usually valid. More properly, however, we should first determine the timing of the arrival of the oil in the reservoir based on our knowledge of when and where it was generated and the duration of migration, and then compute the thermal exposure of the reservoir rock only after arrival of the oil. Even more properly, we could also consider thermal stress experienced by the oil during migration, although the time spent during migration is apt to be much less than that spent in the reservoir (see England, Chapter 12, this volume). From the total amount of thermal exposure, we could in principle compute hydrocarbon composition and volume.

Types of Models

Oil cracking, like hydrocarbon generation, can be modeled in a number of ways. Cracking in reservoirs has been predicted using both the TTI (e.g., Waples, 1980, 1985, 1988) and kinetic methods (e.g., Ungerer et al., 1988a,b; Behar et al., 1988; Burnham, 1989; Ungerer, 1990; Burnham and Sweeney, 1991; Andresen et al., 1993). Like hydrocarbon generation, oil cracking can be better predicted using the kinetic method. However, kinetic parameters for oil cracking are more poorly known than those for oil generation. Different oil types appear to have slightly different cracking parameters, although the practical significance of these differences is still conjectural. Compositional kinetics have been applied to cracking studies in an effort to obtain more detailed information about the products (Ungerer et al., 1988a,b; Behar et al., 1988).

All kinetic models use mass balance considerations to limit the amount of gas that can be formed by cracking of oil. Although the exact proportions vary slightly from model to model and oil to oil, at most about 50% of the cracked oil is converted to gas; the rest becomes carbon residue (Ungerer et al., 1988a,b; Behar et al., 1988; Burnham, 1989; Burnham and Sweeney, 1991). Cracking in the source rock therefore reduces the total mass of hydrocarbons available for expulsion and migration.

Overview of Modeling Procedures

As mentioned earlier, maturity modeling should begin with the development of a conceptual model of regional geologic history that can serve as a framework for reconstruction of the depositional, erosional, and thermal histories. The burial history of sedimentary rocks, including events that occurred during times represented by unconformities, is then reconstructed, and lithologies are assigned to each rock unit. The necessary input data are often obtained from well samples, but important contributions can come from seismic data, well logs, and outcrops. Heat flows and thermal conductivities are then adjusted to give an acceptable fit between measured and calculated present-day temperatures. Finally, paleoheat flow and geologic events during unconformity periods are adjusted to give an acceptable fit between measured and calculated thermal indicators.

Once this "optimization" process is complete, the input burial, thermal, and petrophysical data should be as consistent and correct as possible. Hydrocarbon generation and oil cracking are then calculated using the optimized model. The various steps outlined in this section are discussed in more detail in the following section.

INPUT GEOLOGIC DATA
Burial History

Rock Unit Ages

Maturity modeling requires that ages and thicknesses be specified for all rock units deposited during the time interval being modeled. Ages for extant sedimentary rocks that have been sampled in outcrop or in wells are normally obtained from micropaleontology and are usually precise. Radiometric dates of volcanic rocks can also be useful. Even unusually large uncertainties in rock unit ages will seldom significantly affect the results of maturity modeling (Waples et al., 1992b).

Rock unit ages are depicted relative to depth as in a well bore (Figure 17.2, left), but must be converted to a time history for maturity modeling (Figure 17.2, right). The mechanics of this conversion are simple. The main problem encountered is deciding on the timing and amount of deposition and erosion during periods represented by unconformities.

Water Depth

In principle, maturity calculations can be carried out without specifying water depths. However, some software programs require the user to enter water depths, which are useful for two reasons. First, water depth influences temperatures at the sediment–water interface, which should be usde as the surface temperature in the thermal calculations (see later section on Surface Temperatures). Second, inclusion of water depth information allows one to create geohistory plots (van Hinte, 1978), which are discussed later in this chapter. Water depths are usually obtained from micropaleonto-

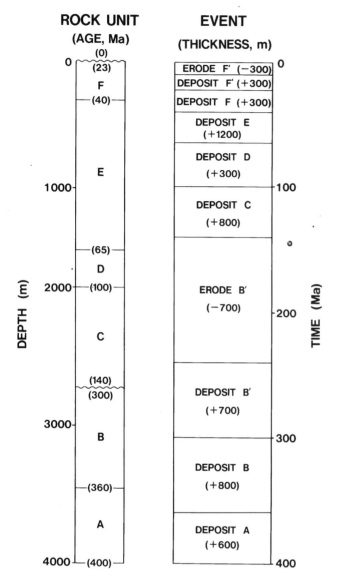

ROCK UNIT
(AGE, Ma)

EVENT
(THICKNESS, m)

Figure 17.2. On the left, rock units in a typical stratigraphic column are plotted on a depth scale. Ages (in Ma) at rock unit boundaries are shown in parentheses. On the right, the same geologic history is plotted on a time scale. The two unconformities were assumed to have had simple histories of deposition (units B' and F') followed by erosion. Numbers in parentheses refer to thickness of interval (+) or amount of erosion (–). All thicknesses of extant rocks are for present-day, and of eroded rocks, at the start of erosion. Depositional thicknesses are greater.

logic data and are thus typically expressed in broad ranges. The distinction between burial history plots and geohistory plots is the absence versus presence of water depth.

Rock Unit Thickness

Some programs allow present-day rock unit thicknesses to be specified directly or to be calculated from rock unit tops, whereas other programs accept only one type of data. Thicknesses are more convenient when using data from outcrops, seismic sections, or geologic cross sections; tops are more useful for modeling wells.

The thicknesses of existing rock units specified by the modeler are present-day thicknesses after compaction. In most software programs, thicknesses of eroded rocks represent the thicknesses the units would have had if preserved today since the amount of missing section is often determined by comparison with preserved sections. Some software programs, however, consider the thickness of an eroded section to be its thickness immediately before erosion. There is usually little practical difference between the two methods.

Original depositional thicknesses are greater than present-day thicknesses by an amount equal to the amount of porosity reduction due to compaction. Compaction is currently calculated in one of two ways. The simplest approach is to compact each rock layer as a function of maximum burial depth according to a lithology-dependent equation provided by the software program. Table 17.4 shows several types of depth-dependent compaction equations used in maturity modeling, including the most popular Athy-type exponential equation. The pros and cons of various types of compaction equations have been reviewed by Baldwin and Butler (1985). The other popular approach is to calculate porosity reduction as a function of effective stress (Ungerer et al., 1990; Schneider et al., 1993).

Overpressuring (undercompaction) could be considered to some degree in the depth-dependent equations by merely changing the equations' constants to yield less compaction. The effective stress approach can directly decrease the rate of porosity reduction during overpressuring. However, Schneider et al. (1993) have concluded that pressure (and therefore also effective stress) cannot be predicted using one-dimensional modeling (that is, z dimension plus time) since in their opinion most fluid flow is horizontal rather than vertical (see England et al., 1987).

Alternative approaches to predicting porosity reduction have been developed to take factors other than depth or stress into consideration (Table 17.4), but none have yet been integrated into maturity or basin models. Porosity reduction has been described as a function of time and temperature history (expressed as TTI or R_o) for limestones (Schmoker, 1984) and sandstones (Schmoker and Gautier, 1988, 1989; Schmoker and Hester, 1990; Bloch, 1991). These equations do not contain a direct depth or pressure dependence, although temperature is closely related to depth. Waples and Kamata (1993) have modeled porosity reduction as a series of seven chemical and physical processes. It is not yet clear whether future porosity reduction calculations will continue to be based on depth or effective stress or will adopt some more sophisticated approach.

When erosion occurs, release of overburden pressure sometimes leads to expansion of the rock and to an increase in porosity. This uncompaction effect is much smaller than the original compaction, however. Some models ignore uncompaction completely; others allow a small increase in porosity—perhaps 10% of the compaction that occurred during deposition of the eroded rock (Ungerer et al., 1990).

Table 17.4. Common Equations for Porosity as a Function of Depth or Maturity

Equations[a]	Associated name	References
Depth-Dependent Compaction Equations		
$\phi = \phi_0 \exp(-bZ)$	Athy; Sclater–Christie	Sclater and Christie, 1980
$1/\phi = 1/\phi_0 + kZ$	Falvey–Middleton	Falvey and Middleton, 1981
$Z = a(1 - \phi)^b$	Power function	Baldwin and Butler, 1985
Maturity-Dependent Compaction Equations		
$\phi = A(TTI)^B$	—	Schmoker, 1984
$\phi = A(R_0)^B$	—	Schmoker and Gautier, 1988, 1989; Schmoker and Hester, 1990
$\phi = A(R_0)^{+B}$	—	Bloch, 1991

[a]Variables: *a*, *b*, *k*, *A*, and *B* are constants, ϕ is porosity, and *Z* is depth.

It is sometimes desirable to change rock thicknesses independently of deposition, erosion, or compaction, such as due to igneous intrusive events (although the high temperatures still remain a problem), salt intrusion or withdrawal, or removal of limestone or sandstone during stylolitization. Using such software, the modeler specifies the beginning and ending times for the event and the amount of section added or subtracted, as well as the lithology of the rock in question. This feature is particularly valuable for describing sections containing salt since even the ephemeral presence of high-conductivity salt can affect temperature and therefore thermal maturity (O'Brien and Lerche, 1988; Carter and Lerche, in press).

Unconformities

When a hiatus or erosional unconformity exists, a description of the missing events must be provided. There is no standard formula or method for reconstructing those events. Comparison with adjacent stratigraphic sections may provide ideas about the amounts and ages of rock deposited and later removed. If used with care, several types of measured data can also yield information about amounts of erosion (e.g., Theis et al., 1993). For example, differences in sonic transit time (Δt values) for shales above and below an unconformity indicate that erosion has occurred (Magara, 1978). When deposition recommences after erosion, the difference in Δt values between shales above an unconformity and those below depends on the amount of erosion that occurred. However, Δt values also depend on the burial history subsequent to the erosional event: as the unconformity is reburied, the difference in Δt values gradually decreases and eventually ceases to be of value in estimating amounts of erosion (Waples et al., 1992b).

Vitrinite reflectance data (and other thermal indicators) can also be used for the same purpose because, like Δt values, they also initially show higher maturities below an erosional unconformity than above. (If little erosion is involved, there is no break in the thermal indicators.) However, like Δt values, breaks in profiles of thermal indicators anneal during reburial and thus must be used cautiously in working out amounts of erosion (Figure 17.3). The graphical approach to estimating removal suggested by Dow (1977) can lead to serious errors where annealing has occurred.

A few guides to the use of R_0 data in estimating amounts of erosion are available (Katz et al., 1988; Armagnac et al., 1989; Waples et al., 1992a,b; Theis et al., 1993). All such reconstructions should be constrained by geologic concepts as well as by mathematical manipulation of data. Illustrative examples of reconstructing thermal histories are given by Deming and Chapman (1989); Feinstein et al., (1989); Hagen and Surdam (1989); and Waples et al. (1992a,b).

The increased degree of compaction (lower porosities) of rocks below an erosional unconformity compared to normal (uneroded) rocks at the same depth affects all other petrophysical properties as well as sonic velocities. Errors in amounts of erosion thus lead to errors in thermal conductivity and permeability (often calculated from porosity; see Chapter 18), and in turn lead to errors in conclusions about maturity and fluid flow. The time spent correctly assessing amounts of erosion is a good investment.

Periods represented by unconformities can consist of complex cycles of burial and erosion, but in most cases little of this complexity can be included in maturity modeling due to lack of data. Fortunately, the missing detail is usually of little practical importance, although the way in which one partitions a time gap into depositional and erosional periods can sometimes significantly affect thermal maturity calculations (e.g., Theis et al., 1993). The larger the break in thermal indicators or D_t values across an unconformity, the more important it will be to reconstruct the events within that unconformity period accurately (e.g., Dahl and Augustson, 1993). From another perspective, detailed knowledge of erosional episodes is most important when the source rocks were at or near their maximum burial depth or temperature during the period in question.

Lithologies

Lithologies specified for rock units control all petrophysical properties of those units, including compaction rates, thermal conductivities, and heat capacities. Consequently, they should be chosen with some care. Lithologies of rock units present in outcrop sections or well

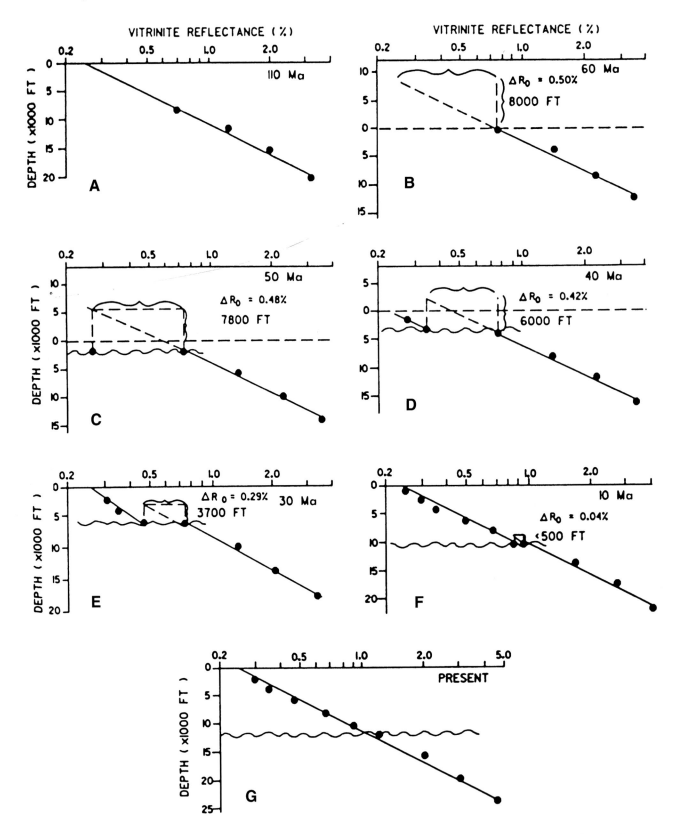

Figure 17.3. Development and gradual annealing of a break in a vitrinite reflectance profile during burial, erosion, and reburial. Erosion between the times represented in (A) and (B) leads to a surface R_o (0.75%) that is 0.5% higher than normal. (C) After 2000 ft of reburial, the gap has shrunk to 0.48%; (D) after 4000 ft, 0.42%; (E) after 6000 ft, 0.29%; (F) after 10,000 ft, 0.04%; and (G) after 12,000 ft, the slope is unbroken. (From Katz et al., 1988.)

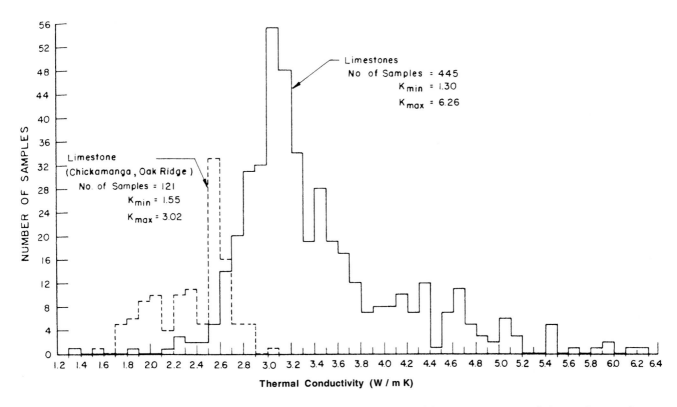

Figure 17.4. Histogram of total thermal conductivities (matrix plus pore fluid) of limestones measured at room temperature. (From Roy et al., 1981; reprinted with permission from McGraw-Hill Cindus.)

bores are normally taken from lithology logs, but can be specified on the basis of any available data.

It is more difficult to define the lithologies of eroded rocks. Some software programs simply assign missing rocks the same lithologies as the extant rocks immediately above or below the missing section. This approach has weaknesses, especially when large amounts of section are missing. In other software programs, the user is allowed to specify the lithologies of the missing rocks. In such cases, lithologies of eroded rocks are usually estimated by analogy with other spatially or temporally related stratigraphic sections using facies concepts.

Petrophysical Properties

Petrophysical properties of rocks are specified in one of three ways, although most programs do not allow all three options. First, if the desired lithology is the same as one of the lithologies in the program's lithology library, petrophysical properties are simply taken from the library. Second, the user can override the library's values with values of his or her own choosing, or third, the program may allow mixing of two or more of the lithologies available in the program's library and will then calculate the petrophysical properties of the mixed lithology.

In most models the lithology library consists of a few standard pure lithologies (such as shale, sandstone, and limestone). The petrophysical properties of any units composed of mixed rock types are then calculated from the values of each of the components using an averaging technique (harmonic, geometric, or arithmetic). The averaging technique selected depends on different factors in different programs. These factors may include relative amounts of each lithology, nature of the mixing (interbedded or grain-by-grain), and the particular petrophysical property of interest.

Calculating properties of mixed lithology rock units as averages presents a number of problems. First, the true values of the various petrophysical parameters for the pure end-member lithologies are difficult to determine because natural variation is large (Figure 17.4). Although some of the variation is undoubtedly due to different porosities and different pore fluids, considerable scatter remains that must be due to lithologic composition. Second, the physical nature of the mixing present within the unit is often unclear from available data. Third, the choice of the best averaging technique is not always obvious. Finally, grain-by-grain mixing, in which small grains often simply fill pore spaces between larger grains (Figure 17.5), cannot be handled by any of the standard averaging equations but rather must be dealt with empirically or by some other mathematical technique (Palciauskas, 1986; Marion, 1990).

The other approach to specifying properties of mixed lithologies is to provide a large number of premixed lithologies whose petrophysical properties have already been assigned based on empirical data. The user does not create additonal lithologies by mixing and thus must fit each layer into a predefined lithologic category. If the empirical data base is large and of good quality, this method is excellent because it is grounded in reality.

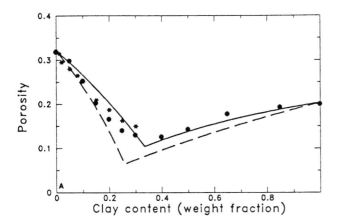

Figure 17.5. Porosity of clay–sand mixtures as related to clay content. Dashed and solid lines represent two mathematical models for predicting porosities of mixtures. (From Marion, 1990; reprinted by permission of the author.)

Faulting

Many current thermal maturity models ignore faulting completely, and those that consider it are unable to handle all kinds of faulting. Two difficult problems must be overcome in developing models to describe faulting: the problem of finding general ways to represent faulted sections and the problem of knowing the thermal regimes associated with faulted sections. The representation problems arise from the fact that any nonvertical fault involves lateral movement of material. Each fault therefore requires construction of two distinct burial and thermal histories, which must be juxtaposed gradually during the period of faulting to create a single final section. Furthermore, rotation occurring along most faults adds a number of complications. The problems related to thermal regimes have been discussed (but not yet solved) by various authors (e.g., Edman and Surdam, 1984; Furlong and Edman, 1984; Warner et al., 1987; Wygrala et al., 1990) and include both basement heat flow and the role of convective heat transfer.

Thermal History

Maturity models require that the temperature be specified at all depths at all times in the past. However, in modeling hydrocarbon generation or cracking or the maturation of thermal indicators, the importance of reconstructing the complete thermal history has probably been overemphasized because most maturation occurs near the maximum paleotemperature (Hermanrud, 1993). Thus, for practical purposes, reconstructing thermal history often reduces to the problem of specifying the maximum paleotemperature, when it occurred, and how long it persisted.

Surface Temperatures

Surface temperatures have generally been given little serious consideration in thermal maturity modeling. Factors that should be considered in estimating the mean annual surface temperature for areas above sea level

include latitudinal position through time and global climatic trends (Frakes, 1979). Conceptual models for surface temperature are often unconsciously based on the present, which is probably a poor model for most of the Phanerozoic.

For areas below sea level, A. Yukler (personal communication, 1989) suggests estimating the temperature at the sediment–water interface by decreasing the ambient land temperature by 4°C/100 m for the uppermost 200 m of water and by 2°C/100 m thereafter, to a minimum value of about 4°C in the open ocean, or a slightly higher temperature in restricted water. It may also be desirable to consider changes in sea floor temperature through time as a function of global circulation.

Geothermal Gradient Method

Subsurface temperatures can in principle be specified (1) directly at all times using geothermal gradients or corrected bottom hole temperatures, or (2) indirectly using the heat flow–conductivity method. If the geothermal gradient method is chosen, gradients can be specified both for the present day and for any desired times in the past and can be made as complex as one wishes. The main weaknesses of the geothermal gradient method are as follows: (1) in most software programs, changes in geothermal gradients are tied to specific depths rather than to rock units, as they should be; (2) modelers often use linear gradients due to lack of data, although actively compacting sedimentary sections normally have nonlinear gradients; and (3) geothermal gradients are effects rather than causes and thus do not provide a sound basis for developing a conceptual model.

Heat Flow–Conductivity Method

Maturity modeling today increasingly favors the heat flow–conductivity method because it deals with more fundamental physical principles. In fact, some software programs have completely abandoned the geothermal gradient method. Using heat flow, one can easily construct complex thermal histories that are probably more realistic than those devised using the geothermal gradient method.

Heat flow across a rock unit represents the product of the thermal conductivity of the unit times the geothermal gradient across the unit. The many present-day heat flow values obtained all over the world from a wide variety of geologic settings vary over a broad range (e.g., Gretener, 1981). However, models for heat flow from the mantle through the crust are still incapable of predicting heat flow values accurately for most cases (see Leadholm et al., 1985; Jensen and Dore, 1993). The intensive studies of the relationship between crustal thickness and heat flow have largely focused on extensional settings (e.g., McKenzie, 1978, 1981; Royden et al., 1980), and there are ongoing controversies about the conceptual and quantitative aspects of such models (e.g., Iliffe et al., 1991). In addition, elevated heat flows associated with crustal stretching are probably of less practical importance than often suggested because source rocks are usually either not yet deposited or only at shallow depths during the times of highest heat flow (but for a contrary example, see Cohen's, 1985, analysis of the Reconcavo basin of Brazil).

Moreover, models generally neglect radiogenic sources of heat within the sedimentary section itself. Rybach (1986) contends that contributions from radiogenic sources may be variable enough as a function of time and lithology that they should be considered in modeling thermal regimes in basins more than 5 km deep or more than 10 Ma. Radiogenic contributions can be indirectly and approximately considered, however, by simply adjusting basement heat flow values.

Heat flow through nonextensional sedimentary basins is even more poorly understood. As a result of these various problems, and also because of local variation, the magnitudes of present or paleoheat flow cannot be predicted precisely from first principles (Blackwell and Steele, 1989). However, by using the idea that crustal thinning leads to higher heat flows, we can often predict trends qualitatively (e.g., McDonald et al., 1989). One must therefore test and calibrate the original estimates of heat flow using measured temperatures and thermal indicators (see section on Optimization).

Convective Heat Transfer and Thermal Refraction

The heat flow–conductivity method applied in one-dimensional modeling necessarily assumes that all heat transfer is by vertical conduction and thus will be deficient wherever convective heat transfer or lateral heat conduction (thermal refraction) is important. These two phenomena are discussed elsewhere in Chapter 18 (Waples, this volume).

Equilibrium versus Disequilibrium

Some software programs assume that sedimentary rocks are always in thermal equilibrium, whereas others allow disequilibrium to occur. Although few sedimentary sections are in true thermal equilibrium, disequilibrium is probably of importance mainly when sedimentation or erosion is rapid (e.g., Deming and Chapman, 1989; Hermanrud et al., 1991; Waples et al., 1992b; Vik and Hermanrud, 1993). Other possible causes for thermal disequilibrium have also been suggested (Powell and Chapman, 1990).

Thermal Conductivities

Thermal conductivities of all sedimentary rocks in the section being modeled are normally provided by the software program from the lithologies entered by the user. Conductivities calculated in this way should be considered as rough first estimates, however, for several reasons: (1) errors in specifying lithologies, (2) deviations of lithologic compositions and properties from the generalized values provided by the software, (3) overpressuring (undercompaction), (4) anisotropy, and (5) errors in averaging procedures and natural variation within a given homogeneous set of lithologies (Figure 17.4 and Table 17.5) (see Roy et al., 1981; Blackwell and Steele, 1989). Geophysical well logs and seismic velocities may be useful in estimating thermal conductivities (Goss et

Table 17.5. Ranges of Thermal Conductivities of Matrix and Pore Fluids

Lithology or Pore Fluid	Thermal Conductivity[a] (mW/m²)
Shale	10.05–1.45
Sandstone	2.50–4.20
Lithic sand	1.25–2.10
Limestone	2.50–3.10
Dolomite	3.75–6.30
Salt	4.80–60.05
Anhydrite	4.90–5.80
Coal	0.18
Granite	2.50–3.35
Basalt and andesite	1.45–2.10
Water	0.59
Kerosene	0.15
Methane	00.044

[a]Conductivities of matrix plus pore fluid at 20°C.

Source: mainly from Blackwell and Steele (1989).

al., 1975; Leadholm et al., 1985; Blackwell and Steele, 1989; Brigaud et al., 1990). Most thermal models assume that pore fluids are similar to sea water since most sedimentary rocks are marine and hydrocarbons can never represent more than a tiny fraction of total pore fluids in a basin. Where large volumes of hydrocarbons have accumulated locally in highly porous rocks, however, the lower conductivities of oil and gas (Table 17.5) can result in thermal anomalies (e.g., Eggen, 1983; Meyer and McGee, 1985).

If available, measured conductivities are of some value, but they are uncommon and, even when available, may not be representative of entire rock units (Powell and Chapman, 1990). Furthermore, conductivities measured parallel and perpendicular to bedding planes are different, particularly in shales (Blackwell and Steele, 1989), but most measured data do not specify orientation. This anisotropy could introduce errors where beds dip steeply or where isotherms have been distorted by faulting or thermal refraction (see Chapter 18, this volume). Deming and Chapman (1989) offer a rare example of measured conductivites abundant enough to provide a valuable local data base, but those data were obtained during many years of sampling and measurement in a well-explored area.

Because of the problems in accurately predicting thermal conductivities from the information available, conductivities must be checked and calibrated with measured temperature data at the same time heat flow is optimized. The differences in conductivities among common lithologies can be large enough to cause distinct changes in geothermal gradient across rock units (e.g., Blackwell and Steele, 1989). Particularly noteworthy are the high conductivities of quartz sandstone (contrasting sharply with lithic sandstone), salt, and anhydrite, and the low conductivities of shale, organic matter, and pore fluids (Table 17.5).

Thermal conductivities of sedimentary rocks decrease sharply with increasing temperature (Roy et al., 1981;

Sekiguchi, 1984; Blackwell and Steele, 1989; Brigaud et al., 1993) and increase with decreasing porosity as low-conductivity pore fluids are expelled. Pressure corrections are small and often omitted (Sekiguchi, 1984). Since the in situ conductivity of a rock unit depends strongly on its temperature and state of compaction, the conductivity entered in most software programs is the conductivity of the rock matrix alone at room temperature.

Optimization

The optimization process begins by comparing present-day subsurface temperatures measured in the well bore with calculated temperatures. Measured subsurface temperatures should always be corrected in some appropriate way for the effects of incomplete thermal equilibration in the well bore. Fertl and Wichman (1977), Gretener (1981), Hagen and Surdam (1989), and Deming (1989) provide some guidelines, techniques, and warnings about standard correction procedures and their uncertainties in the well bore. However, detailed analysis of the precision and accuracy of various temperature correction techniques suggests several things. First, simple methods consistently underestimate true rock unit temperatures, with standard deviations for data sets on the order of 7°C (Hermanrud, 1988). Second, more advanced methods are fairly accurate but still have about the same standard deviations as simple methods (Hermanrud and Shen, 1989; Hermanrud et al., 1990). Finally, the most sophisticated methods (seldom used) can reduce standard deviations to less than 2°C (Hermanrud et al., in press). Deming (1989) has made the important point that it is impossible to expect to correct measured temperatures accurately and that better temperature measurements must be obtained if present-day temperatures are to be known more precisely.

Once present-day temperatures in the well bore have been established, modeling is started using (1) a plausible set of thermal conductivities (probably those given as default values by the software program for the defined lithologies), and (2) an estimate of the present-day heat flow. In subsequent simulations, the present-day heat flow and conductivities of one or more of the rock units can be adjusted to achieve a good fit between measured and calculated temperatures. Thus, heat flow and thermal conductivity are optimized simultaneously rather than separately in an attempt to find a combination of heat flow and conductivity that gives the correct present-day temperature (Waples et al., 1992a). The final choice for a present-day heat flow must also be consistent with the geologic model and must use thermal conductivities that are plausible for those particular rocks. This procedure establishes the present-day heat flow and thermal conductivities for the rock matrices at surface conditions.

Figure 17.6 shows the struggle to fit corrected bottom hole temperatures to calculated temperatures in the MITI Rumoi well (Waples et al., 1992a). Figure 17.6A shows the results using the initial estimate of thermal conductivities (default values for the specified lithologies) and present-day heat flow (38 mW/m²). Figure 17.6B gives

the results after forcing a mathematically good fit by adjusting conductivities (increased by 50%) and heat flow (48.5 mW/m²) without regard for geologic and petrophysical constraints. Figure 17.6C show the final best fit taking all geologic and petrophysical evidence into consideration (conductivities of sandstones decreased to reflect lithic content; heat flow = 45 mW/m²). The imperfect fit in the upper part of the section in Figure 17.6C is attributed to errors in measured temperatures.

The next step is to find a heat flow history that is consistent with the geologic model for regional tectonic evolution and the data from thermal maturity indicators. The heat flow is optimized by varying it through time in a logical way until measured maturity indicators, calculated thermal maturity indicators, and inferred paleotemperatures (from fission track data or fluid inclusions) agree as well as possible. The allowable amount of variation in paleoheat flow is highly dependent on the tectonic history within each area. Because of the large uncertainties in heat flow histories, most workers vary heat flow through time freely during optimization.

Figure 17.7 shows the testing of three alternative hypotheses about paleoheat flow in the MITI Rumoi well (Waples et al., 1992a). Figure 17.7C was finally chosen to represent the "correct" heat flow model, although the predicted R_o values agree less well in the upper part of the section than for the heat flow models in Figures 17.7A and B. The thermal and erosional models required to produce the fits in Figures 17.7A and B were judged to be geologically unreasonable (see Waples et al., 1992a, for details). A key point in justifying the acceptance of the scenario in Figure 17.7C was that the R_o data in the upper part of the well were judged to be unreliable. Poor R_o data are probably much more common than is usually appreciated.

Use of multiple maturity indicators is encouraged because each one gives a different perspective on the time–temperature history and because the suitability of each indicator varies from case to case. Feinstein et al. (1989), He and Lerche (1989), Ritter et al. (1993), and Theis et al. (1993) have presented examples using two or more thermal indicators.

Much emphasis has been placed in the literature on the importance of thermal maturity indicators in constraining paleoheat flow. Mathematical inversion techniques (also known as thermal indicator tomography) have been developed to extract the maximum information from thermal indicators (e.g., Lerche et al., 1984; Lerche, 1988a,b, 1990; He and Lerche, 1989), but few workers have adopted the technology. A major problem with the existing inversion techniques is that they assume that all the geologic uncertainty lies in a single parameter (generally heat flow); every other piece of input geologic data is assumed to be correct. A second problem is that it is tempting to use inversion techniques as a black box replacement for careful geologic analysis. The reality, however, is that inversion technology, like all modeling technology, requires that careful attention be paid to all geologic aspects of the problem, and therefore requires clear thinking. Perhaps the greatest value of thermal indicator tomography is to remind us how

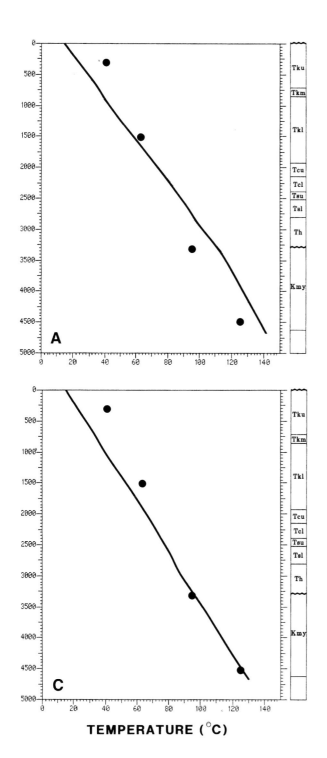

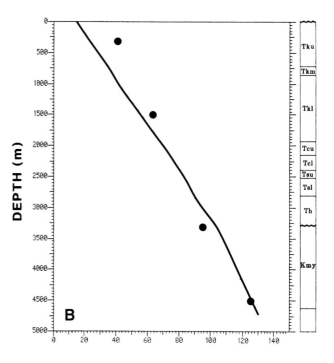

TEMPERATURE (°C)

Figure 17.6. Stepwise fitting of calculated present-day temperature (line) to corrected bottom hole temperatures (dots) in the MITI Rumoi well, Hokkaido, Japan. See text for discussion of graphs A, B, and C. Abbreviations: T, Tertiary; K, Cretaceous; k, Kotanbetsu Formation; c, Chikubetsu Formation; s, Sankebetsu Formation; h, Haboro Formation; my, Middle Yezo Formation; u, upper; m, middle; l, lower. (From Waples et al., 1992a.)

Many workers now recognize the importance of using thermal maturity indicators to constrain paleotemperatures. However, optimization of present-day heat flow and conductivities using present-day temperatures is equally important. Any maturity modeling carried out in the absence of either measured present-day temperatures or measured thermal indicators should be considered speculative (Waples et al., 1992b). While modeling under such conditions is often necessary and valuable, particularly in frontier areas (e.g., Iliffe et al., 1991), it is important to bear in mind the potential errors and uncertainties associated with uncalibrated modeling.

During the process of optimizing heat flows and conductivities, it is also necessary to make a final decision about the amount and timing of erosion during each period represented by an unconformity. (Preliminary estimates of erosion should have been made prior to this stage.) Comparison of measured and calculated values for thermal indicators can now indicate whether the original estimates are plausible. For example, maturity modeling can help estimate the maximum amount of erosion that could have occurred across an unconformity where the measured thermal indicator profile is continuous. In cases where breaks exist, the best estimate of erosion can be made by trial-and-error comparison of measured and calculated profiles of thermal indicators. If a break in a profile of calculated thermal indicators appears where measured data are

poorly our measured data usually constrain paleoheat flows.

Thermal conductivities are generally not adjusted during this optimization step. However, if an acceptable fit cannot be obtained using the previously established present-day thermal conductivities, we may adjust the conductivities, recalibrate the present-day heat flow, and then try again to fit the thermal maturity indicators (see Waples et al., 1992a). The final combined heat flow–conductivity scenario should be as consistent as possible with our conceptual model of the geologic history of the area.

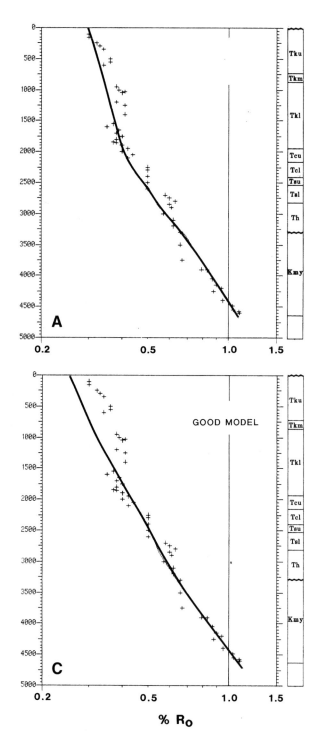

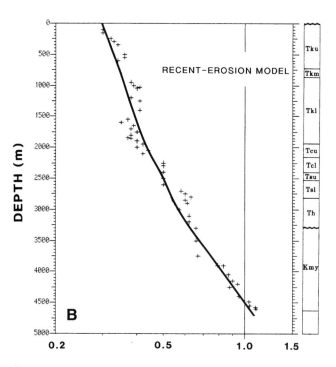

Figure 17.7. Stepwise fitting of calculated R_o data (line) to measured R_o data (+) for three proposed geologic scenarios in the MITI Rumoi well, Hokkaido, Japan, using LLNL kinetic model. See text for discussion of graphs A, B, and C. Abbreviations as in Figure 17.6. (From Waples et al., 1992a.)

selected as the final "best" model is seldom a unique solution and probably contains errors as well. However, by constraining both conductivities and heat flows within geologically plausible limits, we can be reasonably sure that our solution is reasonably close to the truth (Waples et al., 1992b).

DIMENSIONS

Virtually all maturity modeling is carried out in one spatial dimension (one-dimensional), along the z (depth) axis. As a result, we are unable to include directly the effects of convective heat transfer or thermal refraction, both of which might have a significant lateral component. These limitations are usually not troublesome, however. In cases where the effects of convective heat transfer or thermal refraction are significant, they can be included indirectly and approximately in the estimate of conductive heat transfer.

Some software programs offer a multiwell capability, which produces the same output as two-dimensional (x, z, plus time) simulations. With this approach, a number of wells in an area are modeled as independent one-dimensional simulations, and the results are then plotted as plan-view maps on user-selected horizons or as two-dimensional cross sections along user-selected lines (see examples later). For the purposes of maturity modeling, multiwell one-dimensional is probably nearly as good as true two-dimensional modeling and is certainly faster and simpler.

continuous, the estimated amount of erosion is too large. Conversely, if a measured trend shows a break that is absent in the calculated trend, the amount of postulated erosion is too small. In such cases, the modeler simply changes the input data and reruns the simulation. However, natural scatter in thermal indicator data can often make it difficult to determine whether breaks in measured data are actually present (Waples, 1990). Proper use of thermal indicator profiles to reconstruct erosion histories is discussed in Katz et al. (1988), Armagnac et al. (1989), and Waples et al., 1992 a,b).

The combination of thermal factors and erosion

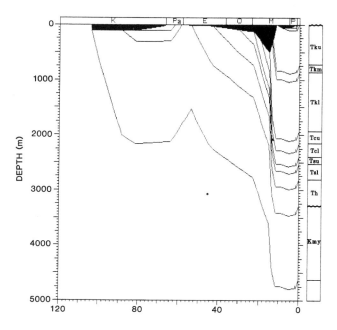

Figure 17.8. Geohistory curve for the MITI Rumoi well, Hokkaido, Japan. Datum is sea level; black areas represent water depth through time. Abbreviations as in Figure 17.6. (From Waples et al., 1992a.)

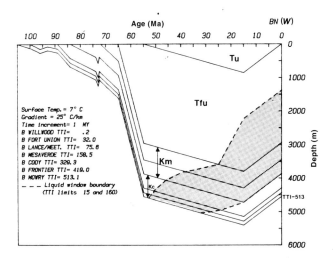

Figure 17.9. Oil or liquid window (shaded) superimposed on burial history diagram for a well in the Big Horn basin, U.S.A. (From Hagen and Surdam, 1984; reprinted with permission of Rocky Mountain Association of Geologists.)

It is worth noting that when we discuss modeling dimensions, we refer only to the number of spatial dimensions. What we call one-dimensional modeling also considers the time dimension in addition to its one spatial dimension and is thus actually two-dimensional. In fact, it is the ability of maturity modeling to include time as a dimension in geologic analysis that in part accounts for its usefulness and popularity.

APPLICATIONS

Of the several ways in which maturity modeling can be applied in petroleum exploration, calculation of timing and extent of oil generation is by far the most common. Other applications are often even more important, however. This section will provide an overview of various ways of extracting useful information from maturity modeling.

Checking the Geologic Model

Many less experienced users of maturity models are unaware of the power and importance of using maturity modeling to check and improve their geologic model. If the input data are not properly tested for internal consistency and reasonableness, any further modeling done with a defective set of input data may be in error. Furthermore, the learning that accompanies development and checking of the geologic model is often as valuable as the final numerical answer about hydrocarbon generation or oil cracking. For example, if one has to struggle with questions about paleoheat flow and amounts and timing of erosion to achieve a fit between measured and calculated thermal indicators, one may

learn much about the geologic evolution of the region, its tectonics, and its depositional patterns (Waples et al., 1992a,b). Previous discussions have shown how the thermal and erosional histories can be resolved with the aid of maturity modeling software (Figures 17.6 and 17.7).

Use of geohistory curves (van Hinte, 1978) instead of burial history curves is of value at this stage because the inclusion of water depth gives a more complete picture of subsidence patterns and the interplay between subsidence and sedimentation. For example, Figure 17.8 shows that although sedimentation was very rapid during the early Miocene in the vicinity of the MITI Rumoi well, water depth increased as sedimentation failed to keep up with basement subsidence.

Hydrocarbon Generation

Maturity modeling can predict the degree and timing of hydrocarbon generation and to some degree the composition of those hydrocarbons. The confidence we have in the results depends on the confidence we have in the input data: how well the thermal history is constrained by thermal maturity and paleotemperature indicators and how well the kerogen type and its kinetic parameters are known. The traditional superposition of the maturity window on the burial history (or geohistory) curves (Figure 17.9) has become less popular as TTI modeling has been gradually replaced by kinetic modeling and as alternative (and possibly superior) methods of displaying output data have been developed. Among these alternatives is plotting hydrocarbon generation for one or more source rocks as a function of time (Figures 17.10) or as a function of depth for the entire stratigraphic section at any desired time (Figure 17.11).

Knowledge of the timing of hydrocarbon generation is important for two reasons. First, migration pathways can change with time through normal compaction processes, diagenesis, cementation, fracturing and faulting, and structural development. To consider where

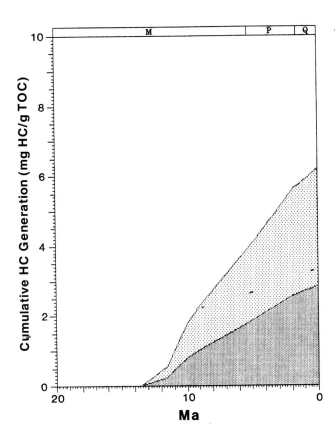

Figure 17.10. Cumulative generation of oil (solid) and gas (shaded) from middle Miocene time from coals at the base of the Haboro Formation, MITI Rumoi well, Hokkaido, Japan. (From Waples et al., 1992a.)

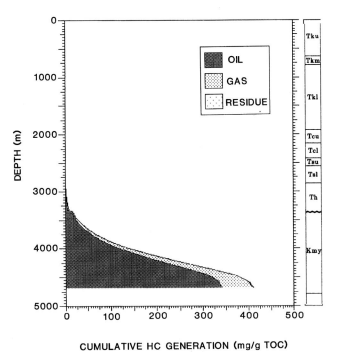

Figure 17.11. Cumulative generation of oil and gas to present day from coals of the Haboro Formation and from a hypothetical source rock in the Middle Yezo Formation in the MITI Rumoi well, Hokkaido, Japan. Abbreviations as in Figure 17.6.

the hydrocarbons went after they left the source rock, we must know approximately when they were moving. Second, the later the generation, the less time there has been for biodegradation, cracking, seal rupture, and other destructive processes that destroy or damage hydrocarbon accumulations.

The amount and composition of hydrocarbons generated can also be determined to some degree by maturity modeling. Most maturity models predict gas–oil ratios (or give even more detailed breakdowns if compositional kinetics are used), but the accuracy of such predictions is limited by how well one can characterize the kerogen. When kerogen type and its kinetic parameters are known reasonably well, such predictions are fairly reliable. Predicting wax contents, API gravities, and other details is beyond the scope of most models today, however. Accurate prediction of volumes of hydrocarbons generated requires not only that we specify total organic carbon content (TOC) values in addition to kerogen type but also that we extrapolate the results of our model to three spatial dimensions. Such extrapolation requires care (Waple, Chapter 18, this volume).

Oil Cracking

Hydrocarbon preservation, like hydrocarbon generation, can easily be shown as a function of time for a particular rock unit in the same fashion as in Figure 17.11, or as a function of depth for the whole section (Figure 17.12). Cracking is shown indirectly by the decrease (or slower increase) in total amount of oil and by the increase in both gas and carbon residue. Carbon residue is the most unambiguous indicator since it is only formed by cracking. Such representations are usually used for source rocks, but could also be applied to reservoirs.

For source rocks at or beyond peak oil generation, there may be considerable differences between the amount of cracking predicted when expulsion is allowed (Figure 17.12A) and that predicted when expulsion is not allowed (Figure 17.12B). The "no-expulsion" model is considerably more pessimistic in predicting mainly gas and condensate, whereas the "expulsion" model predicts considerable oil. The true composition of hydrocarbons emerging from the source rock is probably better predicted using an expulsion model, in spite of our uncertainties about criteria for expulsion (Chapter 18, this volume).

Acknowledgments   I thank JNOC for permission to publish this work and for support in preparation of the manuscript. Christian Hermanrud, Michael Zeitlin, and Les Magoon kindly offered helpful comments on an earlier version, and Nancy Naeser provided perspective on fission track analysis. I also am grateful to the many other workers who have generously shared their knowledge in discussion and through publications.

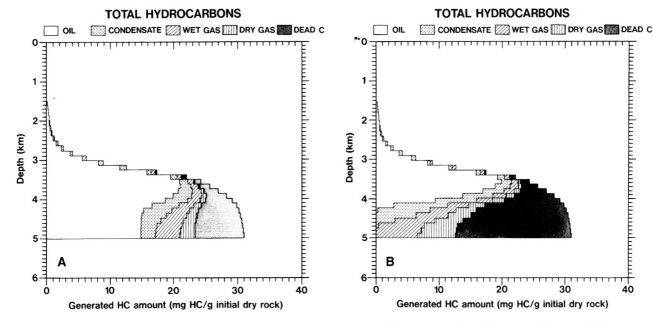

Figure 17.12. Comparison of hydrocarbon yields using (A) a new model of generation that allows expulsion and (B) a conventional model that ignores expulsion. (Output provided courtesy of Beicip; calculated using Genex® software.)

References Cited

Abbott, G. D., and J. R. Maxwell, 1988, Kinetics of the aromatisation of rearranged ring C monoaromatic steroid hydrocarbons, *in* L. Mattavelli and L. Novelli, eds., Advances in Organic Geochemistry 1987: Oxford, Pergamon Press, p. 881–885.

Abbott, G. D., G. Y. Wang, T. I. Eglinton, A. K. Home, and G. S. Petch, 1990, The kinetics of sterane biological marker release and degradation processes during the hydrous pyrolysis of vitrinite kerogen: Geochimica et Cosmochimica Acta, v. 54, p. 2451–2461.

Alexander, R., R. Marzi, and R. I. Kagi, 1990, A new method for assessing the thermal history of sediments: a case study from the Exmouth Plateau in northwestern Australia: APEA Journal, v. 30, pt. 1., p. 364–372.

Alexander, R., P. G. Kralert, R. Marzi, R. I. Kagi, and E. J. Evans, 1991, A geochemical method for assessment of the thermal histories of sediments: a two-well case study from the Gippsland basin, Australia: APEA Journal, pt. 1, p. 325–332.

Andresen, P., N. Mills, H.-J. Schenck, and B. Horsfield, 1993, The importance of kinetic parameters in modelling generation by cracking of oil to gas—a case study in 1D from well 2/4–14, *in* A. G. Dore et al., eds., Basin Modelling: Advances and Applications: Amsterdam, Elsevier, p. 563–572.

Armagnac, C., J. Bucci, C. G. St. C. Kendall, and I. Lerche, 1989, Estimating the thickness of sediment removed at an unconformity using vitrinite reflectance data, *in* N. D. Naeser and T. H. McCulloh, eds., Thermal History of Sedimentary Basins—Methods and Case Histories: New York, Springer Verlag, p. 217–238.

Baldwin, B., and C. O. Butler, 1985, Compaction curves: AAPG Bulletin, v. 69, p. 622–626.

Barker, C. E., and R. H. Goldstein, 1990, Fluid-inclusion technique for determining maximum temperature in calcite and its comparison to the vitrinite reflectance geothermometer: Geology, v. 18, p. 1003–1006.

Behar, F., P. Ungerer, A. Audibert, and M. Villalba, 1988, Experimental study and kinetic modelling of crude oil pyrolysis in relation with enhanced oil recovery processes, *in* F. Meyer and J. Wiggins, eds., Fourth UNITAR/UNDP Conference on Heavy Crudes and Tar Sands: Alberta Oil Sands Technology and Research Authority, p. 747–759.

Blackwell, D. D., and J. L. Steele, 1989, Thermal conductivity of sedimentary rocks: measurement and significance, *in* N. D. Naeser and T. H. McCulloh, eds., Thermal History of Sedimentary Basins—Methods and Case Histories: New York, Springer Verlag, p. 13–36.

Bloch, S., 1991, Empirical prediction of porosity and permeability in sandstones: AAPG Bulletin, v. 75, p. 1145–1160.

Brigaud, F., D. S. Chapman, and S. Le Douaran, 1990, Estimating thermal conductivity in sedimentary basins using lithologic data and geophysical well logs: AAPG Bulletin, v. 74, p. 1459–1474.

Brigaud, F., G. Caillet, and G. Vasseur, 1993, Present thermal state in sedimentary basins predicted from well data: application to the Viking Graben, *in* A. G. Dore et al., eds., Basin Modelling: Advances and Applications: Amsterdam, Elsevier.

Burnham, A. K., 1989, A simple kinetic model of petroleum formation and cracking: Lawrence Livermore National Laboratory Report UCID-21665, 11 p.

Burnham, A. K., 1990, Pyrolysis kinetics and composition for Posidonia shale: Report UCRL-ID-105871, 25 p.

Burnham, A. K., and R. L. Braun, 1990, Development of a detailed model of petroleum formation, destruction, and expulsion from lacustrine and marine source rocks, *in* B. Durand and F. Behar, eds., Advances in Organic Geochemistry 1989: Oxford, Pergamon Press, p. 27–39.

Burnham, A. K., and J. J. Sweeney, 1989, A chemical kinetic model of vitrinite maturation and reflectance: Geochimica et Cosmochimica Acta, v. 53, p. 2649–2657.

Burnham, A. K., and J. J. Sweeney, 1991, Modeling the maturation and migration of petroleum, *in* N. Foster and E. A. Beaumont, eds., AAPG Treatise of Petroleum Geology, p. 55–61.

Burruss, R. C., 1989, Paleotemperatures from fluid inclusions: Advances in theory and technique, *in* N. D. Naeser and T. H.

H. McCulloh, eds., Thermal History of Sedimentary Basins—Methods and Case Histories: New York, Springer Verlag, p. 119–231.

Carter, K., and I. Lerche, in press, Moving salt sheets and sediment maturity: AAPG Bulletin.

Cohen, C. R., 1985, Role of fault rejuvenation in hydrocarbon accumulation and structural evolution of Reconcavo basin, northeastern Brazil: AAPG Bulletin, v. 69, p. 65–76.

Crowley, K. D., M. Cameron, and R. L. Schaefer, 1991, Experimental studies of annealing of etched fission tracks in fluorapatite: Geochimica et Cosmochimica Acta, v. 55, p. 1449–1465.

Curiale, J. A., S. R. Larter, R. E. Sweeney, and B. W. Bromley, 1989, Molecular thermal maturity indicators in oil and gas source rocks, *in* N. D. Naeser and T. H. McCulloh, eds., Thermal History of Sedimentary Basins—Methods and Case Histories: New York, Springer Verlag, p. 53–72.

Dahl, B., and J. H. Augustson, 1993, The influence of Tertiary and Quaternary sedimentation and erosion on hydrocarbon generation in Norwegian offshore basins, *in* A. G. Dore et al., eds., Basin Modelling: Advances and Applications: Amsterdam, Elsevier, p. 419–432.

Deming, D., 1989, Application of bottom-hole temperature corrections in geothermal studies: Geothermics, v. 18, p. 775–786.

Deming, D., and D. S. Chapman, 1989, Thermal histories and hydrocarbon generation: Example from Utah–Wyoming thrust belt: AAPG Bulletin, v. 73, p. 1455–1471.

Dow, W. G., 1977, Kerogen studies and geochemical interpretations: Journal of Geochemical Exploration, v. 7, p. 79–99.

Dykstra, J., 1987, Compaction correction for burial history curves: application to Lopatin's method for source rock maturation determination: Geobyte, v. 2, p. 16–23.

Edman, J. D., and R. C. Surdam, 1984, Influence of overthrusting on maturation of hydrocarbons in Phosphoria Formation, Wyoming–Idaho–Utah overthrust belt: AAPG Bulletin, v. 68, p. 1803–1817.

Eggen, S., 1983, Modelling of subsidence, hydrocarbon generation and heat transport in the Norwegian North Sea, *in* B. Durand, ed., Thermal Phenomena in Sedimentary Basins: Paris, Editions Technip, p. 271–284.

Elphick, R. Y., 1989, Lopatin modeling for hydrocarbon maturity, part 1: Geobyte, v. 4, April, p. 49–54.

Elphick, R. Y., and R. J. Reed, 1989, Lopatin modeling for hydrocarbon maturity, part 2—DOS and Mac programs: Geobyte, v. 4, June, p. 29–37.

England, W. A., A. S. Mackenzie, D. M. Mann, and T. M. Quigley, 1987, The movement and entrapment of petroleum fluids in the subsurface: Journal of the Geological Society, London, v. 144, p. 327–347.

Espitalié, J., P. Ungerer, I. Irwin, and F. Marquis, 1988, Primary cracking of kerogens. Experimenting and modelling C_1, C_2–C_5, C_6–C_{15} and C_{15+} classes of hydrocarbons formed: Organic Geochemistry, v. 13, p. 893–899.

Espitalié, J., F. Marquis, and S. Drouet, 1993, Critical study of kinetic modelling parameters, *in* A. G. Dore et al., eds., Basin Modelling: Advances and Applications: Amsterdam, Elsevier, p. 233–242.

Falvey, D. A., and M. F. Middleton, 1981, Passive continental margins: evidence for a prebreakup deep crustal metamorphic subsidence mechanism: Oceanologica Acta SP, p. 103–114.

Feinstein, S., B. P. Kohn, and M. Eyal, 1989, Significance of combined vitrinite reflectance and fission-track studies in evaluating thermal history of sedimentary basins: an example from southern Israel, *in* N. D. Naeser and T. H. McCulloh, eds., Thermal History of Sedimentary Basins—

Methods and Case Histories: New York, Springer Verlag, p. 197–216.

Fertl, W. H., and P. A. Wichman, 1977, How to determine static BHT from well log data: World Oil, 184/1, p. 105–106.

Forbes, P. L., P. M. Ungerer, A. B. Kuhfuss, F. Riis, and S. Eggen, 1991, Compositional modeling of petroleum generation and expulsion: trial application to a local mass balance in the Smorbukk Sorfield, Haltenbanken area, Norway: AAPG Bulletin, v. 75, p. 873–893.

Frakes, L. A., 1979, Climates Throughout Geologic Time: Amsterdam, Elsevier, 310 p.

Furlong, K. P., and J. D. Edman, 1984, Graphic approach to determination of hydrocarbon maturation in overthrust terrains: AAPG Bulletin, v. 68, p. 1818–1824.

Goff, J. C., 1983, Hydrocarbon generation and migration from Jurassic source rocks in East Shetland basin and Viking graben of the northern North Sea: Journal of the Geological Society of London, v. 140, p. 445–474.

Goldstein, R. H., 1986, Reequilibration of fluid inclusions in low-temperature calcium carbonate cement: Geology, v. 14, p. 792–795.

Goss, R., J. Coumbs, and A. Timur, 1975, Prediction of thermal conductivity in rocks from other physical parameters and from standard geophysical well logs: SPWLA 16th Annual Logging Symposium, p. 1–21.

Gretener, P. E., 1981, Geothermics: using temperature in hydrocarbon exploration: AAPG Education Course Notes Series 17, 156 p.

Hagen, E. S., and R. C. Surdam, 1984, Maturation history and thermal evolution of Cretaceous source rocks of the Bighorn basin, Wyoming and Montana, *in* J. Woodward, F. F. Meissner, and J. L. Clayton, eds., Hydrocarbon source rocks of the greater Rocky Mountain region: Denver, Rocky Mountain Association of Geologists, p. 321–338.

Hagen, E. S., and R. C. Surdam, 1989, Thermal evolution of Laramide-style basins: constraints from the northern Bighorn basin, Wyoming and Montana, *in* N. D. Naeser and T. H. McCulloh, eds., Thermal History of Sedimentary Basins—Methods and Case Histories: New York, Springer Verlag, p. 277–295.

He, Z., and I. Lerche, 1989, Inversion of multiple thermal indicators: quantitative methods of determining paleoheat flux and geological parameters, IV: case histories using thermal indicator tomography: Mathematical Geology, v. 21, p. 523–541.

Hermanrud, C., 1988, Determination of formation temperature from downhole measurements: Ph.D. dissertation, University of South Carolina, Columbia, SC, 203 p.

Hermanrud, C., 1993, Basin modelling techniques—an overview, *in* A. G. Dore et al., eds., Basin Modelling: Advances and Applications: Amsterdam, Elsevier, p. 1–34.

Hermanrud, C., and P. Y. Shen, 1989, Virgin rock temperatures from well logs—accuracy analysis for some advanced inversion models: Marine and Petroleum Geology, v. 6, p. 360–363.

Hermanrud, C., S. Cao, and I. Lerche, 1990, Estimates of virgin rock temperature derived from BHT measurements: bias and error: Geophysics, v. 55, p. 924–931.

Hermanrud, C., S. Eggen, and R. M. Larsen, 1991, Investigation of the thermal regime of the Horda platform by basin modelling: implications for the hydrocarbon potential of the Stord basin, northern North Sea, *in* A. M. Spencer, ed., Generation, Accumulation, and Production of Europe's Hydrocarbon: Oxford, Oxford University Press, p. 65–73.

Hermanrud, C., I. Lerche, and K. K. Meisingset, in press, Determination of virgin rock temperatures from drill stem tests: SPE Formation Evaluation, Society of Petroleum Engineers.

Hunt, J. M., M. D. Lewan, and R. J. C. Hennet, 1991, Modeling oil generation with time–temperature index graphs based on the Arrhenius equation: AAPG Bulletin, v. 75, p. 795–807.

Iliffe, J. E., I. Lerche, and M. DeBuyl, 1991, Basin analysis and hydrocarbon generation of the South Mozambique graben using extensional models of heat flow: Marine and Petroleum Geology, v. 8, p. 152–162.

Issler, D. R., 1984, Calculation of organic maturation levels for offshore eastern Canada—implications for general application of Lopatin's method: Canadian Journal of Earth Sciences, v. 21, p. 477–488.

Jabour, H., and K. Nakayama, 1988, Basin modeling of Tadla basin, Morocco, for hydrocarbon potential: AAPG Bulletin, v. 72, p. 1059–1073.

Jensen, R. P., and A. G. Dore, 1993, A recent Norwegian Shelf heating event—fact or fiction?, in A. G. Dore et al., eds., Basin Modelling: Advances and Applications: Amsterdam, Elsevier, p. 85–106.

Katz, B. J., R. N. Pfeiffer, and D. J. Schunk, 1988, Interpretation of discontinuous vitrinite reflectance profiles: AAPG Bulletin, v. 72, p. 926–931.

Larter, S., 1988, Some pragmatic perspectives in source rock geochemistry: Marine and Petroleum Geology, v. 5, p. 194–204.

Leadholm, R. H., T. T. Y. Ho, and S. K. Sahai, 1985, Heat flow, geothermal gradients and maturation modelling on the Norwegian continental shelf using computer methods, in B. M. Thomas et al., eds., Petroleum Geochemistry in Exploration of the Norwegian Shelf: London, Graham & Trotman, p. 131–143.

Leischner, K., D. H. Welte, and R. Littke, 1993, Fluid inclusions and organic maturity parameters as calibration tools in basin modelling, in A. G. Dore et al., eds., Basin Modelling: Advances and Applications: Amsterdam, Elsevier, p. 161–172.

Lerche, I., 1988a, Inversion of multiple thermal indicators: quantitative methods of determining paleoheat flux and geological parameters, I. Theoretical development for paleoheat flux and geological parameters: Mathematical Geology, v. 20, p. 1–36.

Lerche, I., 1988b, Inversion of multiple thermal indicators: quantitative methods of determining paleoheat flux and geological parameters, II. Theoretical development for chemical, physical, and geological parameters: Mathematical Geology, v. 20, p. 73–96.

Lerche, I., 1990, Basin analysis: Quantitative Methods, Vol. 1: San Diego, Academic Press, 562 p.

Lerche, I., R. F. Yarzab, and C. G. St. C. Kendall, 1984, Determination of paleoheat flux from vitrinite reflectance data: AAPG Bulletin, v. 68, p. 1704–1717.

Lewan, M. D., 1985, Evaluation of petroleum generation by hydrous pyrolysis experimentation: Philosophical Transactions of the Royal Society of London, Ser. A, v. 315, p. 123–134.

Lewan, M. D., and B. Buchardt, 1989, Irradiation of organic matter by uranium decay in the Alum shale, Sweden: Geochimica et Cosmochimica Acta, v. 53, p. 1307–1322.

Lopatin, N. V., 1971, Temperature and geologic time as factors in coalification: Izvestiya Akademiya Nauk SSSR, Ser. Geol., v. 3, p. 95–106 (in Russian).

Mackenzie, A. S., and D. McKenzie, 1983, Isomerization and aromatization of hydrocarbons in sedimentary basins formed by extension: Geological Magazine, v. 120, p. 417, 470.

Magara, K., 1978, Compaction and Fluid Migration: Amsterdam, Elsevier, 319 p.

Marion, D. P., 1990, Acoustical, mechanical, and transport properties of sediments and granular materials: Ph.D. dissertation, Stanford University, Stanford, CA, Stanford Rock & Borehole Project, v. 39, 136 p.

McDonald, A. E., D. U. von Rosenberg, W. R. Jines, W. H. Burke, Jr., and L. M. Uhler, Jr., 1989, A simulator for the computation of paleotemperatures during basin evolution, in N. D. Naeser and T. H. McCulloh, eds., Thermal History of Sedimentary Basins—Methods and Case Histories: New York, Springer Verlag, p. 270–275.

McKenzie, D. P., 1978, Some remarks on the development of sedimentary basins: Earth and Planetary Science Letters, v. 40, p. 25–32.

McKenzie, D. P., 1981, The variation of temperature with time and hydrocarbon maturation in sedimentary basins formed by extension: Earth and Planetary Science Letters, v. 55, p. 87–98.

Meyer, H. J., and H. W. McGee, 1985, Oil and gas fields accompanied by geothermal anomalies in Rocky Mountains region: AAPG Bulletin, v. 69, p. 933–945.

Naeser, N. D., 1993, Apatite fission track analysis in sedimentary basins—a critical appraisal, in A. G. Dore et al., eds., Basin Modelling: Advances and Applications: Amsterdam, Elsevier, p. 147–160.

Naeser, N. D., C. W. Naeser, and T. H. McCulloh, 1989, The application of fission-track dating to the depositional and thermal history of rocks in sedimentary basins, in N. D. Naeser and T. H. McCulloh, eds., Thermal History of Sedimentary Basins—Methods and Case Histories: New York, Springer Verlag, p. 158–180.

Nakayama, K., 1987, Hydrocarbon-expulsion model and its application to Niigata area, Japan: AAPG Bulletin, v. 71, p. 810–821.

Noble, R. A., C. H. Wu, and C. D. Atkinson, 1991, Petroleum generation and migration from Talang Akar coals and shales offshore N.W. Java, Indonesia: Organic Geochemistry, v. 17, p. 363–374.

O'Brien, J. J., and I. Lerche, 1988, Impact of heat flux anomalies around salt diapirs and salt sheets in the Gulf Coast on hydrocarbon maturity: Gulf Coast Association of Geologic Societies, v. 58, p. 231–243.

Palciauskas, V. V., 1986, Models for thermal conductivity and permeability in normally compacting basins, in J. Burrus, ed., Thermal Modeling in Sedimentary Basins: Paris, Editions Technip, p. 323–336.

Peters, K. E., 1986, Guidelines for evaluating petroleum source rock using programmed pyrolysis: AAPG Bulletin, v. 70, p. 318–329.

Powell, W. G., and D. S. Chapman, 1990, A detailed study of heat flow at the Fifth Water Site, Utah, in the Basin and Range–Colorado Plateaus transition: Tectonophysics, v. 176, p. 291–314.

Quigley, T. M., and A. S. Mackenzie, 1988, The temperatures of oil and gas formation in the sub-surface: Nature, v. 333, p. 549–552.

Ritter, M. B. Myhr, U., K. Aareskjold, and L. Schou, 1993, Validation and first application of palaeotemperature models of isomerisation and NMR aromatisation parameters, in A. G. Dore et al., eds., Basin Modelling: Advances and Applications: Amsterdam, Elsevier, p. 185–200.

Roedder, E., 1984, Fluid inclusions: Mineralogical Society of America Reviews in Mineralogy, v. 12, 644 p.

Roy, R. F., A. E. Beck, and Y. S. Touloukian, 1981, Thermophysical properties of rocks, in Y. S. Touloukian, W. R. Judd, and R. F. Roy, eds., Physical Properties of Rocks and Minerals, Vol. II-2: New York, McGraw Hill Cindus, p. 409–502.

Royden, L., J. G. Sclater, and R. P. Von Herzen, 1980, Continental margin subsidence and heat flow: important parameters in formation of petroleum hydrocarbons: AAPG Bulletin, v. 64, p. 173–187.

Rybach, L., 1986, Amount and significance of radioactive heat sources in sediments, *in* J. Burrus, ed., Thermal Modeling in Sedimentary Basins: Paris, Editions Technip, p. 311–322.

Schmoker, J. W., 1984, Empirical relation between carbonate porosity and thermal maturity: an approach to regional porosity prediction: AAPG Bulletin, v. 68, p. 1697–1703.

Schmoker, J. W., and D. L. Gautier, 1988, Sandstone porosity as a function of thermal maturity: Geology, v. 16, p. 1007–1010.

Schmoker, J. W., and D. L. Gautier, 1989, Compaction of basin sediments: modeling based on time–temperature history: Journal of Geophysical Research, v. 94, p. 7379–7386.

Schmoker, J. W., and T. C. Hester, 1990, Regional trends of sandstone porosity versus vitrinite reflectance—a preliminary framework, *in* V. F. Nuccio and C. E. Barker, eds., Applications of thermal maturity studies to energy exploration: Denver, RMS–SEPM, p. 53–60.

Schneider, F., J. Burrus, S. Wolf, B. Doligez, and P. Forbes, 1993, Modelling overpressures by effective stress/porosity relationship: Mathematical artifice or physical reality?, *in* A. G. Dore et al., eds., Basin Modelling: Advances and Applications: Amsterdam, Elsevier.

Sclater, J. G., and P. A. F. Christie, 1980, Continental stretching: an explanation of the post-mid-Cretaceous subsidence of the central North Sea basin: Journal of Geophysical Research, v. 85, p. 3711–3739.

Sekiguchi, K., 1984, A method for determining terrestrial heat flow in oil basinal areas, *in* V. Cermak, L. Rybach, and D. S. Chapman, eds., Terrestrial heat flow studies and the structure of the lithosphere: Tectonophysics, v. 103, p. 67–79.

Sweeney, J. J., 1989, FORTRAN programs for basin analysis and petroleum generation modeling: Lawrence Livermore National Laboratory Report UCID-21859, 43 p.

Sweeney, J. J., 1990, Basinmat FORTRAN program calculates oil and gas generation using a distribution of discrete activation energies: Geobyte, v. 5, April, p. 37–43.

Sweeney, J. J., and A. K. Burnham, 1990, Evaluation of a simple model of vitrinite reflectance based on chemical kinetics: AAPG Bulletin, v. 74, p. 1559–1570.

Tetzlaff, D. M., and J. W. Harbaugh, 1989, Simulating Clastic Sedimentation: New York, Van Nostrand Reinhold, 202 p.

Theis, N. J., H. H. Nielsen, J. K. Sales, and G. J. Gail, 1993, Impact of data integration on basin modelling in the Barents Sea, *in* A. G. Dore et al., eds., Basin Modelling: Advances and Applications: Amsterdam, Elsevier, p. 433–444.

Tissot, B. P., 1969, Premieres donnees sur les mecanismes et la cinetique de la formation du petrole dans les sediments: simulation d'un schema reactionnel sur ordinateur: Revue de l'Institut Français du Petrole, v. 24, p. 470–501.

Tissot, B. P., and J. Espitalié, 1975, L'evolution thermique de la matiere organique des sediments: applications d'une simulation mathematique: Revue de l'Institut Français du Petrole, v. 30, p. 743–777.

Tissot, B. P., R. Pelet, and Ph. Ungerer, 1987, Thermal history of sedimentary basins, maturation indices, and kinetics of oil and gas generation: AAPG Bulletin, v. 71, p. 1445–1466.

Tupper, N. P., and D. M. Burckhardt, 1990, Use of the methylphenanthrene index to characterize expulsion of Cooper and Eromanga basin oils: APEA Journal, p. 373–385.

Ungerer, P., 1990, State of the art of research in kinetic modelling of oil formation and expulsion: Organic Geochemistry, v. 16, p. 1–25.

Ungerer, P., 1993, Modelling of petroleum generation and expulsion—an update to recent reviews, *in* A. G. Dore et al., eds., Basin Modelling: Advances and Applications:

Amsterdam, Elsevier, p. 219–232.

Ungerer, P., F. Behar, M. Villalba, O. R. Heum, and A. Audibert, 1988a, Kinetic modelling of oil cracking: Organic Geochemistry, v. 13, p. 857–868.

Ungerer, P. J. Espitalié, F. Behar, and S. Eggen, 1988b, Modelisation mathematique des interactions entre craquage thermique et migration lors de la formation du petrole et du gaz: Compte Rendus a l'Academie des Sciences, v. 307, Serie II, p. 927–934.

Ungerer, P. J. Burrus, B. Doligez, P. Y. Chenet, and F. Bessis, 1990, Basin evaluation by integrated two-dimensional modeling of heat transfer, fluid flow, hydrocarbon generation, and migration: AAPG Bulletin, v. 74, p. 309–335.

van Hinte, J. E., 1978, Geohistory analysis—application of micropaleontology in exploration geology: AAPG Bulletin, v. 62, p. 201–222.

Vik, E., and C. Hermanrud, 1993, Transient thermal effects of rapid subsidence in the Haltenbanken area, *in* A. G. Dore et al., eds., Basin Modelling: Advances and Applications: Amsterdam, Elsevier, p. 107–118.

Walderhaug, O., and W. Fjeldskaar, 1993, History of hydrocarbon emplacement in the Oseberg field determined by fluid inclusion microthermometry and temperature modelling, *in* A. G. Dore et al., eds., Basin Modelling: Advances and Applications: Amsterdam, Elsevier, p. 485–498.

Waples, D. W., 1980, Time and temperature in petroleum formation: application of Lopatin's method to petroleum exploration: AAPG Bulletin, v. 64, p. 916–926.

Waples, D. W., 1984, Thermal models for oil generation, *in* J. W. Brooks and D. H. Welte, eds., Advances in Petroleum Geochemistry, Vol. 1: London, Academic Press, p. 7–67.

Waples, D. W., 1985, Geochemistry in Petroleum Exploration: Boston, IHRDC, 232 p.

Waples, D. W., 1988, Novel application of maturity modeling for hydrocarbon prospect evaluation: Houston, Proceedings of the 12th World Petroleum Congress, v. 2, p. 3–8.

Waples, D. W., 1990, Kinky vitrinite reflectance well profiles: evidence of paleopore pressure in low-permeability, gas-bearing sequences in Rocky Mountain Foreland basins: Discussion: AAPG Bulletin, v. 74, p. 946–947.

Waples, D. W., and H. Kamata, 1993, Modeling porosity reduction as a series of chemical and physical processes, *in* A. G. Dore et al., eds., Basin Modelling: Advances and Applications: Amsterdam, Elsevier, p. 303–320.

Waples, D. W., and T. Machihara, 1991, Biomarkers for geologists: a practical guide to the application of steranes and triterpanes in petroleum exploration: AAPG Methods in Exploration Series 9, 91 p.

Waples, D. W., H. Kamata, and M. Suizu, 1992a, The art of maturity modeling, part 1: finding a satisfactory geologic model: AAPG Bulletin, v. 76, p. 31–46.

Waples, D. W., M. Suizu, and H. Kamata, 1992b, The art of maturity modeling, part 2: alternative models and sensitivity analysis: AAPG Bulletin, v. 76, p. 47–66.

Warner, M. A., F. Royse, J. D. Edman, and K. P. Furlong, 1987, Thrust faulting and hydrocarbon generation: discussion and reply: AAPG Bulletin, v. 71, p. 882–896.

Wood, D. A., 1988, Relationships between thermal maturity indices calculated using Arrhenius equation and Lopatin method: implications for petroleum exploration: AAPG Bulletin, v. 72, p. 115–134.

Wood, D. A., 1990, Thermal maturation modeling using spreadsheets: Geobyte, v. 5, February, p. 56–61.

Wygrala, B. P., M. N. Yalcin, and L. Dohmen, 1990, Thermal histories and overthrusting—application of numerical simulation techniques: Organic Geochemistry, v. 16, p. 267–285.

Magoon, L. B, and W. G. Dow, eds., 1994, The petroleum
system—from source to trap: AAPG Memoir 60.

Chapter **18**

Modeling of Sedimentary Basins and Petroleum Systems

Douglas W. Waples

Consultant
Denver, Colorado, U.S.A.

Abstract

Basin modeling is the term most often used to describe the modeling of the series of processes that include generation, expulsion, migration, trapping, and preservation of hydrocarbons. This definition includes components of both sedimentary basin modeling and petroleum system modeling. Petroleum system modeling attempts to recreate the history of the hydrocarbons within a specific system. Basin modeling often considers several petroleum systems simultaneously.

Maturity modeling forms one part of system modeling, but system models also describe fluid flow, which is omitted in maturity modeling. Because of these differences and because system and basin models are usually two dimensional, simulation times for system and basin models are longer than for maturity models. Care must be taken in the design of such models to maintain a high degree of user interactiveness and permit convenient optimization of input data and performance of sensitivity analysis. Existing models have yet to solve all these problems. Additional problems that remain unsolved include quantification of expulsion and migration loss, scaling problems and resolution of small features, inability to predict tectonic fracturing and fluid flow through fracture permeability, and inability to handle tectonic complexity. These weaknesses limit applications in some areas and render these models semiquantitative under the best of circumstances.

Petroleum system models are useful tools for describing the behavior of hydrocarbon systems. They are potentially even more powerful for stimulating thinking than for providing final answers. System models have a bright future if some major improvements can be made, if they are designed and built with the technical and philosophical needs of explorationists in mind, and if proper training for model users is provided. Sensitivity analysis is essential for proper application of all models in exploration.

OBJECTIVES

Basin modeling is designed to describe the burial of source rocks, the hydrocarbon generation in those rocks, and the expulsion, migration, trapping, and preservation of those hydrocarbons. The definition of basin modeling as presently used usually corresponds more closely to the concept of a sedimentary basin than to that of a petroleum system. A single basin modeling simulation often includes several petroleum systems, without separating or distinguishing among them.

Sedimentary basin modeling is carried out to recreate the depositional history of a sequence of rock units so as to predict their behavior and properties. Maturity modeling (Waples, Chapter 17, this volume) is therefore an important component of basin modeling. However, the need for basin models to describe the flow of water,

oil, and gas and to specify the conditions that affect fluid flow rates (e.g., permeability, fluid potential, and structure) distinguishes the concept, design, and dimensionality of system models from maturity models.

Modeling of sedimentary basins and modeling of petroleum systems differ in several ways:

1. The physical definition or geometry of a particular sedimentary basin may change through time. The particular package of rock we wish to model may represent a complete basin at one time, part of a larger basin at another time, and multiple basins or subbasins at a third time. The boundary of the sedimentary basin is defined by the depression or by the rock units included, whereas the petroleum system is defined by a line around all hydrocarbon accumulations that emanate from a pod of active source rock.

2. Applications of modeling to petroleum exploration concentrate mainly on generation, migration, accumulation, and preservation of hydrocarbons, that is, on the fundamentals of petroleum systems. Other parts of the sedimentary basin (lithofacies, faults, structures, and water flow) exist as a framework within which this modeling is conducted, but are seldom examined in detail for their own sake (Hermanrud, in press).

3. Sedimentary basins may contain several petroleum systems, each of which may be localized in certain areas or confined to certain strata. Although it is possible to model all systems simultaneously, it is often better to consider each system individually.

Ideally, a system model should tell us (1) the composition and amount of hydrocarbons generated in each block of source rock in each time step; (2) how much hydrocarbon fluid is expelled from each block of source rock in each time step; (3) the relative proportions of each of the oil or gas phases in the expelled hydrocarbon fluid; (4) the total permeability (both parallel and perpendicular to bedding) of each block of rock as a function of time; and (5) the direction and rate of movement of each hydrocarbon fluid phase through the available permeability. To accomplish these objectives, we must be able to specify as a function of time the magnitude of the various driving forces for hydrocarbon fluid movement in each block, absolute matrix permeabilities and relative permeability curves for three coexisting fluid phases (oil, gas, and water) in all kinds of rocks, and the amount of fracture permeability for these rocks, in addition to providing all the information needed to carry out maturity modeling (see Chapter 17, this volume).

In reality, however, much of the information needed to carry out such calculations is inevitably missing. Equations are usually well known, but their ability to describe geologic systems completely is often uncertain. Necessary input data are often unavailable or are plagued by geologic heterogeneity. For practical reasons, it is often impossible to model on as fine a scale as is desirable. Some phenomena are still poorly understood, and others are omitted entirely in existing models. Many empirical relationships must be used in lieu of more fundamental equations.

Modeling of petroleum systems is thus a compromise between what one would like to do and what our limited knowledge permits. As a result, most workers in the field of system modeling are skeptical about the quantitative potential of such models and prefer to use them comparatively or semiquantitatively at most.

BACKGROUND AND LOGISTICS

Dimensions

It is clear that two-dimensional modeling (x, z dimensions, plus time) is at present the preferred choice for both basin and system modeling, although some three-dimensional (x, y, z, plus time) studies have been

performed (e.g., Grigo et al., 1993). Some workers feel that two-dimensional modeling is unable to describe hydrocarbon flow adequately, but the majority believe that carefully executed two-dimensional modeling is usually an adequate representation of reality and is a reasonable compromise between ideal modeling and the real world of petroleum exploration. In most cases, full three-dimensional modeling, which is desirable in principle, requires too much (usually unavailable) input data, too much data preparation time, and too much computer time to be worthwhile. (However, with the advent of faster computers and better ways of entering data, some of the barriers to three-dimensional modeling will disappear.)

One-dimensional modeling, in contrast, is inadequate for completely modeling a petroleum system because of its inability to handle fluid flow in an acceptable way. In practice, most of the optimization in two-dimensional basin and system modeling is carried out using one-dimensional maturity modeling for individual control points (Chapter 17, this volume). Once the input data have been established, final optimization, modeling of hydrocarbon generation, and modeling of fluid flow are then performed using the two-dimensional capability.

Planning the Study

Assume that an explorationist wants to carry out two-dimensional modeling in an area having some well control and several seismic lines. The available data are first plotted on a map and the cross sections to be modeled are selected. These sections should include all the wells since well data are valuable in optimizing the input data for the model. In general, dip lines are more valuable than strike lines since hydrocarbon migration is more likely to occur updip. However, one should be guided by both local geology and data availability when choosing a cross section to model. The number of cross sections selected depends on data density, geologic complexity, the time and budget available for the study, and the objectives of the study.

Each cross section is then divided into a grid system consisting of nodal blocks for the numerical simulations. Most models allow nodal blocks to vary in size and shape. They are generally much longer (x = hundreds of meters to a few kilometers) than they are thick (z = a few tens of meters). Control points for which we have data (such as wells) should be placed in the centers of nodal blocks since a single average value for each property will be calculated for each block. Positions of other vertical lines in the grid should be chosen based on the user's ideas about where lithologic and structural changes occur. Positions of horizontal grid lines on the cross section are controlled by lithology and age and often follow boundaries of rock units (Figure 18.1).

In creating the grid system, the conceptual geologic model is simplified to fit the limits of time, data availability, and computing power. The conceptual model, in turn, is a gross simplification of reality that probably contains many errors (Figure 18.1). These limitations should be borne in mind when interpreting the results of

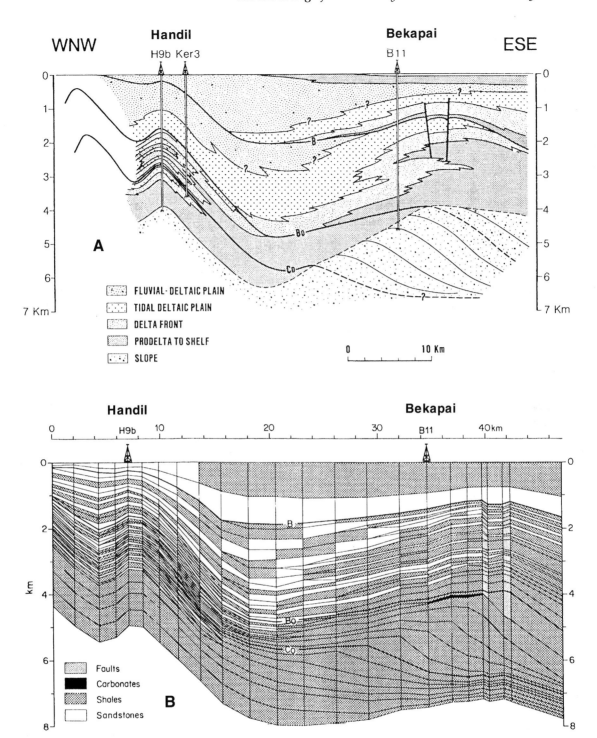

Figure 18.1. (A) Interpreted present-day geologic cross section across the Bekapai and Handil structures, Mahakam Delta, Indonesia. **(B)** Grid for two-dimensional modeling created from the geologic cross section. (From Ungerer et al., 1990.)

simulations using either a basin or a petroleum system model. Some features (such as lithologic inhomogeneity) may occur on a scale smaller than our nodal blocks and thus will be ignored by the model.

Sources of Input Data

Most data for two-dimensional modeling are entered manually at present, but in the future, much of the data will be input in digital form. Software developers are now struggling with problems such as data bases and computing industry standards that are not directly related to basin and system modeling, but which strongly affect how such modeling will be carried out in the future. Additional difficulties to be confronted include how to recognize and clean up erroneous input data. These problems will take considerable time and effort to work out.

Theoretical Foundation

Those interested in studying the fundamental physics and mathematical equations actually used in constructing basin and system models should consult such works as Bethke (1985, 1989), England et al. (1987), Nakayama (1987), Lehner et al. (1988), Zeitlin (1989), Ungerer et al. (1990), and Lerche (1990) for more details and additional references.

BURIAL AND THERMAL HISTORY

Initial Reconstruction

Burial and thermal histories at individual locations are created using the same data and logic as described for maturity modeling (see Chapter 17, this volume). Where lithologies change between wells, prediction of lithology trends can be facilitated by seismic stratigraphic analysis. Measured fluid pressure data can be compared with calculated fluid pressures to constrain permeabilities. (See Chapter 17, this volume, and Schneider et al., 1993, for comments on problems of modeling pressures in one-dimensional.)

Basin models are at present incapable of handling faulting in a general way, although some models allow certain types of faulting (e.g., Wygrala et al., 1990). Most existing models do not properly consider cause and effect in defining the position of economic basement: instead of being controlled by tectonic processes, basement position is defined by the depth required to accomodate a specified rock thickness and water depth. Efforts are now being made to model tectonic subsidence in extensional areas as a primary control on sediment and water thickness in two-dimensional Petroleum system models (Fjeldskaar et al., 1993), but applications to other types of basins are lacking.

Because two-dimensional models can calculate fluid and rock pressures within compacting layers, most models calculate porosity reduction by using effective stress and Darcy's law rather than by assuming some depth-dependent compaction function for each rock type as is usual in one-dimensional modeling (Chapter 17). The advantage of stress-based methods is that they can predict overpressuring (and consequent retention of porosity), whereas depth-dependent compaction functions do not. In stress-based models, fluid flow and porosity reduction during compaction are therefore treated properly as effects rather than as causes. However, other factors such as time and temperature that are not considered by stress-based models may also play a role in porosity reduction (Schmoker, 1984; Schmoker and Hester, 1990; Waples and Kamata, 1993).

Sources of pressure have been discussed by Hermanrud (1993). The most important overall factor in overpressuring is compaction disequilibrium caused by rapid sedimentation. Hydrocarbon generation is of secondary importance overall, but it may be significant locally. Aquathermal pressure and pressure due to mineral diagenesis are of minor importance. How long fluid pressures remain in excess of hydrostatic pressure depends upon the ability of the rocks to release fluids and thus reduce overpressure. Pressures are therefore closely linked to permeabilities as well as to sources of pressure. In discussing formation pressures, it is often forgotten that sources of pressure and mechanisms for dissipating pressure must be addressed simultaneously.

Knowledge of overpressuring is valuable for a number of reasons (such as migration and thermal conductivity) in addition to predicting porosity. The chief disadvantage in calculating compaction from stress is that because most rocks are normally pressured, much time is spent in unnecessary calculations.

Optimization

The initial optimization step in two-dimensional modeling is carried out using one-dimensional modeling for each control point, exactly as described for maturity modeling (Chapter 17). Present-day heat flow and thermal conductivities are established most conveniently by forcing agreement between measured and calculated temperatures. However, since in two-dimensional modeling involves several locations, one must ensure that heat flow and thermal conductivities obtained for each location are consistent within the framework of the conceptual geologic model.

Paleoheat flow and erosion are also established in a manner analogous to that used in one-dimensional thermal maturity modeling. Once again, the trends in these parameters must be consistent with the regional geologic model through time and space. In modeling petroleum systems, the one-dimensional optimized heat flow history may need revision after the two-dimensional simulations are run and the effects of fluid flow and thermal refraction are included. Convective heat transfer by hot water may be important in some tectonically disturbed areas (Oliver, 1986; Deming et al., 1990; Powell and Chapman, 1990). Local cooling by topographically driven groundwater flow from recharge areas, or heating as this water emerges from deeply buried sedimentary rocks, may occur in some places (Smith and Chapman, 1983; Garven and Freeze, 1984; Hitchon, 1984; Willett and Chapman, 1987; Nunn and Deming, 1991).

Heating or cooling in rechargable aquifer systems (such as those fed at outcrop or through subsurface faults) is potentially more effective than in nonrechargable systems, in which the total heat available is constrained by a preexisting volume of connate water (e.g., from within compacting sedimentary rocks) (Waples, 1990; Deming and Nunn, 1991; Nunn and Deming, 1991). It has further been suggested that fluid flow must have a vertical component in excess of 1 mm/yr to alter the thermal environment appreciably (Bredehoeft and Papadopoulos, 1965). The lateral component of fluid movement has little effect on thermal regimes since isotherms are usually nearly horizontal (Nunn and Deming, 1991).

In spite of this theoretical framework, however, the practical effects of fluid movement on thermal maturity of organic matter has received little attention (see Hulen et al., 1991). Most studies thus far have concentrated on hydrothermal systems, where the effect of temperature is much more local and extreme than we normally would want to include in our basin and system models (e.g., Barker and Elders, 1981; Johnsson, 1986).

Thermal refraction can be important where large contrasts in thermal conductivities are combined with structural complexities or abrupt facies changes. The largest contrasts probably occur for steeply dipping beds, salt diapirs, and discontinuous salt sheets (e.g., O'Brien and Lerche, 1988; Wei et al., 1990; Carter and Lerche, in press; Hermanrud, 1993). Lateral heat conduction is probably minor in most other situations, although in principle focusing or defocusing of heat occurs anywhere isotherms are not horizontal. Examples include areas where thrusting has disrupted thermal regimes too quickly for them to have reequilibrated. In any case, to consider thermal refraction properly requires routine differentiation between horizontal and vertical conductivities, which at this time most models fail to do.

Optimization in basin modeling is likely to be long and tedious, as one works out thermal and erosional histories by trial and error for a number of different locations, while at the same time trying to make everything fit a single geologic concept. Mathematical inversion techniques (e.g., Lerche, 1988a,b, 1990) may be of some value, but at most should supplement rather than replace geologic judgment. Software programs could in principle provide a number of aids to make optimization less arduous, but so far none have really met the challenge. Optimization therefore remains a major obstacle to executing good modeling of sedimentary basins.

HYDROCARBON FORMATION AND FLOW

Generation

Hydrocarbon generation in petroleum system modeling, as in maturity modeling, is calculated only after all the input parameters have been optimized. Existing petroleum system models handle hydrocarbon generation in one of two ways. The "qualitative" approach simply calculates the progressive conversion of kerogen to hydrocarbons (Chapter 17). The "quantitative" approach, in contrast, calculates the actual mass or volume of hydrocarbons generated. To use the quantitative approach, we must specify both the richness of the source rock (total organic carbon in weight percent) and the ultimate convertibility of the kerogen to hydrocarbons (in milligrams HC per gram of organic carbon, specified along with kerogen type). The differences between the qualitative and quantitative approaches carry over into discussions of expulsion and migration.

Expulsion

Qualitative Approach

System models using the qualitative approach model only water expulsion and assume that hydrocarbon expulsion parallels water expulsion. These models cannot determine whether hydrocarbon flow actually accompanies water flow and thus are not good at describing the timing or efficiency of expulsion. Consequently, they cannot accurately predict whether oil is cracked to gas prior to its expulsion and therefore may give erroneous predictions of hydrocarbon compositions. Expulsion efficiency, if dealt with at all, is specified by the user or by the program.

Quantitative Approach

It may be useful, interesting, and valid to model hydrocarbon generation in one dimension, but two- or three-dimensional modeling should be used to describe hydrocarbon fluid flow. Most workers today believe that hydrocarbons are expelled as a separate phase and that hydrocarbon expulsion from source rocks depends strongly on hydrocarbon saturation within the pore space (e.g., Welte, 1987; England, Chapter 12, this volume). An increasingly popular view is that the amount of oil adsorbed on kerogen (as opposed to being in the pore space) is also important and may be the controlling factor in some situations (e.g., coals and other rich source rocks, especially those with limited oil-generative potential) (Pepper, in press; Sandvik et al., 1992).

Quantitative models calculate timing and efficiency of expulsion since they calculate hydrocarbon volume or saturation in the source rock, and in some cases, volume of hydrocarbons adsorbed on kerogen. Some quantitative models are "overflow" models, in which once the threshold hydrocarbon saturation is reached, additional hydrocarbons simply flow out of the source rock (Welte, 1987). Others are based on some assumed relationship between hydrocarbon saturation (or quantity) and relative permeabilities to oil, gas, and water (Doligez et al., 1986; Nakayama, 1987). Although there still remain many uncertainties about quantitative saturation-based models, most future models will probably be of this type and those using relative permeability concepts appear to be more popular than overflow models.

In contrast to these models of hydrocarbon flow as a separate phase through water-filled pores, Stainforth and Reinders (1990) have proposed that expulsion occurs by diffusion through a continuous three-dimensional kerogen network rather than by Darcy's flow through pore spaces. Others, however (e.g., Thomas and Clouse, 1990; Hermanrud, in press), believe that such a mechanism is quantitatively unable to account for large accumulations. Diffusion through organic networks is neglected in most existing petroleum system models, and its degree of future acceptance is uncertain. Diffusion of oil molecules through pore water and transport of hydrocarbons in solution are considered to be volumetrically unimportant.

One weakness of the quantitative approach as currently applied is that hydrocarbon flow is modeled as if it were part of a two-phase (water–oil or water–gas) system, instead of the three-phase (oil + gas + water) flow that occurs in many cases. Development of multiphase migration models is now underway.

Experimental work (e.g., Sandvik and Mercer, 1990) indicates that permeabilities of shale source rocks are low during hydrocarbon expulsion and that they vary over several orders of magnitude. However, because absolute permeabilities are seldom measured for source rocks, the permeabilities used in models are usually calculated. One common method is to calculate permeability as a function of porosity, but porosity–permeability relationships have an intrinsic uncertainty of at least an order of magnitude (e.g., Magara, 1986). One can instead use the Kozeny–Carman equation, which calculates porosity as a function of specific surface area of shale particles and effective porosities (Doligez et al., 1986; Ungerer et al., 1990). However, detailed data on source rock fabrics are seldom available. Estimating porosities and permeabilities of mixed lithologies is difficult. Fractal techniques have been used to address the effects on permeability of mixing particles of different sizes. As illustrated by these complications, there is considerable uncertainty in estimating absolute permeabilities of source rocks.

Furthermore, relative permeability curves for source rocks are poorly understood. Most models base their curves on analogy with reservoir rocks (e.g., Ungerer et al., 1990). However, Nakayama (1987) and Okui and Waples (1993) have suggested that relative permeability curves for source rocks are quite different (Figure 18.2). The implications of these differences for expulsion are yet to be fully evaluated, but may be of real importance.

The driving forces for expulsion of hydrocarbons from a source rock probably are hydraulic potential, buoyancy differences between hydrocarbons and water, and capillary pressure at the source rock boundary. Hydraulic potential develops mainly as a deviation from hydrostatic pressure due to sediment loading or hydrocarbon generation, although both contributions are difficult to quantify. Hydraulic potential affects all fluids equally, whereas the other two forces in general favor hydrocarbon movement over water. The relative importance of these three forces varies as a function of such factors as source rock thickness, contrast in pore sizes between source rock and carrier bed, density (composition) of hydrocarbons, sedimentation rate, and source rock permeability. Buoyancy pressure is probably least important in most cases. Capillary pressure effects may play an important role in hydrocarbon expulsion, particularly if generation occurs when porosity is relatively high. However, because capillary pressure depends on the lithology of rocks outside the source rock, because information on the source rock–carrier bed interface is generally poor, and because our knowledge of true hydraulic potentials in compacting rocks is inadequate, our ability to predict the magnitudes of forces promoting hydrocarbon expulsion is limited (Okui and Waples, 1993).

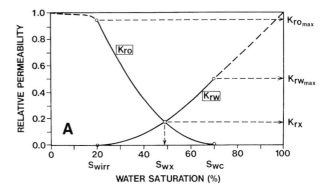

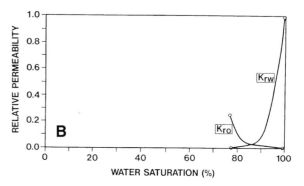

Figure 18.2. (A) Relative permeability curve for a typical reservoir rock compared to that proposed for (B) a typical shale source rock with absolute permeability of 10^{-7} d; $K_{air} = 0.0001$ md. Symbols: K_{ro}, relative permeability to oil; K_{rw}, relative permeability to water; $K_{ro_{max}}$, maximum value of K_{ro} achieved at irreducible water saturation (S_{wirr}); $K_{rw_{max}}$, maximum K_{rw} achieved at the critical water saturation (S_{wc}); S_{wx} and K_{rx}, water saturation and relative permeabilities where the two relative permeability curves cross (where $K_{rw} = K_{ro}$). (From Okui and Waples, 1993; reprinted with permission of Elsevier.)

Fluid expulsion from normally compacting fine-grained rocks is believed by most workers to be mainly vertical (England et al., 1987; but see Schneider et al., in press, for a contrasting opinion) and to occur through matrix permeability. However, under conditions of extreme overpressuring (typically when fluid pressure exceeds about 80–90% of lithostatic pressure), most models assume that microfracturing occurs and that fluid may be expelled through the resulting fracture permeability (e.g., Nakayama, 1987; Welte, 1987).

In quantitative system models, expulsion efficiency is generally not specified by the user or the program and thus does not control expulsion. Instead, expulsion efficiency is calculated later (as output data rather than input) by comparing the amount of expelled hydrocarbons to the total amount of hydrocarbons generated. The amount retained represents some proportion of the total pore volume, approximately equal to $100 - S_{wirr}$ (where S_{wirr} is the irreducible water saturation). As porosity decreases, the amount of hydrocarbons retained decreases due to the increased proportion of irreducible water. Overall expulsion efficiencies of about 80% are commonly accepted today for excellent source rocks, decreasing to values near zero for poor-quality sources (e.g., Mackenzie and Quigley, 1988). Existing numerical expulsion models produce results in accordance with these ideas, although modeling of coals has been a problem (Pepper, in press).

As a consequence of the various uncertainties about expulsion, some of the advantages of the quantitative method over the qualitative may be more apparent than real. Nevertheless, as our understanding of the expulsion process improves, the quantitative approach will become more powerful and will probably be used in most future models.

Secondary Migration and Accumulation

Most petroleum system models calculate rates and volumes of fluids flowing through carrier beds using Darcy's law. One weakness with this calculation is that rock unit permeabilities are often poorly known. Measured permeabilities, where available, may be misleading due to scaling effects (Bethke et al., 1991; Waples, 1991a). Moreover, most system models consider only matrix permeability. If fracturing has occurred, it may greatly increase the permeabilities of existing carrier beds and create new carrier beds from rocks with low matrix permeabilities (Bethke et al., 1991). Some models allow the user to specify the locations of known faults (which are then assigned high permeabilities), but current models are unable to predict faults. A model to predict tectonic fracturing and permeabilities associated with such fracturing is under development (Larson et al., 1993), but has yet to be integrated into any petroleum system models.

The fluid potential driving hydrocarbon migration is calculated for each nodal block on the cross section for each increment of time. If water is taken as the standard fluid, its fluid potential is determined by such factors as compactional forces due to sediment burial, pressure buildup from hydrocarbon generation, and differences in head due to paleorelief. The relative importance of these factors changes as the sedimentary basin evolves. Bethke et al. (1991) have shown, for example, that development of adjacent structures in the Illinois basin during the Mesozoic provided sufficient relief to affect regional fluid flow, whereas compactional forces during the basin's previous slow sedimentation history were much smaller. In contrast, those authors concluded that in basins such as the Gulf Coast compaction disequilibrium is much more important as a driving force for fluids.

Hydrocarbon flow patterns may differ from water flow patterns because capillary pressure and buoyancy (which also contribute to total fluid potential) are different for each phase. Two-phase system models include both capillary and buoyancy effects in describing hydrocarbon migration and thus allow hydrocarbons to move at different speeds and even in different directions from water. Buoyancy effects alone may be unable to account for hydrocarbon movement where dip angles for fluid conduits are low (Bethke et al., 1991). In such situations, a close parallel may exist between water flow and hydrocarbon flow.

Two-phase models assume that oil and gas travel together, with physical properties that may represent either end-member or some average between oil and gas. As noted for hydrocarbon expulsion, modeling of migration as two-phase flow may be adequate. However, the relative proportions of the two hydrocarbon phases can change dramatically through time and space as the result of oil to gas cracking and phase changes (e.g., the condensation of gas or the exsolution of gas from a saturated liquid as pressure is released during upward migration). Interest is growing in developing better phase equilibrium descriptions of migrating fluids to specify more accurately the amount of each hydrocarbon phase actually present at all times (England, Chapter 12, this volume).

Use of a two-phase (hydrocarbon + water) migration model requires knowledge of the volume of hydrocarbons at each point in the system. One must therefore specify the volume of hydrocarbons expelled from the source rock as well as the relative permeabilities of the migration conduits to the fluid phases being considered. Fortunately, relative permeability curves for oil–water systems and gas–oil systems in reservoir rocks are well known. However, few details are yet available for multiphase flow through fractures.

Furthermore, calculation of migration loss due to residual oil saturation is crucial for satisfactory numerical modeling, but the amount of loss that actually occurs is poorly known and probably variable. Oil is believed to follow certain preferential pathways with large pores, high permeability, and near the top of the carrier bed (Dembicki and Anderson, 1989; Miles, 1990; Bethke et al., 1991; England, Chapter 12). Although relative permeability curves for reservoir rocks allow the calculation of the residual oil saturation (irreducible oil saturation) in these preferential pathways, little is known information about what percentage of the total pore volume of a carrier bed is actually saturated with oil. Moreover, any accumulations in structures or stratigraphic traps that are smaller than our nodal blocks are considered as migration loss by the model. It has been suggested that 1–10% (England et al., 1987) or 1–3% (Mackenzie and Quigley, 1988) of carrier bed porosity is filled with residual oil, but these published ranges are too broad to be of much practical value (Waples, 1991b; Hermanrud, 1993; England, Chapter 12). England (Chapter 12) has commented that hydrocarbon migration is "an extremely efficient process, considering the enormous volume of water saturated rock through which the petroleum must pass." While the migration loss is indeed much smaller than it would be if the entire carrier bed were saturated, if we define efficiency as the fraction of original hydrocarbons reaching a commercial accumulation, it may be rather small.

Multiphase models predict that a hydrocarbon phase will accumulate wherever its fluid potential reaches a relative minimum. Since the potential of each phase is calculated for each nodal block for each increment of time, accumulation is easily modeled. However, the capillary pressure at the boundary between the seal rock and the reservoir rock must be calculated with enough accuracy to predict correctly whether hydrocarbons can pass through the seal rock. For lithologies that traditionally provide good sealing capability, this prediction may be quite good, but for seals of marginal quality (e.g., siltstones), there may be considerable uncertainty. Furthermore, our present models are unable to consider possible loss of sealing capability through tectonic fracturing, although most of them do consider fracturing induced by excess pressure.

The qualitative hydrocarbon migration models, in contrast, which only model water flow, assume that hydrocarbons always follow the same pathways as water. Although such approaches fail to take into account differences in direction or velocity due to buoyancy and capillary effects, in most cases they probably give a reasonable general picture of hydrocarbon movement.

One-phase models are less specific than multiphase models about where accumulation is occurring because they are unable to consider the effect of capillary pressure on hydrocarbon movement. Water flow is constrained to be from high fluid potential to low, and accumulation of hydrocarbons is assumed to occur where fluid potentials of water reach local minima.

All migration accumulation models share the common problem that they average the properties that control fluid flow (such as absolute and relative permeability) over large blocks of rock and assume that each block is homogeneous. In fact, rock masses are notoriously heterogeneous, and fluid flow is controlled by (often small) zones of anomalously high or low permeability (e.g., Dembicki and Anderson, 1989). Thus, our models are probably intrinsically too large scale to model migration and accumulation properly. Faster computers would allow modeling of smaller nodal blocks of rock, but there may never be enough detailed data on rock textures to take full advantage of fast computers. If fractal techniques prove applicable for scaling petrophysical properties between laboratory sample sizes and system-modeling nodal block dimensions (Waples, 1991a), it may prove possible to represent fluid flow accurately. For the time being, however, we lack the capability to model fluid flow in the detail required (as emphasized for reservoir studies by van de Graaf and Ealey, 1989), regardless of the sophistication of our equations or computers.

In addition, fluid flow phenomena depend on relationships in three spatial dimensions, whereas our modeling is usually done in two. Careful selection of cross sections to minimize structural changes out of the plane of the section can help minimize this problem, but in structurally complex areas, two-dimensional modeling may be inadequate for describing fluid flow. Areas in which hydrocarbon accumulation is predicted on the basis of two-dimensional simulations should therefore only be considered as "possible" areas for accumulation since structural or lithologic changes in the third dimension might alter migration pathways. Thus, wherever an accumulation is predicted, one should also model a cross section perpendicular to the first one to ascertain that closure of the fluid potential contours occurs in the third dimension.

Preservation

Any hydrocarbon accumulation will be either preserved, degraded, or destroyed (Magoon and Dow, Chapter 1, this volume). Degradation or destruction of accumulated hydrocarbons can occur in at least seven ways: cracking, oxidation, erosion, biodegradation, water washing, leakage through seals, or spillage. The current status of system models in describing each of these phenomena is discussed here.

1. Cracking can be predicted reasonably well using kinetic models. Limitations of current cracking models are discussed by Waples (Chapter 17, this volume).

2. Oxidation mainly involves the rapid conversion of methane to carbon dioxide at high temperatures (about 150°C) in the presence of sulfate. The kinetic equations used for hydrocarbon generation or oil cracking are inappropriate for predicting oxidation (Barker and Kemp, 1982). Since most methane oxidation occurs in carbonate reservoirs at high temperatures, it could probably be predicted using simple temperature and lithologic criteria. However, no models currently consider methane oxidation.

3. Erosion of hydrocarbon accumulations is directly predicted by burial history reconstructions and therefore requires no special consideration.

4. Basin models currently ignore biodegradation, although in principle it should be feasible to predict. Biodegradation requires meteoric water at temperatures below 80°C, with an optimum of about 60°C (Connan, 1984). A combination of hydrodynamics predicted by the fluid flow model, temperature information provided by the heat flow–conductivity model (and modified by fluid flow), and information on the location of hydrocarbons could thus allow the prediction of where biodegradation might occur. Since biodegradation can take place during migration as well as in the reservoir, this biodegradation model should also be applied during migration. The accuracy of modeling biodegradation is controlled by the ability to model the flow of meteoric water. Present-day hydrodynamics are usually the most crucial since much of the biodegradation is recent. Modeling ancient biodegration is difficult because predicting paleohydrodynamics is a major problem due to poor constraint of paleorelief (e.g., Bethke et al., 1991).

5. Water washing results in modest increases in oil density (corresponding to a maximum decrease in oil gravity of about 5° API), but it seldom leads to the formation of asphalt or tar as does biodegradation (Lafargue and Barker, 1988). These facts, and that water washing often accompanies biodegradation (but see Lafargue and Barker, 1988), probably make separate modeling of water washing unnecessary.

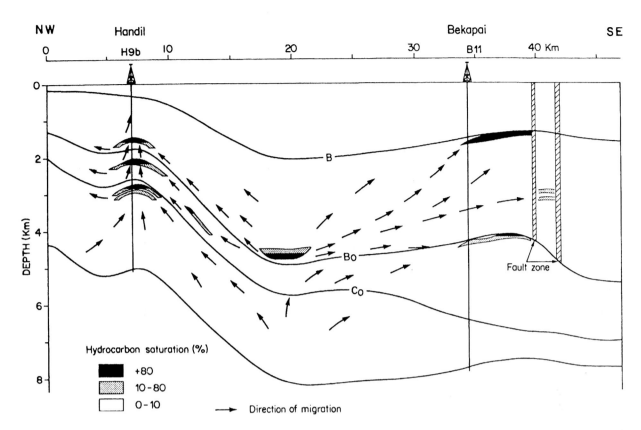

Figure 18.3. Hydrocarbon (oil + gas) saturations and arrows representing directions of present-day gas migration toward the Handil and Bekapai structures, Mahakam Delta, Indonesia, as predicted by two-dimensional modeling (see also Figure 18. 1). (From Ungerer et al., 1990.)

6. Leakage of hydrocarbons from a trap can in principle be modeled using the normal considerations for petroleum fluid flow in the model: fluid moves to a region of lower potential whenever possible. Most models allow hydraulic fracturing of seal rock if the buoyant pressure of the hydrocarbon column becomes large enough (e.g., Ungerer et al., 1990). Leakage due to diffusion has also been considered (Leythaeuser et al., 1982). Inspissation is simply a special case of leakage, in which the lighter components are lost preferentially. However, modeling leakage involves the same problems already discussed for migration: inability of models to consider tectonic fracturing (which may be important in controlling leakage) and averaging the properties controlling fluid flow over large volumes of inhomogeneous rocks. Modeling of leakage is thus one of the weaker parts of the fluid flow scheme.

7. Spillage can be modeled only if trap contours can be modeled accurately. Unfortunately, grid sizes in many system-modeling simulations are too large to represent trap shapes and sizes accurately (but see Ungerer et al., 1990). Sylta (1993) has modeled spillage using ray tracing techniques that differ from flow modeling in most petroleum system models. Sales (1993) has emphasized the need to look at spillage and leakage together.

In summary, except for cracking, modeling of phenomena that destroy hydrocarbon accumulations is poor to nonexistent. A geologist must therefore apply qualitatively the ideas outlined here after the numerical modeling is completed. Considering the frustration involved in finding large quantities of unproducible biodegraded asphalt, or of finding empty reservoirs stained with oil residues, modeling of hydrocarbon loss has been surprisingly neglected.

APPLICATIONS

In recent years, a number of examples of petroleum system modeling have been published that can serve as useful guidelines for those interested in doing modeling themselves. These include the Haltenbanken area of Norway (Ungerer et al., 1990; Forbes et al., 1991; Grigo et al., 1993), the Viking graben (Ungerer et al., 1990; Schroeder and Sylta, 1993; Skjervoy and Sylta, 1993), the Austrian overthrust (Schmidt and Erdogan, 1993), the Mahakam delta of Indonesia (Ungerer et al., 1990), the Tadla basin of Morocco (Jabour and Nakayama, 1988), the Wyoming overthrust belt (Wei and Lerche, 1988), the Illinois basin (Bethke et al., 1991), Mozambique (Iliffe et al., 1991), and an artificial example similar to an Indonesian basin (Zeitlin, 1989). Water flow has also been modeled for purposes unrelated to petroleum exploration (e.g., Bethke et al., 1988; Bethke and Marshak, 1990).

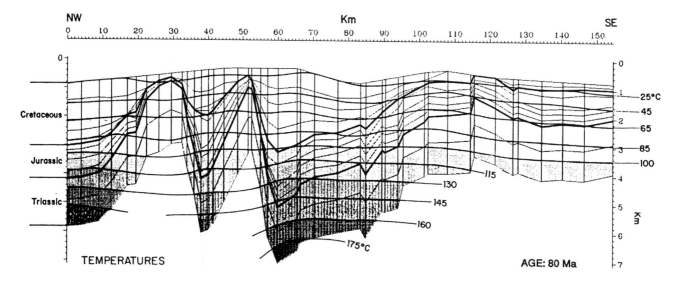

Figure 18.4. Isotherms superimposed on a cross section at 80 Ma through the northern part of the Viking graben. The vertical lines are lateral boundaries of nodal blocks. Light horizontal lines are top and bottom boundaries of nodal blocks. (From Ungerer et al., 1990.)

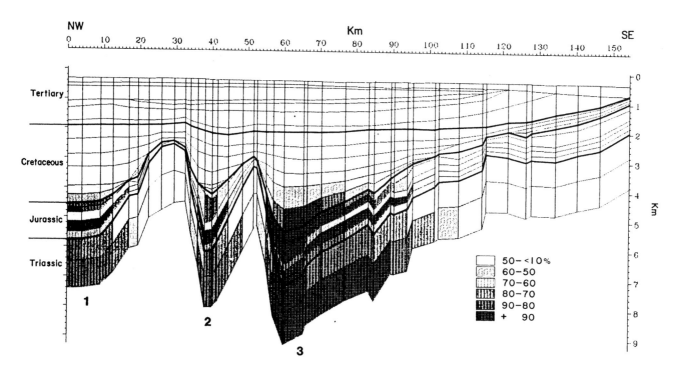

Figure 18.5. Transformation ratios (in %) of kerogen to hydrocarbons (calculated using kinetic modeling) superimposed on a present-day cross section through the northern part of the Viking graben. (From Ungerer et al., 1990.)

Since most petroleum system modeling is two-dimensional, much of the output is also two-dimensional. Here are some examples of data that can be output on cross sections.

Example 1. Hydrocarbon saturations and arrows representing directions of present-day gas migration toward the Handil and Bekapai structures, Mahakam Delta, Indonesia, are shown in

Figure 18.3 as predicted by two-dimensional modeling. A stratigraphic accumulation is predicted in the synclinal area in the middle of the cross section, as well as some spillage to the northwest from overfilled Handil reservoir rocks.

Example 2. Isotherms are shown in Figure 18.4 superimposed on a cross section through the northern part of the Viking graben during the Late Cretaceous. Since heat flow is uniformly 65 mW/m²

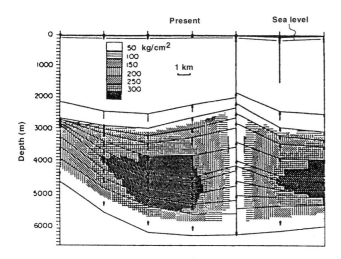

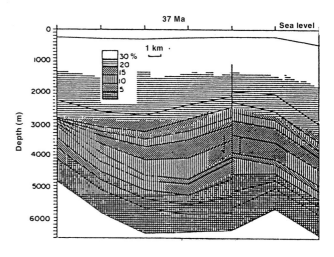

Figure 18.6. Pressure in excess of hydrostatic plotted on a present-day cross section through the Pinedale anticline, western overthrust belt, U.S.A. (From Wei and Lerche, 1988; reprinted with permission of Pergamon Press.)

Figure 18.7. Porosity plotted on a cross section as reconstructed for 37 Ma through the Pinedale anticline, western overthrust belt, U.S.A. (From Wei and Lerche, 1988; reprinted with permission of Pergamon Press.)

across the entire section, the waviness of the isotherms is probably due primarily to differences in thermal conductivities, although convective heat transfer or lateral conduction (thermal refraction) could also contribute.

Example 3. Transformation ratios of kerogen to hydrocarbons in Figure 18.5 (shown by patterns) are superimposed on a present-day cross section through the northern part of the Viking graben. The oil window corresponds to 10–60% conversion and the gas window to 60–100% conversion. (Transformation ratios only represent the degree of hydrocarbon generation; information about the absolute amount of kerogen or hydrocarbons present is lacking.) Zones marked 1, 2, and 3 represent the pods of active source rock from which any hydrocarbons generated would migrate in different directions.

Example 4. Pressure in excess of hydrostatic is plotted on a present-day cross section in Figure 18.6 drawn through the Pinedale anticline, western overthrust belt, U.S.A. The dramatic decrease of excess pressure approaching the fault from both sides (due to its high permeability) is shown by the patterns in the nodal blocks.

Example 5. Figure 18.7 shows porosity by a pattern on a cross section as reconstructed for 37 Ma through the Pinedale anticline in the western overthrust belt of the United States.

Many other parameters can also be plotted at any user-specified time slice. For example, gas–oil ratios (GOR) of recently expelled hydrocarbons from the Are Formation are shown in Figure 18.8 for the drainage area of the Smorbukk Sor field. Plan-view maps at any time can be made for many of these parameters if the data are desired in *x-y* dimensions rather than on cross sections. Figure 18.9 shows calculated R_o values in the Bakken Shale at three different times.

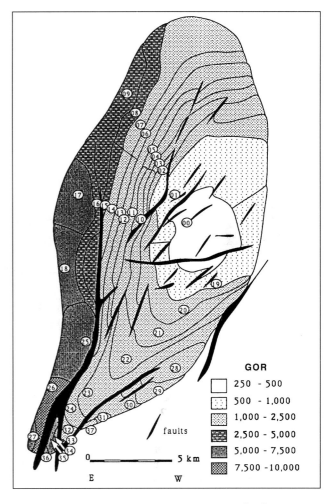

Figure 18.8. Gas–oil ratios (GOR, standard m³/m³) of hydrocarbons expelled from the Are Formation during the last 0.5 m.y. in the drainage area of the Smorbukk Sor field, Haltenbanken area, offshore Norway. Numbers in circles are pseudowells used in simulations. (From Forbes et al., 1991.)

Figure 18.9. Calculated vitrinite reflectance (R_o) values in the Bakken Shale (A) before the Laramide orogeny (70 Ma), (B) after the Laramide orogeny (40 Ma), and (C) present day (on opposite page). Shaded areas indicate $R_o > 0.6\%$; contour interval is $0.05\% R_o$. (From Dembicki and Pirkle, 1985.)

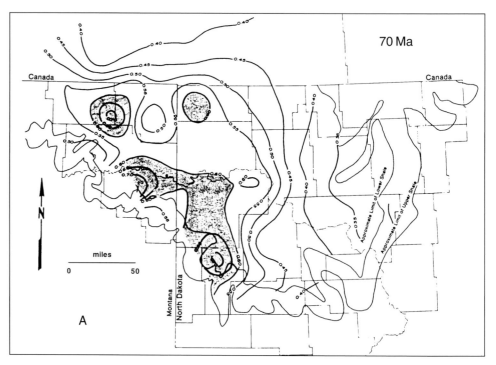

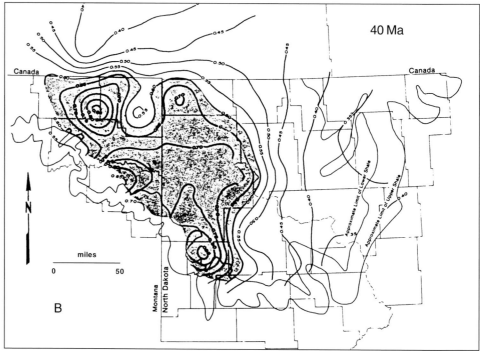

WEAKNESSES OF MODELS AND SENSITIVITY ANALYSIS

Numerous weaknesses in existing petroleum system models have already been mentioned. Among these, the most serious are as follows: (1) the inability of models to provide adequate aid in optimizing input data; (2) lack of consideration of tectonic fracturing and its contribution to total permeability; (3) poor quantification of expulsion, migration, and migration loss; (4) large differences among the scales on which modeling is done and the scales that control important geologic properties such as permeability; (5) inadequate modeling of hydrocarbon destruction and loss in reservoirs; and (6) inability to handle faulting and other structural complexities realistically. Unfortunately, few of our present research efforts are being directed toward these areas. Until these problems are resolved, users of system models must be aware of these weaknesses and deal with them in an ad hoc fashion whenever they are relevant to a particular situation.

As we become increasingly aware of the intrinsic limitations of our knowledge of equations and input data for both sedimentary basin and petroleum system models,

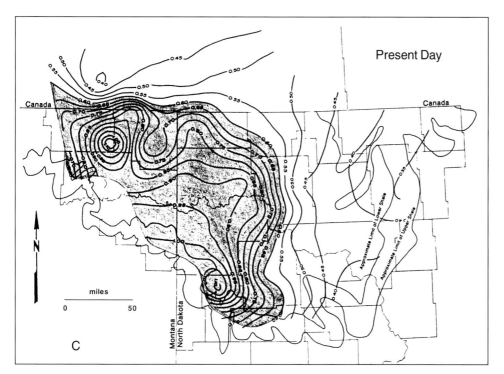

we are also increasingly confronted with the problem of estimating the magnitude of the uncertainty in using such models. Sensitivity analysis is important in any exploration application of modeling because the user must determine whether the intrinsic uncertainties in the input data could affect the final exploration decision (e.g., Waples et al., 1992). Furthermore, because output data from modeling studies is often input into statistical risk assessment calculations, statistical distribution of outcomes is more convenient than a single final answer.

At least three different solutions have been proposed to the problem of sensitivity analysis. One answer is to run multiple simulations using maximum and minimum values for various input parameters (e.g., Iliffe et al., 1991; Waples et al., 1992). The "correct" value should fall somewhere between the largest and smallest output values. However, such an approach is crude because no probability of occurrence is associated with any of the output values. It is most valuable when the final answer turns out to be insensitive to the uncertainties in the input data.

A second answer that is increasingly considered by model builders is to include some probabilistic capability (such as Monte Carlo) in the deterministic model (e.g., Hermanrud et al., 1990; Irwin et al., 1993). Such models would provide output as a range of values, with associated probabilities of occurrence. An advantage of probabilistic methods is that analysis of a range of possible scenarios is more realistic and appropriate than relying on a single "best" answer (Hermanrud, 1993). Monte Carlo technology is well understood; the main problems are to separate variables and to incorporate Monte Carlo technology into system models without making simulation times unbearably long.

A third possibility, not necessarily inconsistent with either of the others, is to run simulations using the same input data using multiple models. Since each model is constructed differently, using a variety of models may provide a feeling for the influence of the model itself on the outcome.

CONCLUDING REMARKS

The speed with which simulations are carried out remains an important but thorny problem. One-dimensional modeling simulations, which dominate maturity modeling, are generally fast. As a result, a geologist can run a simulation, make a change in an input parameter, and test the sensitivity of the result to the change. When simulations only take a minute or less, interactive modeling of this type is feasible and valuable since the geologist can then conveniently and quickly optimize the input data and carry out sensitivity analysis.

Petroleum system simulations require more time than maturity simulations because they are two-dimensional and because they must compute much more information about fluid flow and pressure. As simulation times increase, there is a rapid decline in user interactiveness and the ability to optimize input data conveniently and carry out sensitivity analysis. Maintaining the ability to execute quick simulations should be a high priority for model builders because of the great importance of rapid and convenient optimization and sensitivity analysis.

The dual goals of (1) rapid simulations and (2) more detail, finer-scale, and inclusion of more physical phenomena are incompatible in a single two-dimensional model unless computer speeds increase. In an effort to attain both goals, future system models should provide computer-aided optimization in one dimension, in addition to the final two-dimensional simulations. The modeling process would then consist of (1) initial optimization in one dimension; (2) final optimization in two dimensions; and (3) final simulations in two dimensions.

A fast version of the two-dimensional model might also be helpful for use in sensitivity analysis. Quick models of this type would probably reduce the number of nodal blocks and make some simplifying assumptions to increase simulation speed. The final design of such a system and the particular simplifying assumptions used in constructing the quick two-dimensional option would probably be approached in different ways by different model builders. Some suggestions have already been made (Waples, 1991a).

Model builders are largely interested in creating what is technically the best model possible. Users, however, need a model that accepts the type of data they normally work with and gives them reasonably reliable answers (together with sensitivity analysis or some measure of confidence in the final output) in a reasonable amount of time. Users also need a model that helps them learn during the modeling process, rather than merely functioning as the proverbial "black box." These various needs are sometimes incompatible. Future model development should be done much more from the perspective of the working geologist since it is the geologist's acceptance or rejection of sedimentary basin models and petroleum system models that ultimately determine their impact on petroleum exploration.

Acknowledgments   I thank JNOC for permission to publish this work and for support in preparing the manuscript. Christian Hermanrud, Michael Zeitlin, and Les Magoon offered valuable comments on an earlier version. I am also grateful to the many other workers who have generously shared their knowledge in discussions and through their publications.

References Cited

Barker, C., and M. K. Kemp, 1982, Stability of natural gas at high temperatures, deep subsurface: AAPG Bulletin, v. 66, p. 545.

Barker, C. E., and Elders, W. A., 1981, Vitrinite reflectance geothermometry and apparent heating duration in the Cerro Prieto geothermal field: Geothermics, v. 10, p. 207–223.

Bethke, C. M., 1985, A numerical model of compaction-driven groundwater flow and heat transfer and its application to the paleohydrology of intracratonic sedimentary basins: Journal of Geophysical Research, v. 90, p. 6817–6828.

Bethke, C. M., 1989, Modeling subsurface flow in sedimentary basins: Geologische Rundschau, v. 78, p. 129–154.

Bethke, C. M., and S. Marshak, 1990, Brine migrations across North America—the plate tectonics of groundwater: Annual Reviews of Earth and Planetary Science 1990, v. 18, p. 287–315.

Bethke, C. M., W. J. Harrison, C. Upson, and S. P. Altaner, 1988, Supercomputer analysis of sedimentary basins: Science, v. 239, p. 261–267.

Bethke, C. M., J. D. Reed, and D. F. Oltz, 1991, Long-range petroleum migration in the Illinois basin: AAPG Bulletin, v. 75, p. 925–945.

Bredehoeft, J. D., and I. S. Papadopoulos, 1965, Rates of vertical groundwater movement estimated from the earth's thermal profile: Water Resources Research, v. 1, p. 325–328.

Carter, K., and I. Lerche, in press, Moving salt sheets and sediment maturity: AAPG Bulletin.

Connan, J., 1984, Biodegradation of crude oils in reservoirs, *in* J. Brooks and D. Welte, eds., Advances in Petroleum Geochemistry, Vol. 1: London, Academic Press, p. 299–333.

Dembicki, H., Jr., and M. J. Anderson, 1989, Migration of oil: experiments supporting efficient movement of separate, buoyant oil phase along limited conduits: AAPG Bulletin, v. 73, p. 1018–1021.

Dembicki, H., Jr., and F. J. Pirkle, 1985, Regional source rock mapping using a source potential rating index: AAPG Bulletin, v. 69, p. 567–581.

Deming, D., and J. A. Nunn, 1991, Numerical models of brine migration by topographically driven recharge: Journal of Geophysical Research, v. 96, p. 2485–2499.

Deming, D., J. A. Nunn, and D. G. Evans, 1990, Thermal effects of compaction-driven groundwater flow from overthrust belts: Journal of Geophysical Research, v. 95, p. 6669–6683.

Doligez, B., F. Bessis, J. Burrus, P. Ungerer, and P. Y. Chenet, 1986, Integrated numerical modelling of sedimentation, heat transfer, hydrocarbon formation and fluid migration in a sedimentary basin: the THEMIS model, *in* J. Burrus, ed., Thermal Modeling in Sedimentary Basins: Paris, Editions Technip, p. 173–195.

England, W. A., A. S. Mackenzie, D. M. Mann, and T. M. Quigley, 1987, The movement and entrapment of petroleum fluids in the subsurface, Journal of the Geological Society, London, v. 144, p. 327–347.

Fjeldskaar, E. Prestholm, W., C. Guargena, and N. Gravdal, 1993, Isostatic and tectonic subsidence of the Egersund subbasin, *in* A. G. Dore et al., eds., Basin Modelling: Advances and Applications: Amsterdam, Elsevier, p. 549–562.

Forbes, P. L., P. M. Ungerer, A. B. Kuhfuss, F. Riis, and S. Eggen, 1991, Compositional modeling of petroleum generation and expulsion: Trial application to a local mass balance in the Smorbukk Sor field, Haltenbanken area, Norway: AAPG Bulletin, v. 75, p. 873–893.

Garven, G., and R. A. Freeze, 1984, Theoretical analysis of the role of groundwater flow in the genesis of stratabound ore deposits: American Journal of Science, v. 284, p. 1085–1174.

Grigo, D., B. Maragna, M. T. Arienti, M. Fiorani, A. Paris, M. Marrone, P. Sguazzero, and A. S. Uberg, 1993, Issues in 3D sedimentary basin modelling and application to Haltenbanken area, offshore Norway, *in* A. G. Dore et al., eds., Basin Modelling: Advances and Applications: Amsterdam, Elsevier, p. 445–454.

Hermanrud, C., 1993, Basin modelling techniques—an overview, *in* A. G. Dore et al., eds., Basin Modelling: Advances and Applications: Amsterdam, Elsevier, p. 1–34.

Hermanrud, C., S. Eggen, T. Jacobsen, E,M. Carlsen, and S. Pallesen, 1990, On the accuracy of modelling hydrocarbon generation and migration: The Egersund Basin oil find, Norway: Organic Geochemistry, v. 16, p. 389–399.

Hitchon, B., 1984, Geothermal gradients, hydrodynamics, and hydrocarbon occurrences, Alberta, Canada: AAPG Bulletin, v. 68, p. 713–743.

Hulen, J. B., L. C. Bortz, and S. R. Bereskin, 1991, Geothermal processes in evolution of the Grant Canyon and Bacon Flat oil reservoirs, Railroad Valley, Nye County, Nevada, *in* D. M. H. Flanigan, M. Hansen, and T. E. Flanigan, eds., Geology of White River Valley, the Grant Range, Eastern

Railroad Valley, and Western Egan Range, Nevada: Nevada Petroleum Society, 1991 Fieldtrip Guidebook, Reno, p. 47–54.

Iliffe, J. E., I. Lerche, and M. DeBuyl, 1991, Basin analysis and hydrocarbon generation of the South Mozambique graben using extensional models of heat flow: Marine and Petroleum Geology, v. 8, p. 152–162.

Irwin, H., C. Hermanrud, E. D. Carlsen, J. Vollset, and I. Nordvall, 1993, Basin modelling of hydrocarbon charge in the Egersund Basin, Norwegian North Sea: pre- and post-drilling assessments, *in* A. G. Dore et al., eds., Basin Modelling: Advances and Applications: Amsterdam, Elsevier, p. 539–548.

Jabour, H., and K. Nakayama, 1988, Basin modeling of Tadla basin, Morocco, for hydrocarbon potential: AAPG Bulletin, v. 72, p. 1059–1073.

Johnsson, M. J., 1986, Distribution of maximum burial temperatures across northern Appalachian basin and implications for Carboniferous sedimentation patterns: Geology, v. 14, p. 384–387.

Lafargue, E., and C. Barker, 1988, Effect of water washing on crude oil compositions: AAPG Bulletin, v. 72, p. 263–276.

Larson, K. W., D. W. Waples, Han Fu, and K. Kodama, 1993, Predicting tectonic fractures and fluid flow through fractures in basin modeling, *in* A. G. Dore et al., eds., Basin Modelling: Advances and Applications: Amsterdam, Elsevier, p. 373–384.

Lehner, F. K., D. Marsal, L. Hermans, and A. van Kuyk, 1988, A model of secondary hydrocarbon migration as a buoyancy-driven separate phase flow: Revue de l'Institut Francais du Petrole, v. 43, p. 155–164.

Lerche, I., 1988a, Inversion of multiple thermal indicators: quantitative methods of determining paleoheat flux and geological parameters, I. Theoretical development for paleoheat flux and geological parameters: Mathematical Geology, v. 20, p. 1–36.

Lerche, I., 1988b, Inversion of multiple thermal indicators: quantitative methods of determining paleoheat flux and geological parameters, II. Theoretical development for chemical, physical, and geological parameters: Mathematical Geology, v. 20, p. 73–96.

Lerche, I., 1990, Basin Analysis: Quantitative Methods, Vol. 1: San Diego, Academic Press, 562 p.

Leythaeuser, D., R. G. Schaefer, and A. Yukler, 1982, Role of diffusion in primary migration of hydrocarbons: AAPG Bulletin, v. 66, p. 408–429.

Mackenzie, A. S., and T. M. Quigley, 1988, Principles of geochemical prospect appraisal: AAPG Bulletin, v. 72, p. 399–415.

Magara, K., 1986, Porosity–depth relationship during compaction in hydrostatic and non-hydrostatic cases, *in* J. Burrus, ed., Thermal Modeling in Sedimentary Basins: Paris, Editions Technip, p. 129–147.

Miles, J. A., 1990, Secondary migration routes in the Brent Sandstones of the Viking graben and East Shetland basin: evidence from oil residues and subsurface pressure data: AAPG Bulletin, v. 74, p. 1718–1735.

Nakayama, K., 1987, Hydrocarbon-expulsion model and its application to Niigata area, Japan: AAPG Bulletin, v. 71, p. 810–821.

Nunn, J. A., and D. Deming, 1991, Thermal constraints on basin-scale flow systems, Geophysical Research Letters, v. 18, p. 9676–970.

O'Brien, J. J., and I. Lerche, 1988, Impact of heat flux anomalies around salt diapirs and salt sheets in the Gulf Coast on hydrocarbon maturity: Gulf Coast Association of Geologic Societies, v. 58, p. 231–243.

Okui, A., and D. W. Waples, 1993, Relative permeabilities and hydrocarbon expulsion from source rocks, *in* A. G. Dore et al., eds., Basin Modelling: Advances and Applications: Amsterdam, Elsevier, p. 293–302.

Oliver, J., 1986, Fluids expelled tectonically from orogenic belts, Geology, v. 14, p. 99–102.

Pepper, A. S., in press, Estimating the petroleum expulsion behaviour of source rocks: a novel quantitative approach, *in* W. A. England and A. J. Fleet, eds., Petroleum migration: London Geological Society Special Publication.

Powell, W. G., and D. S. Chapman, 1990, A detailed study of heat flow at the Fifth Water Site, Utah, in the Basin and Range–Colorado Plateaus transition: Tectonophysics, v. 176, p. 291–314.

Sales, J., 1993, Closure vs. seal capacity—a fundamental control on the distribution of oil and gas, *in* A. G. Dore et al., eds., Basin Modelling: Advances and Applications: Amsterdam, Elsevier, p. 399–414.

Sandvik, E. I., and J. N. Mercer, 1990, Primary migration by bulk hydrocarbon flow: Organic Geochemistry, v. 16, p. 83–89.

Sandvik, E. I., W. A. Young, and D. J. Curry, 1992, Expulsion from hydrocarbon sources: the role of organic absorption, *in* C. B. Eckardt et al., eds., Advances in Organic Geochemistry 1991: Oxford, Pergamon, p. 77–88.

Schmidt, F., and T. Erdogan, 1993, Basin modelling in an overthrust area of Austria, *in* A. G. Dore et al., eds., Basin Modelling: Advances and Applications: Amsterdam, Elsevier, p. 573–582.

Schmoker, J. W., 1984, Empirical relation between carbonate porosity and thermal maturity: an approach to regional porosity prediction: AAPG Bulletin, v. 68, p. 1697–1703.

Schmoker, J. W., and T. C. Hester, 1990, Regional trends of sandstone porosity versus vitrinite reflectance—a preliminary framework, *in* V. F. Nuccio and C. E. Barker, eds., Applications of Thermal Maturity Studies to Energy Exploration: Denver, RMS–SEPM, p. 53–60.

Schneider, F., J. Burrus, and S. Wolf, 1993, Modelling overpressures by effective-stress/porosity relationships in low-permeability rocks: empirical artifice or physical reality?, *in* A. G. Dore et al., eds., Basin Modelling: Advances and Applications: Amsterdam, Elsevier, p. 333–342.

Schroeder, F. W., and O. Sylta, 1993, Modelling the hydrocarbon system of the North Viking graben: a case study, *in* A. G. Dore et al., eds., Basin Modelling: Advances and Applications: Amsterdam, Elsevier, p. 469–484.

Skjervoy, A., and O. Sylta, 1993, Modelling of expulsion and secondary migration along the southwestern margin of the Horda platform, *in* A. G. Dore et al., eds., Basin Modelling: Advances and Applications: Amsterdam, Elsevier, p. 499–538.

Smith, L., and D. S. Chapman, 1983, On the thermal effects of groundwater flow, 1—Regional scale systems: Journal of Geophysical Research, v. 88, p. 593–608.

Stainforth, J. G., and J. E. A. Reinders, 1990, Primary migration of hydrocarbons by diffusion through organic matter networks, and its effect on oil and gas generation: Organic Geochemistry, v. 16, p. 61–74.

Sylta, O., 1993, New techniques and their applications in the analysis of secondary migration, *in* A. G. Dore et al., eds., Basin Modelling: Advances and Applications: Amsterdam, Elsevier, p. 385–398.

Thomas, M. M., and J. A. Clouse, 1990, Primary migration by diffusion through kerogen, III. Calculation of geologic fluxes: Geochimica et Cosmochimica Acta, v. 54, p. 2793–2797.

Ungerer, P., J. Burrus, B. Doligez, P. Y. Chenet, and F. Bessis, 1990, Basin evaluation by integrated two–dimensional modeling of heat transfer, fluid flow, hydrocarbon generation, and migration: AAPG Bulletin, v. 74, p. 309–335.

van de Graaf, W. J. E., and P. J. Ealey, 1989, Geological modeling for simulation studies: AAPG Bulletin, v. 73, p. 1436–1444.

Waples, D. W., 1990, Kinky vitrinite reflectance well profiles: evidence of paleopressure in low-permeability, gas-bearing sequences in Rocky Mountain foreland basins: Discussion: AAPG Bulletin, v. 74, p. 946–947.

Waples, D. W., 1991a, Innovative methods for quantifying poorly known parameters necessary for numerical basin modeling: Journal of the Japanese Association of Petroleum Technology, v. 56, p. 96–107.

Waples, D. W., 1991b, Recent developments in petroleum geochemistry: Bulletin of the Geological Society of Malaysia, v. 28, p. 97–108.

Waples, D. W., and H. Kamata, 1993, Modeling porosity reduction as a series of chemical and physical processes, *in* A. G. Dore et al., eds., Basin Modelling: Advances and Applications: Amsterdam, Elsevier, p. 303–320.

Waples, D. W., M. Suizu, and H. Kamata, 1992, The art of maturity modeling, part 2: alternative models and sensitivity analysis: AAPG Bulletin, v. 76, p. 47–66.

Wei, Z. P., and I. Lerche, 1988, Quantitative dynamic geology of the Pinedale anticline, Wyoming, U.S.A.: an application of a two-dimensional simulation model: Applied Geochemistry, v. 3, p. 423–440.

Wei, Z. P., C. Hermanrud, and I. Lerche, 1990, Numerical basin modelling of the Sleipner field, North Sea: Terra Nova, v. 2, p. 31–42.

Welte, D. H., 1987, Migration of hydrocarbons: facts and theory, *in* B. Doligez, ed., Migration of Hydrocarbons in Sedimentary Basins: Paris, Editions Technip, p. 393–413.

Willett, S. D., and D. S. Chapman, 1987, Analysis of temperature and thermal processes in the Uinta basin, *in* C. Beaumont and A. J. Tankard, eds., Sedimentary basins and basin-forming mechanisms: Canadian Society of Petroleum Geologists Memoir 12, p. 447–461.

Wygrala, B. P., M. N. Yalcin, and L. Dohmen, 1990, Thermal histories and overthrusting—application of numerical simulation techniques: Organic Geochemistry, v. 16, p. 267–285.

Zeitlin, M. J., 1989, Dynamic geo-process modelling: a technique to help identify favorable prospects, *in* Proceedings, Indonesian Petroleum Association 18th Annual Convention: Jakarta, IPA, p. 157–193.

Magoon, L. B, and W. G. Dow, eds., 1994, The petroleum
system—from source to trap: AAPG Memoir 60.

Chapter **19**

Volumetric Calculation of Hydrocarbons Generated

James W. Schmoker

U.S. Geological Survey
Denver, Colorado, U.S.A.

Abstract

The problem addressed here is the calculation of the mass of hydrocarbons generated by the active source rock pod of a petroleum system. This calculation method follows a four-step sequence: (1) the source rock is identified and its boundaries defined, (2) the mass of organic carbon in the source rocks is calculated (equation 1), (3) the mass of hydrocarbons generated per gram of organic carbon is estimated (equation 2), and (4) the total mass of hydrocarbons generated is determined by multiplication of these data (equation 3).

The key idea of the calculation is use of the hydrogen index to quantify the fractional conversion of kerogen to hydrocarbons. The hydrogen index, derived from Rock-Eval pyrolysis, represents the potential of a source rock to generate additional hydrocarbons. The difference between the original hydrogen index prior to any petroleum generation and the present-day hydrogen index thus approximates the decrease in generation potential and is equated here to hydrocarbons generated.

INTRODUCTION

This chapter presents guidelines for calculating the amount of hydrocarbons generated within a petroleum system. At least three reasons can be cited for carrying out such calculations. First, volumetric calculations and associated parameters furnish numerical data that help define and describe the petroleum system. Second, estimates of hydrocarbons generated provide a basis for analysis of hydrocarbon expulsion, migration, and accumulation. Third, an internally consistent set of volumetric calculations, representing diverse petroleum systems, offers insights into the workings of petroleum systems in general.

In some cases, the parameters necessary to calculate the amount of hydrocarbons generated are poorly constrained and the calculation error is therefore large. Although disadvantageous, large errors do not necessarily negate the value of volumetric hydrocarbon calculations. For example, it is of value to know if the volume of oil generated is closer to 1 billion, 10 billion, or 100 billion bbl, and such information is not usually obvious from qualitative inspection.

Inefficiencies associated with the expulsion, migration, and trapping of hydrocarbons are often large. Thus, the amount of hydrocarbons generated can be an enormous number compared to the amount in place. McDowell (1975) concluded that recoverable oil is perhaps 10% of oil generated for a few sedimentary basins and is only a few percent of oil generated for most basins. A decade later, Moshier and Waples (1985) reiterated the same general conclusion. The intensive drilling programs of the late 1970s and early 1980s apparently did not alter the perception that the ratio of hydrocarbons generated to hydrocarbons trapped is typically large. It is hoped that the calculations collected in this memoir will shed further light on the efficiencies of petroleum systems.

CALCULATION OF HYDROCARBONS GENERATED

The problem addressed here is that of calculating the mass of hydrocarbons generated by the active source rock pod of a petroleum system. For the purposes of this memoir, the calculation method must be broadly applicable to a diverse set of petroleum systems. The method must balance simplicity against exactness and be understandable to earth scientists of varied backgrounds. Necessary data must be commonly available. These constraints strongly influence the calculation method detailed in the following sections.

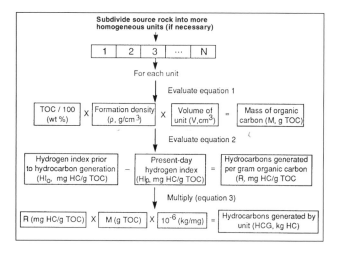

Figure 19.1. Flow diagram of method for approximate calculation of mass of hydrocarbons generated.

Overview

Volumetric methods for calculating hydrocarbons generated differ in approach and in detail (e.g., White and Gehman, 1979; Demaison and Murris, 1984; Waples, 1985; Cooles et al., 1986; Mackenzie and Quigley, 1988). However, many incorporate in one way or another the elements of the following sequence, which is an outline of the calculation approach of this report:

1. The source rock is identified and its boundaries defined.
2. The mass of organic carbon in the source rock is calculated.
3. The mass of hydrocarbons generated per unit mass of organic carbon is estimated.
4. The total mass of hydrocarbons generated is determined by multiplication of these data.

Steps 1 and 2 characterize the present-day availability of organic matter and are straightforward in concept. Step 4 amounts to a tallying up of numbers. Step 3, however, is complex in concept and is a point upon which calculation methods tend to diverge. The mass of hydrocarbons generated per unit mass of organic carbon depends on kerogen type, reaction kinetics, and the time–temperature history to which the kerogen has been exposed. Rather than attempt the quantitative assessment of these factors, an empirical measure of the conversion of kerogen to hydrocarbons based on the hydrogen index is adopted here.

The hydrogen index (HI), expressed as milligrams of hydrocarbons per gram total organic carbon (mg HC/g TOC), is derived from Rock-Eval pyrolysis. The HI measures hydrocarbons produced per gram TOC by the thermal degradation of kerogen during programmed heating. Thus, HI represents the potential of a source rock to generate additional hydrocarbons. The difference between the original hydrogen index (prior to any

hydrocarbon generation) and the present-day hydrogen index can be equated to the hydrocarbons generated by a source rock per unit mass of organic carbon.

Use of the HI to quantify the conversion of kerogen to hydrocarbons is central to the calculation method presented here. A similar concept was used by Merewether and Claypool (1980), Jones (1981), and Schmoker and Hester (1983), although they used pyrolysis data to estimate the mass of hydrocarbons expelled as opposed to the mass generated.

A potential source of experimental error associated with the HI should be noted. The hydrogen index depends on TOC content, and in thermally mature source rocks, TOC is a measure of both the kerogen and the oil concentrations. Variations in expulsion efficiency can thus introduce variations in HI that are not directly related to the geochemical character of the kerogen (Cooles et al., 1986).

Description of Calculation Method

A flow diagram for calculating the mass of hydrocarbons generated within a petroleum system is shown in Figure 19.1. In the initial step, the source rock of a petroleum system is identified and subdivided if necessary into mappable units of more homogeneous physical and geochemical properties. The calculation of hydrocarbons generated is then carried out for each source rock unit, and the results are summed to give a total for the petroleum system.

The objective of the second step is to determine the mass of organic carbon, M (g TOC), in each source rock unit. The data needed to calculate M are the average TOC (wt. %), average formation density, ρ (g/cm^3), and volume, V (cm^3), of the unit. Multiplication of these three parameters gives the mass of organic carbon in the source rock unit:

$$M \text{ (g TOC)} = [\text{TOC (wt. \%)}/100] \times \rho \text{ (g/cm}^3) \times V \text{ (cm}^3) \qquad (1)$$

Note that TOC is divided by 100 to convert from percent abundance to fractional abundance. TOC is commonly derived from pyrolysis analysis but can be determined from wireline logs in organic-rich shales of low porosity (Schmoker and Hester, 1983; Hester et al., 1990). Formation density depends on the mineral matrix and porosity and also on TOC because kerogen is less dense than the rock matrix. Figure 19.2 shows shale density as a function of TOC and porosity and is helpful for estimating the density of shale source rock units in the absence of compensated formation density logs. The volume, V, of the source rock unit is determined from its thickness and areal extent.

The objective of the third step is to determine the mass of hydrocarbons generated per unit mass of organic carbon, R (mg HC/g TOC), for each source rock unit. The data needed to calculate R are the present-day hydrogen index, HI$_p$ (mg HC/g TOC), and the original

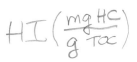

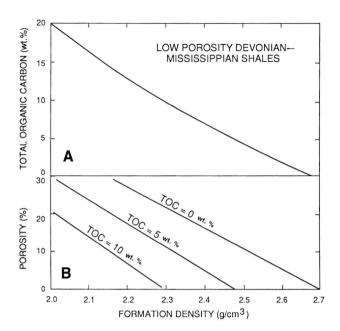

Figure 19.2. Formation density of shale. (A) Empirical relationship between total organic carbon (TOC) and formation density for low porosity Devonian–Mississippian shales. (After Hester et al., 1990, their figure 5). (B) Calculated relationship between porosity and formation density of shale for three values of TOC.

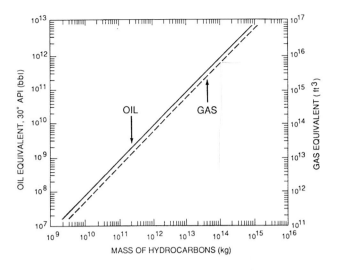

Figure 19.3. Graph to convert mass of hydrocarbons to equivalent barrels of oil or cubic feet of methane.

hydrogen index, HI_o (mg HC/g TOC), of the source rock prior to any petroleum generation. The difference between these two indices approximates the mass of hydrocarbons generated per gram TOC:

$$R \text{ (mg HC/g TOC)} = HI_o \text{ (mg HC/g TOC)} - HI_p \text{ (mg HC/g TOC)} \quad (2)$$

$\triangle HI$

This equation equates the decline in generation potential to hydrocarbons actually generated. HI_p is derived from pyrolysis analysis; HI_o can be derived from pyrolysis analysis of thermally immature samples if it is geologically reasonable to assume no variations in kerogen type. Alternatively, HI_o can be estimated from the generic trends of van Krevelen-type diagrams (e.g., Tissot and Welte, 1984).

The objective of the final step is to compute the total mass of hydrocarbons generated, HCG (kg HC), in each source rock unit. The data needed to calculate HCG are developed in the two previous steps:

$$HCG \text{ (kg HC)} = R \text{ (mg HC/g TOC)} \times M \text{ (g TOC)} \times 10^{-6} \text{ (kg/mg)} \quad (3)$$

Note that multiplying by 10^{-6} converts units of mass from milligrams to kilograms. Volumetric hydrocarbon units (bbl of oil or ft^3 of gas) may be more familiar than the mass units of equation 3. Figure 19.3 provides a graph to convert kilograms of hydrocarbons to equivalent barrels of oil or cubic feet of methane.

SAMPLE CALCULATION

An example may help clarify the procedure for calculating the mass of hydrocarbons generated by the active source rock pod of a petroleum system. The following example parallels the flow diagram of Figure 19.1. If necessary, the source rock of a petroleum system is first subdivided into units of roughly homogeneous physical and geochemical properties. The calculation of hydrocarbons generated is then done for each unit.

Let us assume that a given source rock unit has an average thickness of 20 m (2×10^3 cm) and is 30 km (3×10^6 cm) long by 20 km (2×10^6 cm) wide. The volume, V, of the unit is thus 1.2×10^{16} cm^3. TOC is 6 wt. % on average, and the formation density, assuming a well-compacted shale, is 2.4 g/cm^3 (Figure 19.2). By multiplying these values (equation 1), the mass of organic carbon, M, in the source rock unit is found to be 1.73×10^{15} g TOC.

Let us further assume that kerogen in the source rock has a present-day hydrogen index, HI_p, of 150 mg HC/g TOC. The original hydrogen index, HI_o, prior to the onset of hydrocarbon generation is estimated to have been 380 mg HC/g TOC. By taking the difference of these indices (equation 2), the mass of hydrocarbons generated per gram TOC, R, is found to be 230 mg HC/g TOC.

Finally, by multiplying M times R times 10^{-6} (equation 3), the mass of hydrocarbons generated, HCG, by the source rock unit is found to be 3.98×10^{11} kg HC. Reference to Figure 19.3 indicates that this mass of hydrocarbons is roughly equivalent to 3×10^9 bbl of oil or 2×10^{13} ft^3 of methane.

DISCUSSION

The calculation method detailed here yields a minimum estimate of hydrocarbons derived from the source rocks of a petroleum system. This is for several reasons. First, the approach does not take into consideration hydrocarbons that may already be present in thermally immature shales. Second, as explained by Ehrenberg (1989) and Pate (1989) in the context of porosity loss during burial, a fractional decrease determined by taking the difference of two ratios (e.g., equation 2) is rigorously correct only if the denominators of the two ratios are the same. Because some organic carbon is lost by expulsion of generated hydrocarbons, the denominators (g TOC) of HI_p and HI_o are different, and equation 2 tends to underestimate R. Third, the mass of organic carbon originally present in a source rock unit, M_o (g TOC), is approximated by the present-day mass of organic carbon, M_p. M_o is greater than M_p because a percentage of generated hydrocarbons is expelled from the source rock and because retained generated hydrocarbons lighter than C_5–C_{10} are lost to the laboratory measurement of TOC (Merewether and Claypool, 1980; Cooles et al., 1986; Larter, 1988). Because M_o is greater than M_p, equation 3 gives a minimum estimate of the total mass of hydrocarbons generated. A more correct expression than equation 3 would be

$$HCG = [(HI_o \times M_o) - (HI_p \times M_p)] \times 10^{-6} \qquad (4)$$

The disadvantage of equation 4 is that an additional geochemical parameter, M_o, is introduced, thus adding substantial complexity to the calculation concept. M_o is difficult to determine. Whereas the original hydrogen index, HI_o, depends on the kerogen type and thus has a certain generic predictability, the original mass of organic carbon, M_o, is a property of the formation and cannot be estimated a priori or extrapolated with impunity.

Data presented by Sluijk and Nederlof (1984) permit estimation of the maximum error associated with use of equation 3 instead of equation 4. Assuming a scenario of extreme thermal maturity ($HI_p = 0$) and total expulsion of generated hydrocarbons, M_p/M_o is about equal to C_r/C_o, where C_r is residual carbon after pyrolysis and C_o is total organic carbon before pyrolysis. For type III kerogen, $C_r/C_o \approx 0.75$ (Sluijk and Nederlof, 1984), and the mass of hydrocarbons generated as calculated by equation 3 is three-fourths of that calculated using equation 4. For type II kerogen, $C_r/C_o \approx 0.50$ and the mass of hydrocarbons generated as calculated by equation 3 is one-half of that calculated using equation 4. These are worst-case discrepancies for type II and III kerogens. In practice, differences will be smaller because not all hydrocarbons generated migrate out of the source rock and because hydrocarbon generation has usually not gone to completion. As a cautionary note, C_r/C_o for type I kerogen can be as low as 0.20.

For the purposes of this memoir, the calculation method should strike a balance between practicality and exactness. For this reason, equation 3 is thought to be a better option than equation 4 (except perhaps for the case of highly mature type I kerogens). Equation 3, although yielding a minimum estimate of hydrocarbons generated, uses more straightforward and readily available data.

Acknowledgments   *This chapter benefited from the constructive comments and reviews of Larry A. Beyer, George E. Claypool, Jerry L. Clayton, Gordon L. Dolton, Keith A. Kvenvolden, Leslie B. Magoon, Fred F. Meissner, John T. Smith, and Peter C. van de Kamp.*

References Cited

Cooles, G. P., A. S. Mackenzie, and T. M. Quigley, 1986, Calculation of petroleum masses generated and expelled from source rocks, in D. Leythaeuser and J. Rullkötter, eds., Advances in Organic Geochemistry 1985: Oxford, Pergamon Press, p. 235–245.

Demaison, G., and R. J. Murris, eds., 1984, Petroleum geochemistry and basin evaluation: AAPG Memoir 35, 426 p.

Ehrenberg, S. N., 1989, Assessing the relative importance of compaction processes and cementation to reduction of porosity in sandstones: discussion; compaction and porosity evolution of Pliocene sandstones, Ventura basin, California: discussion: AAPG Bulletin, v. 73, p. 1274–1276.

Hester, T. C., J. W. Schmoker, and H. L. Sahl, 1990, Log-derived regional source rock characteristics of the Woodford Shale, Anadarko basin, Oklahoma: USGS Bulletin 1866-D, 38 p.

Jones, R.W., 1981, Some mass balance and geological constraints on migration mechanisms: AAPG Bulletin, v. 65, p. 103–122.

Larter, S., 1988, Some pragmatic perspectives in source rock geochemistry: Marine and Petroleum Geology, v. 5, p. 194–204.

Mackenzie, A. S., and T. M. Quigley, 1988, Principles of geochemical prospect appraisal: AAPG Bulletin, v. 72, p. 399–415.

McDowell, A. N., 1975, What are the problems in estimating the oil potential of a basin?: Oil and Gas Journal, v. 73, June 9, p. 85–90.

Merewether, E. A., and G. E. Claypool, 1980, Organic composition of some Upper Cretaceous shale, Powder River basin, Wyoming: AAPG Bulletin, v. 64, p. 488–500.

Moshier, S. O., and D. W. Waples, 1985, Quantitative evaluation of Lower Cretaceous Mannville Group as source rock for Alberta's oil sands: AAPG Bulletin, v. 69, p. 161–172.

Pate, C. R., 1989, Assessing the relative importance of compaction processes and cementation to reduction of porosity in sandstones: discussion: AAPG Bulletin, v. 73, p. 1270–1273.

Schmoker, J. W., and T. C. Hester, 1983, Organic carbon in Bakken Formation, United States portion of Williston basin: AAPG Bulletin, v. 67, p. 2165-2174.

Sluijk, D., and M. H. Nederlof, 1984, Worldwide geological experience as a systematic basis for prospect appraisal, in G. Demaison and R. J. Murris, eds., Petroleum geochemistry and basin evaluation: AAPG Memoir 35, p. 15–26.

Tissot, B. P., and D. H. Welte, 1984, Petroleum Formation and Occurrence, 2nd ed.: New York, Springer-Verlag, 699 p.

Waples, D. W., 1985, Geochemistry in Petroleum Exploration: Boston, IHRDC, 232 p.

White, D. A., and H. M. Gehman, 1979, Methods of estimating oil and gas resources: AAPG Bulletin, v. 63, p. 2183–2192.

Part V

Case Studies—
Western Hemisphere

Magoon, L. B., and W. G. Dow, eds., 1994, The petroleum
system—from source to trap: AAPG Memoir 60.

Chapter 20

Overview of Petroleum System Case Studies

Leslie B. Magoon

Zenon C. Valin
Branch of Petroleum Geology
U.S. Geological Survey
Menlo Park, California, U.S.A.

Abstract

Petroleum system case studies provide an important link in understanding the petroleum system concept. Petroleum system case studies from different petroleum provinces of the world demonstrate practical problems that are typical of a petroleum system investigation. Well-documented case studies provide not only an understanding of the present-day distribution of hydrocarbons but also the basis to evaluate petroleum exploration risk in a play or prospect and to carry out petroleum research effectively.

The case studies in the next two units describe and characterize 25 petroleum systems. Some studies address the migration of hydrocarbons from the pod of active source rock to the trap and show the difficulty of determining not only the hydrocarbon migration path but also the loss of petroleum during migration. The case studies also address generation–accumulation efficiency and size so that conclusions can be drawn as to what essential elements and processes most affect efficiency and size. This overview shows that the most prolific petroleum system is not necessarily the most efficient. By comparing several petroleum systems on either an efficiency or size scale and then comparing the essential elements and processes of each system, a general impression is gained of how each system functions.

INTRODUCTION

Petroleum system case studies from different petroleum provinces of the world provide an important link in understanding the petroleum system concept presented in Chapter 1 (Magoon and Dow) and other previous chapters in this volume. The principles and procedures presented in these early chapters are applied to established petroleum provinces so that petroleum systems can be mapped using genetically related accumulations and their pods of active source rock. These case studies demonstrate, at a practical level, the problems encountered during the execution of a petroleum system investigation. Well-documented case studies provide not only an understanding of the present-day distribution of hydrocarbons but also a mechanism to evaluate petroleum exploration risk with respect to a play or prospect and a means to carry out petroleum research more intelligently.

The purpose of this volume is to describe and characterize the petroleum system and how it can be used to investigate the migration of hydrocarbons from the pod of active source rock to traps. The first half of this volume has defined the petroleum system and has provided techniques important to investigating the system. The last half comprises the case studies, which attempt to apply the principles and techniques discussed in the first half. This volume represents only a summary of the geologic, geochemical, and geophysical data and interpretations needed to complete a case study.

If the petroleum system events chart, which itemizes the essential elements and processes of a system, is used as a checklist for a series of maps, then the scope of a full case study becomes apparent. A map of an essential element or process requires many overlays. For example, the reservoir rock needs overlays to show thickness, distribution, lithology, porosity, and permeability for that element; a team of geoscientists using well control, geologic maps, and seismic data would construct these overlays for the reservoir map. Our case studies do not include this kind of detailed reservoir rock interpretation, nor do they include map overlays for the other essential elements and processes. However, if these case studies were internal company reports, such detailed overlays would most likely be available.

Table 20.1. Petroleum Systems Shown in Figure 20.1

Map Symbol	Chapter Number	Petroleum System	Petroleum Province	Location
A	21	Ellesmerian(!)	North Slope	Alaska, U.S.A.
B	22	Tuxedni–Hemlock(!)	Cook Inlet	Alaska, U.S.A.
C	23	Heath–Tyler(!)	Central Montana	Montana, U.S.A.
D	24	Point Pleasant–Brassfield(!)	Appalachian basin	Ohio, U.S.A.
E	25	Green River(!)	Uinta basin	Utah, U.S.A.
F	27	Soda Lake–Painted Rock(!)	Cuyama basin	California, U.S.A.
G	28	Simpson–Ellenburger(.)	Central Basin platform	W. Texas, U.S.A.
H	29	La Luna–Misoa(!)	Maracaibo basin	Venezuela
I	29	Orocue(.)	Maracaibo basin	Venezuela
J	30	Villeta–Monserrate(!)	Magdalena Valley	Colombia
K	30	Villeta–Caballos(!)	Magdalena Valley	Colombia
L	31	Barreirinhas–Itaituba(!)	Salimões basin	Brazil
M	31	Gomo–Marfim(!)	Recôncavo basin	Brazil
N	31	Ibura–Muribeca(!)	Sergipe–Alagoas basin	Brazil
O	31	Lagoa Feia–Carapebus(!)	Campos basin	Brazil
P	32	Los Molles–Tres Esquinas(?)	Neuquén basin	Argentina
Q	32	Vaca Muerta–Sierras Blancas(?)	Neuquén basin	Argentina
R	32	Agrio(?)	Neuquén basin	Argentina
S	33	Mandal–Ekofisk(!)	Central Graben	North Sea
T	34	Lower Saxony basin Jurassic(!)	Lower Saxony basin	Germany
U	34	Lower Saxony basin Lower Cretaceous(!)	Lower Saxony basin	Germany
V	35	Tótkomlós–Szolnok(.)	Pannonian basin	Hungary
W	36	Akata–Agbada(!)	Niger delta	Nigeria
X	37	Cambay–Hazad(!)	South Cambay basin	India
Y	38	Bampo–Peutu(!)	North Sumatra	Indonesia

A petroleum system case study can be carried out in a frontier area, as well as in a well-explored petroleum province. Experience gained from well-executed case studies on well-explored petroleum systems can then be applied to less explored petroleum systems to evaluate prospects. For example, determining the loss of hydrocarbons during migration is important to understanding hydrocarbon charge of a prospect. A complete petroleum system case study includes estimates of the average kerogen type, average immature richness, thickness, and present-day thermal maturity. In addition, there should be one or more burial history charts of locations within the pod of active source rock to determine the critical moment (see Magoon and Dow, Chapter 1, this volume). These data and the kinetic models for the kerogen types can be used to estimate the time of petroleum generation and the volume generated at various locations in the pod. During migration of this petroleum, it forms an economic accumulation, it is lost somewhere in the system, or it is destroyed (see England, Chapter 12, Figure 12.2, this volume). The table of oil and gas fields and other significant noncommercial accumulations of heavy oil to natural bitumen for the petroleum system indicates how much petroleum has accumulated. The volumes of petroleum generated and accumulated can be compared to determine the efficiency of the system. In exploration, this efficiency can be used to evaluate hydrocarbon charge for a prospect.

The generation–accumulation efficiency (GAE) of a petroleum system is influenced by the amount of hydro-

carbons lost within and to the system in the following ways: (1) retention of oil and gas along the primary migration paths; (2) retention of oil and gas along the secondary (and tertiary) migration paths; (3) loss of oil and gas to noncommercial accumulations; (4) loss of oil and gas from the system during active generation before trap formation, such as through surface seeps; (5) loss of oil and gas from the system during active generation because of inadequate trap capacity; and (6) loss of oil and gas from the accumulations during the time of preservation (Chapter 12). The loss of hydrocarbons from any or all of these ways lowers the overall efficiency of the system. Generally, the overall efficiency of a petroleum system has little meaning except to judge such evaluations and to compare different systems. Moreover, the migration efficiency are always higher along a certain migration path with discovered accumulations than for the overall system. To evaluate hydrocarbon charge to a prospect properly, these oil and gas losses in and from the system should be evaluated for the migration path in the petroleum system that will charge the prospect.

In addition to evaluating these hydrocarbon losses, a prospect with an identified pod of active source rock must be evaluated for two additional concerns. First, oil and gas expelled from the active source rock has to be allocated among possible migration paths, and then a determination can be made as to whether a particular prospect has access to the hydrocarbon charge. Second, the volume of oil and gas that has reached the prospect needs to be estimated, particularly when the total trap

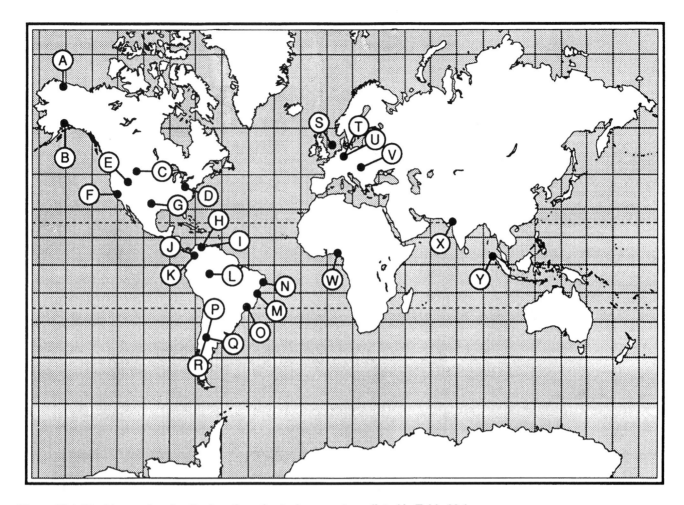

Figure 20.1. World map showing the location of petroleum systems listed in Table 20.1.

volume (oil and gas fields and prospect) along the migration path is large. The properly executed petroleum system case study does not address these two concerns because they are part of prospect evaluation.

The 25 petroleum systems described in the following chapters are in different world petroleum provinces (Table 20.1 and Figure 20.1). Some provinces comprise more than one petroleum system, such as in the Neuquén basin, Argentina, where there are three systems, each with its own source rock. In the Upper Magdalena Valley, Colombia, two petroleum systems are described that share a common source rock, each system having its own separate pod of active source rock. Much can be learned from reading each individual case study. This chapter provides a collective overview for this series of case studies.

CASE STUDY COMPONENTS

Each case study in this volume has something different to offer. Some studies are particularly useful in that they are short but well-done summaries of a particular petroleum system, while others are useful because they are long and detailed. Some of the case studies are particularly good in describing a petroleum system in a

lucid, concise, straightforward manner. A few examples are the Ellesmerian(!) (Bird, Chapter 21), the Akata–Agbada(!) (Ekweozor and Daukoru, Chapter 36), and the Cambay–Hazad(!) petroleum systems (Biswas et al., Chapter 37). In contrast, the chapters on the La Luna–Misoa(!) (Talukdar and Marcano, Chapter 29) and Mandal–Ekofisk(!) (Cornford, Chapter 33) petroleum systems provide detailed descriptions about the processes that combine to create such systems.

Regardless of length, any case study should include certain components, which are outlined in Table 20.2. In the chapters that follow, not all these components are present in each study (Table 20.3). For example, the Green River(!) petroleum system (Fouch et al., Chapter 25) has been given a known level of certainty, even though it has no conclusive oil–source rock correlation. Other studies deviate in other ways. For example, the chapter on the petroleum systems adjacent to the San Andreas fault (Peters et al., Chapter 26) does not include a description of a petroleum system, but does include a detailed oil–oil and oil–source rock correlation that identifies the existence of several petroleum systems, one of which is described in the next chapter (Lillis, Chapter 27). Also, the petroleum systems in the Lower Saxony basin (Kockel et al., Chapter 34) cannot be given names in the

Table 20.2. Components of a Complete Petroleum System Study

Figure or Table	Information Required	Purpose
Map	Locate petroleum fields included in system Indicate whether oil or gas Indicate surface and subsurface oil or gas shows included in system Indicate direction of petroleum migration and Indicate distribution of pod of active source rock	Geographic extent of a petroleum system at critical moment shown by circumscribing the pod of active source rock and the outer limit of migrated hydrocarbons Source rock name from pod of active source rock and Petroleum system burial history chart location
Table	List all oil or gas fields by petroleum system Indicate discovered reserves and in-place petroleum by stratigraphic unit trap type reservoir rock name, age, and lithology and seal rock name, age, and lithology For oil field indicate GOR, API gravity, sulfur content, and Pr/Ph ratio and For gas field indicate GOR, $\delta^{13}C$, and $C_1/C_2 + C_3$ ratio	In-place petroleum for mass balance calculation Reservoir rock name from that reservoir rock with the highest percentage of in-place petroleum Seal rock most commonly occuring in trap and Oil or gas province from average GOR
Cross section	Structural and stratigraphic information such as deformation style and rock units Indicate oil window and gas window Indicate petroleum shows and accumulations Draw at critical moment and Indicate direction and conduits for petroleum migration	Stratigraphic extent of petroleum system at the critical moment by identifying the base of the pod of active source rock or base of hydrocarbon column, whichever is deeper Geographic extent of petroleum system Pod of active source rock shown Overburden rock shown and Petroleum system burial history chart location
Burial history chart	Stratigraphic units penetrated in well Time rock-units were deposited Thickness of rock units Names of rock units Lithology of rock units Present day thermal maturity profile Present day geothermal gradient Computer program to determine time and depth for oil window and gas window and Indicate essential elements of petroleum system	Petroleum system events chart information determined from chart, such as onset and end (at uplift) of petroleum generation, and critical moment Essential elements of petroleum system shown Oil window depth for cross section at critical moment and Gas window depth for cross section at critical moment
Events chart	Age of essential elements of petroleum system Onset and end of trap formation Onset and end of petroleum generation, migration, accumulation Preservation time of petroleum system and Critical moment	Petroleum system events chart summarizes in one diagram the essential elements and processes of the system, as well as the preservation time and critical moment
Petroleum–petroleum correlation	Geochemical evidence, such as bulk properties, biological markers, and isotopic data to show that more than one petroleum accumulation came from the same source rock (but not necessarily the same pod of active source rock)	Geographic and stratigraphic extent of a petroleum system is established with this geochemical correlation in concert with the structure and stratigraphy of the pod of active source rock and the adjacent traps
Petroleum–source rock correlation	Geochemical evidence, such as biological marker and isotopic data, to indicate a certain petroleum originated from a specific source rock	Level of certainty is established using geological and geochemical evidence and indicates the confidence that a specific source rock expelled a given petroleum
Mass balance calculation	TOC and Rock-Eval pyrolysis Source rock density and Volume of pod of active source rock	Mass of petroleum generated to determine petroleum system generation–accumulation efficiency (GAE)

conventional format because data on the volumes of hydrocarbons in multiple reservoir rocks are lacking. Thus, these petroleum systems are provisionally named.

All authors in this volume have indicated the level of certainty for the petroleum systems; nineteen of the systems are known (!), three are hypothetical (.), and three are speculative (?). Except for three petroleum systems, the geographic extent of each petroleum system

has been mapped. Unless the critical moment happens to be present day, the two components absent from most case studies are the petroleum system map and the cross section at the critical moment. This absence is not surprising, as oil and gas maps and most geologic cross sections are easiest to construct for present day. When included in the case studies, these components had been constructed earlier for other purposes than a petroleum

Table 20.3 Summary of Information Available for Each Petroleum System Case Study[a]

Map Symbol	Petroleum System	Petroleum Map PD/GE/PS	CM	Cross Section CM	PD	Burial History	Events Chart	Field Table	Correlation Oil–Oil	Oil–SR	GAE Calc
A	Ellesmerian(!)	+/+/+	o	+	+	+	+	+	+	+	+
B	Tuxedni–Hemlock(!)	+/+/+	o	o	+	+	+	+	+	+	+
C	Heath–Tyler(!)	+/+/+	o	o	+	+	+	+	+	+	+
D	Point Pleasant–Brassfield(!)	+/+/+	o	o	+	+	+	o	o	o	+
E	Green River(!)	+/+/o	o	o	+	+	+	+	o	o	o
F	Soda Lake–Painted Rock(!)	+/o/o	o	o	+	+	+	+	+	+	o
G	Simpson–Ellenburger(.)	+/+/o	o	o	+	+	+	+	+	o	+
H	La Luna–Misoa(!)	+/+/+	o	o	+	+	+	+	o	+	+
I	Orocue(.)	+/+/+	o	o	+	+	+	+	o	o	o
J	Villeta–Monserrate(!)	+/+/+	o	o	+	+	+	+	+	+	+
K	Villeta–Caballos(!)	+/+/+	o	o	+	o	+	+	+	+	+
L	Barreirinhas–Itaituba(!)	+/o/+	o	o	+	o	+	o	o	o	o
M	Gomo–Marfim(!)	+/+/+	o	o	+	o	+	o	o	o	o
N	Ibura–Muribeca(!)	+/+/+	o	o	+	o	+	o	o	o	o
O	Lagoa Feia–Carapebus(!)	+/+/+	o	o	+	o	+	o	o	o	o
P	Los Molles–Tres Esquinas(?)	+/+/+	o	o	+	o	+	+	o	o	o
Q	Vaca Muerta–Sierras Blancas(?)	+/+/+	o	o	+	o	+	+	o	o	o
R	Agrio(?)	+/+/+	o	o	+	o	+	+	o	o	o
S	Mandal–Ekofisk(!)	+/+/+	+	+	+	+	+	+	+	+	+
T	LSB Jurassic(!)	+/+/+	o	+	+	+	+	o	+	+	+
U	LSB Lower Cretaceous(!)	+/+/+	o	o	+	o	+	o	+	+	+
V	Tótkomlós–Szolnok(.)	+/o/o	o	o	+	+	+	o	o	o	o
W	Akata–Agbada(!)	+/+/+	o	o	+	+	+	o	+	+	+
X	Cambay–Hazad(!)	+/+/+	+	+	+	+	+	o	o	o	+
Y	Bampo–Peutu(!)	+/+/+	+	+	+	+	+	+	+	+	+

[a]Symbols and abbreviations: +, available; o, not available; PD, present day; GE, geographic extent of petroleum system; PS, pod of active source rock; CM, critical moment; SR, source rock; calc, calculations.

system study and have simply been recycled. An exception is the cross section at the critical moment for the Ellesmerian petroleum system (Bird, Chapter 21), which was constructed for this study to show the relationship of the pod of active source rock, migration path, and traps to one another when most hydrocarbons migrated in this system.

QUANTIFYING PETROLEUM SYSTEMS

To quantify petroleum systems, two scales are constructed, one for efficiency and one for size. Petroleum systems analyzed with these scales are numerically compared to one another. For example, by evaluating the essential elements and processes of the petroleum systems with respect to the efficiency scale, an insight is gained as to why certain systems are more efficient. For any given petroleum system, this comparison can then be used to evaluate plays and prospects, assess undiscovered petroleum resources, and carry out petroleum research more effectively.

Recovery Efficiency

In Chapter 3, Klemme uses petroleum system recovery efficiency to compare systems. Klemme compares various petroleum systems that have Upper Jurassic source rocks. Using published information and personal experience, he estimates the geochemical properties, physical properties, and volume (pod) of active source rock. In a similar manner, he determines the amount of recoverable petroleum for each system. Klemme then uses these numbers to calculate the petroleum system recovery efficiency. The recovery efficiency for each petroleum system that includes the Upper Jurassic source rock is plotted in descending order in Figure 3.7 (Chapter 3, this volume). Also, the hydrocarbon generated per square mile, the ultimately recoverable hydrocarbons per square mile, and other plumbing ingredients are plotted against recovery efficiency in this figure.

The petroleum system recovery efficiency used by Klemme (Chapter 3) is lower than the generation–accumulation efficiency (GAE) in the case studies that follow, but they can be compared if certain corrections are applied. The numerator for the recovery efficiency is ultimately recoverable oil and gas (in barrels of oil equivalent, or BOE), whereas the GAE is in-place petroleum in kilograms. Klemme's ultimately recoverable BOE can be converted to in-place petroleum by applying a recovery factor for oil or gas, and gas can be converted from energy equivalent to kilograms (6000 ft^3 of gas is 120 kg of petroleum). This correction will increase the numerator four times or more relative to the GAE. For the denominator or petroleum generated, Klemme

Table 20.4 Amount of Recoverable Petroleum by Petroleum System

Map Symbol	Petroleum System	Gravity (°API)	GOR (ft³/bbl)	Oil (10⁶ bbl)	Gas (10⁹ ft³)	Total Petroleum (10⁹ kg)
A	Ellesmerian(!)	25	3,395	12,880	43,731	2682
B	Tuxedni–Hemlock(!)	35	2,100	1,180	2,480	215
C	Heath–Tyler(!)	31	<1,000	96	—	13
D	Point Pleasant–Brassfield(!)	—	<1,000	100	—	14
E	Green River(!)	36	1,624	502	815	86
F	Soda Lake–Painted Rock(!)	32	936	296	277	47
G	Simpson–Ellenburger(.)	45	<1,000	750	—	105
H	La Luna–Misoa(!)	30	995	51,160	50,900	8160
J	Villeta–Monserrate(!)	22	319	263	84	38
K	Villeta–Caballos(!)	30	447	264	118	33
P	Los Molles–Tres Esquinas(?)	33	34,843	287	10,021	243
Q	Vaca Muerta–Sierras Blancas(?)	35	4,947	566	2,831	136
R	Agrio(?)	35	2,021	189	378	34
S	Mandal–Ekofisk(!)	42	1,560	6,540	10,226	1119
T	Lower Saxony basin Jurassic(!)	25	129	897	119	127
U	Lower Saxony basin Lower Cretaceous(!)	30	151	707	98	101
V	Tótkomlós–Szolnok(.)	45	296,190	63	18,660	388
W	Akata–Agbada(!)	42	7,718	758	5,850	224
X	Cambay–Hazad(!)	48	—	—	—	—
Y	Bampo–Peutu(!)	56	15,656	960	15,030	439

decreases the hydrogen index to zero during generation, whereas Schmoker (Chapter 19) only partially matures the source rock in his equations. This correction reduces Klemme's denominator as much as four times. By making these corrections, Klemme's and Schmoker's efficiencies are comparable, but the actual calculations are beyond the scope of this chapter.

Generation–Accumulation Efficiency

The GAE is one scale used to compare the case studies that follow. The data and calculations in the studies are summarized in Tables 20.4–20.7 (see also Appendices A and B). Of these case studies, two included enough information for us to calculate the GAE (Fouch et al., Chapter 25; Lillis, Chapter 27); the authors of the other 14 case studies calculated their own GAE (see Table 20.7). All authors made their calculations independently of one another, and we were unable to revise their figures to fit any preconceived notion about either the efficiency or size of the petroleum systems; therefore, we use their original figures. A description of how we compiled these summary tables from the studies follows.

Using the petroleum system table of accumulations from each case study, we first compiled the amount of recoverable petroleum in each system (Table 20.4). Where this information is absent, it is usually because it is confidential; however, twenty petroleum systems include at least some of this information (Table 20.4). Because GAE compares mass of hydrocarbons, gas is converted from cubic feet to kilograms. The gas–oil ratio (GOR) (ft³/bbl), which is calculated from the amount of recoverable petroleum, distinguishes a gas from an oil system. The most gaseous system is the Tótkomlós–Szolnok(.) petroleum system, with a GOR of 296,190.

GORs > 20,000 tend to indicate gas systems, from 5000–20,000 condensate systems, and <5000 oil systems. Using this criteria and excluding oil gravity (°API), we have two gas systems, two condensate systems, and fifteen oil systems in Table 20.4.

Second, we compiled from the studies the amount of in-place petroleum (Table 20.5). Unless otherwise stated, most of the case studies used recovery factors of 25% for oil and 80% for gas. For purposes of this chapter, the type of petroleum in each system is categorized as gas (Kvenvolden, 1988), condensate (>45° API) (Clayton, 1988), medium gravity oil (20°–45° API) (Clayton, 1988), heavy oil (10°–20° API) (Meyer, 1988), very heavy oil (API < 10°) (Meyer, 1988), or natural bitumen (Meyer, 1988); the total amount of petroleum is in kilograms. Only the Green River petroleum system includes natural bitumen, and only the Ellesmerian and Soda Lake–Painted Rock systems include heavy oil (Table 20.5).

Third, the amount of hydrocarbons generated (HCG) from a pod of active source rock in sixteen petroleum systems was compiled (Table 20.6). The symbols and equations used for these calculations are discussed by Schmoker (Chapter 19). The values listed in Table 20.6 vary in quality because pods of active source rock are sometimes difficult or impossible to map directly (exploratory wells seldom drill where the source rock is buried deepest). Usually, source rock pods are mapped with seismic information and with stratigraphic studies based on well and outcrop information. Even so, the values in Table 20.6 used to calculate HCGs represent the best guesses of the original investigators. Certain parameters vary greatly, such as area (A) and thickness (h); however, other parameters, such as source rock density (ρ), vary much less. The effectiveness of active source rock pods in generating hydrocarbons (HCG) is related

Table 20.5. Estimated Amount of In-Place Petroleum by Petroleum System

Map Symbol	Petroleum System	Natural Bitumen (10^9 bbl)	API[a] <10° (10^9 bbl)	10°–20° (10^9 bbl)	20°–45° (10^9 bbl)	>45° (10^9 bbl)	Total Oil (10^9 bbl)	Gas[b] (10^{12} ft^3)	Total Petroleum (10^9 kg)
A	Ellesmerian(!)	—	—	35.0	32.0	—	67.0	39.0	10,124
B	Tuxedni–Hemlock(!)	—	—	—	3.4	—	3.4	3.1	532
C	Heath–Tyler(!)	—	—	—	0.4	—	0.4	—	53
D	Point Pleasant–Brassfield(!)	—	—	—	0.4	—	0.4	—	56
E	Green River(!)	12.5	—	—	2.4	0.6	14.9	1.0	2,097
F	Soda Lake–Painted Rock(!)	—	—	0.2	0.8	—	1.0	0.3	145
G	Simpson–Ellenburger(.)	—	—	—	—	3.0	3.0	—	418
H	La Luna–Misoa(!)	—	—	—	243.6	—	243.6	63.7	35,220
J	Villeta–Monserrate(!)	—	—	—	0.9	—	0.9	0.1	125
K	Villeta–Caballos(!)	—	—	—	0.9	—	0.9	0.2	127
P	Los Molles–Tres Esquinas(?)	—	—	—	1.2	—	1.2	12.5	414
Q	Vaca Muerta–Sierras Blancas(?)	—	—	—	2.3	—	2.3	3.5	386
R	Agrio(?)	—	—	—	0.8	—	0.8	0.5	115
S	Mandal–Ekofisk(!)	—	—	—	20.7	0.7	21.4	39.4	3,780
T	LSB Jurassic(!)	—	—	—	2.6	—	2.6	0.1	295
U	LSB Lower Cretaceous(!)	—	—	—	2.0	—	2.0	0.1	267
V	Tótkomlós–Szolnok(.)	—	—	—	0.3	—	0.3	23.3	509
W	Akata–Agbada(!)	—	—	—	3.0	—	3.0	7.3	570
X	Cambay–Hazad(!)	—	—	—	—	—	—	—	395
Y	Bampo–Peutu(!)	—	—	—	—	1.2	1.2	18.8	531

[a]API < 10°, extra heavy gravity oil; 10°–20°, heavy gravity oil; 20°–45°, medium gravity oil; API > 45°, condensate.
[b]Gaseous hydrocarbons at STP.

to all the parameters in Table 20.6.

Last, we compiled the GAEs for sixteen petroleum systems in Table 20.7. The GAEs range from a high of 36.3% for the Heath–Tyler(!) petroleum system to a low of 0.3% for the Point Pleasant–Brassfield(!), a large range. For our discussion, GAEs > 10 are very efficient, 1–10 moderately efficient, and <1 inefficient. On this basis, four petroleum systems listed in Table 20.7 are inefficient, eight are moderately efficient, and four are very efficient.

These sixteen petroleum systems can be ranked by their recoverable hydrocarbons (Table 20.8). Rather than converting gas to barrels of oil on the basis of energy equivalent (1 bbl of oil = 6000 ft^3 of gas), gas has been converted to kilograms (2.03×10^{-3} kg/ft^3). For convenience, five categories of petroleum system size that generally correlate with Klemme's sizes, which are based on BOE (Chapter 3, Table 3.1), are as follows: (1) a supergiant petroleum system is >10,000 bkg (billion kilograms) of recoverable hydrocarbons, (2) a giant petroleum system is 5000–10,000 bkg, (3) a large system is 500–5000 bkg, (4) a significant system is 50–500 bkg, and (5) a small system is <50 bkg (Table 20.8). The significant systems outnumber the large systems 4 to 1 and the giant systems 8 to 1; however, the giant system contains more recoverable petroleum than all the other 13 systems combined.

The GAE varies widely in all size categories; that is, a petroleum system does not necessarily become a giant by being more efficient. To understand better the relationship between GAE and petroleum system size, the essential elements and processes of each petroleum system are compared.

COMPARING PETROLEUM SYSTEMS

Comparing petroleum systems is the process of evaluating several systems to determine which essential element or processes most affect the efficiency or size of each system (Tables 20.7 and 20.8). An evaluation can begin by asking certain questions. For example, is a highly efficient petroleum system related more to its type of reservoir rock (such as a carrier bed of porous and permeable quartz sandstone), to the proximity of its accumulations to the pod of active source rock, to its quality of seal rock, or to some other factor? Also, is a supergiant petroleum system large because its source rock is the richest, its pod of active source rock the largest, its seal rock the best (evaporites), or some other factor? By analyzing several petroleum systems with either an efficiency or size scale and then by comparing the essential elements and processes of each system, insight can be gained into how effectively each system component functions.

We use the petroleum system events chart (Chapter 1, Figure 1.5) as a check list to compare the essential elements and processes of each system. Many geologic, geochemical, and geophysical factors affect the performance of each essential element and process in a petroleum system; however, for brevity, only a few of these factors are discussed here.

The Heath–Tyler(!) system (Cole and Drozd, Chapter 23) is the most efficient (GAE = 36.3%) (Table 20.7) and the smallest (13 bkg) (Table 20.8) of the petroleum systems discussed in this volume. This system is the most efficient because its reservoir rock incises into its

Table 20. 6. Values from Case Studies Used to Calculate Amount of Generated Petroleum from Pod of Active Source Rock[a]

Map Symbol	Petroleum System	TOC (wt. %)	ρ (g/cm³)	A (10¹² cm²)	h (10² cm)	V (10¹⁵cm³)	M (10¹² g TOC)	HI_o [b]	HI_p [b]	R [b]	HCG (10⁹ kg)
A	Ellesmerian(!)	3.5	2.4	900	160	14,400	—	—	—	—	—
A		2.0	2.4	1100	800	88,000	5,433,600	—	—	200	1,086,720
B	Tuxedni–Hemlock(!)	1.7	2.6	15	1000	1,500	66,800	300	100	200	13,400
C	Heath–Tyler(!)	7.6	2.3	8	6	5	839	575	400	175	147
D	Point Pleasant–Brassfield(!)	2.5	2.3	400	30	1,200	69,000	600	300	300	20,700
E	Green River(!)	6.0	2.3	21	200	420	58,000	800	350	450	26,100
F	Soda Lake–Painted Rock(!)	2.1	2.4	2.6	300	78	3,990	600	200	400	1,596
G	Simpson–Ellenburger(.)	1.7	2.5	96	35	336	14,600	425	150	275	4,020
H	La Luna–Misoa(!)	5.6	2.7	475	65	3,090	4,550	650	100	550	250,000
J	Villeta–Monserrate(!)	1.8	2.5	9	135	122	—	430	250	180	—
J		2.5	2.5	9	100	90	11,000	725	425	300	2,640
K	Villeta–Caballos(!)	1.8	2.5	7.5	135	101	—	430	250	180	—
K		2.5	2.5	7.5	100	75	9,120	725	425	300	2,197
S	Mandal–Ekofisk(!)	6.7	2.5	11.5	1250	—	—	—	—	—	—
S		6.7	2.5	26.5	750	—	—	—	—	—	—
S		6.7	2.5	74.8	250	1,210	666	—	—	550	66,600
T	LSB Jurassic(!)	8.0	2.3	49.6	25	124	22,820	—	—	300	6,850
U	LSB Lower Cretaceous(!)	4.5	2.3	27.3	25	68	7,064	—	—	370	2,600
W	Akata–Agbada(!)	2.2	2.6	76.8	2310	17,700	1,012,000	232	161	71	71,850
X	Cambay–Hazad(!)	2.6	2.6	54.1	750	4058	272,000	121	93	28	7,610
Y	Bampo–Peutu(!)	0.9	2.6	76	345	2,620	—	200	100	100	—
Y		0.7	2.7	76	460	3,500	127,100	200	70	130	14,800

[a]Variables: ρ, density; A, area; h, thickness; V, volume; M, mass; HI_o, original hydrogen index prior to petroleum generation; HI_p, present-day hydrogen index; R, difference between HI_o and HI_p; HCG, hydrocarbons generated using equations in Schmoker(Chapter 19, this volume).

[b]Units are mg HC/g TOC.

Table 20.7. Petroleum Systems Ranked by Generation–Accumulation Efficiency (GAE) Percentage

Map Symbol	Petroleum System	In–Place Petroleum (10⁹ kg)	Generated Petroleum (10⁹ kg)	GAE (%)
C	Heath–Tyler(!)	53	147	36.3
H	La Luna–Misoa(!)	35,220	250,000	14.0
G	Simpson–Ellenburger(.)	418	4,020	10.4
U	LSB Lower Cretaceous(!)	267	2,614	10.3
F	Soda Lake–Painted Rock(!)	145	1,596	9.0
E	Green River(!)	2,097	26,100	8.0
K	Villeta–Caballos(!)	127	2,197	5.8
X	Cambay–Hazad(!)	395	13,000	5.2
J	Villeta–Monserrate(!)	125	2,640	4.7
T	LSB Jurassic(!)	295	6,850	4.3
B	Tuxedni–Hemlock(!)	532	13,400	4.0
Y	Bampo–Peutu(!)	531	14,800	3.6
A	Ellesmerian(!)	15,439	1,086,000	0.9
W	Akata–Agbada(!)	570	71,850	0.8
S	Mandal–Ekofisk(!)	3,780	666,000	0.6
D	Point Pleasant–Brassfield(!)	56	20,700	0.3

Table 20.8. Petroleum Systems Ranked by Recoverable Hydrocarbons in Billions of Kilograms (bkg)

Map Symbol	Petroleum System	Recoverable Oil (10^6 bbl)	Recoverable Gas (10^9 ft^3)	Recoverable HC (bkg)	In–place HC (bkg)	Generated HC (bkg)	GAE (%)
Giant (5,000–10,000 bkg)							
H	La Luna–Misoa(!)	51,160	50,900	8,160	35,220	250,000	14.0
Large (500–5000 bkg)							
A	Ellesmerian(!)	12,880	43,731	2,682	10,124	1,086,720	0.9
S	Mandal–Ekofisk(!)	6,540	10,226	1,119	3,780	666,000	0.6
Significant (50–500 bkg)							
Y	Bampo–Peutu(!)	960	15,030	439	531	14,800	3.6
W	Akata–Agbada(!)	758	5,850	224	570	71,850	0.8
B	Tuxedni–Hemlock(!)	1,180	2,480	215	532	13,400	4.0
T	LSB Jurassic(!)	897	119	127	295	6,850	4.3
G	Simpson–Ellenburger(.)	750	—	105	418	4,020	10.4
U	LSB Lower Cretaceous(!)	707	98	101	267	2,614	10.3
X	Cambay–Hazad(!)	—	—	—	395	7,610	5.2
E	Green River(!)	502	815	86	2,097	26,100	8.0
Small (<50 bkg)							
F	Soda Lake–Painted Rock(!)	296	277	47	145	1,596	9.0
J	Villeta–Monserrate(!)	263	84	39	125	2,640	4.7
K	Villeta–Caballos(!)	264	118	33	127	2,197	5.8
D	Point Pleasant–Brassfield(!)	100	—	14	56	20,700	0.3
C	Heath–Tyler(!)	96	—	13	53	147	36.3

source rock and migration distance is very short. In addition, this system's reservoir rock is surrounded by shale, a relatively good seal. Even though its inactive source rock is the richest, the Heath–Tyler is the smallest petroleum system because its source rock is not spent and the pod is the smallest (5×10^{15} cm^3) (Table 20.6).

The La Luna–Misoa(!) (Talukdar and Marcano, Chapter 29) is a very efficient (GAE = 14%), giant (8160 bkg) petroleum system. It is very efficient because (1) on the basis of the R value (Table 20.6), the source rock pod expelled most of its oil; (2) the seal rock overlying the primary reservoir rock is regional in extent and of good quality; (3) the reservoir rock blankets the geographic extent of the system and is of good quality; and (4) the critical moment is present day. The La Luna–Misoa is a giant petroleum system because (1) the source rock is very rich (5.6 wt. % TOC) and of high quality (HI$_o$ = 650) (Table 20.6), (2) the volume of the source rock pod is relatively large and mature, (3) comparatively little oil was destroyed, and (4) much of the oil generated made it to traps (GAE = 14%, Table 20.7).

The Simpson–Ellenburger(.) (Katz et al., Chapter 28) is a very efficient (GAE = 10.4%), significant (105 bkg) petroleum system. The efficiency of this system is high because the source rock, reservoir rock, seal rock, and traps are all spatially close and so migration distance is short. Because the critical moment is during the Triassic, the system's seal rock must be excellent to preserve 44° API oil to the present day. The size of this system is reflected in the relatively low source rock richness (1.7 wt. % TOC), low quality (HI$_o$ 425), and small volume of mature source rock pod (336×10^{15} cm^3).

In contrast, the Point Pleasant–Brassfield(!), whose critical moment is also in the Triassic, is an inefficient

(GAE = 0.3%), small (14 bkg) petroleum system. The source rock, reservoir rock, seal rock, and trap in this system are all close so that a high efficiency would be expected, but this is not the case. In addition, the source rock richness and quality values are nearly the same in both the Simpson–Ellenburger and Point Pleasant–Brassfield systems, except that the volume of the active source rock pod is about four times larger in the Point Pleasant–Brassfield. Therefore, five times more hydrocarbons were generated in the Point Pleasant–Brassfield than in the much larger Simpson–Ellenburger(!) system. The inefficiency of the Point Pleasant–Brassfield(!) system is probably due to the small trap volume available for hydrocarbon accumulation relative to the volume of hydrocarbons generated.

Both the Green River(!) and Soda Lake–Painted Rock(!) petroleum systems are moderately efficient (GAE = 8.0 and 9.0%, respectively) and of similar size (86 and 47 bkg, respectively); however, they have some important differences. The richness of the source rock in the Green River system is 6.0 wt. % TOC versus 2.1 wt. % for the Soda Lake–Painted Rock (Table 20.6), and the volume of the Green River active source rock pod is much larger, 420×10^{15} cm^3 versus 78×10^{15} cm^3. Thus, the mass of generated hydrocarbons is large for the Green River system. However, the big difference between the system's sizes is that much of the hydrocarbons generated in the Green River are now natural bitumen (12.5 billion bbl) (Table 20.5), which is presently unrecoverable.

Villeta–Caballos(!) and Villeta–Monserrate(!) are two systems in the same petroleum province that are of similar efficiency and size. There are four oil fields in the former system and fourteen in the latter. In the former, the generated hydrocarbons were expelled into the underlying reservoir rock, and in the latter, the hydrocarbons drained into the overlying reservoir rock. Except for the patterns of their migration paths, both systems are similar.

The Bampo–Peutu(!) and Tuxedni–Hemlock(!) petroleum systems have nearly the same efficiencies (GAE = 3.6 and 4%, respectively) and similar masses of HCGs (14,800 and 13,400 bkg, respectively), as well as similar masses of in-place hydrocarbons (531 versus 532 bkg). However, the recoverable hydrocarbons are 439 and 215 bkg, respectively. The recovery factors for gas (80%) versus those for oil (25%) account for the high recovery of hydrocarbons in the gaseous Bampo–Peutu system; the Tuxedni–Hemlock system is an oil system with only a little gas.

The Ellesmerian(!) petroleum system is an inefficient (GAE = 0.9%), large (2682 bkg) petroleum system. The lack of efficiency in this system as compared to the La Luna–Misoa system suggests some fundamental differences. Although the Ellesmerian system has generated more than four times the hydrocarbons of the La Luna–Misoa system, only half as much in-place hydrocarbon is present in the Ellesmerian system as in the La Luna-Misoa. Both systems have (1) relatively good plumbing systems, (2) adequate seals (the Ellesmerian lacks surface seeps), and (3) overburden rock that was deposited in a foreland basin setting that overmatured the pod of active source rock. We have labeled the Ellesmerian system as large (rather than giant) because the 35 billion bbl of heavy oil in the system are presently considered unconventional (not recoverable), but this is unrelated to its efficiency. That the critical moment for the Ellesmerian system is 75 Ma and for the La Luna–Misoa system is present day contributes, in part, to the difference in their efficiencies. However, the migration distance and number of hydrocarbon accumulations is different in both systems, which probably accounts for most of the difference in their efficiencies. For the Ellesmerian system, the migration distance is up to 350 km into an area of oil accumulations 35 km wide and 75 km long (the Prudhoe Bay area), whereas for the La Luna–Misoa, the migration distance is up to 200 km into a large area of many oil accumulations that is 90 km wide by 150 km long.

The Mandal–Ekofisk(!) system is an inefficient (GAE = 0.6%), large (1119 bkg) petroleum system. On the basis of the amount of petroleum generated (666,000 bkg), it could have been a giant or supergiant petroleum system if the large amount of petroleum generated had been trapped. The efficiency of this system is likely affected by the system's small trap volume and by the large amount of hydrocarbons that has leaked from the system.

CONCLUSIONS

Over half of the recoverable hydrocarbons in the world come from petroleum systems that include Upper Jurassic or middle Cretaceous source rocks (Ulmishek and Klemme, 1990; Klemme and Umishek, 1991). As suggested by Ulmishek and Klemme (1990), the volume of Paleozoic and older source rocks is small in comparison to Mesozoic and younger source rocks. Because active oceanic crust is only as old as the Triassic, source rocks older than Triassic are only preserved on the stable craton, whereas younger source rocks are preserved both on the oceanic crust and the craton. Areas that include younger source rock thus provide more opportunities for thicker, more widespread source rocks. However, a source rock generates petroleum only when it is buried deeply enough to achieve thermal maturity. Only in certain circumstances are young Cenozoic source rocks buried to this depth, and it is likely that Paleozoic source rocks were buried so long ago that the generated oil and gas have been subsequently destroyed. Mesozoic source rocks are old enough to have been buried by overburden rock to sufficient depths for petroleum generation and are young enough that preservation time is minimal. These are optimum conditions for the formation of giant and supergiant petroleum systems, and the case studies in this volume tend to support this assertion.

The case studies in this volume provide specific examples and descriptions of petroleum systems. The connections between petroleum system concepts become clearer and more evident as each case study is read. Readers will become aware of what components a case study should contain and will be better able to integrate and synthesize petroleum system concepts as the studies are examined. The case studies here illustrate the difficulties of gaining insight into some petroleum system processes, especially those affecting petroleum migration losses and migration paths. To better understand petroleum migration, authors of future case studies should choose petroleum systems in which (1) the reservoir rock is not adjacent to the source rock (so that hydrocarbon migration has occurred through several stratigraphic intervals or along faults) and (2) the hydrocarbon losses are due to retention in the active source rock and along the secondary migration path.

References Cited

Clayton, J. L., 1988, Classification and composition of crude oil, *in* Petroleum systems of the United States: USGS Bulletin 1870, p. 54–56.

Klemme, H. D., and G. F. Ulmishek, 1991, Effective petroleum source rocks of the world: stratigraphic distribution and controlling depositional factors: AAPG Bulletin, v. 75, n. 12, p. 1809–1851.

Kvenvolden, K. A., 1988, Natural gas, *in* Petroleum systems of the United States: U.S. Geological Survey Bulletin 1870, p. 46-47.

Meyer, R.F., 1988, Heavy oil and natural bitumen, *in* Petroleum systems of the United States: USGS Bulletin 1870, p. 57-59.

Ulmishek, G. F., and H. D. Klemme, 1990, Depositional controls, distribution, and effectiveness of world's petroleum source rocks: USGS Bulletin 1931, 59 p.

Magoon, L. B, and W. G. Dow, eds., 1994, The petroleum
system—from source to trap: AAPG Memoir 60.

Chapter **21**

Ellesmerian(!) Petroleum System, North Slope of Alaska, U.S.A.

Kenneth J. Bird

Branch of Petroleum Geology
U.S. Geological Survey
Menlo Park, California, U.S.A.

Abstract

The Ellesmerian(!) petroleum system covers an area of about 225,000 km^2 and is the source for about 98% of the in-place hydrocarbons (~77 × 10^9 BOE, or bbl of oil equivalent) and 100% of the commercially recoverable hydrocarbons (~13 × 10^9 bbl of oil) on the North Slope. The system developed when marine shale source rocks of the Triassic Shublik Formation and the Jurassic and Early Cretaceous Kingak Shale were buried sufficiently to begin generating hydrocarbons by the longitudinal filling of the Cretaceous and Tertiary Colville foreland basin. Distinct depocenters in the foreland basin suggest that hydrocarbon generation began in middle to Late Cretaceous time in the western part of the basin and was followed by a separate episode of generation in the east-central part of the basin in early Tertiary time. Reservoir rocks range in age from Mississippian to early Tertiary and are mostly sandstone. Carbonate reservoirs are of Mississippian–Pennsylvanian age. Traps are mainly broad, anticlinal structures with an important component of erosional truncation and thus are classified as combination structural–stratigraphic traps. All hydrocarbon accumulations in this system are located along the Barrow arch, a regional high derived from a buried rift margin. On the basis of average total organic carbon content and assumed hydrogen indices, the mass of hydrocarbons generated by the source rocks is ~8 × 10^{12} bbl of oil. When compared to the amount of known in-place hydrocarbons, these calculations indicate that about 1% of the hydrocarbons generated actually accumulated in traps. If the amount of undiscovered oil and gas estimated for this region is added to the amount already discovered, the percentage increases to 2%.

INTRODUCTION

The North Slope of Alaska lies north of the Brooks Range (the northern extension of the Rocky Mountains) and borders on the Arctic Ocean (Figure 21.1). This region has many geologic similarities to the Alberta basin in Canada and the Rocky Mountain basins in the United States. It is one of North America's most important oil-producing regions. More than thirty oil and gas accumulations have been discovered, and at present, five of these are producing approximately 1.8 million bbl of oil per day, accounting for about one-fourth of daily U. S. oil production. The remote location and harsh climate of this arctic region along with its attendant high cost of exploration and development, are responsible for its relatively late role in oil and gas production. Because large parts of the North Slope and the adjacent continental shelf are lightly explored and have a geology favorable for hydrocarbons, large amounts of oil and gas no doubt remain to be discovered.

Petroleum exploration of the North Slope can be documented for 50 of the last 70 years, and the role of the Federal government in these efforts makes this region unique. Federal exploration was conducted intermittently beginning in 1923, and industry exploration has been continuous since 1958. The first full-scale petroleum exploration program was conducted from 1944 to 1953 by the U.S. Navy (Reed, 1958). This effort focused on Naval Petroleum Reserve No. 4 (now known at the National Petroleum Reserve in Alaska, or NPRA) (Figure 21.1). The second Federal program was limited to the NPRA and was conducted from 1974 to 1981 (Gryc, 1988). These programs resulted in the discovery of three oil fields and seven gas fields, all of which are subeconomic, although accumulation sizes are only approximately known. Industry exploration dates from 1958. The first commercial discovery occurred in 1968, when the Prudhoe Bay field, the largest commercial oil accumulation in North America, was discovered. Since then, an additional 23 oil and gas fields have been found.

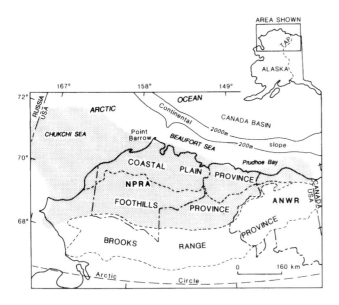

Figure 21.1. Index map showing location of the onshore and offshore North Slope petroleum province (shaded area) and physiographic provinces. NPRA, National Petroleum Reserve in Alaska; ANWR, Arctic National Wildlife Refuge; TAP, Trans-Alaska pipeline.

North Slope oil and gas discoveries now total 36 (Figure 21.2, Tables 21.1–21.3). Although most of these are noncommercial, five are commercial; their total ultimate recovery (reserves plus produced) is estimated to be 13 billion bbl (1.9×10^9 m^3) of oil. Even more indicative of the richness of this province are the total in-place resources shown in Tables 21.1–21.3: nearly 70 billion bbl (11×10^9 m^3) of oil and 40 tcf (trillion cubic feet, or 1.13×10^{12} m^3) of gas, more than 95% of which are concentrated within a 65-km radius of Prudhoe Bay (Figure 21.1).

Recent geologic publications on northern Alaska are numerous. An overview and summary of regional tectonics are provided by Hubbard et al. (1987), Plafker (1990), and Miller and Hudson (1991). Brooks Range and North Slope geology are summarized by Moore et al. (1992), the petroleum geology by Bird (1991), the Colville (foreland) basin by Bird and Molenaar (1992), and the geology of the continental margin of northern Alaska by Grantz et al. (1990). Some of the more recent studies of North Slope petroleum geology have focused on the thermal history of the region (Deming et al., 1992; Howell et al., 1992; Johnsson et al., 1993). Valuable collections of papers on the petroleum geology and related topics are presented for the entire North Slope in Tailleur and Weimer (1987), for the northern Arctic National Wildlife Refuge (ANWR) area (Figure 21.1) in Bird and Magoon (1987), and for the NPRA area in Gryc (1988). A collection of papers focused on the geochemical problem

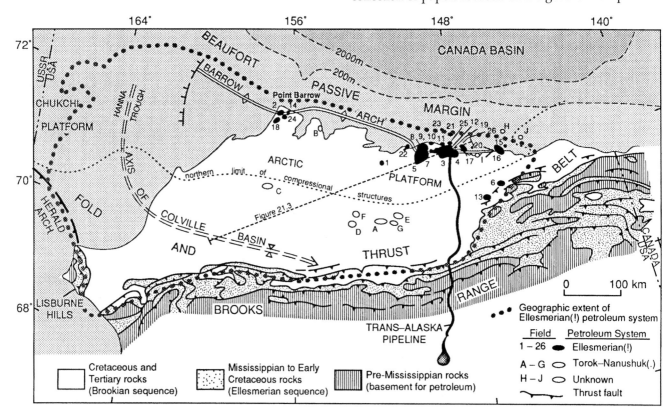

Figure 21.2. Generalized geologic map of the North Slope petroleum province showing locations of oil and gas fields, major tectonic features, and areal extent of the Ellesmerian(!) petroleum system. Numbers and letters coincide with hydrocarbon accumulations listed in Table 21. 1 and located stratigraphically in Figure 21.4.

Table 21.1. Selected Details of the Ellesmerian(!) Petroleum System

Map No.[a]	Accumulation	Date Disc'd	Reservoir	Reservoir Depth (m)	Trap Type[b]	In Place Oil (BBO)	In Place Gas (tcf)	Cum Production Oil (MBO)	Cum Production Gas (bcf)	Reserves Oil (MBO)	Reserves Gas (bcf)	Ref[c]
1	Fish Creek	1949	Nanushuk	915	B?	<<1	—	—	—	?	?	2
2	South Barrow	1949	Barrow	685	A	—	<<1	—	20	—	5	3
3	Prudhoe Bay	1967	Ivishak pool	2440	C	23	27	7,026	11,951	2,700	23,441	5
4	Prudhoe Bay	1967	Lisburne pool	2685	C	3	3	64	382	101	406	6
5	Kuparuk River	1969	Kuparuk	1830	C	~4	~2	723	814	780	634	7
6	Kavik	1969	Ivishak	1435	A	—	<1	—	—	—	?	8
7	West Sak	1969	Sagavanirktok		B?	20[d]	<<1	1	—	—	—	9
8	Ugnu	1969	Sagavanirktok		B?	15[d]	—	—	—	—	—	9
9	Milne Point	1969	Schrader Bluff pool		A	<1	<<1	—	—	—	?	8
10	Milne Point	1969	Kuparuk pool		A	<1	<<1	16	6	84	?	8
11	Gwydyr Bay	1969	Ivishak		A	<1	<<1	—	—	60	?	10
12	North Prudhoe	1970	Ivishak		A	<1	<<1	—	—	75	?	10
13	Kemik	1972	Shublik	2625	A	—	<1	—	—	—	?	8
14	East Barrow	1974	Barrow		A	—	<<1	—	6	—	6	3
15	Flaxman Island	1975	Canning	3810	B?	?	?	—	—	?	?	4
16	Point Thomson	1977	Thomson	3960	C	<1	6	—	—	350	5,000	11
17	Endicott	1978	Kekiktuk		C	1	<2	118	127	272	907	12
18	Walakpa	1980	Walakpa		B	—	<<1	—	—	—	?	13
19	Niakuk	1981	Kuparuk		C	<1	<<1	—	—	58	30	14
20	Tern Island	1982	Kekiktuk		C	?	?	—	—	?	?	15
21	Seal Island	1984	Ivishak		A	<1	<1	—	—	150	?	16
22	Colville Delta	1985	Kuparuk?	1950	C?	?	?	—	—	?	?	16
23	Sandpiper	1986	Ivishak		A	?	?	—	—	?	?	15
24	Sikulik	1988	Barrow		A	—	<<1	—	—	—	?	4
25	Point McIntyre	1988	Kuparuk		C	1	?	—	—	~300	?	17
26	Sag Delta North	1981	Ivishak and Lisburne		C	<1	<<1	2	2	?	?	18
	Totals					**>67**	**>39**	**7,950**	**13,308**	**4,930**	**30,423**	

[a]Map numbers correspond to locations on Figure 21.2.

[b]Trap type: A, structural; B, stratigraphic; C, combination.

[c]References: (2) Collins and Robinson, 1967; Reed, 1958; (3) Lantz, 1981; (4) Well file; (5) State of Alaska, 1977; (6) State of Alaska, 1984; (7) Carman and Hardwick, 1983; van Poollen and Associates, 1978; (8) State of Alaska, 1985; (9) Werner, 1987; (10) Van Dyke, 1980; (11) Oil and Gas Journal, 1984; Bird and Magoon, 1987; Craig et al., 1985; (12) Woidneck et al., 1987; Harris, 1987; (13) Gryc, 1988; (14) Harris, 1988; (15) Minerals Management Service, 1988; (16) Petroleum Information Corp., 1989; (17) Williams, 1989; (18) State of Alaska, 1991.

[d]Midpoint of range of heavy oil.

of matching North Slope oils with source rocks is provided by Magoon and Claypool (1985). Mull and Adams (1989) have produced an informative guidebook with summary papers of the geology observed along the Dalton Highway, which parallels the trans-Alaska pipeline (TAP) (Figure 21.1).

At least three petroleum systems are recognized on the North Slope according to Magoon (1989; in press). These are the Ellesmerian(!), the Hue–Sagavanirktok(!), and the Torok–Nanushuk(.) petroleum systems. This chapter documents the system responsible for most North Slope oil and gas, the Ellesmerian. Following the general format of papers in this volume, this report describes the regional geologic setting, the basis for identification of the Ellesmerian petroleum system, and details of the system's areal extent, source rock characteristics, timing, and amount of hydrocarbon generated.

GEOLOGIC SETTING

The North Slope is part of a continental fragment, the Arctic Alaska plate, that encompasses all of northern Alaska and adjacent parts of northwestern Canada and northeastern Siberia. Although the boundaries and origins of this fragment and its relationship to other regional tectonic elements continue to be debated (Moore et al., 1992), a common interpretation is that this fragment was rifted from the North American plate and rotated while drifting to its present position. In Paleozoic–early Mesozoic time, the Arctic Alaska plate was part of a passive continental margin—probably part of the North American continent north of the Canadian Arctic Islands. During Jurassic–Cretaceous time, rifting occurred along this margin severing the continental connection and creating a separate plate. Drift and coun-

Table 21.2. Selected Details of the Torok–Nanushuk(.) Petroleum System

Map No.[a]	Accumulation	Date Disc'd	Reservoir	Reservoir Depth (m)	Trap Type[b]	In Place Oil (BBO)	In Place Gas (tcf)	Cum Production Oil (MBO)	Cum Production Gas (bcf)	Reserves Oil (MBO)	Reserves Gas (bcf)	Ref[c]
A	Umiat	1946	Nanushuk	300	A	<1	<<1	—	—	70	?	1
B	Simpson	1950	Nanushuk	90	B	<<1	<<1	—	—	12	?	2
C	Meade	1950	Nanushuk	1280	A	—	<<1	—	—	—	20	2
D	Wolf Creek	1951	Nanushuk	460	A	—	<<1	—	—	—	?	2
E	Gubik	1951	Colville	450	A	—	<1	—	—	—	295	2
F	Square Lake	1952	Colville	500	A	—	<<1	—	—	—	58	2
G	East Umiat	1963	Nanushuk	550	A	—	<1	—	—	—	?	4
	Totals					**<1**	**<1**	**—**	**—**	**~82**	**~373**	

[a]Map letters correspond to locations on Figure 21.2.

[b]Trap type: A, structural; B, stratigraphic; C, combination.

[c]References: (1) Molenaar, 1982; (2) Collins and Robinson, 1967; Reed, 1958; (4) Well file.

Table 21.3. Selected details of Unknown Petroleum Systems of the North Slope

Map No.[a]	Accumulation	Date Disc'd	Reservoir	Reservoir Depth (m)	Trap Type[b]	In Place Oil (BBO)	In Place Gas (tcf)	Cum Production Oil (MBO)	Cum Production Gas (bcf)	Reserves Oil (MBO)	Reserves Gas (bcf)	Ref[c]
H	Hammerhead	1985	Sagavanirktok	1570–1700	A	?	?	—	—	?	?	15
I	Badami	1991	Canning?		B?	?	?	—	—	?	?	19
J	Kuvlum	1992	Sagavanirktok	<2590	A			—	—	?	?	19

[a]Map letters correspond to locations on Figure 21.2.

[b]Trap type: A, structural; B, stratigraphic.

[c]References: (15) Minerals Management Service, 1988; (19) Petroleum Information Corp., 1992.

terclockwise rotation of the plate away from North America produced the Canada basin and Beaufort passive margin (Figure 21.2). Concurrent with rifting, on the opposite side of the Arctic Alaska plate, collision with an oceanic island arc produced the Brooks Range orogen and a foreland basin known as the Colville basin.

The continental crust of the Arctic Alaska plate consists mostly of weakly metamorphosed pre-Late Devonian argillite and greenschist facies sedimentary rocks. These basement crustal rocks are overlain by a 1000–2600-m-thick platform sequence of Mississippian–Pennsylvanian carbonate rocks and shelf to basinal clastic Permian–Jurassic rocks. These pre-foreland basin Paleozoic and Mesozoic rocks were deposited on a passive continental margin in which more basinal or distal facies are to the south toward the area of the present Brooks Range.

The foreland basin fill ranges in age from Middle(?) Jurassic to Tertiary or Quaternary. It was filled initially by orogenic deposits dumped into a foredeep flanking the ancestral Brooks Range orogen, followed by thick, northeastward prograding basinal, basin slope, and shallow marine and nonmarine shelf deposits of mudstone, sandstone, and conglomerate derived from the Brooks Range orogen during a stage of crustal thickening and tectonic rebound.

STRUCTURAL SETTING

Most North Slope structures formed in Cretaceous–Tertiary time in response to compressional forces in the south and extensional forces in the north. The Brooks Range and the deformed rocks of the foothills province comprise a fold and thrust belt (Figure 21.2). The Brooks Range is a continental (A-type) subduction orogenic belt (Bally and Snelson, 1980) characterized by east-trending north-vergent structures. The western part of the range, west of long 148°W, is composed of a stack of far-traveled thrust packages (allochthons) characterized by complex folds and imbricate thrust faults. In contrast, the northeastern part of the range displays northeast-trending structures dominated by anticlinoria cored by pre-Carboniferous rocks reflecting regional north-vergent duplex structures (Moore et al., 1992).

Two phases of thrusting are recognized in the Brooks Range: an early phase of great lateral displacement during Late Jurassic–Neocomian time and a late phase of considerably lesser displacement in middle Cretaceous–Tertiary time. The latter deformational episode resulted in uplift of the range and development of many of its conspicuous structures, as well as deformation of foredeep deposits in the foothills province. Patterns of development and filling of the foredeep basin suggest that the latter deformational event was diachronous, being older in the west and becoming progressively younger in the east. Earthquake epicenters and deformed terrace deposits suggest that deformation continues in northern ANWR and offshore in the eastern Beaufort Sea (Grantz et al., 1988).

...ographic province consists of ...eposits and, along its southern ...f older Brooks Range rocks. This ...d by detachment folds which in ... province are remarkable for their ... ...ce. Some anticlines have been mapped on the surface for more than 150 km (Mayfield et al., 1988b). Thrust faults occur at many levels and generally cut stratigraphically upsection to the north. Fault displacements and fold amplitudes diminish northward; their northern extent generally coincides with the northern limit of the foothills province. Structures characteristic of this province extend offshore to the west beneath the southern part of the Chukchi Sea (north of the Herald arch) and to the northeast beneath the Beaufort shelf east of 146°W longitude, offshore from the ANWR (Craig et al., 1985; Thurston and Theiss, 1987; Grantz et al., 1988) (Figure 21.2).

North of the fold and thrust belt, the North Slope petroleum province is characterized by nearly flat-lying Mississippian and younger strata that are cut by extensional and, in some places, strike-slip faults. Prominent structural features of this area are the Arctic and Chukchi platforms, which are separated by the north-trending Hanna trough and the east-trending Barrow arch, which separates the Colville foreland basin from the Beaufort passive margin (Figure 21.2). In the central Chukchi Sea, a broad, northeast-trending zone of complexly faulted anticlinal structures is known as the Hanna wrench-fault zone (Thurston and Theiss, 1987). The Barrow arch, a broad, east-plunging ridge-like feature that underlies the coast of northern Alaska and the northeastern Chukchi Sea, is characterized by broad anticlines cut by normal faults with displacements generally less than a few hundred meters. Much of the faulting relates to the Jurassic and Early Cretaceous episode of rifting. Complex structural–stratigraphic combination traps occur along the Barrow arch as a result of the coincidence of original passive margin stratigraphic pinch-outs, erosional truncation related to rift margin uplift, synrift deposition, and postrift subsidence and sedimentary overlap. Most North Slope oil and gas accumulations occur in traps along the Barrow arch (Figures 21.2 and 21.3, Tables 21.1–21.3).

A structure section (Figure 21.3), constructed from seismic and well data (Bird, 1982; Bruynzeel et al., 1982), illustrates the structural and stratigraphic character of the northern flank of the Colville basin. The section is oriented oblique to the trend of fold and thrust belt structures but parallel to the direction of filling of the Colville basin (Bird and Andrews, 1979) so as to show the probable hydrocarbon "plumbing system." In addition, vitrinite reflectance profiles in selected wells along this section have been used to determine amounts of uplift and to aid in the restoration of the basin in order to determine the time of maximum burial and, hence, the time of oil and gas generation. Elevations of reflectance values corresponding to initial conditions (0.25% R_o), the top of the oil window (0.60% R_o), the base of the oil window (1.3% R_o), and the top of the gas window (2.0% R_o) were determined from regression lines fit to reflectance data in each well (Table 21.4). A reflectance value of 0.25 was selected as the initial value, prior to burial, on the basis of inspection of North Slope reflectance data (Johnsson et al., 1992). These selected vitrinite reflectance values are plotted in Figure 21.3a. The elevation of similar reflectance varies considerably from well to well, especially between wells 2 and 3 and wells 7 and 8, where no evidence of faulting or significant stratigraphic change is known. A set of nearly parallel, gently sloping reflectance isograds was hand-fitted to the data (Figure 21.3a). Such isograds are a gross simplification, particularly in the fold and thrust belt (Foothills province) part of the section, where reflectance isograds are known to be folded along with the rocks (Howell et al., 1992). This degree of simplification, however, is acceptable in determining maximum burial.

Inspection of isograds and stratigraphic relationship in Figure 21.3a suggests that uplift of nearly 3000 m has occurred at the southwest end of the section and that uplift decreases to zero on the coastal plain near the coastline. The time of maximum burial along this section appears to be variable, oldest in the southwest and youngest to the northeast. The northeast end of the section is presently at maximum burial depth because the stratigraphic section there is composed of young (Late Cretaceous–Tertiary) undeformed rocks with no evidence of significant amounts of erosion (e.g., Craig et al. 1985, pl. 5; Molenaar et al., 1986). In contrast, the southwest end of the section was nearly at maximum burial near the end of Cenomanian time because the stratigraphic section is composed primarily of the Aptian(?)–Albian Torok Formation and the Albian–Cenomanian Nanushuk Group.

Furthermore, by tracing the top of the Nanushuk Group (corresponding to ~95-Ma isochron) northeastward from well no. 4, one observes that the region of the Barrow arch at this time was covered by seawater and only a few hundred meters of sediment. The 4-km-thick post-Nanushuk sedimentary package present at the northeast end of the section could not have covered the entire section as a uniform blanket because insufficient space exists between the present-day ground surface and the 0.25 reflectance isograd. This is particularly evident at well no. 4, where space for only about 800 m of section is present between the top of the Nanushuk Group and the 0.25% R_o isograd. Farther to the northeast, in wells no. 6, 7, and 8, the youngest (pre-Gubik Formation) strata 800 m above the top of the Nanushuk Group are Campanian (Witmer et al. 1981), taken to be about 75 Ma in this analysis. This is believed to be the age of maximum burial, at least for the central part of the section, and is the time portrayed in the restoration of the section (Figure 21.3b). This conclusion is based on the assumptions that the 0.25% R_o isograd is a fair approximation of the original land surface and that the thickness of

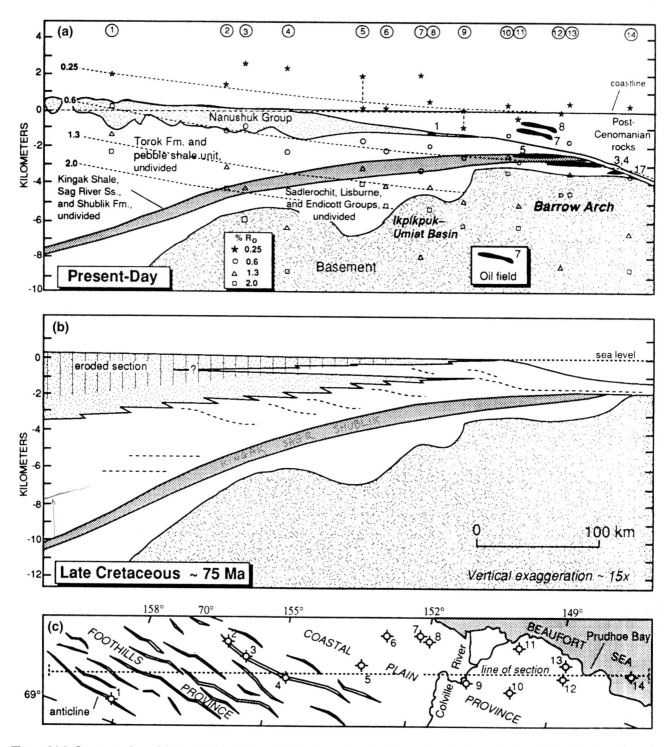

Figure 21.3. Cross section of the central part of the North Slope oriented oblique to structures but parallel to the direction of progradational filling of the Colville basin. (a) Present–day section illustrating major structural–stratigraphic features, occurrence of oil fields, elevation of selected vitrinite reflectance values from wells, and reflectance isograds. (See Table 21. 4 for list of wells and R$_o$ parameters and Figure 21. 2 for location of section.) (b) Reconstruction of section at time of maximum burial of the western half of the section. (c) Index map showing location of section, wells, and physiographic provinces.

projected strata remains relatively constant—a reasonable assumption based on seismic reflection records. If a greater elevation is selected for this isograd, then the time of maximum burial would be younger than 75 Ma. At the far southwest end of the section, maximum burial

cannot be determined by this method for lack of stratigraphic control, but it is believed that maximum burial occurred slightly earlier than 75 Ma, perhaps as early as 95 Ma, at the end of Nanushuk deposition.

In summary, analysis of vitrinite reflectance and strati-

Table 21.4. Selected North Slope Wells Located Along Southwest-Northeast Profile (Figure 21.3) Showing Vitrinite Reflectance Parameters[a]

Well No.	API No. (50-)	Well Name	KB (m)	TD (m)	n	Interval[b] Top	Base	Regression Parameters a	b	R^2	R_o Elevations (m) 0.25	0.6	1.3	2.0
1	155-20001	Awuna #1	344	3414	15	204	2481	0.56311	2.1248E-04	0.967	2004	214	-1366	-2246
2	119-10005	Oumalik #1	59	3619	26	161	3619	0.40893	1.5482E-04	0.941	1440	-1016	-3185	-4394
3	119-10006	East Oumalik #1	89	1839	9	49	1838	0.46197	1.0536E-04	0.804	2620	-988	-4175	-5951
4	119-20001	Koluktak #1	62	1793	10	43	1689	0.38405	7.9780E-05	0.743	2400	-2366	-6575	-8920
5	279-20003	Inigok #1 (entire well)	50	6127	90	134	6066	0.26878	2.1007E-04	0.913	200	-1610	-3209	-4099
5	279-20003	Inigok #1 (upper part)	50	6127	44	134	2883	0.38014	9.4800E-05	0.813	1970	-2041	-5583	-7556
6	103-20017	North Inigok #1	50	3100	19	229	3097	0.25746	1.7016E-04	0.852	125	-2109	-4083	-5182
7	103-20009	West Fish Creek #1	34	3483	15	991	3063	0.34828	7.0901E-05	0.833	2065	-3298	-8034	-10672
8	103-10001	Fish Creek #1	8	2140	7	312	1548	0.30083	1.5048E-04	0.908	542	-1984	-4216	-5459
9	103-20003	Itkillik River Unit #1 (entire well)	19	4670	26	844	4602	0.15290	2.4519E-04	0.908	-852	-2403	-3772	-4535
9	103-20003	Itkillik River Unit #1 (upper part)	19	4670	11	844	2469	0.25155	1.4271E-04	0.838	38	-2626	-4979	-6290
10	029-20051	Toolik Federal #3	107	1835	5	411	1707	0.27996	2.4938E-04	0.927	304	-1220	-2567	-3317
11	029-20699	Kuparuk River Unit #3A-9	27	1960	14	183	1948	0.22112	1.5092E-04	0.802	-327	-2846	-5071	-6311
12	029-20067	Placid et al. State #1	22	3475	8	954	2274	0.25056	8.2769E-04	0.681	34	-4560	-8617	-10877
13	029-20353	Prudhoe Bay Unit #R-1 (entire well)	16	2966	26	146	2965	0.28514	1.1630E-04	0.502	508	-2762	-5649	-7258
13	029-20353	Prudhoe Bay Unit #R-1 (upper part)	16	2966	5	146	694	0.30714	1.8069E-04	0.962	511	-1593	-3451	-4487
14	029-20660	Jeanette Island #1	9	3760	35	64	3603	0.27007	1.0025E-04	0.785	344	-3449	-6799	-8665

[a]Vitrinite reflectance (R_o) data from Johnsson et al. (1992) and regression parameters from Johnsson et al. (1993). Abbreviations: KB, kelly bushing; TD, total depth; n, number of samples; R^2, correlation coefficient; $R_o = a \times 10^{(b \times \text{depth})}$.

[b]Interval refers to measured well depths in meters.

graphic data suggests that the southwestern part of the cross section reached maximum burial during Late Cretaceous time, perhaps as early as 95 Ma but certainly by 75 Ma (Figure 21.3b). At this time, oil generated in the Kingak Shale and Shublik Formation source rocks probably migrated to the north and northeast toward the relatively high-standing Barrow arch where traps had already formed. Since 75 Ma, the southwestern end of the section has undergone folding, uplift, and as much as 2500 m of erosion, whereas the northeastern part of the section has undergone as much as 3000 m of subsidence.

STRATIGRAPHY

The stratigraphic record of the North Slope province extends to the Precambrian, but rocks with petroleum potential are mostly younger than Devonian (Figure 21.4). Traditionally, the petroleum prospective rocks of the North Slope have been grouped into two sequences—Ellesmerian and Brookian—to emphasize provenance areas and genetic relationships. Both sequences contain important petroleum source and reservoir rocks, although most oil production is from Ellesmerian reservoirs. Pre-Mississippian (basement) rocks, especially carbonate rocks, that have been buried and metamorphosed beyond the thermal stage for oil may, under favorable circumstances, provide reservoirs for oil or gas.

Pre-Mississippian

Pre-Mississippian rocks of the North Slope province consist of a complex assemblage of slightly to moderately metamorphosed Proterozoic–Devonian sedimentary and igneous rocks. Precambrian crystalline rocks typical of the Canadian shield are not known to occur in this area. In the subsurface, pre-Carboniferous rocks (known mostly along the Barrow arch) consist of steeply dipping and slightly metamorphosed argillite of Ordovician and Silurian age. Their fine-grained character and apparent great thickness suggest a continental slope depositional environment.

Ellesmerian Sequence

The Ellesmerian sequence records a major northward advance of the sea following the Ellesmerian orogeny. This sequence consists of marine carbonate rocks, marine and nonmarine clastic rocks, and scarce igneous rocks representing about 220 m.y. (Mississippian–Early Cretaceous) of continental margin sedimentation. Northward-directed stratigraphic onlap, convergence, truncation, increasing grain size, and marine to nonmarine facies changes indicate that the ancient shoreline lay near the present-day coast and that the open ocean was to the south. Total Ellesmerian sequence thickness is generally less than 2 km, but in local areas, such as the Umiat basin, it may exceed 6 km. Because the Ellesmerian

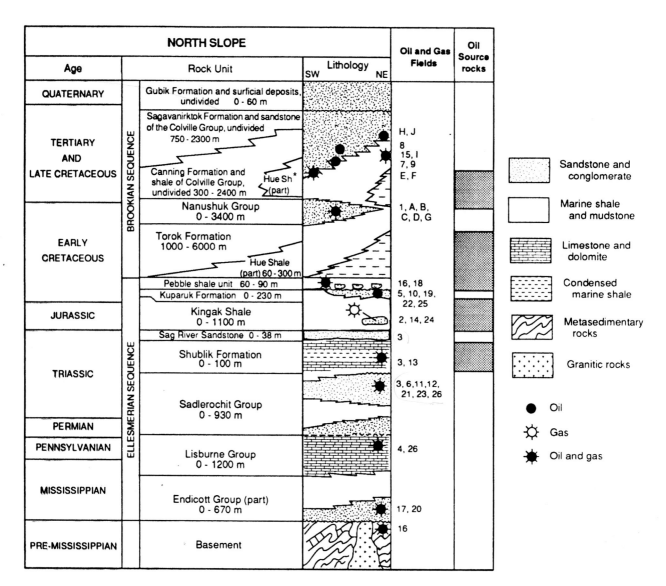

Figure 21.4. Generalized North Slope stratigraphic column showing distribution of oil and gas accumulations and major source rock intervals. Oil and gas field numbers and letters are keyed to Tables 21.1–21.3 and located in Figure 21.2.
*Hue Shale: age assignment for this part of the unit is Late Cretaceous–Paleocene(?).

and don't forget it!

sequence is generally less than 2 km thick, rocks rich in organic material deposited during this time were not capable of generating oil until buried by the much thicker Brookian sequence deposits.

The Mississippian–Lower Permian part of the Ellesmerian sequence constitutes a transgressive megacycle, as much as 4 km thick in some areas. It consists of nonmarine coal-bearing sandstone, shale, and conglomerate (Kekiktuk Conglomerate) that is succeeded by shallow marine black shale (Kayak Shale) or, along the northern basin margin, by red and green shale (Itkilyariak Formation). These clastic deposits are part of the Endicott Group (Figure 21.4). Shale units of the Endicott Group grade upward and laterally into an areally extensive carbonate platform sequence composed of limestone and dolomite (Lisburne Group). Epeirogenic movements in Late Pennsylvanian(?)–Early Permian time caused withdrawal of the sea and development of a

regional unconformity at the top of the Lisburne. Significant oil accumulations occur in the Kekiktuk Conglomerate (Endicott field, no. 17, Figure 21.2 and Table 21.1) and in limestone and dolomite of the Lisburne Group (Lisburne field, no. 4).

Advance of the sea over the eroded Lisburne Group platform resulted in the deposition of the next megacycle, the clastic deposits of the Permian–Triassic Sadlerochit Group. The lower part of the Sadlerochit is a northward-thinning, transgressive marine sandstone and siltstone unit (Echooka Formation). The Echooka is abruptly overlain by prodelta shale and siltstone (Kavik Member of the Ivishak Formation) that grades upward into a southward-prograding clastic wedge of marine to nonmarine sandstone and conglomerate (Ledge Sandstone Member of the Ivishak Formation). The Ledge is the main reservoir of the Prudhoe Bay oil field, where it consists of alluvial fan and deltaic facies (Melvin and

Knight, 1984). The uppermost part of the Sadlerochit Group consists of a transgressive fining-upward and northward-thinning marine siltstone and argillaceous sandstone (Fire Creek Siltstone Member of the Ivishak Formation).

The transgression that began with deposition of the Fire Creek Siltstone Member continued into Middle–Late Triassic time with deposition of as much as 100 m of glauconitic, phosphatic, and richly fossiliferous shale, siltstone, mudstone, and limestone (Shublik Formation). This unit, believed to represent deposition under upwelling oceanic conditions (Parrish, 1987), is an important petroleum source rock. A thin (<30 m), regressive marine sandstone and siltstone (Sag River and Karen Creek sandstones) gradationally overlies the Shublik Formation along the northern basin margin and marks the end of the Shublik transgressive cycle.

Jurassic–Lower Cretaceous (Neocomian) strata consist of as much as 1.5 km of marine shale and siltstone (Kingak Shale and pebble shale unit) with locally developed predominantly marine sandstones (e.g., Kuparuk Formation). The Kingak Shale is an important petroleum source rock composed of a complex of southward-prograding, offlapping, and downlapping wedges of shale and siltstone. It was deposited during an episode of crustal extension and represents the last complete megacycle of the Ellesmerian sequence. Normal faulting and development of sediment-filled grabens and half-grabens, some with as much as 3 km of fill (e.g. Dinkum graben; Grantz et al., 1988), occur mainly north of the present-day coastline. Rock types of the graben fill are unknown because of a lack of well penetrations. Some investigators limit the Ellesmerian sequence by placing the Jurassic and earliest Cretaceous part in a separate sequence called the Barrovian sequence (Carman and Hardwick, 1983; Noonan, 1987) or Beaufortian sequence (Hubbard et al., 1987) on the basis of the association of these rocks with early or prerifting tectonics offshore to the north and northwest. For the purpose of this report, however, the Ellesmerian sequence is used in its broader definition.

Uplift along the rift margin in Early Cretaceous (Valanginian) time resulted in the formation of a northwestward-elongated land mass that, at its maximum, occupied the area beneath most of the present-day coastal plain and the inner continental shelf. Erosion of this landmass produced the regional Lower Cretaceous unconformity (LCU). Subsidence of the rift margin resulted in a marine transgression and, locally, deposition of sandstones such as the Kemik Sandstone. A blanket-like marine shale (pebble shale unit) overlies the LCU and related sandstones. It forms the final deposit of the Ellesmerian sequence, constitutes an important petroleum source rock, and provides the seal for many of the petroleum accumulations in the Prudhoe Bay area. The pebble shale unit is conformably overlain by distal, condensed marine shale deposits (Hue Shale) representing the basal unit of the Brookian sequence on the north flank of the Colville basin (Figure 21.2). The lower part of the Hue Shale is characterized by high gamma ray readings readily identified by gamma ray well logs in the subsurface (Molenaar et al., 1986) or by a hand-held scintillometer in outcrop (Molenaar et al., 1987). This interval of strata is variously known as the gamma ray zone (GRZ) or the highly radioactive zone (HRZ).

Brookian Sequence

The Brookian sequence includes all of the sediments that were shed across northern Alaska from the Brooks Range orogenic belt. This sequence spans Middle or Late Jurassic time to the present and mostly represents foreland basin deposits developed ahead of northward-advancing thrust sheets. The oldest Brookian strata (Jurassic–earliest Cretaceous), probably deposited several hundred kilometers to the south of the present Brooks Range, were tectonically transported in Early Cretaceous time with the Brooks Range allochthons and are now discontinuously preserved in the Brooks Range and adjacent foothills. The majority of Colville basin fill (>8 km thick) is Aptian(?) and younger in age and is that part of the Brookian sequence depicted in Figures 21.2 and 21.4. Filling of the basin occurred from southwest to northeast in a series of migrating depocenters. Because Brookian deposits provided the overburden necessary for petroleum source rocks to be heated to reach maturity, Brookian depocenters provided changing sites of maturity and changing directions of petroleum migration. Shifting depocenters may also reflect geographically and temporally distinct orogenic pulses. Brookian deposits thin northward over the Barrow arch and grade into the passive margin sequence, where they again thicken to as much as 8 km.

The earliest preserved Brookian sequence depocenter developed during Aptian(?)–Cenomanian time in the western and central parts of the North Slope (beneath the Chukchi shelf and the NPRA). During Cenomanian–Eocene time, the depocenter shifted to the central part of the North Slope (approximately the area between the NPRA and the ANWR). From Eocene to the present, the depocenter has been located in the northern ANWR and the adjacent offshore (Moore et al., 1992).

Seismic reflection profiles show that the Brookian sequence is characterized by well-developed sigmoidal reflectors. These reflectors, interpreted as time lines, record successive basin profiles (Molenaar, 1988). Well and outcrop studies show that (1) topset reflections represent deltaic coal-bearing sandstone, conglomerate, and shelf shale deposits; (2) foreset reflections depict slope shale and turbidite sandstone deposits; and (3) bottomset reflections include basin-plain shale and turbidite sandstone deposits and distal, condensed shale with interbedded volcanic ash (Molenaar et al., 1987; Molenaar, 1988). Brookian deltaic deposits form the Nanushuk Group and Sagavanirktok Formation; marine shelf, slope, and basin-plain shale and interbedded sandstone make up the Torok and Canning Formations, and distal, condensed basin-plain shale and bentonites form the Hue Shale.

Petroleum Source Rocks

Chemical analyses of North Slope oils and source rocks indicate that there are multiple oil types that have been generated by multiple source rocks. Prior to the discovery of the Prudhoe Bay field, investigations of North Slope oils from wells and seeps (McKinney et al., 1959) focused on the quality of products that could be derived from these oils rather than their relationships to source rocks or to other oils. This emphasis changed, however, with the discovery of multiple oil-bearing reservoirs in the Prudhoe area. Jones and Speers (1976) reported that oils from widely separated Prudhoe area reservoirs—Sadlerochit, Kuparuk, and Sagavanirktok—were similar and thus from a common source. The most comprehensive study aimed at discovering related types of North Slope oils is that of Magoon and Claypool (1981). From their analyses of 40 samples collected from seeps and wells all across the North Slope, two groups of oil were identified: (1) the Barrow–Prudhoe, from the Sag River Sandstone beneath the Barrow gas field and Prudhoe Bay field, and (2) the Simpson–Umiat, from the Simpson seeps and Umiat field. The Barrow–Prudhoe group, volumetrically the predominant North Slope oil, occurs in reservoirs of Mississippian–Tertiary age. It is characterized by <u>high sulfur</u> content, medium API gravity, light isotopic composition, and a pristane–phytane ratio less than 1.5. The Simpson–Umiat group occurs in Cretaceous–Tertiary reservoirs and, surprisingly, is the only oil found in seeps. This group is characterized by <u>low sulfur</u> content, high API gravity, heavy isotopic composition, and a pristane–phytane ratio greater than 1.5.

Other studies of the same and newly discovered oils (e.g., Seifert et al., 1980; Magoon and Claypool, 1985, 1988; Curiale, 1987; Sedivey et al., 1987; Anders et al., 1987) reveal various oil types within the two groups. Many investigators now regard the Simpson and Umiat oils as being derived from different terrigenous source rock facies. Additional oil types identified within the Simpson–Umiat group include the Manning (from the Manning Point seep), the Jago (from oil-stained rocks along the Jago River), and the Kavik (from oil-stained rocks near the Kavik field) in the ANWR area (Anders et al., 1987) and the pebble shale in the Barrow area (Magoon and Claypool, 1988). The Kingak oil in the Prudhoe area, a type within the Barrow–Prudhoe oil group, is locally derived from the marine Kingak Shale (Seifert et al., 1980).

The total organic carbon (TOC) content of most North Slope rock units exceeds the threshold value of 0.5 wt. % of potential petroleum source rocks, although their hydrogen content varies considerably (Bird, 1991). Generally, the deltaic and prodeltaic units (Endicott, Sadlerochit, Nanushuk, Torok, Colville, Sagavanirktok, and Canning), which have relatively high TOC but low hydrogen content, are considered to be gas-prone source rocks. Marine units such as the Shublik Formation, Kingak Shale, Hue Shale, and parts of the pebble shale unit which have both high TOC and hydrogen content are considered oil-prone source rocks (Figure 21.4). The

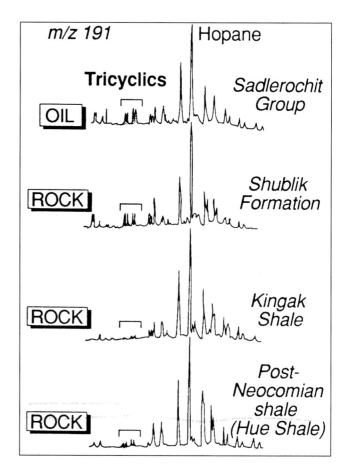

Figure 21.5. Biological marker analysis of a Barrow–Prudhoe oil and candidate source rocks identifying the Shublik Formation, Kingak Shale, and post-Neocomian shale (now known as the Hue Shale) as co-sources of the oil in the Prudhoe Bay oilfield, Sadlerochit Group reservoir. (From Seifert et al., 1980.)

inferred North Slope thermal history indicates that all but the youngest of these rock units are mature to overmature somewhere on the North Slope (Magoon and Bird, 1985, 1987, 1988).

Considerable effort has been devoted to matching North Slope oils with specific source rocks and yet much remains to be learned. The earliest efforts (Morgridge and Smith, 1972) identified Cretaceous shale above the LCU and the Kingak Shale as the most probable source rocks for the Prudhoe Bay oils, on the basis of geologic relationships and bulk geochemical characteristics of the proposed source rocks. Later, Seifert et al. (1980) compared biological marker compounds from rocks and oils (Figure 21.5) and suggested that an assemblage of source rocks, including the Shublik Formation, Kingak Shale, and deeply buried post-Neocomian shale now known as the Hue Shale (Molenaar et al., 1987), had generated these oils. Isotopic correlations of Sedivey et al. (1987) generally complement the biomarker results by showing an excellent correlation between Shublik Formation and Kingak Shale source rocks and the Prudhoe oils (Figure 21.6). Hue Shale isotopic values, however, lie just outside the observed isotopic range of

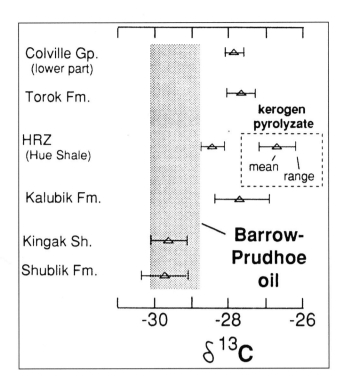

Figure 21.6. Comparison of carbon isotopic compositions of the kerogen pyrolyzate and crude oil showing the match of the Kingak Shale and Shublik Formation with the full range of whole oil isotopic compositons for the Barrow–Prudhoe group of oils. Error bars indicate value ±1 standard deviation from the mean for kerogen pyrolyzate values. (Adapted from Burwood et al., 1985; Sedivy et al., 1987.)

the oils. The USGS-sponsored oil–rock correlation study (Magoon and Claypool, 1985) was a multi-laboratory effort that focused on a common set of oil and candidate source rock samples, mostly from outside the Prudhoe Bay area. The majority (17 of 30 laboratories) agreed that the Shublik Formation and, to a lesser extent (8 laboratories), the Kingak Shale are source rocks for the Prudhoe oils. There was also general agreement (14 laboratories) that the pebble shale unit and, to a lesser extent (7 laboratories), the Torok Formation are source rocks for the Umiat oil type (Claypool and Magoon, 1985).

Reservoir Rocks

Most sandstone and carbonate rock units of the North Slope are known to contain hydrocarbons (Figure 21.4). Most reservoir rocks are sandstone deposited in a variety of environments ranging from deep marine to nonmarine. The most important sandstone reservoirs are the nonmarine to deltaic Sadlerochit Group, the shallow marine Kuparuk Formation, and the nonmarine Kekiktuk Conglomerate (Table 21.1 and Figure 21.4). Platform carbonate rocks, the Lisburne Group, are regionally extensive but provide the reservoir for only one significant hydrocarbon accumulation, the Lisburne pool of the Prudhoe Bay field (Missman and Jameson, 1991). General summaries of North Slope reservoir rocks are provided by Bird et al. (1987), van de Kamp (1988),

and Bird and Molenaar (1992). Details of specific reservoir units can be found in Jones and Speers (1976), Jamison et al. (1980), Carman and Hardwick (1983), Melvin and Knight (1984), Gautier (1987), Tailleur and Weimer (1987), Bartsch-Winkler and Huffman (1988), Gaynor and Scheihing (1988), Molenaar et al. (1988), and Siok (1989).

North Slope pre-foreland basin (Ellesmerian) reservoir rocks are uniformly mature quartz-chert sandstone. In contrast, foreland basin (Brookian) reservoir rocks are generally subquartzose lithic sandstone. In these rocks, there appears to be a general increase in compositional maturity (increasing quartz) with decreasing age. Sandstone with better porosity in both the Brookian and Ellesmerian sequences commonly shows evidence of leaching of both grains and cements.

PETROLEUM SYSTEM

The Ellesmerian(!) petroleum system encompasses the source rocks and hydrocarbon accumulations of the Barrow–Prudhoe family of oils. These oils have been geochemically correlated with considerable confidence with Shublik Formation and Kingak Shale source rocks and less confidently with the Hue Shale (Figures 21.5 and 21.6). Because of the good correlation between oil and source rock, this is considered a known system. A total of 26 hydrocarbon accumulations, representing 98% of discovered North Slope oil and gas, are believed to belong to this system (Table 21.1). A number of associated and nonassociated gas accumulations occur in reservoirs within the Ellesmerian sequence. Although there are no data relating gas to source rocks, these gas accumulations are provisionally included as part of the Ellesmerian petroleum system. Reservoirs containing these oil and gas accumulations range in age from Mississippian to early Tertiary (Figure 21.4). Thus, the system consists of at least two source rock units and at least five significant reservoir rock units. For simplicity, the name *Ellesmerian* is selected for this system because most of the rocks involved are part of the Ellesmerian sequence.

Areal and Stratigraphic Extent

The Ellesmerian petroleum system encompasses the area of mature source rocks and related hydrocarbon accumulations. As shown in Figure 21.2, this system extends from the northern edge of the Brooks Range to just north of the crest of the Barrow arch. The west edge of the system is constrained by the Herald arch and the western limit of the Ellesmerian sequence along the Chukchi platform as seismically mapped by the Minerals Management Service (K. W. Sherwood, personal communication, 1993). As drawn, the system covers ~225,000 km². Prior to Brooks Range crustal shortening, which amounts to several hundred kilometers according to some authors (e.g., Mayfield et al., 1988a), the system could easily have covered twice as much area, including parts of the Yukon Territory of Canada (Poulton, 1982; Norris, 1984).

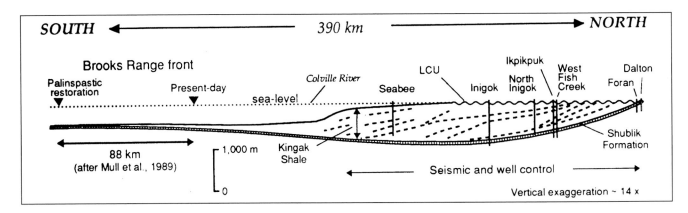

Figure 21.7. Inferred stratigraphic relationship of Ellesmerian(!) petroleum system source rocks, the Shublik Formation and Kingak Shale, and equivalent parts of the Otuk Formation restored to their relative positions at the end of Kingak deposition in Early Cretaceous (Valanginian) time. Dashed lines within Kingak Shale interval represent clinoform features observed on seismic reflection record RCS-8 (Bird, 1985, 1987). Location of section, wells, and outcrops are shown in Figure 21.8. LCU, Lower Cretaceous unconformity.

The stratigraphic extent of the Ellesmerian system is Mississippian–Tertiary and is defined by the ages of reservoir rocks containing the Barrow–Prudhoe family of oils (Figures 21.3 and 21.4). The oldest reservoir is the Mississippian Kekiktuk Conglomerate in the Endicott field, and the youngest is the Paleocene part of the Sagavanirktok Formation in the Ugnu field (Figures 21.2–21.4).

Character and Richness of Source Rocks

General stratigraphic characteristics of the Ellesmerian system source rocks, the Kingak Shale and Shublik Formation, are summarized in a restored north-south cross section across the central part of the North Slope (Figure 21.7). In this and subsequent analyses, the Hue Shale is not considered an important source rock for this petroleum system. Kingak Shale and Shublik Formation age-equivalent strata of the Otuk Formation are exposed along the front of the Brooks Range (Bodnar, 1984, 1989) and provide control for the south end of the section. These outcrops have been incorporated into the section by palinspastically restoring them 88 km south of their present position—a minimum figure for the restoration and likely only half of the true amount according to Mull et al. (1989). The time illustrated by this restoration is the Early Cretaceous (Valanginian), when maximum development of the regional Lower Cretaceous unconformity (LCU) occurred but before deposition of unnamed shales, coquinoid limestone, and the Okpikruak Formation above the Otuk Formation.

This profile shows the relatively uniform thickness of the Shublik Formation and age-equivalent limestone and chert members of the Otuk Formation. In contrast, the Kingak Shale shows pronounced thickness variations and a southward progradational style of deposition. The age-equivalent Blankenship Member of the Otuk Formation is about 20 m thick, probably a minimum thickness because it apparently represents only Early–Middle Jurassic time (Bodnar, 1989). Late Jurassic–earliest Cretaceous strata are missing either by nondeposition or by erosion. The orientation of the profile is

perpendicular to depositional strike as indicated by well data, seismic records, and outcrop studies. In making volumetric calculations, the general thickness, organic carbon richness, and stratigraphic characteristics have been projected laterally from this section.

Organic richness measurements of approximately 300 samples taken along this line of section are tabulated in Table 21.5. These analyses, from drill cuttings, cores, and outcrop samples, show that the Kingak Shale averages about 2 wt. % TOC with a range of <1.0–6.5 wt. %. The partially age-equivalent Blankenship Member of the Otuk Formation shows greater richness, with a 6.5 wt. % mean and <1.0–13.9 wt. % range. The Shublik Formation averages 2.3 wt. % with a range of <1.0–6.7 wt. %. The age-equivalent limestone and chert members of the Otuk Formation are slightly richer, with a mean of 3.3 wt. % and a range of <1.0–10.6 wt. %. Not included in this analysis is the Early Triassic shale member of the Otuk Formation. This shale, as much as 140 m thick with a TOC of about 2 wt. % (Bodnar, 1984), is the age equivalent of the Ivishak Formation.

Regional thermal maturity patterns of the Ellesmerian petroleum system source rocks are summarized in Figure 21.8. Thermal maturity at the top of the Kingak Shale is expressed in terms of petroleum generation stages. For the base of the Kingak Shale and the Shublik Formation, these thermal maturity boundaries would be shifted northward by a few kilometers. This illustration shows that the Kingak Shale and Shublik Formation are mature or overmature with respect to oil generation in most areas; only in the coastal region near Prudhoe Bay and Point Barrow are the rocks immature. Limited data from the Otuk Formation outcrops (Bodnar, 1984, 1989) show a range of maturity from immature in the westernmost outcrop sections to overmature in the easternmost sections. The regional significance of these observations is unknown, although they may be related to the observed westward plunge of allochthons in the Brooks Range. Thermal maturity of the rocks in the Brooks Range is generally interpreted to be the result of tectonic burial, whereas maturity in the foothills region results from sedimentary burial (Harris et al., 1987; Howell et al., 1992).

Table 21.5. Summary of Total Organic Carbon (TOC) Richness for the Kingak Shale and Shublik Formation in Selected Wells and for Lateral Stratigraphic Equivalents in Otuk Formation Outcrops[a]

Wells	Kingak Shale					Shublik Formation				
	Th (m)	n	TOC (wt. %) Mean	Min	Max	Th (m)	n	TOC (wt. %) Mean	Min	Max
Subsurface										
W.T. Foran #1	NP	—	—	—	—	29	5	3.25	1.82	6.73
J.W. Dalton #1	NP	—	—	—	—	79	9	2.00	1.58	2.85
West Fish Creek #1	575	24	1.48	1.06	2.88	70	2	2.13	1.41	2.86
Ikpikpuk #1	721	51	1.90	0.78	6.41	149	16	1.98	0.49	4.26
North Inigok #1	731	22	1.53	0.77	2.38	>24	2	3.11	2.11	4.12
Inigok #1	884	80	1.77	0.52	6.47	73	4	2.67	2.34	3.25
Seabee #1	>735	58	3.02	0.34	5.23	NR	—	—	—	—
Summary		235	2.05	0.34	6.47		38	2.30	0.49	6.73
Outcrop										
Composite of measured sections	Blankenship Member of Otuk Formation					Limestone and Chert Members of Otuk Formation				
	~20	16	6.45	0.31	13.89	~65	15	3.30	0.20	10.63
Combined subsurface and outcrop										
Wells and sections		251	2.34	0.31	13.89		53	2.58	0.20	10.63

[a]Data from Magoon and Bird (1988, tables 17.6 and 17.8) and Bodnar (1984, p. 227–228). See Figures 21.7 and 21.8 for well and measured section locations.
Abbreviations: Th, thickness; n, number of samples; Min, minimum; Max, maximum; NP, not present; NR, not reached.

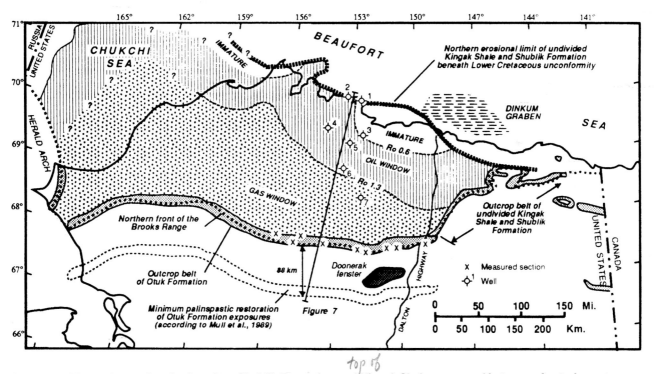

Figure 21.8. Thermal maturity of subsurface Shublik Formation and Kingak Shale expressed in terms of petroleum generative stages. The partially stratigraphic equivalent Otuk Formation, exposed along the northern margin of the Brooks Range, is allochthonous, having been tectonically transported a minimum of 88 km northward. Otuk Formation R_o measurements from measured sections (Bodnar, 1984, 1989) show that westernmost sections are immature, central sections are within the oil window, and eastern sections are within the gas window. Wells are listed in Table 21.5 and shown in cross section in Figure 21.7. (Adapted from Magoon and Bird, 1985, 1987, 1988.)

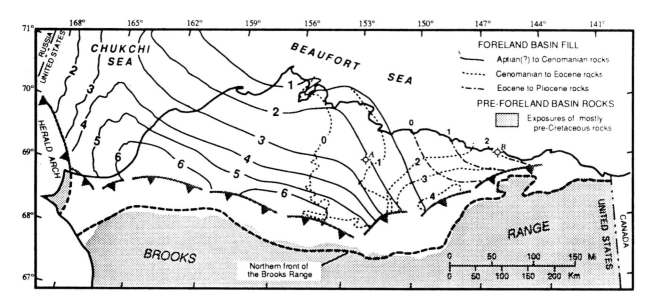

Figure 21.9. Thickness (contours in km) of each of the three sedimentary packages that constitute the Colville foreland basin fill. These rocks are the overburden on presumed Ellesmerian(!) petroleum system source rocks. Note the shifting from west to east of sites of maximum burial and thus of petroleum generation. Location of burial history plots for wells: A, Inigok-1; B, Point Thomson Unit-1.

Timing of Hydrocarbon Generation

The time of maturation of the Ellesmerian system source rocks was governed primarily by sedimentary filling of the Colville foreland basin. The basin fill provided the sedimentary load and burial necessary to heat the source rocks. Analysis of the foreland basin development, summarized in Bird and Molenaar (1992), shows that it occurred in three stages, each with a geographically distinct depocenter (Figure 21.9). The oldest Aptian(?)–Cenomanian depocenter is located in the area of the NPRA and the Chukchi Sea. The burial history of Ellesmerian source rocks on the northeastern margin of this depocenter is shown in the burial history plot of the Inigok well (Figure 21.10a). This analysis from Magoon and Claypool (1983) shows that the onset of oil generation (time–temperature index, or TTI, = 10) occurred in the Shublik Formation in middle Cretaceous time (~100 Ma) and that maximum burial at this location occurred in middle–late Tertiary time. Further analysis and new data now suggest that maximum burial at this location occurred earlier than previously thought. The reconstructed cross section (Figure 21.3b), which is based on maturity isograds that were hand fitted to the vitrinite reflectance data and regional stratigraphic analysis, suggests that maximum burial occurred here in Late Cretaceous time, about 75 Ma, rather than in middle–late Tertiary time. By this reconstruction, the Prudhoe Bay area (and probably other parts of the Barrow arch west of Prudhoe Bay) was in an optimum position to receive and trap migrating hydrocarbons.

The second depocenter (Cenomanian–Eocene) is located in the east-central part of the North Slope, generally south of the Prudhoe Bay area (Figure 21.9). Maximum burial in this area is believed to have occurred in Eocene time, prior to the cutting of a regional unconformity (Molenaar et al., 1987). Thus, the Prudhoe area would have received an additional charge of hydrocarbons from maturing source rocks located to the south of Prudhoe Bay in Eocene time.

The third depocenter (Eocene–Pliocene) is located offshore north of the ANWR. Most of the area beneath this depocenter is believed to lack the Ellesmerian petroleum system source rocks because it lies north and east of the erosional truncation edge of the Shublik Formation and Kingak Shale by the Lower Cretaceous unconformity (Figure 21.8). The burial history of Ellesmerian source rocks on the margin of this and the previous depocenter is shown in the burial history plot of the Point Thomson Unit-1 well (Figure 21.10b). This plot, from Magoon et al. (1987), shows that the Shublik Formation and Kingak Shale are absent at this location, that the onset of oil generation (TTI = 10) occurred in the pebble shale unit in late Tertiary time (~10 Ma), and that maximum burial at this location is the present day.

Trapping and Hydrocarbon Charge

All hydrocarbon accumulations assigned to the Ellesmerian petroleum system are located in structural–stratigraphic traps along the Barrow arch (Figure 21.2 and Table 21.1). The majority of these traps formed during or immediately after the rifting event that separated the Arctic Alaska plate from its former continental connection. Many of the traps, including those for the Prudhoe Bay and Kuparuk River oil fields, were completed when the pebble shale unit (Hauterivian–Barremian) overlapped reservoir units that were exposed and partly eroded during development of the Lower Cretaceous unconformity. The youngest traps and reservoirs in the Ellesmerian system are early Tertiary in age. The trapping mechanism for these accumulations (West Sak and Ugnu, Figures 21.2 and 21.4) is poorly understood but is believed to be related to normal faulting and

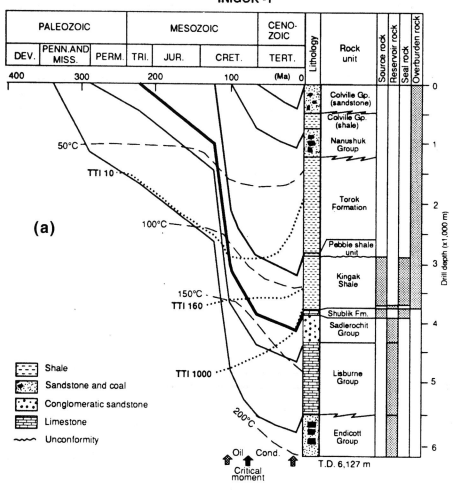

INIGOK -1

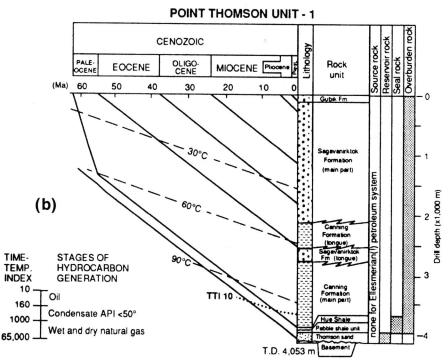

POINT THOMSON UNIT - 1

Figure 21.10. Burial history plots of selected wells illustrating the differences in stratigraphy and burial history between two locations. (a) Inigok well, on the flank of the Colville basin (adapted from Magoon and Claypool, 1983). (b) Point Thomson well, on the Barrow arch (adapted from Magoon et al., 1987). Analysis of vitrinite data and of stratigraphic relationships in Figure 21.3 suggests maximum burial at site A occurred in Late Cretaceous time, ~75 Ma. Well locations shown in Figure 21.9.

perhaps to the occurrence of permafrost (Werner, 1987). The filling of these traps is postulated to have occurred in later Tertiary time as a result of eastward tilting of the Barrow arch, resulting in the spilling of oil from the ancestral Prudhoe Bay oil field which allowed the oil to migrate updip through faults into younger reservoirs.

MASS BALANCE CALCULATIONS

The amount of hydrocarbon generated from mature and overmature Ellesmerian petroleum system source rocks was calculated from the equations of Schmoker (Chapter 19, this volume). This amount was then compared to the amount of hydrocarbons discovered to determine the efficiency of generation–migration–accumulation in the system.

The mass of total organic carbon, M, in the Kingak Shale and Shublik Formation is calculated from Schmoker's equation 1:

$$M \text{ (gTOC)}$$
$$= [\text{TOC (wt. \%)}/100] \times \rho \text{ (g/cm}^3) \times V \text{ (cm}^3) \quad (1)$$

where ρ is the average formation density and V is the volume of the unit.

The calculation is performed on each of the two source rock facies (distal and proximal) south and north, respectively, of the Colville River in the profile (Figure 21.7) because of the distinct differences in TOC and thickness. For each facies, the Kingak Shale and Shublik Formation parameters are combined in this calculation. Furthermore, it is assumed that the profile in Figure 21.7 is typical of organic richness and thickness in other parallel transects across the basin (Table 21.5). For these calculations, the lateral east-west extent was taken to be the Brooks Range mountain front on the east and $166°$W longitude in the Chukchi Sea on the west (Figure 21.8). The distal facies is estimated to have an average TOC of about 3.5 wt. %, a thickness of 160 m and an area of about 90,000 km². None of the area of palinspastic restoration is included in these calculations. The proximal facies is estimated to have an average TOC of 2.0 wt. %, an average thickness of 800 m, and an area (excluding the area of immature source rocks) of 110,000 km². Both source rock facies are estimated to have a density of 2.4.

$$M \text{ (g TOC)}_{\text{distal}}$$
$$= (3.5 \text{ wt. \%}/100) \times 2.4 \text{ g/cm}^3 \times 1.44 \times 10^{19} \text{ cm}^3$$
$$= 1.2096 \times 10^{18} \text{ g}$$

$$M \text{ (g TOC)}_{\text{proximal}}$$
$$= (2.0 \text{ wt.\%}/100) \times 2.4 \text{ g/cm}^3 \times 8.8 \times 10^{19} \text{ cm}^3$$
$$= 4.224 \times 10^{18} \text{ g}$$

$$M \text{ (g TOC)}_{\text{total}}$$
$$= (1.2096 \times 10^{18} \text{ g}) + (4.224 \times 10^{18} \text{ g})$$
$$= 5.4336 \times 10^{18} \text{ g}$$

The mass of hydrocarbons generated per unit mass of organic carbon, R (mg HC/g TOC), is determined by the difference between the present-day hydrogen index, HI_p, and the original hydrogen index, HI_o, prior to petroleum generation (Schmoker's equation 2, Chapter 19):

$$R \text{ (mg HC/g TOC)}$$
$$= HI_o \text{ (mg HC/g TOC)} - HI_p \text{ (mg HC/g TOC)} \quad (2)$$

The parameters required to determine the mass of hydrocarbons generated are obtained from Rock-Eval pyrolysis. Rock-Eval data for the Kingak Shale and Shublik Formation are limited (Magoon and Claypool, 1984, 1985; Magoon et al., 1987), and most analyses are from thermally mature rocks. Determining HI_o from available data is impossible. A fairly conservative value of 200 mg HC/g TOC was assumed in this calculation.

The total mass of hydrocarbons generated, HCG (kg HC), is obtained by multiplying the results of equations 1 and 2, and the result is converted from milligrams to kilograms by multiplying by 10^{-6}:

$$HCG \text{ (kg HC)} \quad (3)$$
$$= R \text{ (mg HC/g TOC)} \times M \text{ (g TOC)} \times 10^{-6} \text{ (kg/mg)}$$

$$HCG \text{ (kg HC)}$$
$$= 200 \times 5.4336 \times 10^{18} \text{ g} \times 10^{-6} \text{ (kg/mg)}$$
$$= 10.8672 \times 10^{14} \text{ kg HC}$$

The total mass of hydrocarbons generated is expressed in kilograms (equation 3). Converting kilograms to barrels of oil using Schmoker's Figure 19.3 yields about 8×10^{12} bbl of 30° API oil. A comparison of the 70×10^9 bbl of in-place oil and 40 tcf of gas (6.7×10^9 BOE) that has been discovered (Table 21.1) with 8×10^{12} bbl generated shows that slightly less than 1% of the generated oil and gas has been trapped. The percentage of trapped hydrocarbon would increase if the mean value estimates of undiscovered recoverable hydrocarbons as reported by Mast et al. (1989) for onshore and offshore North Slope are assumed to be entirely Ellesmerian petroleum system oil and are added to the in-place discovered hydrocarbons. The mean value of undiscovered recoverable oil is estimated to be 24.52×10^9 bbl and of gas, 83.77 tcf. Converting all to in-place oil equivalents (assuming 33% oil recovery and 80% gas recovery), the total is about 91×10^9 bbl. Combined with presently discovered in-place hydrocarbons (77×10^9 bbl), the total is 168×10^9 bbl, or about 2% of the calculated amount of hydrocarbons generated from these source rocks.

SUMMARY

The major features of the Ellesmerian(!) petroleum system are summarized in a time sequence diagram in Figure 21.11. This petroleum system, which occupies an area of about 225,000 km² beneath the Alaskan North Slope and parts of the adjacent continental shelf, is defined by the source rocks of the Barrow–Prudhoe

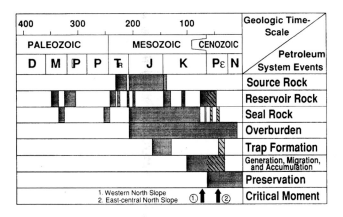

Figure 21.11. Events chart for the Ellesmerian(!) petroleum system. Hatchured pattern indicates estimated time of eastward tilting of the Barrow arch resulting in "spilling" and re-migration of earlier trapped hydrocarbons to traps in younger (early Tertiary) reservoirs. (Time scale from Palmer, 1983.)

family of oils and the accumulations of these oils. Related gas accumulations are provisionally included in the system, acknowledging an absence of data relating gas to source rocks. The Ellesmerian system as thus defined accounts for 98% of all North Slope oil and gas and includes 26 oil and gas accumulations, 5 of which are commercially productive. Reservoir rocks hosting hydrocarbons of this system range in age from Mississippian to Tertiary and record deposition in a wide range of marine to nonmarine environments in both passive margin and foreland basin settings. Included are passive margin Mississippian–Lower Cretaceous mature quartzose sandstones deposited in shallow marine and nonmarine environments and Mississippian and Pennsylvanian platform carbonate rocks. Foreland basin reservoirs are lithic-rich marine and nonmarine sandstone.

Source rocks of the Barrow–Prudhoe oils are identified on the basis of carbon isotope and molecular biomarker analysis as the Triassic Shublik Formation and Jurassic–Lower Cretaceous Kingak Shale. Burial history plots coupled with basin reconstructions show that hydrocarbons were generated from these source rocks by the sedimentary load resulting from filling of the Cretaceous–Tertiary Colville foreland basin. Because the Colville basin was filled longitudinally from west to east, hydrocarbon generation began first beneath the western part of the foreland basin in Late Cretaceous time and beneath the east-central part of the basin in early Tertiary time. Traps are mainly broad, anticlinal structures with an important element of stratigraphic truncation and sealing. These traps are located mainly along the coast, the site of a buried rift margin known as the Barrow arch.

The Ellesmerian petroleum system spans about 360 m.y., from the Mississippian to the present. The last third of this interval was the period of significant trap formation, maturation, generation, migration, and entrapment of hydrocarbons. Regional tilting in middle Tertiary time along the Barrow arch caused earlier formed oil accumulations to spill some of their oil and

gas, which then migrated into younger, stratigraphically higher reservoirs, thus expanding the limits of the system.

The amount of hydrocarbons generated by the Ellesmerian system is calculated to be about 8×10^{12} bbl of oil. Comparison of this amount with discovered hydrocarbons shows an efficiency of about 1%. When mean value estimates of undiscovered hydrocarbons are added to the discovered hydrocarbons, an efficiency of about 2% is indicated.

Acknowledgments This manuscript has benefited from the reviews of L. B. Magoon and K. W. Sherwood. Their efforts are gratefully acknowledged.

References Cited

Anders, D. E., L. B. Magoon, and S. C. Lubeck, 1987, Geochemistry of surface oil shows and potential source rocks, *in* K. J. Bird and L. B. Magoon, eds., Petroleum geology of the northern part of the Arctic National Wildlife Refuge, northeastern Alaska: USGS Bulletin 1778, p. 181–198.

Bally, A. W., and S. Snelson, 1980, Realms of subsidence, *in* A. D. Miall, ed., Facts and principles of world petroleum occurrence: Canadian Society of Petroleum Geologists, Memoir 6, p. 9–94.

Bartsch-Winkler, S., and A. C. Huffman, Jr., 1988, Sandstone petrography of the Nanushuk Group and Torok Formation, *in* G. Gryc, ed., Geology and exploration of the National Petroleum Reserve in Alaska, 1974 to 1982: USGS Professional Paper 1399, p. 801–831.

Bird, K. J., 1982, Rock-unit reports of 228 wells drilled on the North Slope, Alaska: USGS Open-File Report 82-278, 106 p.

Bird, K. J., 1985, Framework geology of the North Slope of Alaska as related to oil–source rock correlations, *in* L. B. Magoon and G. E. Claypool, eds., Alaska North Slope oil–rock correlation study—analysis of North Slope crude: AAPG Studies in Geology 20, p. 3–29.

Bird, K. J., 1987, Framework geology of the North Slope of Alaska as related to oil–source rock correlations, *in* I. Tailleur and P. Weimer, eds., Alaskan North Slope geology: Bakersfield, CA, Pacific Section SEPM, Book 50, p. 121–143.

Bird, K. J., 1991, North Slope of Alaska, *in* H. J. Gluskoter, D. D. Rice, and R. B. Taylor, eds., Economic geology, U.S.: GSA, The Geology of North America Series, v. P-2, p. 447–462.

Bird, K. J., and J. Andrews, 1979, Subsurface studies of the Nanushuk Group, North Slope, Alaska, *in* T. S. Ahlbrandt, ed., Preliminary geologic, petrologic, and paleontologic results of the study of Nanushuk Group rocks, North Slope, Alaska: USGS Circular 794, p. 32–41.

Bird, K. J., and L. B. Magoon, eds., 1987, Petroleum geology of the northern part of the Arctic National Wildlife Refuge, northeastern Alaska: USGS Bulletin 1778, 329 p.

Bird, K. J., and C. M. Molenaar, 1992, The North Slope foreland basin, Alaska, *in* R. W. Macqueen and D. A. Leckie, eds., Foreland basins and foldbelts: AAPG Memoir 55, p. 363–393.

Bird, K. J., S. B. Griscom, S. Bartsch-Winkler, and D. M. Giovannetti, 1987, Petroleum reservoir rocks, *in* K. J. Bird and L. B. Magoon, eds., Petroleum geology of the northern part of the Arctic National Wildlife Refuge, northeastern Alaska: USGS Bulletin 1778, p. 79–99.

Bodnar, D. A., 1984, Stratigraphy, age, depositional environments, and hydrocarbon source rock evaluation of the Otuk Formation, north-central Brooks Range, Alaska: Masters thesis, University of Alaska, Fairbanks, 232 p.

Bodnar, D. A., 1989, Stratigraphy of the Otuk Formation and a Cretaceous coquinoid limestone and shale unit, north-central Brooks Range, Alaska, *in* Mull, C. G. and K. E. Adams, eds., Dalton Highway, Yukon River to Prudhoe Bay, Alaska—bedrock geology of the eastern Koyukuk basin, central Brooks Range, and east-central Arctic slope: State of Alaska Division of Geological and Geophysical Surveys Guidebook 7, v. 2, p. 277–284.

Bruynzeel, J. W., E. C. Guldenzopf, and J. E. Pickard, 1982, Petroleum exploration of NPRA, 1974–1981—final report: Report 8200, Houston, Tetra Tech, 3 vols., 5 boxes of geophysical maps.

Burwood, R., G. A. Cole, R. J. Drozd, H. I. Halpern, I. E. Penfield, and R. A. Sedivy, 1985, Carbon isotopic characterization of some North Slope petroleums and potential source rock kerogen assemblages, *in* L. B. Magoon and G. E. Claypool, eds., Alaska North Slope oil–rock correlation study—analysis of North Slope crude: AAPG Studies in Geology 20, p. 123–137.

Carman, G. J., and Peter Hardwick, 1983, Geology and regional setting of the Kuparuk oil field, Alaska: AAPG Bulletin, v. 67, n. 6, p. 1014–1031.

Claypool, G. E., and Magoon, L. B., 1985, Comparison of oil–source rock correlation data for Alaskan North Slope—techniques, results, and conclusions, *in* L. B. Magoon, and G. E. Claypool, eds., Alaska North Slope oil/rock correlation study: AAPG Secial Studies in Geology 20, p. 49–81.

Collins, F. R., and F. M. Robinson, 1967, Subsurface stratigraphic, structural, and economic geology, northern Alaska: USGS Open-File Report 287, 252 p.

Craig, J. D., K. W. Sherwood, and P. P. Johnson, 1985, Geologic report for the Beaufort Sea planning area, Alaska—regional geology, petroleum geology, environmental geology: Minerals Management Service OCS Report MMS 85-0111, 192 p.

Curiale, J. A., 1987, Crude oil chemistry and classification, Alaska North Slope, *in* I. Tailleur and P. Weimer, eds., Alaskan North Slope geology: Bakersfield, CA, Pacific Section SEPM, Book 50, p. 161–167.

Deming, D., J. H. Sass, A. H. Lachenbruch, and R. F. De Rito, 1992, Heat flow and subsurface temperature as evidence for basin-scale groundwater flow, North Slope of Alaska: GSA Bulletin, v. 104, n. 5, p. 528–542.

Gautier, D. L., 1987, Petrology of Cretaceous and Tertiary reservoir sandstones in the Point Thomson area, *in* K. J. Bird and L. B. Magoon eds., Petroleum geology of the northern part of the Arctic National Wildlife Refuge, northeastern Alaska: USGS Bulletin 1778, p. 117–122.

Gaynor, G. C., and M. H. Scheihing, 1988, Shelf depositional environments and reservoir characteristics of the Kuparuk River Formation (Lower Cretaceous), Kuparuk field, North Slope, Alaska, *in* A. J. Lomando and P. M. Harris, eds., Giant oil and gas fields, a core workshop: SEPM Core Workshop 12, Tulsa, OK, p. 333–389.

Grantz, A., S. D. May, and D. A. Dinter, 1988, Geologic framework, petroleum potential, and environmental geology of the United States Beaufort and northeastern-most Chukchi Seas, *in* G. Gryc, ed., Geology and explo-

ration of the National Petroleum Reserve in Alaska, 1974 to 1982: USGS Professional Paper 1399, p. 231–255.

Grantz, A., S. D. May, and P. E. Hart, 1990, Geology of the arctic continental margin of Alaska, *in* A. Grantz, L. Johnson, and J. F. Sweeney, eds., The Arctic Ocean region: GSA, The Geology of North America Series, v. L, p. 257–288.

Gryc, G., ed., 1988. Geology and exploration of the National Petroleum Reserve in Alaska, 1974 to 1982: USGS Professional Paper 1399, 940 p.

Harris, M., 1987, Endicott benefits from lessons learned: Alaska Construction & Oil, October, p. 15–16.

Harris, M., 1988, Beaufort causeways: Alaska Construction, v. 29, n. 12, p. 12–16.

Harris, A. G., H. R. Lane, I. L. Tailleur, and I. Ellersieck, 1987, Conodont thermal maturation patterns in Paleozoic and Triassic rocks, northern Alaska—geologic and exploration implications, *in* I. Tailleur and P. Weimer, eds., Alaskan North Slope geology: Bakersfield, CA, Pacific Section SEPM, Book 50, p. 181–191.

Howell, D. G., K. J. Bird, Lu Huafu, and M. J. Johnsson, 1992, Tectonics and petroleum potential of the Brooks Range fold and thrust belt—a progress report, *in* D. C. Bradley and A. B. Ford, eds., Geologic studies in Alaska by the USGS during 1990: USGS Bulletin 1999, p. 112–126.

Hubbard, R. J., S. P. Edrich, and R. P. Rattey, 1987, Geologic evolution and hydrocarbon habitat of the "Arctic Alaska microplate," *in* I. Tailleur and P. Weimer, eds., Alaskan North Slope geology: Bakersfield, CA, Pacific Section SEPM, Book 50, p. 797–830.

Jamison, H. C., L. D. Brockett, and R. A. McIntosh, 1980, Prudhoe Bay—a 10-year perspective, *in* M. T. Halbouty, ed., Giant oil fields of the decade 1968–1978: AAPG Memoir 30, p. 289–314.

Johnsson, M. J., M. J. Pawlewicz, A. G. Harris, and Z. C. Valin, 1992, Vitrinite reflectance and conodont color alteration index data from Alaska: data to accompany the thermal maturity map of Alaska: USGS Open-File Report 92-409, 3 computer disks.

Johnsson, M. J., D. G. Howell, and K. J. Bird, 1993, Thermal maturity patterns in Alaska—implications to tectonic evolution and hydrocarbon potential: AAPG Bulletin, v. 77, n. 11, p. 1874–1903.

Jones, H. P., and R. G. Speers, 1976, Permo-Triassic reservoirs of Prudhoe Bay field, North Slope, Alaska, *in* J. Braunstein, ed., North American oil and gas fields: AAPG Memoir 24, p. 23–50.

Lantz, R. J., 1981, Barrow gas fields—North Slope, Alaska: Oil and Gas Journal, v. 79, n. 13, p. 197–200.

Magoon, L. B., 1989, Identified petroleum systems within the United States—1990, *in* L. B. Magoon, ed., The petroleum system—status of research and methods, 1990: USGS Bulletin 1912, p. 2–9.

Magoon, L. B., in press, The geology of known oil and gas resources by petroleum system–onshore Alaska, *in* G. Plafker, D. L. Jones, and H. C. Berg, eds., The Cordilleran orogen: Alaska: GSA, The Geology of North America Series, v. G-1.

Magoon, L. B., and K. J. Bird, 1985, Alaskan North Slope petroleum geochemistry for the Shublik Formation, Kingak Shale, pebble shale unit, and Torok Formation, *in* L. B. Magoon and G. E. Claypool, eds., Alaska North Slope oil–rock correlation study—analysis of North Slope crude: AAPG Studies in Geology 20, p. 31–48.

Magoon, L. B., and K. J. Bird, 1987, Alaskan North Slope petroleum geochemistry for the Shublik Formation, Kingak Shale, pebble shale unit, and Torok Formation, *in* I.

Tailleur and P. Weimer, eds., Alaskan North Slope Geology: Bakersfield, CA, Pacific Section SEPM, v. 1, p. 145–160.

Magoon, L. B., and K. J. Bird, 1988, Evaluation of petroleum source rocks in the National Petroleum Reserve in Alaska, using organic-carbon content, hydrocarbon content, visual kerogen, and vitrinite reflectance, *in* G. Gryc, ed., Geology and exploration of the National Petroleum Reserve in Alaska, 1974 to 1982: USGS Professional Paper 1399, p. 381–450.

Magoon, L. B., and G. E. Claypool, 1981, Two oil types on North Slope of Alaska—implications for exploration: AAPG Bulletin, v. 65, n. 4, p. 644–652.

Magoon, L. B., and G. E. Claypool, 1983, Petroleum geochemistry of the North Slope of Alaska—time and degree of thermal maturity, *in* M. Byorøy et al., eds., Advances in Organic Geochemistry 1981: Chichester, U.K., Wiley Heyden, p. 28–38.

Magoon, L. B., and G. E. Claypool, 1984, The Kingak Shale of northern Alaska—regional variations in organic geochemical properties and petroleum source rock quality: Organic Geochemistry, v. 6, p. 533–542.

Magoon, L. B., and G. E. Claypool, eds., 1985, Alaska North Slope oil–rock correlation study: AAPG Studies in Geology 20, 682 p.

Magoon, L. B., and G. E. Claypool, 1988, Geochemistry of oil occurrences, National Petroleum Reserve in Alaska, *in* G. Gryc, ed., Geology and exploration of the National Petroleum Reserve in Alaska, 1974 to 1982: USGS Professional Paper 1399, p. 519–549.

Magoon, L. B., P. V. Woodward, A. C. Banet, S. B. Griscom, and T. Daws, 1987, Thermal maturity, richness, and type of organic matter of source rocks, *in* K. J. Bird and L. B. Magoon, eds., Petroleum geology of the northern part of the Arctic National Wildlife Refuge, northeastern Alaska: USGS Bulletin 1778, p. 127–179.

Mast, R. F., G. L. Dolton, R. A. Crovelli, D. H. Root, E. D. Attanasi, P. E. Martin, L. W. Cooke, G. B., Carpenter, W. C. Pecora, and M. B. Rose, 1989, Estimates of undiscovered conventional oil and gas resources in the United States—a part of the nation's energy endowment: U.S. Department of the Interior, 44 p.

Mayfield, C. F., I. L. Tailleur, and I. Ellersieck, 1988a, Stratigraphy, structure, and palinspastic synthesis of the western Brooks Range, northwestern Alaska, *in* G. Gryc, ed., Geology and exploration of the National Petroleum Reserve in Alaska, 1974 to 1982: USGS Professional Paper 1399, p. 143–186.

Mayfield, C. F., I. L. Tailleur, and C. E. Kirschner, 1988b, Bedrock geologic map of the National Petroleum Reserve in Alaska, *in* G. Gryc, ed., Geology and exploration of the National Petroleum Reserve in Alaska, 1974 to 1982: USGS Professional Paper 1399, p. 187–190, 2 sheets, 1:500,000 scale.

McKinney, C. M., E. L. Garton, and F. G. Schwartz, 1959, Analyses of some crude oils from Alaska: U.S. Bureau of Mines Report of Investigations 5447, 19 p.

Melvin, J., and A. S. Knight, 1984, Lithofacies, diagenesis and porosity of the Ivishak Formation, Prudhoe Bay area, Alaska, *in* D. A. McDonald and R. C. Surdam, eds., Clastic diagenesis: AAPG Memoir 37, p. 347–365.

Miller, E. L., and T. L. Hudson, 1991, Mid-Cretaceous extensional fragmentation of a Jurassic–Early Cretaceous compressional orogen, Alaska: Tectonics, v. 10, p. 781–796.

Minerals Management Service, 1988, Alaska update—January 1987–August 1988: Minerals Management Service OCS Report MMS 88-0073, 44 p.

Missman, R. A., and J. Jameson, 1991, An evolving description of a fractured carbonate reservoir: the Lisburne field, Prudhoe Bay, Alaska: Society of Petroleum Engineers, Arctic Technology Conference, Anchorage, Alaska, Paper SPE 22161, p. 699–718.

Molenaar, C. M., 1982, Umiat field, an oil accumulation in a thrust-faulted anticline, North Slope, Alaska, *in* R. B. Powers, ed., Geologic studies of the Cordilleran thrust belt: Denver, Rocky Mountain Association of Geologists, p. 537–548.

Molenaar, C. M., 1988, Depositional history and seismic stratigraphy of Lower Cretaceous rocks in the National Petroleum Reserve in Alaska and adjacent areas, *in* G. Gryc, ed., Geology and exploration of the National Petroleum Reserve in Alaska, 1974 to 1982: USGS Professional Paper 1399, p. 593–621.

Molenaar, C. M., K. J. Bird, and T. S. Collett, 1986, Regional correlation sections across the North Slope of Alaska: USGS Miscellaneous Field Studies Map MF-1907.

Molenaar, C. M., K. J. Bird, and A. R. Kirk, 1987, Cretaceous and Tertiary stratigraphy of northeastern Alaska, *in* I. Tailleur and P. Weimer, eds., Alaskan North Slope Geology: Bakersfield, CA, Pacific Section SEPM, Book 50, v. 1, p. 513–528.

Molenaar, C. M., R. M. Egbert, and L. F. Krystinik, 1988, Depositional facies, petrography, and reservoir potential of the Fortress Mountain Formation (Lower Cretaceous), Central North Slope, Alaska, *in* G. Gryc, ed.,Geology and exploration of the National Petroleum Reserve in Alaska, 1974 to 1982: USGS Professional Paper 1399, p. 257–280.

Moore, T. E., W. K. Wallace, K. J. Bird, S. M. Karl, G. G. Mull, and J. T. Dillon, 1992, Stratigraphy, structure, and geologic synthesis of northern Alaska: USGS Open-File Report 92–330, 183 p.

Morgridge, D. L., and W. B. Smith, 1972, Geology and discovery of Prudhoe Bay field, eastern Arctic Slope, *in* R. E. King, ed., Stratigraphic oil and gas fields: AAPG Memoir 16, p. 489–501.

Mull, C. G., and K. E. Adams, eds., 1989, Dalton Highway, Yukon River to Prudhoe Bay, Alaska—Bedrock geology of the eastern Koyukuk basin, central Brooks Range, and east-central Arctic slope: State of Alaska Division of Geological and Geophysical Surveys Guidebook 7, 2 volumes, 309 p.

Mull, C. G., K. E. Adams, and J. T. Dillon, 1989, Stratigraphy and structure of the Doonerak Fenster and Endicott Mountains allochthon, central Brooks Range, *in* C. G. Mull and K. E. Adams, eds., Dalton Highway, Yukon River to Prudhoe Bay, Alaska—Bedrock geology of the eastern Koyukuk basin, central Brooks Range, and eastcentral Arctic Slope: State of Alaska Division of Geological and Geophysical Surveys Guidebook 7, v. 2, p. 203–217.

Noonan, W. G. 1987, Post-Ellesmerian depositional sequences of the North Slope subsurface, *in* I. Tailleur and P. Weimer, eds., Alaskan North Slope geology: Bakersfield, CA, Pacific Section SEPM, Book 50, v. 1, p. 459–477.

Norris, D. K., 1984, Geology of the northern Yukon and northwestern District of Mackenzie: Geological Survey of Canada Map 1581A, scale 1:500,000.

Oil and Gas Journal, 1984, Exxon: N. Slope gas/condensate field is a giant: Oil and Gas Journal, v. 82, n. 11, p. 30.

Palmer, A. R., 1983, The decade of North American geology, 1983 geologic time scale: Geology, v. 11, p. 503–504.

Parrish, J. T., 1987, Lithology, geochemistry, and depositional environment of the Triassic Shublik Formation, northern Alaska, *in* I. Tailleur and P. Weimer, eds., Alaskan North Slope geology: Bakersfield, CA, Pacific Section SEPM, Book 50, v. 1 p. 391–396.

Petroleum Information Corporation, 1989, Consortium seeks extension of Beaufort Sea leases: Alaska Report, v. 35, n. 42, p. 1.

Petroleum Information Corporation, 1992, Arco tests discovery in eastern Beaufort Sea: Alaska Report, v. 38, n. 42, p. 1–3.

Plafker, G., 1990, Regional geology and tectonic evolution of Alaska and adjacent parts of the northeast Pacific Ocean margin: Proceedings of the Pacific Rim Congress 90, Australian Institute of Mining and Metalurgy, Queensland, Australia, p. 841–853.

Poulton, T. P., 1982, Paleogeographic and tectonic implications of the Lower and Middle Jurassic facies patterns in northern Yukon Territory and adjacent Northwest Territories, *in* A. F. Embry and H. R. Balkwill, eds., Arctic geology and geophysics: Canadian Society of Petroleum Geologists Memoir 8, p. 13–27.

Reed, J. C., 1958, Exploration of Naval Petroleum Reserve No. 4 and adjacent areas, northern Alaska, 1944–53; part 1, history of the exploration: USGS Professional Paper 301, 192 p

Sedivy, R. A., I. E. Penfield, H. I. Halpern, R. J. Drozd, G. A. Cole, and R. Burwood, 1987, Investigation of source rock–crude oil relationships in the northern Alaska hydrocarbon habitat, *in* I. Tailleur and P. Weimer, eds., Alaskan North Slope geology: Bakersfield, CA, Pacific Section SEPM, Book 50, p. 169–179.

Seifert, W. K., J. M. Moldowan, and R. W. Jones, 1980, Application of biological marker chemistry to petroleum exploration: Proceedings of the 10th World Petroleum Congress, Bucharest, p. 425–440.

Siok, J. P., 1989, Stratigraphy and petrology of the Okpikruak Formation at Cobblestone Creek, northcentral Brooks Range, *in* C. G. Mull and K. E. Adam, eds., Dalton Highway, Yukon River to Prudhoe Bay, Alaska—Bedrock geology of the eastern Koyukuk basin, central Brooks Range, and east-central Arctic Slope: State of Alaska Division of Geological and Geophysical Surveys Guidebook 7, v. 2, p. 285–292.

State of Alaska, 1977, Prudhoe Bay Unit operating plan: Anchorage, Oil and Gas Conservation Commission, May 5, Conservation Hearing No. 145, Exhibit No. 8.

State of Alaska, 1984, Lisburne field rules: Anchorage, Oil and Gas Conservation Commission, Proceedings of the November 29 Public Hearing, 86 p.

State of Alaska, 1985, 1984 Statistical Report: Anchorage, Oil and Gas Conservation Commission, 177 p.

State of Alaska, 1991, 1985–1990 Statistical Report: Anchorage, Oil and Gas Conservation Commission, 171 p.

Tailleur, I., and P. Weimer, eds., 1987, Alaskan North Slope geology: Bakersfield, CA, Pacific Section SEPM, Book 50, 874 p.

Thurston, D. K., and L. A. Theiss, 1987, Geologic report for the Chukchi Sea planning area, Alaska: Minerals Management Service OCS Report MMS 87-0046, 193 p.

van de Kamp, P. C., 1988, Stratigraphy and diagenetic alteration of Ellesmerian sequence siliciclastic rocks, North Slope, Alaska, *in* G. Gryc, ed., Geology and exploration of the National Petroleum Reserve in Alaska, 1974 to 1982: USGS Professional Paper 1399, p. 833–854.

van Dyke, W. D., 1980, Proven and Probable Oil and Gas Reserves, North Slope, Alaska: Anchorage, State of Alaska Department of Natural Resources, Division of Minerals and Energy Management, 11 p.

van Poollen, H. K., and Associates, Inc., 1978, In-place hydrocarbons determination Kuparuk River Formation Prudhoe Bay area, Alaska: Anchorage, State of Alaska Department of Natural Resources, Division of Oil and Gas, 13 p.

Werner, M. R., 1987, West Sak and Ugnu sands; low-gravity oil zones of the Kuparuk River area, Alaskan North Slope, *in* I. Tailleur and P. Weimer, eds., Alaskan North Slope geology: Bakersfield, CA, Pacific Section SEPM, Book 50, p. 109–118.

Williams, B., 1989, Alaska tax hikes cloud latest giant's prospects: Oil and Gas Journal, v. 87, n. 33, p. 26.

Witmer, R. J., H. Haga, and M. B. Mickey, 1981, Biostratigraphic report of thirty-three wells drilled from 1975 to 1981 in National Petroleum Reserve in Alaska: USGS Open-File Report 81-1166, 47 p.

Woidneck, K., P. Behrman, C. Soule, and J. Wu, 1987, Reservoir description of the Endicott field, North Slope, Alaska, *in* I. Tailleur and P. Weimer, eds., Alaskan North Slope geology: Bakersfield, CA, Pacific Section SEPM, Book 50, p. 43–59.

Magoon, L. B, and W. G. Dow, eds., 1994, The petroleum
system—from source to trap: AAPG Memoir 60.

Chapter 22

Tuxedni–Hemlock(!) Petroleum System in Cook Inlet, Alaska, U.S.A.

Leslie B. Magoon

Branch of Petroleum Geology
U.S. Geological Survey
Menlo Park, California, U.S.A.

Abstract

The Tuxedni-Hemlock(!) petroleum system, situated in the Cook Inlet area in southern Alaska, originally contained discovered recoverable hydrocarbons of about 1.18 billion bbl of oil and 2.48 trillion ft^3 of gas. This system, which covers 2200 km^2, encompasses six commercial oil fields in the Cook Inlet area. Sedimentary rocks of the system, which range in age from Middle Jurassic to Holocene, were deposited in volcanic forearc and backarc basins adjacent to a convergent margin. Carbon isotope and biological marker data indicate that the low sulfur, 28°–42° API gravity oil originated from the source rock in the Middle Jurassic Tuxedni Group. Burial and thermal history reconstructions indicate that the oil was generated and migrated from below the Cenozoic depocenter between the Middle Ground Shoal and Swanson River oil fields during Cenozoic time. Here, the overburden rock is 9.8 km thick and ranges in age from Late Jurassic to Holocene. The principal reservoir rock is the Hemlock Conglomerate of Oligocene age. Traps are anticlines that are commonly faulted and sealed by siltstone; these traps, which are still evolving, started to form during late Cenozoic time.

The essential elements of the petroleum system (source, reservoir, seal, and overburden rocks) were deposited from Middle Jurassic (~170 Ma) to the present. The petroleum system processes (generation–migration–accumulation and trap formation) began in the Paleocene (~63 Ma) and continue to the present.

The quantity of hydrocarbons generated by the Middle Jurassic source rock was calculated and compared to the estimated in-place petroleum to determine the generation–accumulation efficiency of the petroleum system. On the basis of the average organic carbon content (1.7 wt. %), the difference between the original and present-day hydrogen indices (200 mg H/g OC), and the volume of mature source rock (1.5×10^{18} cm^3), 134×10^{11} kg hydrocarbons were generated. In-place hydrocarbons are estimated at 5.3×10^{11} kg. On the basis of these calculations, 4% of the hydrocarbons generated actually accumulated in discovered traps.

INTRODUCTION

The Cook Inlet area in southern Alaska contains commercial oil and natural gas accumulations. Geographically, the area lies between the Alaska–Aleutian Range and Talkeetna Mountains on the northwest and the Kenai Peninsula–Kenai Mountains on the southeast (Figure 22.1). Geologically, the area has been part of a convergent margin since Jurassic time and includes plutonic and volcanic rocks, Middle Jurassic–Cretaceous marine sedimentary rocks, and Cenozoic nonmarine sedimentary rocks.

Almost 60 years of petroleum exploration preceded the discovery in 1957 of the first commercial oil field

(Swanson River) in the Cook Inlet area. This exploration started on the Iniskin Peninsula in 1902, where seven wells were drilled. Between 1921 and 1957, only nine exploratory wells were drilled before the Swanson River oil field was discovered (Parkinson, 1962). By the end of 1987, almost 1.1 billion bbl of oil and 5.3 trillion ft^3 of gas were produced from 6 oil and 14 gas fields (Magoon and Kirschner, 1990).

The history of petroleum exploration and geology in this area has been discussed by many workers (Kelly, 1963, 1968; Detterman and Hartsock, 1966; Crick, 1971; Blasko et al., 1972; Kirschner and Lyon, 1973; MacKevett and Plafker, 1974; Blasko 1974, 1976; Boss et al., 1976; Hite, 1976, Magoon et al., 1976; Fisher and Magoon, 1978;

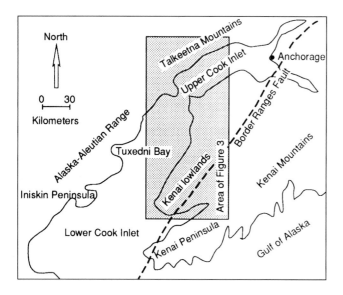

Figure 22.1. Index map of the Cook Inlet area.

Claypool et al., 1980; Magoon et al., 1980; Magoon and Claypool, 1981; Reed et al., 1983; Claypool, 1986; Magoon, 1986; Magoon and Egbert, 1986; Magoon and Anders, 1990, 1992; Magoon and Kirschner, 1990).

Previous work on the origin of the Cook Inlet oil was by Kelly (1963), Osmont et al. (1967), Young et al. (1977), Magoon and Claypool (1981), and Magoon and Anders (1990, 1992). Various theories for the origin of oil in this area have been proposed, the most common of which are that the oil originated (1) from the Tertiary nonmarine rocks, (2) from the Tertiary marine rocks suspected to be present in the center of the basin, or (3) from the marine Jurassic or Cretaceous rocks.

Kelly (1963) indicated on the basis of geologic evidence that oil found in Jurassic rocks on the Iniskin Peninsula in the Cook Inlet is indigenous (migration distance is very short). However, he also considered the oil in the Swanson River oil field to be indigenous to the basal Tertiary rocks or Upper Cretaceous strata. Osmont et al. (1967) preferred the interpretation that the Jurassic rocks are the source of the oil for several reasons. Oil seeps from an exposure of Jurassic rocks on the Iniskin Peninsula are compositionally similar to oil produced from Tertiary reservoirs, and concentrations of several trace elements in both oils correspond closely. Young et al. (1977) used variations in C_5–C_7 and C_{15+} hydrocarbon composition to calculate the age of oils. Cook Inlet oils from Tertiary reservoir rocks were calculated to have the same age as the reservoir rocks, suggesting that the hydrocarbons are from a Tertiary source rock.

On the basis of U.S. Bureau of Mines Hempel distillation analyses (Blasko et al., 1972), all oils from Tertiary reservoirs here are found to be similar (Magoon and Claypool, 1981). Gas chromatograms of C_{15+} hydrocarbons from rocks of the Middle Jurassic Tuxedni Group and of oils from Tertiary reservoirs were judged similar enough to indicate a reasonable oil–source rock pair (Magoon and Claypool, 1981). For commercial oil in upper Cook Inlet, this conclusion was confirmed by Magoon and Anders (1990, 1992) using carbon isotopic

and biological marker information. However, for oils recovered on drill-stem tests in lower Cook Inlet, these analyses suggest that both the Upper Triassic and Middle Jurassic are the source rocks.

Nonassociated natural gas deposits are found in shallower, younger reservoir rocks (Figures 22.2 and 22.3) and are responsible for most Cook Inlet natural gas production (Magoon and Kirschner, 1990). On the basis of association, Kelly (1968) suggested that the gas originated from the Tertiary coals. On the basis of carbon isotopic data, Claypool et al. (1980) determined the origin of this gas as biogenic. In some cases, liquids are associated with these gas accumulations. Carbon isotopic information on both the associated liquids and rock extracts from Tertiary coals indicates that they are very similar (Magoon and Anders, 1992).

Three petroleum systems, two oil and one natural gas, are identified in the Cook Inlet area (Magoon, 1989; Magoon and Anders, 1992). Commercial biogenic gas from the Neogene rocks constitutes the Beluga–Sterling(!) system. Only one oil system, the Tuxedni–Hemlock(!), is commercial. The noncommercial petroleum system, the Tuxedni–Kaguyak(!), is located in lower Cook Inlet.

This chapter is a case study of the Tuxedni–Hemlock petroleum system and includes (1) a brief description of the sedimentary basin setting, (2) the basis on which this system is identified, and (3) an estimate of the generation–accumulation efficiency of this system.

SEDIMENTARY BASIN SETTING

The tectonic evolution of the Cook Inlet area is complex because it is part of the northern Pacific margin, which has been the site of continuous convergence throughout the Mesozoic and Cenozoic (Coney and Jones, 1985). The Cook Inlet area is bounded on the northwest by granitic batholiths that make up the Alaska–Aleutian Range and by the Talkeetna Mountains, and on the southeast by the Chugach terrane that makes up the Kenai Mountains. The stratigraphy between the batholiths and the Chugach terrane consists of Jurassic and Lower Cretaceous rocks, which are included in the Peninsular terrane (Silberling et al., in press), and the Upper Cretaceous and Cenozoic rocks that compose a postamalgamation overlap sequence (Figure 22.2).

Structural Setting

The Cook Inlet area has evolved from a backarc basin during the Jurassic to a forearc basin in the Cenozoic. On the basis of chemical variations and polarity in Jurassic plutons (Reed et al., 1983) and the presence of a basin floored by continental or intermediate crust associated with a B-subduction zone (Bally and Snelson, 1980), it is interpreted that the Cook Inlet area was a backarc basin during Jurassic time. A reversal of the subduction polarity accompanied the Cenozoic forearc basin, also associated with the B-subduction (Kirschner and Lyon, 1973; Seely and Dickinson, 1977; Bally and Snelson, 1980).

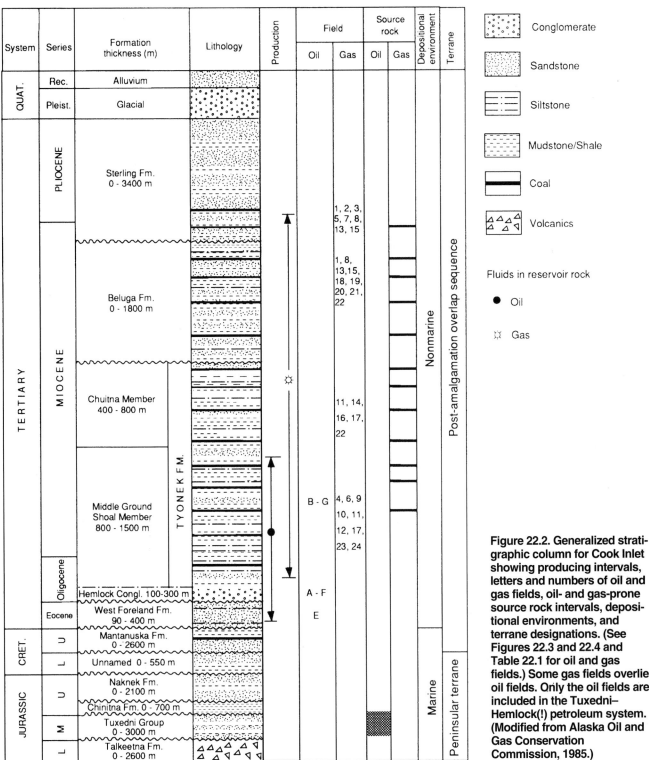

Figure 22.2. Generalized stratigraphic column for Cook Inlet showing producing intervals, letters and numbers of oil and gas fields, oil- and gas-prone source rock intervals, depositional environments, and terrane designations. (See Figures 22.3 and 22.4 and Table 22.1 for oil and gas fields.) Some gas fields overlie oil fields. Only the oil fields are included in the Tuxedni–Hemlock(!) petroleum system. (Modified from Alaska Oil and Gas Conservation Commission, 1985.)

Cross section A–A′ in Figure 22.4 (based on the work of Boss et al., 1976, and Plafker et al., 1982) shows the generalized structural style and rock units in the Cook Inlet area. Numerous high-angle reverse faults indicate considerable compression throughout the Mesozoic and Cenozoic with only minor normal faults near Swanson River field. Except for the deepest part of the basin, well information controls the thickness of the Cenozoic rocks. Except for a few well penetrations, the configuration of the pre-Cenozoic rocks is based on inference and geophysical information. The top of the oil and gas windows is based on publicly available vitrinite reflectance data (Geologic Materials Center, Eagle, Alaska).

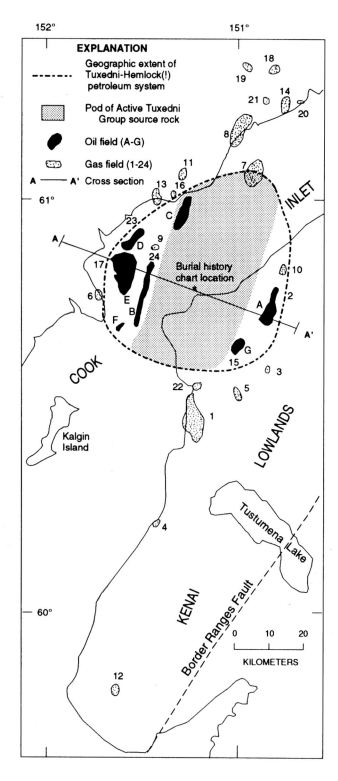

Figure 22.3. Cook Inlet oil and gas fields, and location of cross section A–A' in Figure 22.4. Letters refer to oil fields in Table 22.1 and Figure 22.2, and numbers to gas fields in Figure 22.2. Dashed line represents the geographic extent of the Tuxedni–Hemlock(!) petroleum system. (Modified from Alaska Oil and Gas Conservation Commission, 1985.)

Stratigraphic Section

In the Cook Inlet area, the pre-Upper Cretaceous sequence and correlative plutonic rocks of the Alaska–Aleutian Range batholith constitute the Peninsular terrane (Silberling et al., 1994). The Border Ranges fault separates this terrane from the accreted Chugach terrane on the southeast. The Chugach terrane is composed of highly deformed sedimentary rocks without petroleum potential. Detailed descriptions of rock units in this area are in Detterman and Hartsock (1966) and Magoon and Egbert (1986).

The Lower Jurassic Talkeetna Formation, a volcaniclastic sequence, and the Alaska–Aleutian batholith are economic basement for this petroleum province (Figures 22.2 and 22.4). The Tuxedni Group is a dark gray, clay-rich siltstone of Middle Jurassic age and is important because it contains the petroleum source rock for the commercial oil in the area (Magoon and Anders, 1990, 1992). The Upper Jurassic Naknek Formation contains a high percentage of feldspathic sandstone and conglomerate, but because of laumontite cementation, it is a poor reservoir (Franks and Hite, 1980; Bolm and McCulloh, 1986). The Lower Cretaceous *Inoceramus*-rich sandstone and siltstone were deposited on a broad, shallow marine shelf.

An unconformity separates the Lower Cretaceous rocks from the Upper Cretaceous rocks. The Matanuska and Kaguyak Formations of Late Cretaceous age contain little organic matter but do contain sandstone that, in places, is a reservoir. These rocks change rapidly from fluvial facies to deep water turbidite fan facies that formed in a forearc sedimentary basin (Fisher and Magoon, 1978; Magoon et al., 1980). The Peninsular terrane units and Upper Cretaceous rocks were deposited in a coastal to deep marine environment and unconformably underlie the petroleum-bearing Cenozoic rocks (Figure 22.2).

The Cenozoic rocks in the Cook Inlet area overlap the Alaska–Aleutian batholith on the northwest and the Border Ranges fault on the southeast. Calderwood and Fackler (1972) defined and named the critical Cenozoic units—West Foreland Formation, Hemlock Conglomerate, Tyonek Formation, Beluga Formation, and Sterling Formation—that are regionally correlated (Alaska Geological Society, 1969a–d, 1970a,b) and mapped (Hartman et al., 1972). These rock units were deposited in a nonmarine forearc basin setting. The West Foreland Formation consists of tuffaceous conglomerates to siltstones with a minor amount of coal. The Hemlock Conglomerate consists of conglomeratic sandstone, and the Tyonek, Beluga, and Sterling formations consist of varying amounts of sandstone, siltstone, shale, and coal. The provenance for the conglomerate, sandstone, siltstone, shale, and volcaniclastic debris was local highs flanking the basin as well as more distal sources in interior Alaska. Each of these rock units is a reservoir for oil or gas somewhere in the basin.

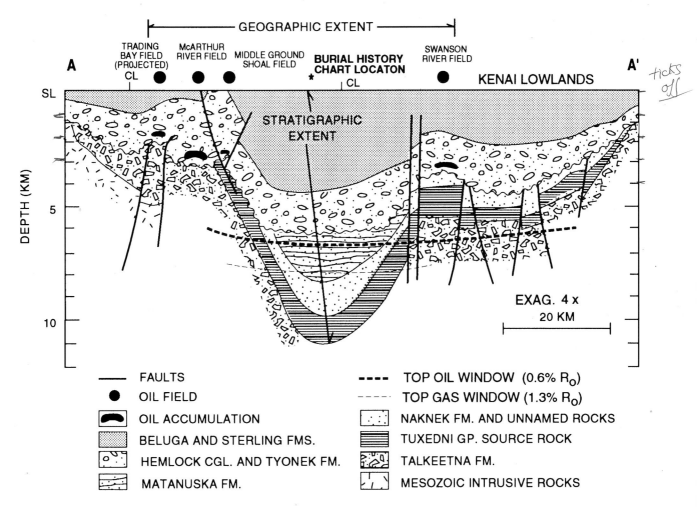

Figure 22.4. Cross section A–A' of Cook Inlet showing the geographic (horizontal) and stratigraphic (vertical) extent of the Tuxedni–Hemlock(!) petroleum system. The critical moment for this petroleum system is present day. (See Figure 22.3 for location of section.) Abbreviations: SL, sea level; CL, coast line. (Modified from Boss et al., 1976; Plafker et al., 1982.)

THE PETROLEUM SYSTEM

A petroleum system investigation requires that a series of hydrocarbon accumulations be attributed to a pod of mature source rock. To more clearly understand the system, the relationship between the petroleum system events and processes are described and shown relative to the geologic time scale in Figure 22.5.

Petroleum Source Rock

The Middle Jurassic Tuxedni Group (187–163 Ma) is the source rock for the commercial oil in the Cook Inlet area. The Tuxedni Group underlies much of the Cook Inlet area east of the Middle Ground Shoal oil field and subcrops beneath the Cenozoic rocks east of the Swanson River oil field (Figure 22.4). In outcrops between Tuxedni Bay and the Iniskin Peninsula, the Tuxedni Group is over 1687 m thick (Detterman and Hartsock, 1966), and at the south end of the Swanson River field, the Soldatna 33-33 well penetrated 997 m of Middle Jurassic rocks. Based on this information and the regional setting (Plafker et al., 1982), the Middle Jurassic is estimated to be 1 km thick in the deepest part of the basin, between the McArthur River and Swanson River fields.

The amount and type of organic matter from the Middle Jurassic rock samples indicate a marginal oil source rock (Magoon and Anders, 1992). Total organic carbon (TOC) content and hydrogen indices (HI) are available for the Middle Jurassic rocks from two wells: four immature samples from the Soldatna 33-33 well and three mature samples from the Beal 1 well on the Iniskin Peninsula. TOC content for the immature samples ranges from 0.8 to 2.1 wt. %, averaging 1.7 wt. %, and for the mature samples from 0.9 to 1.1 wt. %, averaging 0.9 wt. %. Rock-Eval pyrolysis data show that the HI for the four immature Soldatna 33-33 samples averages 296 and for the three mature Beal 1 samples averages 134 (Figure 22.6).

Where measured, the thermal maturity of this Middle Jurassic source rock ranges from immature to mature, and based on a burial diagram, is postmature in the deepest part of the basin (Figures 22.4 and 22.7). The Middle Jurassic rocks in the Soldatna 33-33 are immature, with a Rock-Eval pyrolysis T_{max} of <435°C and a vitrinite reflectance value of <0.6% R_o, whereas the uplifted Middle Jurassic rocks penetrated in the Beal 1 well and the nearby Zappa 1 well are mature, with a T_{max} of >440°C and a reflectance value >0.6% R_o.

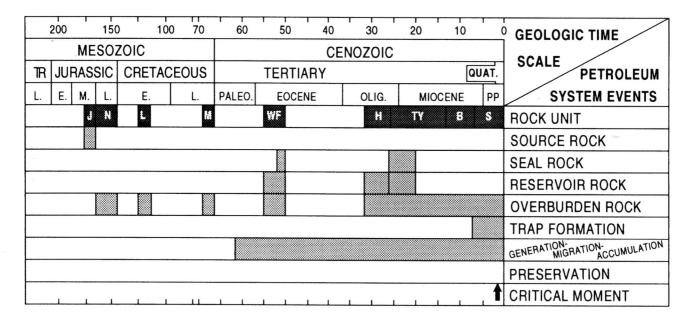

Figure 22.5. The events chart for the Tuxedni–Hemlock(!) petroleum system. The geologic time scale is after Palmer (1983) and it changes scale at 70 Ma. Abbreviations: J, Tuxedni Group; N, Naknek Formation; L, Unnamed rocks; M, Matanuska Formation; WF, West Foreland Formation; H, Hemlock Conglomerate; Ty, Tyonek Formation; B, Beluga Formation; S, Sterling Formation and Quaternary deposits; PP, Pliocene and Pleistocene (includes Holocene).

The burial history chart is constructed for the area where the system's source rock is the most deeply buried to determine the time and depth that the petroleum was generated. It is assumed that migration and accumulation of the petroleum immediately follows hydrocarbon generation. Figure 22.7 was constructed using the computer program BasinMod (Platte River Assoc.) with the following assumptions: (1) the geothermal gradient has always been 20°C/km or near the present-day gradient, (2) depth and thickness information for the overburden rock (Figure 22.5) from Plafker et al. (1982) is correct, (3) 0.6% R_o is presently at 6.5 km and 1.3% R_o is presently at 8 km, and (4) the Middle Jurassic Tuxedni Group is the source rock for the commercial oil in the area. Based on these assumptions, a time–temperature index (TTI) of 10 (top oil window) was achieved for the Paleocene (63 Ma) and a TTI of 180 (top gas window) was achieved for the late Miocene (10 Ma).

Reservoir Rocks and Accumulations

Approximately 80% of the recoverable oil is contained in the Hemlock Conglomerate, 20% in the Middle Ground Shoal member (Debelius, 1974) of the Tyonek Formation, and minor amounts in the West Foreland Formation (Figure 22.5). The Hemlock is a conglomeratic sandstone of Oligocene age (37–24 Ma) (Magoon et al., 1976; Wolfe, 1981). Of the six oil fields, the McArthur River field is the largest, with original reserves of almost 570 million bbl of oil, of which almost 500 million bbl are from the Hemlock Conglomerate (Table 22.1).

The seal rocks for these accumulations are presumed to be the siltstone within the West Foreland and Tyonek Formations, and underclays associated with coals within the Tyonek Formation (Figure 22.5).

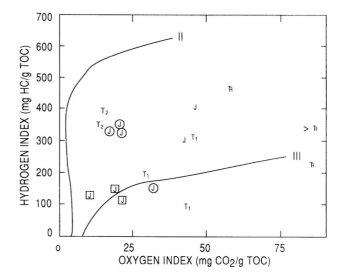

Figure 22.6. Rock-Eval pyrolysis and total organic carbon data plotted on a modified van Krevelen diagram to show kerogen type. Symbols: T_1, Tyonek Formation; T_2, West Foreland Formation; J (in circle), immature Tuxedni Group rocks from Soldatna 33-33 well; J (in square), thermally mature Tuxedni Group rocks from Beal 1 well; J, thermally mature Middle Jurassic at Puale Bay; Tr, Upper Triassic at Puale Bay. (From Magoon and Anders, 1992.)

A typical oil pool in this petroleum system is located in a faulted anticline at an average drill depth of 2560 m (range 765–4500 m). The pool covers 1000 ha (195–5000 ha) and has a net pay of 90 m (21–300 m). The reservoir rock is a conglomeratic sandstone with an average porosity of 17% (12–22%), an average permeability of 80 md (10–360 md), a reservoir pressure of 29,650 kPa (14,045–52,071 kPa), and a temperature of 72°C (44–102°C). The typical oil

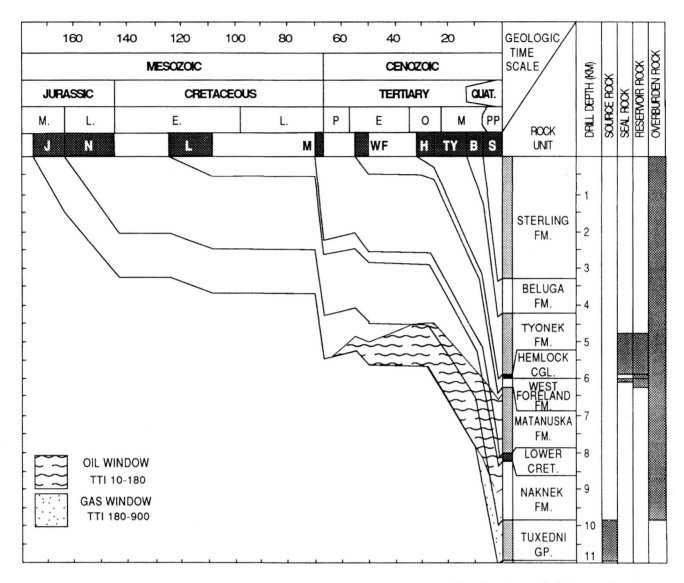

Figure 22.7. The burial history chart for the Tuxedni–Hemlock(!) petroleum system. The oil and gas windows are shown relative to maximum present-day burial depth of the Tuxedni Group, as shown in Figure 22.4. The essential elements of the system are on the right. The TTI is 10–180 for oil and 180–900 for gas using the BasinMod program. Abbreviations as in Figure 22.5.

in this reservoir has an API oil gravity of 34° ± 6°, a gas–oil ratio (GOR) of 600 (175–3850), a sulfur content of 0.1%, a pristane–phytane ratio of 2.7 (1.6–3.4), and carbon isotope values for saturated hydrocarbons of –30‰ (–30.4 to –29.6‰) and for aromatic hydrocarbons of –28‰ (–29.1 to –27.8‰). This and other information are tabulated in Magoon and Kirschner (1990).

Level of Certainty

The level of certainty indicates how confident one is that a given hydrocarbon accumulation originated from a particular pod of active source rock. Based on carbon isotopic and biological marker information, there is a high degree of confidence that the six commercial oil accumulations originated from the Middle Jurassic Tuxedni Group (Magoon and Anders, 1992). Oil–oil correlations from the commercial accumulations as well

as from drill-stem tests from within the geographic extent of the Tuxedni–Hemlock petroleum system are similar based on biological marker data and carbon isotopic compositions.

The carbon isotopic compositions of the 24 oil samples and 12 source rock samples are nearly identical (Figure 22.8). The δ13C value of the saturated hydrocarbons in these 12 rock extracts (bitumen) ranges from –31.2 to –28.9‰, a 2.3‰ difference, and for 24 oils from –30.8 to –29.4‰, a 1.4‰ difference. The δ13C values of the aromatic hydrocarbons in these rock extracts range from –30.2 to –28.1‰, a 2.1‰ difference, and for oils from –29.9 to –27.4‰, a 2.5‰ difference. The range in the isotopic ratio for saturated hydrocarbons in the rocks completely overlaps that of the oils, and the range for aromatic hydrocarbons partially overlaps that of the oil. Isotopic data for the condensates associated with the gas accumulations and the rock extracts from Tertiary coals

Table 22.1. Tuxedni–Hemlock(!) Oil Accumulations by Discovery Date, Indicating Cumulative Production as of December 31, 1987, Remaining Reserves, and Reservoir Characteristics[a]

Map[b] Symbol	Accumulation Name	Year Dis'd	Prod Unit	Pool	Res Lith	Prod Status	Trap Type	Prod Depth (m)	Oil Gravity (°API)	Orig GOR (SCF/STB)	Cum Prod Oil (×10³ bbl)	Cum Prod Gas (bcf)	Reserves Oil (×10⁶ bbl)	Reserves Gas (bcf)
A	Swanson River	1957	Hemlock	34-10	cg	prod	A	3285	30	175	–	–	–	–
A	Swanson River		Hemlock	Center	cg	prod	A	3220	30	175	–	–	–	–
A	Swanson River		Hemlock	SCU	cg	prod	A	3140	37	350	–	–	–	–
										Field totals	208,469	1752	10	250
B	Mid Grd Shl	1962	Tyonek	A	ss	prod	FA	765	42	3850	2,000	4	–	–
B	Mid Grd Shl		Tyonek	B, C, D	ss	prod	FA	1830	36	650	10,420	7	–	–
B	Mid Grd Shl		Ty-Hem	E, F, G	ss-cg	prod	FA	2590	35	381	140,683	65	–	–
										Field totals	153,103	77	11	7
C	Granite Point	1965	Tyonek	MGS	ss	prod	A	2675	42	1110	106,838	92	–	–
C	Granite Point		Hemlock	–	cg	prod	A	–	–	–	3	–	–	–
										Field totals	106,841	92	19	15
D	Trading Bay	1965	Tyonek	C	ss	prod	FA	1340	28	–	–	–	–	–
D	Trading Bay		Tyonek	D	ss	prod	FA	1715	28	268	–	–	–	–
D	Trading Bay		Ty-Hem	–	ss-cg	prod	A	2990	36	275	–	–	–	–
D	Trading Bay		Hemlock	–	cg	prod	FA	1860	31	318	–	–	–	–
										Field totals	89,424	61	2	2
E	McArthur River	1965	Tyonek	MGS	ss	prod	A	2695	36	297	36,769	18	–	–
E	McArthur River		Hemlock	–	cg	prod	A	2820	35	404	474,421	171	–	–
E	McArthur River		W Foreland	–	ss	prod	A	2940	33	271	19,317	6	–	–
										Field totals	530,507	194	47	25
F	Redoubt Shoal	1968	Hemlock	–	cg	abd	–	–	28		2	–	–	–
G	Beaver Creek	1972	Tyonek	MGS	ss	prod	–	4510	35	280	3521	1	1	1

[a]Symbols: A, anticlinal trap; abd, abandoned; cg, conglomeratic sandstone; cum prod, cumulative production through 12/31/87; FA, faulted anticlinal trap; lith, lithology; MGS, Middle Ground Shoal Member of Debelius (1974); Mid Grd Shl, Middle Ground Shoal; pools A–G, industry pool designation; prod, producing; res, reservoir; SCU, Soldatna Creek unit; ss, sandstone; Ty-Hem, Tyonek Formation and Hemlock Conglomerate, undivided.

[b]Map symbols correspond to locations on Figure 22.3.

References used for this table: Alaska Oil and Gas Conservation Commission, 1985, 1991; R. P. Crandall, written communication, 1988; Oil and Gas Journal, 1988.

are unlike the oils. Based on carbon isotopic data, rock extracts from Upper Triassic marine shale at Puale Bay (over 400 km to the southwest of the McArthur River field) and the Middle Jurassic Tuxedni Group are similar. Upper Triassic metasedimentary rocks are present in outcrop in the Iniskin Peninsula–Tuxedni Bay area, but are too mature to be evaluated for their source rock characteristics.

Representative m/z 191 fragmentograms are shown for Upper Triassic and Middle Jurassic rock extracts and for two oils (Figure 22.9). Tricyclic hydrocarbons are present in above-normal amounts in both the rock extracts from the Upper Triassic rocks and the oils recovered by drill-stem tests in lower Cook Inlet. In contrast, the commercial oils in upper Cook Inlet and extracts from Middle Jurassic rocks contain only small amounts of tricyclic hydrocarbons. On the basis of biological marker compounds, the small amounts of oil recovered from reservoir rocks in lower Cook Inlet appear to be co-sourced by the Upper Triassic and

Middle Jurassic rocks; the commercial oil in upper Cook Inlet is from the Middle Jurassic Tuxedni Group. The biomarkers in rock extracts from the Tertiary source rocks are unlike the Mesozoic marine rock extracts.

Geographic, Stratigraphic, and Temporal Extent

The geographic extent of the Tuxedni–Hemlock petroleum system includes both the pod of mature Middle Jurassic source rock and the oil accumulations charged by that pod (A–G in Figure 22.3). The geographic extent includes the North Cook Inlet gas field (#7, Figure 22.3) because oil from a marine source rock was recovered from the Hemlock Conglomerate (Magoon and Anders, 1992). Since oil exploration has occurred intermittently for almost 90 years, the presumption is that most all of the large accumulations have been found. A single oil type for the included accumulations firmly establishes the extent of the system for migrated

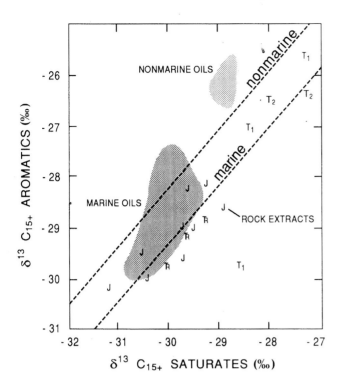

Figure 22.8. Carbon isotopic ratios of saturated versus aromatic hydrocarbons in rock extracts (letters) and 3 nonmarine and 24 marine oil (shaded) samples from the Cook Inlet–Alaska Peninsula area (from Magoon and Anders, 1992). Diagonal lines (from Sofer, 1984) refer to the isotope composition of waxy nonmarine oils and nonwaxy marine oils. Symbols: T_1, Tyonek Formation; T_2, West Foreland Formation; J, Tuxedni Group; Tr, Upper Triassic.

oil, but insufficient geologic and geochemical information is available to map the pod of active source rock directly since no wells penetrate the source rock where it is most deeply buried today. However, information about the source rock where it is less deeply buried was extrapolated into the area where it is more deeply buried (Figure 22.7). Therefore, the geographic extent is constrained by the accumulations (Table 22.1) and the fact that the Middle Jurassic Tuxedni Group, the only source for these accumulations, is most deeply buried between these oil fields.

The stratigraphic and temporal extent of this petroleum system is defined by the essential elements and processes of the system (Figures 22.4, 22.5, and 22.7). The stratigraphic extent is the depth range over which the essential elements occur, and the temporal extent is the time span of these elements and processes. The essential elements are as follows: (1) the Middle Jurassic Tuxedni Group is the source rock; (2) the West Foreland and Tyonek formations are the seal rocks; (3) the West Foreland Formation, Hemlock Conglomerate, and Tyonek Formation are the reservoir rocks; and (4) Upper Jurassic–Holocene rock units that overlie the source rock are the overburden rocks. The generation–migration–accumulation of petroleum started during the Paleocene (~63 Ma) where the source rock is buried deepest and is probably continuing today in some areas (Figures 22.5

and 22.7). In this convergent margin setting, trap formation is estimated to have started in the Late Miocene (~10 Ma) and persists today. These petroleum system events are summarized on the events chart in Figure 22.5.

EFFICIENCY OF THE SYSTEM

The generation–accumulation efficiency of a petroleum system is a comparison of the known amount of in-place hydrocarbons that have accumulated to the estimated or calculated amount generated, and it is expressed as a percentage. The amount of hydrocarbons generated is calculated using Schmoker's method (Chapter 19, this volume), and the in-place hydrocarbons are estimated using Table 22.1 and a reasonable recovery factor. The efficiency of the Tuxedni–Hemlock petroleum system is calculated as follows.

First, the amount of generated hydrocarbons is determined. The mass (M) in grams of TOC and the density (ρ) for the pod of Middle Jurassic mature source rock in Figure 22.3 are calculated according to equation 1 in Schmoker as follows:

$$M \text{ (g TOC)} = [\text{TOC (wt. \%)}/100] \times \rho \text{ (g/cm}^3)$$
$$\times V \text{ (cm}^3) \qquad (1)$$

where V is the volume of mature source rock.

As previously estimated, the average TOC content for the immature source rock is 1.7 wt. %, and the estimated density for this organic-rich rock is 2.62 g/cm^3 (from Figure 19.2, Schmoker, this volume). The area of mature source rock from Figure 22.3 is 1500 km^2, or 1.5×10^{13} cm^2. The thickness as estimated earlier is 1 km or 1×10^5 cm. The volume is thus 1.5×10^{18} cm^3. Solving equation 1, we then have

$$M \text{ (g TOC)} = [(1.7 \text{ wt. \% TOC})/100] \times 2.62 \text{ g/cm}^3$$
$$\times 1.5 \times 10^{18} \text{ cm}^3$$
$$= 6.68 \times 10^{16} \text{ g TOC}$$

The mass of hydrocarbons generated per unit mass of TOC for each source rock unit (R) is calculated according to equation 2 of Schmoker as follows:

$$R \text{ (mg HC/g TOC)} = \text{HI}_o \text{ (mg HC/g TOC)}$$
$$- \text{HI}_p \text{ (mg HC/g TOC)} \qquad (2)$$

where HI_o is the original hydrogen index for an immature source rock, estimated at 300 mg HC/g TOC, and HI_p is the present-day HI for mature to overmature source rock, estimated at 100 mg HC/g TOC. Solving equation 2, we have

$$R \text{ (mg HC/g TOC)} = 300 - 100 \text{ mg HC/g TOC}$$
$$= 200 \text{ mg HC/g TOC}$$

A minimum estimate for the total mass of hydrocarbons (HCG) generated (either oil and/or gas) is calcu-

(a)

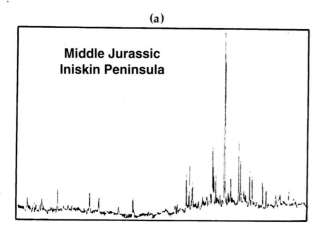

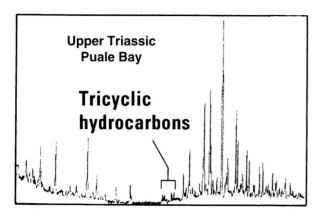

(b)

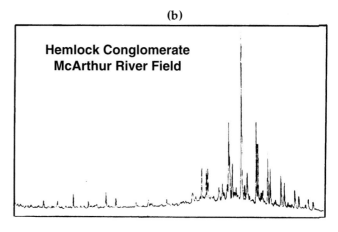

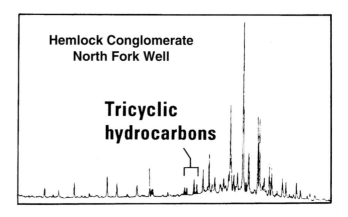

Figure 22.9. Biological marker information (*m/z* 191) for (a) rock extracts and (b) marine oils. The North Fork well is located in the North Fork gas accumulation (12 on Figure 22.3), and Puale Bay is 400 km southwest of Anchorage on the Alaska Peninsula. (From Magoon and Anders, 1992.)

lated from these results according to equation 3 of Schmoker as follows:

$$HCG \text{ (kg HC)} = 200 \text{ mg HC/g TOC}$$
$$\times (6.68 \times 10^{16} \text{ g TOC}) \times 10^{-6} \text{ kg/mg}$$
$$= 1.34 \times 10^{13} \text{ kg HC}$$

The amount of in-place hydrocarbons in kilograms is calculated from recoverable hydrocarbons (Table 22.1) using a recovery factor of 35% for oil and 80% for gas. Total recoverable resources (Table 22.1) are 1.18×10^9 bbl of oil and 2.48×10^{12} ft^3 of gas. Calculated hydrocarbons in-place are 3.37×10^9 bbl of oil ($1.18/0.35 \times 10^9$) and 3.1×10^{12} ft^3 of gas ($2.48/0.80 \times 10^{12}$). Kilograms of hydrocarbons are 469.4×10^9 kg of oil (139.3 kg/bbl), and 62.9×10^9 kg of gas (2.03×10^{-2} kg/ft^3), which totals 5.32×10^{11} kg in-place.

Finally, the amount of generated hydrocarbons is compared to the amount of accumulated hydrocarbons to determine the system's generation–accumulation efficiency (GAE) in the following manner:

$$GAE \text{ (\%)} = \text{(accumulated kg HC/generated kg HC)} \times 100$$
$$= [(5.32 \times 10^{11})/(134 \times 10^{11})] \times 100 = 4\%$$

Thus, according to these calculations, 4% of all hydrocarbons generated actually accumulated.

MIGRATION AND ACCUMULATION

The migration of oil from the active source rock to the trap within the Tuxedni–Hemlock petroleum system can only be inferred. Based on the cross section (Figure 22.4) and the burial history chart (Figure 22.7), the source rock first became mature during the Paleocene (~63 Ma) and is presently in the gas window. Evidently, very little gas was generated, as the GOR is <1000; thus, the oil that was generated over the last 63 m.y. apparently migrated updip to the flanks of the basin and was trapped stratigraphically until the structural traps formed (10 Ma). Oil that generated and migrated before the Hemlock Conglomerate was deposited (~30 Ma) may have been detroyed by erosion. The source rock in the gas window is evidently spent. Based on the synclinal geometry of the basin, any oil generated must have migrated laterally through sandstone within the source rock or in the overlying Naknek Formation to the Cretaceous–Tertiary unconformity, across the unconformity, and through the West Foreland Formation and into the Hemlock Conglomerate, a widespread reservoir rock unit. After the oil migrated into the Hemlock Conglomerate, it migrated into stratigraphic traps (not found) or later-formed structural traps (discovered).

The migration–accumulation scenario raises inportant questions about the low generation–accumulation efficiency of 4% and about the whereabouts of the oil that was generated before the structural traps were formed and filled. If the geographic extent of the system is divided into quadrants by using the axis of the basin (northeast-southwest) and by a line just northeast of the Trading Bay (D in Figure 22.3) and Swanson River (A) fields (northwest-southeast), most of the oil is in the west quadrant (B, D, E, and F) followed by the south (A and G) and north (C). Very little is in the east quadrant. Using the previous equations for the west quadrant (25% of generated hydrocarbons is 33.5×10^{11} kg, for recoverable petroleum is 933×10^{6} bbl of oil and 366×10^{9} ft^3 of gas, or 3.85×10^{11} kg), the generation–accumulation efficiency is 11.5 %. Either the plumbing system and traps are best developed in the west quadrant, or the stratigraphically trapped oil in the other quadrants is yet to be found either within or beyond the geographic extent of the system. Since surface seeps are unreported, then this oil is still in undiscovered stratigraphic traps. If this interpretation is valid, then a great deal more oil has been generated (overcharged system) and trapped stratigraphically than has been discovered.

SUMMARY

The Tuxedni–Hemlock(!) petroleum system originally contained discovered recoverable hydrocarbons of about 1.18 billion bbl of oil and 2.48 trillion ft^3 of gas in six commercial oil fields. Carbon isotope and biological marker data indicate that the low sulfur, 35° API gravity oil from all these fields has the same chemical composition and that, based on rock extracts, it originated from the Middle Jurassic Tuxedni Group source rock.

Essential elements of the petroleum system (source, reservoir, seal, and overburden rocks) were deposited from the Middle Jurassic (~170 Ma) to the present in volcanic forearc and backarc basins adjacent to a convergent margin. The generation–migration–accumulation process started in the Paleocene (~63 Ma) and continues today, while trap formation occurred much later in the late Miocene (~10 Ma).

Burial and thermal history reconstructions show that the oil and gas were generated and migrated from the deepest part of the basin between the Middle Ground Shoal and Swanson River oil fields during Cenozoic time. Here, the overburden rock is 9.8 km thick and ranges in age from Late Jurassic to Holocene. Although several large faults are present, petroleum migration was mainly lateral because the accumulations presently overlie immature source rocks. The principal oil reservoir rock is the Oligocene Hemlock Conglomerate. Traps are anticlines that are commonly faulted and sealed by siltstone; these traps, which are still evolving, started to form during late Cenozoic time.

The major reservoir rock (Hemlock) was deposited about 30 m.y. after some oil migration, suggesting that early oil was lost to erosion. However, some oil must have been preserved in stratigraphic traps prior to remigrating into structural traps that formed during the late Miocene to present.

The mass of hydrocarbons generated by the Middle Jurassic source rock was calculated and compared to the estimated in-place petroleum to determine the efficiency of the petroleum system. On the basis of the average TOC content (1.7 wt. %), the difference between the original and present-day hydrogen indices (200 mg H/g TOC), and the volume of mature source rock (1.5×10^{18} cm^3), 1.34×10^{13} kg hydrocarbons were generated. In-place hydrocarbons are estimated at 4.9×10^{11} kg. On the basis of these calculations, almost 4% of the hydrocarbons generated actually accumulated in known traps. When the petroleum system is divided into quadrants, the western quadrant has a GAE of 11.5%, or three times the other three quadrants. These other quadrants apparently lack the trap volume, have inadequate plumbing systems, or the accumulations are present in stratigraphic traps but as yet undiscovered.

Acknowledgments   *I wish to acknowledge K. J. Bird and J. W. Schmoker for critically reviewing an early version of this chapter and for their helpful suggestions. John T. Smith, Peter van de Kamp, Minor B. Long, and Gerard Demaison made helpful suggestions when they reviewed a later version.*

References Cited

Alaska Geological Society, 1969a, Northwest to southeast stratigraphic correlation section, Drift River to Anchor River, Cook Inlet basin, Alaska: Anchorage, vertical scale 1 in. = 500 ft.

Alaska Geological Society, 1969b, South to north stratigraphic correlation section, Anchor Point to Campbell Point, Cook Inlet basin, Alaska: Anchorage, vertical scale 1 in. = 500 ft.

Alaska Geological Society, 1969c, South to north stratigraphic correlation section, Kalgin Island to Beluga River, Cook Inlet basin, Alaska: Anchorage, vertical scale 1 in. = 500 ft.

Alaska Geological Society, 1969d, West to east stratigraphic correlation section, West Foreland to Swan Lake, Cook Inlet basin, Alaska: Anchorage, vertical scale 1 in. = 500 ft.

Alaska Geological Society, 1970a, South to north stratigraphic correlation section, Campbell Point to Rosetta, Cook Inlet basin, Alaska: Anchorage, vertical scale 1 in. = 500 ft.

Alaska Geological Society, 1970b, West to east stratigraphic correlation section, Beluga River to Wasilla, Cook Inlet basin, Alaska: Anchorage, vertical scale 1 in. = 500 ft.

Alaska Oil and Gas Conservation Commission, 1985, 1984 Statistical Report: Alaska Oil and Gas Conservation Commission, 187 p.

Alaska Oil and Gas Conservation Commission, 1991, 1985–1990 Statistical Report: Alaska Oil and Gas Conservation Commission, p. 14–17.

Bally, A. W., and S. Snelson, 1980, Realms of subsidence, *in* A. D. Miall, ed., Facts and principles of world petroleum occurrence: Canadian Society of Petroleum Geologists Memoir 6, p. 9–94.

Blasko, D. P., 1974, Natural gas fields—Cook Inlet basin, Alaska: Bureau of Mines Open-File Report 35-74, 29 p.

Blasko, D. P., 1976, Oil and gas seeps in Alaska—Alaska Peninsula, Western Gulf of Alaska: U.S. Bureau of Mines Report of Investigations 8122, 78 p.

Blasko, D. P., W. J. Wenger, and J. C. Morris, 1972, Oilfields and crude oil characteristics, Cook Inlet basin, Alaska: U.S. Bureau of Mines Report of Investigations 7688, 44 p.

Bolm, J. G., and T. H. McCulloh, 1986, Sandstone diagenesis, *in* L. B. Magoon, ed., Geologic studies of the lower Cook Inlet COST No. 1 well, Alaska Outer Continental Shelf: U.S.G.S. Bulletin 1596, p. 51–53.

Boss, R. F., R. B. Lennon, and B. W. Wilson, 1976, Middle Ground Shoal oil field, Alaska, *in* J. Braunstein, ed., North American oil and gas fields: AAPG Memoir 24, p. 1–22.

Calderwood, K. W., and W. C. Fackler, 1972, Proposed stratigraphic nomenclature for Kenai Group, Cook Inlet basin, Alaska: AAPG Bulletin, v. 56, p. 739–754.

Claypool, G. E., 1986, Petroleum geochemistry, *in* L. B. Magoon, ed., Geologic studies of the lower Cook Inlet COST No. 1 well, Alaska Outer Continental Shelf: U.S.G.S. Bulletin 1596, p. 33–39.

Claypool, G. E., C. N. Threlkeld, and L. B. Magoon, 1980, Biogenic and thermogenic origins of natural gas in Cook Inlet basin, Alaska. AAPG Bulletin, v. 64, p. 1131–1139.

Coney, P. J., and D. L. Jones, 1985, Accretion tectonics and crustal structure in Alaska: Tectonophysics, v. 119, p. 265–283.

Crick, R. W. 1971, Potential petroleum reserves, Cook Inlet, Alaska, *in* I. H. Cram, ed., Future petroleum provinces of the United States—their geology and potential: AAPG Memoir 15, v. 1, p. 109–119.

Debelius, C. A., 1974, Environmental impact statement, offshore oil and gas development in Cook Inlet, Alaska (final): Alaska District, Corps of Engineers, 446 p.

Detterman, R. L., and J. K. Hartsock, 1966, Geology of the Iniskin–Tuxedni Region, Alaska: U.S.G.S. Professional Paper 512, 78 p.

Fisher, M. A., and L. B. Magoon, 1978, Geologic framework of lower Cook Inlet Alaska: AAPG Bulletin, v. 62, p. 373–402.

Franks, S. G., and D. M. Hite, 1980, Controls of zeolite cementation in Upper Jurassic sandstones, lower Cook Inlet, Alaska (abs.): AAPG Bulletin, v. 64, p. 708–709.

Hartman, D. C., G. H. Pessel, and D. L. McGee, 1972, Preliminary report on stratigraphy of Kenai Group, upper Cook Inlet, Alaska. Alaska Division of Geological Surveys, Special Report No. 5, 4 p., 7 maps, scale 1:500,000, 1 pl.

Hite, D. M., 1976, Some sedimentary aspects of the Kenai Group, Cook Inlet, Alaska, *in* T. P. Miller, ed., Recent and ancient sedimentary environments in Alaska: Alaska Geological Society, Anchorage, Alaska, p. I1–I23.

Kelly, T. E., 1963, Geology and hydrocarbons in Cook Inlet basin, Alaska, *in* O. E. Childs and B. W. Beebe, eds., Backbone of the Americas: AAPG Memoir 2, p. 278–296.

Kelly, T. E., 1968, Gas accumulations in nonmarine strata, Cook Inlet basin, Alaska, *in* W. B. Beebe and B. F. Curtis, eds., Natural gases of North America: AAPG Memoir 9, v. 1, p. 49–64.

Kirschner, C. E., and C. A. Lyon, 1973, Stratigraphic and tectonic development of Cook Inlet petroleum province, *in* M. G. Pitcher, ed., Arctic geology: AAPG Memoir 19, p. 396–407.

MacKevett, E. M., Jr., and G. Plafker, 1974, The Border Ranges fault in south-central Alaska: U.S.G.S. Journal of Research, v. 2, p. 323–329.

Magoon, L. B., ed., 1986, Geologic studies of the lower Cook Inlet COST No. 1 well, Alaska Outer Continental Shelf: U.S.G.S. Bulletin 1596, 99 p.

Magoon, L. B., 1989, Identified petroleum systems within the United States—1990, *in* L. B. Magoon, ed., The petroleum system—status of research and methods, 1990: U.S.G.S. Bulletin 1912, p. 2–9.

Magoon, L. B., and D. E. Anders, 1990, Oil–source rock correlation using carbon isotope data and biological marker compounds, Cook Inlet—Alaska Peninsula, Alaska (abs.): AAPG Bulletin, v. 74, p. 711.

Magoon, L. B., and D. E. Anders, 1992, Oil-to-source rock correlation using carbon-isotopic data and biological marker compounds, Cook Inlet–Alaska Peninsula, Alaska, *in* J. M. Moldowan, P. Albrecht, and R. P. Philp, eds., Biological markers in sediments and petroleum: Englewood Cliffs, NJ, Prentice-Hall, p. 241–274.

Magoon, L. B., and G. E. Claypool, 1981, Petroleum geology of Cook Inlet basin, Alaska—an exploration model: AAPG Bulletin, v. 65, p. 1043–1061.

Magoon, L. B., and R. M. Egbert, 1986, Framework geology and sandstone composition, *in* L. B. Magoon, ed., Geologic studies of the lower Cook Inlet COST No. 1 well, Alaska Outer Continental Shelf: U.S.G.S. Bulletin 1596, p. 65–90.

Magoon, L. B., and C. E. Kirschner, 1990, Alaska onshore national assessment program—geology and petroleum resource potential of six onshore Alaska provinces: U.S.G.S. Open-File Report 88-450T, 47 p.

Magoon, L. B., W. L. Adkison, and R. M. Egbert, 1976, Map showing geology, wildcat wells, Tertiary plant-fossil localities, K-Ar age dates, and petroleum operations, Cook Inlet area, Alaska. U.S.G.S. Miscellaneous Investigations Map I-1019, 3 sheets, scale 1:250,000.

Magoon, L. B., F. R. Griesbach, and R. M. Egbert, 1980, Nonmarine Upper Cretaceous rocks, Cook Inlet, Alaska: AAPG Bulletin, v. 64, p. 1259–1266.

Oil and Gas Journal, 1988, U.S. fields with reserves exceeding 100 million bbl: Oil and Gas Journal, v. 86, n. 4, p. 60.

Osmont, F. C., R. M. Marrow, and R. W. Craig, 1967, Petroleum geology and development of the Cook Inlet basin of Alaska (with French abs.): Seventh World Petroleum Congress Proceedings, Mexico City, v. 2, p. 141–150.

Palmer, A. R., 1983, The decade of North American Geology, 1983 geologic time scale: Geology, v. 11, p. 503–504.

Parkinson, L. J., 1962, One field, one giant—the story of Swanson River: Oil and Gas Journal, v. 60, n. 13, p. 180–183.

Plafker, G., T. R. Bruns, G. R. Winkler, and R. G. Tysdal, 1982, Cross section of the eastern arc, from Mount Spurr to the Aleutian trench near Middleton Island, Alaska: Geological Society of America Map and Chart Series MC-28-P, 1 sheet.

Reed, B. L., A. T. Miesch, and M. A. Lanphere, 1983, Plutonic rocks of Jurassic age in the Alaska–Aleutian Range batholith: chemical variations and polarity: GSA Bulletin, v. 94, p. 1232–1240.

Seely, D. R., and W. R. Dickinson, 1977, Structure and stratigraphy of forearc regions: AAPG Continuing Education Course Notes, Series 5, p. C1–C23.

Silberling, N. J., D. L. Jones, P. J. Coney, H. C. Berg, and G. Plafker,1994, Lithotectonic terrane map of Alaska, *in* G. Plafker, D. L. Jones, and H. C. Berg, eds., Geology of Alaska: Geological Society of America, plate III.

Sofer, Z., 1984, Stable carbon isotope compositions of crude oils: application to source depositional environments and petroleum alteration: AAPG Bulletin, v. 68, p. 31–49.

Wolfe, J. A., 1981, A chronologic framework for Cenozoic megafossil floras of northwestern North America and its relation to marine geochronology: GSA Special Paper 184, p. 39–42.

Young, A., P. H. Monaghan, and R. T. Schweisberger, 1977, Calculation of ages of hydrocarbons in oils—physical chemistry applied to petroleum geochemistry I: AAPG Bulletin, v. 61, p. 573–600.

Magoon, L. B, and W. G. Dow, eds., 1994, The petroleum
system—from source to trap: AAPG Memoir 60.

Chapter 23

Heath–Tyler(!) Petroleum System in Central Montana, U.S.A.

Gary A. Cole*

Richard J. Drozd**

BP Exploration
Houston, Texas, U.S.A.

Abstract

The Heath–Tyler(!) petroleum system, located in the Big Snowy trough in central Montana, has produced about 100 million bbl of oil from over 25 fields in an area covering 800–1200 km^2. This petroleum system is relatively simple in that it has a source rock, the Heath Formation of Mississippian age, overlain by a sandstone reservoir rock, the Pennsylvanian Tyler Formation. The lower part of the Heath Formation was deposited in a deep neritic (outer shelf) environment which grades upward into a shallow, restricted, nearshore marine environment. The organic-rich mudstones and carbonates of the upper part of the Heath Formation have good to excellent source rock characteristics. Reservoir rocks within the overlying lower Tyler Formation are lenticular channel sandstones, probably resulting of a limited fluviolacustrine, deltaic phase of erosion and deposition that incised into the underlying Heath source rock when it was uplifted and deformed prior to deposition of the Tyler Formation.

By using stable carbon isotopic and biological marker data, the moderate API gravity, low sulfur oils recovered from the Tyler correlate to the Heath Formation, an oil-prone source rock. Burial history–thermal modeling and measured thermal maturity results show an increase in maturity from west to east with maximum maturity occurring with maximum burial just preceding uplift and erosion during the Laramide orogeny in early Tertiary (40 Ma). The pod of active source rock is estimated to cover 800 km^2, and the thermally most mature source rock is found in pre-Laramide synclines. The generation–migration–accumulation phase occurred in early Tertiary (52–40 Ma), but subsequent oil remigration occurred as a result of Laramide deformation.

The volume of in-place hydrocarbons is estimated to be 38% of the volume of generated hydrocarbons. This high efficiency is due to the juxtaposition of the source rock and reservoir rock. Only limited volumes of oil are yet to be discovered.

INTRODUCTION

The Heath–Tyler(!) petroleum system is located in central Montana and lies almost totally within northern Musselshell and western Rosebud counties (Figure 23.1). The Heath–Tyler petroleum system contains more than 25 oil fields (Table 23.1) that began to produce oil from the Heath or Tyler Formations around 1920. The largest fields (e.g., Melstone and Sumatra) were found in the late 1940s or early 1950s (Montana Oil and Gas Conservation Division, 1987).

The Mississippian Heath Formation in central Montana (Figure 23.2) is an economically important stratigraphic unit because of its high total organic carbon content (Williams, 1974; Swetland et al., 1978; Derkey et al., 1985; Rinaldi, 1988). The Heath is considered a petroleum source rock for oil in the overlying sandstone within the Pennsylvanian Tyler Formation (Kranzler, 1966; Swetland et al., 1978; Maughn, 1984) as well as a good to excellent oil shale as shown by Fischer assay analyses (Cox, 1973; Cox and Cole, 1981; Desborough et al., 1981; Derkey et al., 1985). The purposes of this case study are to (1) define the type of source rock based on routine analyses, (2) map the area of thermally mature source rock, (3) determine the timing of oil expulsion and migration, (4) present the data that correlate the Tyler oil to the organic matter in the Heath shale–carbonate, and (5) demonstrate how oil migrated from the Heath source

*Present address: Saudi Aramco, Dhahran, Saudi Arabia.
**Present address: Westport Technology Center International,
Houston, Texas, U.S.A.

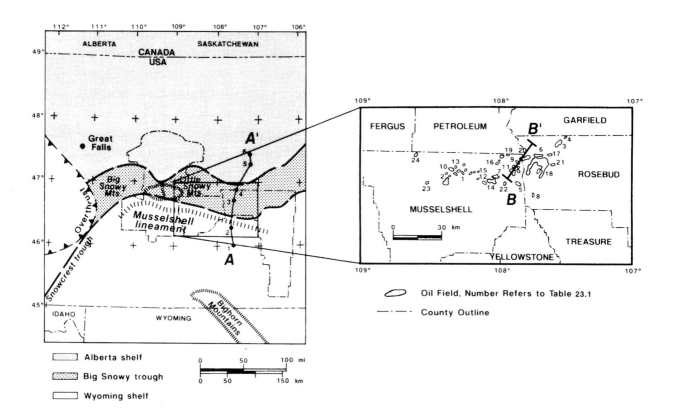

Figure 23.1. Index map showing the oil fields producing from the Tyler Formation in central Montana in relation to paleogeographic features, such as the Big Snowy trough and the Alberta and Wyoming shelfs, and to the present-day Big Snowy and Little Snowy mountains. The numbered oil fields on the right-hand map are listed in Table 23.1. Cross section A–A' is shown (with numbered wells) in Figure 23.4, and B–B' is shown in Figure 23.13. (Maps modified from Maughn, 1984.)

rock to traps in the Tyler sandstone reservoirs. An events chart (Figure 23.3) provides a view of the Heath–Tyler petroleum system with respect to the Big Snowy Group and the regional Middle Jurassic unconformity (modified from Peterson and MacCary, 1987).

GEOLOGY OF SOURCE ROCK AND RESERVOIR ROCK

The Heath Formation (Scott, 1935) and the Tyler Formation (Freeman, 1922) are shown in the generalized stratigraphic column for the Heath–Tyler petroleum system (Figure 23.2).

The Heath Formation is part of the Big Snowy Group and conformably overlies the Otter Formation which rests on the Kibbey Formation, the basal unit of the group. As proposed by Mundt (1956), the Heath and overlying Tyler are separate formations with the Tyler disconformably overlying the Heath. The contact between the two formations is placed at the base of the lowest sandstone unit, typically a well-sorted, medium-grained sandstone with local basal lag or conglomeratic beds. Smith and Gilmour (1979) have cited references placing the Pennsylvanian–Mississippian contact within the Tyler rather than at the contact between the two formations.

In central Montana, the pattern of shallow marine sedimentary basins and uplifts was drastically changed during the Late Devonian–Early Mississippian (Smith and Gilmour, 1979). Tectonically, the Big Snowy trough began its development as a downward flexure between the Wyoming and Alberta shelves (Figure 23.1). This flexure remained relatively stable throughout Mississippian time. The first sequence of sedimentary rocks to accumulate in this trough and on adjacent shelves were the thick carbonates of the Madison Group. Following Madison deposition (Meramecian–Chesterian time), differential uplift on the Alberta and Wyoming shelves further defined the Big Snowy trough (Smith and Gilmour, 1979; Maughn, 1984). The sediment shed from the uplift of the adjacent shelves provided the clastic material for the basal unit of the Big Snowy Group, the Kibbey Formation.

Uplift and erosion in Middle Jurassic time and during the Laramide orogenic pulse (Roberts, 1979; Smith and Gilmour, 1979; Maughn, 1984) caused the original extent and geometry of the Big Snowy trough to be altered, which has restricted our knowledge of the burial history for this petroleum system (Figure 23.4). From the limited paleogeographic data available (Maughn, 1984), we know that the Big Snowy Group was deposited over a much broader area.

The Kibbey Formation, the basal unit of the Big

Table 23.1. Oil Production from Tyler Formation, Central Montana[a]

Map No.	Field	Cumulative Production (bbl)
—	Bean Blossom	290,569
1	Big Gully	98,964
2	Big Wall	7,518,896
3	Breed Creek	1,092,603
3	Devil's Basin	107,278
3	Devil's Pocket	37,277
4	Gumbo Ridge	579,181
5	Hiawatha	1,515,741
6	High Five	2,103,213
7	Howard Coulee	124,578
8	Injun Creek	117,387
9	Ivanhoe	4,496,528
10	Jim Coulee	4,108,861
11	Keg Coulee	5,465,460
11	Keg Coulee, North	437,149
12	Kelley	977,976
12	Kinchloe Ranch West	512,550
13	Little Wall Creek	3,515,921
14	Melstone	3,355,250
14	Musselshell	30,318
15	North Willow Creek	322,975
16	Ragged Point	3,777,950
17	Rattler Butte	843,647
18	Rosebud	439,071
19	Sheepherder	76,044
20	Stensvad	10,109,080
20	Studhorse	156,790
21	Sumatra	42,486,205
22	Tippy Buttes	120,130
23	Wagon Box	21,024
24	Winnett Junction	840,648
	Total Production through 1987	95,679,264

[a]From Montana Oil and Gas (1987).

Snowy Group, consists mostly of a clastic carbonate sequence derived from erosion of the uplifted Alberta and Wyoming shelves. The Kibbey, which conformably overlies the Madison Group (Maughn and Roberts, 1967), was deposited in sabhka, intertidal, and shallow subtidal environments (Maughn, 1984). The Otter Formation, the middle unit of the Big Snowy Group, consists of calcareous mudstones and thin-bedded limestones and dolomites. The Otter is thought to have been deposited in a shallow, wave-dominated marine environment (Maughn, 1984).

The uppermost formation of the Big Snowy Group, and the most important due to the presence of organic-rich beds, is the Heath Formation. The Heath consists of dark, organic-rich mudstones interbedded with dark gray argillaceous carbonates. Gypsum beds are also present in the upper part of the formation. The fauna and organic-rich nature of some intervals within the Heath suggest that it was deposited in a biologically productive, neritic environment and grades into a restricted marine environment. Using core descriptions, Derkey et al. (1985) showed this gradation.

Informally the Heath is divided into a lower, middle (Forestgrove member, from Derkey et al., 1985), and upper member (Figure 23.2). The lower member is interpreted as marine. The Forestgrove member ranges from a nearshore, restricted marine environment, based on thin coaly intervals and algal-rich oil shales, to a hypersaline–sabkha environment, based on evaporite intervals (Loco Ridge gypsum zone). The upper member is interpreted to be nearshore marine. Past studies have shown that the Heath Formation contains excellent source rock and oil shale characteristics (Cox, 1973; Swetland et al., 1978; Cox and Cole, 1981; Desborough et al., 1981; Derkey et al; 1985; Rinaldi, 1988). The oil recovered from the Tyler Formation to the east in the Williston basin is thought to have originated from a source rock in the Tyler (Dow, 1974; Williams, 1974).

A period of uplift and erosion followed deposition of the Big Snowy Group as evidenced by the unconformable contact between the Heath and Tyler Formations (Maughn, 1984). Illustrations of the unconformable contact between the two formations have been shown in several papers by documenting where the Tyler incised into the Heath (Foster, 1956; Mundt, 1956; Staggs, 1959; Kranzler, 1966). The Tyler Formation is composed of a sequence of mostly siliciclastics (mudstones, sandstones, and minor coals) with occasional carbonates, and the reservoir sandstone is located in the lower part. Differential uplift north of the Big Snowy trough (Maughn, 1984; Smith and Gilmour, 1979) provided the majority of terrigenous clastics that were deposited in a fluviodeltaic setting.

To complete the generalized geology that includes the burial and structural history for this petroleum system, one must understand how these erosional events relate to the thermal maturation of the source rock. The source rock described in this chapter is from the western part of the Big Snowy trough in Fergus County. Due to a Middle Jurassic erosional episode, this unit is presently at the surface (Smith and Gilmour, 1979). From thermal maturity measurements made on Heath coals within 0.3 km (1000 ft) of the surface, Cole and Daniel (1984) estimated that about 1.5–2.0 km (5000–6500 ft) of erosion occurred in the Fergus County area. In the main petroleum trend (Musselshell and Rosebud counties), a more complete Mesozoic and Tertiary section is present and was responsible for the thermal maturation of the source rock. Although erosion has occurred here, it is to a lesser degree.

ORGANIC GEOCHEMISTRY

Source Rock

Heath Formation rock samples were obtained from shallow core holes drilled in Fergus County by the Montana Bureau of Mines and Geology and are described in Derkey et al. (1985). These samples were selected based on Fischer retort analyses from Derkey et

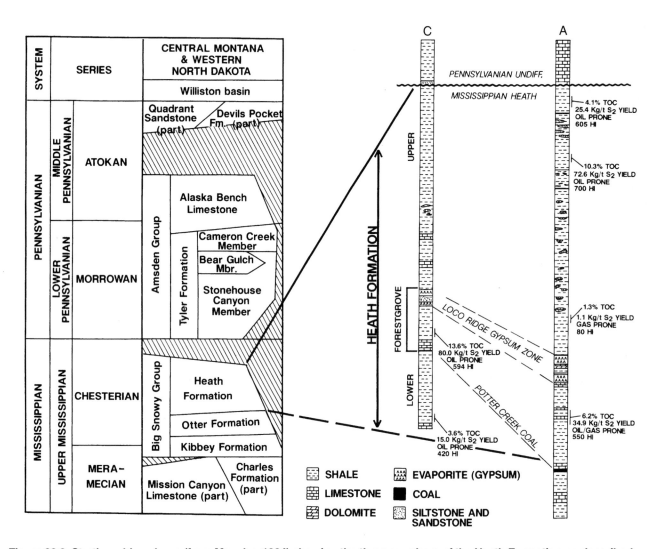

Figure 23.2. Stratigraphic column (from Maughn, 1984) showing the three members of the Heath Formation as described from core holes (Derkey et al., 1985). Geochemical data indicate the organic-rich zones. Locations of wells C and A are shown in Figure 23.11.

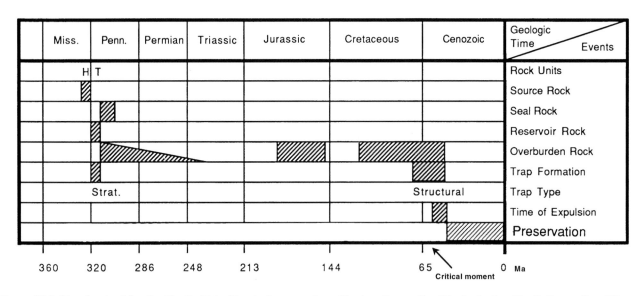

Figure 23.3. Events chart for the Heath–Tyler(!) petroleum system. Rock units are the Mississippian Heath Formation (H), which is the source rock, and the Pennsylvanian Tyler (T) sandstone, the reservoir rock. Maximum burial depth of the source rock occurred in early Tertiary time, which coincides with structural inversion by the Laramide orogeny.

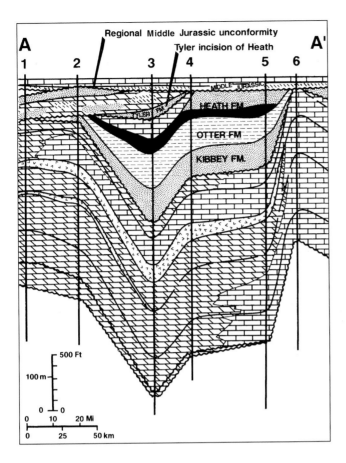

Figure 23.4. Cross section A–A' shows the relationship of the Big Snowy Group (Kibbey, Otter, and Heath formations) to the underlying Madison Group and to the overlying Tyler Formation, the basal unit of the Pennsylvanian Amsden Group. Three members of the Heath Formation are shown: lower (black), Forestgrove (dotted), and upper (brick pattern). Note how the Tyler Formation incises into the Heath Formation. (Modified from Peterson and MacCary, 1987.)

al. (1985) and from the general color of the rocks (black to dark gray means potential as a good source rock; light color indicates little or no source rock potential). Samples were analyzed for total organic carbon (TOC, wt. %), Rock-Eval pyrolysis (S_2 peak), source rock extract, $\delta^{13}C$ isotopic composition of kerogen and kerogen pyrolyzate, and pyrolysis–gas chromatography (gas to oil generation index, GOGI).

Thirty-two core samples from the Heath Formation from Fergus County, central Montana, were used to determine source rock characteristics and to compare with the oil from the central Montana fields. These samples were chosen because of their relative immaturity. Cole and Daniel (1984) showed that these samples had not yet entered the main phase of oil generation considered to be 0.6% vitrinite reflectance. From the analyses of the selected 32 core chips, 31 had TOC > 1 wt. % (27 had TOC > 3 wt. %), and 22 had a pyrolytic yield of S_2 > 20 kg/t. On average, these units had TOC = 7.6 wt. % and S_2 = 40.0 kg/t. The Heath Formation contains excellent source rock intervals.

The source rock data on these 32 samples from seven drill holes (Table 23.2) graphically illustrate the source rock character of the Heath Formation (Figure 23.5). Each site had excellent source rock character in limited intervals. Although only a selected number of core chips were analyzed, the lithologic descriptions from Derkey et al. (1985) and these analyses suggest that only a small amount of the Heath Formation is truly an excellent source rock. These analyses suggest that the source rock interval for the Heath is <10 m (20–30 ft) thick and is found in two intervals within the middle Heath (Forestgrove of Derkey et al., 1985). The best Heath source rock potential is in the calcareous shales, not the carbonates, even though they occasionally contain excellent source character.

Previous studies have also shown that the Heath Formation is a good candidate for the source of the Tyler oil. Williams (1974) stated that the Heath and Tyler contained sufficient organic matter, but concluded that to the east in the Williston basin, the Tyler was the more likely source rock. Swetland et al. (1978) suggested that the Heath Formation was the better source rock as determined from outcrop material acquired from Fergus County. From limited source rock material collected 6 km (4 mi) south of Piper, Montana, Rinaldi (1988) correlated oil produced from the Tyler Formation to the Heath. Even so, these few samples had a TOC range of 5–20 wt. %, contained 80% algal material, and had a bitumen content of up to 3500 ppm. One sample had a TOC of 12.6 wt. %, a T_{max} of 416°C (immature), an S_2 of 91.6 kg/t, and a HI of 727 mg HC/g TOC. In summary, the Heath Formation is an excellent source rock.

Oil–Source Rock Correlation

The oil being produced from the Tyler Formation in Rosebud and Musselshell counties has a moderate API gravity of 29–33° API, a low sulfur content of up to 0.7 wt. %, low concentrations of nickel and vanadium, a low asphaltene content averaging 3.4%, and a saturated hydrocarbon content of 42–50%.

For this study, crude oil from Big Wall, Little Wall Creek, and Sumatra fields were analyzed using gas chromatography and mass spectrometry for C_{12+} gas chromatograms and biological markers and stable carbon isotopes. These geochemical data for the three oils were compared to several Heath source rock extracts (Table 23.3). Rinaldi (1988) also studied oils from the Big Wall and Sumatra fields which showed excellent agreement with the data presented here.

Figure 23.6 compares the chromatograms of the three oils having C_{12+} saturated hydrocarbons with a similar chromatogram for an extract of the thermally immature Heath source rock. Each oil had a peak normal alkane of C_{15}, and a pristane–phytane ratio of ≤1.0, which is indicative of marine algal–planktonic organic material preserved under anoxic conditions. The oils also appear to have been expelled at low thermal maturity based on their chromatographic profiles, such as high pristane to n-C_{17} and phytane to n-C_{18} ratios (Figure 23.7), as well as on the light hydrocarbon ratios described by Thompson (1979, 1983).

Table 23.2. Summary of source rock data for the Heath Formation[a]

Core Site	Depth (m)	TOC (wt. %)	S$_2$ Yield (mg HC/g rock)	Gas vs. Oil (Pyrolysis-GC)	δ^{13}C$_{KPY}$ (‰)	D$_o$	δ^{13}C Correlation
A	32.0–33.2	4.14	25.4	Dominant oil	−28.8	2.0	Poor
	47.9–48.5	10.34	72.6	Dominant oil	−29.5	1.3	Poor
	91.4–92.1	1.33	1.1	Mixed oil/gas	−30.1	0.7	Acceptable
	117.3–120.7	6.19	34.9	Dominant oil	−29.8	1.0	Fair
B	70.1–75.3	7.34	39.8	Dominant oil	−30.6	0.2	Excellent
	105.5–106.1	0.38	0.0	—	—	—	—
C	82.6–83.8	13.63	80.0	Dominant oil	−31.2	−0.4	Excellent
	106.7–107.3	3.59	15.0	Dominant oil	−30.4	0.4	Excellent
D	66.4–67.1	2.67	9.2	Dominant oil	−30.2	0.6	Acceptable
	71.3–74.1	9.48	54.9	Dominant oil	−30.8	0.0	Excellent
E	15.5–18.3	9.22	48.8	Dominant oil	−31.0	−0.2	Excellent
F	44.5–47.5	9.33	48.1	Dominant oil	−30.7	0.1	Excellent
G	29.9–31.1	6.68	4.5	Dominant gas	−31.1	−0.3	Excellent
					−25.6[b]	5.2[b]	Poor[b]

[a]Abbreviations: KPY, kerogen pyrolyzate; D$_o$, difference between δ^{13}C whole oil and pyrolyzate values (<0.5, excellent correlation; <1.0, acceptable; <1.3, fair; ≥1.3, poor).
[b]Sample from a coal stringer at 30.5 m.

These C$_{12+}$ chromatographic data on the pristane–phytane ratios agree well with those published by Rinaldi (1988). He has suggested an environment of deposition such as a lake or a shallow mesohaline lagoon. When these data are placed in the geologic framework previously discussed, the environment of deposition indicated is a partially restricted, shallow marine environment, grading upward into shallow hypersaline or sabkha environments (based on the presence of evaporites). However, since the Heath source rock is widespread, a restricted marine environment is probably a more reasonable interpretation.

The most compelling evidence that the Heath Formation is the source rock for the oil in the Tyler Formation comes from a comparison of the stable carbon isotopic composition of kerogen and kerogen pyrolyzate in the source rocks with the stable carbon isotopic values of the whole oil and its fractions. The biological marker data from gas chromatography–mass spectrometry (GC-MS) analysis further refines this oil–source rock correlation. Oil–source rock correlations in the past have been performed by comparing the carbon isotopic composition of kerogen isolates to the values from oil or oil fractions (Stahl, 1977; Powell et al., 1984). This case study uses an approach in which the kerogen, kerogen pyrolyzate, and source rock extract are compared to the carbon isotopic composition of the oil (described in Burwood et al., 1985, 1988; Cole et al., 1987). Previous studies indicate that an excellent correlation results when the kerogen pyrolyzate and source rock extract values are within ±0.5‰ of the oil. An acceptable correlation is within ±1.0‰.

The relationship of the δ^{13}C values for kerogen pyrolyzate, kerogen, and extract of the Heath source rock to that of the whole oil illustrates that the oil correlates best with the kerogen pyrolyzate (Figure 23.5). Generally, the kerogen pyrolyzate is about 1.0–1.5‰ lighter than the kerogen and is most similar to the oil. The only exception is from site A at 302 ft (92 m) where the pyrolyzate is 4.5‰ lighter than the kerogen. However, this anomalous value was from an isotopically heavier, coaly interval, but the pyrolyzate was similar to the oil-prone values observed in the source rock intervals. This suggests that the oil-prone material in the coal intervals may be the same as the marine shales.

Excluding the anomalous values from the coal intervals, the δ^{13}C values for the kerogen and kerogen pyrolyzate average −28.9‰ and −30.4‰, respectively, for the Heath source rock. By using an average δ^{13}C value of −30.8‰ for the whole oil (Table 23.3), an excellent correlation (±0.5‰) results when compared to the kerogen pyrolyzate. If the Heath source rock data from each location are compared to the oils, six of the sites have excellent matches to the oils. Only the source rock samples from site A do not match the oil. At the other sites, almost all the δ^{13}C values for the source rock extract were about 0.5–1.0‰ heavier than the oils, suggesting that only longer chain hydrocarbons were extracted and that perhaps thermal maturity (a pyrolyzate is acquired by heating the kerogen) plays a role in comparison of δ^{13}C values. Figure 23.8 compares the range of values and average value for the kerogen pyrolyzate (solid triangle, excluding the coal data) with isotopic data for the three oils to show the excellent correlation.

Biological marker data acquired from GC-MS for both the oil and source rock extract are additional evidence for the oil–source rock correlation. Figure 23.9 compares the hopanes (m/z 191) and the steranes (m/z 217) from the

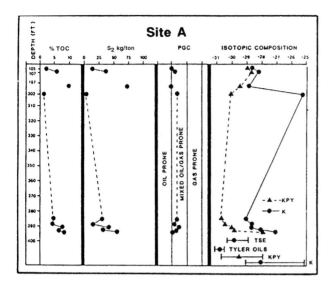

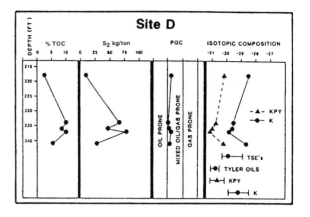

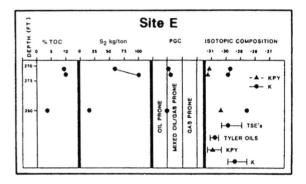

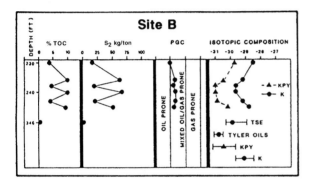

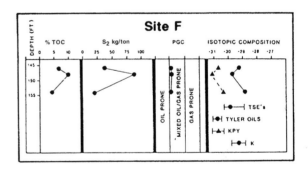

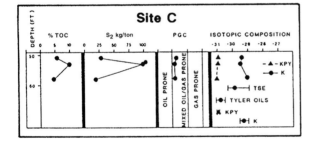

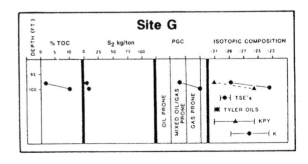

Figure 23.5. Source rock and oil data for seven shallow (<400 m) core holes drilled by the Montana Bureau of Mines and Geology. Corehole locations (A–G) are shown in Figure 23.11. Abbreviations: KPY, kerogen pyrolyzate; K, kerogen; TSE, source rock extract. (From Derkey et al., 1985.)

Table 23.3. Geochemical Data Characterizing Oil in Tyler Formation and a Source Rock Extract from Heath Formation

Data	Sample ID Number			
	HCB-656	HCB-657	HCB-658	HCB-647
Field	Big Wall	Little Wall	Sumatra	Site B
Depth (m)	915	915	1432	72-74
Formation	Tyler	Tyler	Tyler	Heath
API°	29.3	33.6	33.3	—
% Sulfur	0.97	0.69	0.44	—
% Asphaltene	6.0	2.1	2.1	42.5
% Distillate	15.9	19.4	20.4	0
% Saturate[a]	43.9	42.5	50.5	9.8
Carbon preference index	1.07	1.06	1.11	1.23
pristane/phytane	0.93	0.97	1.02	1.06
pristane/n-C_{17}	1.4	1.5	1.2	1.6
phytane/n-C_{18}	1.6	1.8	1.2	1.5
Paraffin index I[b]	0.95	0.62	0.72	—
Paraffin index II[b]	22.3	18.7	19.4	—
$\delta^{13}C_{oil}$ (‰)	−31.1	−30.8	−30.5	−30.1
Gammacerane	Yes	Yes	Yes	Yes

[a]Percentage opped and deasphalted oil.

[b]From Thompson (1979, 1983).

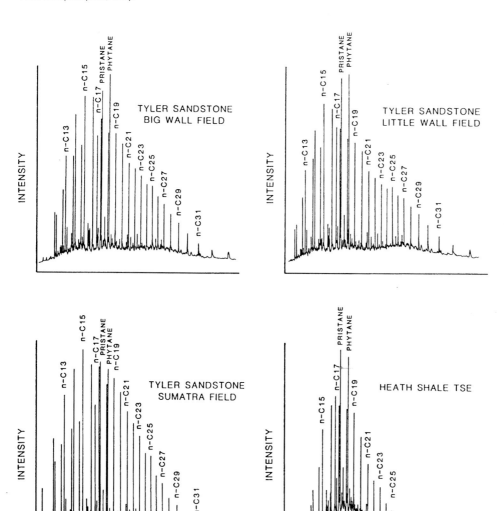

Figure 23.6. Gas chromatograms for saturated hydrocarbon fraction (C_{12+}) for three representative oils and a source rock extract (TSE) that show similar *n*-alkane and isoprenoid distributions.

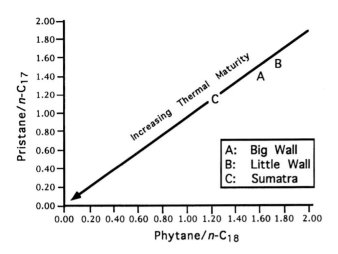

Figure 23.7. Pristane to *n*–C₁₇ versus phytane to *n*–C₁₈ ratios of the three representative oils showing their relative thermal maturities.

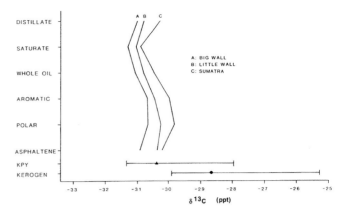

Figure 23.8. Plot comparing the carbon isotopic curves (Galimov plots) for three representative oils and their relationship to the carbon isotopic values of kerogen pyrolyzate (triangle) and kerogen (closed circle).

total soluble extracts of the source units (Figure 23.9a) to the three Tyler Formation oils (Figure 23.9b). From these biological marker traces, distinct similarities can be seen between the oils and source rocks. For the hopane peaks, these similarities are as follows: the C_{29} norhopane (peak 1) is less than C_{30} hopane (peak 2); gammacerane is abundant (indicates hypersaline environments, such as evaporites); the C_{35} hopane peak height is higher than the two peaks (C_{34}) to the left; and lower molecular weight hopanes are abundant (peaks left of peak 1). In most samples and source intervals, the steranes are characterized by abundant diasteranes and a dominance of $C_{29} > C_{27} > C_{28}$ steranes (Figure 23.10). Since the Heath source rock varies significantly, as shown by the carbon isotopes and the general source rock data, some variability in the GC-MS ratios exist. However, comparison of the data between the oil and source rock strongly suggest that the oil being produced from the Tyler Formation originated from the Heath Formation. For these reasons, the Heath–Tyler is a known petroleum system.

EXPULSION AND TRAPPING OF HEATH-DERIVED OILS

The generation and subsequent expulsion of oil from a source rock is controlled by the thermal maturity and, most importantly, the kinetics that apply to the kerogen type. The maturity parameters used to define generation and expulsion are in the literature and are based on kinetic parameters initially described by Tissot and Espitalié (1975). Based on the source rock parameters that identify the marine algal Heath Formation as an oil-prone source rock, the modified kinetic parameters assume a low heating rate. Thus, the Heath kerogen probably attained the onset of generation at 105–110°C and expulsion at 125–130°C. Applying the time–temperature equation from Roydon et al. (1980), these tempera-

tures translate into vitrinite reflectances of 0.55 and 0.75%, respectively. By applying these results to the geochemical data, we can show where the Heath source rock is thermally mature for hydrocarbon generation and expulsion (Figure 23.11).

Since the region where the Heath is mature is established, the timing of oil expulsion must be defined. This is accomplished by modeling the burial and thermal history of the source rock. To construct a model, certain parameters are required: the burial history (previously discussed) where the source rock is buried deepest, the present-day geothermal gradient (assumed to be about 40°C/km, or 2.2°F/100 ft), and thermal maturity values of the source rock (0.8–0.9% R_o) for calibration of the model. In addition, an estimate of both the surface temperature and heat flow back through time to the age of the source rock is required.

If 1200–1500 m (4000–5000 ft) of erosion is assumed as a result of the Laramide orogeny, then the burial history for the most thermally mature part of the Heath source rock can be constructed (Figure 23.12). Other periods of erosion prior to the Laramide orogeny are less important. The north-south cross section across the Big Snowy trough shows several periods of erosion (Figure 23.4). Erosion first occurred in the Pennsylvanian during deposition of the Tyler Formation. Erosion during the Middle Jurassic created an unconformity (Figures 23.4 and 23.13). The Laramide orogeny occurred during Late Cretaceous–early Tertiary and is the most important erosional event described in the literature (Fanshawe, 1978; Maughn, 1984; Peterson and MacCary, 1987).

The Tyler erosional event occurred as the fluvial system downcut into the Heath Formation. This event would not have influenced the thermal maturation of the source rock. The Middle Jurassic erosional event is believed to have only eroded up to 500–700 m (1500–2200 ft) of section. This event would also not have influenced maturation of the source rock for the following reason. If enough section was present to have thermally matured the Heath source rock prior to Jurassic erosion, then the present-day location and composition of the oil should be questioned. Because this

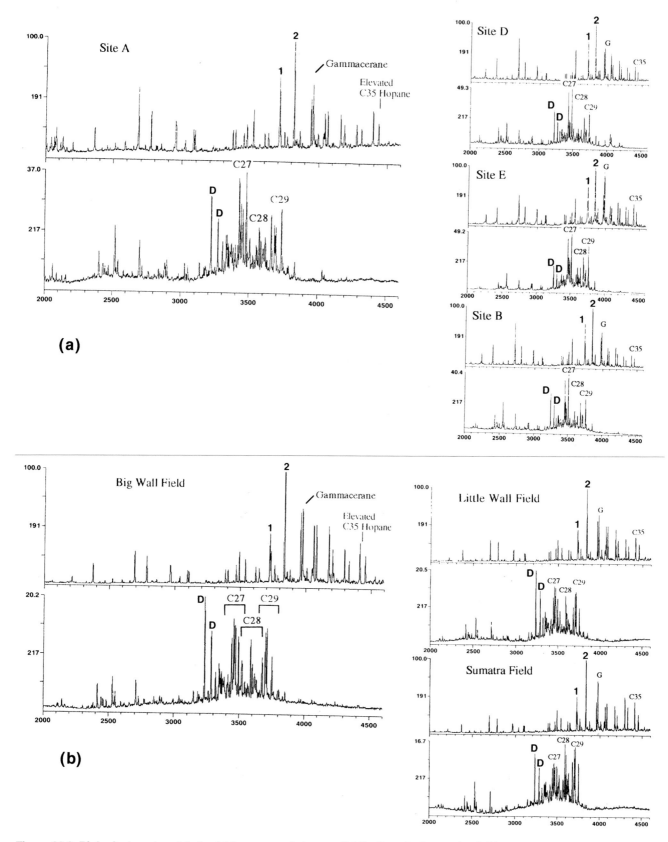

Figure 23.9. Biological marker data for (a) hopane and sterane distributions in the total soluble extracts from the Heath Formation source units from four core sites and (b) hopane and sterane distributions from three representative Tyler reservoired oils. Two biological marker traces or fragmentograms are shown for each sample: top is *m/z* 191 trace (hopanes) and bottom is *m/z* 217 trace (steranes). Peaks: 1, norhopane; 2, hopane; G, gammacerane; D, diasterane; C_{27}–C_{29}, steranes with 27–29 carbon atoms.

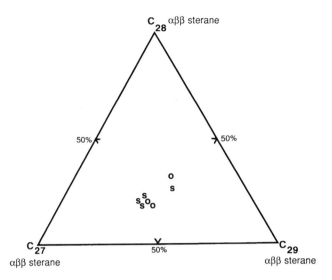

Figure 23.10. Ternary plot showing the relationship between the αββ C$_{27}$–C$_{29}$ steranes for the oils (o) and source rock extract (s).

erosional event removed section overlying the Tyler Formation (Peterson and MacCary, 1987), the reservoir rocks in the Tyler would have been breached, resulting in loss of reservoir integrity (no longer any seals), and what oils remained would have been biodegraded. Neither of these scenarios has happened.

The only plausible scenario for expelling and trapping oil in Tyler reservoir rocks without biodegradation or alteration is the one modeled in Figure 23.13. In this model, maximum burial of the source rock occurred during the early Tertiary, when hydrocarbon expulsion

was achieved. Then structural inversion of the Big Snowy trough during the Laramide orogeny formed anticlinal traps into which the oil remigrated. The stratigraphic traps were filled where the active source rock juxtaposed the reservoir rock. Where thermal maturity was sufficient to expel oil, the stratigraphic traps were filled. For this reason, the geographic extent of the Heath–Tyler petroleum system is coincident with the pod of active source rock (Figure 23.11).

PETROLEUM SYSTEM EFFICIENCY

Since the previous scenario is the most plausible one for thermal maturation of the Heath source rock to expulsion temperatures and then migration of the oil to potential traps, we need to estimate the amount of hydrocarbons that were most likely expelled, which can then be compared to the in-place oil to determine the generation–accumulation efficiency (GAE). To achieve this estimate, we use the method described in Schmoker (Chapter 19, this volume). To determine the mass of hydrocarbons generated, M, we use the following:

$$M \text{ (g TOC)} = [\text{TOC (wt. \%)}/100] \times \rho \text{ (g/cm}^3) \times V \text{ (cm}^3) \quad (1)$$

where ρ is the density of the source rock and V is the volume of mature source rock. For this case, we assumed a density of 2.3 g/cm^3, an average TOC of 7.6 wt. % where immature, and a volume of 800 km^2 × 6.0 m of source rock. This results in 8.39 × 10^{14} g TOC available for conversion to oil or gas.

By using the Rock-Eval pyrolysis data, or hydrogen

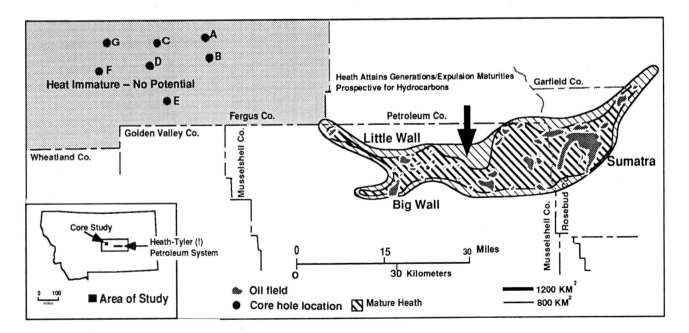

Figure 23.11. Map showing the pod of active source rock (inner line at 800 km^2) based on a peak expulsion of 0.75% R$_o$. Maximum R$_o$ (about 0.85–0.9%) is attained near the Sumatra field. The outer line (1200 km^2) is the geographic extent of the Heath–Tyler(!) petroleum system. The location of the shallow (<400 m) core holes in Fergus County are shown (see Figure 23.5). Here the source rock is immature, with R$_o$ ranging from 0.45 to 0.6%.

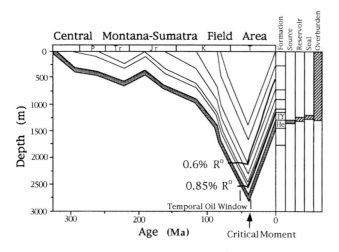

Figure 23.12. Burial history and thermal maturation models for the Heath source rock show that expulsion occurred during maximum burial (at the critical moment) during the Tertiary (~40 Ma). The essential elements are shown, relative to depth, on the right. R$_o$ values are shown relative to time.

index (HI) values, we can estimate hydrocarbons generated, R. For this determination, we use the following equation:

$$R \text{ (mg HC/g TOC)} = \text{HI}_o \text{ (mg HC/g TOC)} - \text{HI}_p \text{ (mg HC/g TOC)} \quad (2)$$

where HI$_o$ is the original and HI$_p$ the present-day hydrogen index. For the Heath source rock, we assume an HI$_o$ of 575 where immature and an average of 400 for the mature area. For the most mature part of the system, this value is actually about 200 since the Heath has attained postpeak maturation. However, this area is small. From equation 2, R = 175 mg HC/g TOC.

Calculation of the mass of hydrocarbons generated, HCG, is done as follows:

$$\text{HCG (kg HC)} \quad (3)$$
$$= R \text{ (mg HC/g TOC)} \times M \text{ (g TOC)} \times 10^{-6} \text{ (kg/mg)}$$

which results in 1.46×10^{11} kg HC. If instead, we assumed the 1200-km^2 case (Figure 23.11), the HCG would be 2.20×10^{11} kg HC.

These calculations indicate the amount of oil generated from the pod of active source rock within the petroleum system. To determine the efficiency of this system, these values (using the 800-km^2 area) for oil generated and expelled must be compared to the amount of in-place hydrocarbons. As of 1988, the Tyler sandstones have produced almost 100 million bbl of oil (Table 23.1) (Maughn, 1984; Rinaldi, 1988). If we assume a recovery factor of 25% for oil (most Tyler production is oil), the Tyler fields account for a total of about 0.56×10^{11} kg (400 million bbl) of in-place oil.

By comparing the in-place oil to the amount of oil generated, we can estimate the generation–accumulation

efficiency for the 800-km^2 area as 38% for this system. This means that for every barrel of oil generated, about 0.4 bbl has been found trapped and 0.1 bbl will be or has been recovered.

Since the Heath Formation ranges from marginal to peak maturity, these numbers indicate fair expulsion efficiencies, Thus, we can assume that a large portion of generated hydrocarbons remained within the source rock interval. We can expect little loss along the short oil migration route and little loss to leakage because (1) the petroleum system is sealed in a relatively restrictive, compact area, (2) the carrier beds are lenticular fluvial sandstones belonging to the Tyler Formation, and (3) the reservoir rocks are in close proximity or in direct contact with the active source rock. Therefore, most of the oil not accounted for remains in the Heath shale itself, with a smaller amount yet to be discovered in adjacent reservoirs.

RESERVOIR AND TRAPPING MECHANISMS

Several papers have addressed the factors that control the occurrence, size, and position of the oil fields, whose reservoir rock is in the Tyler sandstone, relative to the thermally mature Heath source rock. Most oil production is from the lenticular sandstone bodies of the Stonehouse Canyon Member in the Tyler Formation (Maughn, 1984). Since these sandstone bodies usually incise the active source rock, they are easily charged with oil.

In addition, Kranzler (1966) showed that present-day structure is helpful but not the controlling factor in locating the Tyler fields. He did, however, attribute the location of the fields to the lenticular nature of the sandstone bodies and paleostructure. Kranzler illustrated the coincidence of Tyler fields to the subcrop of the Heath, the source rock he suspected of charging the sandstone bodies. He showed that this subcrop was beneath every field except for Ivanhoe, which is located on a migration pathway. Present-day and paleostructural reconstructions by Kranzler (Figures 23.13) show how these sandstone bodies would be charged using his concept. Kranzler, as well as Norwood (1965), also noted how the structural inversion during the Laramide orogeny may have caused redistribution of Tyler fields. Simply stated, the Laramide orogeny inversion caused synclines to become anticlines and anticlines to become synclines.

Fanshawe (1978) stated that the distribution of Tyler fields is without rhyme or reason regarding present-day structure. He shows that the Alice dome, a "textbook" structure that is empty, and the Breed Creek and Gumbo Ridge oil fields do not relate to any structural anomaly, and that Stensvad field appears to be a fault trap but is not. He further suggests that the controlling factor in exploring for Tyler oil may be found in the pre-Piper structure. Fanshawe states that, based on this structure, Breed Creek and Gumbo Ridge are stratigraphically controlled, while Alice dome is a structural low. He also suggests that the Stensvad and Sumatra fields are stratigraphic traps modified by the Laramide inversion.

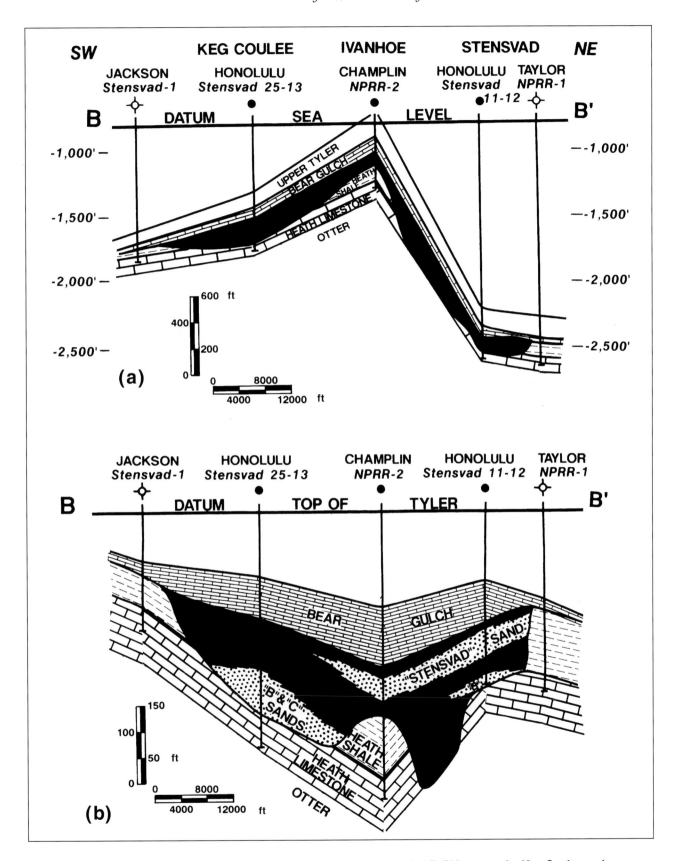

Figure 23.13. (a) Present-day structural and (b) paleostructural cross section B–B' between the Keg Coulee and Stensvad oil fields in central Montana. Cross section location shown on Figure 23.1. Note the structural inversion (synclines to anticlines) caused by the Laramide orogeny. The black unit is the lower Tyler Formation incising the Heath Formation. (From Kranzler, 1966.)

The distribution of Tyler oil fields can probably be determined by using a combination of paleostructural reconstructions of the Tyler Formation during Mesozoic time and the Laramide orogeny and by locating the sandstone bodies in the Stonehouse Canyon Member. Most importantly, it is necessary to know where these sandstone bodies lie in relation to the active source rock, as suggested by Rinaldi (1988).

Alice dome is a good case for analyzing where Tyler oil fields should or should not be. As discussed in many papers, Alice dome is a large but dry structure (Kranzler, 1966; Fanshawe, 1978; Rinaldi, 1988). Using paleotectonic structure maps, both Kranzler (1966) and Fanshawe (1978) showed that this area was relatively flat prior to the Laramide orogeny. Kranzler further suggested that the position of Alice dome during the Pennsylvanian did not lie in the migration pathway. Rinaldi (1988) further refined this by stating that the Heath source rock was not mature enough in this area and was never able to charge the structure. Rinaldi further suggests that the paleostructural position of Alice dome, a shallow synclinal feature, never contained enough overburden rock above the source rock to generate petroleum. This is undoubtedly true, but since Alice Dome is dry, we can also assume that post-Laramide remigration of oil never reached this structural trap. This suggests either that insufficient oil was expelled from the active Heath source rock to provide an oil show or that the dome was not in the oil migration pathway.

The remigration of oil caused by the Laramide structural inversion is an important question. We believe the answer to this question can be resolved by addressing the amount of oil expelled from the Heath source rock, the amount found in-place in the Tyler reservoir rocks in relation to the pod of active source rock, and the amount of oil that is still in the source rock. According to our calculations, for every 100 bbl of oil generated, 10 bbl is recoverable (38 bbl of oil in-place). These numbers suggest that most of the expelled oil charged the juxtaposed Tyler sandstone reservoirs. Those fields that were located along a viable migration route and within the pod of active source rock were also charged. This leaves a considerable amount of oil still in the Heath shale or yet to be found.

SUMMARY

From source rock and oil characterization data, a successful oil–source rock correlation between the two primary components of the petroleum system has been established. When incorporated with the burial and thermal history modeling, these results show that the Heath–Tyler(!) petroleum system is limited to that portion of the Big Snowy trough in central Montana where the pod of active source rock is mapped. As shown by the volumetric calculations, this petroleum system still has some remaining oil potential. The critical moment of this system is that time of maximum burial during early Tertiary when expulsion occurred. This moment is almost coincident with the structural develop-

ment of the anticlinal trends. The system contains two types of traps: lenticular channel sandstone bodies that incised into the source rock formed stratigraphic traps and late forming anticlines created structural traps. Since this is a well-explored hydrocarbon province, all known structural traps have been tested with at least one exploratory hole.

The yet-to-find oil accumulations probably exist as stratigraphic traps within the geographic extent of the Heath–Tyler petroleum system and along the migration pathway of the sandstone bodies. As stated by Fanshawe (1978), understanding the paleosandstone body distribution along this migration route undoubtedly holds the key to finding the undiscovered oil accumulations.

Acknowledgments   *The authors wish to express their gratitude to BP Exploration for permission to publish this scientific paper. We also want to thank Joe Devay and Roger Sassen at BP Exploration for reviewing this paper and John Daniel at the University of Minnesota–Morris who has contributed data and samples throughout the years.*

References Cited

Burwood, R., G. A. Cole, R. J. Drozd, H. I. Halpern, I. E. Penfield, and R. A. Sedivy, 1985, Carbon isotopic characterization of some north Alaska petroleums and potential source rock kerogen assemblages, *in* L. B. Magoon and G. E. Claypool, eds., Alaska North Slope Oil–Rock Correlation Study: AAPG Studies in Geology 20, p. 123–137.

Burwood, R., R. J. Drozd, H. I. Halpern, and R. A. Sedivy, 1988, Carbon isotopic variations of kerogen pyrolyzates: Organic Geochemistry, v. 12, n. 2, p. 195–205.

Cole, G. A., and J. A. Daniel, 1984, Thermal maturity trends of the Heath Formation, Fergus County, Montana, *in* J. Woodward, F. F. Meissner, and J. L. Clayton, eds., Hydrocarbon Source Rocks of the Greater Rocky Mountain Region: Denver, Rocky Mountain Association of Geologists, p. 275–280.

Cole, G. A., R. J. Drozd, R. A. Sedivy, and H. I. Halpern, 1987, Organic geochemistry and oil–source correlations, Paleozoic of Ohio: AAPG Bulletin, v. 71, n. 7, p. 788–809.

Cox, W. E., 1973, Fergus County research project—evaluation of Heath–Tyler oil shales, with laboratory analyses by John W. Blumer: Montana Bureau of Mines and Geology Open-File Report 15, 85 p.

Cox, W. E., and G. A. Cole, 1981, Oil shale potential in the Heath and Tyler Formations, central Montana: Montana Bureau of Mines and Geology Geologic Map 19, 2 sheets.

Derkey, P. D., F. N. Abercrombie, S. M. Vuke, and J. A. Daniel, 1985, Geology and oil shale resources of the Heath Formation, Fergus County, Montana: Montana Bureau of Mines and Geology Memoir 57, 100 p.

Desborough, G. A., F. G. Poole, and G. N. Green, 1981, Metalliferous oil shales in central Montana and northeastern Nevada: USGS Open-File Report 81-121, 14 p.

Dow, W. G., 1974, Application of oil correlation and source rock data to exploration in Williston basin: AAPG Bulletin, v. 58, n. 7, p. 1253–1262.

Fanshawe, J. R., 1978, Central Montana tectonics and the Tyler Formation, *in* The economic geology of the Williston basin, Montana, North Dakota, South Dakota, Saskatchewan, Manitoba: 24th Annual Conference, Williston Basin Symposium, Montana Geological Society, p. 239–248.

Foster, D. I., 1956, N.W. Sumatra field (Montana), *in* Judith Mountains, central Montana: 7th Annual Field Conference, Billings Geological Society, p. 116–123.

Freeman, O. W., 1922, Oil in the Quadrant Formation in Montana: Engineering and Mining Journal, v. 113, n. 19, p. 825–827.

Galimov, E. M., 1973, Carbon isotopes in oil and gas geology [izotopy ugleroda v neftgazovoy geologic]: Nedra, Moscow, NASA, Washington, D.C., 1974, p. 384.

Kranzler, I., 1966, Origin of oil in lower member of Tyler Formation of central Montana: AAPG Bulletin, v. 50, n. 10, p. 2245–2259.

Maughn, E. K., 1984, Paleogeographic setting of Pennsylvanian Tyler Formation and underlying Mississippian rocks in Montana and North Dakota: AAPB Bulletin, v. 68, n. 2, p. 178–195.

Maughn, E. K. and A. E. Roberts, 1967, Big Snowy and Amsden groups and the Mississippian–Pennsylvanian boundary in Montana: USGS Professional Paper 554-B, 27 p.

Montana Oil and Gas Conservation Division, 1987, Montana oil and gas Annual review 1987: Dept. of Natural Resources and Conservation, State of Montana, vol. 31, 62 p.

Mundt, P. A., 1956, The Tyler and Alaska Bench Formations, *in* Judith Mountains, central Montana, 7th Annual Field Conference: Billings Geological Society, Billings, Montana, p. 46–51.

Norwood, E. E., 1965, Geological history of central and south-central Montana: AAPG Bulletin, v. 49, p. 1824–1832.

Peterson, J. A., and L. M. MacCary, 1987, Regional stratigraphy and general petroleum geology of the U.S. portion of the Williston basin and adjacent areas, *in* J. A. Peterson et al., eds., Williston basin: anatomy of a cratonic oil province: Denver, Rocky Mountain Association of Geologists, p. 9–44.

Powell, T. G., R. W. MacQueen, J. F. Barker, and D. G. Bree, 1984, Geochemical character and origin of Ontario oils: Bulletin of Canadian Petroleum Geology, v. 32, p. 289–312.

Rinaldi, G. G. L., 1988, Oil–source studies in central Montana: Correlations and migration implications, *in* Advances in Organic Geochemistry: Organic Geochemistry 1987, v. 13, n. 1–3, p. 373–376.

Roberts, A. E., 1979, Northern Rocky Mountains and adjacent plains region, *in* L. C. Craig et al., eds., Paleotectonic investigations of the Mississippian System in the United States—part 1: USGS Professional Paper 1010, p. 221–248.

Roydon, L., J. G. Sclater, and R. P. von Herzen, 1980, Continental margin subsidence and heat flow: important parameters for formation of petroleum hydrocarbons: AAPG Bulletin, v. 64, p. 173–187.

Scott, H. W., 1935, Some Carboniferous stratigraphy in Montana and northwestern Wyoming: Journal of Geology, v. 43, p. 1011–1032.

Smith, D. L., and E. H. Gilmour, 1979, The Mississippian and Pennsylvanian (Carboniferous) Systems in the United States: USGS Professional Paper 1110-X, p. X1–X32.

Staggs, J. O., 1959, Stensvad field, *in* Billings Geological Society Guidebook: 10th Annual Field Conference, Billings Geological Society, p. 69–74.

Stahl, W. J., 1977, Carbon and nitrogen isotopes in hydrocarbon research and exploration: Chemical Geology, v. 20, p. 121–149.

Swetland, P. J., J. L. Clayton, and E. G. Sable, 1978, Petroleum source bed potential of Mississippian–Pennsylvanian rocks in parts of Montana, Idaho, Utah, and Colorado: The Mountain Geologist, Rocky Mountain Association of Geologists, v. 14, n. 3, p. 79–87.

Thompson, K. F. M., 1979, Light hydrocarbons in subsurface sediments: Geochimica et Cosmochimica Acta, v. 43, p. 657–672.

Thompson, K. F. M., 1983, Classification and thermal history of petroleum based on light hydrocarbons: Geochimica et Cosmochimica Acta, v. 47, p. 303–316.

Tissot, B., and J. Espitalié, 1975, Lé Evolution thermique de la matiere organiques des sediments: application úne simulation mathimatique: Review Institute Français du Petrole, v. 30, p. 43–77.

Williams, J. A., 1974, Characterization of oil types in Williston basin: AAPG Bulletin, v. 58, n. 7, p. 1243–1252.

*"The most important factor in the
origin of petroleum is the thermal
history of the source rock."*
—John M. Hunt

Passage from Hunt, J. M., 1979, Petroleum Geochemistry and Geology: W.H. Freeman, p. 148.

Magoon, L. B, and W. G. Dow, eds., 1994, The petroleum
system—from source to trap: AAPG Memoir 60.

Chapter **24**

Point Pleasant–Brassfield(!) Petroleum System, Appalachian Basin, U.S.A.

Richard J. Drozd*

Gary A. Cole**

BP Research
Houston, Texas, U.S.A.

Abstract

The Point Pleasant–Brassfield(!) petroleum system, located in eastern Ohio and western parts of Pennsylvania and West Virginia, created a charge of 150 billion bbl of oil equivalent. The system covers 40,000 km^2 and encompasses numerous small oil and gas fields in eastern Ohio. Sedimentary rocks included in this system are Ordovician–Triassic in age and were deposited in the Appalachian basin. Several source rocks exist within the basin, including shales of the Ordvocian Point Pleasant Formation, the Devonian Ohio Shale and Olentangy Shale, and the Mississippian Sunbury Shale. Most of the oil in the Silurian Clinton reservoir rock (Brassfield Formation) originated from the Point Pleasant Formation. Oil generated from the Point Pleasant source rock has chemical characteristics similar to early Paleozoic oils. Based on paraffin indices, oil from this source rock is very mature to supermature and has lost most biological markers.

Generation–migration–accumulation lasted from Point Pleasant deposition in Middle Ordovician time through maximum deposition in the Late Triassic–Early Jurassic, a duration of about 250 m.y. The mass of hydrocarbons generated by the source rock in the Point Pleasant Formation totaled 75 billion bbl of oil. Of this, some found its way to traps with Silurian reservoir rocks on the east flank of the Cincinnati–Findlay arch. Only 400 million bbl of in-place oil can be accounted for in known fields. The remaining oil and gas generated by the Point Pleasant source rock was probably lost in subeconomic accumulations along the migration pathway between the pod of active source rock and the geographic extent of the Point Pleasant–Brassfield petroleum system.

INTRODUCTION

Oil and gas production from the Point Pleasant–Brassfield(!) petroleum system is in eastern Ohio and western Pennsylvania and West Virginia. During the late 1800s, Ohio was the leading producer of petroleum from fields along the prolific Lima–Indiana trend northwest of the Cincinnati–Findlay arch in central Indiana and northwestern Ohio. These fields produce from reservoir rocks within the Cambrian Knox Dolomite and Ordovician Trenton Limestone. Although the oil from these fields has a composition similar to the oil in the Point Pleasant–Brassfield petroleum system, the Lima–Indiana oil is part of a separate petroleum system in the Michigan basin. The Point Pleasant–Brassfield petroleum system lies southeast of the Cincinnati–Findlay arch in the

Appalachian basin. Here, the lower Paleozoic rocks produce oil that is similar in composition to that found in the Lima–Indiana trend but in more deeply buried reservoir rocks in eastern Ohio (Figure 24.1).

Work by Cole et al. (1987) demonstrated that the top of the oil window in the Appalachian basin is presently about 3000 ft (~1000 m) subsea and that the axis of the Cincinnati–Findlay arch is thermally immature above the basement rock. Furthermore, they demonstrated that the onset of oil generation for source rocks in the Appalachian basin occurred in Permian time or well after the arch developed during the Devonian. The lack of significant oil accumulations along the axis of the arch, the prevalence of stratigraphic traps on both flanks of the arch, and the significant amounts of gas in these fields all indicate that the oil generated downdip in the

*Present address: Westport Technology Center International, Houston, Texas, U.S.A.
**Present address: Saudi Aramco, Dhahran, Saudi Arabia.

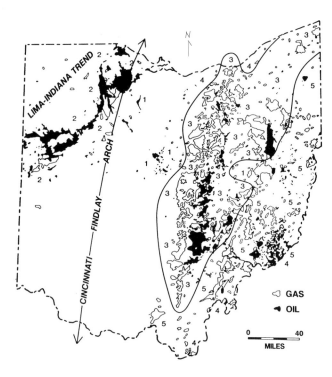

Figure 24.1. Map showing the location of oil and gas fields in Ohio. Map numbers: (1) Cambrian–Ordovician Knox Dolomite, (2) Ordovician Trenton Limestone, (3) Silurian Clinton Sandstone, (4) Devonian Ohio Shale, (5) Mississippian Berea Sandstone; outline indicates production from Clinton sands. Except for small oil fields that produce from the Knox Dolomite, the oil and gas fields for the Point Pleasant–Brassfield(!) petroleum system produce from the Silurian Clinton sandstone. The oil fields in the Lima–Indiana trend in northwestern Ohio are in a separate petroleum system, as are the oil fields that produce from the Devonian Ohio Shale and the Mississippian Berea Sandstone. (After Gray, 1983.)

Appalachian basin was unable to migrate freely to the arch axis. Much of the oil was trapped downdip and cracked to gas. Thus, the Cincinnati–Findlay arch separates two petroleum systems even though the oil being produced from Lima–Indiana trend northwest of the arch is similar to the early Paleozoic oil southeast of the arch in eastern Ohio.

Cole et al. (1987), as part of a wider study of Ohio oils and source rocks, used oil–oil and oil–source rock correlations to determine that three groups of oils produced from the Appalachian basin could be correlated to three different source rocks. Oil from group 1, from Cambrian–Silurian reservoir rocks, is correlated to the Point Pleasant Formation. More recently Wallace and Roen (1989) have reviewed the source rock potential of the Point Pleasant shale and equivalent units over a wider area of the Appalachian basin. In addition to formally naming this petroleum system, this case study reviews pertinent geology and geochemistry to map its geographic, stratigrapic, and temporal extent.

REGIONAL GEOLOGY

The stratigraphic column of the Appalachian basin shows the formation names, potential source rocks, and producing reservoir rocks for the entire basin as well as the essential elements for the Point Pleasant–Brassfield(!) petroleum system (Figure 24.2). Of the four source rocks, only the Point Pleasant Formation is important to this petroleum system. Based on less than adequate data, the Brassfield Formation (or Silurian Clinton Sandstone* on Figure 24.1), which unconformably overlies the Ordovician rocks, contains the most oil in this system, followed by the Cabot Head and Whitewater formations and the Knox Dolomite. The Knox Dolomite contains a minor amount of oil east of the axis and directly downdip of the Cincinnati–Findlay arch. The Trenton Limestone lacks oil in the Appalachian basin. Oil and gas found in Devonian and younger strata are attributed to the younger source rocks (Cole et al., 1987).

Major structural features of Ohio are the Cincinnati–Findlay arch, which trends northward through western Ohio, and the Ohio–Indiana platform on the west, which the arch grades into (Figure 24.3). This arch and platform form a persistent structural high between the Appalachian basin to the east in Ohio, the Illinois basin to the southwest in Illinois, and the Michigan basin to the northwest in northwestern Ohio and Michigan. The structural contours on top of the Precambrian basement rock illustrate the general configuration of the overlying Paleozoic sedimentary rocks throughout Ohio.

A regional cross section through Ohio from Michigan to West Virginia shows the general configuration of the Paleozoic sedimentary rocks (Figure 24.4). Drill depth to the Precambrian basement rock is about 1000 m on the Cincinnatti–Findlay arch and is more than 4000 m in the Appalachian basin. Present-day burial depth of the Point Pleasant shale is 300–3700 m and of the Clinton sands is 0–3000 m. Many of the stratigraphic units thicken from the arch into the Appalachian basin, but the greatest thickening occurs within the Devonian Ohio Shale interval. Surface exposures are youngest (Pennsylvanian age) in the axis of the basin and get progressively older (Ordovician age) as the arch axis is approached. This cross section indicates that the Cincinnatti–Findlay arch is a Paleozoic high and that the overburden rock above the Point Pleasant shale is all Paleozoic, which suggests that hydrocarbon generation took place from Late Devonian time to near the end of Paleozoic time.

The depositional history of the Paleozoic sedimentary rocks (Figure 24.2) is well established due to the long history of hydrocarbon exploration and coal production within Ohio. The sedimentary succession relevant to this petroleum system can be summarized as follows. First, all Cambrian–Ordovician stratigraphic units are carbonate rocks that were deposited on a shallow platform with some shale representing an occasional influx of siliciclastic sediment. The Ordovician Trenton Limestone was deposited in a subtidal environment, which ranged from open shelf to platform facies.

---

*We use the term "Clinton sands to Big Lime sequence" to encompass a number of local colloquial drillers' names used in Ohio throughout the years (see Figure 24.2).

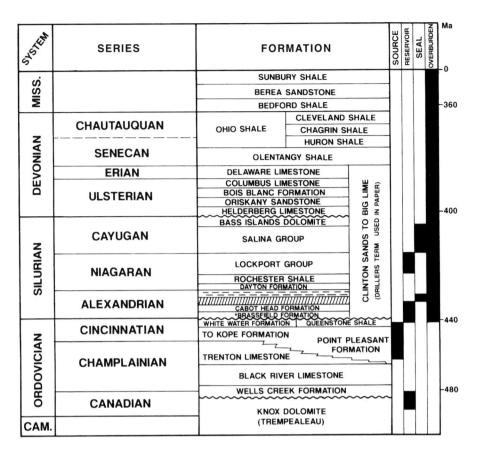

Figure 24.2. Stratigraphic section showing relationship of Point Pleasant Formation source rock with basal Silurian Clinton sands reservoir rock, as well as the seal and overburden rocks for this petroleum system in Ohio. (From Janssens, 1973; Schwietering, 1979; Cole et al., 1987.)

Southeast of the carbonate buildup on the platform, the Point Pleasant Formation was deposited in an interplatform basin setting with restricted water circulation. The deposition of the Trenton Limestone and Point Pleasant Formation ended with an influx of siliciclastic sediments from the westward-migrating Utica sea (Stith, 1979; Wickstrom and Gray, 1988). Wickstrom (1990) has concluded that Precambrian zones of weakness profoundly affected early Paleozoic sedimentation, diagenesis, and potential for hydrocarbon accumulation, leading in part to the formation of the restricted interplatform basin in which the Point Pleasant Formation was deposited.

Second, Silurian stratigraphic units, which unconformably overlie Ordovician rocks, represent a major regressive sequence containing sandstone within the Silurian portion of the Clinton sands to Big Lime sequence. The Silurian Clinton sandstone bodies were deposited as deltaic stream channels and offshore bars that interfinger with shales and siltstones (Knight, 1969; Cumberlidge and McCullough, 1985). These sandstone bodies are lenticular in central Ohio and more sheetlike in eastern Ohio. Hydrocarbon reserves are estimated at less than 60 bbl of oil or 250 mcf of gas/ac-ft, with net pay less than 7 m (20 ft), and production declining rapidly in the first few years. The Upper Silurian is characterized by deposition of prominent evaporite beds in the Salina Group, a regional seal that separates the lower Paleozoic oil from the upper Paleozoic oil (Cole et al., 1987).

Third, the Silurian Clinton sand (most of which is the Brassfield Formation) is the dominant drilling target in eastern Ohio and accounts for 71% of the completions (Gray, 1983). The only Silurian Clinton sand of this age that includes a producing reservoir is the Brassfield and Cabot Head formations (Figure 24.2). Because the Brassfield Formation is at the base of the Clinton sand and stratigraphically closest to the Point Pleasant source rock, it is in the most likely position to be charged with hydrocarbons coming from the active source rock. Thus, Brassfield Formation is used as the reservoir name for the Point Pleasant–Brassfield(!) petroleum system.

Finally, Devonian stratigraphic units, which unconformably overlie Silurian rocks, represent the return of transgressive seas and end with a major regressive unit. The Lower Devonian transgressive rocks, represented by formations in the Clinton sands to Big Lime sequence, are predominantly limestone with some siliciclastic sandstone. However, these sands lack Point Pleasant oil (Cole et al., 1987). During Middle–Late Devonian time, the Catskill delta built westward, filling the Appalachian basin. This basin fill thinned rapidly up the flank of the Cincinnatti–Findlay arch and is represented by the Upper Devonian shales of the Senecan and Chautauquan series.

Two transgressive events are related to two major orogenic pulses during the Acadian. The first event, beginning in the Early Devonian, resulted in deposition of the Oriskany Sandstone through the lower Olentangy Shale. The second event in Late Devonian yielded the

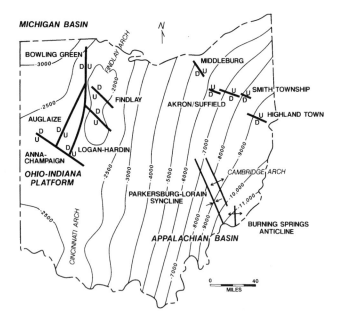

Figure 24.3. Map of major structural features in Ohio. Contour interval is 500 ft in western Ohio and 1000 ft in eastern Ohio and is drawn on top of Precambrian basement rock. (Drawn from Cole et al., 1987.)

marine shales of the upper Olentangy and Ohio shales (Johnson and Friedman, 1969; Schwietering, 1979). The Olentangy shale represents an important Upper Devonian source rock. As indicated by Cole et al. (1987), the oil in these Upper Devonian reservoir rocks are in group 2 of Cole et al. (1987) (upper Paleozoic), which originated from Upper Devonian source rocks and thus are part of a shallower petroleum system. However, this sequence of rock and all overlying units are important to the Point Pleasant–Brassfield petroleum sytem because they are the overburden rock that buries the Point Pleasant source rock (Figure 24.2).

ORGANIC GEOCHEMISTRY

Source Rock Quality

Source quality data are available from Cole et al. (1987) and Wallace and Roen (1989). Their evaluations consist of measurements of total organic carbon (TOC) content and Rock-Eval pyrolysis. Cole et al. (1987) found that most pre-Pennsylvanian strata of Ohio were of marginal organic richness. Within the pre-Devonian, only the shales of the Ordovician Point Pleasant Formation are of good source rock potential.

Based on 150 measurements from core and drill cuttings taken throughout Ohio, the Point Pleasant

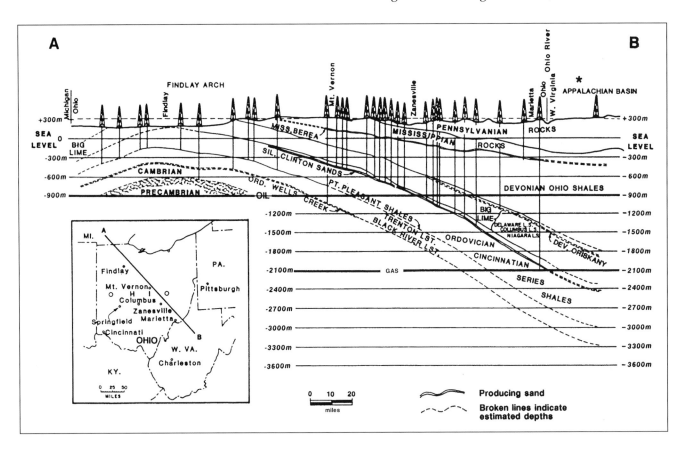

Figure 24.4. Cross section A–B illustrating the eastward thickening of sedimentary section from 790 m (2600 ft) over the Cincinnati–Finlay arch to over 3650 m (12,000 ft) in the Appalachian basin in southeastern Ohio. Location of section A–B is shown on map inset. Asterisk (∗) indicates location of burial history diagram. (Modified from Gray, 1983; Cole et al., 1987.)

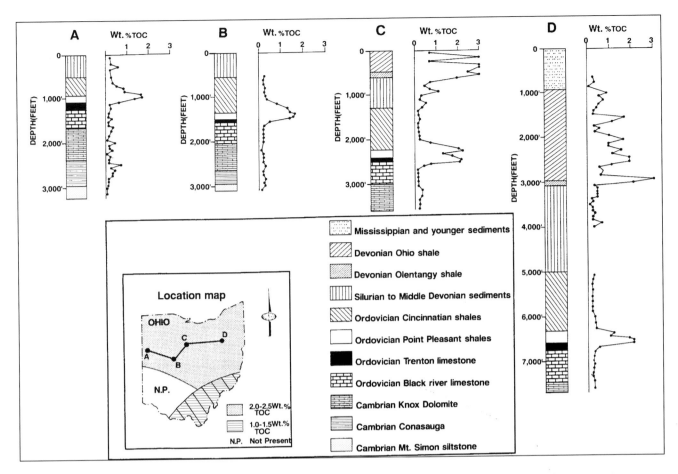

Figure 24.5. Geochemical log showing the TOC profiles for four wells in Ohio. Well locations (A–D) are shown on the map inset. Only three rock units have consistently high TOC contents: Devonian Ohio and Olentangy shales and shales of the Ordovician Point Pleasant Formation.

Formation averaged 1.3 wt. % TOC and 3.94 kg HC/t rock using the S_2 peak from Rock-Eval pyrolysis. Pyrolytic yields were slightly lower due to the more advanced thermal maturity of this unit (see next section). Where immature, a TOC of 2–3 wt. % is projected to have an S_2 yield of more than 20 kg HC/t rock (Figure 24.5). Adequate samples of immature Point Pleasant source rocks are difficult to obtain.

Powell et al. (1984) described similar results from the Ordovician Collingwood Formation in Ontario, equivalent to the Point Pleasant Formation, which has TOC values of up to 5.68 wt. %. Results from a study by Henderson and Timm (1985) showed similar TOC trends for the Ordovician rocks in central New York. Here they found that the Utica Shale was a good source rock. Wallace and Roen (1989) reported similar source quality parameters for the Utica Shale. Their data were also impacted by the higher levels of thermal maturity in the samples analyzed.

Oil–Oil Correlation

Oils in Ohio are found in reservoir rocks that range in age from Cambrian to Pennsylvanian (Cole et al., 1987). The oil (and gas) in only the Silurian and older reservoir rocks is derived from the shale in the Point Pleasant Formation (Figure 24.2). Oils from other source rocks must first be distinguished from oils derived from the Point Pleasant source rock.

Figure 24.6 shows a comparison of gas chromatograms of the C_{12+} saturated hydrocarbons for a representative oil from each of the two groups, the upper and lower Paleozoic (as defined by Cole et al., 1987), with chromatograms of oils from the Silurian Clinton sands. The maximum n-alkane abundance between n-C_{13} and n-C_{15} and the lack of a naphthene "hump" below the baseline show that all of the oils are very mature to supermature. The general distribution of n-alkanes shows distinct differences between the two groups. The lower Paleozoic oils have a distinct, strong odd–even carbon preference over the n-C_{13}–n-C_{21} range (Figures 24.6A and C) compared to a more typical chromatogram for Devonian and younger oils (Figure 24.6B). This relationship has been discussed by other workers (Powell et al, 1984; Fowler et al., 1986; Reed et al., 1985; Longman and Palmer, 1987; Fowler, 1988; Guthrie, 1989). The oils from Clinton reservoir rocks (Figures 24.6C and D) are of both chromatographic types, which indicates an organic facies change in the Point Pleasant source rock or mixing during migration from a different source rock.

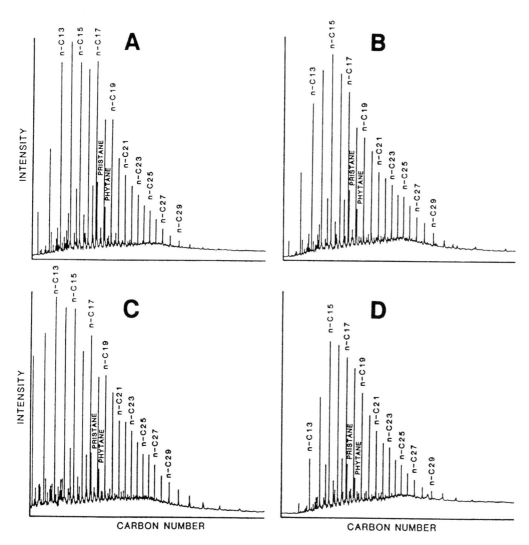

Figure 24.6. Representative gas chromatograms for the C_{12+} saturated hydrocarbon fraction for oils from (A) a lower Paleozoic reservoir, (B) an upper Paleozoic reservoir, and (C and D) Silurian Clinton sandstone.

Similarly, a plot of pristane to n-C_{17} versus phytane to n-C_{18} (Figure 24.7) separates the upper from the lower Paleozoic oil except for one Silurian oil (solid dot). The Ordovician oil from the Indiana part of the Lima–Indiana trend (white squares in Figure 24.7) are included in the lower Paleozoic oil. Most oils (6 of 10) from the Silurian Clinton sand fall into the lower Paleozoic oil group (group 1). However, some oils (4 of 10) fall into the upper Paleozoic oil group (group 2), but may have originated from a different organic facies in the Point Pleasant Formation or other unidentified pre-Devonian source rock. Similarly, Galimov (1973) style isotopic curves separate the Silurian Clinton sand oil into their respective subgroups (Figure 24.8).

Oil–Source Rock Correlation

On the basis of stable carbon isotopic composition of oil and kerogen pyrolyzates, Cole et al. (1987) correlated the early Paleozoic oil and most of the oils from the Silurian Clinton sands with the Point Pleasant source rock. The Cambrian–Ordovician oils plot with subgroup 1 and the Devonian and younger oils plot with subgroup 2. Although there is considerable overlap among the four source rocks, the kerogen pyrolyzate (KPY) for the Point

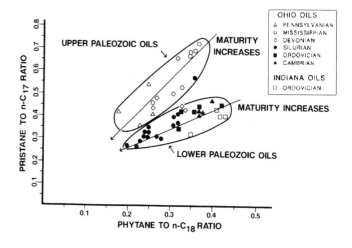

Figure 24.7. Comparison of trends in pristane/n-C_{17} with phytane/n-C_{18} for oils from the upper Paleozoic (group 2) and lower Paleozoic (group 1).

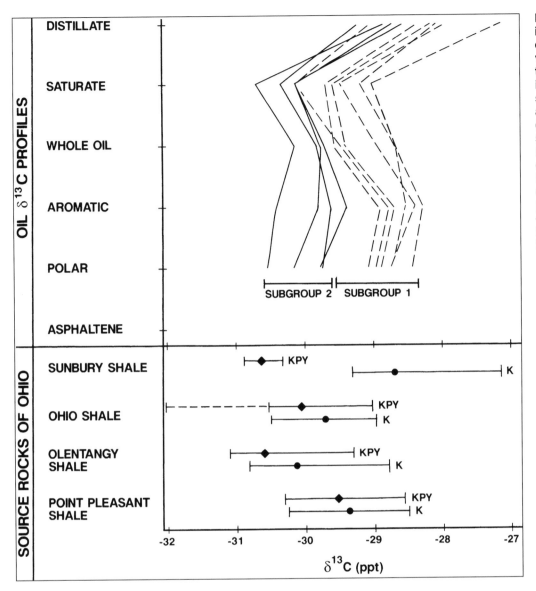

Figure 24.8. Carbon isotopic type curves for oil from Silurian reservoirs subdivided into two groups. Comparison of isotopic compositions of kerogen (K) and kerogen pyrolyzate (KPY) for their potential source rock are shown below these oil type curves. (Dashed line at bottom represents expanded Ohio Shale pyrolyzate range if −32.14 ppt value is included.) (Modified from Cole et al., 1987.)

Pleasant source rock is isotopically heaviest and is the best match for the Silurian and older oils (Figure 24.8).

This oil–source rock correlation indicates that a pod of active Point Pleasant source rock buried in the Appalachian basin provided the oil and gas that charged the Silurian and older fields on the east flank of the Cincinnati–Findlay arch. Thus, the Point Pleasant–Brassfield(!) petroleum system has a known level of certainty.

EXPULSION AND TRAPPING

Thermal maturity assessment of the Point Pleasant Formation is complicated by the lack of vitrinite in these Ordovician aged rocks. Qualitative techniques, such as thermal alteration index (TAI) (Staplin, 1969, 1977, 1982; Burgess, 1974; Peters et al., 1977), conodont color alteration index (CAI) (Epstein et al., 1977; Harris, 1979), qualitative fluorescence (van Gijzel, 1982), and transformation ratios ($S_1/S_1 + S_2$ from Rock-Eval pyrolysis) (Tissot and Welte, 1978; Hunt, 1979) were used instead because

vitrinite is a product formed by higher vascular plants, which did not evolve until the Late Silurian.

The thermal maturity trends for the Ordovician Point Pleasant shales parallel the structural contours on top of the basement rock (Figures 24.3 and 24.9). The least mature area lies along the Cincinnati–Findlay arch, with a rapid increase in maturity as the rocks plunge northwest into the Michigan basin and southeastward into the Appalachian basin (Figures 24.9 and 24.10). The Ordovician rocks attain a very mature status (>1.0% R_o equivalent) in southeastern Ohio owing to a greater burial depth from a thickening sequence of upper Paleozoic rocks. Within the Appalachian basin, data are scarce, but Wallace and Roen (1989) have concluded that most of the Utica Shale was beyond the oil floor except for a narrow band along Lake Erie in Pennsylvania and New York.

Cole et al. (1987) modeled the expulsion of oil from thermally mature shales of the Point Pleasant Formation. Present geothermal gradients in Ohio are in the range of 19–33°C/km (1.0°–1.8°F/100 ft), with the coolest

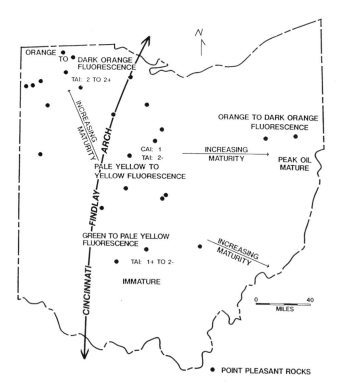

Figure 24.9. Thermal maturity trends for Ordovician source rock from the Point Pleasant Formation. Maturity is based on qualitative methods: thermal alteration index (TAI), conodont color alteration index (CAI), and qualitative fluorescence.

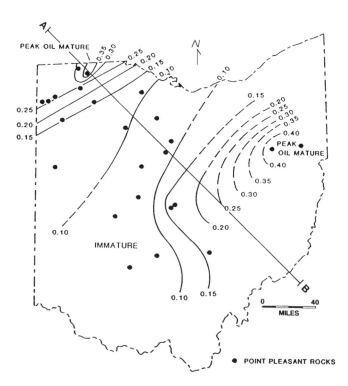

Figure 24.10. Thermal maturity trends based on the production index calculated from Rock-Eval pyrolysis is shown for the Point Pleasant source rock. (Cross section A–B is shown in Figure 24.4.)

gradients located on the platform in central Ohio (Kinney, 1976). Maximum paleogeothermal gradients for the Appalachian basin may have been 45–70°C/km (2.5–3.8°F/100 ft) in the center of the basin, with lower gradients along the margin of the basin (Hower, 1978; Chyi et al., 1987).

PEAK EXPULSION

Based on heat flow and burial histories, one can estimate the time over which hydrocarbon generation took place by using thermal models (Roydon et al., 1980). A simplified model was constructed for eastern Ohio. Basic assumptions made were (1) a constant additional 1.5 km (4900 ft) of burial in Permian–Triassic time, (2) a 10°C (50°F) surface temperature, and (3) an initial geothermal gradient of 29°C/km (1.6°F/100 ft). Matching observed and calculated R_0 values required additional heating in the form of a heat pulse during the Appalachian orogeny. A gradient of 54°C/km (3.0°F/100 ft) at the time of maximum burial (about 230 Ma) resulted in the best match.

Under these assumptions, the burial history diagram (Figure 24.11) shows the time and depth that oil and gas generation began in eastern Ohio for the Point Pleasant source rock. The source rock reached the top of the oil window at about 2 km depth in Early Mississippian time (350 Ma); the top of the gas window at 3.1 km by the Late Permian (260 Ma); and after 200 m of erosion, ceased to

generate hydrocarbons by Middle Jurassic time (170 Ma). The critical moment for this petroleum system was when the Point Pleasant source rock was buried to its greatest depth of 3.4 km in the Triassic (230 Ma).

The critical moment is usually that time when the freshly generated oil and gas have migrated and accumulated in the closest trap. If severe deformation and uplift follows the critical moment, then much of this oil and gas remigrates or is destroyed. For the Point Pleasant–Brassfield petroleum system, the regional geology and burial history diagram suggests little compressional tectonics since the beginning of uplift in Triassic. Uplift was about 1 km and regional in nature. Thus, the present-day geometry of the basement rock (Figure 24.3) and the stratigraphic units in the cross section (Figure 24.4) are essentially unchanged since the Triassic. The structural configuration of this system at the critical moment is essentially the same as present day, with the exception of more overburden.

PETROLEUM SYSTEM EVENTS

To create a petroleum system in the earth's crust, the essential processes must occur and the essential elements must be present, including the source rock, reservoir rock, seal rock, and overburden rock. The Point Pleasant Formation has been identified as the source rock using TOC and Rock–Eval pyrolysis analyses for the oil in the reservoir rock immediately overlying it. The ages of the source and reservoir rocks are determined from the stratigraphic column (Figure 24.2). Identification of the

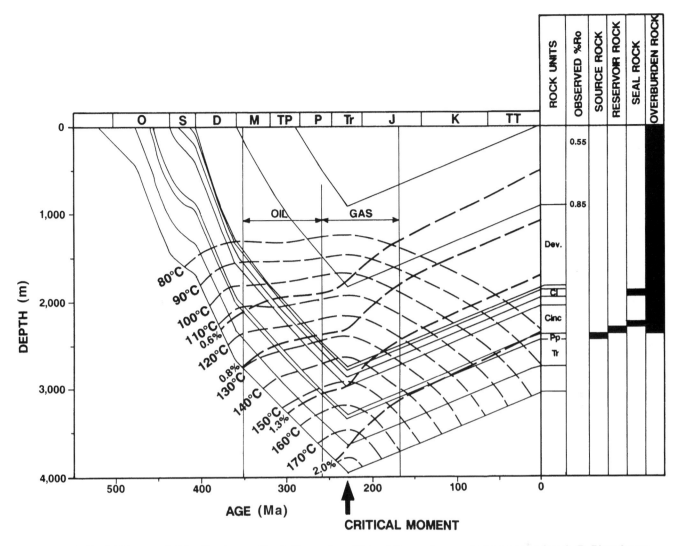

Figure 24.11. Burial history plot for the deepest burial in eastern Ohio at the eastern end of cross section A–B. Plot shows the depth and time of oil and gas generation along with the critical moment. (After Royden et al., 1980.)

seal rocks is more difficult. The regional seal is the evaporites sequence of the Salina Group, but the rocks that encase the sandstone lenses are more likely the effective hydrocarbon seals for each accumulation. The age of known overburden rocks is Late Ordovician–Permian (440–260 Ma), but regional geology indicates that Triassic rocks should be included as overburden rock. Therefore, the maximum burial depth or the critical moment is during the Triassic (Figure 24.12).

The processes include the generation–migration–accumulation of hydrocarbons and formation of the traps. Since most of the traps are stratigraphic, they formed at the time of deposition of the reservoir rock. The burial history chart, which shows the time the source rock reached the tops of the oil and gas windows, in conjunction with the hydrocarbon generation curve determines the time within which the oil and gas accumulations formed. From the Late Ordovician to Middle Triassic is the duration over which the Point Pleasant–Brassfield petroleum system formed, after which the hydrocarbons generated had to be preserved until today (Figure 24.12).

VOLUMETRIC ASSESSMENT

To determine the generation–accumulation efficiency (GAE) of the Point Pleasant–Brassfield petroleum system, we make several assumptions. First, although this petroleum system extends beyond Ohio to the north, east, and south, the amount of oil found in Ohio is proportional to the amount of hydrocarbons generated in Ohio. Gas is more likely to have migrated into this restricted area because of its mobility, but we assume that it is balanced by outflow. Second, the amount of recoverable hydrocarbons is assumed to be about 100 million bbl of oil equivalent and in-place oil equivalent is 400 million bbl using a 25% recovery factor. Third, no appreciable amount of remigration is assumed to have occurred. Last, we assume that hydrocarbons have never migrated into the Cincinnati–Findlay arch axis.

Next, the geographic extent and the pod of active source rock for this petroleum system must be mapped (Figure 24.13). The updip limit of accumulations (Figure 24.1), is used to map the geographic extent of this

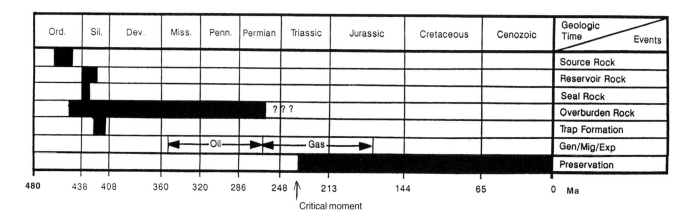

Ord.	Sil.	Dev.	Miss.	Penn.	Permian	Triassic	Jurassic	Cretaceous	Cenozoic	Geologic Time / Events
										Source Rock
										Reservoir Rock
										Seal Rock
					? ? ?					Overburden Rock
										Trap Formation
			←—Oil—►	◄	—Gas—►					Gen/Mig/Exp
										Preservation

480   438   408   360   320   286   248 ↑ 213   144   65   0   Ma

                                     Critical moment

Figure 24.12. Events chart for the Point Pleasant–Brassfield (!) petroleum system, indicating the essential elements and processes. Uncertainties involve the extent and thickness of Mesozoic overburden.

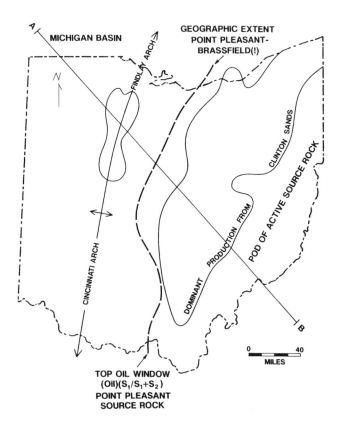

Figure 24.13. Map showing the geographic extent of the Point Pleasant–Brassfield(!) petroleum system, which is coincident with the updip extent of hydrocarbon accumulation and the threshold of maturity for the source rock. The pod of active source rock, the provenance for the hydrocarbons, covers eastern Ohio. This figure is a composite of Figures 24.1, 24.3, 24.9, and 24.10.

petroleum system. The thermal maturity data on the Point Pleasant source rock allows the provenance of these hydrocarbons to be determined. The production index contour line of 0.10 (Figure 24.10) provides the updip limit of the pod of active source rock in Ohio (Figure 24.13), which is almost coincident with the updip limit of production. The area and thickness of this active

source rock pod is the volume from which 100 million bbl of oil equivalent originated. Using the equations of Schmoker (Chapter 19, this volume), we can determine the amount of hydrocarbons generated.

To determine the mass of hydrocarbons generated, M, we use the following formula:

$$M \text{ (g TOC)} = [\text{TOC (wt. \%)}/100] \times \rho \text{ (g/cm}^3) \times V \text{ (cm}^3) \qquad (1)$$

where ρ is the density of the source rock and V is the volume of the pod of active source rock. For this case, we assume a density of 2.3 g/cm^3 and an average TOC of 2.5% where immature. The area involved Point Pleasant Formation source units (or equivalent) in Ohio, western Pennsylvania, and West Virginia and is estimated at 40,000 km^2. Because only the Ohio portion of the source rock interval impacted the Ohio reservoirs, only a 20,000-km^2 area was considered in further calculations. A thickness of 30 m was estimated from available well data, resulting in 35×10^{15} g of organic carbon available.

The mass of hydrocarbon generated per unit organic carbon, R, was calculated as follows:

$$R \text{ (mg HC/gTOC)} = \text{HI}_o \text{ (mg HC/g TOC)} - \text{HI}_p \text{ (mg HC/g TOC)} \qquad (2)$$

where HI$_o$ is the original hydrogen index and HIp is the present-day hyrdrogen index (Schmoker, Chapter 19, this volume). Pyrolysis data were obtained from Cole et al. (1987). For the Point Pleasant, we assumed a HI$_o$ of 600 where immature and an average of 300 for the mature area. However, this is minimal. From equation 2, $R = 300$ mg/g TOC. The total mass of hydrocarbon generated, HCG, is as follows:

$$\text{HCG (kg HC)} \qquad\qquad\qquad\qquad\qquad (3)$$
$$= R \text{ (mg HC/g TOC)} \times M \text{ (g TOC)} \times 10^{-6} \text{ (kg/mg)}$$

This equation indicates that 1.03×10^{13} kg HC (7.5×10^{10} BOE) were generated. Because the assumptions are different, this result is about five times higher than the 13×10^9 bbl calculated by Wallace and Roen (1989).

The in-place hydrocarbon value of 400×10^6 BOE (55.72×10^9 kg) gives a GAE for this petroleum system of 0.54%, a very low value. This low efficiency may be attributed to oil leakage during the 175-m.y. period of preservation, but this is unlikely because more group 1 oil would be mixed with group 2 oil in upper Paleozoic reservoir rocks. Some of this charge may have been lost as gas or at the updip eroded Clinton sand outcrop. It is possible that there is a great deal left in minor accumulations. This also illustrates the difficulty in extrapolating source rock distribution from limited measurements.

SUMMARY

From the known source rocks and oil characteristics, a successful oil–source rock correlation was made between the Point Pleasant Formation source rock and oil in the Silurian Clinton sands (mostly the Brassfield Formation). From these results, we were able to identify, determine the name of, and assign a level of certainty to the Point Pleasant–Brassfield(!) petroleum system. Mapping the updip extent of the hydrocarbon accumulations in the Silurian and older reservoir rocks outlined the petroleum system in Ohio. By mapping the pod of active Point Pleasant source rock, the provenance of the group 1 oil in this system was identified. By modeling the thermal and burial histories for the Point Pleasant source rock where it was buried to the greatest depth, we were able to ascertain the time and depth over which hydrocarbons were generated. All this timing information about essential elements and processes for this petroleum system is summarized on an events chart (Figure 24.12). Calculations that compared the amount of petroleum generated to the amount of in-place petroleum indicate that only a small percentage of hydrocarbons have been discovered.

References Cited

Burgess, J. D., 1974, Microscopic examination of kerogen (dispersed organic matter) in petroleum exploration, *in* R. R. Dutcher, P. A. Hacquebard, J. M. Schopf, and J. A. Simon, eds., Carbonaceous materials as indicators of metamorphism: GSA Special Paper 153, p. 19–30.

Chyi, L. L., R. G. Barnett, A. E. Burford, T. J. Quick, and R. G. Gray, 1987, Coalification patterns of the Pittsburgh coal: their origin and bearing on hydrocarbon generation: International Journal of Coal Geology, v. 7, p. 69–84.

Cole, G. A., R. J. Drozd, R. A. Sedivy, and H. I. Halpern, 1987, Organic geochemistry and oil–source correlations, Paleozoic of Ohio: AAPG Bulletin, v. 71, p. 788–809.

Cumberlidge, J. T., and W. D. McCullough, 1985, Economic profile of Ohio's Clinton sand: Oil and Gas Journal, v. 83, May 13, p. 91–103.

Epstein, A. G., J. B. Epstein, and L. D. Harris, 1977, Conodont color alteration: an index to organic metamorphism: USGS Professional Paper 995, 27p.

Fowler, A. G., 1988, Organic geochemistry of oils and organic-rich rocks of Ordovician age from Canada: Terra Cognita v. 8, p. 218.

Fowler, A. G., P. Abolins and A. G. Douglas, 1986, Monocylic alkanes in Ordovician organic matter, *in* D. Leythaeuser and J. Rullkotter eds., Advances in Organic Geochemistry 1985; Oxford, Pergamon Press, v. 2, p. 815–824.

Galimov, E. M., 1973, Carbon isotopes in oil and gas geology, *in* Izotopy ugleroda v neftgazovoy geologic, Nedra, Moscow: NASA, Washington, D.C., 1974, p. 384.

Gray, J., 1983, Prospects for deep drilling in Ohio: Ohio Oil and Gas Association Winter Meeting, Columbus, Ohio, 27 p.

Guthrie, J., 1989, Organic geochemistry and corrlation of Paleozoic source rocks and Trenton crude oils, Indiana: AAPG Bulletin, v. 73, p. 1032.

Harris, A. G., 1979, Conodont color alteration, an organo-mineral metamorphic index, and its application to Appalachian basin geology, *in* P. A. Scholle and P. R. Schluger, eds., Aspects of diagenesis: SEPM Special Publication 26, p. 3–16.

Henderson, G. J., and C. M. Timm, 1985, Ordovician stratigraphic hydrocarbon entrapment potential of Appalachia: Oil & Gas Journal, v. 83, p. 118–125.

Hower, J. C., 1978, Anisotropy of vitrinite reflectance in relation to coal metamorphism for selected United States coals: Ph.D. dissertation, Pennsylvania State University, University Park, PA, 356 p.

Hunt, J. M., 1979, Petroleum Geochemistry and Geology: San Francisco, W.H. Freeman, 617 p.

Janssens, A., 1973, Stratigraphy of the Cambrian and Lower Ordovician rocks in Ohio: Ohio Geological Survey Bulletin, v. 64, 197 p.

Johnson, K. G., and G. M. Friedman, 1969, The Tully clastic correlatives (Upper Devonian) of New York state—a model for recognition of alluvial, dune, tidal, nearshore (bar and lagoon), and offshore sedimentary environments in a tectonic delta complex: Journal of Sedimentary Petrology, v. 39, p. 451–485.

Kinney, D. M., ed., 1976, Geothermal Gradient Map of North America: USGS Map, 2 sheets.

Knight, W. V., 1969, Historical and economic geology of Lower Silurian Clinton sandstone of northeastern Ohio: AAPG Bulletin, v. 53, p. 1421–1452.

Longman, M. W., and S. E. Palmer, 1987, Organic geochemistry of mid-continent Middle and Late Ordovician oils: AAPG Bulletin, v. 71, 938–950.

Peters, K. E., R. Ishiwatari, and I. R. Kaplan, 1977, Color of kerogen as index of organic maturity: AAPG Bulletin, v. 61 p. 504–510.

Powell, T. G., R. W. Macqueen, J. F. Barker, and D. G. Bree, 1984, Geochemical character and origin of Ontario oils: Bulletin of Canadian Petroleum Geology, v. 32, p. 289–312.

Reed, J. D., H. A. Illich, and B. Horsfield, 1985, Biochemical evolutionary significance of Ordovician oils and their sources, *in* D. Leythaeuser and J. Rullkötter, eds., Advances in Organic Geochemistry 1986: Oxford, Pergamon Press, v. 1, p. 347–358.

Roydon, L., J. G. Sclater, and R. P. Von Herzen, 1980, Continental margin subsidence and heat flow: important parameters for formation of petroleum hydrocarbons: AAPG Bulletin, v. 64, p. 173–187.

Schwietering, J. F., 1979, Devonian shales of Ohio and their eastern and southern equivalents: Morgantown Energy Technology Center., U.S. Department of Energy, METC/CR-79/2, 68 p.

Staplin, F. L., 1969, Sedimentary organic matter, organic metamorphism, and oil and gas occurrence: Bulletin of Canadian Petroleum Geology, v. 17, p. 47–66.

Staplin, F. L., 1977, Interpretation of thermal history from color of particulate organic matter: a review, *in* R. L. Pierce, ed., Palynology, v. 1, p. 9–18.

Staplin, F. L., 1982, Determination of thermal alteration index from color of exinite (pollen, spores), *in* How to assess maturation and paleotemperatures: SEPM Short Course 7, p. 7–11.

Stith, D. A., 1979, Chemical composition, stratigraphy, and depositional environments of the Black River Group (Middle Ordovician), southwestern Ohio: Ohio Geological Survey Report of Investigations 113, 36 p.

Tissot, B. P., and D. H. Welte, 1978, Petroleum formation and occurrence; a new approach to oil and gas exploration: New York, Springer-Verlag, 521 p.

Wallace, L. G., and J. B. Roen, 1989, Petroleum source rock potential of the Upper Ordovician black shale sequence, northern Appalachian Basin: USGS Open File Report 89-488, 66 p.

Wickstrom, L. H., 1990, A new look at Trenton (Ordovician) structure in northwestern Ohio: Northeastern Geology, v. 12, p. 103–113.

Wickstrom, L. H., and J. D. Gray, 1988, Geology of the Trenton Limestone in northwestern Ohio, *in* B. G. Keith, ed., The Trenton Group, Upper Ordovician series of eastern North America: deposition, diagenesis, and petroleum: AAPG Studies in Geology 29, p. 159–172.

van Gijzel, P., 1982, Characterization and identification of kerogen and bitumen and determination of thermal maturity by means of qualittative and quantitative micro-scopical techniques, *in* How to assess maturity and paleo-temperatures: SEPM Short Course 7, p. 159–216.

Magoon, L. B, and W. G. Dow, eds., 1994, The petroleum
system—from source to trap: AAPG Memoir 60.

Chapter **25**

Green River(!) Petroleum System, Uinta Basin, Utah, U.S.A.

Thomas D. Fouch

Vito F. Nuccio

Donald E. Anders

Dudley D. Rice

Janet K. Pitman

Richard F. Mast

U.S. Geological Survey
Denver, Colorado, U.S.A.

Abstract

The Green River(!) petroleum system, located in northeast Utah in the Uinta Basin, is responsible for almost 500 million bbl of recoverable high pour-point and paraffinic oil, 12–13 billion bbl of inferred Tertiary and Cretaceous tar sandstone accumulations. It is a prolific complex of rocks that includes gilsonite, oil shales, and lacustrine source rocks in the Paleocene–Eocene Green River Formation. These source rocks include an open lacustrine facies containing mainly type I kerogen, a marginal lacustrine facies with types I, II, and III kerogens, and an alluvial facies with mostly type III kerogen. Some type I kerogens have TOC contents as high as 60 wt. % and average ~6.0 wt. %. These kerogenous carbonate beds (oil shale) have hydrogen indices greater than 500 mg HC/g TOC.

Oil is produced primarily from lenticular reservoirs that are parts of larger regional hydrocarbon accumulations, some of which span major structural elements. Regionally, alluvial rocks stratigraphically trap most oil in down-dip open and marginal lacustrine reservoirs. The exposed bitumen-bearing sandstones (tar sands) represent the surface expression of migrated oil in marginal lacustrine strata that are continuous with the downdip oil fields. Economically viable oil is recovered from the subsurface where the oil is above pour-point temperatures and is moveable and where strata are especially porous and permeable. However, oil-bearing reservoir rocks commonly extend beyond field limits. In the deep subsurface, wells are completed in overpressured strata where pods of open fractures provide high formation permeability sufficient to drain "tight" oil reservoirs. High fluid pressure gradients associated with these pods occur where impermeable rocks with abundant type I kerogen have been subjected to temperatures sufficient to generate hydrocarbons at a rate greater than the rate of fluid migration.

INTRODUCTION

The lacustrine and fluvial Paleocene and Eocene Green River Formation of the greater Uinta–Piceance basin in northeastern Utah and northwestern Colorado has long has been recognized for its extensive oil shales, gilsonite, and other solid hydrocarbon species. In addition, numerous oil and gas fields are developed within and produce petroleum from Paleozoic, Mesozoic, and Cenozoic reservoir rocks. Other petroleum-bearing Tertiary strata have been identified in drill holes distributed over much of the central and eastern parts of the Uinta Basin, and bituminous sandstones (tar sands or natural bitumen) are exposed along the basin's southern margin in the Roan Cliffs (Figures 25.1 and 25.2).

Based on oil and gas composition, at least three petroleum systems are identified within the greater Unita–Piceance basin (Figure 25.2). The nonassociated gas fields produce mostly from Mesozoic reservoir rocks, with some gas migrating up into the overlying Tertiary rocks. Most of this gas is thought to originate from the underlying Cretaceous Mancos Formation and/or Mesaverde Group and is interpreted to be part of one or more gas systems. The second petroleum system is represented by the relatively high sulfur oil in the Ashley Valley and Rangely oil fields. This oil probably originated from the Phosphoria Formation source rock sometime in late Mesozoic time. The third system, which is the subject of this chapter, is the Green River(!) petroleum system, which is largely restricted to the Uinta

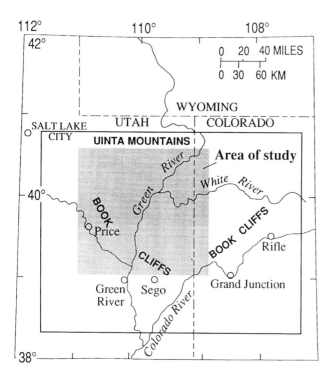

Figure 25.1. Index map of study area in northeastern Utah and northwestern Colorado, showing the areas of Figure 25.2 (rectangle) and Figure 25.3 (shaded).

Basin in northeastern Utah (Figures 25.2 and 25.3a). In this prolific petroleum system, the Green River Formation contains the source rock as well as most of the reservoir and seal rocks (Figure 25.4).

Greater Uinta–Piceance Basin

The greater Uinta–Piceance basin is bounded on the west by the Wasatch Mountains and Wasatch Plateau, on the north by the Uinta Mountains, and on the east by the White River Uplift and Elk Mountains (Figure 25.2). The greater basin is commonly divided into two lesser basins with the eastern segment, lying east of the Douglas Creek arch, called the Piceance basin. The segment west of the Douglas Creek arch is the Uinta Basin, the proper name for the topographic basin of the same name. The southern boundary for the greater Uinta–Piceance basin is topographically defined by the Uncompahgre and San Rafael uplifts and the Book Cliffs. It is common for the southern boundary of the basin to be defined by the lower limit of Tertiary sedimentary rocks in the Roan and Book Cliffs. However, it should be noted that most Tertiary rocks once extended far south of their present-day erosional limits in the cliffs.

The greater Uinta–Piceance basin is a structural and topographic basin of latest Cretaceous and Tertiary age that trends east-southeast in northeastern Utah and northwestern Colorado and roughly parallels the Uinta Mountains to the north. It is an asymmetrical structural trough filled by as much as 5000 m (17,000 ft) of Maastrichtian and Paleogene lacustrine and fluvial sedimen-

tary rocks. Uppermost Cretaceous and lowermost Tertiary strata dip 4°–6° north from the Roan and Book Cliffs, and drill holes penetrate them in the subsurface of the north-central part of the Uinta Basin at the Altamont–Bluebell oil-producing complex at a drill depth of 6100 m (20,000 ft) (Figure 25.4).

This chapter focuses on the Uinta Basin because it is where the Green River Formation is petroliferous. Here, oil is produced primarily from diagenetically enhanced lenticular fluvial and lacustrine sandstone and lacustrine carbonate reservoirs that are parts of larger regional hydrocarbon accumulations crossing structural boundaries (compare Figures 25.2 and 25.5). Alluvial rocks, which are the most peripheral facies of the Lake Uinta depositional system, serve primarily as impermeable or nontransmissive complexes that stratigraphically trap most oil accumulations in down-dip open and marginal lacustrine reservoirs. The oil-bearing outcrops (tar sands of natural bitumen) represent the surface expression of oil that has migrated up structural dip to the surface through marginal lacustrine strata that are continuous with the more deeply buried oil fields. Economically viable oil with associated gas is recovered from the subsurface where the oil is above pour-point temperatures and is moveable, and where strata are especially porous or permeable. Oil with associated gas is recovered from deeply buried and overpressured strata along and spanning the synclinal axis of the basin where pods of open fractures provide permeable networks that drain "tight" oil reservoirs characterized by low values of matrix porosity and permeability.

Oil and Gas Reserves

Up to the end of 1990, approximately 365 million bbl (MMbbl) of oil and more than 630 billion ft³ (bcf) of associated gas derived from the source rock in the Green River Formation had been produced from reservoirs (gas–oil ratio, or GOR, = 1730) in the formation or from units in the laterally and temporally equivalent Wasatch and Colton formations (Utah Division of Oil, Gas, and Mining, 1991) (Figure 25.4; Table 25.1). Nonassociated gas (GOR > 20,000) is also produced from these reservoir rocks but originates from a deeper source (Figure 25.4; Table 25.2).

As of 1991, cumulative production from the principal oil fields was as follows: greater Altamont–Bluebell, 221 MMbbl of oil and 326 bcf of gas from Paleocene and Eocene strata of the Green River, Wasatch, and Colton formations; greater Red Wash, more than 127 MMbbl of oil and 326 bcf of gas from lower–upper Eocene units of the Green River and Wasatch formations; and greater Natural Buttes, more than 6 MMbbl of oil and 286 bcf of gas from Eocene fluvial and lacustrine reservoirs in the Wasatch (mostly nonassociated) and Green River formations (mostly associated gas) (Utah Division of Oil, Gas, and Mining, 1991). Some gas at Natural Buttes is derived from organic matter in the underlying Upper Cretaceous Mesaverde Group and is mixed with gas generated in the Green River Formation (Rice et al., 1992; Osmond, 1992; Fouch et al., 1992a) (Table 25.2). The cumulative

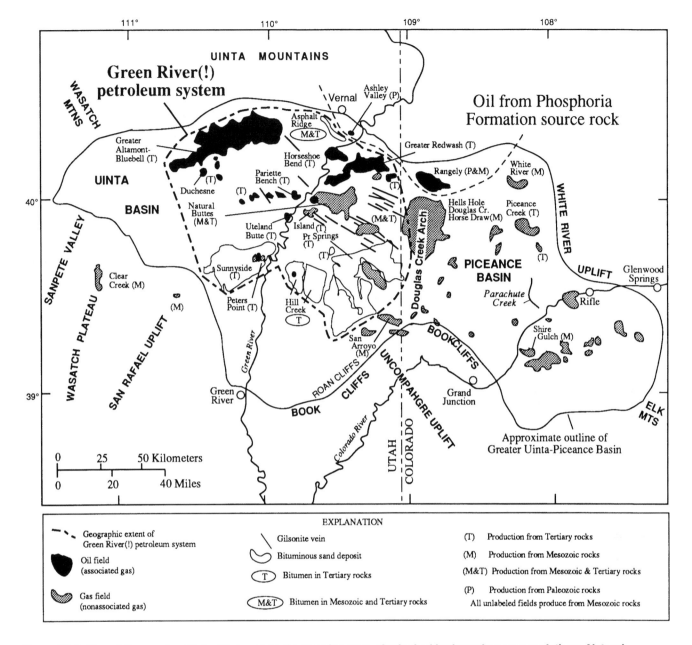

Figure 25.2. Map of the greater Uinta–Piceance basin showing area of principal hydrocarbon accumulations. Natural bitumen-bearing sandstones are abundant in surface exposures in regions between areas shown as tar sands or bitumens.

production figures for gas (and GOR) are generally low because (1) most gas was flared during early stages of production and (2) gas used at production sites for heating high pour-point oil was not reported on state records until recently.

Table 25.1 shows 1989 cumulative production and reserve data for fields in the Green River(!) petroleum system. The table also provides a basis for predicting future production from this system. The extent of existing production, when compared to our maps of productive lithofacies, suggest areas of future production. We expect that future drilling and production will link many small oil fields on the south flank of the basin, such as Pariette Bench, to the greater Altamont–Bluebell

and Red Wash fields. This linkage will form a region of continuous production extending from the northeast end of the Altamont–Bluebell complex east to Red Wash and southwest and west to rejoin the southwest tip of the Altamont–Bluebell complex (Figure 25.3A). More than 750 MMbbl of oil are expected to be produced from this area (Fouch et al., 1992a).

Anders et al. (1992) indicate that natural bitumen in tar sands of the Uinta Basin originated from source rocks in the middle Eocene part of the Green River Formation. Estimates by Ritzma (1979), and Oblad et al. (1987) indicate that 12–13 billion bbl of measured, indicated, and inferred oil is present in these Tertiary and Cretaceous natural bitumen deposits.

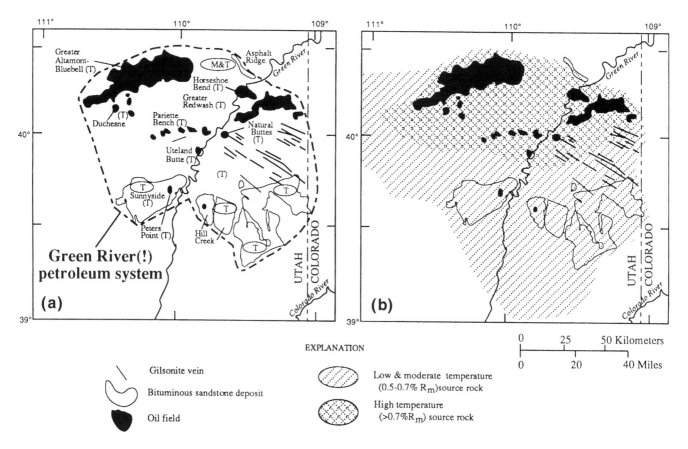

Figure 25.3. (a) Map of Uinta Basin showing the principal oil fields, bituminous sandstone deposits, and gilsonite veins in the Green River(!) petroleum system. (b) Map of high temperature and low to moderate temperature zones of source rock for the Green River petroleum system.

All large commercial oil accumulations in the Green River petroleum system are associated primarily with source rock and reservoir rock having vitrinite reflectance values greater than 0.5% R_m. However, billions of barrels of oil in-place, or natural bitumen, are in sandstones that are at a lower thermal maturity, and in some small oil fields, they are encased by source rock whose vitrinite reflectance values are less than 0.5% R_m. This natural bitumen and oil are interpreted to have been generated and expelled from low maturity source rock. For this reason we use the expressions low (<0.5% R_m), moderate (0.5–0.7% R_m), and high temperature (>0.7% R_m) for the source rock and the characteristic oil rather than immature, mature, and overmature.

GREEN RIVER(!) PETROLEUM SYSTEM

Lake Uinta Depositional System

Two early Tertiary lakes, Lake Uinta and Lake Gosiute, were separated by the ancestral Uinta Mountains. Lake Gosiute, located north of the ancestral Uinta Mountains, represents the hydrologic and depositional counterpart of Lake Uinta. Lake Gosiute was the site of deposition for the Green River Formation strata that now occupies the greater Green River basin in north-

western Colorado and southwestern Wyoming. Lake Uinta, south of the ancestral Uinta Mountains in northeastern Utah and northwestern Colorado, was the depositional and hydrologic center of an internally drained topographic depression now represented by the Tertiary rocks of the greater Uinta–Piceance basin. Rocks of the Green River Formation represent sediments that were deposited in and around the margin of this Paleocene and Eocene lake. Only the depositional system of Lake Uinta is discussed here.

Stratigraphic and Geochemical Cycles

Upper Paleocene–upper Eocene lake deposits are characterized by calcium sulfate salts (upper Paleocene–lowest Eocene), halite, sodium bicarbonate salts (lower–upper Eocene), and kerogen-rich shales containing biologically derived carbonate minerals, indicating a highly organically productive, closed hydrologic system. Because Lake Uinta had no outlet, the chemistry and geometry of the water mass were especially sensitive to external factors such as changes in climate and tectonically induced reconfiguration of the topographic and hydrologic basin. These changes provided a mechanism for the production and preservation of intercalated petroleum source, reservoir, and seal rocks.

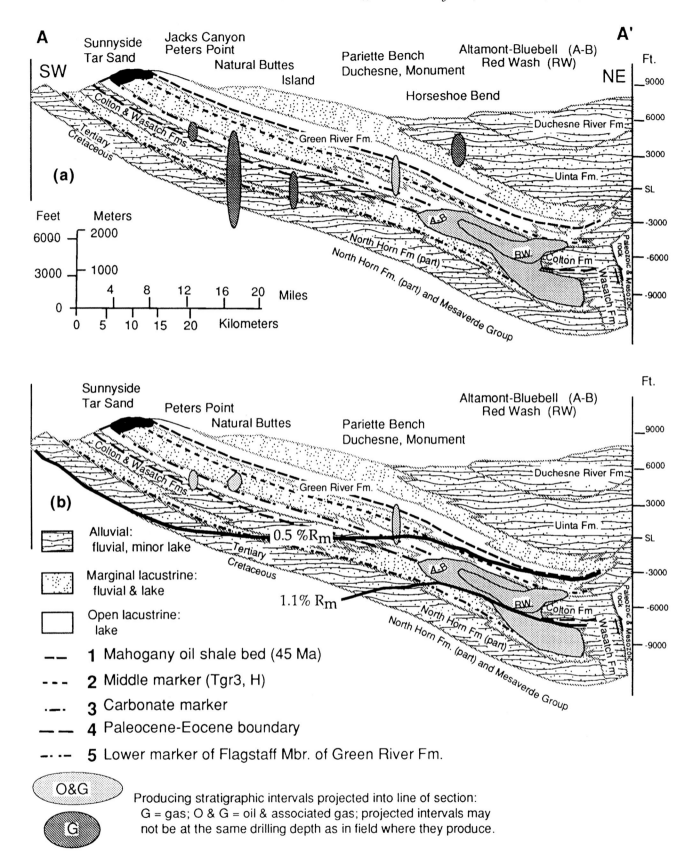

Figure 25.4. Cross section A–A' extending from outcrops on the southwestern flank of the Uinta Basin, through Duchesne and Altamont–Bluebell oil fields, to the north-central part of the basin. (Modified from Fouch, 1975; stratigraphy from Fouch, 1975, 1981; Fouch et al., 1976; Ryder et al.,1976; Bryant et al.,1989; Bryant, 1991; see Figure 25.6.) See Figure 25.5 for line of section. (a) Producing intervals for many fields are projected into the line of section. (b) Only those accumulations included in the Green River(!) petroleum system are shown.

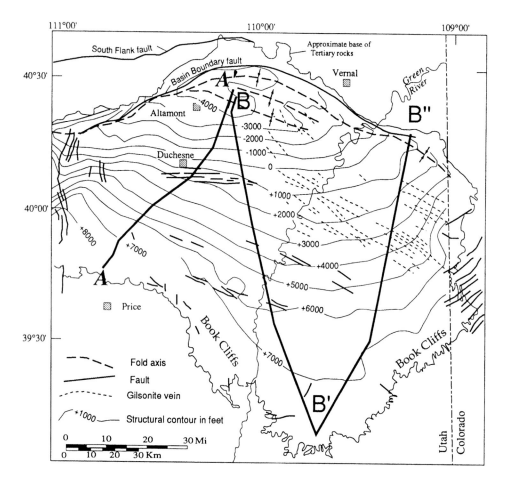

Figure 25.5. Map showing present-day structural contours developed on the middle Eocene middle marker (#2 on Figure 25.6) of the Green River Formation. Gilsonite veins, major fold axis, and faults in Tertiary rocks as well as locations for sections A–A' and B–B'–B" are shown.

Table 25.1. Oil Fields That Produce Oil, Natural Gas Liquids (NGL), and Associated Gas, Green River(!) Petroleum System, Uinta Basin[a]

Field or Area Name	Year Disc'd	Trap Type[b]	Oil (°API)	GOR (ft3/bbl)	Form-ation[c]	Lith-ology	Depth (ft)	Net Pay (ft)	Porosity (%)	Perm (md)
Altamont-Bluebell	1971	Comb	42	1170	GR,W,C	Ss,ls	12,400	575	5	—
Altamont-Bluebell	1949	Comb	32	852	GR	Ss,ls	9351	69	8	—
Antelope Creek	1983	—	40	3754	GR	Ss	5634	269	—	—
Brennan Bottom	1953	Strat	32	1075	GR	Ls	6870	54	5	—
Brundage Canyon	1983	—	34	1662	GR	Ss	4907	759	—	—
Castle Peak	1962	Comb	34	2728	GR	Ss	3568	7245	—	—
Coyote Basin	1964	—	31	387	GR	Ss	4202	2	—	—
Duchesne	1958	Comb	22	1696	GR	Ss	2330	300	—	—
Duchesne	1951	Comb	20	647	C	Ss	7486	100	—	—
Eight Mile Flat, North	1982	—	34	1900	GR	Ss	3738	2326	—	—
Horseshoe Bend	1964	Comb	27	1346	GR	Ss	6488	28	—	—
Monument Butte	1964	Comb	32	2555	GR	Ss	4735	20	—	—
Natural Buttes	1956	Comb	29	7984	GR	Ss,ls	3384	25	—	—
Pariette Bench	1962	Comb	32	756	GR	Ss	4862	1041	—	—
Peters Point	1954	Comb	28	>20,000	GR	Ss	2800	29	—	—
Red Wash	1951	Comb	30	2396	GR	Ss,ls	5500	90	—	95

[a]Production data are through 1990 and from Utah Division of Oil, Gas, and Mining (1991): reserve data are through 1989 and from NRG Associates (1990).
[b]Comb, combination; strat, stratigraphic.
[c]GR, Green River; W, Wasatch; C, Colton.

Both long- and short-term changes in climate and tectonic regime are recorded in the Green River Formation (Fouch and Pitman, 1991; Fouch and Pitman, 1992; Fouch et al., 1992a; also see Remy, 1991). Most regionally extensive reconfigurations of Lake Uinta were probably in response to faulting, which commonly expanded the hydrologic and topographic basin giving rise to relatively thick (few to several hundred meters), lithologically distinct, areally extensive (tens of kilometers of lake expansion) stratigraphic sequences. Simultaneous changes in climate brought on by variations in solar radiation initiated rapid rises and falls of lake level. These changes, coupled with shifts in alkalinity and salinity of the water, resulted in the development of carbonate geochemical and sedimentary cycles (parasequences) of up to tens of meters thick. Tectonically induced regionally extensive stratigraphic sequences represent environments that lasted several million years, whereas many climate-induced parasequences lasted several thousand years. Thus, both long- and short-term changes in climate and tectonic regime served as the heartbeat of the lake system, inducing the development of carbonate geochemical and sedimentary cycles that resulted in the development of source, reservoir, and seal rocks.

Major open lacustrine units reflect rises of lake level and regional expansions of the lake such as those associated with the middle Eocene middle marker and carbonate marker zones of Ryder et al. (1976), the upper Paleocene–lower Eocene Flagstaff Member of the Green River Formation, and the middle Eocene Mahogany oil shale zone (ledge) of the Green River Formation (Figure 25.6). The carbonate marker zone approximates the stratigraphic position of the Uteland Butte limestone of

Osmond (1992), an informal local name in the Uinta Basin, and the Long Point Bed of the Green River Formation of Johnson (1985) in the greater Uinta–Piceance basin.

These major expansions of lake facies appear to correspond to episodes of tectonic reactivation of regional faults such as the subsurface Basin Boundary fault (Utah Geological and Mineral Survey, 1967; Ritzma, 1974; Campbell, 1975) and the South Flank fault, which together bound the north flank of the Uinta Basin (Campbell, 1975; Ryder et al., 1976; Gries, 1983; Bruhn et al., 1986; Benson, 1992) (Figure 25.5). These regionally extensive reconfigurations of the depositional system are locally unconformity bounded near the faulted margins of the depositional system. In addition, strata associated with the regional reconfigurations thicken toward the faulted margins of the basin where subsidence was presumably most rapid and continuous during faulting (compare Figures 25.4, 25.5, and 25.7). Strata that bracket these boundaries represent major cycles and consist of thick, lithologically distinct tongues of open lacustrine, marginal lacustrine, and alluvial rocks extending over large regions of the depositional system.

Green River Formation strata contain more numerous cycles of smaller dimensions than the large regional sequences just discussed. Recurrent and continuing climate change initiated very rapid expansions and contractions (and rises and falls) of the lake as well as shifts in alkalinity and salinity of its water. These changes resulted in small- to large-scale carbonate geochemical and sedimentary parasequences within the larger regional sequences. Climate-induced sedimentary and geochemical cycles are similar in style to tectonic cycles, except that they are commonly recorded within a sedimentary thickness of 3–30 m (10–100 ft). We suggest that they represent a few to tens of thousands of years.

In kerogenous open lacustrine source rock, the 3–30 m climate-induced sedimentary cycles just discussed result in carbon and oxygen isotope fluctuations in carbonate that correspond to cyclic variations in total organic carbon (TOC) content (Figure 25.8). Variations in carbon and TOC document changes in organic matter productivity and the amount of reduced carbon available for carbonate precipitation by way of bacterial methanogenesis (J. K. Pitman, USGS, written comm. 1992). Variations in oxygen record climate-induced salinity changes resulting from alterations in the lake's hydrologic balance.

Study of exposures on the basin's south flank and of core from several of the basin's fields shows that, throughout the lake system, a cyclic depositional sequence was deposited in a early–middle Eocene marginal lacustrine setting. From oldest to youngest, this sequence consists of the following:

Unit 1. Laterally continuous (as much as several kilometers), mud-supported, laminated carbonate rock or oil shale with a flooding surface at its base shoaling to an ostracode , pisolite , and oolite grainstone;

Table 25.1. *(continued)*

Cumulative Production[d]			Reserves[d]		
Oil	NGL	Gas	Oil	NGL	Gas
(10^3 bbl)	(10^3 bbl)	(10^6 ft^3)	(10^3 bbl)	(10^3 bbl)	(10^6 ft^3)
188,536	18,604	241,079	61,464	8,746	112,921
21,446	1,519	19,519	3,554	831	10,481
962	0	3,612	638	0	3,888
1,221	0	1,312	199	0	308
906	0	1,506	394	0	744
489	0	1,334	261	0	1,216
1,056	0	409	164	0	149
477	0	809	223	0	3,181
402	0	260	198	0	206
1,191	0	2,263	509	0	1,037
848	0	1,141	544	0	945
4,461	0	11,396	2,039	0	7,504
1,343	0	10,723	257	0	8,177
873	0	660	127	0	150
143	0	2753	0	0	1,057
137,399	1,690	333,529	37,326	170	33,671
361,610	**21,813**	**629,552**	**107,897**	**9,747**	**184,578**

[d]Cumulative production and reserves as of December 1989.

Table 25.2. Gas Fields Producing Nonassociated Gas and Natural Gas Liquids as Part of Deeper Gas System, Uinta Basin[a]

Field or Area Name	Year Disc'd	Trap Type[b]	Oil (°API)	GOR (ft³/bbl)	Reservoir Rock					
					Form-ation[c]	Lith-ology	Depth (ft)	Net Pay (ft)	Porosity (%)	Perm (md)
Horseshoe Bend	1964	Comb	—	>20,000	U	Ss	3170	23	—	—
Natural Buttes	1960	Comb	—	>20,000	W	Ss	5000	56	10	1.5
Peters Point	1953	Comb	—	19,251	C	Ss	4800	31	—	18
Red Wash	1965	Comb	—	>20,000	W	Ss	4936	35	—	—
Rock House	1960	Strat	—	>20,000	W	Ss	2982	34	20	—

[a]Production data are through 1990 and from Utah Division of Oil, Gas, and Mining (1991): reserve data are through 1989 and from NRG Associates (1990).
[b]Comb, combination; strat, stratigraphic.
[c]W, Wasatch; C, Colton; U, Uinta.

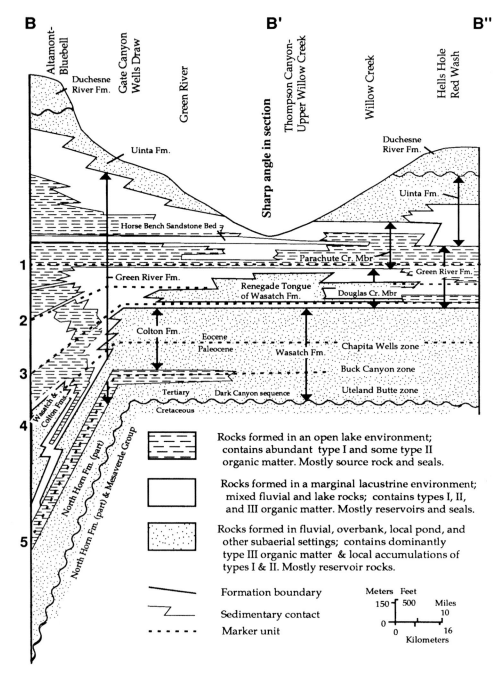

Figure 25.6. Stratigraphic diagram B–B'–B" extending east from the Altamont–Bluebell oil field to the Red Wash and Hells Hole areas of the eastern end of the basin by way of Gate Canyon and Thompson Canyon on the basin's south flank. Marker beds are designated #1–5 and correspond to those on Figures 25.4, 25.11, and 25.13: (1) Mahoganey oil shale bed (45 Ma); (2) Middle marker (Tgr3, H); (3) Carbonate marker approx. equivalent to Uteland Butte limestone and Long Point Bed of Green River Fm.; (4) Paleocene–Eocene boundary; (5) Lower marker of Flagstaff Mbr. of Green River Fm. See Figure 25.5 for line of section.

Table 25.2. *(continued)*

Cumulative Production[d]			Reserves[d]		
Oil	NGL	Gas	Oil	NGL	Gas
(10^3 bbl)	(10^3 bbl)	(10^6 ft^3)	(10^3 bbl)	(10^3 bbl)	(10^6 ft^3)
0	8	16,366	0	0	1,934
0	432	232,862	0	458	214,138
0	0	1,289	0	0	31
0	0	6,221	0	0	709
0	7	7,119	0	1	3,441
0	**440**	**263,857**	**0**	**459**	**220,253**

[d]Cumulative production and reserves as of December 1989.

Unit 2. Mudcracked mudstone and stromatolitic carbonate
Unit 3. Mudcracked overbank mudstone or sandstone
Unit 4. Coalesced channel sandstone that locally eroded down to the underlying carbonate (unit 1) and aggraded laterally to form a composite sandstone sheet (Figure 25.9) (Fouch et al., 1992a).

This depositional sequence is important because similar sequences are recorded in cores of producing intervals of similar age in the Red Wash, Altamont–Bluebell, and other oil fields (Fouch et al., 1992a,b). Each genetic unit within the sequence can vary greatly in thickness and areal extent depending on its position within the depositional system and the chemistry of lake water at the time of formation.

Source Rocks

A modified van Krevelen diagram compares the hydrogen index (HI) to the oxygen index (OI) of low temperature ($R_m < 0.5\%$) source rocks to determined kerogen type (Figure 25.10). The samples are Green River Formation kerogenous calcareous mudrocks, carbonate units, and algal coals. The HI and OI relate the amounts of pyrolyzable hydrocarbons (S_2) and CO_2 (S_3), respectively, to the TOC content of the rock samples. Type III kerogen is dominant in the rocks of the alluvial depositional facies (not illustrated); marginal lacustrine rocks contain type I, II, and III kerogen; and open lacustrine rocks contain abundant type I kerogen with local accumulations of type II. Lacustrine algal coals, associated with Lake Uinta's shore, are rich in both type II and III kerogen. These coals are particularly well preserved in upper Paleocene and upper lower Eocene or lower middle Eocene beds in the western part of the Uinta Basin (Fouch et al., 1976), the same stratigraphic interval that is most productive from overpressured reservoirs at Altamont–Bluebell.

Information from Tissot et al., (1978), Anders and Gerrild (1984), Powell (1986), and Anders et al. (1992) indicates that low temperature middle Eocene lacustrine rocks (maximum 150 m above the Mahogany oil shale bed and extending down to the middle marker) have TOC contents as high as 21 wt. % and average about 6.0 wt. %. A few rock samples reach 60 wt. %. Comparable

upper Paleocene–middle Eocene lacustrine lithofacies beneath the middle marker zone show significantly lower values; low temperature rocks average 1.8 wt. % TOC and higher temperature >0.5% R_m units average 1.6 wt. % TOC. The more hydrogen-rich samples (HI > 500) are from post-middle marker middle Eocene open lacustrine kerogenous carbonate (oil shale) beds of the southeastern part of the Uinta Basin, whereas the samples with HI < 350 are from upper Paleocene–middle Eocene rocks in the subsurface of the Altamont–Bluebell area. However, exposed upper Paleocene rocks in the southwestern part of the basin contain algal coals and kerogenous limestone with TOC values as high as 75 wt. % (Fouch and Hanley, 1977).

Reservoir Rocks

The reservoir rocks in Tertiary strata are controlled by the geometry of the lake–nonlake geochemical and sedimentary cycles. Principal reservoir rocks include diagenetically altered fluvial channel, deltaic, and open lacustrine sandstones (including turbidites in Altamont–Bluebell field) that formed near the lake margin and nearshore lacustrine bars and beaches that apparently developed parallel to the northeastern margin of the lake in Utah (Koesoemadinata, 1970; Chatfield, 1972; Fouch, 1975; Lucas and Drexler, 1976; Fouch and Cashion, 1979; Fouch, 1981; Narr and Currie, 1982; Pitman et al., 1982; Clem, 1985; Colburn et al., 1985; Castle, 1990; Kelly and Castle, 1992). Marginal lacustrine channel sandstones comprise the principal reservoirs for oil and associated gas in Tertiary strata, and alluvial channel sandstones formed in peripheral settings are the basin's principal Tertiary reservoirs for nonassociated gas. The channel sequences (depositional unit 4) occur within the parasequences.

In the Uinta Basin, most oil and associated gas is recovered from pores (most being secondary) in the basal parts of marginal lacustrine channel sandstone units that are intercalated with carbonate and gray and green mudstone units (Fouch, 1975; Keighin and Fouch, 1981; Pitman et al., 1982; Fouch, 1985). The sequence contains units with great contrast in ductility; as a result, the reservoir rocks are commonly fractured in response to differential brittle failure during periods of changes in stress.

Fluvial channels that developed in alluvial settings well outside the margin of the lake (alluvial–fluvial) are intercalated with, and encased within, relatively ductile claystones. Brittle carbonate units are rare to absent. As a result, oil has not migrated laterally through fractures from lacustrine source rocks into the fluvial–alluvial channels. Thus, for much of the petroleum system, the alluvial facies serves as a regional impermeable barrier (seal) to oil migration.

Paleogeographic Maps

Paleogeographic maps in Figure 25.11 illustrate these facies and elements for three periods of geologic time in the Paleogene. The maps characterize units within 30 m (100 ft) of strata approximated by the upper Paleocene

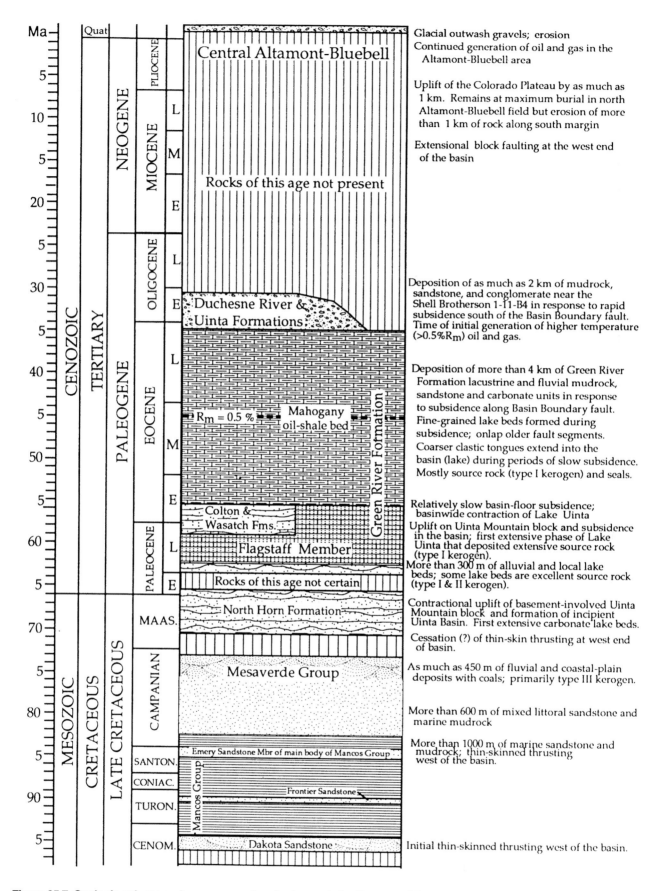

Figure 25.7. Geologic column and a summary of geologic events for the area of the central part of the greater Altamont–Bluebell field, Uinta Basin. (Data from Fouch, 1975, 1981; Ryder et al., 1976; Fouch et al., 1983, 1992a,b; Hansen,1984, 1990; Johnson, 1985; Bruhn et al.,1986; Bryant et al., 1989; Bryant, 1991; Franczyk et al., 1992; Nuccio et al.,1992.)

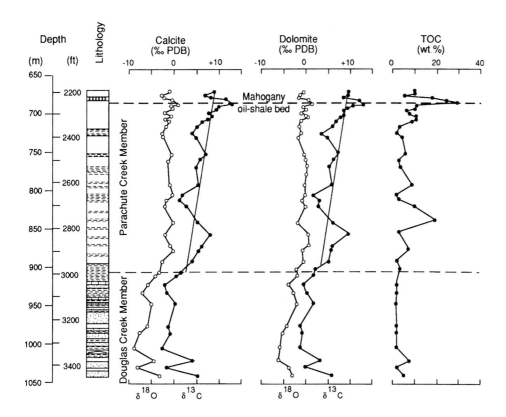

Figure 25.8. Carbonate isotope and TOC data for the Green River Formation from Coyote Wash well, located outside the southeastern end of the greater Red Wash field. Straight lines represent major trends on the curves. Where sample density is adequate, geochemical cycles of several dimensions are apparent, including depositional cycles of 10–30 m that correspond to climatic change (parasequences) in marginal lacustrine rocks. See Figure 25.2 for location of Red Wash field.

lower marker of the Flagstaff Member of the Green River Formation, the Paleocene–Eocene boundary, and the middle Eocene middle marker of the Green River Formation respectively. These and other markers can be traced from the surface to the subsurface (see Koesoemadinata, 1970; Fouch, 1975; Ryder et al., 1976; Fouch and Cashion, 1979; Fouch, 1981; Castle, 1990; Osmond, 1992). Figures 25.4 and 25.6 provide a cross-sectional stratigraphic frame of reference for examining the paleogeographic distribution of depositional facies and formational elements in the petroleum system.

Lower marker rocks are the oldest Tertiary units in the basin that have yielded large volumes of oil or gas (Figure 25.11a). Lower marker rocks produce from marginal and open lacustrine units in the region of the Altamont–Bluebell producing area along the northern margin of Lake Uinta. In the southeastern part of the basin, beds of this age onlap Cretaceous units along the northwestern margin of the Uncompahgre uplift, thus their limits and potential as gas reservoirs do not extend far east of the Green River (Stone, 1977; Fouch and Cashion, 1979).

Oil and associated gas have been recovered from marginal lacustrine rocks near the Paleocene–Eocene boundary in the central and eastern part of the basin (Figure 25.11b). Like those of the lower marker, the distribution of beds and potential reservoirs of this age are limited where they pinchout against the Uncompahgre uplift southeast of the present-day course of the Green River. Middle marker reservoirs yield large volumes of oil and gas in the region of the Red Wash producing complex (Figure 25.11c). Marginal lacustrine units within this sequence contain gas in many of the eastern and

northern parts of the basin. Beds from this stratigraphic sequence also contain the impermeable (tight) alluvial sandstone reservoirs of the Wasatch and Colton Formations in the greater Natural Buttes producing area.

Most reservoir rocks are lenticular fluvial and lacustrine sandstones that are part of a major nonmarine intermontane depositional system. Figures 25.4 and 25.6 illustrate this system in stratigraphic cross sections and Figure 25.7 is a Cretaceous and Tertiary stratigraphic column that summarizes information for the central Altamont–Bluebell area. The depositional system consists of rocks that occur in the Maastrichtian–lower Eocene North Horn Formation and in the Paleocene–Eocene Green River, Wasatch, and Colton Formations.

Group I Reservoir Rocks

Analysis of drill-stem test (DST) data, core plug values, and the distribution of fluid pressures and productive lithofacies indicate three groups of reservoir rocks (Fouch et al., 1992b). Group I reservoir rocks are composed of deeply buried, overpressured, oil-bearing and associated gas-bearing strata that contain reservoirs whose *in situ* matrix permeability values are commonly below 0.1 md and whose porosity values (mostly secondary porosity) average 5%, ranging from 3 to 10%. Group I overpressured rocks host oil in a complex generally without oil–water contacts. Group I strata can be said to contain "tight oil" reservoirs. However, these strata contain open fractures and transmissivity (T = permeability × height) values through producing intervals that are commonly high. Many zones tested in deeply buried Group I rocks below depths of 3048 m (10,000 ft) at Altamont–Bluebell oil field are naturally

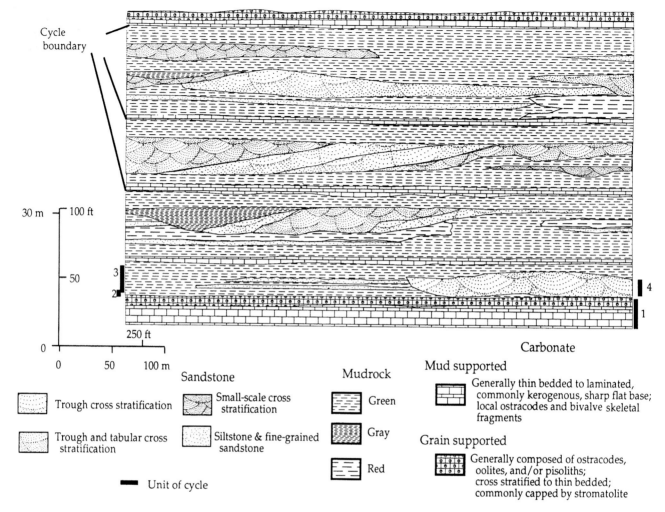

Cycle boundary

30 m — 100 ft

50

3
2

1

4

0

250 ft

0   50   100 m

Sandstone   Mudrock

Trough cross stratification   Small-scale cross stratification   Green

Trough and tabular cross stratification   Siltstone & fine-grained sandstone   Gray

Red

Unit of cycle

Carbonate

Mud supported

Generally thin bedded to laminated, commonly kerogenous, sharp flat base; local ostracodes and bivalve skeletal fragments

Grain supported

Generally composed of ostracodes, oolites, and/or pisoliths; cross stratified to thin bedded; commonly capped by stromatolite

Figure 25.9. Depositional cycles (parasequences) between the carbonate and middle markers (#3 on Figure 25.6) of the Green River Formation in a marginal lacustrine setting exposed in strata near the intersection of Nine Mile and Gate Canyons. Carbonate beds (unit 1) can be traced over large areas using borehole logs. This sequence is typical of lower–middle Eocene strata; it formed in a marginal lacustrine setting crossed by numerous streams (see Ryder et al., 1976). (From Fouch et al., 1992a.)

fractured (Fouch, 1981). Natural open fractures provide major conduits to move fluids and gases to the wellbore in otherwise low permeability strata (Fouch, 1975; Lucas and Drexler, 1976; Wesley, 1990; Fouch et al., 1992b; Wesley et al., 1993).

Group II Reservoir Rocks

Group II rocks contain normally pressured Tertiary oil and associated gas reservoirs characterized by matrix permeability values as high as 1 darcy (d) and combined primary and secondary porosity values of 10–16%. Group II fields generally contain oil–water contacts. Transmissivity values for Group II strata are locally high because of high matrix permeability and local networks of open fractures. Group II reservoirs are common in the Red Wash, Pariette Bench, Duchesne, and Horseshoe Bend fields and in reservoirs less than 2895 m (9500 ft) drill depth in the Altamont–Bluebell producing complex. Group II strata in and north of the large Red Wash field in the northeastern Uinta Basin, especially shallower fluvial and lacustrine reservoirs, are characterized by

high matrix permeability (Castle, 1990). Despite relatively few open fractures, transmissivity values for such sequences are relatively high because of their high matrix permeability.

Group III Reservoir Rocks

Group III rocks include nonassociated gas sandstone reservoirs with *in situ* permeability values throughout the pay or gas-producing section of 0.1 md or less to gas (exclusive of fracture permeability) and porosity values of 8–18%; they are classified as tight gas sandstones. Transmissivity values for many productive tight gas intervals are very low because of relatively few natural open fractures. Group III impermeable Tertiary producing intervals of much of the southeastern part in the Uinta Basin are devoid of significant natural open fractures,` which has resulted in relatively low producibility for many units. Many of the gas-producing zones within the Wasatch Formation at Natural Buttes field are characterized by Group III reservoirs (Fouch et al., 1992b).

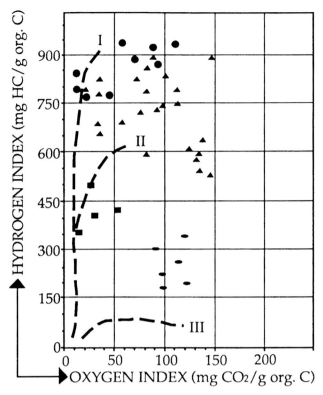

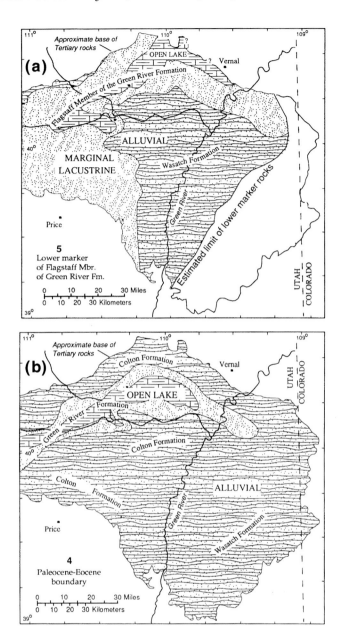

- Marginal lacustrine carbonaceous and coaly mudrock
■ Nearshore lacustrine algal coal
▲ Marginal lacustrine kerogenous mudrock and carbonate
● Open lacustrine mudrock and carbonate

Figure 25.10. Modified van Krevelen diagram showing hydrogen index (mg HC/g TOC) and oxygen index (mg CO_2/g TOC) determined from Rock-Eval pyrolysis of thermally immature (<0.5% R_m) Green River open lacustrine and marginal lacustrine calcareous mudrocks and upper Paleocene–middle Eocene algal coals. The more hydrogen-rich samples (HI > 500) are from middle Eocene oil shale beds in the southeastern part of the Uinta Basin, and the samples with HI < 350 are from the subsurface of the Altamont–Bluebell area.

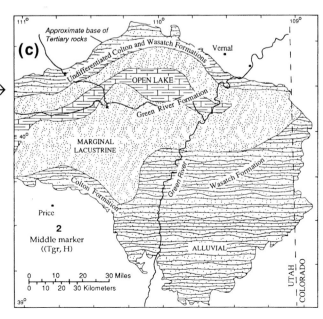

Figure 25.11. Paleogeographic maps on three marker beds. (a) Depositional facies in beds adjacent and equivalent to the lower marker (#5 on Figure 25.6) of the Flagstaff Member of the Green River Formation (modified from Fouch, 1975; Fouch et al., 1992a). Oil and gas are produced from the Altamont–Bluebell area along the northern margin of the lake. (b) Depositional facies in beds adjacent and equivalent to the Paleocene–Eocene boundary (#4) (modified from Fouch, 1975). (c) Depositional facies in beds adjacent and equivalent to the middle marker (#2) of the Green River Formation (modified from Fouch, 1975). Middle marker reservoirs yield large volumes of oil and gas at Red Wash field (Figure 25.2a). Marginal lacustrine units in this sequence contain gas in the eastern and northern parts of the basin. The Wasatch and Colton formations of this sequence contain tight alluvial sandstone reservoirs in the Natural Buttes area.

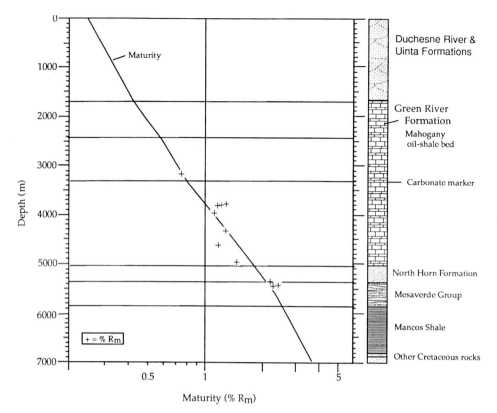

Figure 25.12. Vitrinite reflectance profile as predicted by the model (solid line) and the measured vitrinite reflectance profile (+). Note "kink" where the measured vitrinite reflectance data points are connected between 3800 and 4950 m. The vertical section in the R_m profile corresponds approximately to the zone of overpressuring described by Fouch and Cashion (1979) and may be due to a perturbation of heat transfer.

Thermal Maturation History

Several workers have tried to determine amounts of overburden eroded from various areas of the Uinta Basin. Tissot et al. (1978) estimated 1780 m (5840 ft) of overburden removal from the site of the Shell 1-23-B4 Brotherson well in the Altamont–Bluebell field. Narr and Currie (1982) used fluid inclusions to determine overburden removal from the Altamont–Bluebell area and had greatly varying results ranging from 339 to 2892 m (1112 to 9482 ft) of removal. Using a combination of vitrinite reflectance, burial history modeling, and organic geochemistry, Pitman et al. (1982) estimated no more than 1006 m (~3300 ft) of erosion from the Pariette Bench field, and Pitman et al. (1987) estimated that 1000 m (3300 ft) of overburden have been removed from the Natural Buttes field area. Using kerogen kinetic modeling, Sweeney et al. (1987) estimated that between 1525 and 2745 m (5000 and 9000 ft) of rock have been eroded from the north-central part of the basin.

Johnson and Nuccio (1993) have used R_m–depth profiles to estimate amounts of overburden removed in three different parts of the Uinta Basin. One profile for a well near the eastern edge of the basin extrapolated to 0.30% R_m indicates that the thickness of overburden removed is about 1220 m (4000 ft). If the profile is extrapolated to 0.20% R_m, about 2745 m (9000 ft) of overburden is estimated to have been eroded. These amounts contrast markedly with the estimated section eroded in the Island field area. The R_m–depth profile for Island field does not plot in a straight line but rather has a kink near the middle of the Mesaverde Group. The kink most likely marks the approximate original boundary between normally pressured water-bearing strata and underlying overpressured gas- and water-bearing rocks (see Law et al., 1989; Johnson and Nuccio, 1993). The extrapolation of this profile to 0.30% R_m yields a depth of about 275 m (900 ft) below the present-day surface, while extrapolating to 0.20% R_m gives an estimate of about 700 m (2300 ft) of overburden removed.

An R_m profile has been constructed for the Shell Brotherson 1-11-B4 well in the Altamont–Bluebell field from which cores were taken from selected units between about 3050 and 5490 m (10,000 and 18,000 ft). For this Shell Brotherson 1-11-B4 profile, extrapolation to 0.30% R_m gives an estimate of 1890 m (6200 ft) of overburden removed, and extrapolation to 0.20% R_m yields an estimate of 3355 m (11,000 ft) removed (Figure 25.12) (Johnson and Nuccio, 1993).

The R_m data for the Shell Brotherson 1-11-B4 well are fairly sparse, but they indicate a discontinuous or kinky profile. Between depths of about 3050 and 3352 m (10,000 and 11,000 ft), the profile trends in a "normal" fashion of increasing with depth. From about 3800 to 4950 m (12,500 to 16,250 ft), the profile is vertical and does not increase with depth. Below 4950 m (16,250 ft), the profile once again increases with depth (Figure 25.12). It is unlikely that the kink is due to differences in rock conductivity because it does not correspond to a stratigraphic or lithologic break. Furthermore, we feel that it is not coincidental that the vertical section in the R_m profile corresponds to the zone of overpressuring as described by Fouch and Cashion (1979). The vertical section of the profile represents either a perturbation of heat transfer

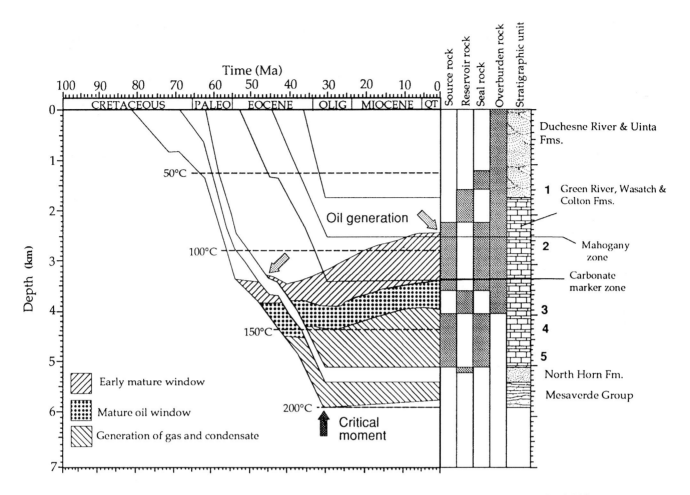

Figure 25.13. Burial history curve and petroleum kinetic model for the Shell Brotherson 1-11-B4 well. Burial history was reconstructed using formation thicknesses from geophysical logs. A geothermal gradient of 31°C/km and no overburden removal were assumed for the model.

associated with the zone of overpressuring and hydrocarbon generation (Law et al., 1989) or a suppression of the vitrinite kinetic reaction in the overpressured system.

Although estimated amounts of erosion from the area of the Shell Brotherson 1-11-B4 range from 1830 to 3355 m (6000 to 11,000 ft), our data indicate that much less rock has been eroded from the area of the well and northward. Figure 25.7 provides stratigraphic and other geologic information for the area of the central part of the Altamont–Bluebell field. Restoration of eroded units of the Duchesne River and Uinta Formations suggests that less than 1 km of rock and perhaps no sediment has been eroded from the well area and northward. In addition, field mapping (Bryant, 1991) and stratigraphic information (Anderson and Picard, 1972) indicate that no faults or folds are exposed south of the Basin Boundary or South Flank faults that demonstrate uplift of more than a few meters as would be expected if the north and central Altamont–Bluebell area had been greatly elevated and eroded since the Oligocene. It is likely that amounts of erosion vary considerably within the Altamont–Bluebell field, and areas north of the Shell Brotherson 1-11-B4 well could have had less erosion or possibly none at all.

Figure 25.13 is a burial curve and petroleum genera-

tion kinetic model for the Shell Brotherson 1-11-B4 well. The burial history was reconstructed using formation thicknesses from geophysical logs (Fouch, 1981). Based on geologic reconstructions, we assume that there has been no erosion at the well site. The vitrinite reflectance profile for the Brotherson 1-11-B4 well described earlier was constructed by choosing high quality vitrinite samples in marlstones to avoid the possible effects of suppression due to association with lipid-rich kerogen. We feel that the profile gives a reliable determination of the thermal maturity of rocks in the area. The vitrinite reflectance profile allows the ability to calibrate the burial and petroleum generation model to measured parameters, thus the maximum maturity of the rocks does not have to be estimated. Assuming the burial history is representative of the area, the paleogeothermal gradient can be adjusted until the vitrinite reflectance values predicted by the model approximate the measured reflectance values (Figure 25.12). It follows that an increased amount of eroded section would require a lower paleogeothermal gradient to match the measured values, whereas a lower amount of eroded section would require a higher paleogeothermal gradient to match the measured values.

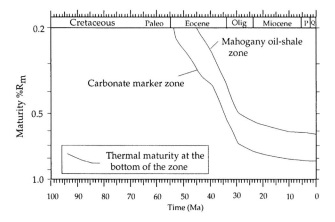

Figure 25.14. Maturity rate (% R$_m$) through time for the Carbonate marker and Mahogany zones of the Green River Formation. Rates of maturity were highest 50–30 Ma during the time of rapid burial and have slowed, but not stopped, from 30 Ma to present.

The present-day geothermal gradient for the area around Altamont–Bluebell is about 25°C/km (Chapman et al., 1984). Sweeney et al. (1987) state that it is likely that the geothermal gradient in this area was fairly constant from the Tertiary to the present time. The geothermal gradient required for our model is about 31°C/km, which is slightly higher than that established by Pitman et al. (1987) for the Natural Buttes field in the south-central part of the basin. If we were to use the present-day geothermal gradient of 25°C/km, we would have to increase the amount of overburden removed for the area by several thousand meters. As discussed earlier, this is not geologically reasonable. An alternate way to match the modeled vitrinite profile with the measured profile is to increase the geothermal gradient sometime in the past and then lower it to the present-day gradient beginning sometime late in the burial history.

The present-day topographic profile of the surface is illustrated in a transect that extends north from the basin's south flank through the Altamont–Bluebell field (Figure 25.4). The cross section also demonstrates the variable amount and uplift within the limits of the field. Uplift and subsequent erosion have resulted in more than 1830 m (6000 ft) of strata being removed from southern parts of the field, while strata underlying the northern limits of the field remain at maximum burial. The thermal maturity level of the beds as indicated by the values of 0.5 and 1.1% R$_m$, respectively, largely parallel the surface topography. In addition, source rocks at the level of the Mahogany oil shale bed that reached temperatures greater than those represented by 0.5% R$_m$ (moderate and high temperatures) are restricted largely to where they are buried deeply enough to transform the kerogen to hydrocarbons, like those of the Altamont–Bluebell and Red Wash fields. In our interpretation, moderate and high temperature oil and gas were being generated from Green River lacustrine source rocks that achieved a level of R$_m$ > 0.5%. The interpretation suggests that beds in the central part of the Altamont–Bluebell field are presently at or near maximum burial

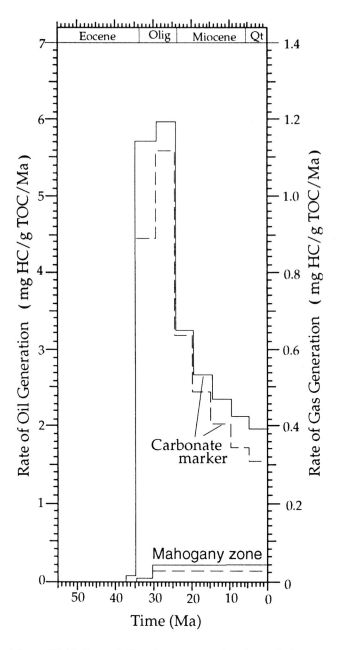

Figure 25.15. Rate of oil and gas generation through time for the Carbonate marker and Mahogany zone of the Green River Formation. Oil and gas generation for the Carbonate marker was highest 30 Ma and has slowed through time. Generation for the Mahogany began 30 Ma and has maintained a constant generation rate to the present.

and that moderate and high temperature oil and gas are currently being generated below ~3050 m (~10,000 ft) burial depth.

Our interpretation of the petroleum generation history of the Green River Formation near the area of the Shell Brotherson 1-11-B4 well (Figure 25.13) indicates that oil and gas generation began near the base of the Green River Formation around 40 Ma at a depth of ~3350 m (~11,000 ft). Peak oil generation probably occurred during rapid burial to maximum burial at 30–40 Ma. Rates of generation slowed during the period of maximum burial from 30 Ma to the present, and the zone of generation has risen stratigraphically through time (Figure 25.13). Figure 25.14 illustrates that maturation rates have also slowed through time, but that they have not stopped. Oil in the lower part of the Green River Formation has likely been undergoing thermal cracking to gas and condensate since about 35 Ma. Because gas generation from either oil cracking or conversion of coals can continue to R_m values of at least 3.0%, it is likely that some gas generation is ongoing for source rocks near the base of the Green River Formation. This lower Green River Formation high temperature zone also corresponds to the zone of highest fluid pressures. Oil and gas generation for the stratigraphically higher carbonate marker did not begin until 25–30 Ma, and it is likely that this zone is presently still in the oil generation window (although the rate of generation has slowed) (Figure 25.15). Figure 25.15 also shows that the Mahogany zone began to generate some oil and gas as early as 30 Ma, and rates of generation, although small, have not dropped significantly since then.

Fluid Pressure Gradients *a disappointing summary*

Fluid pressure gradients can be estimated using a variety of techniques such as drill-stem tests (DSTs) and comparison of mud weights to drilling depths. For this chapter, fluid pressure gradients were calculated using extrapolated shut-in pressures for DSTs that were of long duration (see Willet and Chapman, 1987; Wesley, 1990; Wesley et al., 1993). The regional distribution of the DST-derived fluid pressure gradients illustrates where in the subsurface the fluid pressure gradient exceeds 0.5 psi/ft (11.31 kPa/m) (Figure 25.16). The depth and geometry of this pod of abnormally high fluid pressure spans the synclinal axis of the basin and is almost identical with the producing interval in the Altamont–Bluebell field (Figure 25.4). Subsurface temperatures calculated from DST analyses (Wesley, 1990; Wesley et al., 1993) show that, in the Altamont–Bluebell area, temperatures at drilling depths near 4420 m (14,500 ft) in Tertiary strata are currently near 132°C (270°F) and that underlying Mesaverde Group rocks are hotter (see Nuccio et al., 1992). Our fluid pressure gradients largely agree with the pressures given by Lucas and Drexler (1976) and Spencer (1987), and they concur with the cross-sectional view of pressure gradients in Fouch (1975).

The results of our study suggest that the highest fluid pressure gradients are located in the subsurface where impermeable rocks with abundant type I hydrogen-rich kerogen have been subjected to sufficient heat to transform their organic matter thermochemically into petroleum-like compounds at such a rate and in such volume that the increase in volume of petroleum has resulted in an increase in fluid pressure gradients (see Bredehoeft et al., in press).

It should be noted that inspection of density logs indicates that the overpresured and "thermally mature" carbonate, mudrock, and sandstone lithologies near and inside the envelope of impermeable strata are denser than similar rocks outside the zone of abnormally high

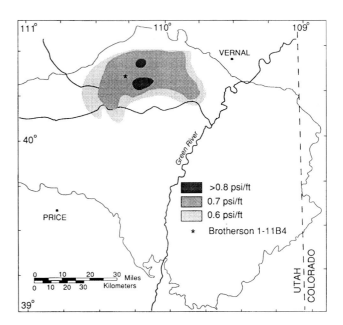

Figure 25.16. Fluid pressure gradients from 0. 6 psi/ft and higher for Tertiary strata in the Uinta Basin The depth and geometry of this pod of abnormally high fluid pressure is similar to the producing interval of the Altamont–Bluebell field (Figure 25.4). (Data from Fouch, 1975; Lucas and Drexler, 1976; Wesley, 1990; Spencer 1987; Fouch et al., 1992b.)

gradients. Figure 25.16 shows that fluid pressure gradients in the deep Altamont–Bluebell strata decrease in the North Horn Formation, a unit that does not contain abundant hydrogen-rich type I organic matter in the area. The fluid pressure gradients decrease in rocks where pressures have nearly equilibrated to normal hydrostatic gradients. In these rocks, the rate of hydrocarbon and other fluid production in the zone of thermal generation is equal to the rate of fluid migration away from the generation zone. Data from Fouch (1975), Lucas and Drexler (1976), Bredehoeft et al. (1992; in press), and Fouch et al. (1992a) suggest that open fracture networks are much more common in overpressured strata. This relationship of abnormally high fluid pressure gradients, excellent source rocks, high maturation temperatures, and networks of open fractures surrounded by strata with few connected open fractures suggests that many open fractures may be the result of the rapid and ongoing generation of hydrocarbons within the largely impermeable subsurface rock cell.

Figures 25.4 and 25.16 demonstrate that the areal distribution of fluid pressure gradients more than 0.5 psi/ft (11.31 kPa/m) approximates the areal distribution of moderate to high temperature (>0.5% R_m) Tertiary source rocks. As a result, the pattern of these fluid pressure gradients can be used to estimate the stratigraphic and subareal distribution of Group I impermeable rocks that can be expected to contain natural open fractures and abnormally high formation pressures such as those in the greater Altamont–Bluebell field. In addition, these gradients provide a basis for determining the volume and distribution of source rocks that have been subjected to moderate and high temperature (>0.5% R_m) thermochemical transformation of their kerogen to petroleum-like compounds. Our studies strongly suggest that oil and gas is currently being generated in strata rich in organic matter at levels of >0.5% R_m and that some hydrocarbons have migrated as far east as the Red Wash field in the eastern part of the basin (Fouch et al., 1992a; Anders et al., 1992; Rice et al., 1992).

Oil

Gas chromatograms in Figure 25.17 of C_{10+} alkanes of oils produced from the Green River Formation in the Uinta Basin are typical for oils recovered from reservoir rocks subjected to low (<0.5% R_m), moderate (0.5–0.7% R_m), and high temperatures (>0.7% R_m). Thermal maturities were estimated by vitrinite reflectance, Rock-Eval T_{max}, Rock-Eval transformation ratio, atomic hydrogen to carbon (H/C) ratio, light hydrocarbon yield (C_5–C_7), Lopatin time–temperature indices (TTI), and biological marker ratios associated with thermal isomerization and degradation reactions (see Anders et al., 1992; Hatcher et al., 1992). This information, combined with new data on the geologic setting of the source rocks and oils, better constrain the geographic and stratigraphic extent of the Green River(!) petroleum system.

Oils in reservoirs of the greater Altamont–Bluebell field at depths of less than 2562 m (8400 ft) appear to be derived from low temperature, bitumen-rich middle–upper Eocene source rocks of the Green River Formation having <0.7% R_m. Oils in fractured reservoirs at depths of 2562–4270 m (8400–14,000 ft) appear to have been derived from upper Paleocene–lower Eocene rocks of the Flagstaff Member of the Green River Formation with vitrinite reflectance values of 0.7–1.3% R_m.

Most oil in the Red Wash field is in middle Eocene beds of the Green River Formation at depths of 1525–1830 m (5000–6000 ft) (Castle, 1990; Kelly and Castle, 1992). Green River Formation rocks at these depths have vitrinite reflectance values in the range of 0.40–0.55% R_m, yet the oils have thermal maturity geochemical indices equivalent to values of 0.7–0.8% R_m. These thermal maturity differences suggest that the Red Wash oils have migrated from more deeply buried, higher temperature upper Paleocene–middle Eocene Green River Formation source rocks to the west (Anders et al., 1992). This eastward migration of oil to relatively low temperature rocks in the Red Wash field from higher temperature source rocks to the west is along a migration pathway for fluid and gas flow that can be predicted by fluid pressure gradients (Wesley, 1990), the composition of natural gases (Rice et al., 1992), and the formation waters (Wanty et al., 1991). This flow pattern also follows an anticlinal structure in the Green River Formation that extends from the north-central part of the Uinta Basin as far east as Red Wash field (compare Figures 25.2 and 25.5).

The natural bitumen in sandstones and the many small oil fields along the basin's south flank are in strata that have not been subjected to temperature and time levels represented by 0.5% R_m (Figure 25.3). On the basis

of biomarker ratios, the oils associated with the asphaltic sands range from thermally low to moderate at Sunnyside and Asphalt Ridge (0.5–0.7% R_m) and thermally moderate to high at P.R. Spring (>0.7% R_m) (Anders et al., 1992; Hatcher et al., 1992). Most vitrinite reflectance values for asphaltic sand reservoir strata are below 0.5% R_m. The association of billions of barrels of low and moderate temperature oil in tar sands with rocks of low thermal maturity most likely indicates that much moveable oil has been formed at relatively shallow depths (<9500 ft) and at low and moderate temperatures near the Altamont–Bluebell field.

Natural Gas

On the basis of isotopic composition ($\delta^{13}C_1$, δD_1, and $\delta^{13}C_2$) and gas wetness (C_{2+}), two groups of gases are distinguished in the Uinta Basin (Rice et al., 1992). Additional plots of molecular and isotopic composition that assist in identifying these unique types of gas are presented in Rice et al. (1992).

Gases generated and produced from the Green River(!) petroleum system are mainly associated with oil. Where sampled in the greater Altamont–Bluebell and greater Red Wash fields, gases are characterized by methane $\delta^{13}C$ values of –58.1 to –46.9‰, ethane $\delta^{13}C$ values of –39.4 to –34.1‰, and methane δD values of –286 to –228‰ (Figure 25.18). C_{2+} values vary considerably from 0 to 23.3%. Based on composition, stratigraphic position, and association with a distinct type of oil, Group B gases are interpreted to have been generated mainly from type I kerogen preserved in the open lacustrine facies of the Green River Formation during catagenesis (oil window) when both oil and associated gas were generated. As discussed previously, these thermogenic hydrocarbons were generated in the Altamont–Bluebell area but have since migrated beyond the area where they were generated. As compared to gases generated from type II and III kerogen, gases generated from type I are characterized by (1) a wide spread in methane and ethane $\delta^{13}C$ values, (2) lighter carbon isotope compositions at similar levels of thermal maturity, and (3) wetter molecular composition at intermediate levels of thermal maturity (James 1983, 1990; Rice 1983; Schoell, 1983; Rice et al., 1989; Johnson and Rice, 1990).

The scatter in isotopic composition in the gas samples results from (1) mixing of biogenic gas in shallower reservoirs in the greater Altamont–Bluebell area and (2) migration processes in the greater Red Wash field. Gases and oils in Red Wash field occur in reservoirs that are lithologically similar and coeval to those in lower–middle Eocene reservoirs in Altamont–Bluebell field, but the depth of production and the level of thermal maturity (immature with respect to oil window) are much less. These gases are interpreted to have been generated in and to have migrated from the central basin area (Altamont–Bluebell field). Migration was along the pathways of the hydrodynamic flow, as documented by Bredehoeft et al. (in press) and Wesley (1990) and away from the area of high fluid pressures (as described in the previous section). A similar history of migration is inter-

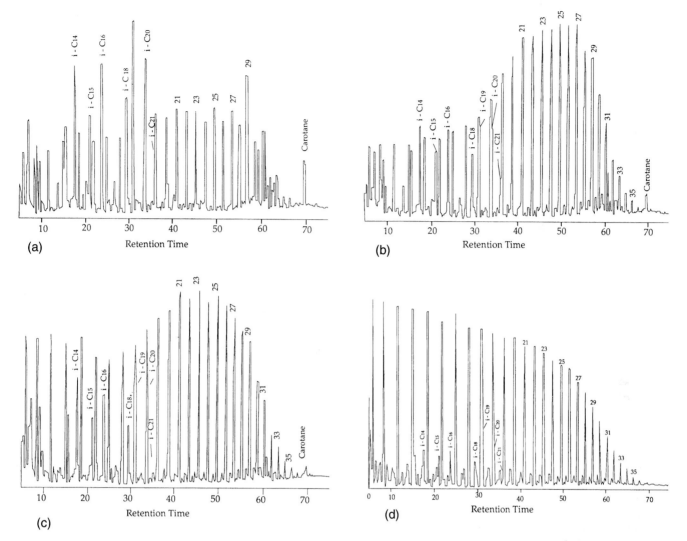

Figure 25.17. Gas chromatograms of C$_{10+}$ alkanes from Green River Formation oils. Numbers refer to carbon chain length of *n*–alkanes, and those preceded by *i* are carbon numbers of the regular isoprenoids. (a) Low temperature, black, tarry oil from the Federal 1 well in the Twelve Mile Wash field (7396 ft) at the eastern end of the greater Altamont–Bluebell field. (b) Moderate temperature, black, paraffinic oil from the Red Wash 64164 well in Red Wash field. (c) Moderate temperature, black, paraffinic oil from the Victor Brown 1 well, Bluebell field (9042 ft) from that part of the greater Altamont–Bluebell field at drilling depths shallower than 10,000 ft. (d) Deeply buried, high temperature, brown to yellow paraffinic oil extracted from upper Paleocene–lower Eocene units at 12, 341 ft in the Shell Miles well in the Altamont–Bluebell field.

preted for the oils, as discussed previously. This migration probably resulted in an increase of the original GOR and enrichment of the methane fraction of the gases. GORs calculated from the cumulative production figures for the Altamont–Bluebell and Red Wash fields give a relative sense of the original GORs, although the gas numbers are undoubtedly low because of flaring and use on the production sites.

The Natural Buttes gas field contains Group A gas (Rice et al., 1992) (Figure 25.18). In this gas field, fluvial reservoirs of the Tertiary Wasatch Formation produce gases characterized by methane $\delta^{13}C$ values of –35.7 to –35.2‰, ethane $\delta^{13}C$ values of –26.2 to –26.0‰, and methane δD values of –167 to –166‰. In addition, the C_{2+} values of these samples are closely grouped in the range of about 4.9–9.1%. This group of thermogenic

gases is interpreted to have been generated from structured kerogen (type III) in the underlying Upper Cretaceous Mesaverde Group and thus represents leakage of gas from a source rock outside the Green River petroleum system. Type III kerogen generates mostly natural gas throughout its thermogenic history (Tissot and Welte, 1984). The gases are interpreted to have migrated vertically from the Mesaverde into shallower reservoirs of the Wasatch Formation along faults and fractures typical of the area. In contrast, gases produced from lacustrine reservoirs in tongues of the Green River Formation in the Natural Buttes field are mixtures of the two groups of gases just described, the associated gas generated in the Green River petroleum system, and the nonassociated gas that migrated from the Mesaverde Group (Rice et al., 1992).

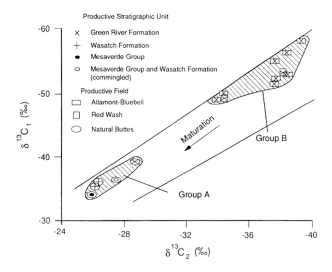

Figure 25.18. Methane ($\delta^{13}C_1$) versus ethane ($\delta^{13}C_2$) carbon isotope ratios showing two groups of gases in the Uinta Basin. Group A was generated from type III kerogen in the Upper Cretaceous Mesaverde Group and is produced from the Wasatch Formation and Mesaverde Group in some areas of the greater Natural Buttes field. Group B was generated from type I kerogen in the Tertiary Green River Formation and is produced from Green River, Colton, and Wasatch formations in the Altamont–Bluebell field and from Green River and Wasatch formations in the Red Wash field and the Natural Buttes field. (From Rice et al., 1992.)

Events Chart

The events chart summarizes those times when deposition of essential elements and important processes took place in the Green River(!) petroleum system (Figure 25.19). Deposition of essential elements took place in Paleocene–Oligocene time (64–30 Ma). The time of deposition for the source, reservoir, and seal rocks is only generally shown because the depositional system of the Green River Formation varies laterally and vertically within the Lake Uinta area. The overburden rock, required to thermally mature the source rock, includes the upper part of the Green River Formation and the overlying rock units. Since the hydrocarbon traps are strongly stratigraphic, trap formation mostly occurred during deposition of the Green River Formation. Recent uplift (<3 Ma) of a part of the Uinta Basin area enhanced the structural component. Based on the burial history chart (Figure 25.13), petroleum generation for much of the Altamont–Bluebell area occured 35–20 Ma, with peak generation (critical moment) occurring about 30 Ma. However, the abnormally high fluid pressure in the Altamont–Bluebell field convinces us that hydrocarbon generation is presently ongoing in the central and northern regions of the field complex (see Bredehoeft et al., in press). During the time of preservation (<20 Ma), already generated hydrocarbons were either preserved in their original state (oil fields) or biodegraded and eroded away (natural bitumen).

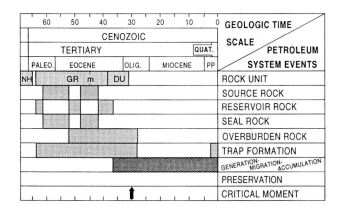

Figure 25.19. Events chart for the Green River(!) petroleum system. Abbreviations: NH, North Horn Formation; GR, Green River Formation; m, Mahogany oil shale bed; DU, Duchesne River and Uinta formations.

CONCLUSIONS

In the Green River(!) petroleum system, most oil and associated gas is recovered from pores (most secondary) in the basal parts of marginal lacustrine channel sandstone units that are intercalated with clay mudrock and carbonate mudstone units. Future drilling and production will link many small oil fields on the south flank of the Uinta Basin to the greater Altamont–Bluebell and Red Wash fields to form a region of continuous production extending from the northeastern end of the Altamont–Bluebell complex eastward to Red Wash and southwestward and westward to rejoin the southwestern tip of the Altamont–Bluebell complex.

Productive oil-bearing and associated gas-bearing rocks in the Green River system can be separated into three groups of reservoir rocks:

1. Deeply buried, overpressured, fractured, oil- and associated gas-bearing strata with low matrix permeability, low porosity, and rare to absent oil–water contacts
2. Normally pressured Tertiary oil and associated gas reservoirs with relatively high matrix permeability, high porosity, and oil–water contact
3. Sandstone reservoirs with low matrix permeability, moderate to high porosity, and some natural fractures containing nonassociated gas with minor amounts of oil

Because the Lake Uinta hydrologic system was closed, the chemistry and geometry of the water mass were especially sensitive to external factors such as changes in climate and tectonically induced reconfigurations of the topographic and hydrologic basin. Simultaneous changes in climate initiated rapid rises and falls in lake level, as well as shifts in alkalinity and salinity of the water, which resulted in the development of carbonate geochemical and sedimentary cycles (parasequences) of up to tens of meters thick. Regionally extensive reconfigurations of the Lake Uinta depositional system were probably in response to faulting. Long- and short-term changes in climate and tectonic regime induced the development of carbonate geochemical and sedimentary cycles that resulted in the source, seal, and reservoir rocks of the Green River(!) petroleum system.

Green River Formation source rocks include an open lacustrine facies containing mainly type I kerogen, a marginal lacustrine facies containing types I, II, and III kerogens, and an alluvial facies with dominantly type III kerogen.

The trend of thermal maturity level of the beds largely parallels the present-day surface topography. Moderate and high temperature oil and gas were generated from lacustrine source rocks in the Green River Formation that have achieved a level of >0.5% R_m. Beds in the northern and central part of the Altamont–Bluebell field are presently at or near maximum burial, and moderate and high temperature oil and gases are currently being generated below ~3050 m (~10,000 ft).

Although accumulations such as the greater Altamont–Bluebell field are associated with reservoir strata with vitrinite reflectance values of >0.5% R_m, billions of barrels of oil in-place in the subsurface and in bituminous sandstones are encased in strata with R_m values equal to or less than that. Much of that oil was probably derived from source rocks of low and moderate temperatures as approximated by vitrinite reflectance values, and many rocks have generated and expelled large volumes of oil and are by definition mature, even though some source beds have values of 0.5% R_m or less. Biomarker ratios of oils associated with the tar sands and stratigraphic considerations indicate that oil formed at relatively shallow depths (<2900 m) and at low to moderate temperatures and has migrated to the basin margin from the central part of the basin.

In the Green River(!) petroleum system, the highest fluid pressure gradients and the most extensive open fractures networks are located in the deeply buried subsurface. Here, impermeable source rocks with abundant type I kerogen have been and continue to be subjected to sufficient heat to transform their organic matter thermochemically into petroleum-like compounds at such a rate and in such volume that the increase in the volume of petroleum has resulted in (1) an increase in fluid pressure gradients and (2) pods of open fractures.

References Cited

Anders, D. E., and P. M. Gerrild, 1984, Hydrocarbon generation in lacustrine rocks of Tertiary age, Uinta Basin, Utah–organic carbon, pyrolysis yield, and light hydrocarbons, *in* J. Woodward, F. F. Meissner, and J. L. Clayton, eds., Hydrocarbon source rocks of the Greater Rocky Mountain Region: Denver, Rocky Mountain Association of Geologists, p. 513–529.

Anders, D. E., J. G. Palacas, and R. C. Johnson, 1992, Thermal maturity of rocks and hydrocarbon deposits, Uinta Basin, Utah, *in* T. D. Fouch, V. F. Nuccio, and T. C. Chidsey, Jr.,

eds., Hydrocarbon and Mineral Resources of the Uinta Basin, Utah and Colorado: Utah Geological Association Guidebook 20: Salt Lake City, Utah, p. 53–76.

Andersen, D. W., and M. D. Picard, 1972, Stratigraphy of the Duchesne River Formation, northern Uinta Basin, northeastern Utah: Utah Geological and Mineralogical Survey Bulletin 97, 23 p.

Benson, A. K., 1992, Determination of depth models through self-consistent structural modeling to help delineate hydrocarbon traps in the Uinta Basin, *in* T. D. Fouch, V. F. Nuccio, and T. C. Chidsey, Jr., eds., Hydrocarbon and Mineral Resources of the Uinta Basin, Utah and Colorado: Utah Geological Association Guidebook 20, Salt Lake City, Utah, p. 219–226.

Bredehoeft, J. D., J. B. Wesley, and T. D. Fouch, 1992, Origin of fluid pressure, fracture generation, and the movement of fluids in the Uinta Basin, Utah, (abs.) *in* L. M. H. Carter, ed., USGS Research on Energy Resources, 1992, program and abstracts: USGS Circular 1074, p. 13.

Bredehoeft, J. D., J. B. Wesley, and T. D. Fouch, in press, The origin of fluid pressures, fracture generation, and the movement of fluid in the Uinta Basin, Utah: AAPG Bulletin.

Bruhn, R. L., M. D. Picard, and J. S. Isby, 1986, Tectonics and sedimentology of Uinta arch, western Uinta Mountains and Uinta Basin, *in* J. A. Peterson, ed., Paleotectonics and sedimentation in the Rocky Mountain region, United States: AAPG Memoir 32, p. 333–352.

Bryant, B., 1991, Geologic map of the Salt Lake City 1°×2° quadrangle, Utah and Wyoming: USGS Miscellaneous Investigations Series Map I-1997, 2 sheets.

Bryant, B., C. W. Naeser, R. F. Marvin, and H. H. Mehnert, 1989, Upper Cretaceous and Paleogene sedimentary rocks and isotopic ages of Paleogene tuffs, Uinta Basin, Utah: USGS Bulletin 1787-J, 22 p.

Campbell, J. A., 1975, Structural geology and petroleum potential of the south flank of the Uinta Mountain uplift, northeastern Utah: Utah Geology, v. 2, n. 2, p. 129–132.

Castle, J. W., 1990, Sedimentation in Eocene Lake Uinta (Lower Green River Formation), northeastern Uinta Basin, Utah, *in* B. J. Katz, ed., Lacustrine basin exploration—case studies and modern analogs: AAPG Memoir 50, p. 243–264.

Chapman, D. S., T. H. Keho, M. S. Bauer, and M. D. Picard, 1984, Heat flow in the Uinta Basin determined from bottom hole temperature (BHT) data: Geophysics, v. 49, n. 4, p. 453–466.

Chatfield, J., 1972, Case history of Red Wash field, Uintah County, Utah, *in* R. E. King, ed., Stratigraphic oil and gas fields—classification, exploration methods, and case histories: AAPG Memoir 16, p. 343–353.

Clem, K., 1985, Oil and gas production summary of the Uinta Basin, *in* M. D. Picard, ed., Utah Geological Association Publication 12: Geology and Energy Resources, Uinta Basin of Utah, p. 159–168.

Colburn, J. A., S. R. Bereskin, D. C. McGinley, and D. M. Schiller, 1985, Lower Green River Formation in the Pleasant Valley Producing area, Duchesne and Uintah counties, Utah, *in* M. D. Picard, ed., Utah Geological Association Publication 12: Geology and Energy Resources, Uinta Basin of Utah, p. 177–186.

Fouch, T. D., 1975, Lithofacies and related hydrocarbon accumulations in Tertiary strata of the western and central Uinta Basin, Utah, *in* D. W. Bolyard, ed., Deep drilling frontiers of the central Rocky Mountains: Rocky Mountain Association of Petroleum Geologists Symposium, Denver, p. 163–174.

Fouch, T. D., 1981, Distribution of rock types, lithologic groups, and interpreted depositional environments for some lower Tertiary and Upper Cretaceous rocks from outcrops at Willow Creek–Indian Canyon through the subsurface of Duchesne and Altamont oil fields, southwest to north central parts of the Uinta Basin, Utah: USGS Oil and Gas Investigations Chart OC-81, 2 sheets.

Fouch, T. D., 1985, Oil- and Gas-bearing Upper Cretaceous and Paleogene fluvial rocks in central and northeast Utah, *in* Recognition of fluvial depositional systems and their resource potential: SEPM Short Course 19, p. 241–272.

Fouch, T. D., and W. B. Cashion, 1979, Distribution of rock types, lithologic groups, and depositional environments for some lower Tertiary and Upper Cretaceous, and Upper and Middle Jurassic rocks in the subsurface between Altamont oil field and San Arroyo gas field, northcentral to southeast Uinta Basin, Utah: USGS Open File Report 79-365, 2 sheets.

Fouch, T. D., and J. H. Hanley, 1977, Interdisciplinary analysis of some petroleum source rocks in east-central Utah— Implications for hydrocarbon exploration in nonmarine rocks of western United States (abs.): AAPG Bulletin, v. 61, n. 8, p. 1377–1378.

Fouch, T. D., and J. K. Pitman, 1991, Tectonic and climate changes expressed as sedimentary cycles and stratigraphic sequences in the Paleogene Lake Uinta system, central Rocky Mountains, Utah and Colorado, (abs.): AAPG Bulletin, v. 75, n. 3, p. 575

Fouch, T. D., and J. K. Pitman, 1992, Tectonic and climate changes expressed as sedimentary and geochemical cycles: Paleogene Lake systems, Utah and Colorado: implications for petroleum source and reservoir rocks (abs.), *in* L. M. H. Carter, ed., USGS Research on Energy Resources, 1992, Program and Abstracts: USGS Circular 1074, p. 29–30.

Fouch, T. D., W. B. Cashion, R. T. Ryder, and J. A. Campbell, 1976, Field guide to lacustrine and related nonmarine depositional environments in Tertiary rocks, Uinta Basin, Utah, *in* R. C. Epis and R. J. Weimer, eds., Studies in Colorado field geology: Professional Contributions of Colorado School of Mines, n. 8, p. 358–385.

Fouch, T. D., T. F. Lawton, D. J. Nichols, W. B. Cashion, and W. A. Cobban, 1983, Patterns and timing of synorogenic sedimentation in Upper Cretaceous rocks of central and northeast Utah, *in* M. W. Reynolds and E. D. Dolly, eds., Mesozoic paleogeography of the west-central United States: Second SEPM Paleogeography Symposium, Rocky Mountain Section, Denver, p. 305–336.

Fouch, T. D., V. F. Nuccio, J. C. Osmond, L. MacMillan, W. B. Cashion, and C. J. Wandrey, 1992a, Oil and Gas in uppermost Cretaceous and Tertiary rock, Uinta Basin, Utah, *in* T. D. Fouch, V. F. Nuccio, and T. C. Chidsey Jr., eds., Hydrocarbon and mineral resources of the Uinta Basin, Utah and Colorado: Utah Geological Association Guidebook 20: Salt Lake City, Utah, p. 9–47.

Fouch, T. D., C. J. Wandrey, J. K. Pitman, V. F. Nuccio, J. W. Schmoker, D. D. Rice, R. C. Johnson, and G. L. Dolton, 1992b, Natural gas accumulations in low-permeability Tertiary and Cretaceous (Maastrichtian–Campanian) rock, Uinta Basin, Utah: U.S. Department of Energy Report DOE/MC/20422-3051 (DE92001132), 81 p.

Franczyk, K. J., T. D. Fouch, R. C. Johnson, and C. M. Molenaar, 1992, Cretaceous and Tertiary paleogeographic reconstructions for the Uinta–Piceance study area: USGS Bulletin 1787, Chapter Q, 37 p.

Gries, R., 1983, Oil and gas prospecting beneath Precambrian of foreland thrust plates in the Rocky Mountains, AAPG, v. 67, p. 1–28.

Hansen, W. R., 1984, Post-Laramide tectonic history of the eastern Uinta Mountains, Utah, Colorado, and Wyoming: The Mountain Geologist, v. 21, n. 1, p. 5–29.

Hansen, W. R., 1990, Paleogeographic and paleotectonic setting of Laramide sedimentary basins in the central Rocky Mountain region: Alternative interpretation and reply: Geological Society of America Bulletin, v. 102, n. 2, p. 280–282.

Hatcher, H. J., H. L. C. Meuzelaar, and D. T. Urban, 1992, A comparison of biomarkers in gilsonite, oil shale, tar sand, and petroleum from Threemile Canyon and adjacent areas in the Uinta Basin, Utah, *in* T. D. Fouch, V. F. Nuccio, and T. C. Chidsey, Jr., eds., Hydrocarbon and mineral resources of the Uinta Basin, Utah and Colorado: Utah Geological Association Guidebook 20, Salt Lake City, Utah, p. 271–288.

James, A. T., 1983, Correlation of natural gas by use of carbon isotopic distribution between hydrocarbon components: AAPG Bulletin, v. 67, p. 1176–1191.

James, A. T., 1990, Correlation of reservoired gases using the carbon isotopic composition of wet gas components: AAPG Bulletin, v. 74, p. 1441–1458.

Johnson, R. C., 1985, Early Cenozoic history of the Uinta and Piceance Creek basins, Utah and Colorado, with special reference to the development of Eocene Lake Uinta, *in* R. M. Flores and S. S. Kaplan, eds., Cenozoic paleogeography of the west-central United States: SEPM Symposium, Rocky Mountain Section, p. 247–276.

Johnson, R. C., and V. F. Nuccio, 1993, Surface vitrinite reflectance study of the Uinta and Piceance Basins area, eastern Utah and western Colorado—implications for the development of Laramide basins and uplifts: USGS Bulletin 1787-DD, 38 p.

Johnson R. C., and D. D. Rice, 1990, Occurrence and geochemistry of natural gases, Piceance basin, northwest Colorado: AAPG Bulletin, v. 74, p. 805–829.

Keighin, C. W., and T. D. Fouch, 1981, Depositional environments and diagenesis of some nonmarine Upper Cretaceous reservoir rocks, Uinta Basin, Utah, *in* F. G. Ethridge and R. M. Flores, eds., Recent and ancient nonmarine depositional environments: models for exploration: SEPM Special Publication 31, p. 109–125.

Kelly, J. M., and Castle, J. W., 1992, Red Wash field—U. S. A. Uinta Basin, Utah, *in* N. H. Foster and E. A. Beaumont, eds., Stratigraphic traps III: AAPG, Treatise of Petroleum Geology, Atlas of Oil and Gas Fields, p. 231–256.

Koesoemadinata, R. P., 1970, Stratigraphy and petroleum occurrence, Green River Formation, Red Wash Field, Utah: Quarterly of the Colorado School of Mines, v. 65, n. 1, p. 1–77.

Law, B. E., V. F. Nuccio, and C. E. Barker, 1989, Kinky vitrinite reflectance well profiles: evidence of paleopore pressure in low-permeability, gas-bearing sequences in Rocky Mountain Foreland basins: AAPG Bulletin, v. 73, p. 999–1010.

Lucas, P. T., and J. M. Drexler, 1976, Altamont–Bluebell—a major naturally fractured stratigraphic trap, *in* North American oil and gas fields: AAPG Memoir 24, p. 121–135.

Narr, W., and J. B. Currie, 1982, Origin of fracture porosity—example from Altamont Field, Utah: AAPG, v. 66, p. 1231–1247.

Natural Petroleum Council, 1992, Energy and environmental analysis, 1991–92 NPC tight gas resources and well recoveries—lower 48: Committee on Natural Gas, Nonconventional Gas Subgroup, 40 p.

NRG Associates, Inc., 1990, The significant oil and gas fields of the United States (through December 1989): Unpublished computer database, Colorado Springs, CO, Nehring Associates, Inc.

Nuccio, V. F., J. W. Schmoker, and T. D. Fouch, 1992, Thermal maturity, porosity, and lithofacies relationship applied to gas generation and production in Tertiary and Cretaceous low-permeability (tight) sandstones, Uinta Basin, Utah, *in* T. D. Fouch, V. F. Nuccio, and T. C. Chidsey, Jr., eds., Hydrocarbon and mineral resources of the Uinta Basin, Utah and Colorado: Utah Geological Association Guidebook 20: Salt Lake, City, Utah, p. 77–93.

Oblad, A. G., J. W. Bunger, F. V. Hanson, J. D. Miller, H. R. Ritzma, and J. D. Seader, 1987, Tar sand research and development at the University of Utah, *in* J. M. Hollander, H. Brooks, and D. Sternlight, eds., Annual Review of Energy, v. 12: Palo Alto, CA, Annual Reviews, Inc., p. 283–357.

Osmond, J. C., 1992, Greater Natural Buttes gas field, Uintah County, Utah, *in* T. D. Fouch, V. F. Nuccio, and T. C. Chidsey, Jr., eds., Hydrocarbon and mineral resources of the Uinta Basin, Utah and Colorado: Utah Geological Association Guidebook 20: Salt Lake City, Utah, p. 143–163.

Pitman, J. K., T. D. Fouch, and M. B. Goldhaber, 1982, Sedimentologic and diagenetic evolution of some Tertiary nonmarine unconventional reservoir rocks, Uinta Basin, Utah: AAPG Bulletin, v. 66, n. 10, p. 1581–1596.

Pitman, J. K., K. J. Franczyk, and D. E. Anders, 1987, Marine and nonmarine gas-bearing rocks in Upper Cretaceous Blackhawk and Neslen formations, eastern Uinta Basin, Utah: AAPG Bulletin, v. 71, p. 76–94.

Powell, T. G., 1986, Petroleum geochemistry and depositional settings of lacustrine source rocks: Marine and Petroleum Geology, v. 3, p. 200–219.

Remy, R. R., 1991, Analysis of lacustrine deltaic sedimentation in the Green River Formation, southern Uinta Basin, Utah: Ph.D. dissertation, Louisiana State University, Baton Rouge, LA, 394 p.

Rice, D. D., 1983, Relation of natural gas composition to thermal maturity and source rock type in San Juan basin, northwestern New Mexico and southwestern Colorado: AAPG Bulletin, v. 67, p. 1199–1218.

Rice, D. D., J. L. Clayton, and M. J. Pawlewicz, 1989, Characterization of coal-derived hydrocarbons and source rock potential of coal beds, San Juan basin, New Mexico and Colorado, U.S.A.: International Journal of Coal Geology, v. 13, p. 597–623.

Rice, D. D., T. D. Fouch, and R. C. Johnson 1992, Influence of source rock type, thermal maturity, and migration on composition and distribution of natural gases, Uinta Basin, Utah, *in* T. D. Fouch, V. F. Nuccio, and T. C. Chidsey, Jr., eds., Hydrocarbon and mineral resources of the Uinta Basin, Utah and Colorado: Utah Geological Association Guidebook 20: Salt Lake City, Utah, p. 95–109.

Ritzma, H. R., 1974, Cross-section southeast Asphalt Ridge,

Uintah County, Utah, *in* Energy resources of the Uinta Basin: Utah Geological Association Publication 4, p. 60.

Ritzma, H. R., 1979, Oil-impregnated rock deposits of Utah: Utah Geological and Mineral Survey Map 47, scale 1:1,000,000, 2 sheets.

Ryder, R. T., T. D. Fouch, and J. H. Elison, 1976, Early Tertiary sedimentation in the western Uinta Basin, Utah: GSA Bulletin, v. 87, n. 4, p. 496–512.

Schoell, M. 1983, Genetic characterization of natural gases: AAPG Bulletin, v. 67, p. 2225–2238.

Spencer, C. W., 1987, Hydrocarbon generation as a mechanism for overpressuring in Rocky Mountain region, AAPG Bulletin, v. 71, n. 4, p. 368–388.

Stone, D. S., 1977, Tectonic history of the Uncompahgre uplift, *in* H. K. Veal, ed., Exploration frontiers of the central and southern Rockies: Denver, Rocky Mountain Association of Geologists, p. 23–30.

Sweeney, J. J., A. K. Burnham, and R. L. Bruan, 1987, A model of hydrocarbon generation from type I kerogen, application to Uinta Basin, Utah: AAPG Bulletin, v. 71, n. 8, p. 967–985.

Tissot, B. P., and D. H. Welte, 1984, Petroleum Formation and Occurrence: New York, Springer-Verlag, 699 p.

Tissot, B. P., G. Deroo, and A. Hood, 1978, Geochemical study of the Uinta Basin: formation of petroleum from the Green River Formation: Geochimica et Cosmochimica Acta, v. 42, p. 1469–1485.

Utah Division of Oil, Gas, and Mining, 1991, December 1990 oil and gas production report: Salt Lake City, State of Utah Department of Natural Resources, Division of Oil, Gas, and Mining, 227 p.

Utah Geological and Mineral Survey, 1967, Reflection seismograph survey, Asphalt Ridge area, Uintah County, Utah: Petty Geophysical Engineering Company, Utah Geological and Mineral Survey Unnumbered Open-File Report, November.

Wanty, R. B., J. K. Pitman, and T. D. Fouch 1991, Groundwater chemistry and diagenetic reactions in Tertiary sandstones of the Green River and Wasatch formations, Uinta Basin, Utah: USGS Bulletin 1787-X, 21 p.

Wesley, J. B., 1990, Finite difference modeling of present-day overpressures maintained by hydrocarbon generation and regional fluid flow in the Green River Formation, Uinta Basin, Utah: Master's thesis, Colorado School of Mines, Golden, CO, 139 p.

Wesley, J. B., Wandrey, C. J., and Fouch, T. D., 1993, Principal drill stem test database (UBDST) and documentation: analysis of Uinta Basin, Utah gas-bearing Cretaceous and Tertiary strata: USGS Open-File Report 93-193, 18 p.

Willet, S. D., and D. S. Chapman, 1987, Analysis of temperatures and thermal processes in the Uinta Basin, *in* C. Beaumont and A. J. Tankard, eds., Sedimentary basins and basin-forming environments: Canadian Society of Petroleum Geologists Memoir 12, p. 447–461.

*"The continually rising standards of
petroleum geoscience and oil search require
an ever greater knowledge of the
fundamental nature of petroleum, its origin,
and its behavior in the rocks of
the earth's crust."*

—Hollis D. Hedberg

Passage from Hedberg, H. D., 1979, Petroleum Geochemistry and Geology, J. M. Hunt, ed.: W.H. Freeman, p. xi.

Magoon, L. B., and W. G. Dow, eds., 1994, The petroleum
system—from source to trap: AAPG Memoir 60.

Chapter **26**

Identification of Petroleum Systems Adjacent to the San Andreas Fault, California, U.S.A.

K. E. Peters*

Chevron Overseas Petroleum Inc.
San Ramon, California, U.S.A.

M. H. Pytte

Chevron Overseas Petroleum Inc.
San Ramon, California, U.S.A.

T. D. Elam

Chevron U.S.A. Inc.
Bakersfield, California, U.S.A.

P. Sundararaman

Chevron Petroleum Technology Company
La Habra, California, U.S.A.

Abstract

Based on stable carbon isotope and porphyrin data, most oil, oil seep, and oil-stained samples examined from the west flank of the San Joaquin basin and east flank of the Cuyama and Salinas basins, all adjacent to the San Andreas fault, were generated from source rocks of Cretaceous (group IV), Eocene (group I), or Miocene (groups II and III) age. Based on similar analysis of source rock samples from wells and outcrops in the same area, the Eocene and Miocene source rocks compare favorably with oil samples. These oil–oil and oil–source rock correlations identify at least two unnamed petroleum systems.

Oil, oil seep, and oil-stained samples show stable carbon isotope values ranging from about –27 to –29‰ for the Eocene and –22 to –26‰ for the Miocene petroleum systems. Wide variations in the Ni/(Ni + V) porphyrin ratio among these samples indicate oil mixing or considerable variations in the organic facies of the source rocks. For example, group III represents a single family of petroleums derived from different organic facies of the Miocene source rock. These oil samples show similar stable carbon isotope compositions but different Ni/(Ni + V) porphyrin ratios.

In general, oils from the northern study area can be tied to Eocene Kreyenhagen source rock (group I). Oil stains on the east side of the San Andreas fault can be tied to low-maturity Miocene McDonald shales (group III), a lateral equivalent to the Monterey Formation. Samples on the west side of the San Andreas fault can be tied to the Soda Lake Shale Member of the Vaqueros Formation (group II). Oil (group IV) from the Oil City field is suspected to originate from the Moreno Formation.

INTRODUCTION

Regional Geology

The San Joaquin basin (Figure 26.1) is an asymmetric trough with a gently sloping eastern flank and a narrow, tectonically deformed western flank (Figure 26.2). The trough is filled with upper Mesozoic and Cenozoic sedimentary rocks reaching thicknesses of over 9 km. The basin is bounded on the north by the Stockton arch (Bartow, 1987; Crowell, 1987), on the south by the Tehachapi–San Emigdio Mountains (Bandy and Arnal, 1969), on the west by the San Andreas fault, and on the east by the Sierra Nevada batholith.

Petroleum Geology

The paleotectonic settings during deposition of sediments in the San Joaquin basin have been discussed by various authors (e.g. Bartow, 1987; Dickinson et al., 1987; Graham, 1987; Nilsen, 1987). Some of the most likely petroleum source rocks in the basin include the Cretaceous–Paleocene Moreno, the Eocene Kreyenhagen, and the Miocene Monterey shales.

The Upper Cretaceous portion of the Moreno Formation along the western flank of the San Joaquin basin in the northern part of the study from the Vallecitos field to south of the Coalinga field contains laminated dolomites and is rich in oil-prone organic

---

*Present address: Mobil Exploration and Producing Technical
Center, Dallas, Texas, U.S.A.

423

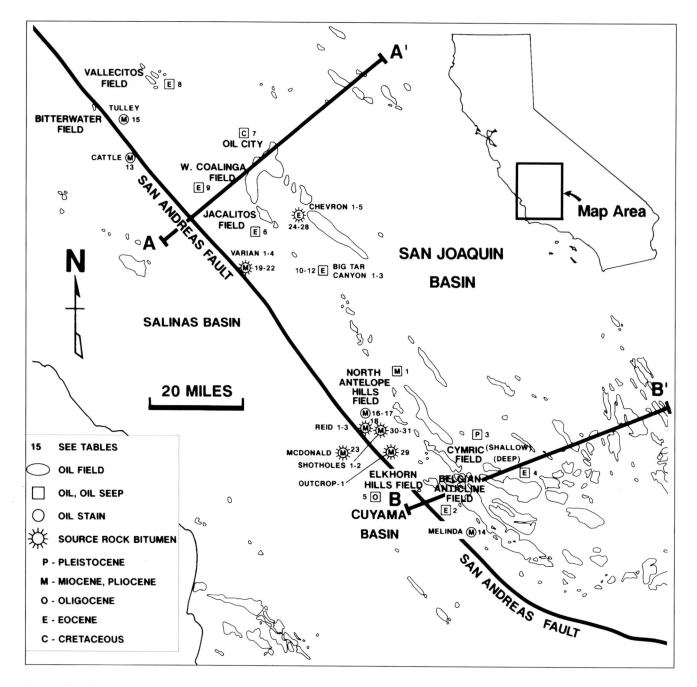

Figure 26.1. Map showing the location of the oil and source rock samples relative to the San Andreas fault and the San Joaquin, Salinas, and Cuyama basins. Locations of cross sections A–A' and B–B' in Figure 26.2 are shown.

matter. For example, in a well near W. Coalinga field, the Moreno is dominated by oil-prone type II kerogen and contains up to 7.25 wt. % total organic carbon (TOC) (McGuire, 1988). These sedimentary rocks thin to the northwest onto the Stockton arch (Nilsen, 1987) and become dominated by oxidized, structured organic matter with poor petroleum potential (McGuire, 1988).

Depositional environments during the Eocene were complex but generally consisted of fluvial, marine shelf, slope, basin, and deep sea fan deposits that generally prograded from the east flank of the basin to the west toward the study area. The deep marine Kreyenhagen

Formation contains well-laminated, organic-rich, oil-prone intervals (Milam, 1985) inferred to have generated significant quantities of oil (Graham, 1987).

During the Miocene and early Pliocene, thick accumulations of diatomaceous sediments were deposited in the southern San Joaquin basin. The Miocene Monterey Formation contains dominantly oil-prone type II kerogen from marine plankton (Graham, 1987). Most workers acknowledge the Monterey Formation as the source rock for most of the petroleum in San Joaquin basin.

The literature shows a remarkable lack of geochemical evidence on the source rocks for oils found in and

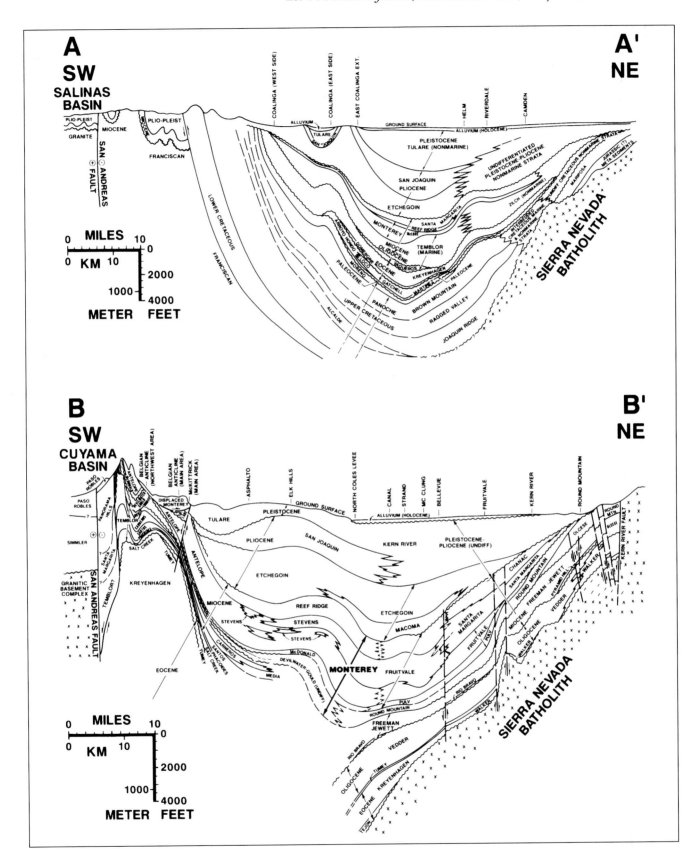

Figure 26.2. Cross sections A–A' and B–B' showing the stratigraphic units and the structural relationships of the sedimentary rocks in the basins and on both sides of the San Andreas fault. (Modified from California Department of Conservation, 1985.)

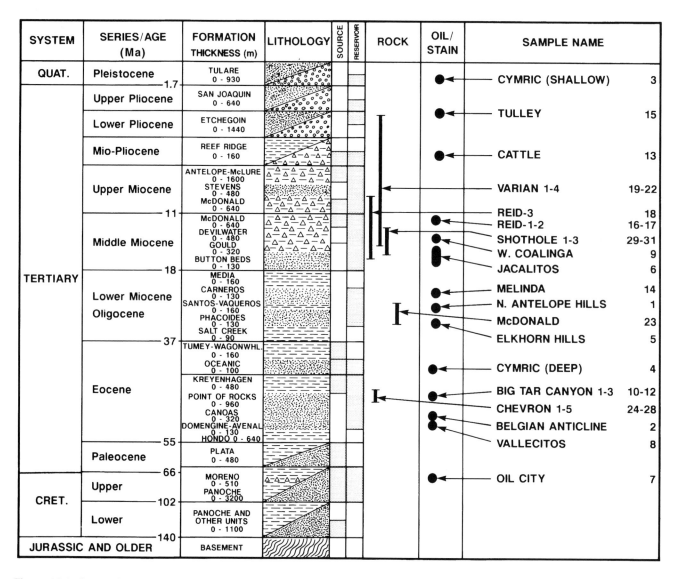

Figure 26.3. Generalized stratigraphic column for San Joaquin basin showing the ages of the source rock samples and of the reservoir rocks for the oil samples. Stratigraphic location for the Cattle and McDonald samples are based on correlative age and formation.

around the San Joaquin basin. Limited data for the Eocene Kreyenhagen Formation (Milam, 1985) suggest it is a petroleum source rock in the central San Joaquin basin, whereas the organic-rich Miocene Monterey Formation is too shallow to have reached the oil window (Graham and Williams, 1985). Biological marker maturity parameters show that oil generation from the Monterey Formation occurs only at depths in excess of 4 km in the south-central San Joaquin basin (Kruge, 1985). Oil-prone shales have been described in the Oligocene–Miocene Temblor Formation from Kettleman North Dome (Kuespert, 1985).

Oil seeps and oil stains occur in the hills of the Temblor and southern Diablo Ranges, commonly on the east side of the San Andreas fault at the west end of cross section A–A' (Figure 26.1) in rocks ranging in age from Cretaceous to Pleistocene (Figure 26.3). The occurrence of oil just east of the fault (Figure 26.2A) is problematic because San Joaquin basin source rocks are believed to be

thermally immature or absent due to erosion or nondeposition. For example, the Paleocene–Cretaceous Moreno and Eocene Kreyenhagen Formations are thin or absent in this area, while the Miocene Monterey and McLure shales in the Varian well appear to be thermally immature (Figure 26.1). Furthermore, long distance migration of oil from a source rock buried in the axis of the San Joaquin basin in the present structural setting requires that oil migrate downsection through low-permeability Cretaceous shales.

An important exploration question is whether oil on the east side of the San Andreas fault, such as in the Vallecitos, Belgian anticline, and Jacalitos fields and in the Temblor–Diablo Range oil shows, might be partially the result of migration across the fault from thermally mature source rocks buried in the Cuyama or Salinas basins. Alternately, these oils might originate from thermally mature source rocks in the western San Joaquin basin east of the San Andreas fault.

The objective of this case study is to identify and determine the number of petroleum systems present along the west flank of the San Joaquin basin by using oil–oil and oil–source rock correlations. To accomplish this, we evaluate the genetic relationships among various potential source rocks, oils, oil seeps, and oil stains from the western San Joaquin and adjacent Cuyama and Salinas basins (Figure 26.1).

METHODS

This geochemical reconnaissance of the western San Joaquin basin samples was completed using rapid low-cost analyses. Relying on methods described by Peters (1986) and Peters and Cassa (Chapter 5, this volume), we analyzed whole rock samples for TOC and pyrolysis response using a Leco Analyzer and a Rock-Eval II Pyro-analyzer. Bitumens were extracted from ground whole rock using methylene chloride. Oils, bitumens, and kerogens as well as saturated and aromatic hydrocarbons were separated (Peters and Moldowan, 1993) and analyzed for stable carbon isotopic composition (Schoell et al., 1983). Stable carbon isotope ratios are reported relative to the PeeDee belemnite (PDB) standard. In our laboratory, NBS-22 (National Bureau of Standards) oil is used for calibration, measuring $-29.75 \pm 0.05‰$ against PDB. Porphyrin analyses were completed using the method of Sundararaman et al. (1988). Selected oils and bitumens were spiked with internal standards (Peters and Moldowan, 1993) and analyzed for biomarkers using a Hewlett-Packard gas chromatograph–mass selective detector (GC-MSD).

RESULTS

Analytical results show that certain measurements effectively define genetic relationships among samples (groups) from the western San Joaquin basin: (1) stable carbon isotope ratios of saturated and aromatic hydrocarbons, and (2) nickel versus vanadyl porphyrin content (Table 26.1). Stable carbon isotope values for these samples show distinct differences that help organize them into genetic types. For example, when the stable carbon isotope ratios for the saturate versus aromatic hydrocarbon fractions of the samples are plotted, several petroleum types are suggested (Figure 26.4). Because stable carbon isotope analyses for unrelated samples can be fortuitously similar, the sample types designated were grouped using additional information provided by the relative amounts of nickel and vanadyl porphyrins, or the Ni/(Ni + V) ratio (Sundararaman et al., 1988) (Figure 26.5).

Group I

Group I (Table 26.1) consists of oil (samples 2, 4, 6, 8, and 9) and oil seeps (10–12) from reservoir rocks of Miocene and Eocene age east of the San Andreas fault in the western San Joaquin basin and bitumen (sample 25) extracted from Eocene Kreyenhagen source rock in the

74X-21H well (Figure 26.1). The oil samples are from the Belgian anticline, Cymric (deep), Jacalitos, Vallecitos, and West Coalinga fields and from an oil seep in the Eocene Point of Rocks Formation just beneath the Kreyenhagen shale in Big Tar Canyon (Figure 26.3). These samples show stable carbon isotope ratios in the range -29.08 to $-27.28‰$ and Ni/(Ni + V) ratios of 0.24–0.71 (subgroup IA). The Belgian anticline oil (subgroup IA) shows only trace porphyrins, and a reliable Ni/(Ni + V) ratio could not be measured.

The Vallecitos oil is located north of the other samples (Figure 26.1). This oil also differs from the other group I samples because it is more depleted in ^{13}C (whole oil = $-29.08‰$) (Figure 26.4;) and shows a higher Ni/(Ni + V) ratio (0.71) (Figure 26.5). The Monterey Formation is an unlikely source rock for this oil because the adjacent Vallecitos syncline lacks thermally mature Monterey source rock, whereas the Kreyenhagen source rock is present (McGuire, 1988). Bac and Schulein (1990) suggest that Vallecitos oil, which comes from a reservoir rock in the San Carlos sandstone member of the Lodo Formation (late Paleocene age, equivalent to Plata Formation in Figure 26.3), was generated from the underlying Moreno Formation. We view this as unlikely because an oil from the nearby Oil City Field is being produced from the Moreno Formation and it shows an isotopic and porphyrin composition unlike the Vallecitos oil or oil from the Miocene source rock. Thus, we conclude that the Vallecitos oil came from the Kreyenhagen source rock.

Big Tar Canyon (Figure 26.1) contains three oil seeps (Kuespert, 1990), all of which were sampled for this case study. These seeps show stable carbon isotope ratios of -27.94 to $-28.77‰$ and Ni/(Ni + V) ratios of 0.24–0.38, consistent with classification into group I. Although these seep oils probably migrated from depth (see later), they appear to come from the Kreyenhagen source rock where it is thermally mature.

Five bitumens extracted from Kreyenhagen source rock in the Kreyenhagen 74X-21H well (10,040–10,460 ft) show Ni/(Ni + V) porphyrin ratios (0.10–0.57) similar to the range for group I samples (0.24–0.71). Values of the porphyrin maturity parameter (PMP) (Sundararaman et al., 1988) in the range of 0.12–0.18 for these samples indicate thermal maturity within the oil window. Stable carbon isotope analyses completed on one of these bitumens (10,130–10,160 ft) also support a relationship between the Eocene source rock and the group I oils (Figures 26.4 and 26.5).

Classification of the Belgian anticline oil in group I is tentative because it is comparatively enriched in ^{13}C (Figure 26.4) and lacks sufficient porphyrins to give a reliable Ni/(Ni + V) ratio. For these reasons, it is classified into subgroup IA, while all others are IB. This oil field is closer to the San Andreas fault and south of others in group I (Figure 26.1). The Belgian anticline oil could represent a mixture containing some ^{13}C-rich input from one of the other groups (Figure 26.4). The PMP (0.30), low sulfur content (0.10 wt. %), and high API gravity ($32°$) for this oil indicate thermal maturity within the oil window.

Table 26.1. Geochemical Data for Oils and Bitumens from the West Flank of the San Joaquin Basin

Sample No.	Field or Sample	Well Name and Number	Group	Depth (ft)	COFRC[a] No.
Oils					
1	N. Antelope Hills	Shell Hopkins 8-61X	IIIC	2,352–2,478	32,835
2	Belgian Anticline	CWOD 3-31-21V	IA	4,195–4,425	13,838
3	Cymric (shallow)	Chevron 22-11A-31X	IIIA	620–700	32,723
4	Cymric (deep)	Chevron 585-R-72	IB	8,840–8,964	25,322
5	Elkhorn Hills	Hotchkiss U. 24-25	IIIB	3,720–4,014	34,758
6	Jacalitos	Chevron 75-21E	IB	3,396–3,968	14,740
7	Oil City	Chevron 4-20A	IV	800	13,334
8	Vallecitos	Artnell Ashurst 3-5	IB	5,345–5,508	15,329
9	W. Coalinga	Chevron 3-8	IB	900	30,482
Oil seeps					
10	Big Tar Canyon-1	NA	IB	0	49,198
11	Big Tar Canyon-2	NA	IB	0	49,199
12	Big Tar Canyon-3	NA	IB	0	49,200
Oil stains					
13	Cattle	Texaco Calif. Land & Cattle 1	II	4,693–4,703	49,203
14	Melinda	Frank Short Melinda 2	IIIC	1,598–1,604	49,202
15	Tulley	Texaco Tulley 1	IIIB	1,670–1,678	49,205
16	Reid-1	Gene Reid 53-36	IIIA	1,660–1,674	49,204-3
17	Reid-2	Gene Reid 53-36	IIIA	1,674–1,692	49,204-4
Source rocks					
18	Reid-3	Gene Reid 53-36	IIIA	988–998	49,204-1
19	Varian-1	Phillips Varian A1	IIIB	3,360–3,390	48,683-1
20	Varian-2	Phillips Varian A1	IIIB	3,630–3,660	48,683-2
21	Varian-3	Phillips Varian A1	IIIB	3,990–4,020	48,683-3
22	Varian-4	Phillips Varian A1	IIIB	4,170–4,200	48,683-4
23	McDonald	Shell McDonald 28	II	8,533–8,541	49,207
24	Chevron-1	Chevron Kreyenhagen 74x-21H	—	10,040–10,070	49,799-1
25	Chevron-2	Chevron Kreyenhagen 74x-21H	IB	10,130–10,160	49,799-2
26	Chevron-3	Chevron Kreyenhagen 74x-21H	—	10,220–10,250	49,799-3
27	Chevron-4	Chevron Kreyenhagen 74x-21H	—	10,340–10,370	49,799-4
28	Chevron-5	Chevron Kreyenhagen 74x-21H	—	10,430–10,460	49,799-5
29	Outcrop-1	McDonald/Devilwater Fm. 36776-1	IIIB	0	49,509-4
30	Shothole-1	McDonald/Devilwater Fm. 36786-153.5'	IIIB	0	49,509-6
31	Shothole-2	McDonald/Devilwater Fm. 36786-155.5'	IIIC	0	49,509-8

[a]COFRC, Chevron Oil Field Research Company.
[b]PMP, porphyrin maturity parameter.

Significant quantities of nickel porphyrins combined with low sulfur (0.10–0.66 wt. %) in the group I samples suggest a suboxic depositional environment for the probable Kreyenhagen source rock. The considerable range in the Ni/(Ni + V) ratio from 0.24 to 0.71 for the group I samples indicates a wide variation in oxicity of the source rock's depositional environment (higher ratios mean more oxic). Interestingly, Ni/(Ni + V) ratios are lowest in group I samples near Big Tar Canyon (0.24–0.38) and increase to the northwest (0.39–0.71) at Vallecitos, West Coalinga, and Jacalitos and to the southeast (0.58) at Cymric. This implies that the depocenter for Eocene age source rocks was located near Big Tar Canyon and that more oxic conditions prevailed to the northwest and southeast during this time.

The PMP indicates that all group I samples are moderately mature (prior to the peak oil-generative stage), except two seep samples from Big Tar Canyon (see later). For example, the Cymric (deep) oil from the Eocene reservoir rock shows a high PMP (0.35) and a high API gravity (32°) and was produced from one of the deepest intervals in the study area (8840–8964 ft). Based on the West Coalinga oil's low API gravity (13°), shallow reservoir (900 ft), and gas chromatographic character, this mature (PMP = 0.41) oil appears to be biodegraded.

Two oil seep samples from Big Tar Canyon have a higher thermal maturity when compared to the inferred lower maturity from the surrounding Kreyenhagen shale. This indicates that these seeps must have migrated from deeper, more mature, equivalent rocks. Two of the

Table 26.1 (*continued*)

Gravity (°API)	Sulfur (wt. %)	Stable Carbon Isotope Ratio (PDB, ‰)				Porphyrins		Sample No.
		Kerogen	Oil/Bitumen	Saturates	Aromatics	Ni/(Ni + V)	PMP[b]	
15	1.00	NA	−25.50	−26.23	−25.66	0.61	0.23	1
32	0.10	NA	−27.28	−28.44	−26.06	-	0.30	2
12	1.22	NA	−23.56	−24.35	−23.84	0.26	0.11	3
32	0.66	NA	−28.02	−28.95	−27.39	0.58	0.35	4
26	0.24	NA	−24.65	−25.30	−24.20	0.74	0.56	5
35	0.37	NA	−28.91	−29.48	−28.52	0.39	0.33	6
33	0.21	NA	−26.61	−27.72	−25.20	0.00	0.12	7
21	0.28	NA	−29.08	−29.75	−28.95	0.71	0.24	8
13	0.32	NA	−28.25	−28.82	−28.34	0.46	0.41	9
NA	0.59	NA	−28.77	−29.28	−28.65	0.38	0.65	10
NA	0.66	NA	−28.74	−29.35	−28.66	0.35	0.67	11
NA	0.57	NA	−27.94	−28.65	−28.12	0.24	0.30	12
NA	4.73	−19.32	−22.10	−24.06	−22.77	0.10	0.18	13
NA	0.65	−27.16	−25.58	−26.29	−25.32	0.50	0.28	14
NA	1.50	−19.03	−23.96	−25.85	−24.31	1.00	—	15
NA	1.90	−23.58	−23.38	−24.70	−23.65	0.50	0.10	16
NA	1.78	−23.57	−23.37	−24.46	−23.78	0.48	0.11	17
NA	1.91	−24.12	−23.94	−25.05	−23.88	0.42	0.00	18
NA	0.52	—	—	−25.43	−24.52	1.00	—	19
NA	0.17	—	—	−25.29	−23.81	1.00	—	20
NA	0.08	—	—	−25.64	−24.21	1.00	—	21
NA	0.18	—	—	−25.60	−24.32	1.00	—	22
NA	0.59	−20.12	−21.69	−23.77	−21.43	0.00	0.51	23
NA	—	—	—	—	—	0.57	0.12	24
NA	—	—	—	−28.33	−28.82	0.34	0.16	25
NA	—	—	—	—	—	0.24	0.16	26
NA	—	—	—	—	—	0.11	0.14	27
NA	—	—	—	—	—	0.10	0.18	28
NA	—	—	—	−25.30	−23.42	0.80	0.00	29
NA	—	—	—	−25.58	−24.55	0.79	0.00	30
NA	—	—	—	−26.01	−24.07	0.59	0.00	31

seep samples from Big Tar Canyon (10 and 11 on Table 26.1) are very mature (PMP = 0.65–0.67; past peak oil generation), while all other samples in group I show lower thermal maturity (0.24–0.35). Although we lack data on the maturity of the Kreyenhagen shale in Big Tar Canyon, geologic reconstruction indicates it was never buried sufficiently to have entered the oil window. On-strike but more deeply buried equivalents of the Kreyenhagen source rock in the Chevron Jacalitos No. 67 well (3995–4748 ft), about 10 mi from Big Tar Canyon (Section 17, T21S, R15E), show good quantities (1.29–5.49 wt. % TOC) of predominantly oil-prone organic matter (HI = 125–525 mg HC/g TOC) that is thermally immature (T_{max} = 410°–429°C) (Milam, 1985).

The Monterey Formation is thermally immature in this area, and the only likely source rock for group I is the Kreyenhagen Formation. The maximum burial depth of the Kreyenhagen Formation varies widely over short distances near Big Tar Canyon. Reflection seismic data show that downdip and 5 mi northeast of Big Tar Canyon the Kreyenhagen is buried as deeply as 17,000–20,000 ft in the Pleasant Valley syncline. Here, the Kreyenhagen should be thermally mature to postmature. These local but wide variations in maximum burial depth support the conclusion that the more mature Big Tar Canyon oil seep samples originated from more deeply buried Kreyenhagen source rock and migrated updip to their present position. Thus, the group I oils derived from the Kreyenhagen source rock represent part of one petroleum system.

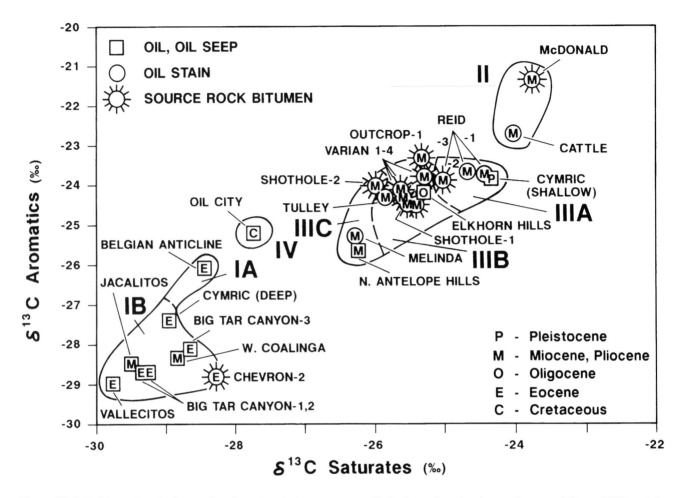

Figure 26.4. Stable carbon isotope ratios for saturated versus aromatic hydrocarbon (parts per thousand, ‰, on PDB scale) for oil and source rock samples. Four oil–source rock groups (I–IV) are shown. Dashed lines break group III into subgroups IIIA, IIIB, and IIIC and group I into subgroups IA and IB. The ages of the samples are also shown on Figure 26.3.

Group II

The group II samples (13 and 23) are isotopically enriched in ^{13}C compared to group I (Figure 26.4). Whole-oil or bitumen stable carbon isotope ratios range from –22.10 to –21.69‰ for group II and from –29.08 to –27.28‰ for group I. Such large differences in stable isotope composition (at least 5.18‰) cannot be explained by differences in thermal maturity among related petroleums, but must be caused by origins from different source rocks. Both group II samples are from widely spaced Miocene rocks to the west of the San Andreas fault (Figure 26.1) (see Lillis, Chapter 27, this volume).

Group II samples consist of one oil-stained core from the Texaco California Land and Cattle #1 well on the east flank of the Salinas basin and apparently indigenous bitumen in a core from the Shell McDonald #28 well at the north end of the Cuyama basin. These two samples are isotopically enriched in ^{13}C (–22.10 to –21.69‰) and show lower Ni/(Ni + V) porphyrin ratios (0–0.1) than the other groups in the study. High vanadyl porphyrins reflected by these ratios indicate an anoxic marine depositional environment for the source rock.

The high sulfur content of the oil stain (sample 13) compared to the bitumen (sample 23) of 4.73 versus 0.59 wt. % is consistent with gas chromatographic evidence indicating biodegradation of the oil stain. Some of this difference could be due to the higher thermal maturity of the bitumen sample as sulfur content decreases with increasing thermal maturity compared to that of the oil stain, as indicated by a higher PMP (0.51 versus 0.18) and greater present burial depth (8533–8541 versus 4693–4703 ft). This interpretation suggests that sulfur was originally higher than 0.59 wt. % in the bitumen sample but was reduced during thermal maturation.

The oil extracted from the oil-stained core appears to be migrated oil based on the lithology (called "oil-stained clayey siltstone" on the well logs), a high extract to TOC ratio (432 mg extract/g TOC), and the large difference in stable carbon isotope ratio between the kerogen and oil (2.78‰). The carbon isotopic value kerogen comes from the organic matter in the clayey siltstone. The reservoir rock for this oil stain is late middle Miocene in age. Although the oil shows a PMP (0.18) typical of mature petroleum, the organic matter in the host reservoir rock is immature based on vitrinite reflectance ($R_o = 0.57\%$),

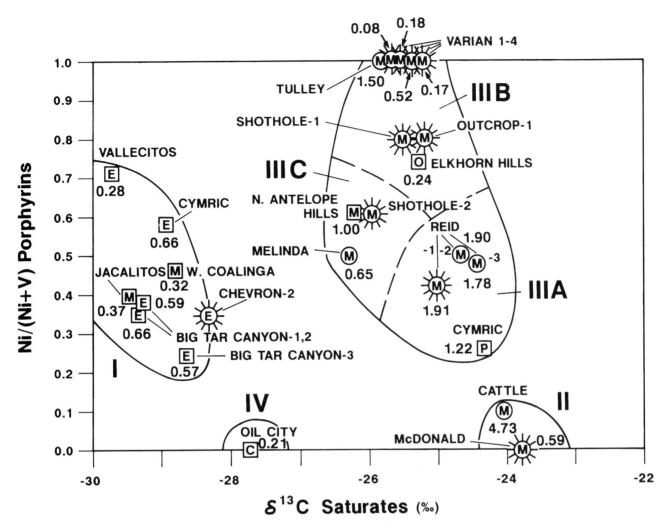

Figure 26.5. Stable carbon isotope ratio of saturated hydrocarbons (‰ on PDB scale) relative to the porphyrin Ni/(Ni + V) ratio. Sulfur content (in wt. %) is shown beneath each symbol. Four oil–source rock groups (I–IV) are shown. Dashed lines break group III into subgroups IIIA, IIIB, and IIIC. See Figure 26.4 for explanation of symbols.

and Rock-Eval pyrolysis ($T_{max} = 423°C$) data, indicating that the oil stain is migrated oil.

Bitumen extracted from the Shell McDonald #28 core was obtained from the Soda Lake Shale Member of the lower Miocene Vaqueros Formation. This member has been described as containing black, slickensided, oil-stained shale. The bitumen appears to be indigenous based on a low bitumen to TOC ratio (12 mg bitumen/g TOC), a low S_1 (0.22 mg HC/g rock), and a low production index (PI = 0.05), that is, the organic matter is thermally immature. Likewise, the stable carbon isotope data are consistent with indigenous material (Table 26.1) because the kerogen is only 1.57‰ enriched in ^{13}C compared to the bitumen.

The Soda Lake Shale Member appears to be the source rock for group II oil. Lundell and Gordon (1988) concluded that the lower Miocene Soda Lake rather than the lower middle Miocene Saltos Shale Member of the Monterey Formation rock is the source rock for oil in the Cuyama basin. Similar conclusions were made by Kornacki (1988) and Lillis (1988). Lillis (Chapter 27, this

volume) describes the Soda Lake–Painted Rock(!) petroleum system for the Cuyama basin. The results of our study indicate that there is a second petroleum system that includes the group II oil stain.

Group III

Group III represents a family of oils derived from different organic facies of the Miocene Monterey source rock. Seven oil samples and eight rock samples are further divided into subgroups IIIA, IIIB, and IIIC (Table 26.1). These samples show similar stable carbon isotope compositions, but variable Ni/(Ni + V) porphyrin ratios. For example, the bitumens from the three organic-rich outcrop and shothole samples of middle Miocene age (Figure 26.5 and Table 26.1) are isotopically similar for both the saturated and aromatic hydrocarbons, but show a range of Ni/(Ni + V) porphyrin ratios from 0.59 to 0.80. Based on these porphyrin ratios, we interpret three subgroups.

Subgroup IIIA

Subgroup IIIA is based on three oil samples and one source rock sample. Of the three oil samples, one is from the Amnicola Formation, a reservoir rock of Pleistocene age in the Cymric field (shallow), and the other two are oil stains in cores from the Gene Reid #53-36 well in the Carneros Creek area. The cores are middle–late Miocene age from a depth interval of 1660–1692 ft. The one source rock is from this same well but much shallower at 988–998 ft. The subgroup IIIA samples show similar stable carbon isotope ratios (–23.94 to –23.37‰), Ni/(Ni + V) ratios (0.26–0.50), and sulfur content (1.22–1.91 wt. %). PMP values range from 0 to 0.11 and indicate low thermal maturity.

The shallow Gene Reid core (988–998 ft) is an immature organic-rich source rock. It contains excellent quantities (6.25 wt. % TOC) of oil-prone organic matter (HI = 410 mg HC/g TOC). Bitumen extracted from this rock appears to be indigenous or locally generated because it has a low PMP (0), indicating immature organic matter. The high Rock-Eval pyrolysis PI (0.14) and low T_{max} (410°C) for this sample do not necessarily indicate contamination by migrated petroleum because these results are typical of immature Monterey-equivalent organic-rich rocks. For these reasons, the shallow Gene Reid core bitumen is marked as a source rock in Figures 26.4 and 26.5.

The two deep Reid cores appear to contain locally generated migrated oil. For example, the sample from 1660–1674 ft is described on the well log as "oil-stained sandstone." These deep Gene Reid reservoir rock extracts show PMP values of 0.10 (1660–1674 ft) and 0.11 (1674–1692 ft) indicating marginally mature organic matter. Carbon isotopic ratios of the extracts (16, 17) are similar to the kerogen in the source rock. In fact, all three Reid extracts are isotopically similar to their corresponding kerogens. This is consistent with generation of this oil and bitumen from the surrounding middle–upper Miocene source rock.

The oil from the shallower (620–700 ft) Pleistocene Amnicola Member of the Tulare Formation in the Cymric field is geochemically distinct from the deeper (8840–8964 ft) group I oil in Eocene reservoir rocks in the same field. The shallower Cymric oil has a higher sulfur content (1.22 versus 0.66 wt. %), a more positive stable carbon isotope ratio (–23.56 versus –28.02‰), a lower Ni/(Ni + V) ratio (0.26 versus 0.58), a lower PMP (0.11 versus 0.35), and a lower API gravity (12° versus 32°), than the deeper Cymric oil, indicating it was derived from a different source rock at a lower thermal maturity.

The shallower Cymric field oil appears to be derived from thermally mature equivalents of middle–late Miocene source rocks like those in the Reid well (Figures 26.4 and 26.5). Although less likely, this oil could be a mixture of groups II and III because it shows Ni/(Ni + V) and stable carbon isotope ratios for saturates and aromatics between these two groups. Input from group II would require unlikely long distance migration across the San Andreas fault.

Subgroup IIIB

The samples included in subgroup IIIB consist of two oil samples and six source rock samples. One oil (sample 5) is from the Elkhorn Hills field near the west end of cross section B–B' and the other (sample 15) is an oil-stained reservoir rock from the Texaco Tulley #1 well near the west end of cross section A–A' (Figure 26.1). Four bitumen samples (19–22) are from the depth range of 3360–4200 ft in the Phillips Varian A-1 well, and two others (29 and 30) are from the McDonald outcrop and shothole samples in the McDonald Formation on Carneros Creek. The Varian bitumens are middle Miocene–early Pliocene in age, and the McDonald outcrop and shothole samples are middle Miocene. The two oil samples are located on the east side of the San Andreas fault, but are about 100 mi apart. The two localities for the source rock samples are between the oil samples on the same side of the fault with the Varian well about 45 mi northwest of the outcrop and shothole samples. All sample localities are within 4 mi of the San Andreas fault (nearer to the fault than group I).

These subgroup IIIB samples differ from others in this study because of the high Ni/(Ni + V) ratios (0.74–1.0). High proportions of nickel porphyrins indicate suboxic to oxic conditions during deposition of the source rock. Although the source rock samples in the Varian well are from rock units (McLure and Reef Ridge formations) that are equivalent in age to the Monterey Formation (middle Miocene–early Pliocene), the well is located in that part of the San Joaquin basin that was dominated by siliciclastic deposition (Santa Margarita and Temblor formations). Thus, the depositional environment for this source rock was probably more oxic and shallower than other Monterey equivalents to the south in the southern San Joaquin basin, or even across the San Andreas fault in the Salinas and Cuyama basins.

Oil stain in the Tulley well (sample 15) and source rock extracts of the four drill cuttings from the Varian well (samples 19–22) show identical Ni/(Ni + V) values (1.0) and, except for the Tulley oil (1.50 wt. %), similar sulfur contents (0.08–0.52 wt. %). Stable carbon isotope ratios for saturated hydrocarbons (–25.85 to –25.29‰) and aromatic hydrocarbons (–24.52 to –24.21‰) for these samples are also similar (Figure 26.4 and Table 26.1).

The light brown oil stain in the Tulley sample (15) is migrated oil because the isotope data for the indigenous kerogen (–19.03‰) is very different for the oil stain (–23.96‰). The kerogen is 4.93‰ enriched in ^{13}C compared to oil in the sample. The stain shows a Ni/(Ni + V) ratio of 1.0, and stable carbon isotope ratios for saturated and aromatic hydrocarbons similar to those of the Varian samples. Unlike other group III samples, this sample has a high sulfur content (1.50 wt. %, biodegraded) and a more negative stable carbon isotope ratio for the whole extract (–23.96‰).

The extracts from the Varian well represent indigenous bitumen based on low S_1 (0.24–0.56) and low PI (0.04–0.05) values. The rocks are immature (T_{max} = 420–425°C and 0.33–0.35% R_o) and contain good quantities (1.51–2.42 wt. % TOC) of oil-prone organic matter.

Elkhorn Hills oil (sample 5) from Oligocene reservoir rocks and two bitumen samples (29 and 30) extracted from source rocks in shothole and outcrop samples in the McDonald shale in Carneros Creek are isotopically similar to the Varian and Tulley samples, but differ in lower Ni/(Ni + V) ratios (0.74–0.80) (Figure 26.5). These two source rocks have high quantities (4.71–4.94 wt. % TOC) of oil-prone organic matter, but there is little evidence to support widespread thermal maturity in this area. All three outcrop and shothole source rock samples (29–31) from the McDonald Formation are immature (PMP = 0). Low thermal maturity is confirmed by the low bitumen to TOC ratios for these two rocks (13.0 and 24.5 mg bitumen/g TOC).

The high Ni/(Ni + V) porphyrin ratios (0.79–0.80) for the two outcrop and shothole samples indicate suboxic to oxic conditions during deposition of these rocks. This observation is consistent with stratigraphic relationships indicating that this area was a submarine high that received siliciclastic input during the middle Miocene– early late Miocene.

The low sulfur content (0.24 wt. %) and the stable carbon isotope ratios for saturates and aromatics from the Elkhorn Hills oil (Figure 26.4) are similar to those of the Varian and Tulley samples, indicating a common source rock. However, unlike these samples, the Elkhorn Hills oil has a lower Ni/(Ni + V) ratio (0.74). This oil has a high PMP (0.56), moderate API gravity (26°), and a low sulfur content (0.24 wt. %), indicating thermal maturity within the oil window.

Subgroup IIIC

Samples of subgroup IIIC include two oils and one source rock. One oil (sample 1) is from the North Antelope Hills field, and the other oil (sample 14) was extracted from Miocene age oil-stained sandstone core in the Frank Short Melinda #2 well. The carbon isotope data indicate that the Melinda extract consists of migrated oil because it is 1.58‰ enriched in ^{13}C compared to the indigenous kerogen (Table 26.1). These two oil samples show similar stable carbon isotope ratios for saturated hydrocarbons, aromatic hydrocarbons (Figure 26.4), and whole oil (–25.58 versus –25.50‰), as well as similar Ni/(Ni + V) ratios (0.50 versus 0.61), sulfur contents (0.65 versus 1.0 wt. %), and PMP values (0.28 versus 0.23).

One source rock (sample 31) analyzed from the middle Miocene McDonald and Devilwater formations shothole belongs in this subgroup (see later). However, the stable carbon isotope composition for this bitumen differs slightly from the Melinda and North Antelope Hills oil samples (Figure 26.4).

The porphyrin maturity parameter (PMP) for the North Antelope Hills oil (0.23) indicates thermal maturity within the oil window. Consequently, the low API gravity (15°) and moderate sulfur content (1.0 wt. %) for this oil appear to result from biodegradation rather than low thermal maturity.

Group IV

Oil (sample 7) from the Oil City field near the Coalinga field is unrelated to other samples in this study. Because of its stable carbon isotope composition for saturated and aromatic hydrocarbons and its low Ni/(Ni + V) ratio (0), this oil sample is different from the oils in the Eocene (group I) and Miocene source rocks (groups II and III).

The Oil City sample is thermally mature (PMP = 0.12, API gravity = 33°), but it is found at a shallow depth (800 ft) in the Cretaceous–Paleocene Moreno Formation. Previous biomarker work on five oil samples (McGuire, 1988) from the Moreno in the Oil City field and from the Griswold Canyon area of the Vallecitos field suggests that these oils are geochemically distinct from other oils in the area. These other oils are being produced from Miocene and Eocene reservoir rocks. For example, Moreno oils lack 28,30-bisnorhopane and show high concentrations of diasteranes, while Miocene oil of similar thermal maturity shows abundant 28,30-bisnorhopane and low concentrations of diasteranes. Furthermore, the oils in Eocene reservoir rocks have higher hopane to sterane and C_{23}-tricyclic terpane to C_{30}-hopane ratios than do the oils from the Moreno Formation.

This oil–oil correlation indicates that the Oil City oil is unique from other oil found in the area and that the most likely source rock is the Moreno Formation. Source rock data on this formation discussed earlier indicates that there is oil-prone organic matter present. However, until a positive oil–source rock correlation can be achieved, the level of certainty of this petroleum system remains hypothetical.

Biomarker Analyses

Routine biological marker analyses by gas chromatography–mass spectrometry (GC-MS) in the multiple ion detection mode (MID) do not effectively separate the groups of samples defined by the previous isotopic and porphyrin results. For example, all analyzed samples from groups I, III, and IV show similar plot locations on the sterane ternary diagram (Figure 26.6 and Table 26.2), except for the oil (sample 3) from the shallow reservoir rock in the Cymric field. Based on the character of the mass chromatogram, the lack of *n*-paraffins, and the high sulfur content (1.22 wt. %), we believe that the sterane distribution in this oil has been altered by biodegradation.

Like the steranes, diasterane distributions for most of the samples are similar (Table 26.2). However, the Oil City oil (sample 7) and Big Tar Canyon seep (samples 10–12) show higher C_{28}-diasteranes than the other samples. This difference between the Oil City oil (group IV) and other samples (groups I and III) is expected because of the carbon isotopic and porphyrin results previously discussed. However, the difference in diasterane composition between the Big Tar Canyon and

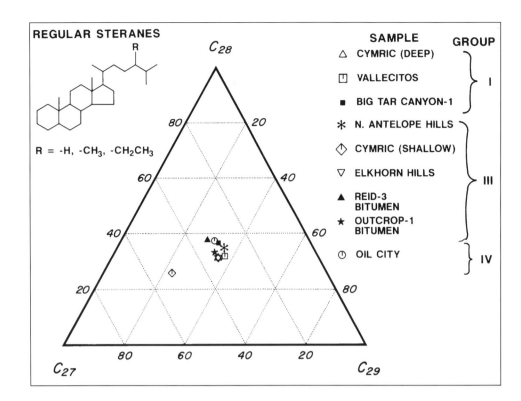

Figure 26.6. Ternary diagram showing relative abundances of C_{27}, C_{28}, and C_{29} regular steranes [5α(H), 14α(H), 17α(H), $20R$] in the saturated hydrocarbon fraction of selected oils and bitumens determined by multiple ion detection GC-MS (m/z 217). Group designations are given with sample names. The shallow Cymric oil shows evidence of biodegradation of the steranes.

Table 26.2. Relative Abundances of C_{27}, C_{28}, and C_{29} Regular Steranes and Diasteranes in Saturated Hydrocarbon Fractions of Selected Oils and Bitumens[a]

Sample No.	Field or Sample Name	Depth (ft)	$C_{27}/(C_{27}$ to $C_{29})$ Steranes (%)	$C_{27}/(C_{27}$ to $C_{29})$ Diasteranes (%)	$C_{28}/(C_{27}$ to $C_{29})$ Steranes (%)	$C_{28}/(C_{27}$ to $C_{29})$ Diasteranes (%)	$C_{29}/(C_{27}$ to $C_{29})$ Steranes (%)	$C_{29}/(C_{27}$ to $C_{29})$ Diasteranes (%)
Group I								
4	Cymric (deep)	8840–8964	33.6	39.7	31.0	28.2	35.4	32.1
8	Vallecitos	5345–5508	31.0	37.2	31.7	30.4	37.3	32.4
10	Big Tar Canyon-1	0	30.7	33.3	36.8	37.0	32.6	29.7
Group III								
1	N. Antelope Hills	2352–2478	29.8	41.4	34.8	29.2	35.5	29.4
3	Cymric (shallow)	620–700	51.5	37.0	25.8	28.3	22.7	34.7
5	Elkhorn Hills	3720–4014	33.5	38.8	31.4	27.5	35.1	33.7
18	Reid-3	988–998	33.9	41.0	37.8	27.5	28.4	31.5
29	Outcrop-1	0	33.7	43.6	33.5	27.6	32.8	28.8
Group IV								
7	Oil City	800	31.6	35.6	37.4	36.5	31.0	27.9

[a]5α(H),14α(H),17α(H),$20R$-steranes by multiple ion detection gas chromatography mass spectrometry (GC-MS MID) (m/z 217) and 13β(H),17α(H),$20S$ + $20R$-diasteranes by GC-MS MID (m/z 259).

other group III samples is puzzling. GC-MS in MID mode commonly results in interference by ions from various parent molecules (Peters and Moldowan, 1993). It is possible that the ion trace used to monitor diasteranes in this sample (m/z 259) was affected by interference. More detailed biological marker analyses of these samples are needed and should include GC-MS of steranes in the metastable reaction monitoring (MRM) mode and analysis of terpanes and monoaromatic and triaromatic steroids.

CONCLUSIONS

The purpose for carrying out oil–oil and oil–source rock correlations is to identify the minimum number of petroleum systems in an area and to determine the level of certainty that a particular source rock generated a given oil group. Based on carbon isotopic data of the saturated and aromatic hydrocarbons and the Ni/(Ni + V) ratio, four oil groups, I–IV, have been established. Each of these oil groups are geochemically distinct

Table 26.3. Oil–Oil and Oil–Source Rock Correlations by Group

Sample No.	Group	Field or Well Name	Sample[a] Source	Type	Gravity (°API)	Sulfur (%)	Oil/Bit. (‰)	Saturates (‰)	Aromatics (‰)	Porphyrins Ni/(Ni + V)	PMP
Kreyenhagen source rock and related oils											
2	IA	Belgian anticline	OL	OL	32	0.10	−27.28	−28.44	−26.06	—	0.30
4	IB	Cymric (deep)	OL	OL	32	0.66	−28.02	−28.95	−27.39	0.58	0.35
6	IB	Jacalitos	OL	OL	35	0.37	−28.91	−29.48	−28.52	0.39	0.33
8	IB	Vallecitos	OL	OL	21	0.28	−29.08	−29.75	−28.95	0.71	0.24
9	IB	W. Coalinga	OL	OL	13	0.32	−28.25	−28.82	−28.34	0.46	0.41
10	IB	Big Tar Canyon-1	SE	OL	NA	0.59	−28.77	−29.28	−28.65	0.38	0.65
11	IB	Big Tar Canyon-2	SE	OL	NA	0.66	−28.74	−29.35	−28.66	0.35	0.67
12	IB	Big Tar Canyon-3	SE	OL	NA	0.57	−27.94	−28.65	−28.12	0.24	0.30
24	—	Chevron-1	CO	SR	NA	—	—	—	—	0.57	0.12
25	IB	Chevron-2	CO	SR	NA	—	—	−28.33	−28.82	0.34	0.16
26	—	Chevron-3	CO	SR	NA	—	—	—	—	0.24	0.16
27	—	Chevron-4	CO	SR	NA	—	—	—	—	0.11	0.14
28	—	Chevron-5	CO	SR	NA	—	—	—	—	0.10	0.18
Soda Lake Shale source rock and related oil											
13	II	Cattle	ST	OL	NA	4.73	−22.10	−24.06	−22.77	0.10	0.18
23	II	McDonald	CO	SR	NA	0.59	−21.69	−23.77	−21.43	0.00	0.51
McDonald–McLure source rock and related oils											
3	IIIA	Cymric (shallow)	OL	OL	12	1.22	−23.56	−24.35	−23.84	0.26	0.11
16	IIIA	Reid-1	ST	OL	NA	1.90	−23.38	−24.70	−23.65	0.50	0.10
17	IIIA	Reid-2	ST	OL	NA	1.78	−23.37	−24.46	−23.78	0.48	0.11
18	IIIA	Reid-3	CO	SR	NA	1.91	−23.94	−25.05	−23.88	0.42	0.00
5	IIIB	Elkhorn Hills	OL	OL	26	0.24	−24.65	−25.30	−24.20	0.74	0.56
15	IIIB	Tulley	ST	OL	NA	1.50	−23.96	−25.85	−24.31	1.00	—
19	IIIB	Varian-1	CT	SR	NA	0.52	—	−25.43	−24.52	1.00	—
20	IIIB	Varian-2	CT	SR	NA	0.17	—	−25.29	−23.81	1.00	—
21	IIIB	Varian-3	CT	SR	NA	0.08	—	−25.64	−24.21	1.00	—
22	IIIB	Varian-4	CT	SR	NA	0.18	—	−25.60	−24.32	1.00	—
29	IIIB	Outcrop-1	CO	SR	NA	—	—	−25.30	−23.42	0.80	0.00
30	IIIB	Shothole-1	CT	SR	NA	—	—	−25.58	−24.55	0.79	0.00
1	IIIC	N. Antelope Hills	OL	OL	15	1.00	−25.50	−26.23	−25.66	0.61	0.23
14	IIIC	Melinda	ST	OL	NA	0.65	−25.58	−26.29	−25.32	0.50	0.28
31	IIIC	Shothole-2	CT	SR	NA	—	—	−26.01	−24.07	0.59	0.00
Oil from Moreno source rock											
7	IV	Oil City	OL	OL	33	0.21	−26.61	−27.72	−25.20	0.00	0.12

[a]OL, oil; CO, conventional core; SE, seep oil; ST, oil-stained rock; CT, drill cuttings; SR, source rock.

enough to conclude that each can be attributed to a particular source rock. Furthermore, one oil group (III) can be further subdivided in such a way that a certain oil can be related back to a particular organic facies within the source rock. The oil–source rock correlations for three of the four oil groups are successful enough to identify their respective source rock. For the fourth oil group, sufficient information exists in the literature to establish the source rock reasonably well.

What is absent from this study is the total number of petroleum systems that these oil and source rock samples may represent. Since a specific source rock interval can be responsible for more than one petroleum system (see Klemme, Chapter 3, this volume), and since four different source rock intervals are included in this study, the number of systems in this area could be much more than four. However, to determine the geographic, stratigraphic, and temporal extent of the petroleum systems in this area is beyond the scope of this study.

On the basis of groups established in the literature and in this study, we have identified the following petroleum systems. The data for these conclusions are shown in Figures 26.4 and 26.5 and in Table 26.3. Oil–source rock correlation of group I indicates that the Kreyenhagen Formation of Eocene age is its source rock. Oils from the Cymric (deep), Jacalitos, Vallecitos, West Coalinga, and Belgian anticline fields and from the oil seeps at Big Tar Canyon are derived from the Kreyenhagen and Point of Rocks source rock as found in the Kreyenhagen 74X-21H well.

Correlation of group II indicates that the lower Miocene Soda Lake Shale Member of the Vaqueros Formation is the source rock. In the Cuyama basin, this source rock is part of the Soda Lake–Painted Rock(!) petroleum system (Lillis, Chapter 27, this volume). However, there is a good possibility that the oil sample (13) from the Texaco Land & Cattle well is part of a separate petroleum system in the Salinas basin area.

Oil–source rock correlation work on group III samples indicates that the middle–upper Miocene is the source rock and that this source rock has three organic facies. The middle–upper Miocene includes all the Monterey source rock and its equivalent rock units, which together cover a large area in central and southern California. This source rock interval is responsible for much of the onshore and offshore oil in California. Within the study area, there is at least one petroleum system that includes the Cymric (shallow), Elkhorn Hills, and North Antelope Hills oil fields.

Group IV is based on one oil from the Oil City field and the literature. Geology indicates that this oil was probably generated from a source rock within the Paleocene–Cretaceous Moreno Formation.

Acknowledgments *We thank the management of Chevron U.S.A. Inc. for permission to publish this paper, R. J. Hwang, who completed GC-MSD analyses on selected samples, and L. B. Magoon, J. T. Smith, and P. van de Kamp for their useful editorial comments.*

References Cited

Bac, M. G., and B. J. Schulein, 1990, Stratigraphic variations in the biomarker distribution of the Moreno Formation: their correlation with San Joaquin basin oils (abs.): AAPG Bulletin, v. 74, p. 603.

Bandy, O. L., and R. E. Arnal, 1969, Middle Tertiary basin development, San Joaquin Valley, California: GSA Bulletin, v. 80, p. 783–820.

Bartow, J. A., 1987, Cenozoic non-marine sedimentation in the San Joaquin basin, central California, *in* R. V. Ingersoll and W. G. Ernst, eds., Cenozoic basin development of coastal California: Rubey Volume VI, Englewood Cliffs, NJ, Prentice Hall, p. 146–171.

California Department of Conservation, 1985, California oil and gas fields, central California, 3rd ed.: California Division of Oil and Gas, v. 1 (map).

Crowell, J. C., 1987, Late Cenozoic basins of onshore southern California: complexity is the hallmark of their tectonic history, *in* R. V. Ingersoll and W. G. Ernst, eds., Cenozoic basin development of coastal California: Rubey Volume VI, Englewood Cliffs, NJ, Prentice Hall, p. 207–241.

Dickinson, W. R., R. A. Armin, N. Beckvar, T. C. Goodlin, S. U. Janecke, R. A. Mark, R. D. Norris, G. Radell, and A. A. Wortman, 1987, Geohistory analysis of rates of sediment accumulation and subsidence for selected California basins, *in* R. V. Ingersoll and W. G. Ernst, eds., Cenozoic basin development of coastal California: Rubey Volume VI, Englewood Cliffs, NJ, Prentice Hall, p. 1–23.

Graham, S. A., 1987, Tectonic controls on petroleum occurrence in central California, *in* R. V. Ingersoll and W. G.

Ernst, eds., Cenozoic basin development of coastal California: Rubey Volume VI, Englewood Cliffs, NJ, Prentice Hall, p. 47–63.

Graham, S. A., and L. A. Williams, 1985, Tectonic, depositional, and diagenetic history of Miocene Monterey Formation, central San Joaquin basin, California: AAPG Bulletin, v. 69, p. 385–411.

Kruge, M. A., 1985, Organic geochemistry and comparative diagenesis: Monterey Formation, Lost Hills oil field and vicinity, west San Joaquin basin, California: Ph.D. dissertation, University of California, Berkeley, 266 p.

Kuespert, J. G., 1985, Depositional environments and sedimentary history of the Miocene Temblor Formation and associated Oligo-Miocene units in the vicinity of Kettleman North Dome, San Joaquin Valley, California, *in* S. A. Graham, ed., Geology of the Temblor Formation, western San Joaquin basin, California: SEPM Pacific Section, v. 4, p. 53–67.

Kuespert, J. G., 1990, Temblor Formation at Big Tar Canyon: Reef ridge, Fresno County, California, *in* J. G. Kuespert and S. A. Reid, eds., Structure, stratigraphy, and hydrocarbon occurrences of the San Joaquin basin, California: SEPM, n. 64, p. 357–364.

Lillis, P. G., 1988, Correlation and characterization of oils using biological markers, Cuyama basin, California, *in* W. J. M. Bazeley, ed., Tertiary tectonics and sedimentation in the Cuyama basin, San Luis Obispo, Santa Barbara, and Ventura counties, California: SEPM Pacific Section, v. 59, p. 39–48.

Lundell, L. L., and S. A. Gordon, 1988, Origin of Cuyama basin oils, *in* W. J. M. Bazeley, ed., Tertiary tectonics and sedimentation in the Cuyama basin, San Luis Obispo, Santa Barbara, and Ventura counties, California: SEPM Pacific Section, v. 59, p. 29–37.

McGuire, D. J., 1988, Stratigraphy, depositional history, and hydrocarbon source-rock potential of the Upper Cretaceous–lower Tertiary Moreno Formation, central San Joaquin Basin, California: Ph.D. dissertation, Stanford University, Stanford, CA, 308 p.

Milam, R. W., 1985, Biostratigraphy and sedimentation of the Eocene and Oligocene Kreyenhagen Formation, central California: Ph.D. dissertation, Stanford University, Stanford, CA, 240 p.

Nilsen, T. H., 1987, Paleogene tectonics and sedimentation of coastal California, *in* R. V. Ingersoll and W. G. Ernst, eds., Cenozoic basin development of coastal California: Rubey Volume VI, Englewood Cliffs, NJ, Prentice Hall, p. 81–123.

Peters, K. E., 1986, Guidelines for evaluating petroleum source rock using programmed pyrolysis: AAPG Bulletin, v. 70, p. 318–329.

Peters, K. E., and J. M. Moldowan, 1993, The Biomarker Guide: Englewood Cliffs, NJ, Prentice Hall, 363 p.

Schoell, M., E. Faber, and M. L. Coleman, 1983, Carbon and hydrogen isotopic compositions of the NBS22 and NBS21 stable isotope reference materials: an interlaboratory comparison: Organic Geochemistry, v. 5, p. 3–6.

Sundararaman, P., W. R. Biggs, J. G. Reynolds, and J. C. Fetzer, 1988, Vanadyl porphyrins, indicators of kerogen breakdown and generation of petroleum: Geochimica Cosmochimica Acta, v. 52, p. 2337–2341.

Magoon, L. B., and W. G. Dow, eds., 1994, The petroleum
system—from source to trap: AAPG Memoir 60.

Chapter 27

Soda Lake–Painted Rock(!) Petroleum System in the Cuyama Basin, California, U.S.A.

Paul G. Lillis

Branch of Petroleum Geology
U.S. Geological Survey
Denver, Colorado, U.S.A.

Abstract

The Cuyama basin, located in the central California Coast Ranges, was formed by extension during early Miocene time and was filled with a variety of nonmarine, marginal marine, and neritic to bathyal marine sediments. Low sulfur oil is produced primarily from the lower Miocene Painted Rock Sandstone Member of the Vaqueros Formation along a structural trend parallel to the Russell fault, which was active from 23 to 5 Ma. A major fold and thrust belt beginning about 3 Ma formed the Caliente and Sierra Madre ranges and partially obscures the Miocene extensional basin.

Stable carbon isotope and biomarker data indicate that the lower Miocene Soda Lake Shale Member of the Vaqueros Formation is the predominant source rock for the oil in the Cuyama area. Burial and thermal history modeling shows that oil generation began in middle–late Miocene time and that oil migrated into existing traps. Younger traps that formed in the overthrust are barren of oil because migration occurred prior to the development of the fold and thrust belt or because subthrust oil was unable to migrate into the overthrust.

INTRODUCTION

The Neogene Cuyama basin is located in the southern Coast Ranges of central California, west of the San Andreas fault, in an area now occupied by the Caliente and Sierra Madre ranges, Cuyama Valley, and Carrizo Plain (Figure 27.1). Pre-Neogene rocks include undivided Cretaceous and Eocene sedimentary rock and Mesozoic crystalline rock (Vedder, 1973). The basin fill, which is late Oligocene–late Miocene in age, has been deformed by strike-slip faulting and low angle thrust faulting. Nonmarine sedimentary rocks of Pliocene–Holocene age unconformably overlie the Cuyama basin fill.

Oil accumulations discovered in 1948–1951 are confined to one structural trend and include, from southeast to northwest, South Cuyama, Russell Ranch, Morales Canyon, and Taylor Canyon fields (Figure 27.1). Three fields are currently producing oil (South Cuyama, Russell Ranch, and Morales Canyon) and two are abandoned (Taylor Canyona and Central Cuyama). South Cuyama is the largest oil field (225 million bbl of oil) followed by Russell Ranch (69 million bbl), Morales Canyon (2 million bbl), Taylor Canyon (<1 million bbl),

and Central Cuyama (Table 27.1). Oil is produced mainly from the lower Miocene Painted Rock Sandstone Member of the Vaqueros Formation at depths of about 1000–1500 m. It has a low sulfur content (<0.5 wt. %) and moderately high API gravity (33° API) (Tables 27.1, 27.2).

The Cuyama oils are a single genetic family (Lillis, 1988; Lundell and Gordon, 1988) with minor geochemical variations caused by biodegradation in the shallow reservoirs. The two potential source rocks are the Saltos Shale Member of the Monterey Formation and the Soda Lake Shale Member of the Vaqueros Formation (Figure 27.2). All other rock units in the area have low organic carbon content or are immature.

Previous studies have shown that the Miocene Monterey Formation is a source rock for oils in several California basins (Phillipi, 1965; Taylor, 1976; Seifert and Moldowan, 1978; Kruge, 1986; Orr, 1986). However, clear differences exist between the composition of Cuyama oils and typical Monterey oils in adjacent basins (Lillis, 1988). For example, the Cuyama oils have a lower sulfur content (0.30–0.47 wt. %) and higher pristane/phytane ratios (1.6–1.9), while"typical" Monterey oils have a high sulfur content (>1.0 wt. %) and lower pristane/phytane

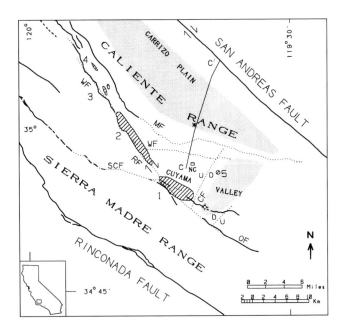

Figure 27.1. Map of Cuyama area (insert shows location of map in California). Symbols: WF, Whiterock thrust fault; MF, Morales thrust fault; SCF, South Cuyama thrust fault; OF, Ozena thrust fault; RF, Russell fault; CF, Cox fault; NC, town of New Cuyama; C–C', location of Davis et al. (1988) cross section (see Figure 27.3); shaded areas, Soda Lake shale is mature to overmature; cross-hatchured areas, oil fields; ∗, location of geohistory diagram (see Figure 27.13); ◇, dry hole, location of Roco James #1 well. Faults: dashed where approximate, dotted where covered. Oil fields: 1. South Cuyama; 2. Russell Ranch; 3. Morales Canyon; 4. Taylor Canyon; 5. Central Cuyama. (Modified from Dibblee, 1973b; Davis et al., 1988.)

ratios (≤1.0). Based on geologic considerations, Cross (1959) proposed that the source of the Cuyama oils may be the Soda Lake Shale Member of the Vaqueros Formation. More recently published organic geochemical work by Lundell and Gordon (1988), Kornacki (1988), and Lillis (1988) suggest that the Soda Lake Shale Member is the source rock for the Cuyama oils.

The geologic and geochemical studies just mentioned and data presented in this chapter indicate that the Soda Lake Shale Member, rather than the Monterey Formation, is the source rock responsible for most of the oil in this petroleum province. Therefore, this system has a known level of certainty and is named the Soda Lake–Painted Rock(!) petroleum system. However, the Monterey has probably produced a small quantity of oil that may have mixed locally with Soda Lake oil. In addition to presenting geochemical data, the remainder of this chapter defines the geographic, stratigraphic, and temporal extent of the Soda Lake–Painted Rock petroleum system.

Biological marker data are used in the oil–oil and oil–source rock correlation. A *biological marker* (or *biomarker*) is an organic compound found in the geosphere that can be linked to a biological precursor molecule from living organisms (Eglinton and Calvin,

1967; Brassell et al., 1983). Because of their unique signature in oil and bitumen, biomarkers are excellent tools for oil–oil and oil–source rock correlation (Seifert and Moldowan, 1981). Biomarkers can also be used as thermal maturity indicators for petroleum and source rocks. A computer program (BasinMod, Platte River Associates) that combines geohistory diagrams (van Hinte, 1978) with thermal history and kinetics of petroleum generation is used to determine the timing of generation–migration–accumulation. A petroleum system events chart is used to summarize which stratigraphic units are the essential elements and when trap formation occurred, as well as when other important events took place.

METHODS

Rock-Eval pyrolysis was performed on 41 core samples from potential source facies to determine the quality and quantity of organic matter. From this set, a subset of 36 core samples were powdered and extracted with chloroform for 24 hr in a Soxhlet apparatus. The extracted bitumen and 11 oil samples from South Cuyama, Russell Ranch, and Morales Canyon fields were separated by elution chromatography into saturated hydrocarbon, aromatic hydrocarbon, resin, and asphaltene fractions. Ten core samples extracted and fractionated by ARCO Oil and Gas Company were also included in the study. Gas chromatography of the C_{9+} saturated hydrocarbon fractions was performed on a Hewlett Packard 5880A gas chromatograph (GC). Biological marker distributions were determined by running whole oil samples and bitumen extracts on a computerized gas chromatograph–mass spectrometer (GC-MS) using the GC described above coupled with a Kratos MS 30 mass spectrometer. The fragment ions monitored were m/z 191 (tricyclic and pentacyclic terpanes), m/z 217 (steranes), m/z 231 (triaromatic steroids), and m/z 253 (monoaromatic steroids). Peak identifications were based on elution time and mass spectra (Philp, 1985).

Stable carbon isotope ratios were determined on the C_{15+} saturate and aromatic hydrocarbon fractions and are reported in the standard delta notation (δ) in units of parts per thousand (‰) relative to the Peedee belemnite standard (PDB). (See Lillis, 1992, for more details of analytical methods.)

GEOLOGY

Detailed discussions of the geology of the Cuyama basin have been given by Hill et al. (1958), Schwade et al. (1958), Dibblee (1973a), Clifton (1981) Lagoe (1982, 1984, 1985, 1987a,b), and Davis et al. (1988). The basin fill consists of an unconformity-bounded middle Cenozoic succession that overlies either Cretaceous–Eocene marine rocks or Cretaceous and older gneissic–granitic basement (Vedder, 1973).

Table 27.1. Oil and Gas Fields in the Cuyama Area, California

Map No.	Field or Area	Year Disc'd	Trap Type[a]	Pool	Status[b]	Formation	Member	Depth (ft)	Gravity (°API)	Oil (10³ bbl)	Gas (10³ mcf)
1	**South Cuyama**	1949	FA		Prod					**224,992**	**225,011**
	East			L. Miocene	Abd	Vaqueros	Painted Rock	8400	37.0	42	30
	Main			52-1		Santa Margarita		2011	25.3	891	497
	Main			Branch Canyon		Branch Canyon		2778	27.7	1,581	538
	Main			Homan		Vaqueros	Painted Rock	4495	32.0	213,296	220,542
	Main			Hibberd	Abd	Vaqueros	Quail Canyon	4287	35.2	3,679	1,381
	S.E.			Cox	Abd	Vaqueros	Quail Canyon	5248	36.7	109	19
	S.E.			Gas Zone		Santa Margarita		2956	—	—	—
2	**Russell Ranch**	1948	FH		Prod					**68,560**	**50,240**
	Main			138-5		Santa Margarita		1534	13.2	—	—
	Main			Sloan		Santa Margarita		2224	24.6	1,789	1,659
	Main			Dibblee		Vaqueros	Painted Rock	3258	34.0	56,630	38,642
	Main			Colgrove N.		Vaqueros	Quail Canyon	3672	36.3	3,825	2,484
	Main			Colgrove S	Abd	Vaqueros	Quail Canyon	3511	38.5	4,381	1,646
	Norris			Norris	Abd	Santa Margarita		2044	25.0	18	35
	Norris			Griggs-Dibblee		Vaqueros	Painted Rock	3441	33.0	649	280
	S.E.			Russell 15-9		Vaqueros	Painted Rock	3713	39.2	645	3,160
	West				Abd	Morales		1107	—	0.1	—
3	**Morales Canyon**	1950	FA		Prod					**2,420**	**1,771**
				Clayton		Morales		2181	31.9	1,023	488
				Government 18		Vaqueros	Quail Canyon	5939	38.5	1,401	1,282
4	**Taylor Canyon**	1951	FN		Abd	Vaqueros	Quail Canyon	5935	38.7	**484**	**141**
5	**Central Cuyama**	1951	FH		Abd	Branch Canyon		7372	40.0[c]	**33**	**12**
							Totals			**296,472**	**277,175**

[a]FA, faulted anticline; FH, faulted homocline; FN, faulted nose.
[b]Prod, producing; abd, abandoned.
[c]California Division of Oil and Gas (1974) reports Central Cuyama oil gravity of 46° API.
Modified from CCOP (1993) and California Division of Oil and Gas (1974, 1991). Note that pool production is cumulative only (CCOP, 1993).

Table 27.2. Geochemical Data for Oils in Cuyama Area, California

Oil	Oil Field	Well Name	Zone/Formation	Pr/Ph	CPI[a]	Sulfur (wt. %)	Gravity (°API)
1	S. Cuyama	SCU 43-6	Dibblee/Vaqueros	1.64	1.05	—	32.2[b]
2	S. Cuyama	SCU 28-36	Dibblee/Vaqueros	1.69	1.05	0.43	32.2[b]
3	Russell Ranch	RRU 187-25A	Dibblee/Vaqueros	1.67	1.07	—	33.0[b]
4	Russell Ranch	RRU 45-25	Dibblee/Vaqueros	1.84	1.08	0.42	32.6[b]
5	Russell Ranch	Sloan C81-26	Colgrove/Vaqueros	1.87	1.04	—	32.2[b]
6	Russell Ranch	Sloan C181-26	Dibblee/Vaqueros	1.75	1.04	—	31.5[b]
7	Russell Ranch	Sloan C184-26	Santa Margarita	—	—	0.47	23.8
8	Russell Ranch	Sloan C83-26	Colgrove/Vaqueros	1.84	1.10	—	35.6[b]
9	Morales Canyon	Ritter C22-11	Government Oil/Vaqueros	1.93	1.08	0.30	34.2[b]
14	S. Cuyama	Hibberd 211-6	Bittercreek/Branch Canyon	1.64	—	—	26.5
15	S. Cuyama	SCU 55-6	Dibblee/Vaqueros	1.66	1.12	—	29.0

[a]Carbon preference index, n-C_{24}–n-C_{34}.
[b]Oil gravity from Lundell and Gordon (1988).

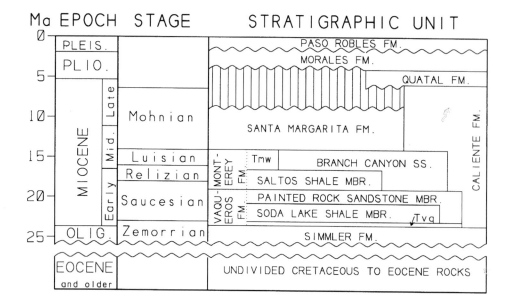

Figure 27.2. Stratigraphy of the Cuyama area, California. Tvq, Quail Canyon Sandstone Member of the Vaqueros Formation; Tmw, Whiterock Bluff Shale Member of the Monterey Formation. (Modified from Lagoe, 1987b and references therein.)

Two cycles of rapid subsidence followed by basin filling are represented starting about 23 Ma with the lower Miocene shallow marine Quail Canyon Sandstone Member of the Vaqueros Formation (Figure 27.2). This sandstone is overlain by the middle–upper bathyal Soda Lake Shale Member of the Vaqueros Formation, which in turn is overlain by the neritic Painted Rock Sandstone Member of the Vaqueros Formation. Rapid subsidence again resulted in deposition of the overlying middle bathyal Saltos Shale Member of the Monterey Formation. Locally, the Saltos is overlain by the middle Miocene upper bathyal–outer neritic Whiterock Bluff Shale Member of the Monterey Formation. The Monterey laterally interfingers with the shallow marine Branch Canyon Sandstone and is overlain by the upper Miocene shallow marine Santa Margarita Formation. The entire Miocene marine section grades laterally eastward into the nonmarine Caliente Formation. The Santa Margarita Formation is unconformably overlain by nonmarine sandstones and mudstones of the Pliocene Morales Formation and the Pleistocene Paso Robles Formation.

The Cuyama basin formed in the early Miocene by extension accompanied by strike-slip faulting (e.g. Russell fault) and normal faulting (e.g. Cox fault) (Figure 27.1). Dramatic thickness variations in the Vaqueros and Monterey formations are associated with paleohighs and basin deeps resulting from tilted blocks and growth faults. A compressional tectonic regime began about 3 Ma (Davis et al., 1988) forming major folds and thrusts that deform and partially obscure the older extensional Cuyama basin (Figure 27.3). The upper plates of the thrusts now constitute the topographic highs in the area (Caliente and Sierra Madre ranges).

The Vaqueros reaches a maximum thickness of greater than 2400 m in the Caliente Range, although thicker sections are thought to be present in the subthrust deep areas below the northern Caliente Range (Davis et al. 1988). The Saltos Shale Member reaches a maximum thickness of more than 1580 m in the southeastern Cuyama Valley in the Cox fault graben (Spitz, 1988).

OIL OCCURRENCE

All the oil fields except the abandoned Central Cuyama field lie on a structural trend adjacent to the Russell fault system, which has had predominantly strike-slip motion (Yeats et al., 1989). The fault system acts as the primary trap for the fields except in South Cuyama field, which also has domal closure (Schwade et al., 1958). The Russell fault was most active prior to and during Painted Rock deposition, and some activity up to 5 Ma is evident (pre-Morales Formation) (Yeats et al., 1989). South Cuyama field lies over an early Miocene paleohigh as suggested by thinning of the Vaqueros Formation and Saltos Shale Member. Some contemporaneous folding may have occurred associated with movement along the Russell fault (Schwade et al. 1958; Yeats et al., 1989). However, younger Miocene sediments in the oil field are also folded, indicating that some closure formed after 11 Ma. Minor traps were formed by the normal Cox fault (19–16 Ma) along the southeastern edge of the South Cuyama field. The fields are concealed in part beneath the late Cenozoic thrust blocks, but the thrusts aid in trapping oil in only one small pool (Clayton zone, Morales Canyon field). All of the Pliocene and Pleistocene anticlinal traps formed in the thrust belt that have been tested are barren of oil, indicating that the Cuyama oil migrated before thrusting (3 Ma). Alternatively, migration of oil from the subthrust into the overthrust has been obstructed since thrusting began.

Although locally called the "Dibblee sand," the formal name of the main reservoir rock is the Painted Rock Sandstone Member of the Vaqueros Formation (Table 27.1). Minor amounts of oil and gas are produced from the Santa Margarita Formation, the Branch Canyon Sandstone, the Quail Canyon Sandstone Member, and the Morales Formation (Table 27.1). The oil from the Santa Margarita Formation and the Branch Canyon Sandstone has a slightly lower gravity (average 25° API). ARCO drilled three wells into the deep subthrust basin under the Caliente Range: ARCO Drake Federal #1

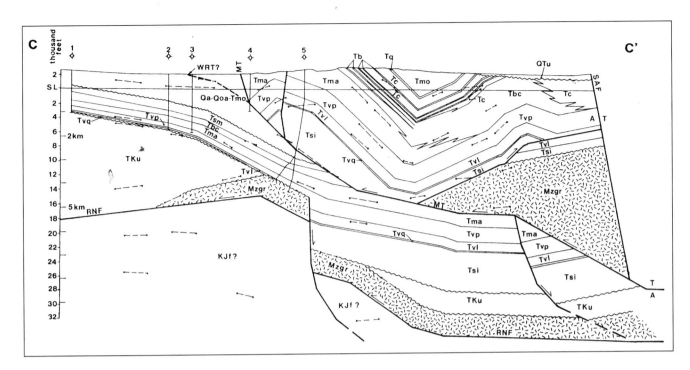

Figure 27.3. Cross section (C–C') from the Cuyama Valley north across southern Caliente Range to the San Andreas fault. Symbols: dashed lines ending in dots, major reflectors from seismic data; WRT, Whiterock thrust; MT, Morales thrust; RNF, Rinconada fault; SAF, San Andreas fault; Mzgr, Mesozoic granitic rocks; TKu, undivided Cretaceous–Eocene; Tsi, Simmler Fm.; Tvq, Quail Canyon Sandstone Member; Tvl, Soda Lake Shale Member; Tvp, Painted Rock Sandstone Member; Tma, Saltos Shale Member; Tmw, Whiterock Bluff Shale Member; Tbc, Branch Canyon Sandstone; Tsm, Santa Margarita Fm.; Tc, Caliente Fm.; Tq, Quatal Fm.; Tmo, Morales Fm.; QTu, Paso Robles Fm. (See Figure 27. 2 for details.) Wells: 1. Bell Buzzard #1; 2. Texaco Kirschenman; 3. Colgrove Russell #33-7; 4. Colgrove Russell 33-5A; 5. ARCO Drake Federal #1. (From Davis et al.,1988; used with permission.)

(sec. 31, T. 11 N, R. 26 W), ARCO Federal Caliente Unit #1 (sec. 35, T. 11 N, R. 27 W), and ARCO Stone #1 (sec. 21, T. 32 S, R. 20 E). In the Drake Federal #1 and the Federal Caliente Unit #1 wells, a minor amount of oil (about 1600 bbl) was swabbed from the fractured Saltos Shale Member of the Monterey Formation.

RESULTS

Petroleum Geochemistry

The petroleum geochemistry of the Cuyama oils discussed here is a summary of previous work (Lillis, 1988) combined with new data. The abandoned Taylor Canyon field and the Central Cuyama field are not discussed because samples are unavailable. Data from the gas chromatograms of the saturated hydrocarbon fraction and the sulfur determinations are listed in Table 27.2. With the exception of two samples (oils #7 and #14, Table 27.2), the oils have a marginally mature character with a slight odd-numbered *n*-alkane predominance (the carbon preference index or CPI = 1.04–1.12) (Bray and Evans, 1961), a relatively high pristane/phytane ratio (1.6–1.9), moderately high gravity (29–36° API), and low sulfur content (0.30–0.47 wt. %). The normal, branched, and cyclic alkanes and the isoprenoid hydrocarbon distributions are similar in all the Cuyama oils, and pristane is usually the dominant peak (Figure 27.4b). Oils

produced from younger reservoirs (Branch Canyon Sandstone and Santa Margarita Formation) have slightly lower API gravity, and the normal alkanes are reduced (oil #7) or missing (oil #14, Figure 27.4a). Oil #7 is unusual because it lacks acyclic isoprenoids (pristane and phytane) yet contains normal alkanes.

Figure 27.5 shows stable carbon isotopes of the Cuyama oils and rock extracts (bitumen) determined by Lundell and Gordon (1988) and by the USGS (Table 27.3). Cuyama oils are isotopically heavy, with saturated hydrocarbon $\delta^{13}C$ values ranging from –22.0 to –22.6‰ and aromatic hydrocarbon $\delta^{13}C$ values ranging from –21.3 to –22.0‰. Data from Curiale et al. (1985) show that these values are within the range of Monterey oils from the Santa Maria basin, but are isotopically heavier than Monterey oils from the San Joaquin, Ventura, and Los Angeles basins.

Peak identifications of biological markers are listed in Table 27.4, and example mass chromatograms are shown in Figure 27.6. Biological marker ratios based on peak areas are summarized in Table 27.5. The tricyclic and pentacyclic terpane distributions (m/z 191) and the sterane distributions (m/z 217) from the three fields (oils #2, 4, 7, and 9 in Table 27.2) are generally correlative (Lillis, 1988). Cuyama oils are characterized by relatively high C_{27} steranes, moderate diasteranes, minor C_{30} steranes, moderate amounts of oleanane, and hopanes dominating over steranes (Table 27.5). The Cuyama oils

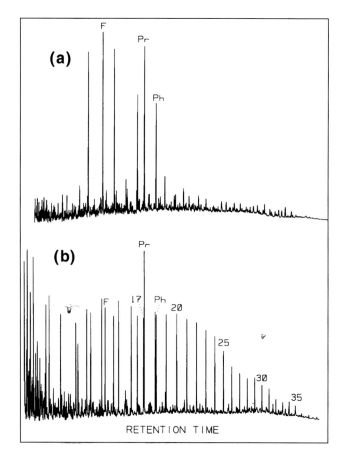

Figure 27.4. Gas chromatograms of the saturated hydrocarbon fraction of oil from South Cuyama field. (a) Biodegraded oil from shallow production, Bittercreek pool, Branch Canyon Sandstone (oil #14, 26.5° API). (b) Oil from the main reservoir, Dibblee pool, Painted Rock Sandstone Member (oil #2, 32.2° API). Pr, pristane; Ph, phytane; F, farnesane; numbers are the carbon numbers of the corresponding normal alkanes.

notably lack significant amounts of 28,30-bisnorhopane, a biomarker that is abundant in Monterey oils in adjacent basins (Curiale et al., 1985).

Source Rock Geochemistry

A summary of the Rock-Eval pyrolysis data is presented in Table 27.6, including 41 samples from this study and 22 samples from Lundell and Gordon (1988) (see Lillis, 1992, for a detailed listing). The Saltos Shale Member of the Monterey Formation and the Soda Lake Shale Member of the Vaqueros Formation have the best source rock potential, with total organic carbon (TOC) values averaging 3.03 and 2.13 wt. % and pyrolyzable hydrocarbon yields (S_2) averaging 11.95 and 7.73 mg HC/g rock, respectively. The other possible source rocks, shales in the undivided Branch Canyon–Santa Margarita, the Painted Rock Sandstone Member, and the undivided Cretaceous–Eocene units, have poor source rock potential based on low TOC and S_2 yields (Table 27.6). The Whiterock Bluff Shale Member was not analyzed because of its limited extent and low thermal maturity.

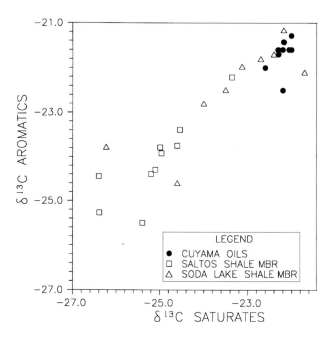

Figure 27.5. Stable carbon isotope ratios ($\delta^{13}C$) of the saturated and aromatic hydrocarbon fractions of oils and rock extracts from the Cuyama area, California. Ratios in parts per thousand (‰) relative to PDB standard. (Data from Table 27. 3 and Lundell and Gordon, 1988.)

Figure 27.7 shows the hydrogen index (HI) versus oxygen index (OI) plot, which is similar to a van Krevelan diagram and thought to be useful for classifying kerogen type (Tissot et al., 1974; Espitalié et al., 1977). The Saltos and Soda Lake members fall within the type II–III kerogen region with some scatter. A method for determining "true average" HI is a plot of S_2 versus TOC (Figure 27.8), in which the slope of the regression line yields the average HI (Langford and Blanc-Valleron, 1990). The Saltos member has a slope of 4.79 or an average HI of 479 (Table 27.6), while the Soda Lake member has a slope of 4.02 or an average HI of 402. However, if one outlier point is excluded (see Figure 27.8), the Soda Lake has a slope of 6.07 or an average HI of 607, with a significant improvement in the regression coefficient (Table 27.6).

Gas chromatograms of the saturated hydrocarbon fraction of the Saltos and Soda Lake members (Figure 27.9) are variable. The Saltos has pristane/phytane ratios ranging from 0.4 to almost 4.4, while the Soda Lake ranges from 0.8 to 4.9. However, most of the values of both units are less than 2.0 (median values are 1.2; see Table 27.5). Both the Saltos and Soda Lake generally have odd numbered *n*-alkane predominance with CPI values of 0.91–1.75 and 1.04–1.43, respectively.

The stable carbon isotope ratios for saturated and aromatic hydrocarbon fractions of selected rock extracts (bitumen) are shown in Figure 27.5, which includes data from Table 27.3 and from Lundell and Gordon (1988). The $\delta^{13}C$ values are variable, but the Soda Lake values are generally heavier than the Saltos values and are closer to the values of the Cuyama oils.

Table 27.3. Stable Carbon Isotope Ratios (δ^{13}C) of Saturated and Aromatic Hydrocarbon Fractions of Oils and Rock Extracts from the Cuyama Area, California

Well	Depth (m)	Member/Stage	δ^{13}C (‰ PDB) Saturated	Aromatic
Oils				
2 SCU 28-36	—	—	−22.2	−21.4
4 RRU 45-25	—	—	−22.3	−21.6
7 Sloan C184-26	—	—	−22.1	−21.6
Rock extracts (bitumen)				
ROCO James #1	2235.4	Saltos/Relizian	−24.6	−23.8
ROCO James #1	2349.4	Saltos/Relizian	−25.0	−23.8
ROCO James #1	2670.0	Saltos/Saucesian	−24.5	−23.4
ROCO James #1	2728.9	Saltos/Saucesian	−25.0	−23.9
ROCO James #1	2863.3	Saltos/Saucesian	−26.4	−24.4
ROCO James #1	2999.2	Saltos/Saucesian	−26.4	−25.3
ROCO James #1	3122.4	Saltos/Saucesian	−23.4	−22.2
ROCO James #1	3248.3	Painted Rock/Saucesian	−21.9	−21.0
ROCO James #1	3304.6	Soda Lake/Saucesian	−22.2	−21.2
ROCO James #1	3383.3	Soda Lake/Saucesian	−23.1	−22.0
ROCO James #1	3436.9	Soda Lake/Saucesian	−26.2	−23.8

Table 27.4. Biomarker Compound Assignments for Peaks in *m/z* 191 and *m/z* 217 Mass Chromatograms

Peak No.	Compound
1	C_{20} tricyclic terpane
2	C_{21} tricyclic terpane
3	C_{23} tricyclic terpane
4	C_{24} tricyclic terpane
5	Unidentified terpane (A)
6	C_{25} tricyclic terpane
7	Unidentified terpane (B)
8	C_{26} tricyclic terpane + C_{24} tetracyclic terpane
9	C_{26} tricyclic terpane
10	18α(H)-22,29,30-trisnorneohopane (Ts)
11	17α(H)-22,29,30-trisnorhopane (Tm)
12	28,30-bisnorhopane
13	Norhopane
14	18α(H)-30-norneohopane (C_{29} Ts)
15	Oleanane
16	17α(H),21β(H) C_{30} hopane
17	moretane
18	C_{31} hopane 22S
19	C_{31} hopane 22R
20	C_{32} hopane 22S
21	C_{32} hopane 22R
22	C_{33} hopane 22S
23	C_{33} hopane 22R
24	C_{27} diasterane (13β,17α) 20R
25	C_{27} sterane (5α,14α,17α) 20R
26	C_{28} sterane (5α,14α,17α) 20R
27	C_{29} sterane (5α,14α,17α) 20S
28	C_{29} sterane (5α,14β,17β) 20R
29	C_{29} sterane (5α,14β,17β) 20S
30	4α-methyl 24-methyl C_{29} sterane (tentative)
31	C_{29} sterane (5α,14α,17α) 20R
32	C_{30} sterane

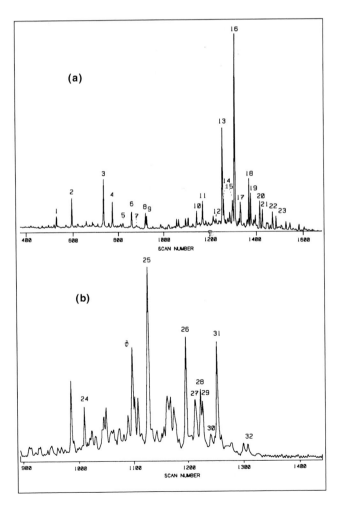

Figure 27.6. Mass chromatograms of a typical oil from South Cuyama field (oil #2) showing (a) terpane (*m/z* 191) and (b) sterane (*m/z* 217) distributions. Numbered peaks are identified in Table 27.4.

Table 27.5. Biomarker Data from Oils and Rock Extracts of the Saltos and Soda Lake Shale Members from the Cuyama Area, California[a]

Biomarker	Saltos Shale Member (20 Samples)				Soda Lake Shale Member (11 Samples)				Oils (#'s from Table 27.2)				
	Min	Max	Ave	Med	Min	Max	Ave	Med	Ave	#9	#7	#4	#2
C_{20} Tr/C_{23} Tr	0.16	0.75	0.39	0.32	0.24	0.92	0.48	0.43	0.22	0.21	0.21	0.25	0.21
C_{21} Tr/C_{23} Tr	0.43	1.24	0.79	0.72	0.43	1.11	0.69	0.65	0.56	0.58	0.49	0.61	0.55
C_{23} T$_s$/Hop	0.03	0.45	0.13	0.10	0.02	0.26	0.11	0.07	0.31	0.44	0.25	0.31	0.25
C_{24} Tr/C_{23} Tr	0.42	1.10	0.59	0.53	0.39	0.80	0.56	0.55	0.47	0.44	0.50	0.43	0.52
P#5/Hop	0.01	2.35	0.18	0.07	0.01	0.18	0.05	0.03	0.04	0.06	0.03	0.04	0.02
C_{25} Tr/C_{23} Tr	0.19	8.43	0.99	0.61	0.30	1.84	0.70	0.53	0.46	0.40	0.50	0.42	0.50
P#7/Hop	0.00	0.99	0.06	0.02	0.00	0.04	0.01	0.01	0.01	0.01	0.00	0.01	0.01
P#8/P#9	0.71	1.77	1.33	1.29	0.42	3.03	1.73	1.84	1.68	1.84	2.03	1.33	1.53
P#9/C_{23} Tr	0.21	0.85	0.44	0.36	0.10	1.54	0.50	0.29	0.18	0.17	0.14	0.19	0.20
Tm/Ts	1.38	10.9	3.71	2.62	0.72	7.28	2.25	1.62	2.07	1.67	2.26	2.21	2.15
Bis/Hop	0.01	2.56	0.21	0.04	0.00	0.15	0.05	0.05	0.03	0.04	0.04	0.02	0.02
Nor/Hop	0.28	1.43	0.59	0.55	0.20	1.65	0.53	0.42	0.49	0.49	0.49	0.50	0.48
P#14/Hop	0.07	0.31	0.15	0.15	0.02	0.43	0.16	0.16	0.13	0.16	0.13	0.12	0.11
Ole/Hop	0.13	6.91	0.76	0.38	0.15	0.68	0.35	0.24	0.23	0.24	0.21	0.26	0.21
Mor/Hop	0.15	0.82	0.30	0.20	0.16	0.89	0.29	0.21	0.15	0.15	0.14	0.16	0.16
C_{31} Ho($S+R$)/Hop	0.17	0.80	0.40	0.41	0.23	0.92	0.61	0.63	0.48	0.52	0.38	0.57	0.44
C_{32} Ho($S+R$)/Hop	0.0	0.62	0.20	0.15	0.10	0.58	0.33	0.29	0.32	0.44	0.21	0.35	0.29
C_{33} Ho($S+R$)/Hop	0.02	0.40	0.14	0.11	0.05	0.49	0.27	0.27	0.22	0.30	0.14	0.25	0.18
C_{31} Ho $S/S+R$	0.10	0.63	0.45	0.48	0.20	0.67	0.49	0.51	0.57	0.58	0.57	0.55	0.56
C_{32} Ho $S/S+R$	0.03	0.61	0.41	0.45	0.08	0.68	0.43	0.41	0.56	0.55	0.56	0.55	0.58
C_{33} Ho $S/S+R$	0.00	0.75	0.47	0.51	0.33	0.71	0.55	0.59	0.58	0.59	0.58	0.58	0.58
$\beta\beta/\beta\beta+\alpha\alpha$ Ste	0.21	0.42	0.31	0.28	0.23	0.49	0.37	0.35	0.36	0.41	0.37	0.33	0.34
C_{29} St $S/S+R$	0.04	0.55	0.18	0.11	0.05	0.51	0.26	0.33	0.34	0.33	0.34	0.35	0.35
C_{27} R St/Σ St	0.29	0.49	0.38	0.38	0.25	0.47	0.37	0.36	0.42	0.43	0.45	0.38	0.43
C_{28} R St/Σ St	0.12	0.41	0.33	0.34	0.10	0.49	0.31	0.30	0.28	0.26	0.25	0.29	0.30
C_{29} R St/Σ St	0.18	0.57	0.29	0.25	0.04	0.51	0.33	0.34	0.30	0.31	0.30	0.33	0.27
Dia/C_{27} R St	0.02	0.38	0.12	0.09	0.07	1.09	0.27	0.12	0.29	0.42	0.24	0.27	0.22
C_{30} St/Σ St	0.01	0.04	0.03	0.03	0.02	0.06	0.03	0.04	0.03	0.03	0.03	0.03	0.03
P#30/Σ St	0.01	0.21	0.07	0.05	0.03	0.40	0.12	0.09	0.07	0.09	0.06	0.07	0.06
(Hop+Mor)/Stn	0.15	1.91	0.74	0.57	0.12	6.08	1.67	1.15	2.23	2.07	2.56	2.28	1.99
Pr/Ph	0.42	4.42	1.43	1.20	0.82	4.91	1.59	1.19	1.82	1.93	—	1.84	1.69
Tri/Mono+Tri	—	—	—	—	—	—	—	—	0.83	0.74	0.85	0.85	0.88

[a]Ratios based on peak areas of *m/z* 191, 217, 231, and 253 mass chromatograms. Pristane/phytane ratios based on peak areas from gas chromatogram of C_{9+} saturate hydrocarbon fraction. Minimum (min), maximum (max), average (ave), and median (med) values are given for the extracts. Average and individual values for four oils are given. Abbreviations: P#, peak number in Table 27.4; Tr, tricyclic terpane; Hop, 17α(H),21β(H) C_{30} hopane (peak 16); Tm, 17α(H)-22,29,30-trisnorhopane (peak 11); Ts, 18α(H)-22,29,30-trisnorhopane (peak 10); Bis, 28,30-bisnorhopane (peak 12); Nor, norhopane (peak 13); Ole, oleanane (peak 15); Mor, moretane (peak 17); Ho, hopane; $\beta\beta/\beta\beta+\alpha\alpha$ Ste, C_{29} 14α(H),17α(H)- and 14β(H),17β(H) 20($R+S$) steranes (peaks 28+29/27+28+28+31); St, sterane, 5α,14α,17α; Σ St, sum of C_{27}, C_{28}, C_{29}, and C_{30} 5α(H),14α(H),17α(H) 20R steranes; Dia, C_{27} 13β,17α 20R diasterane (peak 24); Stn, sum of all C_{29} steranes/(C_{29} R St/Σ St)0.333; Pr, pristane; Ph, phytane; Tri/Mono+Tri, triaromatic steranes/mono + tri aromatic steranes ratio after Mackenzie et al. (1981). See Lillis (1988) for peak identifications.

The biological marker data of the source rocks is summarized in Table 27.5. The ranges of the biomarker ratios for the Saltos Shale Member and the Soda Lake Shale Member overlap considerably, thus no single biomarker has been found that clearly distinguishes the two units. However, relationships between biomarker composition and formation can be recognized based on median values. For example, the diasterane/sterane, $C_{29}/C_{27}+C_{28}+C_{29}$ steranes, 4-methyl sterane/sterane, hopane/sterane, C_{32}/C_{30} hopane, and C_{33}/C_{30} hopane ratios are generally higher in the Soda Lake than in the Saltos (Table 27.5). A few samples of the Saltos and Soda Lake contain high concentrations of oleanane and C_{29} steranes. Finally, the only two samples having significant amounts of 28,30-bisnorhopane are from the Monterey Formation.

Samples from the ROCO James #1 well, located in the graben east of the Cox fault (Figure 27.1), were processed for vitrinite reflectance analysis (Table 27.7). None of the samples contain enough vitrinite to make the desired 50 measurements per sample. However, a fairly consistent downhole trend is observed increasing in mean reflectance from 0.32% R_m (2235 m) to 0.55% R_m (3437 m).

DISCUSSION

Oil–Oil Correlation

Lillis (1988) determined that all the significant petroleum accumulations in the Cuyama basin were derived from a common source (i.e., a single family). The

Table 27.6. Summary of Rock-Eval Pyrolysis Data from the Cuyama Area, California

	Average Rock-Eval Values				
	TOC (wt. %)	T_{max} (°C)	HI (mg HC/g TOC)	Oxygen Index (mg CO_2/g TOC)	No. of Samples
Undivided Branch Canyon Ss to Santa Margarita Fm	0.46	424	188	110	3
Saltos Shale Member	3.03	426	361	101	28
Painted Rock Ss Member	0.48	424	133	67	4
Soda Lake Shale Member	2.13	435	295	62	24
Undivided Cretaceous–Eocene	1.03	445	43	65	4
				Total	63

	S_2 versus TOC Linear Regression Results				
	Slope	HI	*y* intercept	*x* intercept	*R*
Saltos	4.79	479	–2.62	0.55	0.91
Soda Lake	4.02	402	–0.87	0.22	0.66
Soda Lake excluding outlier	6.07	607	–4.17	0.69	0.93

[a]Including data from Lundell and Gordon (1988). In S2 versus TOC plot (Figure 27.8), the slope of linear regression determines "true" average HI (Langford and Blanc-Valleron, 1990) for Saltos and Soda Lake. See Lillis (1992) for a complete list of all Rock-Eval pyrolysis data.

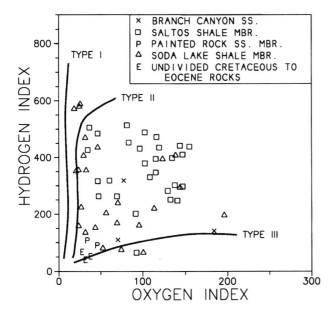

Figure 27.7. Hydrogen index (mg HC/g TOC) versus oxygen index (mg CO_2/g TOC) plot from Rock-Eval data in the Cuyama area, California. Curved solid lines are type I, II, and III kerogen evolution pathways after Espitalié et al. (1977) and Peters (1986).

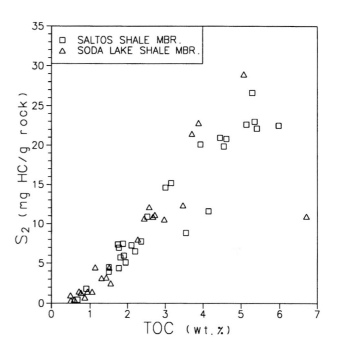

Figure 27.8. S_2 (mg HC/g rock) versus TOC plot from Rock-Eval pyrolysis data in the Cuyama area, California.

distribution patterns of the saturated hydrocarbons and the biomarkers are essentially identical for the three oil fields. The correlation is confirmed by Lundell and Gordon (1988) and Kornacki (1988) and by the isotope data presented here. This conclusion was expected since the oil fields generally lie in close proximity along a structural trend and have the same reservoir rocks.

The saturated hydrocarbon gas chromatograms of the oils produced from younger reservoirs (Branch Canyon Sandstone and Santa Margarita Formation) appear quite different from the oils in the main producing reservoir (Painted Rock Sandstone Member) due to biodegradation. Because biological markers are more resistant to biodegradation than *n*-alkanes, the biomarker composition of the altered oils can be correlated with the deeper oil production (compare oils #4 and #7 in Table 27.5). Oil #7 is unusual because it lacks acyclic isoprenoids (pristane and phytane) yet contains normal alkanes. Normally, bacteria preferentially consume *n*-alkanes leaving behind acyclic isoprenoids (Volkman et al. 1983),

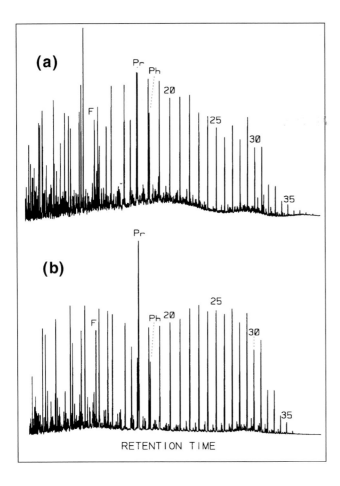

Figure 27.9. Gas chromatograms of the saturated hydrocarbon fraction of rock extracts from (a) the Saltos Shale Member and (b) the Soda Lake Shale Member in the Cuyama area, California. Pr, pristane; Ph, phytane; F, farnesane; numbers are the carbon numbers of the corresponding normal alkanes.

as observed in oil #14 (Figure 27.4a). One explanation for the anomalous composition is that the oil was partially biodegraded, removing the *n*-alkanes and acyclic isoprenoids, and subsequently mixed with a very mature crude oil having abundant *n*-alkanes and very low concentrations of acyclic isoprenoids (Lillis, 1992).

Cuyama oils do not correlate with Monterey oils in surrounding basins (Lillis, 1988). Monterey oils typically have lower gravity, higher sulfur content, lower pristane/phytane ratios, lower diasterane/sterane ratios, higher bisnorhopane content, and lighter carbon isotope values. Orr (1986) plotted API gravity versus sulfur content and noted a good linear relationship for Monterey oils in the Santa Maria basin. While most Monterey oils plot along his calculated regression line, the Cuyama oils do not (Lillis, 1988). Furthermore, the apparent slope of the Cuyama oil data is different from that of the Monterey oils, although not enough data exist to calculate a regression line. Differences in slope are probably related to differences in kerogen composition of the source rocks.

Oil–Source Rock Correlation

Based on geologic and geochemical constraints, the Cuyama basin contains only two potential source rocks, the Saltos Shale Member of the Monterey Formation and the Soda Lake Shale Member of the Vaqueros Formation. Thus, this discussion is limited to these two units. Rock-Eval pyrolysis data indicate that both the Saltos Shale Member and the Soda Lake Shale Member are oil-prone source rocks with good potential (Peters, 1986). If we exclude one outlier data point, the Soda Lake has better quality organic matter (true average HI = 607) than the Saltos (HI = 479).

Because the Monterey Formation is a proven source rock in surrounding basins, it is logical to speculate that it is the effective source rock for the Cuyama oils. However, the Soda Lake Shale Member is stratigraphically lower and thus has more favorable thermal maturity. The primary reservoir rock, the Painted Rock Sandstone Member, lies directly above the Soda Lake, allowing optimal oil migration upward, while oil derived from the Saltos Shale Member of the Monterey Formation would have to migrate downward into the reservoir or by a complex structural scenario.

The observation by Lillis (1988) and Kornacki (1988) that the Cuyama oils are unlike typical Monterey oil implies that a different source is required. However, the Monterey Formation in the Cuyama basin is quite different in composition from the Monterey in other basins—the Saltos Shale Member has a higher clay content, pristane/phytane ratio, diasterane content, and oleanane content and a lower bisnorhopane content. It is possible that the Monterey Formation in the Cuyama basin could produce a low sulfur, high gravity oil with a composition similar to the Cuyama oils.

Indeed, the organic matter of the Saltos and Soda Lake members are quite similar in composition—predominantly marine algal- and bacterial-derived organic matter. This is not surprising because both units accumulated in similar depositional environments; both were deposited near the Miocene strandline into a marine basin of bathyal depth (Lagoe, 1987a). Both units received pulses of allochthonous terrigenous organic matter as indicated by a few samples containing high oleanane (Ekweozor et al. 1979), C_{29} steranes (Huang and Meinschein, 1979), and terrestrial plant wax components (n-C_{27}, n-C_{29}, and n-C_{31}). However, both units show some variation in the saturated hydrocarbon gas chromatograms and in biomarker composition due to a range in thermal maturity and organic matter type.

The biomarker ratios for the Cuyama oils usually fall within the range of both the Saltos and the Soda Lake members (Table 27.5). For example, the ternary diagram of C_{27}, C_{28}, and C_{29} $\alpha\alpha\alpha$ R steranes (Figure 27.10) shows both source rocks with considerable range in composition, and the Cuyama oils plot within the range of both facies. The pristane/phytane ratios of the oils are also within the range of both formations (Figure 27.11). However, the median biomarker composition of the Soda Lake is closer to the average Cuyama oil in many

Table 27.7. Vitrinite Reflectance Data and Biomarker Maturity Data of Core Samples from the Roco James #1 Well in the Graben East of the Cox Fault[a]

Depth (m)	% R_m	Standard Deviation	Range (% R_m)	Number of Measurements	Biomarker Ratio ($S/S+R$)	
					C_{29} St	C_{31} Ho
2235.4	0.32	0.03	0.29–0.36	4	0.05	0.37
2349.4	0.37	0.05	0.27–0.51	31	0.07	0.27
2670.0	0.37	0.06	0.26–0.51	21	0.05	0.43
2728.9	0.50	0.05	0.42–0.56	4	0.08	0.44
2863.3	0.49	0.04	0.43–0.57	14	0.18	0.63
2999.2			No data		0.29	0.55
3122.4	0.51	0.01	0.50–0.52	2	0.32	0.60
3248.3	0.52	0.06	0.40–0.63	9	0.45	0.57
3304.6	0.47	0.08	0.36–0.57	5	0.38	0.62
3383.3	0.63	0.06	0.58–0.74	6	0.44	0.60
3436.9	0.55	0.06	0.45–0.65	8	0.49	0.67

[a]Biomarker abbreviations same as in Table 27.5.; R_m, mean reflectance. See Figure 27.1 for well location.

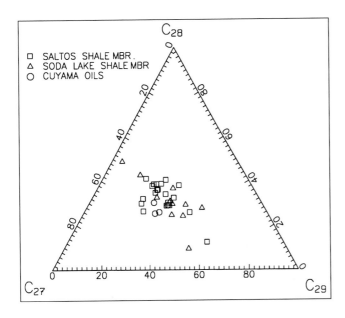

Figure 27.10. Ternary plot of normalized percentages $\alpha\alpha\alpha$ *R* steranes $C_{27}:C_{28}:C_{29}$ of oils and rock extracts from the Cuyama area, California.

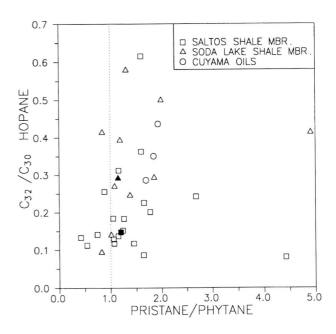

Figure 27.11. Plot of C_{32}/C_{30} hopane versus pristane/phytane of oils and rock extracts from the Cuyama area, California. Solid symbols are median values.

more cases than the median value of the Saltos (Table 27.5) (namely, diasterane/sterane, percent C_{28} sterane, hopane/sterane, C_{25}/C_{23} tricyclics, C_{26} *R*/C_{23} tricyclics, peak A/hopane, peak B/hopane, oleanane/hopane, and C_{32}/C_{30} hopane). For example, in Figure 27.11 (C_{32}/C_{30} hopane versus pristane/phytane), the oils plot closer to the median value (and the average value) of the Soda Lake Shale Member. The only two biomarker ratios where the median value of the Saltos Shale Member correlates better with the oil are the C_{20}/C_{23} tricyclic and the C_{23} tricyclic/hopane. These data suggest that the Cuyama oils correlate with the Soda Lake slightly better than the Saltos, but the possibility of the Saltos being a subordinate source of oil cannot be discounted.

Oil #9 (Table 27.2) from the Morales Canyon field is produced from the Quail Canyon Sandstone Member, which is stratigraphically below the Soda Lake.

Biomarker data (Table 27.5) suggest that the correlation of oil #9 to the Soda Lake is slightly better than the correlation of the average Cuyama oil just described. This might be expected because it would be even more difficult to migrate Monterey oil into a reservoir below the Soda Lake Shale Member.

Although no single biomarker clearly differentiates the Saltos Shale Member from the Soda Lake Shale Member, the stable carbon isotope data do distinguish the two units (Figure 27.5). Furthermore, the isotope data suggest that the Soda Lake is the primary source of the Cuyama oils. To summarize, the geochemical data indicate that the Soda Lake is the main source for oil in the Cuyama basin. However, the Monterey may have also contributed a minor amount of oil to the known accumulations.

Timing of Generation–Migration–Accumulation and Trap Formation

Most of the rock samples available are from the shallow parts of the basin and thus are not representative of the full range of thermal maturity. Maturity data obtained from rock samples include vitrinite reflectance, T_{max} from Rock-Eval pyrolysis, and biomarker maturity ratios. The biomarker ratios selected are mostly related to organic matter type but some are influenced by maturity (Table 27.5). Ratios of stereoisomers of the pentacyclic terpanes and steranes are used to evaluate the thermal maturity of source rocks and oils (Seifert and Moldowan, 1981) (Table 27.7). Many of these ratios reach an equilibrium value at low maturities, often before significant oil generation, depending on the kinetics of the reaction (Mackenzie and McKenzie, 1983). For example, the $S/S+R$ C_{31} hopane ratio and the moretane/hopane ratio are at or near equilibrium in the Cuyama oils (Figure 27.12). However, the oils are significantly below the equilibrium values for $S/S+R$ steranes (0.54) (Figure 27.12) and $\beta\beta/\beta\beta+\alpha\alpha$ steranes (0.66–0.75) (Table 27.5) (Seifert and Moldowan, 1986).

The maturity at which oil is generated and expelled depends on many factors, including type of organic matter, mineral matrix, confining pressure, and thermal history. The biomarker maturity ratios of the oils can be compared with those in the source rocks (of known maturity) to determine the approximate maturity level of oil expulsion (Suzuki, 1990). Vitrinite reflectance values of Cuyama source rocks with the same thermal maturity as the oils are about 0.52% R_m (Figure 27.12), while measured T_{max} values (not shown) are about 440°C. This level of maturity is slightly below the commonly cited onset of oil generation (Dow, 1977). However, high heating rates have been shown to produce oil at low vitrinite reflectance values (Suzuki, 1990). Based on a comparison of aromatization of steroids to isomerization of steranes in Cuyama oils, Lillis (1988) concluded that high heating rates of the source rock generated Cuyama oils. Oil #9 from the Morales Canyon field appears to have a slightly higher maturity than the oils from the Russell Ranch and South Cuyama fields based on Tm/Ts, $\beta\beta/\beta\beta+\alpha\alpha$ sterane, and diasterane/sterane ratios. However, these ratios may also be influenced by organic facies.

Geohistory diagrams (van Hinte, 1978) were constructed for wells in the area and for the possible deep source areas to the northeast (Figure 27.13). Age, paleobathymetry, and lithology data were taken from the literature (see references in Geology section), and thicknesses were taken from well log data and from the cross sections of Davis et al. (1988). Bottom hole temperatures combined with thermal maturity estimates from T_{max}, vitrinite reflectance, and biomarker ratios were used to estimate a thermal history. Calculated heat flow ranges from 65 to 72 mW/m². Generation and migration is assumed to start at a thermal maturity equivalent to a vitrinite reflectance of 0.52% R_m based on the reasoning presented earlier. On the basis of limited geochemical data, the base of the oil window is placed at a vitrinite

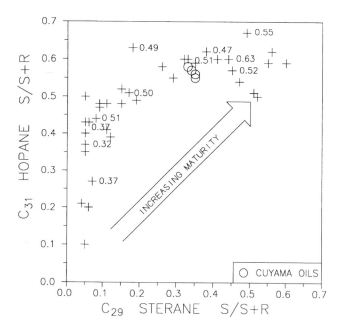

Figure 27.12. Biological marker thermal maturity ratios from oils (circles) and rock extracts (crosses) from the Cuyama area, California; isomerization of C_{31} hopane at carbon 22 versus C_{29} sterane at carbon 20. Numbers are mean vitrinite reflectance values (% R_m) shown for corresponding samples (see Table 27.7).

reflectance of 0.7 %R_m which is lower than commonly cited values (1.0 %R_m) (Dow, 1977). However, lower reflectance values for the oil window may be expected because vitrinite maturation is less affected by high heating rates than oil generation.

Figure 27.13 shows the essential elements of the petroleum system with respect to burial history for the southern Caliente Range area. The first episode of subsidence (23 Ma) was followed by deposition of the source rock and reservoir rock, respectively. A second subsidence episode (19 Ma) was followed by deposition of the seal rock and subsequent overburden. The calculated oil window shows that oil generation in the Soda Lake began about 10 Ma and continued until about 1.2 Ma.

The maturity modeling and timing of structures support a Soda Lake Shale Member source. Furthermore, modeling and Rock-Eval pyrolysis data from Lundell and Gordon (1988) indicate that the Saltos Shale Member is immature to marginally mature in much of the basin. However, modeling also shows that within the last 1 m.y. oil generated from the Saltos in the grabens beneath the southern Caliente Range and east of the Cox fault may have contributed to already trapped oil. The biomarker data suggest that the Saltos may be a cosource for oil in the Russell Ranch and South Cuyama fields but that the Morales Canyon field contains mostly Soda Lake oil. Below the main thrust in the southern Caliente Range (Figure 27.3), oil in the "Saltos" (an oil-saturated sandstone) appears to be derived from the Saltos (Lillis, 1992).

The events chart summarizes the essential elements and the processes of the Soda Lake–Painted Rocks(!)

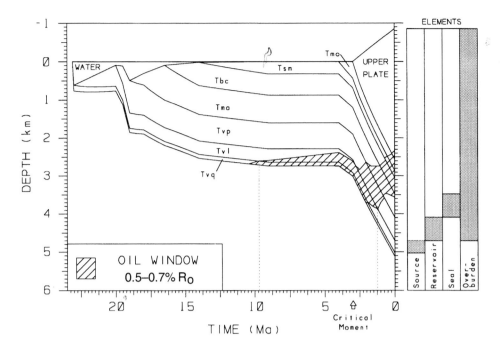

Figure 27.13. Geohistory diagram for deep area in the southern Caliente Range using the BasinMod program of Platte River Associates. Location shown in Figure 27.1.

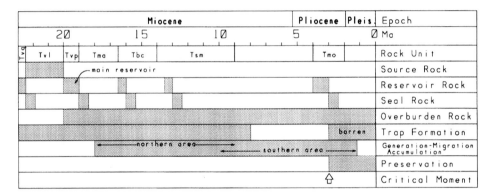

Figure 27.14. Summary of timing for critical petroleum system elements for the Cuyama area, California. Rock unit abbreviations same as in Figure 27.3.

petroleum system (Figure 27.14). The stratigraphic units above the basement rock are indicated. The Painted Rock Sandstone Member is the major reservoir rock and was deposited immediately after the source rock (the Soda Lake Shale Member). The seal rock, the Saltos Shale Member, was deposited immediately after the reservoir rocks. The overburden rock includes all the Cenozoic rocks deposited after the Soda Lake prior to thrusting about 3 Ma, after which the thrust sheet added to the burial depth of the source rock. Traps formed by extensional and strike-slip faulting from 23 Ma to about 8 Ma.

The process of generation–migration–accumulation of oil commenced between 18 and 10 Ma depending on the overburden thickness (and sedimentation rate). In the northern Caliente Range where the Painted Rock is up to 2380 m thick, the Soda Lake reached the oil window earlier (18 Ma), while the Monterey remained immature. Closer to the oil fields in the southern Caliente Range, the Painted Rock is only about 610 m thick and the Soda Lake reached the oil window about 10 Ma (Figure 27.13). The traps containing oil were formed in early–late Miocene, while barren traps in the overthrust were formed since 3 Ma. Therefore, most of the migration

occurred between 19 and 3 Ma, assuming migration pathways have been available from the subthrust to the upper plate. Because migration occurred prior to 3 Ma, the critical moment is placed at 3 Ma. If migrating petroleum has been restricted to the subthrust by permeability barriers, then the critical moment would be at about 1 Ma (the end of generation–migration in the system).

The geographic extent of mature Soda Lake shale is shown in Figure 27.1. The northwestern boundary of the petroleum system is undefined, but the absence of oil accumulations suggests that one of the essential elements may be missing.

CONCLUSIONS

The Soda Lake–Painted Rock(!) petroleum system involving lower Miocene source rocks and reservoir rocks has been defined in the Cuyama basin. The main source facies, the lower Miocene Soda Lake Shale Member of the Vaqueros Formation, was deposited in middle–upper bathyal marginal marine environments.

The Soda Lake is overlain by the main reservoir rock, the shallow marine Painted Rock Sandstone Member of the Vaqueros Formation. Due to high sedimentation and heating rates, oil generation–migration began in middle–late Miocene time from the deep graben areas into existent structural traps associated with the Miocene Russell fault. Because the Painted Rock is very thick in much of the deep graben area, the overlying source facies, the Saltos Shale Member of the Monterey Formation, is immature to marginally mature and may have only contributed a subordinate proportion of petroleum to the Cuyama oil fields.

Under the southern Caliente Range where the Painted Rock Sandstone Member is much thinner, the Saltos Shale Member has reached the onset of oil generation in the last few million years. The Saltos is also mature enough to generate hydrocarbons in the graben east of the Cox fault. However, significant accumulations of Saltos-derived oil have not been discovered to date. The Saltos Shale Member is different in composition from typical Monterey Formation in adjacent basins. The organic matter in the Saltos has relatively low bisnorhopane, moderate oleanane (and other higher plant debris biomarkers), higher diasterane content, and higher pristane/phytane ratios. Thus, a Saltos-derived oil would not be a typical Monterey oil; it would be sweet, light oil similar to Soda Lake oils found in the Cuyama basin.

Acknowledgments   I am indebted to Donald Anders, Jerry Clayton, Michael Lewan, and James Palacas of the U.S. Geological Survey for insightful discussions. I acknowledge J. David King, Ted Daws, Augusta Warden, and Mark Pawlewicz of the U.S. Geological Survey for the biomarker, Rock-Eval, carbon isotope, and vitrinite reflectance data, respectively. I thank ARCO Oil and Gas Company for providing the oil and rock samples and pertinent data. Ben Law and Jerry Clayton gave thoughtful and constructive reviews of the manuscript. Dorothy Malone and Les Magoon provided editorial assistance. I also thank Martin Lagoe, William Bazeley, Lee Lundell, and Tom Wildeman for their continued support and guidance. Permission to use Figure 27.3 by Davis et al. (1988) was obtained from SEPM representative Reinhard Suchsland. Use of product names does not constitute endorsement by the U.S. Geological Survey.

References Cited

Brassell, S. C., G. Eglinton, and R. Maxwell, 1983, The geochemistry of terpenoids and steroids: Biochemistry Society Transactions 603rd Meeting, Liverpool, v. 11, p. 575–586.

Bray, E. E., and E. D. Evans, 1961, Distribution of *n*-paraffins as a clue to recognition of source beds: Geochimica Cosmochimica Acta, v. 22, p. 2–15.

California Division of Oil and Gas, 1974, California oil and gas fields, Vol. II, south, central, and offshore California: California Department of Conservation, Division of Oil and Gas, Report TR12.

California Division of Oil and Gas, 1991, 76th annual report of the state oil & gas supervisor 1990: California Department of Conservation, Division of Oil and Gas, Publication No. PRO6, 165 p.

CCOP, 1993, Annual review of California oil and gas production—1992: Los Angeles, Conservation Committee of California Oil and Gas Producers, p. G-50.

Clifton, H. E., 1981, Progradational sequences in Miocene shoreline deposits, southeastern Caliente Range, California: Journal of Sedimentary Petrology, v. 51, p. 165–184.

Cross, R. K., 1959, Review of Cuyama oil province: AAPG Bulletin, v. 43, p. 259.

Curiale, J. A., D. Cameron, and D. V. Davis, 1985, Biological marker distribution and significance in oils and rocks of the Monterey Formation, California: Geochimica Cosmochimica Acta, v. 49, p. 271–288.

Davis, T. L., M. B. Lagoe, W. J. M. Bazeley, S. Gordon, K. McIntosh, and J. S. Namson, 1988, Structure of the Cuyama Valley, Caliente Range, and Carrizo Plain and its significance to the structural style of the southern Coast Ranges and western Transverse Ranges, in W. J. M. Bazeley, ed., 1988, Tertiary tectonics and sedimentation in the Cuyama basin, San Luis Obispo, Santa Barbara, and Ventura counties, California: SEPM Pacific Section, v. 59, p. 141–158.

Dibblee, T. W., Jr., 1973a, Stratigraphy of the Southern Coast Ranges near the San Andreas fault from Cholame to Maricopa, California: USGS Professional Paper 764, 45 p.

Dibblee, T. W., Jr., 1973b, Regional geologic map of San Andreas and related faults in Carrizo Plain, Temblor, Caliente, and La Panza ranges and vicinity, California: USGS Miscellaneous Geological Investigations, Map I-757.

Dow, W. G., 1977, Kerogen studies and geological interpretations: Journal of Geochemical Exploration, v. 7, p. 79–99.

Eglinton, G., and M. Calvin, 1967, Chemical fossils: Scientific American, v. 216, p. 32–43.

Ekweozor, C. M., J. I. Okogun, D. E. V. Ekong, and J. R. Maxwell, 1979, Preliminary organic geochemical studies of samples from the Niger delta, Nigeria, Part 2: analysis of shales for triterpane derivatives: Chemical Geology, v. 27, p. 29–37.

Espitalié, J., M. Madec, B. Tissot, J. J. Mennig, and P. Leplat, 1977, Source rock characterization method for petroleum exploration: Proceedings of the Ninth Annual Offshore Technology Conference, v. 3, p. 439–448.

Hill, M. L., S. A. Carlson, and T. W. Dibblee, Jr., 1958, Stratigraphy of Cuyama Valley–Caliente Range area, California: AAPG Bulletin, v. 42, n. 12, p. 2973–3000.

Huang, W. Y., and W. G. Meinschein, 1979, Sterols as ecological indicators: Geochimica Cosmochimica Acta, v. 43, p. 739–745.

Kornacki, A. J., 1988, Provenance of oil in southern Cuyama Basin, California: AAPG Bulletin, v. 72, n. 2, p. 207.

Kruge, M. A., 1986, Biomarker geochemistry of the Miocene Monterey Formation, West San Joaquin basin, California: implications for petroleum generation: Organic Geochemistry, v. 10, p. 517–530.

Lagoe, M. B., 1982, Stratigraphy and paleoenvironments of the Monterey Formation and associated rocks, Cuyama basin, California: Ph.D. dissertation, Stanford University, Stanford, CA, 216 p.

Lagoe, M. B., 1984, Paleogeography of Monterey Formation, Cuyama basin, California: AAPG Bulletin, v. 68, p. 610–627.

Lagoe, M. B., 1985, Depositional environments in the Monterey Formation, Cuyama basin, California: GSA Bulletin, v. 96, p. 1296–1312.

Lagoe, M. B., 1987a, Middle Cenozoic basin development, Cuyama basin, California, *in* R. V. Ingersoll and W. G. Ernst, eds., Cenozoic basin development of coastal California, Rubey Vol. VI: Englewood Cliffs, NJ, Prentice Hall, p. 172–206.

Lagoe, M. B., 1987b, Middle Cenozoic unconformity-bounded stratigraphic units in the Cuyama and southern San Joaquin basins, California: record of eustatic and tectonic events in active margin basins: Cushman Foundation of Foraminiferal Research, Special Publication 24, p. 15–32.

Langford, F. F., and M. M. Blanc-Valleron, 1990, Interpreting Rock-Eval pyrolysis data using graphs of pyrolyzable hydrocarbons vs. total organic carbon: AAPG Bulletin, v. 74, n. 6, p. 799–804.

Lillis, P. G., 1988, Correlation and characterization of oils using biological markers, Cuyama basin, California, *in* W. J. M. Bazeley, ed., 1988, Tertiary tectonics and sedimentation in the Cuyama basin, San Luis Obispo, Santa Barbara, and Ventura counties, California: SEPM Pacific Section, v. 59, p. 39–48.

Lillis, P. G., 1992, Organic geochemistry of the Miocene marine rocks and petroleum accumulations, Cuyama basin, California: Ph.D. dissertation, Colorado School of Mines, Golden, CO, 274 p.

Lundell, L., and S. Gordon, 1988, Origin of Cuyama oils, *in* W. J. M. Bazeley, ed., 1988, Tertiary tectonics and sedimentation in the Cuyama basin, San Luis Obispo, Santa Barbara, and Ventura counties, California: SEPM Pacific Section, v. 59, p. 29–37.

Mackenzie, A. S., C. F. Hoffmann, and J. R. Maxwell, 1981, Molecular parameters of maturation in the Toarcian shales, Paris basin, France, III—changes in aromatic steroid hydrocarbons: Geochimica Cosmochimica Acta, v. 45, p. 1345–1355.

Mackenzie, A. S., and D. McKenzie, 1983, Isomerization and aromatization of steroid hydrocarbons in sedimentary basins formed by extension: Geology Magazine, v. 120, p. 417–470.

Orr, W. L., 1986, Kerogen/asphaltene/sulfur relationships in sulfur-rich Monterey oils: Organic Geochemistry, v. 10, p. 499–516.

Peters, K. E., 1986, Guidelines for evaluating petroleum source rock using programmed pyrolysis: AAPG Bulletin, v. 70, n. 3, p. 318–329.

Philippi, G. T., 1965, On the depth, time, and mechanism of petroleum generation: Geochimica Cosmochimica Acta, v. 29, p. 1021–1049.

Philp, R. P., 1985, Fossil Fuel Biomarkers—Applications and Spectra: Amsterdam, Elsevier, 294p.

Schwade, I. T., S. A. Carlson, and J. B. O'Flynn, 1958, Geologic environment of Cuyama Valley oil fields, California, *in* L. G. Weeks, ed., Habitat of oil: AAPG Symposium, p. 78–98.

Seifert, W. K., and J. M. Moldowan, 1978, Applications of steranes, terpanes, and monoaromatics to the maturation, migration, and source of crude oils: Geochimica Cosmochimica Acta, v. 42, p. 77–95.

Seifert, W. K., and J. M. Moldowan, 1981, Paleoreconstruction by biological markers: Geochimica Cosmochimica Acta, v. 45, p. 783–794.

Seifert, W. K., and J. M. Moldowan, 1986, Use of biological markers in petroleum exploration, *in* R. B. Johns, ed., Biological Markers in the Sedimentary Record: Amsterdam, Elsevier, p. 261–290.

Spitz, H. M., 1988, Structure of the Cox trough, southeastern Cuyama Valley, southern California, *in* W. J. M. Bazeley, ed., 1988, Tertiary tectonics and sedimentation in the Cuyama basin, San Luis Obispo, Santa Barbara, and Ventura counties, California: SEPM Pacific Section, v. 59, p. 113–126.

Suzuki, N., 1990, Application of sterane epimerization to evaluation of Yoshii gas and condensate reservoir, Niigata basin, Japan: AAPG Bulletin, v. 74, n. 10, p. 1571–1589.

Taylor, J. C., 1976, Geologic appraisal of the petroleum potential of offshore southern California: the Borderland compared to onshore coastal basins: USGS Circular 730, 43 p.

Tissot, B. P., B. Durand, J. Espitalié, and A. Combaz, 1974, Influence of nature and diagenesis of organic matter in formation of petroleum: AAPG Bulletin, v. 58, p. 499–506.

van Hinte, J. E., 1978, Geohistory analysis—application of micropaleontology in exploration geology: AAPG Bulletin, v. 62, n. 2, p. 201–222.

Vedder, J. G., 1973, Geologic framework and correlation of Miocene rocks in the Caliente Range, California, *in* Sedimentary facies changes in Tertiary rocks—California Transverse and southern Coast Ranges: Field Trip Guidebook, SEPM Pacific Section 1973 Annual Meeting, Anaheim, CA, p. 42–53.

Volkman, J. K, R. Alexander, R. I. Kagi, and G. W. Woodhouse, 1983, Demethylated hopanes in crude oils and their applications in petroleum geology: Geochimica Cosmochimica Acta, v. 47, p. 785–794.

Yeats, R. S., J. A. Calhoun, B. B. Nevins, H. F. Schwing, and H. M. Spitz, 1989, Russell fault: Early strike-slip fault of California Coast Ranges: AAPG Bulletin, v. 73, p. 1089–1102.

"The outstanding contribution of methane generation to petroleum migration is as a major source of internal energy to move fluids within the petroleum source system."

—Hollis D. Hedberg

Passage from Hedberg, H. D., 1980, Methane generation and petroleum migration: AAPG Studies in Geology 10, p. 179.

Magoon, L. B, and W. G. Dow, eds., 1994, The petroleum
system—from source to trap: AAPG Memoir 60.

Chapter **28**

Simpson–Ellenburger(.) Petroleum System of the Central Basin Platform, West Texas, U.S.A.

B. J. Katz

V. D. Robison

W. C. Dawson

L. W. Elrod

*Texaco EPTD
Houston, Texas, U.S.A.*

Abstract

The Simpson–Ellenburger(.) petroleum system is located in the Central Basin platform of the greater Permian basin of west Texas and southeastern New Mexico. It originally contained about 3.0 billion bbl of oil in-place. This petroleum system covers about 9600 km^2 and includes more than 50 fields. Sedimentary rocks within the study area range from Early Ordovician toTertiary. However, the section is dominated by Paleozoic strata, of which about 50% in thickness are Permian. Geochemical data, including carbon isotopic composition and gas chromatographic results obtained on 10 crude oils, strongly support an Ordovician source rock. Geochemical data further suggest that this oil-prone Ordovician source rock was probably limited to shales within the Simpson Group. Burial and thermal reconstructions indicate that the oil was generated and expelled over an approximately 210-m.y. period. The principal reservoir rock of this petroleum system occurs within karstified Ellenburger dolomites (Early Ordovician). Hydrocarbon traps that developed by Ochoan time (Late Permian) are mainly faulted anticlines.

The source rock, primary reservoir rock, and seal rock were deposited over a 52-m.y. period. The necessary overburden rock for hydrocarbon generation and migration occurred over a 418-m.y. period ending during the Oligocene (~35 Ma). An estimated 180–540 billion bbl of oil generated by the Simpson Group suggests that the trapping efficiency of this system is about 4.3–14.3% when compared to original estimates of oil in-place.

INTRODUCTION

The greater Permian basin of west Texas contains several petroleum systems with hydrocarbons generated from source rocks of Ordovician, Devonian–Mississippian, Pennsylvanian, and Permian age (Guevara and Mukhopadhyay, 1987; Dow et al., 1990). This chapter describes the Simpson–Ellenburger(.) petroleum system, which has a source rock of Ordovician age and is largely restricted to the Central Basin platform (Figure 28.1).

The Simpson–Ellenburger petroleum system covers about 9600 km^2 (3700 mi^2) and includes parts of Andrews, Crane, Ector, Midland, Upton, and Winkler counties in Texas and Lea County in New Mexico. Production from this system was established in 1942 with the discovery of Wheeler field (Ector and Winkler counties, Texas). To date, this system has produced about 1.0 billion bbl of oil and very little gas, with a remaining recoverable potential of about 200 million bbl. The high API oil gravity, ranging from 35 to 53° API, allows for a 40% recovery factor. On this basis, we estimate original oil in-place for this system to be about 3.0 billion bbl. Converting to kilograms (139.3 kg/bbl) gives 4.2 × 10^{11} kg of oil (Schmoker, Chapter 19, this volume).

As noted previously, other oil fields on the Central Basin platform are unrelated to the Simpson–Ellenburger petroleum system, but these fields are excluded from this case study. These excluded oil fields add up to 23.4 billion bbl of in-place oil. The oil fields included in the Simpson–Ellenburger petroleum system are shown on Figure 28.2, and the fields with geochemical and/or geologic data are listed in Table 28.1.

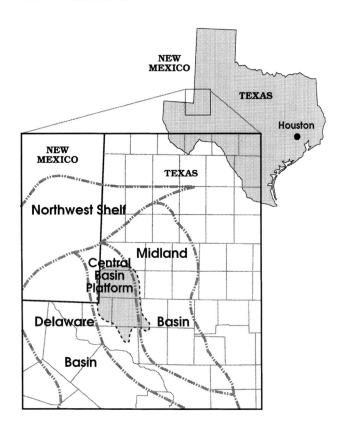

Figure 28.1. Location of the Central Basin platform in west Texas and southeastern New Mexico. Shaded area indicates the location of the Simpson–Ellenberger(.) petroleum system. The greater Permian includes the Delaware and Midland basins, the Central Basin platform, and the Northwest Shelf.

SEDIMENTARY BASIN SETTING

Structural Setting

Galley (1958) and Wright (1979) have provided a general overview of both the structural and sedimentologic framework of the greater Permian basin. This greater basin includes the Northwest shelf, Delaware and Midland basins, and the Central Basin platform (Figure 28.1). Galley (1958) noted that no evidence exists for the Central Basin platform prior to Montoya time in the Late Ordovician (~435 Ma). Up to this time, stratigraphic evidence indicates that the Ellenburger Formation and Simpson Group were deposited over a broad carbonate shelf. Subtle stratigraphic evidence for the ancestral Central Basin platform that began to form as a structural high in Montoya time is suggested by a thickening wedge of Silurian–Lower Carboniferous sedimentary rock in the Delaware and Midland basins. This structural high persisted throughout the Early Carboniferous.

In pre-Permian time, major uplift of the ancestral platform by block faulting formed the Central Basin platform. When the Lower Permian unconformity is used as a datum, as much as 2.5 km of structural relief in the Delaware basin and over 0.5 km of relief in the

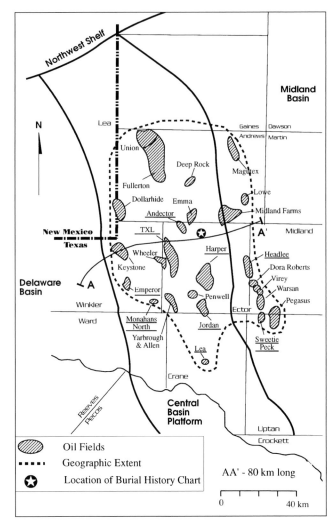

Figure 28.2. Location of all oil fields within the Simpson–Ellenburger(.) petroleum system, whose present-day geographic extent is shown as a dashed line. Province outlines compare with those on Figure 28.1. Cross section A–A' is shown in Figure 28.3 and the burial history chart is shown in Figure 28.6. Underlined field names are referred to on Table 28.1.

Midland basin has been measured (Figure 28.3). It is believed that the trend of these faults was controlled largely by preexisting Proterozoic lines of weakness (Hills, 1984).

Following this uplift, Permian sedimentary rock filled the block-faulted Delaware and Midland basins and overlapped the Central Basin platform and Northwest Shelf to form the greater Permian basin. These Permian rocks range in thickness from 1.6 km over the Central Basin platform to 4.2 km in the Delaware basin, and in turn are overlain by as much as 0.7 km of Triassic rocks. Jurassic rocks are absent either by nondeposition or erosion prior to deposition of the Lower Cretaceous. Overlying the Lower Cretaceous sedimentary rocks is a thin veneer (<100 m) of Cenozoic rocks (Figure 28.3). Uplift of the entire region occurred relatively recently.

Table 28.1. Characteristics of Oil Fields in the Simpson–Ellenburger(.) Petroleum System

Field	Year Disc'd	Producing Unit[a]	Reservoir Lithology	Trap Type[b]	Depth (ft)	Oil Gravity (°API)	Original GOR (SCF/STB)	Cum. Prod. (10⁶ bbl)	Ult. Recov. (10⁶ bbl)
Andector	1946	Ellbrg	Dolo	FA	8,500	44	553	154.1	195.7
TXL	1945	Ellbrg	Dolo	FBA	9,600	44	1063	126.3	128.0
Headlee	1953	Ellbrg	Dolo	SA	13,300	51	1259	36.8	40.0
Jordan	1947	Ellbrg	Dolo	FA	8,800	45	710	30.2	31.0
Harper	1962	Ellbrg	Dolo, Ls	FA	12,300	46	—	20.5	21.5
Lea	1953	Ellbrg	Dolo	FBA	8,200	43	367	19.6	20.9
Sweetie Peck	1950	Ellbrg	Dolo	—	13,128	53	—	9.5	—
Monahans North	1955	Thirtyone	Ls	—	11,540	44	—	—	—
Monahans North	1955	Ellbrg	Dolo	—	12,030	43	—	7.3	—
Emperor	1954	Ellbrg	Dolo	—	11,480	35	—	0.04	—

[a]Ellbrg, Ellenburger.
[b]FA, faulted anticline; FBA, fault-bounded anticline; SA, simple anticline.
References: Galloway et al. (1983); International Oil Scouts Association (1989).

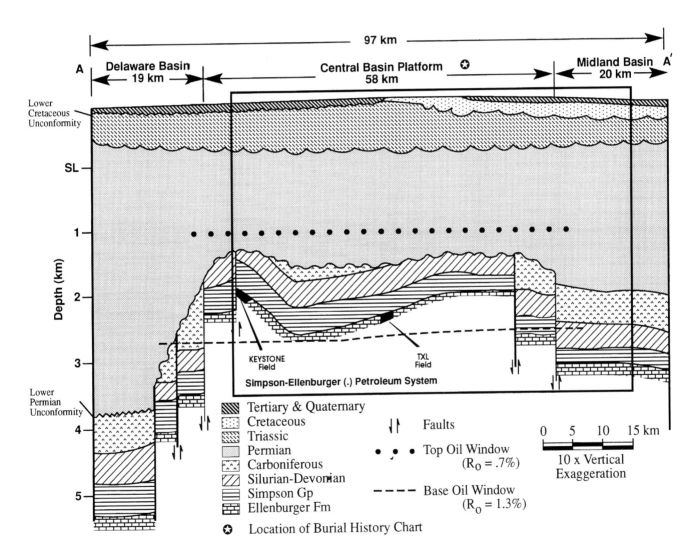

Figure 28.3. West–east cross section across the Central Basin platform. Location is shown on Figure 28.2. The block faulting is pre-Permian and the basal Lower Permian unconformity truncates all older units after uplift. Permian sedimentary rocks fill the Delaware and Midland basin and overlap the Central Basin platform to form the greater Permian basin.

Stratigraphic Section

A generalized stratigraphic column is presented in Figure 28.4. The thicknesses presented are the maximum thicknesses noted in the COSUNA (1983) chart. The variation in thickness across the Central Basin platform is shown in Figure 28.3.

The Ellenburger Formation (Lower Ordovician) is composed mainly of finely to coarsely crystalline light-colored carbonates and is predominantly dolomite up to 400 m thick. Limestones and cherty limestones are largely restricted to lower portions of the Ellenburger. The Ellenburger was deposited in a broad, shallow epicontinental sea with an estimated water depth of less than 15 m (50 ft) and contains numerous minor unconformities throughout. These unconformities reflect fluctuations in sea level during the Early Ordovician.

Disconformably overlying the Ellenburger is the Simpson Group, which is up to 400 m thick and divided into five formations: Joins, Oil Creek, McLish, Tulip Creek, and Bromide. The Joins Formation is composed principally of gray to brown, shallow marine, shaley limestones and dolomites. The Joins is slightly glauconitic near its base. The Oil Creek, McLish, and Tulip Creek formations are mostly shale units with thin layers of fossiliferous limestones and calcareous (or siliciclastic?) sandstones. In general, these lower formations represent the transgressive phase of the Simpson sea. This sea probably extended from present-day west Texas and southern New Mexico through Oklahoma and Kansas because lithologic characteristics are uniform and persistent throughout this broad region. The uppermost Bromide Formation is dominated by light gray to brown massive limestones with minor shale interbeds. Deposition of the Bromide occurred during a minor regressive episode. The source rocks for the petroleum system under discussion are the shales of the Simpson Group. Source rock properties are described in more detail later. Overlying the Simpson Group is the Montoya Dolomite. This Late Ordovician cherty carbonate is up to 70 m thick and characteristically finely crystalline.

The Silurian–Carboniferous section includes carbonates and shales. The Ordovician Montoya Dolomite is overlain by 50–70 m of Silurian Fusselman Dolomite, a largely cherty dolomite, and 30–60 m of Wristen Formation shales. The Devonian section is mostly a massive carbonate section, the Thirtyone Formation, that is up to 300 m thick. Capping the Devonian sequence is up to 30 m of Devonian–Carboniferous Woodford Formation. The Woodford is an organic-rich, brownish black, pyritic, fissile shale with carbonate and sandstone interbeds. It represents a major transgressive episode with deposition occurring under largely stagnant conditions. Except for the dark-colored Barnett Shale, the remaining Carboniferous section is a finely crystalline limestone. On the Central Basin platform, the Barnett Shale is overlain by limestone units: the Strawn Limestone, Canyon Limestone, and Gisco Limestone.

During Early Permian time, deposition on the Central Basin platform was dominated by carbonates repre-

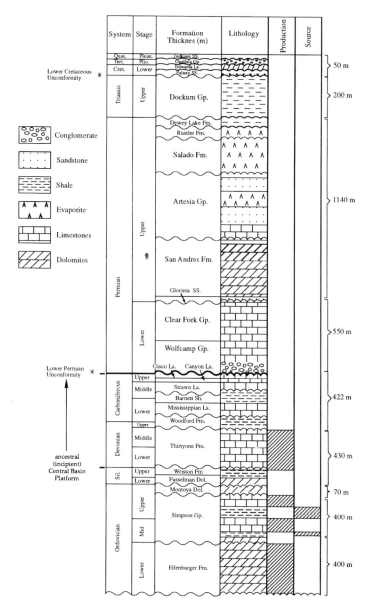

Figure 28.4. Generalized stratigraphic column for the Central Basin platform where the burial history chart is located. The unconformities at the basal Montoya Dolomite, basal Lower Permian, and basal Lower Cretaceous are important to the development of this petroleum system. Thickness represents maximum values presented in the COSUNA (1983) chart. Absolute ages are based on DNAG assignments (Palmer, 1983).

sented by the Wolfcamp and Clear Fork groups. These two groups contain large proportions of dolomite that together are as much as 550 m thick. During Late Permian time, there was a shift toward deposition of more evaporitic units on the platform. Collectively, the Permian section accounts for more than half of the total sedimentary thickness and is the most important overburden rock for this petroleum system. The post-Paleozoic sequence is of relatively minor stratigraphic importance and is composed principally of shales, sandstones, and conglomerates.

THE PETROLEUM SYSTEM

Petroleum Source Rock

The Simpson–Ellenburger(.) petroleum system remains problematic. Only limited geochemical data are available to establish the source rock potential of the Simpson Group. However, there is considerable circumstantial evidence supporting the source–reservoir association.

The oil being produced from the Ellenburger Formation is geochemically unique, displaying characteristics typical of Ordovician oils derived from the algae *Gloeocapsamorpha prisca.* (These oils are described in detail later.) This stratigraphically restricts the source rock sequence to the Ellenburger Formation, the Simpson Group, or the Montoya Dolomite. Geologic and geochemical data favor the Simpson Group as the source rock for these oils. The arguments are as follows:

1. The Ellenburger Formation is lean with respect to organic matter (Cardwell, 1977) and is incapable of generating commercial quantities of hydrocarbons. Total organic carbon (TOC) content of the Ellenburger is typically less than 0.5 wt. %.
2. The geochemically distinct oils are almost exclusively found in Ellenburger reservoir rocks wherever they are overlain by the Simpson Group. Elsewhere in the greater Permian basin where the Simpson is lacking, Ellenburger oils appear to have been generated from the Woodford Shale (Kvenvolden and Squires, 1967).
3. The limited source rock data from the study area (Philippi, 1981) (Figure 28.5) suggest that the Simpson Group does contain at least some organic-rich, oil-prone intervals, with TOC contents in excess of 1.0 wt. % and extractable hydrocarbon contents greater than 1.0‰.

In addition to Philippi's data from the study area, geochemical data from equivalent units in Oklahoma reveal excellent oil source rock potential (Figure 28.5). These units are richer and more oil prone than the west Texas samples. This may in part reflect differences in the level of thermal maturity between the two sample suites. Available data and thermal modeling results suggest that the west Texas samples are more mature than the material analyzed from Oklahoma.

Reservoir Rocks and Accumulations

The Ellenburger Formation penetrated in wells drilled in Crane, Ector, and Winkler counties, Texas (Figure 28.2), consists mainly of dark gray, finely crystalline, massively bedded dolomite. The Ellenburger sequence on the Central Basin platform and throughout most of west Texas represents cyclic, shallowing-upward carbonate sedimentation in restricted marine (subtidal, intertidal, and supratidal) paleoenvironments. According to Loucks and Anderson (1980, 1985), the Ellenburger contains a variety of shallow marine carbonate lithofacies, including algal boundstone, intraclastic packstone,

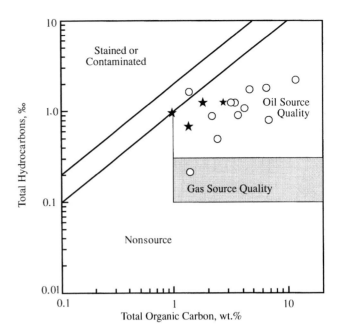

Figure 28.5. Relationship between TOC content and total extractable hydrocarbons for the Simpson source rock. Data from west Texas (stars) are from Philippi (1981), and data from Oklahoma (open circles) are presented to show that the source rock is oil prone.

laminated mudstone, burrowed mudstone, peloidal packstone, and ooid packstone–grainstone. Typically, these shallowing-upward Ellenburger cycles are capped by pedogenic carbonates. Locally, the lower Ellenburger contains interstratified siliciclastic units recording alluvial fan to fan delta progradation onto the Ellenburger carbonate shelf.

The Ellenburger Formation has undergone multiple episodes of dolomitization and karstification. Extensive karstification of Ellenburger carbonates and coeval formations appears to have coincided with a Middle Ordovician eustatic sea level lowstand prior to deposition of the Simpson Group siliciclastics (Kerans, 1988). This subaerial exposure resulted in the development of solution collapse breccias and vuggy to cavernous porosity (Loucks and Anderson, 1985; Kerans, 1988). However, because the Ellenburger was repeatedly exposed (and probably karstified) throughout the middle Paleozoic, the timing of karstification, dolomitization, and porosity development is somewhat speculative (Mazzullo, 1990). In addition to karst-related pore systems, Ellenburger reservoirs have fault-related fracture systems that developed during middle–late Paleozoic tectonism (pre-Permian). Well sample logs and core descriptions also record the presence of abundant intercrystalline porosity in the Ellenburger dolomites. The origin and timing of such porous strata and their relationship, if any, to karst surfaces are equivocal but undoubtedly pre-Permian.

The depth of Ellenburger reservoirs in the study area ranges from 2600 to 4035 m. These dolomites have an average porosity of 2% (range 1–4%) and an average permeability of 179 md (range 5–300 md).

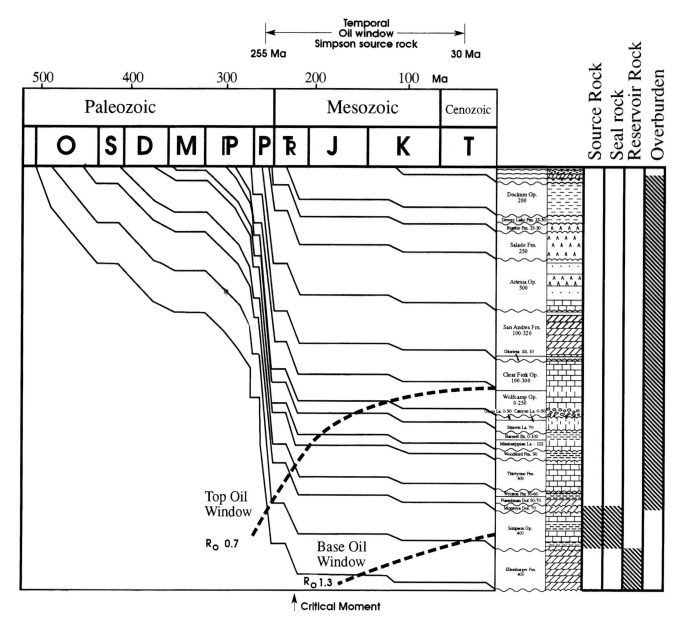

Figure 28.6. Burial history diagram assuming maximum stratigraphic thicknesses present in the Central Basin platform, with all unconformities represented by sedimentary hiatuses. The position of the oil window is based on a constant geothermal gradient of 1.54°F/100 ft. Burial of the source rock was mostly over by the end of the Triassic. Oil generation in the Simpson source rock started in Late Permian (255 Ma), peaked in Late Triassic (210 Ma), and was over by middle Tertiary (30 Ma) time.

Petroleum System Timing

A Lopatin-type approach was used to estimate the present level of thermal maturity and the timing of hydrocarbon generation and migration. The burial history diagram and the position of the oil window are shown in Figure 28.6. The model assumes maximum stratigraphic thickness for the region and nearly continuous deposition, with unconformities being represented as periods of nondeposition. A constant geothermal gradient of 1.54°F/100 ft was also assumed (Hills, 1984).

These simplifying assumptions tend to result in underestimation of the level of thermal maturity. This is

particularly true in light of the structural and stratigraphic history of the region. There is clear evidence that erosion occurred following deposition of both the Ellenburger Formation and Simpson Group. Furthermore, the region underwent compression from the southeast during the Late Carboniferous–Permian. This compressional episode resulted in uplift and significant erosion across parts of the Central Basin platform and the Delaware basin. This has resulted in local erosional truncation down to the Ellenburger or, in some cases, even the Precambrian (Ijirigho, 1989).

An analysis of Figure 28.6 indicates that the Simpson–Ellenburger petroleum system was active for about 470

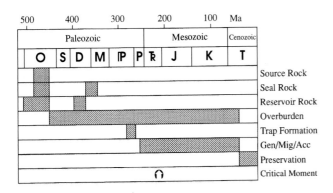

Figure 28.7. Events chart for the Simpson–Ellenburger(.) petroleum system showing the temporal relationships of the essential elements and processes.

m.y. beginning with deposition of the Ellenburger Formation 505 Ma. Deposition of the Simpson, which acts as both the source rock and primary seal for the system, occurred between 488 and 453 Ma. By the end of the Paleozoic, about 245 Ma, the Simpson source rock was buried in places to sufficient depths for it to enter the oil window. From near the close of Dewey Lake sedimentation (~255 Ma) until after deposition of the Edwards Limestone, the Simpson source rock was in the oil window and may have been actively generating and expelling hydrocarbons. This suggests that hydrocarbons were actively generating, migrating, and accumulating for a duration of about 210 m.y. However, by the end of Dockum deposition (~215 Ma), the Simpson source rock approached its maximum burial depth and the bulk of the hydrocarbons had probably been generated and expelled. The Simpson Group moved out of the oil window about 35 Ma.

Trap development was associated with the collisional event that resulted in the subdivision of the greater Permian basin into the Delaware and Midland basins, the Northwest Shelf, and the Central Basin platform in pre-Permian time. This event establishes the time of development of the faulted anticlinal traps as pre-Permian, about 290 Ma. The major events associated with the petroleum system are summarized in Figure 28.7.

Level of Certainty

Ten oils were geochemically examined as part of this case study (Table 28.1). Nine of these oils are from reservoir rocks of Ordovician age and one is from Devonian. These ten oils are characterized by a high proportion of gasoline-range paraffins, a pronounced odd predominance of normal paraffins in the C_{15}–C_{19} range, low concentrations of pristane and phytane, and very light stable carbon isotope values. These characteristics strongly suggest an Ordovician source rock (Reed et al., 1986; Longman and Palmer, 1987).

The oils generally have a high concentration of straight-chain paraffins when compared to branched paraffins and naphthenes and a high concentration of

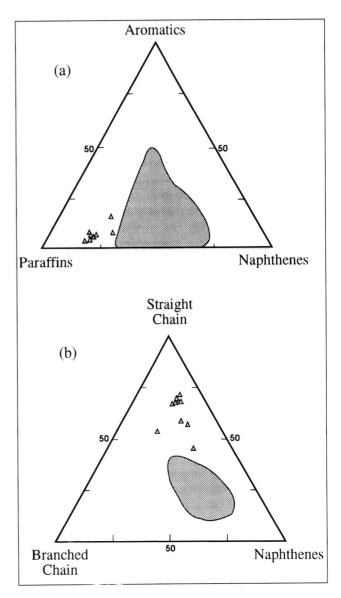

Figure 28.8. Ternary diagrams of (a) total gasoline range (C_4–C_7) hydrocarbons and (b) nonaromatic hydrocarbons for oils from the Simpson–Ellenburger(.) petroleum system depicting enrichment in straight-chain n-paraffins. Shaded areas represent different oil types from source rocks other than the Simpson in the greater Permian basin.

total paraffins when compared to aromatics and naphthenes (Figure 28.8). The oils display n-paraffin distributions that are distinctive. They show a marked odd carbon number predominance in the C_{15}–C_{19} n-paraffin range and very low concentrations of both pristane and phytane (Figure 28.9), both of which are characteristic of oil derived from an Ordovician source rock containing the algae *Gloeocapsamorpha prisca* (Reed et al., 1986; Longman and Palmer, 1987).

These oils are isotopically light, with saturated hydrocarbon fractions at –33 to –35.5‰ (relative to PDB standard) (Figure 28.10). Similar isotopic compositions were reported by Kvenvolden and Squires (1967) for Ellenburger oil production from regions where the Ellen-

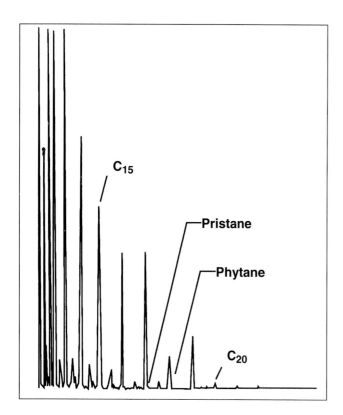

Figure 28.9. Representative gas chromatogram of the C₁₅₊ hydrocarbon fraction of an oil that originated from the Simpson source rock. Note the low concentration of pristane and phytane and the odd carbon number predominance in the C₁₅–C₁₉ range.

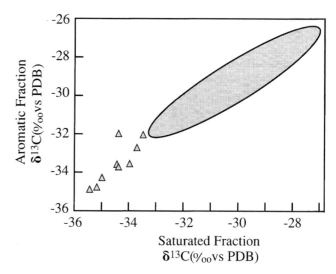

Figure 28.10. Comparison of the carbon isotopic composition of saturated and aromatic fraction hydrocarbons. Shaded area represents different oil types from source rocks other than the Simpson in the greater Permian basin.

burger Formation is overlain by the Simpson Group. This stratigraphic relationship further suggests a genetic relationship between the Simpson Group source rocks and the Ellenburger reservoir rocks. Such light isotopic compositions are also associated with oil from Ordovician or older source rocks in other regions.

Geographic and Stratigraphic Extent

The Simpson–Ellenburger petroleum system(.) is geographically restricted to that part of the greater Permian basin where oil accumulations charged by the Simpson source rock occur. Stratigraphically, most of the oil is found in reservoir rocks within the Ellenburger Formation. However, oil from the Simpson source rock is also found in Simpson reservoir rocks and a limited number of accumulations are in Devonian reservoir rocks.

It is important to note that not all of the multipay fields associated with the Simpson–Ellenburger system share a common source rock. Coester and Williams (1968) noted that in some multipay fields, oil from the Simpson source rock may be present in Ellenburger reservoir rocks, while other source rocks may supply oil to the shallower Devonian, Carboniferous, and Permian reservoir rocks. However, these shallower oils are part of a different petroleum system(s).

EFFICIENCY OF SYSTEM

There are several limitations in the resource assessment of a hypothetical petroleum system. Most of these are related to the lack of sufficient source rock data to fully characterize the richness, quality, and thermal maturity of the organic matter and the areal extent of the pod of active source rock. This inability to establish source rock richness, quality, thermal maturity, and volume accurately reduces the accuracy of the estimate of a system's efficiency. Thus, we show the assumptions used in our calculations.

The efficiency of the petroleum system is dependent on both the amount of hydrocarbons generated and the amount of trapped hydrocarbons. The amount of hydrocarbons generated from the pod of active source rock in the petroleum system can be estimated through a series of steps outlined by Schmoker (Chapter 19, this volume). These estimates are partially based on the level of organic enrichment of the source rock. Within the system currently under examination, source rock data are limited. The observed levels of organic enrichment range from 1.00 to 2.78 wt. % TOC, with a mean of 1.74 wt. % (Philippi, 1981).

This weight percent of TOC content can be converted to mass if the volume and density of the effective source rock are known. Based on the current burial depth, a shale porosity of about 10% is assumed for the Simpson source rock. Using Schmoker's relationship, we can equate this to a source rock density of 2.5 g/cm³. If the Simpson source rock is assumed to be present throughout the system's geographic extent and a net source rock thickness of 20–50 m is assumed, this equates to a source rock volume of 192–480 km³.

By combining the mean TOC, shale porosity, and source volume, the mass of TOC is estimated to be $1.9–4.8 \times 10^{17}$ g. If we then assume that the kerogen could originally be classified as type II according to the scheme of Tissot et al. (1974), then an original HI of between 350 and 500 mg HC/g C can be assumed. Considering the average present level of thermal maturity of the Simpson source rock interval, the present HI is estimated to be about 150 mg HC/g C. This equates to 2.9–7.3×10^{12} t of oil generated. When the calculated amount of oil generated is compared to the estimated original oil in-place, the generation–accumulation efficiency of the system appears to be 5.7–14.3%. Peak hydrocarbon generation and expulsion occur after trap development (Figure 28.7).

It should also be noted that these calculations do not take into consideration the reduction in present-day TOC content through hydrocarbon generation and expulsion. If the method of Daley and Edman (1987) is used to calculate the initial levels of organic carbon, a mean of 2.3 wt. % TOC would be assumed rather than the 1.74 wt. % used in the current calculations. This increase in initial TOC content would reduce the overall generation–accumulation efficiency of this system to 4.3–10.8%.

SUMMARY

The Simpson–Ellenburger(.) petroleum system remains speculative because no definitive oil–source rock correlation has been performed. Geologic and geochemical data, however, support an Ordovician source, specifically the shales within the Simpson Group. This petroleum system is geographically restricted to the Central Basin platform. Although the primary reservoirs are within the Ellenburger Formation, other reservoirs are stratigraphically present within Ordovician–Devonian strata.

Peak hydrocarbon generation began about 245 Ma. Traps had been formed and in place for about 50 m.y. before peak generation. The generation–accumulation efficiency of the Simpson–Ellenburger petroleum system is between 4.3 and 14.3%, depending on the assumptions used in the calculations.

Acknowledgments   *The authors thank Texaco Inc. for permission to publish this work. Assistance with manuscript preparation was provided by Mary Hill. The authors would also like to thank Les Magoon and Wally Dow for inviting us to contribute this manuscript.*

References Cited

Cardwell, A. L., 1977. Petroleum source-rock potential of Arbuckle and Ellenburger Groups of southern Mid-Continent, United States: Quarterly of the Colorado School of Mines, v. 72, n. 3, p. 1–134.

Coester, B. B., and J. L. Williams, 1968, Relationships of oil composition and stratigraphy in multipay fields (abs.): AAPG Bulletin, v. 52, p. 195.

COSUNA, 1983, Southwest/Southwest Mid-Continent Region: AAPG, Correlation of Stratigraphic Units of North America Project, 1 sheet.

Daley, A. R., and J. D. Edman, 1987, Loss of organic carbon from source rocks during thermal maturation: AAPG Bulletin, v. 71, p. 546.

Dow, W. G., S. C. Talukdar, and L. Harmon, 1990. Exploration applications of geochemistry in the Midland Basin, Texas (abs.): AAPG Bulletin, v. 74, p. 644–645.

Galley, J. E., 1958. Oil and geology in the Permian basin of Texas and New Mexico, in L. G. Weeks, ed., Habitat of oil: Tulsa, OK, AAPG, p. 395–446.

Galloway, W. E., T. E. Ewing, C. M. Garret, N. Tyler, and D. G. Bebout, 1983, Atlas of Major Texas Oil Reservoirs: The University of Texas at Austin, Bureau of Economic Geology.

Guevara, E. H., and P. K. Mukhopadhyay, 1987, Source rock potential and oil source correlation, Permian (Leonardian) strata, central Spraberry trend, Midland basin, Texas—preliminary study (abs.): AAPG Bulletin, v. 71, p. 561–562.

Hills, J. M., 1984, Sedimentation, tectonism, and hydrocarbon generation in Delaware basin, west Texas and southeastern New Mexico: AAPG Bulletin, v. 68, p. 250–267.

Ijirigho, B. T., 1989, Tectono-structural evolution and hydrocarbon distribution in fractured carbonate reservoirs, Permian basin, west Texas, in B.K. Cunningham and D. W. Cromell, eds., The lower Paleozoic of west Texas and southern New Mexico—modern exploration concepts: SEPM Publication 89-31, p. 159–168.

International Oil Scouts Association, 1989, International Oil and Gas Development Yearbook, v. 60.

Kerans, C., 1988, Karst-controlled reservoir heterogeneity in Ellenburger Group carbonates of west Texas: AAPG Bulletin, v. 72, p. 1160–1183.

Kvenvolden, K. A., and R. M. Squires, 1967, Carbon isotopic composition of crude oils from Ellenburger Group (Lower Ordovician), Permian basin, west Texas and eastern New Mexico: AAPG Bulletin, v. 51, p. 1293–1303.

Longman, M. W., and S. E. Palmer, 1987, Organic geochemistry of mid-continent Middle and Late Ordovician oils: AAPG Bulletin, v. 71, p. 938–950.

Loucks, R. G., and J. H. Anderson, 1980, Depositional facies and porosity development in Lower Ordovician Ellenburger dolomite, Puckett field, Pecos County, Texas: Carbonate Reservoir Rocks, SEPM Core Workshop, n. 1, p. 1–31.

Loucks, R. R. G., and J. H. Anderson, 1985, Depositional facies, diagenetic terranes, and porosity development in Lower Ordovician Ellenburger dolomite, Puckett field, west Texas, in P. O. Roehl and P. W. Choquette, eds., Carbonate Petroleum Reservoirs: New York, Springer-Verlag, p. 21–37.

Mazzullo, S. J., 1990, Karst-controlled reservoir heterogeneity in Ellenburger Group carbonates of west Texas—discussion: AAPG Bulletin, v. 74, p. 1119–1123.

Palmer, A. R., 1983, The decade of North American geology, 1983 geologic time scale: Geology, v. 11, p. 503–504.

Philippi, G. T., 1981, Correlation of crude oils with their source formation, using high resolution GLC C_6–C_7 component analyses: Geochimica Cosmochimica Acta, v. 45, p. 1495–1513.

Reed, J. D., H. A. Illich, and B. Horsfield, 1986, Biochemical evolutionary significance of Ordovician oils and their sources: Organic Geochemistry, v. 10, p. 347–358.

Tissot, B., B. Durand, J. Espitalié, and A. Combaz, 1974, Influence of nature and diagenesis of organic matter in formation of petroleum: AAPG Bulletin, v. 58, p. 499–506.

Wright, W. F., 1979, Petroleum geology of the Permian basin: West Texas Geological Society, 98 p.

"To explore is to synthesize. In a succession of exploration cycles, that is only occasionally reqarded by discovereies, earth scientistists find themselves involved in a perennial learning process, that ultimately will deepen our understanding of the earth and its resources."

—A. W. Bally

Passage from Bally A. W., in preface of Perrodon, A., 1983, Dynamics of Oil and Gas Accumulations: Elf Aquitaine, p. 2..

Magoon, L. B, and W. G. Dow, eds., 1994, The petroleum
system—from source to trap: AAPG Memoir 60.

Chapter **29**

Petroleum Systems of the Maracaibo Basin, Venezuela

Suhas C. Talukdar
DGSI
The Woodlands, Texas, U.S.A.

Fernando Marcano
MARAVEN, S.A.
Caracas, Venezuela

Abstract

The La Luna–Misoa(!) petroleum system covers an area of about 47,500 km^2 and contributes more than 98% of the total recoverable oil reserves of 52.20 billion bbl and gas reserves of 51.97 tcf in the Maracaibo basin. The system developed in two phases, with each phase having the characteristics of a unique petroleum system but both sharing the Upper Cretaceous La Luna source rock. The development of each phase is related to two separate mature to overmature pods of the La Luna source rock. Biological markers indicate that the oil in this system is correlated to the oil-prone type II kerogen of the La Luna Formation, a marine source rock. Reservoir rocks of Eocene and Miocene age are the most important, contributing 50% and 44%, respectively, of the total recoverable oil in the basin. Based on average TOC content and consumed hydrogen from hydrogen indices, the mass of hydrocarbons generated by the La Luna source rock is 2.50×10^{14} kg and the in-place hydrocarbon in known oil fields is estimated at 352.25×10^{11} kg. These calculations indicate that 14% of the hydrocarbons generated from the La Luna source rock actually accumulated in known traps.

The Orocue(.) petroleum system, located in the southwestern part of the basin, contributes less than 2% of the total hydrocarbon reserves in the basin. It covers 10,500 km^2 and encompasses the mature to overmature pod of Paleocene Orocue Formation, a coaly source rock containing type III kerogen and genetically related oil accumulations. Some of these accumulations contain a mixture of oils from the Orocue and La Luna source rocks.

INTRODUCTION

The Maracaibo basin is located in western Venezuela (Figure 29.1). Only a small part of the basin extends to the southwest into Colombia. This basin is the most important oil-producing area of Venezuela and accounts for about 70% of Venezuela's annual production (average 685 million bbl, 1980–1987 production data). It also accounts for about 76% of the cumulative Venezuelan oil production of 45,440 million bbl as of December 1993.

The Maracaibo basin occupies an area of about 50,000 km^2 (19,300 mi^2) and is bounded on the northwest by the Perija Range, on the southwest by the Santander massif of Colombia, and on the southeast by the Venezuelan Andes (Figures 29.1 and 29.2). The northeastern boundary of the basin is formed by the zone of the western foothills of the Trujillo Range, which separates it from the Falcon basin. The northern boundary is formed by the Gulf of Venezuela. Lake Maracaibo covers about one-third of the total area and receives water drained

from the Perija Range, Venezulan Andes, and Trujillo ranges. The lake is connected to the Gulf of Venezuela through the El Tablazo Bay.

The geologic history of the Maracaibo basin changed through time as it evolved from a passive continental margin setting in Cretaceous–Eocene time to a foreland basin setting in post-Eocene time. Development of this basin is related to interactions among the Pacific, Caribbean, and South American plates.

Oil exploration in the Maracaibo basin began early because of known occurrences of oil and gas seeps. In 1914, commercial oil was first discovered in Mene Grande field where oil seeps were known. By 1970, forty fields had been discovered of which eight were giants with individual oil reserves of at least 500 million bbl (Halbouty et al., 1970). Tables 29.1 and 29.2 give the discovery dates of all fields or areas presently known, and Figure 29.2 shows their locations. These oil fields produce from siliciclastic and carbonate reservoir rocks of which the Eocene and Miocene are the most important (Figures 29.2 and 29.3). About 17,000 wells have been drilled in the Maracaibo basin.

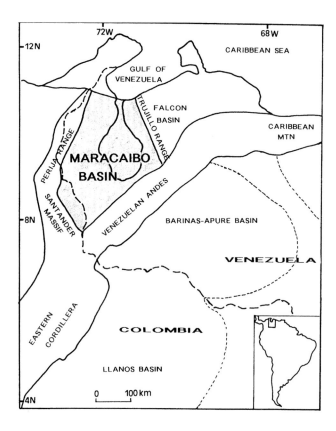

Figure 29.1. Location of the Maracaibo basin and adjacent provinces.

Total in-place oil was calulated in three steps. First, cumulative production reached 32.86 billion bbl of oil (bbo) and 35.97 trillion cubic feet of gas (tcfg) by the end of 1990. Proven reserves are estimated at 19.34 bbo and 16 tcfg, of which 93% is solution gas. The subtotal of produced and proven reserves are 52.20 bbo and 51.97 tcfg. If we use a recovery factor of 21% for oil and 80% for gas, which seems reasonable for these reservoir rocks, the in-place petroleum at the time of discovery (produced plus proven reserves) was 249 bbo and 65 tcfg. Second, if we add the probable and possible resources (6.59 bbo and 21.24 tcfg) to these, the recoverable resources are 58.79 bbo and 73.21 tcfg. The same recovery factor gives the in-place resources as 280 bbo and 92 tcfg. Last, when we add the oil resources assessed by probabilistic methods, the hypothetical (1.20 bbo) and speculative (6.76 bbo) reserves, we get total recoverable oil resources of 66.75 bbo. Thus, the total hydrocarbons in-place are 318 bbo and 92 tcfg.

The basin is at a mature stage of exploration in its northern half but is still poorly explored in the south toward the North Andean foredeep. Recent exploratory efforts have targeted the Andean flank south of Lake Maracaibo, Perija in Zulia state, and Ceuta on Lake Maracaibo. Proven oil reserves were recently increased by the discovery of 1.2 billion bbl of light oil between the Ceuta and Barua structural highs (near fields 5 and 9, Figure 29.2) (Roberto et al., 1990). A more recent estimate has lowered this newly discovered oil reserve in Ceuta

field to 764 million bbl of light and medium gravity oil (F. Marcano, unpublished data, 1992).

Previous studies of the geology of the Maracaibo basin are numerous (cited in Gonzalez de Juana et al., 1980). An outline of the basin's geology has been given by Zambrano et al. (1971) and Gonzalez de Juana et al. (1980). The characterization, origin, and alteration of oil from the Maracaibo basin have been published by several authors (Brenneman, 1960; Bockmeulen et al., 1983; Blaser and White, 1984; Gallango et al., 1985; Talukdar et al., 1985, 1986).

The debate about the origin of oil from the Maracaibo basin has centered around whether all oils are the same genetic type and thus whether all are derived from the Upper Cretaceous La Luna source rock, or if other source rocks exist that have contributed significantly to the oil accumulations. Based on biological markers, Talukdar et al. (1985, 1986) identified three genetic oil types: a marine oil, that is, an oil derived from a marine kerogen in the La Luna Formation; a terrestrial oil, or an oil derived from terrestrial kerogen, possibly from Paleocene shales or coals; and a third type, a mixed oil derived from both the marine and terrestrial oil. The marine oil type is distributed throughout the basin, whereas the terrestrial and mixed oils are found only in the southwestern part of the basin. Talukdar et al. (1985, 1986) and Gallango et. al. (1985) also subdivided the marine oils of the La Luna source rock based on alteration (biodegradation) and maturity.

Characteristics of the La Luna source rocks, a marine type II kerogen, have been discussed by Blaser and White (1984) and Talukdar et al. (1985, 1986, 1987). On the basis of source rock and thermal maturity data and modeling, Blaser and White have suggested that the Paleocene Orocue Formation, a coaly type III kerogen in the North Andean foredeep and the Colon district in southwestern Maraciabo basin, has the capability to generate oil.

Using thermal maturity modeling, Blaser and White (1984) have determined the present-day maturity of the La Luna and Orocue formations and have reconstructed the time when the La Luna source rock reached various levels of maturity in different parts of the basin. Talukdar et al. (1985, 1986) outlined the generation and migration of hydrocarbons in the Maracaibo basin. Reconstruction of the areas where hydrocarbons were generated at different geologic times using time–temperature index (TTI) diagrams suggested that oil and gas emanated from the La Luna source rock during two phases. The first phase occurred during the middle–late Eocene in the northeastern part of the basin, while the second phase took place during the late Miocene–Holocene in the central, western, and southern parts. Based on chemical kinetic parameters derived from Rock-Eval pyrolysis and Pyromat instruments and using the same time–temperature history of Talukdar et al. (1985, 1986), Sweeney et. al. (1990) predicted the timing and extent of oil generation in the basin.

This case study integrates available geologic and geochemical data to describe the petroleum systems of

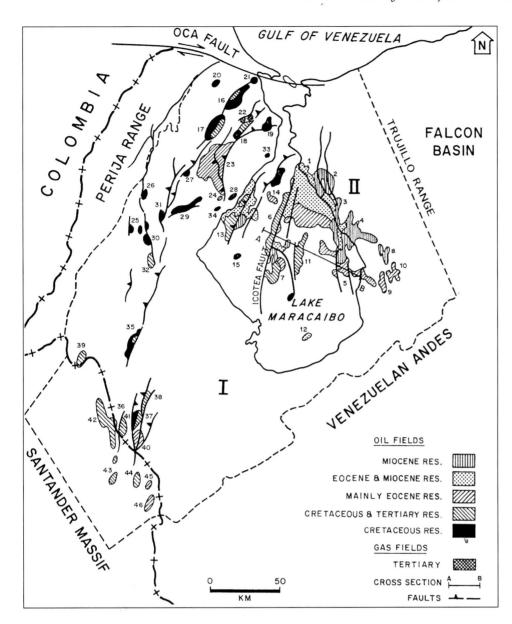

Figure 29.2. Location of oil and gas fields in the Maracaibo basin, within dashed outline. Shown are ages of reservoir rocks, important faults, and location of cross section A–B in Figure 29.4. Roman numerals refer to stratigraphic columns in Figure 29.3. Numbers refer to oil and gas fields in Figures 29.8, 29.9, and 29.13 and Tables 29.1 and 29.2.

the Maracaibo basin. Petroleum system concepts as developed by Magoon (1988) and Magoon and Dow (Chapter 1, this volume) are included. This chapter includes a brief description of the stratigraphic and structural setting of the basin and discusses the essential elements, processes, and events of the petroleum systems.

SEDIMENTARY BASIN SETTING

The geologic evolution of the Maracaibo basin relevant to development of the petroleum systems includes sedimentation and tectonics from Cretaceous to Holocene time. Cretaceous sedimentation began on top of the basement rock, which is mostly continental sedimentary rocks and silicic volcanic rocks of the La Quinta Formation of Triassic–Jurassic age and some Paleozoic igneous and metamorphic rocks (Figure 29.3).

Stratigraphic Section

Sedimentation of the Cretaceous rocks on the Maracaibo platform started in the Barremian with the deposition of coarse continental clastics of the Rio Negro Formation (Figure 29.3). This formation reached great thicknesses in certain troughs, while on the main part of the platform, it is quite thin. Siliciclastic sandstones within the Rio Negro form secondary reservoir rocks in the north. Secondary reservoirs contain significantly smaller volumes of oil than primary reservoir rocks (Figure 29.3 and Table 29.1).

During Aptian–Albian time, a marine transgression deposited thick, shallow water platform carbonates and associated sedimentary rocks that comprise the Apon, Lisure, and Maraca formations of the Cogollo Group and their equivalents. Fractured limestone within this group is secondary reservoir rock. In the southern part of the basin to the north of the Venezuelan Andes, sandstone of

Table 29.1. Oil Fields of the La Luna–Misoa(!) Petroleum System

Map No.	Field Name	Year Disc'd	Producing Unit	Producing Depth (m)	Lithology Reservoir	Lithology Seal	Trap Type	Cum. Oil Production (10³ bbl)	Est. Oil Reserves (10³ bbl)
1	Cabimas	1917	Lagunillas	520–1830	Ss	Sh	FB–S	465,797	23,535
			Misoa	1700	Ss	Sh	FB	7,346	17,075
2	Tia Juana	1925	Lagunillas	600–1800	Ss	Sh	S	4,146,708	903,114
			La Rosa	750–2050	Ss	Sh	FB	172,788	47,749
			Icotea	1000	Ss	Sh	FB	4,373	4,812
			Misoa	750–2100	Ss	Sh	FB	4,848,476	3,321,339
			Cretaceous	4550–5150	Ls	Ls	FB	6,294	6,806
3	Lagunillas	1926	Lagunillas	600–1800	Ss	Sh	FB–S	3,603,945	1,654,087
			La Rosa	1000–1700	Ss	Sh	FB	309	4,456
			Misoa	1250–3050	Ss	Sh	FB	718,023	412,056
4	Bachaquero	1930	Lagunillas	400–3150	Ss	Sh	FB–S	5,389,502	2,728,393
			La Rosa	1600–2850	Ss	Sh	FB	44,778	11,060
			Misoa	800–4000	Ss	Sh	FB	442,334	372,627
5	Ceuta	1957	Lagunillas	2100–4100	Ss	Sh	FA	1,214,341	436,992
			La Rosa	3050–3100	Ss	Sh	FA	73	2,110
			Misoa	3050–4500	Ss	Sh	FA	160,871	836,350
			Cretaceous	5050	Ls	Ls, Sh	FA	420	10,232
6	Lama	1957	Lagunillas	1400	Ss	Sh	FA	90	30
			La Rosa	2300–2650	Ss	Sh	FA	4876	1,914
			Misoa	1300–4850	Ss	Sh	FA	4,018,213	1,402,259
			Guasare	2300–2950	Ss	Sh?	FA	732	1,231
			Cretaceous	3650–4600	Ls	Ls, Sh	FA	156,979	144,445
7	Lamar	1958	La Rosa	3050–3500	Ss	Sh	FA	6162	6,945
			Icotea	3600	Ss	Sh	FA	3,366	3,126
			Misoa	3050–4500	Ss	Sh	FA	1,182,527	430,468
			Cretaceous	3650–4840	Ls	Ls, Sh	FA	962	23,906
8	Mene Grande	1914	Lagunillas	150–1050	Ss	Sh	S	561,309	47,487
			Misoa	600–2400	Ss	Sh	FA	82,395	16,503
9	Barua	1958	Misoa	4100	Ss	Sh	FA	45,072	57,316
10	Motatan	1952	Misoa–Pauji	2700–4100	Ss	Sh	FA	108,685	234,457
11	Centro	1957	La Rosa	2950–3750	Ss	Sh	FA	1,404	24,733
			Misoa	2500–3900	Ss	Sh	FA	700,142	534,884
			Cretaceous	4600–4780	Ls	Ls, Sh	FA	155,563	111,303
12	Sur Lago	1973	Oligocene	5500	Ss	Sh	FB	7,026	9,170
			Cretaceous	5300–5550	Ls	Ls, Sh	FB	18,503	40,568
13	Urdaneta Oeste	1970	La Rosa	2180	Ss	Sh	FA	100	258
			Icotea	2460	Ss	Sh	FA	19	14,130
			Misoa	2470	Ss	Sh	FA	88,437	1,353,229
			Cretaceous	4700–5100	Ss	Ls, Sh	FA	36,830	127,821

aFA, faulted anticline; FB, faulted block; S, stratigraphic.
bGas only, in million cubic feet.

(continued)

the Aguardiente Formation was deposited, which is partly equivalent to the Apon and Lisure formations in the north. This sandstone is a potential reservoir rock.

At maximum marine transgression in Cenomanian–Santonian time, organic material that originated in the pelagic zone was preserved in an euxinic environment and is represented by dark gray limestone and calcareous shale of the La Luna Formation (and in part by the Capacho Formation in the southwestern part of the basin). The La Luna Formation (and its equivalents) is the most important petroleum source rock and accounts for more than 98% of the oil in this basin (Talukdar et al., 1986). In addition, fractured La Luna limestone acts as a secondary reservoir rock in the north.

During the Campanian–Maastrichtian, sedimentation took place in open marine (oxic) conditions represented by the thick shale of the Colon Formation and the overlying siltstone of the Mito-Juan Formation. The Colon Formation acts as a regional seal. Fine-grained sandstone of the Mito-Juan Formation sometimes acts as a secondary reservoir rock.

Sedimentation changed from marine to nonmarine in some areas during the Paleocene. In the southwest of the basin, nonmarine shale, sandstone, and coal of the Orocue Formation were deposited. Among its three members, the Catatumbo, Barco, and Los Cuervos Members, the lower Catatumbo and the upper Barco contain coal that is a secondary source rock for oil. In the

Table 29.1 *(continued)*

Map No.	Field Name	Year Disc'd	Producing Unit	Producing Depth (m)	Lithology Reservoir	Seal	Trap Type	Cum. Oil Production (10^3 bbl)	Est. Oil Reserves (10^3 bbl)
14	Urdaneta Este	1970	Lagunillas	600	Ss	Sh	FB	85	1,540
			La Rosa	1300	Ss	Sh	FB	6	1,065
			Misoa	1300–3500	Ss	Sh	FB	17,043	85,086
			Cretaceous	4050–5300	Ls, Ss	Ls, Sh	FB	25,273	41,527
15	Sol	1981	Cretaceous	4550–5200	Ls	Ls, Sh	FB	198	7,323
16	Mara	1944	Paleoc–Eoc	800–1800	Ss	Sh	FA	26,947	4,729
			Cretaceous	1800–3100	Ls	Ls, Sh	FA	278,858	16,521
			Basement	2750–3200	Bsmt	–	FA	26,947	4,729
17	La Paz	1923	Paleoc–Eoc	520	Ss	Sh	FA	48,953	6,264
			Cretaceous	2750–3500	Ls	Ls, Sh	FA	572,142	87,026
			Basement	2750–3500	Bsmt	–	FA	246,486	81,246
18	La Concepcion	1924	Misoa	610	Ss	Sh	FA	75,778	21,327
			Cretaceous	2400–3050	Ls	Ls, Sh	FA	63,955	27,867
19	Sibucara	1927	Cretaceous	3900	Ls	Ls, Sh	FB	43,600	8,400
20	West Mara	1951	Cretaceous	1800	Ls	Ls, Sh	FA	14,604	18,352
21	El Mojan	1953	Cretaceous	2700	Ls	Ls, Sh	FA	5,109	1,290
22	Los Llanudos	1984	Misoa	–	Ss	Sh	FB	87,978[b]	80,624[b]
23	Boscan	1946	Misoa/Icotea	2300	Ss	Sh	FB	759,351	1,711,819
24	Los Claros	1962	Misoa/Icotea	2300	Ss	Sh	FB	43,827	52,812
25	Machiques	1984	Cretaceous	5250–5400	Ls	Ls, Sh	FB	355	47,465
26	Macoa	1974	Cretaceous	2000	Ls	Ls, Sh	FB	5	3
27	Totumos	1929	Cretaceous	3800–4250	Ls	Ls, Sh	FB	3,738	21,746
28	Urdaneta	1956	Misoa	2500	Ss	Sh	FA	12	4,958
			Cretaceous	5000–5050	Ls, Ss	Ls, Sh	FA	928	20,061
29	Alpuf	1980	Cretaceous	4038–4968	Ls	Ls, Sh	FB	6,231	73,595
30	San Julian	1980	Cretaceous	5000	Ls	Ls, Sh	FB	748	27,854
31	San Jose	1948	Cretaceous	4800–4850	Ls	Ls, Sh	FB	3,154	13,263
32	Alturitas	1950	Paleocene	3200–3681	Ss	Sh	FA	547	129,651
			Cretaceous	4781–4877	Ls	Ls, Sh	–	4,776	38,082
33	Ensenada	1946	Colon	4270	Ss	Sh	FB	471	3,113
34	Garcia	1963	Misoa	2850	Ss	Sh	FB	21	9,069
			Cretaceous	4700–5200	Ls	Ls, Sh	–	344	26,876
35	Rosario	1937	Mirador/Carbonera	2300	Ss	Sh	FA	4,381	13,516
			Cretaceous	4300	Ls	Ls, Sh	FA	11,720	37,063
	Totals							30,692,363	18,024,214
	Total from other fields								2,443,423
	Grand total								**51,160,000**

western part of the basin (area I in Figure 29.2), deposition took place in shallow-marine to near-shore deltaic conditions. The deposits include limestone, sandstone, shale, and coal of the Marcelina Formation. In the rest of the basin, sedimentation occurred on a shallow-water marine platform, represented mostly by limestone and marl of the Guasare Formation. Siliciclastic sandstone of Paleocene age acts as secondary reservoir rock.

During early–middle Eocene time, a large delta developed whose stream flowed from southwest to northeast. Eocene sedimentation was mostly fluvial (Mirador Formation) in the southwest, fluviodeltaic to deltaic (Mirador and Misoa Formations) on the platform up to the hinge line (shelf break), deep water marine shale (Pauji Formation) overlying the Misoa Formation in the northeast, and turbidite and flysch deposits in the Barquisimeto trough beyond the northeastern limit of the

basin. Sandstones in the Misoa and Mirador formations are primary and secondary reservoir rocks, respectively.

During the late Eocene–early Oligocene, the sedimentary rocks on the Maracaibo platform were subjected to intense deformation, uplift, and erosion. This event set the stage for the next period of deposition as great thicknesses of Eocene sedimentary rock were eroded and deposited in the newly formed Maracaibo foreland basin.

In the late Eocene–early Oligocene to early Miocene, nonmarine sedimentary rocks of the Carbonera and Leon formations were deposited in the southwestern and western parts of the area. During late Oligocene–early Miocene time, a marine transgression covered the central part of the area over the subsided structural high of eroded Eocene rock. During this marine transgression, the La Rosa Formation, which consists of sandstone and

Table 29.2. Oil Accumulations of the Orocue(.) Petroleum System

Map No.	Field Name	Year Disc'd	Producing Unit	Producing Depth (m)	Lithology Reservoir	Seal	Trap Type	Cum. Oil Production (10³ bbl)	Est. Oil Reserves (10³ bbl)
36	Tarra[b]	1947	Catatumbo	1700	Ss	Sh	FA	45,761	25,549
			Cretaceous	2050–2750	Ls	Ls, Sh	FA	17,021	1,824
37	Las Cruces[b]	1917	Mirador	100–800	Ss	Sh	FA	59,313	13,649
			Orocue	850–1450	Ss	Sh	FA	56,973	2,458
			Cretaceous	2300–2700	Ls	Ls, Sh	FA	738	5,295
38	Los Manueles[b]	1927	Carbonera	700–1150	Ss	Sh	FA	7,608	13,166
			Mirador	1100–1300	Ss	Sh	FA	50,381	16,462
			Cretaceous	3600	Ls	Ls, Sh	FA	24	2,276
39	Rio de Oro	1915	Paleocene	1720	Ss	Sh	FA	67	–
			Cretaceous	–	Ls	Ls, Sh	FA	40	–
40	Concordia	1955	Barco	400–800	Ss	Sh	FB	4310	467
41	Bonito	1954	Cretaceous	2300–2600	Ls	Sh	FB	5,786	2,233
42	Socuavo/Tibu	–	Barco	–	Ss	Sh	FA	2,832	193
			Cretaceous	2600	Ls	Ls, Sh	–	2,869	2,748
			Cret–Tertiary	–	Ls, Ss	Ls, Sh	–	214,076	–
43	Sardinata	–	Cret–Tertiary	–	Ls, Ss	Ls, Sh	FA	7,470	–
44	Petrolea	–	Cret–Tertiary	–	Ls, Sh	Ls, Sh	FA	36,560	–
45	Carbonera	–	Tertiary	–	Ss	Sh	FA	455	–
46	Rio Zulia	–	Tertiary	–	Ss	Sh	FA	123,085[c]	–
	Totals							512,284	86,320
	Grand total								598,604

[a]FA, faulted anticline; FB, faulted block.
[b]Oils are mixed with oils from the La Luna source rock.
[c]Gas only, in million cubic feet.

sparsely fossiliferous shale, was deposited first. Overlying this unit is the lower–middle Miocene Lagunillas Formation, which consists of sandstone, shale, and coal deposited in fluvial to deltaic environments. Sandstones of the Lagunillas and La Rosa are the primary and secondary reservoir rocks, respectively.

The subsidence of this foreland basin continued throughout late Miocene–Pliocene time during which the direction of maximum subsidence shifted from north to south along the Venezuelan Andes foredeep. Thick siliciclastic continental sedimentary rocks of the late Miocene Betijoque Formation were deposited in this foredeep. In general, since late Miocene time, continental sedimentation has filled more and more of the foredeep. Presently, the filling of Lake Maracaibo is the continuation of this sedimentation process.

Structural Evolution

The structural depression of the Maracaibo platform occurred in response to erosion and peneplanation after the Permian–Triassic orogenic event and extension during Triassic–Jurassic time. Locally, troughlike grabens marginal to the central part of the platform were formed into which Cretaceous sedimentation began.

The Maracaibo platform was part of the passive margin of the South American continent during the Cretaceous–Eocene. Basin configuration changed drastically during the late Eocene–early Oligocene from a platform to a foreland basin. The tectonic setting since

the Miocene has been an intermontane foreland basin because this depression is surrounded by mountain ranges.

Three periods of deformation are recorded in the Cretaceous–Holocene sedimentary rocks: Late Cretaceous–Paleocene, late Eocene–early Oligocene, and Miocene–Pliocene. Deformation related to the second and third periods are extremely important to generation–migration–accumulation of hydrocarbons in the Maracaibo basin.

The first deformation, in Late Cretaceous–Paleocene time, only slightly affected the sedimentary rocks as evidenced by the lack of any type of unconformity in the section. However, the trap-forming process was initiated. The deformation probably formed some broad north-northeast trending anticlines and faults, which became more deformed during later periods of more intense deformation. Of particular interest are the early formed anticlinal structures that are now the Icotea, Sibucara, Sol, and Pueblo Viejo oil fields (Figure 29.2 and Table 29.1). During this deformation, parts of the Venezuelan Andes and the Perija Range began to emerge as topographic highs. At the end of this deformation, the Marcelina Formation on the western part of the platform was subjected to uplift and erosion. Structural development in this period appears to have been controlled by northwest compression created by the interaction of the Caribbean and South American plates (James, 1990).

The second deformation during the late Eocene–early Oligocene was related to a northeastward compression

(a)

(b)

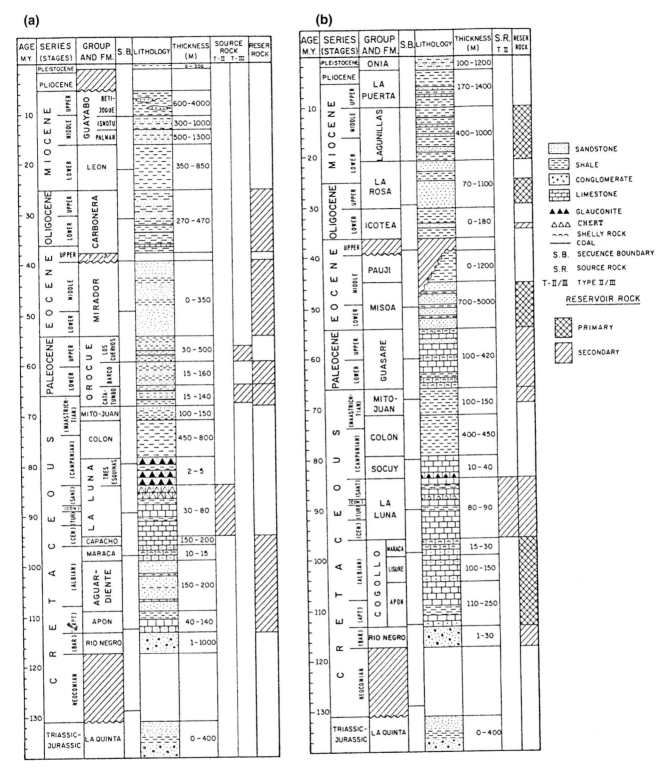

Figure 29.3. Generalized stratigraphic columns for the (a) southern area (I) and (b) northern area (II) of Maracaibo basin showing rock units, thicknesses, lithologies, and intervals of source rocks and reservoir rocks. Locations of columns shown in Figure 29.2.

against northwestern South America due to movement of the Cocos plate and the northern part of the Nazca plate in response to spreading along both the north-south trending East Pacific Rise and the east-west trending Cocos–Nazca plate boundary (James, 1990).

This deformation gave rise to large-scale north-northeast trending uplifts of Boscan and Sibucara oil fields, as well as similarly trending smaller transpressive structures of La Conception, Mara, and La Paz oil fields. Other important lineaments formed during this time are the

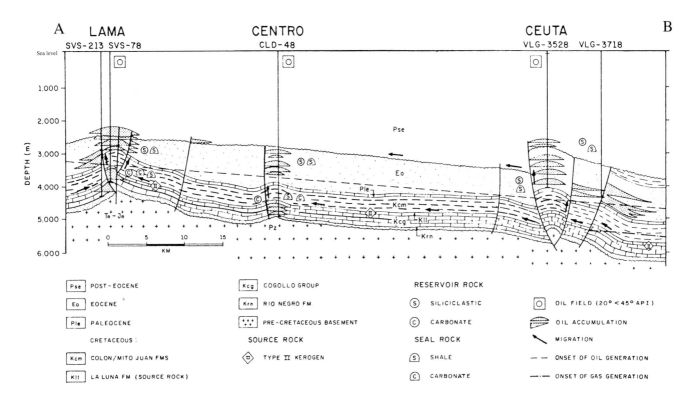

Figure 29.4. Cross section A–B across Lama, Centro, and Ceuta oil fields. See Figure 29.2 for section location. The section shows the stratigraphic (vertical) extent of the La Luna–Misoa(!) petroelum system in phase 2, La Luna source rock, onset of oil and gas generation, migration paths, reservoir rocks, seals, trap styles, and oil accumulations.

structural highs of Tarra, Las Cruces, Los Manueles, Lama, Lamar, Bachaquero, Ceuta, Mene Grande, and Motatan oil fields (see Table 29.1). During this deformation, structures developed earlier were also reactivated. This deformation marked the structural inversion of the platform, with the thickest Eocene section being deposited in the northeast, to an intermontane foreland basin with the depocenter to the southwest (Zambrano et al., 1971).

Marine sedimentation ceased during the Oligocene, and only continental sediments were deposited locally as a result of uplift and erosion of large areas where the Eocene section was exposed. More of the Eocene section in the northeast was uplifted and eroded in comparison to the same section to the south, southwest, and west (Talukdar et. al., 1986; James, 1990).

The last period of deformation in the Miocene–Pliocene was characterized by intense structural deformation. Open folds, minor faults, and some uplifts were formed in the post-Eocene sedimentary rocks as well as the reactivation of the earlier structures in Eocene and older rock units. Compressional structures developed at the north end of the Venezuelan Andes and in the east end of the Perija Range. In the Maracaibo foreland basin, the general structure that related to this period is a southward-opening fan whose ribs are north-northeast and north trending sinistral faults (Figure 29.2). Of these, the Icotea fault, which extends over 200 km, is the best known example (James, 1990). The main folds are subparallel to and were generated by movement along these faults. The sinistral displacements along these

faults change in the north and south into northeast trending thrust faults. These sinistral faults are antithetic to the east-west trending Caribbean–South American transform plate boundary, the site of the Oca fault (Figure 29.2). Cross section A–B in Figure 29.4 is a present-day geologic section across oil-bearing structures of Lama, Centro, and Ceuta fields that are related to the development of Icotea and other north-northeast trending sinistral faults.

During the last deformation period, the Maracaibo foreland basin became part of an independent block or microplate that appears to have a northward translation toward the Caribbean plate. This northward shift is due to dextral movement along the northeast-southwest trending Bocono fault which extends through the entire Venezuelan Andes. Transpression along this fault is the cause of uplift and northwestward thrusting of the Venezuelan Andes against the adjacent Andean foredeep in the south Maracaibo foreland basin.

THE PETROLEUM SYSTEMS

Accumulations of oil and gas in the Maracaibo basin are related to two petroleum systems. The main petroleum system, which contributes more than 98% of the total oil reserves (produced plus proven) of 52.20 bbo, involves the genetic relationship between the Upper Cretaceous La Luna source rock and the resulting petroleum accumulations (Table 29.1). Oils of this system are widespread throughout the basin and are found in several different reservoir rocks, which from the most to

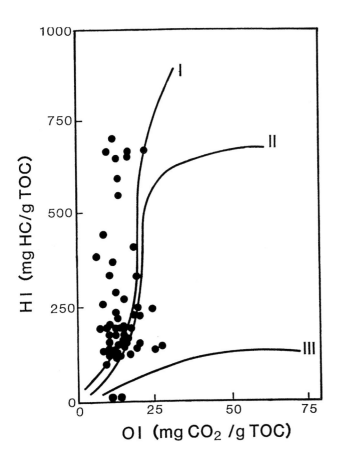

Figure 29.5. Plot of the hydrogen index (HI) versus oxygen index (OI) of the La Luna source rock, a type II kerogen. The reduction in HI is related to increasing thermal maturity.

least important are as follows: Misoa Formation (50% discovered oil), Lagunillas Formation (44%), Cretaceous rocks (<5%), La Rosa Formation (<1%), and igneous–metamorphic basement rocks (<1%). The oil plumbing system is most effective from the La Luna source rock to the Misoa reservoir rock. Leakage from the Misoa reservoir has charged the overlying Lagunillas reservoir rocks. Based on the volume of oil, the Misoa is the major reservoir rock. A positive oil–source rock correlation is reported by Talukdar et al. (1985, 1986). Therefore this known petroleum system is named the La Luna–Misoa(!).

The other petroleum system encompasses the upper Maastrichtian–Paleocene Orocue Group source rocks and the resulting oil accumulations (Table 29.2). This system is restricted to the southwestern part of the Maracaibo basin and has contributed less than 2% (0.7 billion bbl) of the oil discovered. Most of the oil occurs in the Orocue Group and Cretaceous–Tertiary reservoir rocks (47%), followed by Mirador Formation and Tertiary rocks (37%), Carbonera Formation (11%), and Cretaceous rocks (5%). Because most of the hydrocarbons originate from and reside in the Orocue Group, this hypothetical system is named the Orocue(.) petroleum system. It is hypothetical because the geochemistry of the source rock and the hydrocarbons suggest a genetic relationship, but a definite oil–source rock correlation is lacking.

La Luna–Misoa(!) Petroleum System

The La Luna–Misoa petroleum system evolved in two phases. Oil accumulations for both phases are genetically related to the same La Luna source rock but each phase has some characteristics of a separate petroleum system with its own stratigraphic, areal, and temporal extents.

Petroleum Source Rock

The Late Cretaceous La Luna Formation contains the source rock for the La Luna–Misoa petroleum system. The source rock was deposited under anoxic conditions during a marine transgression on a broad open marine outer shelf during the Late Cretaceous sea level rise. It contains mostly fine-grained limestone with some calcareous shale and large amounts of organic matter.

The La Luna Formation varies in thickness from 61 to 213 m (Talukdar et al., 1986, 1987). The regional variation in thickness over most of the area was mapped by Blaser and White (1984) who found that where the thickness varies from 75 to 150 m, the net thickness of source rock is from one-third to two-thirds of the total thickness. Lithologic variations, both vertically and laterally, and organic matter content are discussed by Talukdar et al. (1988).

The limestone and shale in the La Luna Formation are excellent oil-prone type II kerogen source rocks that are rich in hydrogen. The organic carbon (TOC) content generally ranges from 1.5 to 9.6 wt. % with an average of 3.8 wt. %. Calculated original TOC ranges from 2.5 to 10.8 wt. %, averaging 5.6 wt. %. About 80% of the samples show a TOC content of 2–6 wt. %; some range up to 11 wt. % and samples with less than 1 wt. % are rare. Regional variations in TOC content are given in Talukdar et al. (1985, 1986).

The organic matter in the source rocks is mainly of the structureless marine amorphous type with only minor algal fragments and rare vitrinite particles. Rock-Eval pyrolysis data reveal the oil-prone type II nature of the kerogen (Figure 29.5). The hydrogen index (HI) of immature samples is a maximum of 700 mg HC/g TOC, and it decreases with increasing thermal maturity (Figure 29.6). The average HI of immature samples is about 650 mg HC/g TOC. The average HI at the end of the oil window (T_{max} 460°C, 1.3% R_o) is about 100 mg HC/g TOC.

Thermal maturity patterns of the La Luna Formation in the Maracaibo basin are known from maturity measurements (T_{max}, R_o) and from thermal maturity modeling of 81 wells (Talukdar et al., 1986). Thermal maturity modeling shows the geographic evolution of oil and gas generation through time; it also provides a basis to predict when and how much oil and gas has been generated (Blaser and White, 1984: Talukdar et al., 1986; Sweeney et al., 1990). Based on this information, we can construct the mature to overmature pods of La Luna source rock at the end of Eocene (38 Ma) and Holocene (0 Ma) times. Thes two times are the two critical moments for the La Luna–Misoa petroleum system and correspond to phases 1 and 2 on Figure 29.7. The well used to construct this model is in the Centro oil field (field 11, Figure 29.2).

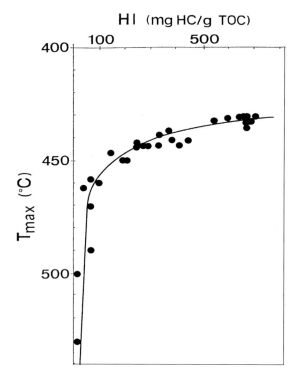

Figure 29.6. Plot showing the reduction in HI with increasing thermal maturity (T$_{max}$) in the La Luna source rock.

The areal extent of thermally mature La Luna source rock for phase 1 at the end of Eocene time is restricted to an elongate area southwest of the Trujillo Range (Figure 29.8). For phase 2, thermally mature La Luna source rock covers a much larger area to the southwest of the area covered by phase 1, and in places is generating gas (Figure 29.9). Today, this source rock is actively generating oil and gas over most of the area.

Reservoir Rocks and Traps

Oil from the La Luna source rocks comprises over 98% of the total recoverable oil from 35 fields (Table 29.1). Most of these fields are located in the northeastern part of the basin, with the only exception being the Rosario oil field. A few fields from the southwestern part contain a mixture of oil from the La Luna Formation and the Orocue Group source rocks (Figures 29.2 and 29.9; Table 29.2).

Oil from the La Luna source rock accumulated at two different times: during the middle–late Eocene (phase 1) and the late Miocene–Holocene (phase 2). Because the oil from each phase originates from the same source rock, the composition of both oils are identical, except that phase 1 oil is biodegraded. Based on the reconstructed generation–migration–accumulation history and the composition of the mixed oils (unaltered oil mixed with highly altered oil residue) in Eocene reservoir rocks of Motatan, Lamar, Ceuta, Centro, and Bachaquero fields, Talukdar et al. (1986) has suggested that the component of highly altered oil residue was originally biodegraded in the reservoir during the Oligocene and that the unaltered oil component migrated into the reservoir during the Miocene–Holocene. Since oil residues are found only in Eocene reservoir rocks and since a large thickness of the Eocene rocks were eroded during the Oligocene, it is possible that Eocene oils of phase 1 were mostly lost. If this is true, then almost all of the recoverable oil accumulated during phase 2 of the La Luna–Misoa petroleum system. Reservoir rocks for the phase 1 oil range in age from Late Cretaceous to Eocene (Figure 29.10). Reservoir rocks for the phase 2 oil are basement rocks, Cretaceous sandstones and limestones, and Paleocene–Miocene sandstones (Figure 29.11).

Reservoir rocks for all La Luna oil include basement rocks, Cretaceous, Paleocene, Eocene, Oligocene, and

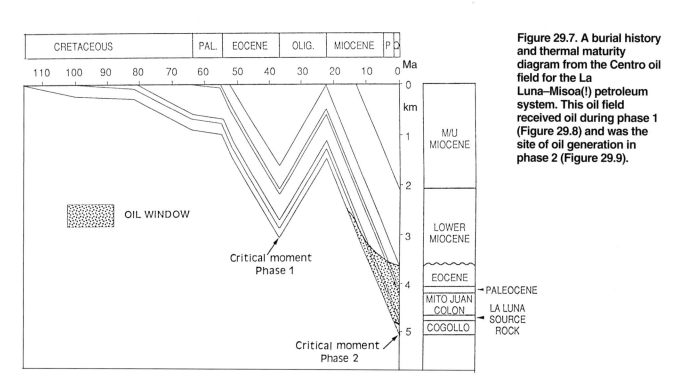

Figure 29.7. A burial history and thermal maturity diagram from the Centro oil field for the La Luna–Misoa(!) petroleum system. This oil field received oil during phase 1 (Figure 29.8) and was the site of oil generation in phase 2 (Figure 29.9).

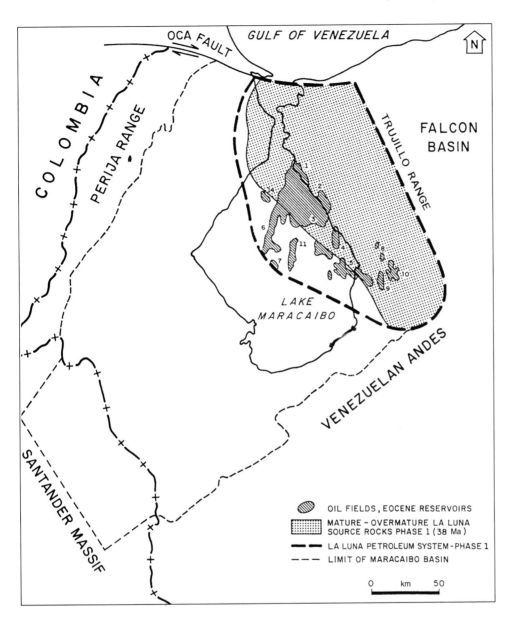

Figure 29.8. Map showing the geographic extent of the La Luna–Misoa(!) petroleum system at the critical moment for phase 1, which was late Eocene (38 Ma).

Miocene rock units. Of these, Eocene and Miocene reservoirs are the most important, contributing about 50% and 44%, respectively, of the total recoverable oil in the basin. Minor reservoirs include the Cretaceous (<5%) and Paleocene, Oligocene, and basement reservoir rocks, which together contribute about 6% of the total recoverable oil. Table 29.1 gives the details of producing formation, depth, reservoir lithology, cumulative oil production, and remaining reserves in different fields for the La Luna–Misoa system.

Eocene reservoir rocks include several sandstone units (B and C) of the Misoa Formation and sandstones of the Mirador Formation. The porosity of these sandstones is dominantly intergranular, varying between 12 and 28%, with an average of 20% (Gonzalez de Juana et al., 1980). Permeability varies considerably, but a reasonable average is about 240 md.

Miocene reservoir rocks include sandstones of the Lagunillas and La Rosa formations. The porosity of these sandstones is high, mainly intergranular and varies between 10 and 40% (Gonzalez de Juana et al., 1980). The

average porosity value for Miocene sandstone is 33%, and the average permeability for both rock units is about 610 md.

The secondary oil reservoir rocks are as follows. Basement reservoir rocks are known only in Mara and La Paz fields and are fractured schist, quartzite, and granite. In Urdaneta fields, sandstones of the Rio Negro Formation and Cretaceous limestones are the oil reservoir rocks. The oils accumulated in these limestones commonly contain dissolved H_2S gas (Talukdar et al., 1989). Other Cretaceous reservoir rocks are mainly fractured limestones of the Cogollo Group and, in some cases, the La Luna Formation. The Upper Cretaceous Mito Juan, the Paleocene Guasare Formation, the Oligocene Icotea Formation, and the La Rosa Formation are sandstone reservoirs.

Seal rocks for the Paleocene–Miocene reservoir rocks that trap oil accumulations are the overlying shales of these same rock units (Figures 29.10 and 29.11). The hydrocarbon seals for the Cretaceous accumulations are formed by the overlying shales of the Upper Cretaceous

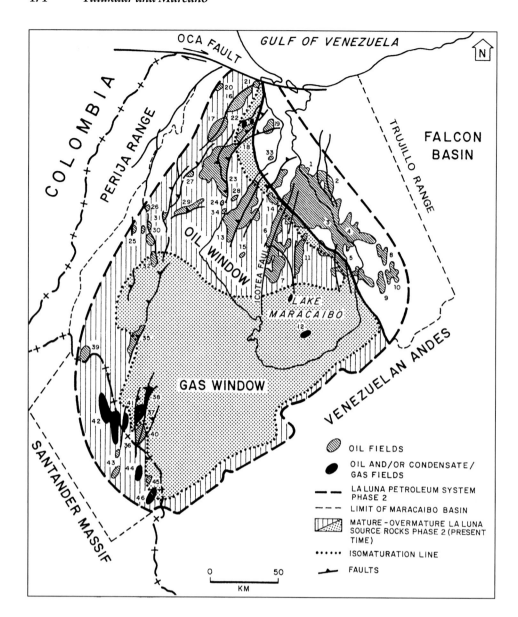

Figure 29.9. Map showing the geographic extent of the La Luna–Misoa(!) petroleum system at the critical moment for phase 2, which is present day.

Colon Formation or the associated and immediately overlying shale and limestone.

Trap styles for oil accumulations in fractured basement, Cretaceous, Paleocene, Oligocene, and Eocene reservoir rocks for the different fields are structural and can be described as faulted anticlines or faulted blocks (Table 29.1). Hydrocarbon traps that contain the Miocene reservoir rocks are structural, combined structural–stratigraphic, or stratigraphic traps (Table 29.1). Stratigraphic or combined fault block–stratigraphic traps are found in Miocene Lagunillas reservoirs of the Cabimas, Tia Juana, Lagunillas, Bachaquero, and Mene Grande oil fields. Structural traps are associated with north-south trending, sinistral, strike-slip faults. Stratigraphic traps require a pinch-out of a sandstone or a truncation of a reservoir rock that is sealed by a shale or heavy oil plug.

Oil Composition

Oil from the La Luna source rock is separated into two main groups: unaltered and altered marine oils. On the basis of biological markers, the unaltered oils can be further subdivided according to maturity into marginally mature oils, mature oils, and highly mature oils.

Marginally mature oils are only known in the shallow Cretaceous reservoirs of the Mara field and the Eocene reservoirs of the Boscan field. These oils are characterized by low API gravity (11–16° API), high vanadium (914–1173 ppm), high sulfur (4.8–5.2%), low saturated hydrocarbons (20–26%), and high concentrations of resins and asphaltenes (34–44%). The marginally mature oil is clearly distinguished from the altered oil by the presence of a complete range of *n*-alkanes and unaltered steranes.

Mature oils, on the other hand, are widely distributed in the Maracaibo basin and occur in the Cretaceous, Eocene, and Miocene reservoir rocks. The oils have API gravities of 20°–39° API, sulfur contents of 0.7–1.3%, vanadium contents of 20–235 ppm, saturated hydrocarbons of 53–69%, and concentrations of resins and asphaltenes of 8–22%.

The highly mature oils are restricted to Cretaceous–lower Eocene reservoirs of the southwestern, central,

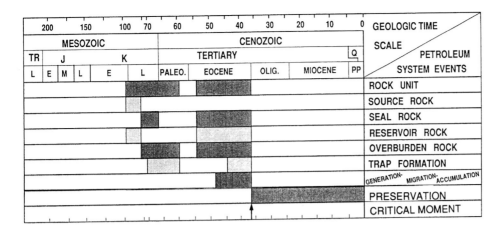

Figure 29.10. Events chart for the La Luna–Misoa(!) petroleum system for phase 1.

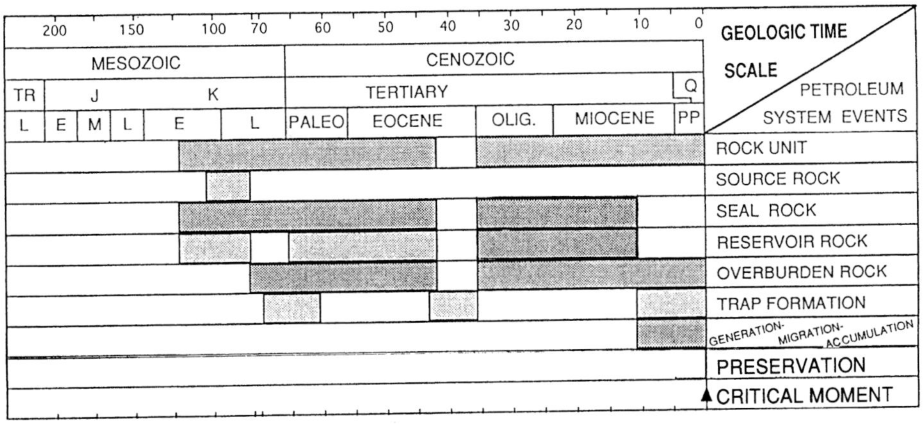

Figure 29.11. Events chart for the La Luna–Misoa(!) petroleum system for phase 2.

southeastern, and northeastern parts and have high API gravities (37°–55°), low vandium contents (<8 ppm), low sulfur contents (<0.5%), high concentrations of saturated hydrocarbons (72–93%), and low concentrations of resins and asphaltenes (0.2–8.8%). In the Maracaibo basin, some unaltered oils from Motatan, Lamar, Ceuta, Centro, and Bachaquero fields show mixing of unaltered marine oils with highly altered residues of earlier generated oils (Talukdar et al., 1986).

The altered oils occur only in shallow reservoir rocks of Miocene and Eocene in the northeastern part of the basin. These oils are characterized by the absence of *n*-alkanes, high sulfur content (>1.3%), moderate to high vanadium content (200-500 ppm), low API gravity(<25° API) and a low saturate to aromatic hydrocarbon ratio (<2.0).

Natural gas in the La Luna–Misoa petroleum system is mainly solution gas. This gas represents 93% of the total recoverable gas and is produced from different reservoir rocks, particularly those of Cretaceous and Eocene age. Free gas is produced from the Los Llanudos and Rio Zulia oil fields. Gas in Los Llanudos is of mixed origin (thermogenic and biogenic), with the thermogenic component derived from the La Luna source rock (Lew, 1985).

Level of Certainty

The La Luna–Misoa(!) is a known petroleum sytem because there is a high degree of confidence that the oil accumulations in different fields distributed throughout the basin originated from the La Luna source rock. Docu-

mented evidence for the oil–source rock correlation exists in the literature (Blaser and White, 1984; Talukdar et al., 1986).

Correlation of the oil to the La Luna source rock extract in the Maracaibo basin was established initially by the close similarity in certain geochemical characteristics such as their high metal porphyrin content, V/Ni ratio, high sulfur content, and a uniform gas chromatographic pattern (Blaser and White, 1984). In addition, the similarity of the rock extract from the La Luna source rock and the oil from producing fields was established by comparing the C_{15+} gas chromatograms and biomarker terpanes and steranes (Gallango et al., 1985; Talukdar et al., 1985, 1986).

Oil–source rock and oil–oil correlation studies are based on extensive gas chromatography (GC) and gas chromatography–mass spectrometry (GC-MS) data. These data include saturate GC of 130 oils and 66 rock extracts, and GC-MS analysis of terpane and sterane biomarkers in 57 oils and 22 rock extracts. The results of these studies have firmly established that the oil from the producing fields originated from the La Luna source rock (Talukdar et al., 1986). The distribution of *n*-alkanes in unaltered marine oils is very similar to that of the La Luna rock extracts. In addition, the *n*-alkanes less than C_{24} are predominant, the pristane/phytane ratio is always less than 1.0, and the pristane/*n*-C_{17} ratio is less than 0.5, suggesting that marine organic matter was deposited and preserved in an anoxic environment.

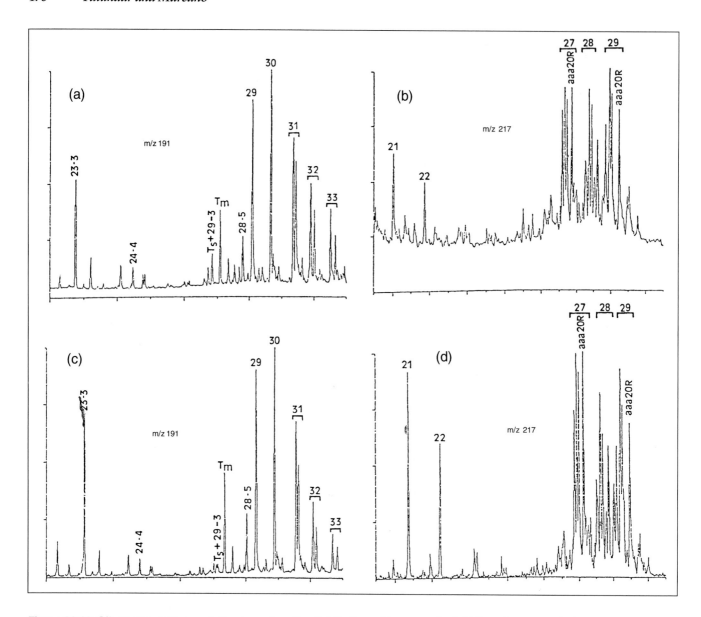

Figure 29.12. Oil–source rock correlation based on the distribution of terpanes (*m/z* 191) and steranes (*m/z* 217): (a) and (b) an oil from Cretaceous reservoir; (c) and (d) bitumen from a La Luna source rock.

The fingerprints or peak patterns of the terpane and sterane biomarkers for both the unaltered and altered marine oils are very similar to those of the La Luna rock extracts. The terpane distribution (*m/z* 191) of both marine oils and the La Luna rock extracts includes abundant tricyclic terpanes, a predominance of C_{23} tricyclic terpane among the tricyclics, and mostly hopanes among the total terpanes with C_{29} norhopane and C_{30} hopane as the dominant peaks ($C_{30} > C_{29}$). This distribution is characteristic of both marine oils and the La Luna rock extracts. The sterane distribution (*m/z* 217) for both unaltered and partially altered marine oils and of the La Luna rock extracts shows the C_{27} $\alpha\alpha\alpha$(20R) sterane in greater relative abundance than the C_{29} $\alpha\alpha\alpha$(20R) sterane. Figure 29.12 shows an example of oil–source rock correlation based on terpane and sterane biomarkers.

Characteristics and Limits of Phase 1

The La Luna–Misoa petroleum system can be best understood if the essential elements, processes, and events are described independently in two phases (1 and 2) as defined earlier (Figures 29.8–29.11). Through the development of these phases, the La Luna source rock became mature for oil and gas generation over most of the Maracaibo basin except for a narrow belt of immature source rocks on the west.

The system in phase 1 covers an area of about 19,000 km2 and includes 15,000 km2 of thermally mature to overmature La Luna source rock and 12 oil fields that partially extend out into the additional 4000 km2. Phase 1 developed during middle–late Eocene time, and oil from this pod of mature La Luna source rock charged Eocene and probably some Cretaceous reservoir rocks by 38 Ma (Figures 29.8 and 29.10).

The essential elements of the system in phase 1 include (1) the Upper Cretaceous La Luna Formation as the source rock; (2) fractured limestone in the La Luna Formation and sandstone in the Misoa Formation as the reservoir rocks; (3) shales in the Colon and Misoa formations as the seal rocks; and (4) the Colon through Misoa formations as the overburden rocks (Figure 29.10).

The formation of structural traps occurred during the Late Cretaceous–Paleocene deformation, and development of stratigraphic traps occurred as a result of the deposition of couplets of Eocene sandstone and shale. The generation–migration–accumulation of oil and gas occurred in the middle–late Eocene, or just prior to late Eocene uplift and Oligocene erosion. Oil and gas migrated vertically out of the Upper Cretaceous La Luna source rock and fractured reservoir rock into overlying Eocene deltaic sandstones wherever fractures and faults broke the shale seals of the Upper Cretaceous and Paleocene (Talukdar et al., 1986). Updip lateral migration to the west along Eocene sandstone carrier beds may have continued until the final accumulation in Eocene stratigraphic traps.

The duration time of this system is about 58 m.y. from the Late Cretaceous to late Eocene (96–38 Ma). Preservation time started 38 Ma and has continued to the Holocene. Uplift of the La Luna source rock, oil remigration, partial removal of Eocene reservoir rocks, and intense bacterial degradation of oil in the remaining Eocene reservoirs apparently took place during the Oligocene following uplift 38 Ma.

Characteristics and Limits of Phase 2

The La Luna–Misoa(!) petroleum system for phase 2 covers 38,500 km² and includes 32,500 km² of thermally mature to overmature La Luna source rock. This phase developed from Miocene to Holocene time (Figure 29.9) and is responsible for most of the present-day oil accumulations in the Maracaibo basin.

The essential elements of the system in phase 2 are as follows: (1) La Luna Formation as the source rock; (2) Cretaceous sandstone and fractured limestone and Paleocene–Miocene sandstones as the reservoir rocks; (3) Cretaceous limestone and shale and Paleocene–Miocene shales as the seal rocks; and (4) Upper Cretaceous to Pliocene–Pleistocene units overlying the source rock as the overburden rocks (Figure 29.11).

Trap formation took place during deformation in Late Cretaceous–Paleocene, late Eocene, and late Miocene–Pleistocene times. Generation–migration–accumulation of oil and gas occurred during the late Miocene–Holocene. During this time, large mature to overmature pods of the La Luna source rock developed.

The southern and southwestern parts corresponding to the Andean foredeep presently contain the most mature pod (gas window). Most of the generated oil from this pod migrated outward in all directions prior to its entering the gas window. Updip migration of oil occurred to the south toward the northern flank of the Venezuelan Andes and to the west, northwest, and north toward the structures of the different oil fields. Oil and

gas migration involved intrasource (primary) migration into Cretaceous structural highs and secondary migration vertically through faults and fractures. Migration occurred across the Colon Formation, into Paleocene–Eocene and post-Eocene rock units, laterally through Eocene–Miocene sandtones, and under a post-Eocene unconformity (Talukdar et al., 1986). In cross section A–B drawn across Lama, Centro, and Ceuta oil fields, migration paths and accumulations of oil from actively generating La Luna source rock of phase 2 are depicted (Figure 29.4).

Phase 2 of the La Luna–Misoa(!) petroleum system is still in its duration time. It lasted about 120 m.y., including the time of deposition of the Lower Cretaceous Rio Negro Formation through rock units of Pliocene–Pleistocene age. Significant migration and accumulation occurred from late Miocene to Holocene time (12 m.y. duration). Severely biodegraded oils occur in shallow Miocene reservoirs in the Bolivar Coastal oil fields (Talukdar et al., 1986).

Efficiency of the System

The efficiency of a petroleum system gives an estimate of the amount of generated hydrocarbons that accumulate in known traps. The efficiency is the amount of in-place hydrocarbons expressed as a percent of total hydrocarbons generated. In this paper, calculation of hydrocarbons generated is based on Schmoker's method (Chapter 19, this volume). The same method is followed for other petroleum systems described in this volume and thus provides an opportunity to compare efficiencies of different petroleum systems. Calculations for the La Luna–Misoa petroleum system are based on basinwide average values of source rock geochemistry, density, and net thickness.

For calculating the total mass of organic carbon for the mature La Luna source rock the following data are considered: (1) an average TOC of 5.56 wt.% for immature source rocks, (2) an average density (ρ) of 2.65 g/cm³, (3) an area of 47,500 km² for mature La Luna source rock (obtained by adding the areas of mature to overmature pods of La Luna that developed in phases 1 and 2), and (4) an average of 65 m for the net thickness of source rock. The volume of mature source rock is thus 30.88×10^{17} cm³.

The following equation from Schmoker (Chapter 19) was used to determine the total mass (M) of organic matter for the mature La Luna source rocks in the basin:

$$M \text{ (g TOC)} = [\text{TOC (wt. \%)}/100] \times \rho \text{ (g/cm}^3) \times V \text{ (cm}^3)$$

where ρ is the density and V the volume of the source rock. Inserting our data, we obtain

$$M \text{ (g TOC)} = [(5.5 \text{ wt. \% TOC})/100] \times 2.65 \text{ g/cm}^3$$
$$\times (30.88 \times 10^{17} \text{ cm}^3)$$
$$= 4.55 \times 10^{17} \text{ g TOC}$$

The mass of hydrocarbons generated per unit mass of

organic carbon (R) in the La Luna source rocks is calculated as follows (Schmoker, Chapter 19):

$$R \text{ (mg HC/g TOC)} = \text{HI}_o \text{ (mg HC/g TOC)} - \text{HI}_p \text{ (mg HC/g TOC)}$$

where HI_o is the original hydrogen index and HI_p is the present-day hydrogen index. Using an HI_o of 650 mg HC/g TOC (the average for the immature La Luna rock) and an HI_p of 100 mg HC/g TOC (the average for La Luna rock mature beyond the oil window), we obtain

$$R = (650 - 100) \text{ mg HC/g TOC} = 550 \text{ mg HC/g TOC}$$

The total mass of hydrocarbons generated (HCG) in the oil-prone La Luna source rock is

$$\text{HCG (kg HC)} = (550 \text{ mg HC/g TOC}) \times (4.55 \times 10^{17} \text{g TOC})$$
$$= 2.50 \times 10^{20} \text{ mg HC} = 2.50 \times 10^{14} \text{ kg HC}$$

The amount of in-place hydrocarbons can be estimated roughly from known total recoverable oil and gas reserves. Total recoverable oil reserves (produced and known remaining reserves) is estimated at 52.20 bbo and total recoverable gas reserves at 51.97 tcfg. As an approximation, if 98% of the total recoverable oil and gas resources were derived from the La Luna source rock, then the total resources for the La Luna–Misoa(!) petroleum system would be 51.16 bbo and 50.93 tcf. Calculated hydrocarbons in-place, using a recovery factor of 21% for oil and 80% for gas, are 243.6 bbo and 63.66 tcfg. Kilograms of hydrocarbons are 339.33×10^{11} kg of oil (139.30 kg/bbl) and 12.92×10^{11} kg of gas (2.03×10^{-2} kg/ft^3), which totals to 352.25×10^{11} kg HC in-place.

The generation–accumulation efficiency (GAE) of the system is

$$\text{GAE} = [\text{HC}_{acc} \text{ kg/HC}_{gen} \text{ kg}] \times 100$$
$$= (352.25 \times 10^{11} / 2.50 \times 10^{14}) \times 100 = 14\%$$

where HC_{acc} is the accumulated hydrocarbons and HC_{gen} the generated HC. By these calculations, about 14% of all hydrocarbons generated from La Luna source rocks are in known accumulations. It is believed that the efficiency of the La Luna–Misoa(!) petroleum system in reality is even greater because these calculations are based only on known oil and gas resources.

Orocue(.) Petroleum System

The Orocue(.) petroleum system is responsible for several oil accumulations in the southwestern part of the basin and for the occurrence of oil seeps at the base of the Venezuelan Andes. This oil is thought to be derived from nonmarine source rocks containing terrestrial organic matter and type III kerogen (Talukdar et al., 1986; Cassani et al., 1989; Tocco et al., 1990). Sometimes this oil is mixed with oil from the marine organic matter of the La Luna source rock. Because of the limited available data, only a

brief description of the Orocue system is given here. Stratigraphic, areal, and temporal extents of this petroleum system are shown in Figures 29.13 and 29.14.

Petroleum Source Rock

The Orocue Formation of Paleocene age was deposited in the southwestern part of the Maracaibo basin and contains the source rock for the Orocue(.) petroleum system (Figures 29.13 and 29.14). This formation consists of siliciclastic rocks intercalated with locally significant coals and carbonaceous shales. Among the three members of the formation, the lower Catatumbo Member and upper Barco Member contain coal beds (Figure 29.3a). Rock-Eval pyrolysis shows the coals to be type III kerogen, relatively hydrogen-rich source rocks that are comparable with the coaly source rocks that produce oil in Borneo and Indonesia (Blaser and White, 1989). Published geochemical data on the source rock quality are unavailable on these Orocue coals. Exposed on the north Andean flank, the thermally immature to mature coaly shales of the Orocue Formation are type III kerogen with high TOC contents (7.59–39.36 wt. %) with oil- and gas-generating capacity (Cassani et al., 1989). Carbonaceous shales of the Orocue Formation from the subsurface contain similar type III kerogen, but the TOC contents are generally low (0.4–0.55 wt. %) and hydrocarbon potentials are low (<2 kg HC/t rock) (Talukdar et al., 1985).

Thermally mature Orocue source rocks were penetrated only locally in the Tarra, Las Cruces, Los Manueles, and Concordia oil fields. The Orocue Formation appears to be mature in the southwestern part of the area as determined from thermal maturity modeling (Blaser and White, 1984; Talukdar et al., 1986). Figure 29.13 shows the mature to overmature pod of Paleocene Orocue source rocks at the present time, which are presently at their maximum depth of burial.

Reservoir Rocks and Accumulations

Oil derived from the coaly type III kerogen Orocue source rocks are known to occur in the Eocene sandstone reservoirs of Los Manueles oil field. This oil is also mixed with oil from the La Luna source rock and is found in Paleocene and Eocene sandstone reservoirs of the Las Cruces oil field, Paleocene sandstone reservoirs of Tarra field, and Eocene sandstones of Los Manueles field (Talukdar et al., 1986). The Orocue oil of Los Manueles field is compositionally mature, has an API gravity of about 36° API, and has low sulfur (<0.5%) and vanadium (4 ppm) contents. The oil originated from terrestrial organic matter as shown by the following: abundant *n*-alkanes in the C_{25}–C_{35} range (waxy component), high pristane/phytane (>3) and pristane/*n*-C_{17} ratios (>0.6), higher concentration of C_{29} $\alpha\alpha\alpha(20R)$ sterane relative to C_{27} $\alpha\alpha\alpha(20R)$ sterane in the sterane distribution (m/z 217), low tricyclic terpanes and significant $18\alpha(H)$ oleanane in the terpane distribution (m/z 191), and high hopane/sterane ratios (Talukdar et al., 1986).

Seal rocks for the oil accumulations in Paleocene and Eocene reservoir rocks are the associated or overlying

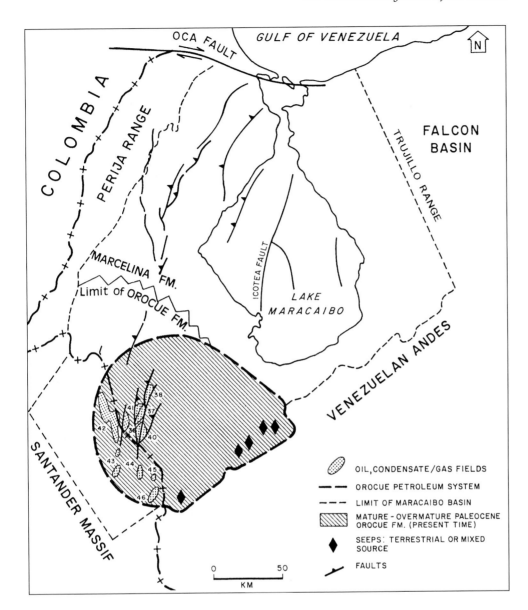

Figure 29.13. Map showing the geographic extent of the Orocue(.) petroleum system, which encompasses the mature to overmature pod of Paleocene Orocue source rock and all related accumulations at the critical moment, which is present day.

shale within the same rock unit (Figure 29.14). Hydrocarbon traps are faulted anticlines (Figure 29.13).

Level of Certainty

The Orocue(.) petroleum system is considered hypothetical. Peaks on the gas chromatograms and sterane and terpane biomarkers are characteristic of oils from terrestrial organic matter. However, their geochemical correlation is not unique to Paleocene Orocue source rocks (Talukdar et al., 1985, 1986; Cassani et al., 1989; Tocco et al., 1990). The oils also seem to correlate to carbonaceous shales of other Tertiary rock units such as the Oligocene Carbonera Formation (Cassani et al., 1989; Tocco et al., 1990). However, the Carbonera carbonaceous shales can be discarded as an oil source because they all lack the thermal maturity to generate and expel oil.

Characteristics and Limits

The Orocue(.) petroleum system covers an area of about 10,500 km² and is restricted to the southwestern part of the Maracaibo basin. It encompasses the mature to overmature Paleocene Orocue source rocks (coals) and all oil accumulations (Figure 29.13) charged from this source rock in Pliocene–Holocene time (5 Ma to present).

The essential elements of the system include (1) coals of the Paleocene Orocue Formation as the source rock, (2) Paleocene Orocue sandstones and Eocene Mirador sandstones as the reservoir rocks, (3) Paleocene Orocue shales and Eocene Mirador shales as the seal rocks, and (4) Eocene–Holocene rock units as the overburden rocks (Figure 29.14).

Traps are structures that formed during late Eocene and Pliocene–Holocene time (particularly in the North Andean front). Generation–migration–accumulation took place during the Pliocene–Holocene (Figure 29.14). Secondary migration probably involved both lateral migration through sandstone carrier rocks in Paleocene and Eocene units and vertical migration through faults. The Orocue(.) petroleum system is still in its duration time. Information needed to calculate the efficiency of this system is lacking.

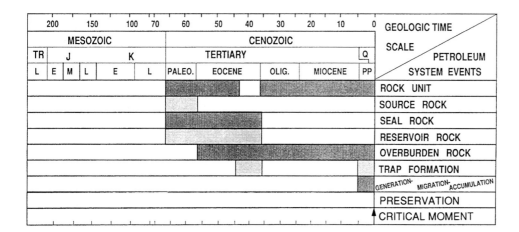

Figure 29.14. Events chart for the Orocue(.) petroleum system.

SUMMARY

The La Luna–Misoa(!) petroleum system contributes over 98% of the total recoverable reserves (produced plus known remaining reserves) of oil (52.20 bbo) and gas (51.97 tcfg) in the Maracaibo basin. This system covers about 47,500 km² and includes the mature to overmature area of La Luna source rock developed in phase 1 during the Eocene and phase 2 during the late Miocene–Holocene. Each phase of the system has characteristics of a unique petroleum system with its own stratigraphic, areal, and temporal extents, but both have the same La Luna source rock. The two phases are related to two episodes of burial that provided sufficient overburden rock to thermally mature the La Luna source rock.

The essential elements of the system in phase 1 are La Luna Formation as the source rock, La Luna limestones and Misoa sandstones as the reservoir rocks, Colon and Misoa shales as the seal rocks, and Colon through Misoa formations as the overburden rocks. Structural traps formed during the Late Cretaceous–Paleocene deformation and stratigraphic traps during the deposition of the Eocene sequence. Essential elements were deposited and critical processes occurred from Late Cretaceous to late Eocene (96–38 Ma), a 58-m.y. duration. The essential elements of phase 2 are La Luna Formation as the source rock, Cretaceous sandstones and limestones and Tertiary sandstones as the reservoir rocks, Cretaceous limestones and shales and Tertiary shales as the seal rocks, and Colon through Pliocene–Pleistocene rocks as the overburden. Trap formation occurred during periods of deformation in the Late Cretaceous, late Eocene, and late Miocene–Pleistocene. Essential elements were deposited and critical processes extended from Early Cretaceous to Holocene, a 120-m.y. duration.

The oils of this system were generated from the Upper Cretaceous La Luna source rock, an oil-prone type II kerogen deposited in a marine environment. This oil–source rock correlation is based on the similarity of biomarkers in the oils and source rock extracts. The oils include both unaltered and altered (biodegraded) oils; the unaltered oils are classified as marginally mature, mature, and highly mature. With increasing thermal maturity, the API gravity of the oil increases and the amount of sulfur, vanadium, and polar compounds decreases.

The mass of hydrocarbons generated by the Upper Cretaceous La Luna source rock is 2.50×10^{14} kg. In-place hydrocarbons are estimated at 352.25×10^{11} kg. Thus, about 14% of hydrocarbons generated from La Luna source rock actually accumulated in known traps.

The Orocue(.) petroleum system, located in the southwestern part of the basin, is less definitely known and plays a secondary role in hydrocarbon contribution (<2% of the total hydrocarbon reserve). Its geographic extent is 10,500 km², and it coincides with the mature to overmature pod of Paleocene Orocue Formation, a coaly source rock containing type III kerogen. The oil from this source rock is sometimes mixed with oils from the marine La Luna source rock. The essential elements of the system are the Orocue Formation as the source rock, Orocue and Mirador sandstones as the reservoir rocks, Orocue and Mirador shales as the seal rocks, and Eocene to Pliocene–Pleistocene units as the overburden rocks. Structural traps formed during periods of deformation in the late Eocene and Pliocene–Pleistocene. Processes took place during the Pliocene–Holocene, and the system's time duration was Paleocene–Holocene, about 66 m.y.

Acknowledgments   *MARAVEN S.A. approved the participation of Fernando Marcano, an author, in this study. The authors are particularly thankful to Gonzalo Gamero and Luis Mompart for their support and encouragement during the preparation of this manuscript. Approval of MARAVEN S.A. and PDVSA to publish the production and reserve data is gratefully acknowledged. Authors are, however, responsible for the conclusions given in this paper. The authors greatly benefitted from discussions with Wallace G. Dow of DGSI while preparing the manuscript. Review of this paper by Wallace G. Dow and Leslie B. Magoon of USGS is deeply appreciated.*

References Cited

Blaser, R., and C. White, 1984, Source rock and carbonization study, *in* G. Demaison and R. J. Murris, eds., Petroleum geochemistry and basin evaluation: AAPG Memoir 35, 426 p.

Bockmeulen, H., C. Barker, and P. A. Dickey, 1983, Geology and geochemistry of crude oils, Bolivar costal fields, Venezuela: AAPG Bulletin, v. 67, p. 242–270.

Brenneman, M. C. 1960, Estudio geoquimico de crudos de la Cuenca de Maracaibo: Memoir, Third Venezuelan Geological Congress, Caracas, Venezuela, v. 3, p. 1025–1069.

Cassani, F., O. Gallango, and N. Jordán, 1989, Geoquímica del Flanco Norandino en el sector Lobateria-El Vigia: Memoir, Seventh Venezuelan Geological Congress, Caracas, Venezuela, v. 3, p. 1368–1391.

Gallango, O., S. Talukdar, and M. Chin-A-Lien, 1985, Caracteristicas de los crudos marinos en la Cuenca de Maracaibo, Venezuela Occidental: Memoir, Sixth Venezuelan Geological Congress, Caracas, Venezuela, v. 3, p. 1661–1693.

Gonzalez de Juana, C., J. Iturralde de Arozena, and X. Picard Cadillat, 1980, Geologia de Venezuela y de sus cuencas petroliferas: Caracas, Venezuela, Edition FONINVES, v. 1 and 2, 1031 p.

Halbouty, M. T., A. A. Meyerhoff, R. E. King, R. E. Dott, R. H. Klemme, and H. D. Shabadt, 1970, World's giant oil and gas fields: geological factors affecting their formation and basin classification, *in* M. T. Halbouty, ed., Geology of giant petroleum fields: AAPG Memoir 14, 575 p.

James, K. H., 1990, The Venezuelan hydrocarbon habitat, *in* J. Brooks, ed., Classic petroleum provinces: Geological Society of London, Special Publication 50, p. 9–35.

Lew, M., 1985, Origen de los gases en el area de Mara-Maracaibo: Memoir, Sixth Venezuelan Geological Congress, Caracas, Venezuela, v. 3, p. 1726–1756.

Magoon, L. B., 1988, The petroleum system—a classification scheme for research, exploration, and resource assessment, *in* L. B. Magoon, ed., Petroleum systems of the United States: USGS Bulletin 1870, p. 2–15.

Roberto, M., L. Mompart, E. Puche, and F. Scherer, 1990, New oil discoveries in the Ceuta area, SE Lake Maracaibo, Venezuela, *in* J. Brooks, ed., Classic petroleum provinces: Geological Society of London, Special Publication 50, p. 77–89.

Sweeney, J., S. Talukdar, A. Burnham, and C. Vallejos, 1990, Pyrolysis kinetics applied to prediction of oil generation in the Maracaibo basin, Venezuela, *in* Advances in Organic Geochemistry 1989: Organic Geochemistry, v. 16, n. 1–3, p. 189–196.

Talukdar, S., O. Gallango, and M. Chin-A-Lien, 1985, Generation and migration of hydrocarbons in the Maracaibo basin: Memoir, Second Bolivarian Symposium on Petroleum Exploration in Subandean Basins, Colombia, v. 2, 44 p.

Talukdar, S., O. Gallango, and M. Chin-A-Lien, 1986, Generation and migration of hydrocarbons in the Maracaibo basin, Venezuela: an integrated basin study, *in* D. Leythaeuser and J Rullkötter, eds., Advances in Organic Geochemistry 1985, part I: Organic Geochemistry, v. 10, p. 261–279.

Talukdar, S., O. Gallango, C. Vallejos, and A. Ruggiero, 1987, Observations on the primary migration of oil in the La Luna source rocks of the Maracaibo basin, Venezuela, *in* B. Doliguez, ed., Migration of hydrocarbons in sedimentary basins: Paris, Technip, p. 59–78.

Talukdar, S., O. Gallango, and C. Vallejos, 1989, Origen y distribución del H_2S en el area de Urdaneta Lago, Cuenca de Maracaibo: Revista Tecnica INTEVEP, v. 9, n. 1, p. 55–70.

Tocco, R., S. Peinado, M. Escobar, F. Galarraga, R. Falcon, D. Loureiro, M. Ostos, O. Rojas, F. Urbani, and F. Yoris, 1990, Estudio de correlación de menes y rocas madres en el flanco norandino, Venezuela (abs.): Second Latin American Congress on Organic Geochemistry, Caracas, Venezuela, 92 p.

Zambrano, E., E. Vasquez, B. Duval, M. Latreille, and B. Coffinieres, 1971, Sintesis paleogeografica y petrolera del occidente de Venezuela: Memoir, Fourth Venezuelan Geological Congress, Caracas, Venezuela, Special Publication 5, p. 483–545.

"The approach to the truth follows complex paths, in which logic and intellectual satisfaction sometimes experience rude shocks. Knowledge has advanced in rapid strides and also interminable detours which sometimes look like reversals. But seen in the right perspective, these contradictions, which are more apparent than real, are so often merely components of vaster and more complex overall views of the image that we try to develop, and the model, which we believed to be fixed and unchanging, is ceaselessly enriched."

—Alain Perrodon

Passage from Perrodon, A., 1983, Dynamics of Oil and Gas Accumulations: Elf Aquitaine, p. 19.

Magoon, L. B, and W. G. Dow, eds., 1994, The petroleum
system—from source to trap: AAPG Memoir 60.

Chapter **30**

Petroleum Systems of the Neiva Area, Upper Magdalena Valley, Colombia

Jaime Buitrago

Exxon Exploration Company
Houston, Texas, U.S.A.

Abstract

The Villeta–Caballos(!) and Villeta–Monserrate(!) petroleum systems of the Neiva area, situated in the upper Magdalena Valley of central Colombia, cover 5120 km² and include 18 fields with ultimate recoverable reserves of 83.8 million m³ (527 million bbl) of oil and 5.7 billion m³ (201 bcf) of gas. Aptian–Holocene sedimentary rocks in the area were deposited in rift, margin sag, and foreland basins. Geochemistry data show that the hydrocarbons were generated mainly from two intervals within the Albian–Santonian Villeta Formation. Thermal maturation modeling indicates that the hydrocarbons were generated from a pod of active source rock along the footwall of the Chusma fault (Villeta–Caballos system) and in the central Neiva syncline (Villeta–Monserrate system) from the end of the Oligocene to the present. Overburden rocks are mostly Eocene–Pleistocene molassic sedimentary rocks. The two main reservoirs are Cretaceous sandstones of the Caballos and Monserrate formations. Secondary reservoirs of significance are fluvial sandstones of the Miocene Honda Group. Traps are mainly structures (anticlines and faulted anticlines) associated with a fold and thrust belt that began in the Oligocene and is still active.

Essential elements and processes of these petroleum systems in the Neiva area occurred from the Aptian (110 Ma) to the present. First, the fluvial sandstones of lower Caballos reservoir rock were deposited. The source rock was deposited a few million years later and reached thermal maturity in synchronism with the formation of structural traps during the last 25 m.y. Destruction of some accumulations in the Villeta–Caballos system by uplift and erosion of reservoir rocks in the Monserate Formation in the fold belt started in the Miocene. The volume of hydrocarbons generated by both systems was calculated using an average TOC content of 2.1 wt. % for 235 m of total source interval in two intervals and a total area of mature source of 1650 km². A hydrocarbon generation of 325 mg HC/g TOC was used based on the HI measurements of immature Villeta source rock and a hydrocarbon generation algorithm. The generation–accumulation efficiency of the systems is about 5%.

INTRODUCTION

The Neiva basin is located in central Colombia (Figure 30.1). It is the southernmost Miocene depocenter along the Magdalena Valley. It contains commercial accumulations of oil and gas. Geographically, the Neiva basin occupies the upstream portion of an elongated valley between the Central and Eastern mountain chains of the Colombian Andes, along which the Magdalena River flows north toward the Caribbean Sea. It is physiographically separated from the next basin to the north, the Girardot basin, by a narrowing of the river valley.

Geologically, the Neiva basin has a complex history that can be traced back with some certainty to the Aptian. Since then, the area has been successively part of (1) a basin that was in the latest stage of a backarc rift, (2) a margin sag basin, (3) a collision-related foreland basin, (4) a backarc foreland basin, and most recently, (5) an intramontane basin that is part of a collision-related deformation belt. Pre-Aptian basement rocks include Mesozoic and older magmatic and metamorphic rocks, while the younger basin fill includes Mesozoic and Cenozoic continental sedimentary rocks, as well as Mesozoic marine sedimentary rocks.

The first well drilled in the Neiva basin was in 1962, the Dina-1, and resulted in the discovery of commercial oil. Although this first discovery found oil in the Tertiary section, the first producing trend was established from

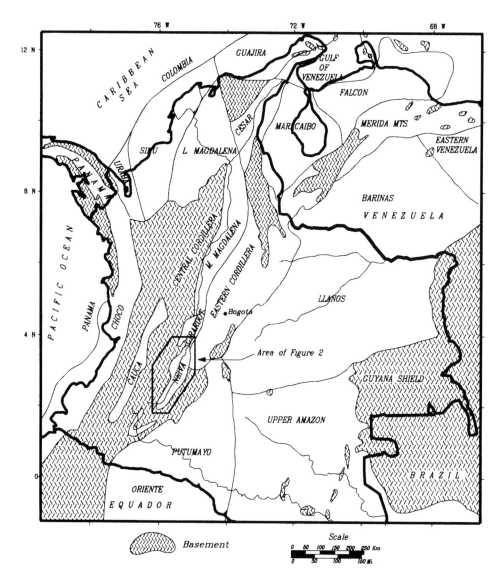

Figure 30.1. Map of northwestern South America showing the sedimentary basins and the location of the Neiva area.

1962 through 1982 in the Cretaceous Monserrate Formation just north of the city of Neiva (Dina–Tello trend) (Figure 30.2). During this 20-year period, almost 50 wildcats were drilled. In 1984, a new exploration stage started when the Hato Nuevo-1 well encountered oil in the Albian–Aptian Caballos Formation. Since then, more than 50 wildcats have been drilled, and a new producing trend has been established along the Dina–San Jacinto fault (Balcon–Yaguara trend). By the end of 1990, 83.8 million m^3 (527 million bbl) of recoverable oil and 5.7 billion m^3 (201 billion ft^3) of recoverable gas had been discovered in 18 accumulations, and 30.7 million m^3 (193 million bbl) of oil and 1.6 billion m^3 (56 billion ft^3) of gas had been produced from 16 fields (Tables 30.1 and 30.2). A total of 98 exploration wells and over 300 appraisal and development wells have been drilled in the Neiva basin.

Work on the geology of this area has been published by many authors, including the following: Torres et al. (1959), Beltran and Gallo (1968), Van Houten and Travis (1968), Wellman (1970), Anderson (1972), Pedreira and Rosenman (1973), Howe (1974), Van Houten (1976),

Butler (1983), Mojica and Macias (1983), Waddell (1985), Butler and Schamel (1988), and Schamel (1991). Previous work on geochemistry has been done by Maldonado and Mantilla (1991).

The Villeta–Caballos(!) and the Villeta–Monserrate(!) petroleum systems are identified in the Neiva basin. Both systems rely on the same source rock which was deposited in a sedimentary basin much larger than the Neiva basin. Thus, it extends beyond this basin into the Putumayo and Girardot basins (Figure 30.1) and may be present in other parts of Colombia. Therefore, these system names could be used in other parts of Colombia. Each system has a main reservoir rock: the Caballos Formation for the system associated with the Chusma fault area and the Monserrate Formation for the Neiva syncline (Figure 30.3). Because the source rock is thermally mature in two areas—along the Neiva syncline and along the footwall of the Chusma fault—there are two pods of active source rock (Figures 30.2 and 30.4). This paper includes a description of the sedimentary and structural settings of the systems, the basis for their identification, and a calculation of their efficiency.

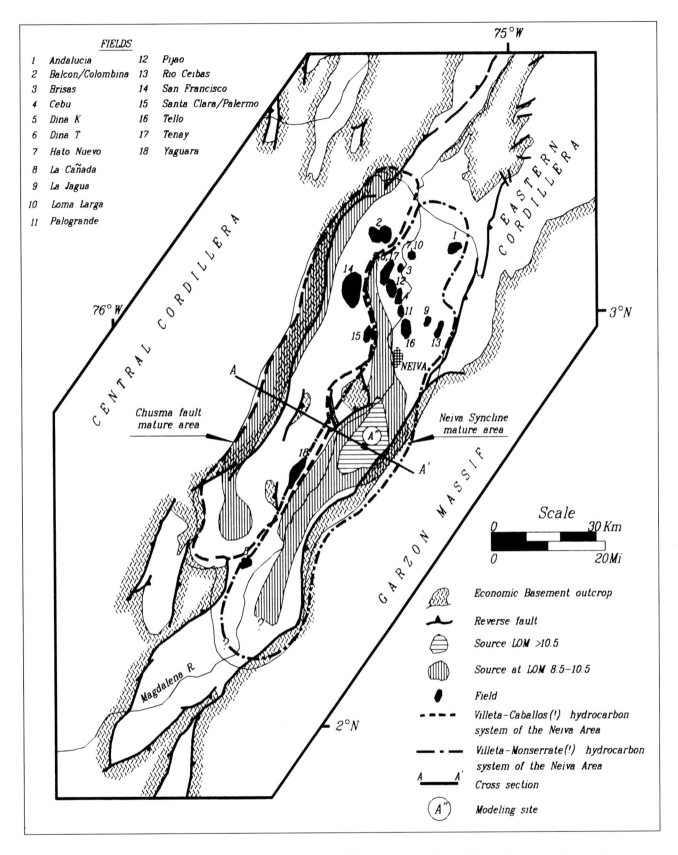

Figure 30.2. Map of the Neiva basin showing the extent of the Villeta–Caballos(!) and Villeta–Monserrate(!) petroleum systems of the Neiva area and the locations of the fields and pods of active source rock. Location of cross section A–A' (Figure 30.4) and burial history chart A" (Figure 30.7) are shown. LOM, level of organic metamorphism.

Table 30.1. Petroleum Accumulations in the Villeta–Caballos(!) Petroleum System[a]

Field No.	Field Name	Year Disc'd	Producing Formation	Depth (m)	Reservoir Lith	Seal Lith	Trap Type[b]	Oil (°API)	Cumulative Oil (10^6 m³)	Cumulative Gas (10^6 m³)	Remaining Oil (10^6 m³)	Remaining Gas (10^6 m³)
2	Balcon/ Colombina	1988	Caballos	3000	Ss	Sh	F	33	0.01	0.6	9.53	868.7
14	San Francisco	1985	Caballos	800	Ss	Sh	A	27	5.38	362.5	19.39	1306.4
15	Santa Clara/ Palermo	1987	Caballos	800	Ss	Sh	FA	18	0.22	16.7	1.65	122.8
18	Yaguara	1987	Caballos	800	ss	sh	FA	22	0.00	0.0	5.85	668.4

[a]Cumulative production as of December 1, 1990. From A.C.I.P.E.T. (1990).
[b]F, fault; A, anticline; FA, faulted anticline.

Table 30.2. Petroleum Accumulations in the Villeta–Monseratte(!) Petroleum System[a]

Field No.	Field Name	Year Disc'd	Producing Formation	Depth (m)	Reservoir Lith	Seal Lith[b]	Trap Type[c]	Oil (°API)	Cumulative Oil (10^6 m³)	Cumulative Gas (10^6 m³)	Remaining Oil (10^6 m³)	Remaining Gas (10^6 m³)
1	Andalucia	1979	Honda	650	Ss	Cly	FA	34	0.95	0.9	3.33	3.2
3	Brisas	1973	Monserrate	1250	Ss	Cly	F	23	0.86	23.8	0.10	2.7
4	Cebu	1981	Monserrate	2000	Ss	Cly	F	19	0.97	25.7	1.15	30.5
5	Dina K	1969	Monserrate	2000	Ss	Cly	FA	22	5.52	157.5	4.63	107.7
6	Dina T	1962	Honda/ Doima	950	Ss, Cgl	Cly	FA	20	4.12	412.3	2.65	206.5
7	Hato Nuevo	1984	Caballos	2100	Ss	Sh	F	36	0.28	30.2	0.52	55.9
8	La Cañada	1969	Monserrate	250	Ss	Cly	A	21	0.19	3.9	0.19	3.8
9	La Jagua	1986	Honda	1650	Ss	Cly	F	22	0.06	1.1	0.81	14.4
10	Loma Larga	1985	Monserrate	1100	Ss	Cly	F	22	0.00	0.1	0.16	2.4
11	Pologrande	1979	Monserrate	2000	Ss	Cly	F	20	3.79	167.4	0.19	8.4
12	Pijao	1982	Monserrate	2150	Ss	Cly	F	21	0.67	15.3	0.47	10.7
13	Rio Ceibas	1988	Honda	1100	Ss	Cly	F	20	0.00	0.0	0.00	566.4
16	Tello	1972	Monserrate	2450	Ss	Cly	FS	22	7.06	215.0	2.19	66.8
17	Tenay	1985	Caballos	3650	Ss	Sh	F	36	0.57	154.3	0.30	81.4

[a]Cumulative production as of December 1, 1990. From A.C.I.P.E.T. (1990).
[b]Cly, claystone; Sh, shale.
[c]F, fault; A, anticline; FA, faulted anticline; FS, faulted syncline.

SEDIMENTARY BASIN SETTING

Stratigraphic Section

The crystalline basement rock is an igneous and metamorphic complex that ranges in age from Precambrian to Jurassic. Unconformably overlying this crystalline rock is up to 4000 m of sedimentary and volcanic rock, which in this area is considered economic basement for petroleum. Unconformably overlying this basement rock are sedimentary rocks of Cretaceous (Aptian) to Pleistocene age that are important to the petroleum potential of the area (Figure 30.3).

Within these sedimentary rocks, four megacycles of sedimentation can be distinguished (Figure 30.3). The oldest one, Aptian–Paleocene, is in general a typical depositional wedge with continental sedimentary rocks at the base and top and marine sedimentary rocks in the middle. It contains the source rock and the two main reservoir rocks for both petroleum systems. This

megacycle is less than 2 km thick. The second cycle of late Eocene–Oligocene sedimentary rocks is up to 3 km thick and can be characterized as a typical molasse. The third megacycle is Miocene and includes up to 5.3 km of mostly fluvial and some lacustrine sedimentary rocks. This section includes reservoir rocks that contain commercial oil accumulations. Finally, the fourth megacycle consists of up to 1 km of late Miocene and younger fan and terrace deposits that are related to volcanic activity in the Central Cordillera.

The oldest Cretaceous (Aptian) sedimentary rocks in the area are those of the Yavi Formation. The Yavi was deposited during the latest stages of the backarc rift phase of development of the much larger ancestral Central basin of Colombia, of which the Yavi in the Neiva basin is only a small part. The Yavi is of limited extent in the area, so it is frequently absent. Similar pre-Aptian rift deposits occur more continuously to the north of the Neiva basin. The Yavi Formation is a clastic sequence of claystones, siltstones, and low porosity sand-

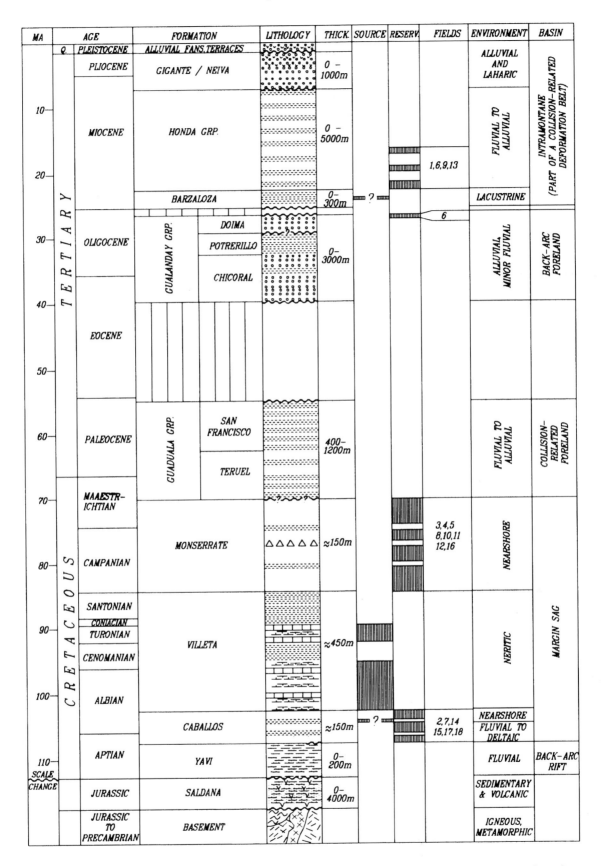

Figure 30.3. Generalized stratigraphic column of the Neiva area showing source rock and reservoir rock intervals with reference to the fields in which they are productive, environment of deposition, and basin type. Linear time scale is to the base of the Yavi Formation. The number key for the fields is in Tables 30.1 and 30.2. Figure 30.2 shows number key and locations of the fields.

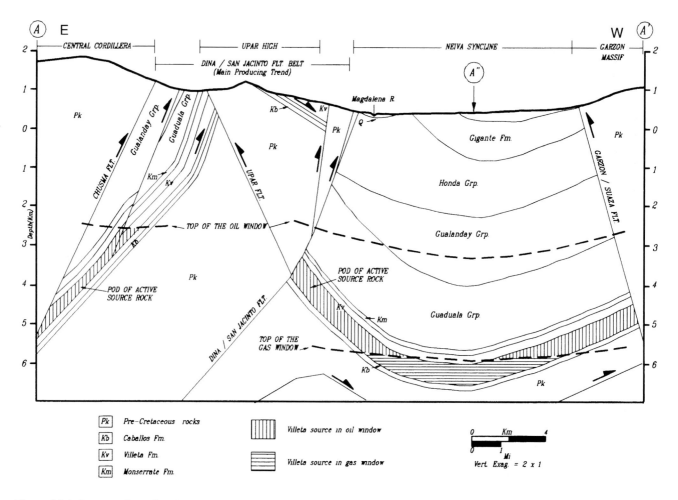

Figure 30.4. Structural section A–A' across the deepest portion of the Neiva syncline (see Figure 30.2 for location), which is opposite a large uplifted block within the Dina–San Jacinto fold belt, the Upar high. The section shows the major faults and the top of oil and gas generation. Notice the relationship of the pod of active source rock relative to the Chusma fault and Neiva syncline. A" is location of burial history chart.

stones deposited in a continental environment. Where the Yavi is present, the contact with the overlaying Caballos Formation is sometimes unconformable.

The Caballos Formation of Aptian–Albian age is composed of a series of sedimentary sequences that stack up in a retrogradational pattern, becoming more marine toward the top. The Caballos sequences were deposited in the area at the start of the margin sag phase of the Central basin of Colombia. Provenance of the sediments was mainly from the craton, across the present-day Garzon massif (Figure 30.2) and locally from uplifted areas of the Central Cordillera. In addition to reservoir-quality sandstones, the Caballos contains organic-rich marine shales, limestones, continental claystones, and a couple of glauconitic horizons. Locally, these horizons form good correlation markers in the subsurface due to their obvious response on the density log and to their conspicuous red color when oxidized at the surface. The contact between the Caballos Formation and the overlying Villeta Formation is transitional and occasionally subject to interpretation where the upper Caballos sandstones are locally absent.

The Albian–Santonian Villeta Formation represents

the main phase of margin sag of the Central basin of Colombia. During the Turonian, marine deposits extended across a continuous margin that wrapped around the shield from eastern Venezuela to Peru and transgressed all the way to the center of the present Llanos basin. In the Neiva basin, water depths rarely exceeded 100–200 m, decreasing during periods of lowstand to zero. Evidence of this lowstand is in surface outcrops in the San Antonio syncline east of the city of Neiva; here, coals occur toward the middle of the Villeta Formation (Figure 30.2). Coarse siliciclastic sedimentation was shut off in this region, probably due to the absence of a nearby delta. However, farther south in the area of the present-day Putumayo basin, the Villeta Formation contains lowstand sandstone bodies that are productive. In the Neiva basin area, the Villeta Formation consists of dark gray marine shales with varying amounts of calcareous material that occasionally become marls, which are interbedded with micritic limestones (mudstones). The more calcareous portions of the formation are either toward the base or in the middle of the section. The contact with the overlying Monserrate Formation is conformable to transitional.

The Monserrate Formation of Campanian–Maastrichtian age is formed by parasequences that stack in a general progradational pattern, with more massive sandstone beds toward the top. The environment of deposition is nearshore, with parasequences grading up from the offshore to beach environments. Provenance of the clasts is from the east where a major deltaic system prograded westward over the area. The upper contact of the Monserrate with the Guaduala Group is abrupt and may be unconformable.

These continental sedimentary rocks of the Guaduala Group are part of the regressive wedge of the Cretaceous–Paleocene cycle of deposition. They range in thickness from 400 to 1200 m and were deposited in a collision-related foreland basin. The group is characterized by multicolor, but predominantly violet, claystones. Some interbedded sandstone horizons are occasional markers on seismic profiles and at the surface. The contact of the Guaduala Group with the overlaying Gualanday Group is a regional unconformity that represents a depositional hiatus spanning the early–middle Eocene.

The 3-km-thick Gualanday Group, the second megacycle, is a molasse of late Eocene–Oligocene age. The group includes two or three distinct conglomerates that form prominent ridges along the western margin of the basin. Interbedded lithologies include red claystones and sandstones. The provenance of the coarse siliciclastics was the emerging Central Cordillera. The unconformity formed by the upper contact of the Gualanday Group with the base of the Miocene sedimentary rocks is angular and easily observable on a seismic profile.

The present-day geometry of the intermontane Neiva basin developed as the Andean foreland belt deformed during the Miocene (Dengo and Covey, 1991). The oldest Miocene sedimentary rocks in the Neiva basin appear to be conglomerates that cover a limited area. They can be difficult to differentiate from the underlying Gualanday Group. However, around the city of Neiva, there is a persistent shale interval at the base of the Miocene in many wells. For example, in the Florentina-1 well just south of the city, drill cuttings from this interval contain abundant Miocene flora and high TOC values. This interval also has a characteristic carbon isotopic composition that can be correlated from well to well. This unit is informally referred to here as the "Barzalosa Formation." The depositional environment is most likely lacustrine. Its lateral extent is unclear, but it is usually absent by onlap beyond the area of the city of Neiva. The Barzalosa Formation is a top seal for pre-Miocene reservoir rocks (Butler, 1983).

The 5-km-thick fluvial sequences of the Honda Group onlap in an angular relationship with pre-Miocene rocks. The lower Honda is predominantly claystone with interbedded sandstone beds. The upper Honda has the opposite ratio, with a predominance of sandstones, which are occasionally conglomeratic. Together, the Barzaloza Formation and the Honda Group are the third and thickest megacycle.

The last and thinnest megacycle is the Neiva and Gigante formations of late Miocene–Pliocene age. It consists of several alluvial fans, valley fills, debris flows, and fluvial sedimentary rocks related to volcanism in the Central Cordillera. Graywackes with a high content of lithic fragments are characteristic of the Gigante Formation.

Structural Setting

Strong deformation of the post-Aptian section apparently did not occur until late Oligocene time. Prior to that, there is evidence for limited normal faulting during the Cretaceous. In Maastrichtian time, the collision of the Dagua terrane with South America initiated a regional uplift of the area, probably causing the poorly expressed unconformity at the base of the Guaduala Group. However, as the collision continued, it created the hiatus in the rock column that probably covers some of the upper Paleocene but most definitely the lower–middle Eocene sequence. However, deformation in the area was minimum, and the Eocene unconformity is generally not angular (Figures 30.3 and 30.4). This is remarkably different from the situation in other basins to the north.

Toward the end of the Oligocene, a fold and thrust belt with east vergence started to develop along the foreland, or eastern flank, of the Central Cordillera in the area of the present-day Neiva and Girardot basins. The style of deformation for the main faults is moderate-angle thrusting involving at least the Paleozoic–Jurassic basement rock. Abundant splays occur as detached low-angle thrusts extending east of the main faults. Out-of-sequence thrusting and back-thrusting are also present. Folds are associated with the thrusting, originating mostly as fault-bend folds. The pre-Miocene age of this deformation is documented in numerous instances by the fossilization of the thrusts beneath the unconformity at the base of the Miocene section. There is significant onlap of the Miocene sedimentary rocks over the area of the Oligocene fold belt, suggesting continuous tectonism during deposition of the Honda Formation.

The main phase of the Andean orogeny began during the Miocene. The Neiva basin proper was formed as an intermontane basin or as a less deformed, sediment-receiving portion of the large fold and thrust belt. A major "back-thrust" fault to the overall east-verging belt (Dengo and Covey, 1991), the Garzon–Suaza fault, separates the Neiva basin from the uplifted Garzon massif and Eastern Cordillera. Reactivation of the Oligocene faults during and after Honda deposition is evident from the data.

THE PETROLEUM SYSTEMS

Petroleum Source Rock

The Cretaceous Villeta Formation is the source rock for the commercial oil found in the Neiva basin. The Villeta is present over most of the area except where it has been truncated by the angular unconformity at the base of the Miocene, over some of the northern and northeastern parts of the area, and where it has been

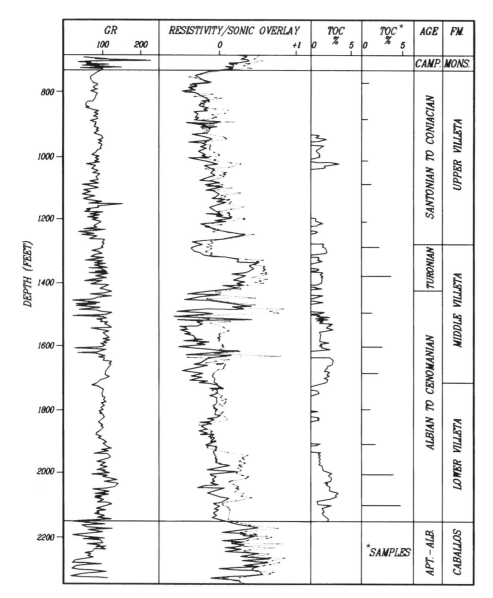

Figure 30.5. Log geochemistry display for the Villeta Formation in the Los Mangos-1 well, with values of TOC measured from cuttings for comparison. Log TOC is calculated using the separation of the resistivity and acoustic transit time overlay and the LOM (level of organic metamorphism) values from samples (Data from Exxon Production Research laboratory.)

eroded at the surface on structural highs of the fold belt, along the western margin (Figures 30.2 and 30.4). Total thickness of the Villeta is about 450 m in wells drilled in the area.

Based on log and sample geochemistry, the source rock intervals within the Villeta Formation are located mainly in the middle and lowermost portion of the section (Figure 30.5). The geochemical log in Figure 30.5 shows two values for TOC: the one on the left is calculated from wireline log data and the one on the right is from geochemical analyses. The age zonation of the Villeta formation in the Los Mangos-1 well is based on micropaleontology. The middle zone of organic-rich shales with interbeds of limestone correlates with a worldwide suite of Turonian source rocks and is equivalent to the La Luna and Querecual formations of northern Colombia and Venezuela. The lowermost portion of the Villeta, directly overlying the Caballos Formation, is an organic-rich, marly source rock. Its proximity to the underlying reservoir beds facilitates a top-loading mechanism of primary migration.

The visual organic matter present in the source rock intervals of the Villeta Formation is mixed, mostly marine algal material along with some terrigenous material. Lateral variations in the visual type of organic matter are common. Rock-Eval pyrolysis and TOC data are used to calculate the hydrogen and oxygen indices (HI and OI) plotted on the modified van Krevelen diagram in Figure 30.6. These indices show that the Villeta source rock contains three kerogen types: the lower Villeta contains type I to II, the middle Villeta has a mixture of types II and III, and the upper Villeta has type III kerogen.

Hydrocarbon Generation

Thermal maturity measurements for the Villeta Formation in the Neiva basin are available only from outcrops and on-structure wells. The Villeta is immature in all of these locations (Maldonado et al., 1991), which

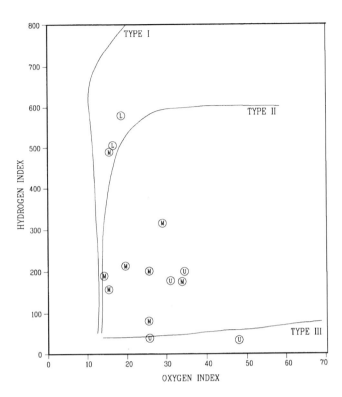

Figure 30.6. Data from Rock-Eval pyrolysis analysis of Villeta source rock samples on a van Krevelen diagram. L, lower Villeta; M, middle Villeta; U, upper Villeta. (Data from Exxon Production Research laboratory.)

indicates that recent burial rather than pre-Miocene tectonics and burial provided the necessary overburden rock to thermally mature the source rock. Seismic profiles that cross the basin parallel to cross section A–A' indicate that the Villeta Formation is buried more than 6 km (Figure 30.4).

Geohistory modeling of the Villeta source rock where it is buried deeper in the basin (such as at location A" in Figure 30.2) indicates areas of thermally mature and overmature source rock. The burial history chart of Figure 30.7 shows that the source rock has been continually buried deeper and is presently at its maximum burial depth, thus, the critical moment is present day. A thermal maturity model was constructed with an Exxon basin modeling system, incorporating heat flow and compaction considerations and using proprietary algorithms based on the Arrhenius equation to calculate the generation of oil and gas (Figure 30.7). Where the Villeta source rock is buried deepest in the Neiva syncline, oil generation started 30 Ma in Oligocene time, and gas generation began 10 Ma in late Miocene. If we assume that hydrocarbon generation is similar within the length of the Neiva syncline, the thermally mature source rock can be mapped (Figure 30.2) as a pod of active source rock. Using the same assumptions about hydrocarbon generation as modeled in the Neiva syncline, we can identify a similar pod of active source rock along the footwall of the Chusma fault.

Reservoir Rocks

The sandstones of the Caballos Formation are the producing reservoir rocks for the oil that came from the pod of active source rock along the footwall of the Chusma fault (Figure 30.2). In general they improve in reservoir quality toward the top, as they grade from fluvial at the base to nearshore marine higher in the section. However, the marine sandstones near the top have less lateral continuity, and carbonate cementation is locally a problem. Porosities in the Caballos are typically 12–17%, with the more marine sandstones in the upper part of the section having the best averages. The Caballos sandstones have mixed wettability in some of the fields.

The sandstone of the Monserrate Formation is the primary reservoir rock for the oil that came from the pod of active source rock in the Neiva syncline (Figure 30.2). Porosities are generally 15–22%. Secondary porosity development can be significant when close to the Miocene unconformity (Waddell, 1985). Other reservoirs of significance are the argillaceous sandstones of the Honda Formation, which have porosities of 20–25% and irreducible water saturations that commonly reach 50%.

Seal Rocks

The Villeta Formation is the seal rock for over half of the oil and gas, by volume, in the Neiva basin (Tables 30.1 and 30.2). Most of this oil is found in one field, the San Francisco, with recoverable hydrocarbons of nearly 25 million m^3 of oil and 17 billion m^3 of gas. Since the Villeta Formation is the source rock for this oil, this lithology serves a dual function as a source rock and a seal rock, though in different places.

The second most important seal rock is the basal claystone of the Guaduala Group. One-third, by volume of the oil and gas is trapped within the reservoir rocks of the Monserrate Formation, indicating that the sealing lithology is very effective. Additional seal rocks are the intraformational claystones within the Honda Group. They seal almost 15% of the recoverable oil and gas discovered.

Overburden Rocks

The overburden rocks in the Neiva basin can be as thick as 7 km (Figure 30.4) and are important because they bury the source rock to generate hydrocarbons as well as contain some of the reservoir and seal rocks. The burial history plot (Figure 30.7) shows that except for some uplift and erosion during the early–middle Eocene, burial of the source rock has been continuous from the Maastrichtian. The stratigraphic column (Figure 30.3) shows that the upper Eocene–Pliocene section represents as much as 80% of the overburden rock and is thick enough to generate thermal gas. However, except for the Rio Ceibas gas field, all the remaining fields contain mostly oil, as the gas–oil ratio (GOR) is low. This may indicate that the migration paths from the pods of active

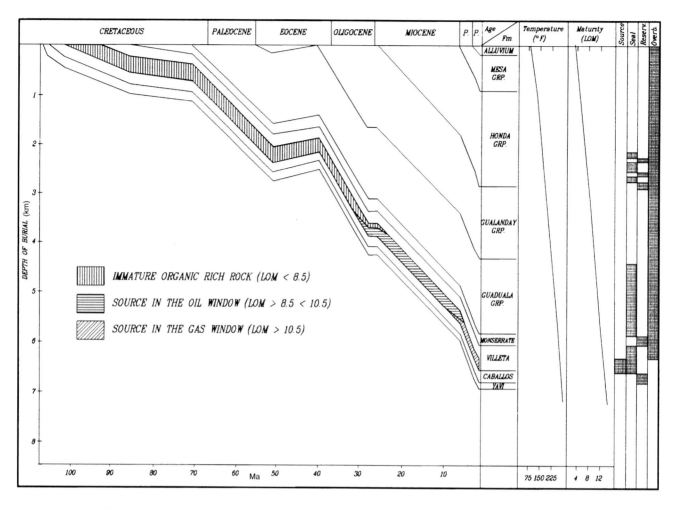

Figure 30.7. Burial history chart of the Aptian and older beds at location A" (see Figure 30.2) showing the time, depth, and temperature at which the Villeta source rock started oil and gas generation in the Villeta–Monseratte(!) petroleum system. Constructed from seismic data using an Exxon proprietary basin modeling system.

source rock from the onset of oil migration were unimpeded and that the source rock was depleted before it entered the gas window.

Traps

The hydrocarbon traps appear to be full to the spill or leak points. A possible exception is the La Cañada field whose conduit from the active source rock to the trap may have been poorly plumbed (Figure 30.2). Field sizes and producing depths as well as API gravities for each field are given in Tables 30.1 and 30.2. Almost all traps are structural or have strong structural components. The largest field, the San Francisco, is an anticline, while all the remaining fields include a fault in the form of a faulted anticline, a fault and a subunconformity, or just a fault trap. The fields producing from the Honda Group also have a stratigraphic component due to the lenticularity of the reservoirs.

The absence of producing reservoirs in the Monserrate Formation in the Villeta–Caballos petroleum system of the Neiva area (Table 30.1) is due in three of the fields to erosion and exposure of this reservoir in the

immediate area, with the resulting destruction of the trap. This takes place either at the surface, as in the Yaruara field, or beneath the unconformity at the base of the Miocene section, as in the Santa Clara–Palermo and San Francisco fields.

The Monserrate–Villeta petroleum system of the Neiva area includes only two fields producing from reservoirs of the Caballos Formation (Table 30.2). This is due to the lower trap density of this reservoir rock as compared to that of the Monserrate Formation. The lower trap density is caused by the presence of the thick shales of the Villeta Formation between the two reservoirs. Many of the thrust faults that create the traps in the Monserrate Formation sole out within the Villeta formation and do not involve the reservoir rocks in the Caballos Formation. More detailed descriptions of the structural styles and configuration of the traps in these two petroleum systems have been given previously by Butler (1983), Butler and Schamel (1988), and Schamel (1991).

The fields in the Neiva basin have interesting physiographical settings. Some of them have spectacular mountain locations, such as the San Francisco, Santa

Clara–Palermo, and La Cañada fields. The Yaguara field is now almost surrounded by a man-made lake, the waters of which were rising as the discovery well was being drilled. Others are close to large population centers, such as the fields of the Dina–Tello trend in the vicinity of the city of Neiva.

Level of Certainty

The Villeta–Caballos(!) and the Villeta–Monserrate(!) petroleum systems of the Neiva area can both be classified as a known level of certainty. The shales and marls of the Villeta Formation are the documented source rocks for hydrocarbons in several of the commercial petroleum accumulations in the Neiva area. They are the dominant source rock in the area. Candidates for additional and minor contributors are the marine shales in the uppermost part of the Caballos Formation and the lacustrine shales of the Barzalosa Formation. Previous published geochemistry (Maldonado and Mantilla, 1991) also point to the lower unit of the Villeta Formation as the source of hydrocarbons in the area.

Based on the carbon isotopic composition of the saturated and aromatic hydrocarbons, the Villeta source rock extracts from both outcrop and drill cuttings samples show a positive correlation with oils from several fields. In addition, a negative correlation exists between these same oils and rock extracts from the Gualanday Group and the Barzalosa Formation (Figure 30.8). The oils in the Andalucia and La Jagua fields have a carbon isotopic composition that is slightly displaced toward the Barzalosa oil extract. The significance of this last observation is not clear.

Gas chromatograms of an oil and rock extract from the same well, the Los Mangos-1 drilled in the Yagura field, are compared in Figure 30.9. The oil was produced from the Caballos Formation, and the source rock extract was acquired from drill cuttings of the thermally immature Villeta Formation. Based on the odd-carbon predominance and the pristine and phytane peaks being higher than the adjacent *n*-alkane peaks, the rock extract

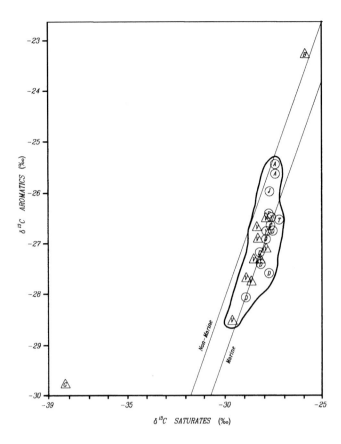

Figure 30.8. Carbon isotopic ratios for oils and rock extracts in the Neiva area. Oils (circles): A, Andalucia; C, La Cañada; D, Dina; F, San Francisco; J, La Jagua; T, Tello; Y, Yaguara. Rock extracts (triangles): B, Barzalosa; G, Gualanday; V, Villeta. (Data from Exxon Production Research laboratory.)

is immature when compared to the oil. Even so, the similarity of the chromatograms support the interpretation that the oil in the reservoir rock originates from a more mature organic facies within the Villeta some distance from the field (Figures 30.2 and 30.4).

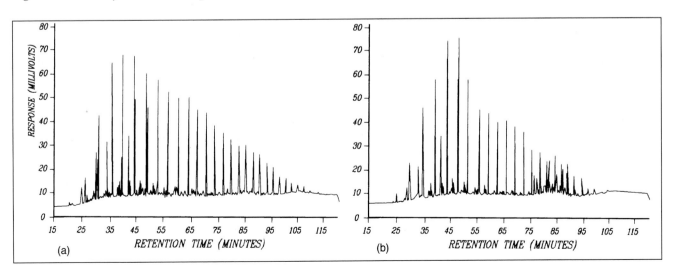

Figure 30.9. C$_{15+}$ (saturate) chromatograms for (a) an oil and (b) a rock extract from Villeta drill cuttings; both from the Los Mangos-1 well (Yaguara field). (Data from Exxon Production Research laboratory.)

Work on the oils from the Yaguara field done at the Exxon Production Research lab indicates, on the basis of biomarkers, that the oils originated from a marine source with mixed marine algal and terrigenous components, with the algal component being dominant. This description is consistent with the organic matter types found in the Villeta Formation, with the proposed shallow marine environment of deposition, and with the paleogeographic setting of the area in an interior sea or embayment.

Extent and Migration Pathways

Two pods of active source rock, each of which contributed hydrocarbons to the fields in the Neiva area, dictate the presence of two petroleum systems. These two systems are the Villeta–Caballos(!) petroleum system along the footwall of the Chusma fault and the Villeta–Monserrate(!) system of the Neiva syncline (Figure 30.2). All commercial oil and gas accumulations in the Neiva basin are included in one of these systems (Tables 30.1 and 30.2). Their southern limit is poorly defined, but their extension farther south is unlikely based on thermal maturation modeling and seismic data, both of which indicate the absence of mature source rocks due to lesser burial (Figure 30.2). The northern end of both systems is against the Natagaima arch, of Oligocene age, which also separates the Neiva basin from the Girardot basin to the north. These systems are separated down the long axis of the basin by the Dina–San Jacinto fault, which acts as a barrier to petroleum migration from west to east (Figure 30.4).

The Villeta–Caballos system extends stratigraphically from the oldest reservoir, the lower Caballos sandstones, to the top of the Pliocene–Pleistocene molasse, part of the overburden section responsible for the thermal maturation of the source rock. The Villeta–Monserrate system has a similar stratigraphic extent, although the main reservoir rock is the younger Monserrate Formation.

Migration pathways present several alternatives. The most likely migration route in the Villeta–Caballos is from the active source rock pod along the Chusma fault toward the east and to the fields within the same large-scale thrust sheet (Figures 30.2 and 30.4). Oil probably migrated to both the Caballos and Monserrate reservoirs and seems to have accumulated in both reservoirs in some of the structures (Yaguara). However, the Monserrate reservoirs were either breached at the time of migration or were subsequently breached by erosion.

Hydrocarbon migration in the Villeta–Monserrate system is most likely from the active source rock pod in the Neiva syncline. Here, the longest lateral migration paths to discovered accumulations are to the Andalucia field for oil (20–25 km) and to the Rio Ceibas field for gas (25–30 km to the area of gas generation). However, migration from east to west across major faults may explain certain peculiarities, such as the presence of gas in the Caballos Formation in the Caimito-1 well, just south of the Santa Clara–Palermo field, which is on the opposite side of the Dina–San Jacinto fault from the pod of active source rock with gas generation capability.

Faults may have provided vertical migration

pathways in some instances, but the relationship between Honda production and areas where the Honda rests directly on basement indicates that a thick Guaduala Group is an effective regional seal. Likely, migration to the Honda reservoirs took place along the basal unconformity of the Miocene and then either up to the Honda beds, in areas where the Barzalosa Formation is absent, or up along faults with post-Miocene movement, in such areas as the Dina field.

Events Chart

The events chart for each petroleum system in Figure 30.10 shows the essential elements and processes relative to geologic time. Both systems started with deposition of the Caballos Formation reservoir rock and have source rocks that are still active at the present time because the overburden rock is presently being deposited. However, in some areas along the western margin of the Neiva basin, the destruction of the Villeta–Caballos system is ongoing due to erosion of the seal and reservoir beds in structures within the active fold belt (Figures 30.2 and 30.4). The Monserrate reservoir in the Yaguara field structure, for instance, is saturated with tar. The high concentrations of degraded hydrocarbons in these sandstones indicate that a paleoaccumulation of oil existed in the Monserrate at Yaguara and that it was subsequently exposed and degraded. A slightly less intense deformation along this fold belt would have resulted in better preserved traps containing considerably greater recoverable reserves. Key to the presence of the systems in the Neiva area was deposition of the thick molasse during the Tertiary.

Mass Balance Calculations

The mass balance calculations done here for both petroleum systems follow Schmoker (Chapter 19, this volume). The same two source rock units within the Villeta Formation are considered for the calculation (Figure 30.5). The first one, the middle Villeta, is 135 m thick and has an average TOC of 1.8 wt. %. The second one, the lower Villeta, is 100 m thick and has an average TOC of 2.5 wt. %. An average formation density of 2.47 g/cm³, obtained from wireline logs, was used for both intervals. The area of thermally mature Villeta source rock for the Villeta–Caballos petroleum system is 750 km² and for the Villeta–Monserrate system is 900 km² (Figure 30.2).

The total mass of organic carbon (M) present in the middle Villeta of the Villeta–Caballos system is

$$M \text{ (g TOC)}$$
$$= (1.8/100)(2.47 \text{ g/cm}^3)(13.5 \times 10^3 \text{ cm})(75 \times 10^{11} \text{ cm}^2)$$
$$= 45.02 \times 10^{14}$$

and in the lower Villeta is

$$M \text{ (g TOC)}$$
$$= (2.5/100)(2.47 \text{ g/cm}^3)(10^4 \text{ cm})(75 \times 10^{11} \text{ cm}^2)$$
$$= 46.31 \times 10^{14}$$

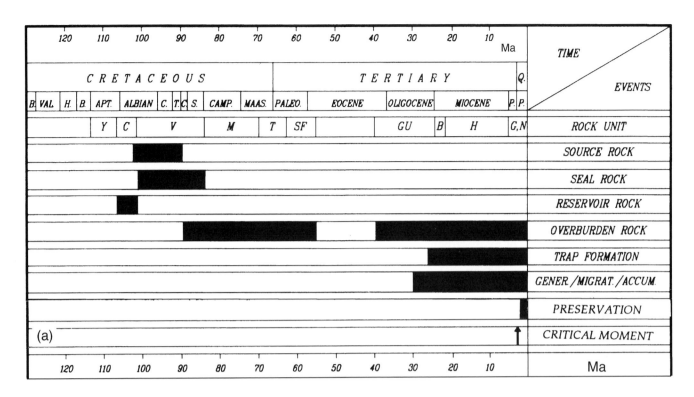

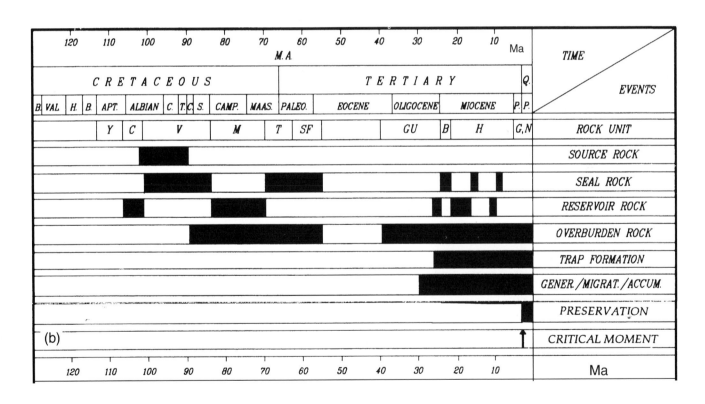

Figure 30.10. Events charts for (a) the Villeta–Caballos(!) petroleum system in the Chusma fault area and (b) the Villeta–Monserrate(!) petroleum system in the Neiva syncline area, related to geologic time. Arrow indicates time represented on the map (Figure 30.2) and cross section (Figure 30.4). Units: Y, Yavi Formation; C, Caballos Formation; V, Villeta Formation; M, Monserrate Formation; T, Teruel Formation; SF, San Francisco Formation; GU, Gualanday Group; B, Barzalosa Formation; H, Honda Group; G, Gigante Formation; N, Neiva Formation.

The total mass of organic carbon (M) present in the middle Villeta of the Villeta–Monserrate system is

$$M \text{ (g TOC)}$$
$$= (1.8/100)(2.47 \text{ g/cm}^3)(13.5 \times 10^3 \text{ cm})(9 \times 10^{12} \text{ cm}^2)$$
$$= 54.02 \times 10^{14}$$

and in the lower Villeta is

$$M \text{ (gTOC)}$$
$$= (2.5/100)(2.47 \text{ g/cm}^3)(10^4 \text{ cm})(9 \times 10^{12} \text{ cm}^2)$$
$$= 55.57 \times 10^{14}$$

The method proposed by Schmoker (Chapter 19) for the calculation of the mass of hydrocarbons generated per unit mass of organic carbon (R) can not be used because all available samples of Villeta are immature. Instead, the measured values for the present-day hydrogen index (HI_p) in the Villeta samples (Figure 30.6) were used instead of the original hydrogen index (HI_o), and an Exxon proprietary algorithm for hydrocarbon generation was used to calculate R. Measured values of HI average 250 mg HC/g TOC for the middle Villeta and 425 mg HC/g TOC for the lower Villeta. The calculated values of R are 180 and 300 mg HC/g TOC for the two units, respectively.

The total mass of hydrocarbons generated (HGC) in the middle Villeta of the Villeta–Caballos system is

$$HGC \text{ (kg HC)} = (180 \text{ mg HC/g TOC})$$
$$\times (45.02 \times 10^{14} \text{ g TOC})(10^{-6} \text{ kg/mg})$$
$$= 810 \times 10^9 \text{ kg HC}$$

and in the lower Villeta is

$$HGC \text{ (kg HC)} = (300 \text{ mg HC/g TOC})$$
$$\times (46.31 \times 10^{14} \text{ g TOC})(10^{-6} \text{ kg/mg})$$
$$= 1389 \times 10^9 \text{ kg HC}$$

The total in the system is thus 2.2×10^{12} kg HC, or 1.96×10^9 m^3 of oil (12.3×10^9 bbl), using an average API gravity of $27°$ API.

The total mass of hydrocarbons generated (HGC) in the middle Villeta of the Villeta–Monseratte system is

$$HGC \text{ (kg HC)} = (180 \text{ mg HC/g TOC})$$
$$\times (54.02 \times 10^{14} \text{ g TOC})(10^{-6} \text{ kg/mg})$$
$$= 972 \times 10^9 \text{ kg HC}$$

and in the lower Villeta is

$$HGC \text{ (kg HC)} = (300 \text{ mg HC/g TOC})$$
$$\times (55.57 \times 10^{14} \text{ g TOC})(10^{-6} \text{ kg/mg})$$
$$= 1667 \times 10^9 \text{ kg HC}$$

The total in the system is thus 2.64×10^{12} kg HC, or 2.42×10^9 m^3 of oil (15.2×10^9 bbl), using an average API gravity of $23°$ API.

The amount of in-place hydrocarbons (HC_{ip}) can be calculated from the discovered reserves (Tables 30. 1 and 30.2) using average recovery factors of 30% for the oil and 60% for the gas, which is mostly associated, and a gas gravity of 0.72. For the Villeta–Caballos system, this value is

$$HC_{ip} \text{ (kg HC)}$$
$$= (42.03 \times 10^6 \text{ m}^3 \text{ oil})(0.89 \times 10^3 \text{ kg HC/m}^3/0.3)$$
$$+ (3.3 \times 10^9 \text{ m}^3 \text{ gas})(0.72 \text{ kg HC/m}^3/0.6)$$
$$= 0.13 \times 10^{12}$$

and for the Villeta–Monserrate system it is

$$HC_{ip} \text{ (kg HC)}$$
$$= (41.73 \times 10^6 \text{ m}^3 \text{ oil})(0.91 \times 10^3 \text{ kg HC/m}^3/0.3)$$
$$+ (2.4 \times 10^9 \text{ m}^3 \text{ gas})(0.72 \text{ kg HC/m}^3/0.6)$$
$$= 0.13 \times 10^{12}$$

The generation–accumulation efficiency (GAE) of the Villeta–Caballos system is

$$GAE \text{ (\%)} = (0.13 \times 10^{12} \text{ kg HC}/2.2 \times 10^{12} \text{ kg HC})(100)$$
$$= 5.9\%$$

and the GAE of the Villeta–Monserrate system is

$$GAE \text{ (\%)} = (0.13 \times 10^{12} \text{ kg HC}/2.64 \times 10^{12} \text{ kg HC})(100)$$
$$= 4.9\%$$

which are fair efficiencies if we consider that the systems contain active plays that may still yield new discoveries.

Acknowledgments   *I would like to thank Ecopetrol, Exxon, and Total for their permission to include data from the exploration work conducted by them in the area of Neiva. Many of the conclusions in this paper are based on internal company reports emanating from that effort. I would like to acknowledge in particular the contributions of Esso Colombiana's geologists Jose Maria Jaramillo and Ricardo Escovar and the staff of Exxon Production Research Company.*

References Cited

ACIPET, 1990, Produccion acumulada por campo: Boletin estadistico mensual, Asociacion Colombiana de Ingenieros del Petroleo, v. 281., 3 p.

Anderson, T. A., 1972, Paleogene non-marine Gualanday Group, Neiva basin, Colombia, and regional development of the Colombian Andes: GSA Bulletin, v. 83, p. 2423–2438.

Beltran, N., and J. Gallo, 1968, The geology of the Neiva subbasin, Upper Magdalena basin, southern portion: Ninth Annual Field Conference, Colombian Association of Petroleum Geologists and Geophysicists, 44 p.

Butler, K., 1983, Andean-type foreland deformation: structural development of the Neiva basin, upper Magdalena valley, Colombia: Ph.D. dissertation, University of South Carolina, Columbia, SC, 272 p.

Butler, K., and S. Schamel, 1988, Structure along the eastern margin of the Central Cordillera, upper Magdalena valley, Colombia: Journal of South American Earth Science, v. 1, p. 109-120.

Dengo, C. A., and M. C. Covey, 1991, La estructura de la Cordillera Oriental de Colombia: un modelo tectonico de los Andes Colombianos: IV Simposio Bolivariano, Asociacion Colombiana de Geologos y Geofisicos del Petroleo, Bogota, v. 3.

Howe, M. W., 1974, Nonmarine Neiva Formation (Pliocene?), upper Magdalena valley, Colombia: regional tectonism: GSA Bulletin, v. 85, p. 1031–1042.

Maldonado, A., and J. A. Mantilla, 1991, Geoquimica de roca fuente de hidrocarburos en la subcuenca de Neiva (Colombia): IV Simposio Bolivariano, Asociacion Colombiana de Geologos y Geofisicos del Petroleo, Bogota, v. 1, 29 p.

Mojica, J., and C. Macia, 1983, Caracteristicas estratigraficas y edad de la Formacion Yavi, Mesozoico de la region entre Prado y Dolores, Tolima, Colombia: Geologia Colombiana, v. 12, p. 7–32.

Pedreira, A. J., and H. L. Rosenman, 1973, Geologia del area de Palermo, Departamento del Huila, Republica de Colombia: Actas, V Congreso Geologico Argentino, Cordoba, v. 4, p. 133-157.

Schamel, S., 1991, Middle and Upper Magdalena basins, Colombia, *in* K. T. Biddle, ed., Active margin basins: case histories and examples: AAPG Memoir 52, p. 283–301.

Torres, G., et al., 1959, Mapa geologico de la Republica de Colombia, plancha N-8, Neiva, escala 1:200,000: Bogota, Servicio Geologico Nacional.

Van Houten, F. B., 1976, Late Cenozoic deposits, Andean foredeep, Colombia: AAPG Bulletin, v. 87, p. 481–495.

Van Houten, F. B., and R.B. Travis, 1968, Cenozoic deposits, upper Magdalena valley, Colombia: AAPG Bulletin, v. 52, p. 675–702.

Waddell, M. G., 1985, The relationship of porosity development and diagenesis in the Upper Cretaceous Guadalupe Formation, Neiva basin, Colombia: II Simposio Bolivariano, Asociacion Colombiana de Geologos y Geofisicos del Petroleo, Bogota, v. 2, 18 p.

Wellman, S. S., 1970, Stratigraphy and petrology of the nonmarine Honda Group (Miocene), upper Magdalena valley, Colombia: GSA Bulletin, v. 81, p. 2358–2374.

"During the past ten to fifteen years, organic geochemistry has become a widely accepted tool in oil and gas exploration. The concept that oil and most of the gas is generated in organic-rich source rocks, which are matured through elevated temperature and time, and from which the hydrocarbons are then expelled to migrate along carrier beds and other conduits to the traps, has proved to be a very fruitful one, with considerable impact on exploration thinking."

—R. J. Murris

Passage from Murris, R. J., 1984, Petroleum Geochemistry and Basin Evaluation, G. Demaison and R. J. Murris, eds.: AAPG Memoir 35.

Magoon, L. B, and W. G. Dow, eds., 1994, The petroleum
system—from source to trap: AAPG Memoir 60.

Chapter **31**

Selected Petroleum Systems in Brazil

M. R. Mello

E. A. M. Koutsoukos

Petrobras R & D Center, Petrobras/CENPES
Cidade University
Rio de Janeiro, Brazil

W. U. Mohriak

G. Bacoccoli

Petróleo Brasileiro S/A Petrobras Depex
Rio de Janeiro, Brazil

Abstract

The application of a multidisciplinary approach involving geochemical, sedimentologic, geophysical, and microbiostratigraphic research has greatly enhanced the level of understanding of some of the most representative petroleum systems in Brazil. Investigation of the data allowed the characterization in time and space of petroleum pathways from source rock to trap, which represent oil in-place in reservoir rocks ranging in age from Paleozoic to Tertiary.

Four major petroleum systems were selected as representative case studies from various stages of basin formation in Brazil: (1) the intracratonic sequence in the Solimões basin in the Amazon region; (2) the prerift and synrift sequence in the Recôncavo basin near the eastern tip of Brazil; (3) the protomarine sequence in the Sergipe–Alagoas basin on the northeastern coast of Brazil; and (4) the drift sequence in the Campos basin, offshore Rio de Janeiro in southeastern Brazil.

Although there are locally important oil source rocks of Paleozoic, Aptian, and Tertiary ages, about 90% of the discovered petroleum in Brazil originates from Lower Cretaceous source rocks that were deposited in the proto-Atlantic rift. The most prolific oil-bearing reservoir rocks, by volume, are siliciclastic turbidites deposited in bathyal water depths during the Late Cretaceous and Paleogene.

INTRODUCTION

In recent years, many hydrocarbon exploratory efforts have been directed toward identifying and characterizing petroleum systems (e.g., Magoon, 1988, 1990). A petroleum system investigation emphasizes the genetic relationship between a particular pod of active source rock and the related hydrocarbons in the reservoir rock by focusing all geochemical, stratigraphic, and structural research on the essential elements and processes (Magoon, 1990).

In Brazilian sedimentary basins, the first approach aiming to characterize petroleum systems was carried out by Estrella et al. (1984) in the Espirito Santo basin on the eastern Brazilian margin. Multidisciplinary investigations, based on geochemical, sedimentologic, geophysical, and microbiostratigraphic studies, have been undertaken in the Brazilian sedimentary basins with the intent of understanding the petroleum pathways, from source to trap. Such an approach opened a new era in hydrocarbon exploration in the sedimentary basins of Brazil.

Four major petroleum systems, responsible for about 90% of the known petroleum reserves in Brazil, were chosen as representative case studies. The petroleum systems studied were examined with respect to the tectono-sedimentary evolutionary phases of the basins and are classified on that basis (Asmus and Ponte, 1973; Ojeda, 1982). The four evolutionary sequences are as follows (Figure 31.1):

I. **Intracratonic sequence,** which describes a cratonic sag before rifting. It is represented by the Paleozoic Solimões sag basin in the Amazon region.

II. **Prerift and synrift sequence,** which describes a rift basin just before and during rifting. It is represented by the Recôncavo rift basin on the southeastern coast of Brazil

III. **Protomarine sequence,** which describes a rift basin that fluctuates between marine and evaporite depositional environments. It is represented by the Sergipe rift basin near the eastern tip of Brazil.

IV. **Drift sequence,** which describes a basin that is entirely marine and part of the Atlantic passive margin (Figure 31.2). It is represented by the continental drift margin in the deep water Campos basin in southeastern Brazil.

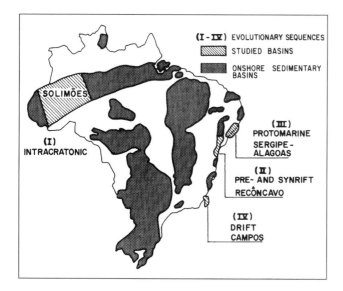

Figure 31.1. Location of the four sedimentary basins in Brazil, with the evolutionary sequences indicated, and the four petroleum systems incorporated.

EVOLUTIONARY SEQUENCE	TYPICAL CASES					BOEIP x10⁶
	BASIN	OIL FIELD	RESERVOIR	SOURCE ROCK	PETROLEUM SYSTEM	
IV DRIFT	CAMPOS	MARLIM	PALEOGENE TURBIDITIC SANDSTONE	LK-LACUST. SALINE SHALE	LAGOA FEIA-CARAPEBUS	13,900
III PROTO-MARINE	SERGIPE-ALAGOAS	CARMÓPOLIS	APTIAN CONGLOM.	APTIAN EVAPORITIC MARLS	IBURA-MURIBECA	1,200
II PRE-& SYNRIFT	RECÔNCAVO	ÁGUA GRANDE MIRANGA	UJ-FLUVIAL LK-TURBD. SANDST.	LK-LACUST. FRESHWATER SHALE	GOMO-MARFIM	1,152
I INTRA-CRATONIC	SOLIMÕES	URUCU	CARBONIF. EOLIAN SANDST.	UD-SHALLOW MARINE SHALE	BARREIRINHAS-ITAITUBA	73

LEGEND: LK = Lower Cretaceous
UJ = Upper Jurassic
UD = Upper Devonian
BOEIP = barrel of oil equivalent in-place

Figure 31.2. Evolutionary sequence, with oldest at the bottom, of rift basin development indicating which oil field is discussed as a typical trap type. The major reservoir rock and source rock of the oil along with the oil in-place are also given.

BARREIRINHAS–ITAITUBA(!) PETROLEUM SYSTEM

The Barreirinhas–Itaituba(!) petroleum system was chosen to represent a system located in an intracratonic sag, the Solimões basin (Figure 31.3). The Solimões basin, which covers 600,000 km² in the Amazon region of northern Brazil, is filled with upper Paleozoic sedimentary rocks and Mesozoic diabase sills. This sag basin is separated from the Acre basin to the west, which is probably part of the sub-Andean trough, near the Iquitos arch, and on the east by the Purus arch. Its northern and southern limits are the Guyana and Brazilian Precambrian shields, respectively. The sag is filled with approximately 2500 m of mostly Devonian and Carboniferous strata, intruded by Mesozoic diabase sills and unconformably overlain by up to 500 m of Cretaceous and Tertiary sedimentary rocks (Figure 31.4) (Mosmann et al., 1987; Brazil, 1990).

The Urucu oil field, which produces from a Carboniferous reservoir rock, is located in a structure that trends northeast-southwest and contains about 73 million bbl of oil in-place (Figure 31.5).

Tectono-Stratigraphic Setting

The geologic history of the Solimões basin began with the deposition of Upper Devonian sandstones and black shales (Barreirinhas Member) of the Curuá Formation over Precambrian basement rocks. An unknown thickness of eolian sandstones and evaporites of the Carboniferous Itaituba Formation unconformably overlie these sedimentary rocks. During the Triassic–Jurassic, the area was intruded by diabase sills which, along with the underlying sedimentary rocks, were deformed in Early Jurassic–Early Cretaceous time. This period of

deformation created many of the structural features observed today. Unconformably overlying this sequence are about 500 m of undeformed deposits of the Alter do Chão Formation of Albian age, and Tertiary rocks of minor thickness.

Regional studies in the Solimões basin (Caputo and Silva, 1990; Brazil, 1990) indicate that the Solimões megashear is responsible for the formation of an array of transpressional structures, particularly anticlinal structures associated with reverse faults and en echelon folds in the Monte Alegre and Itaituba formations (Figure 31.4).

The main reservoir rocks in the area are Pennsylvanian eolian sandstones at the base of the Itaituba Formation. The underlying delta plain sandstones of the Monte Alegre Formation (Figures 31.2 and 31.4) are minor reservoir rocks. These sandstones are up to 80 m thick and presently have porosities ranging from 10 to 30% and permeabilities up to 1200 md (Neves et al., 1989; Rodrigues et al., 1991). An efficient seal is provided by the presence of an overlying thick evaporitic layer of the Itaituba Formation.

The Solimões megashear corresponds to a zone of deformation extending for about 1000 km in a northeast-southwest direction. Caputo and Silva (1990) suggest that subduction in the Andean region associated with the formation of the South Atlantic Ocean in the Early Cretaceous gave rise to a compressional regime. The compressive stress was accommodated by shearing in a N 70°–80° E direction. In the Solimões megashear, the main deformation zone is associated with positive flower structures in the seismic sections, and movement is accommodated by faults with subvertical planes. Horizontal movement along the main deformation zone was about 20 km (Porsche, 1985). The deformation caused by shearing in the Solimões megashear is also responsible for the formation of folds and reverse faults trending N 65° E and dipping toward the northwest and subordi-

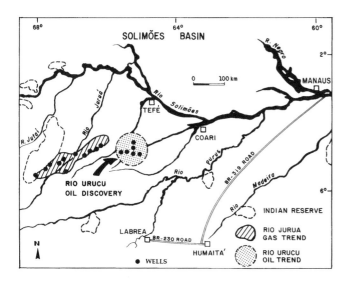

Figure 31.3. Urucu oil field and the Juruá gas field in the Solimões basin, northern Brazil.

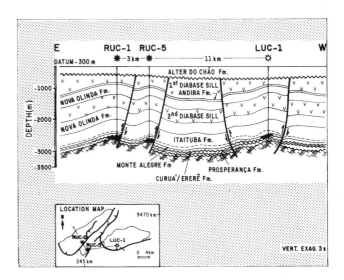

Figure 31.4. Cross section of the Urucu oil field (location on Figures 31.3 and 31.5). (Modified from Tsubone et al., 1988.)

nately toward the southeast. They have been mapped as anastomosing faults at an angle of 10°–45° to the main transcurrent fault zone. They form a group of folds trending in the same direction with an en echelon pattern that forms the following hydrocarbon field trends (from west to east): the Jandiatuba, Jutaí, Juruá, and Urucu. Structural closures for trapping hydrocarbons are observed in some of these elongated folds (Figure 31.4).

During the opening of the North Atlantic Ocean in Triassic–Jurassic time, the northern region of Brazil was affected by several episodes of magmatic extrusion in the Tacutu basin, and diabase sills were emplaced in the late Paleozoic section of the Solimões basin (Figure 31.4). The thickest sills are found close to the en echelon petroliferous trend, suggesting that magmatic conduits were present in this region. These sills were deformed by the compressional episode that occurred in Late Jurassic–Early Cretaceous, as evidenced by faulting, folding, and flexing of the older sedimentary rocks and sills. Faulting and folding is not observed in the Albian Alter do Chão Formation, indicating that by this time, tectonic activity had ceased. Consequently, tectonic activity associated with formation of present petroliferous structural trends occurred between the end of the Jurassic and the end of the Aptian (140–110 Ma), which is the probable age of remigration and entrapment of the hydrocarbons into anticlines.

Source Rock and Hydrocarbon Characterization

Detailed geochemical analyses were carried out on core and oil samples from wells drilled in the Solimões basin. Integration of the data show that the source rock for the Rio Urucu oil accumulation is the radioactive restricted-marine black shales in the Upper Devonian Barreirinhas Member of the Curuá Formation (Figure 31.6).

These radioactive black shales have an average thickness of about 50 m, with a total organic carbon

(TOC) content of up to 6 wt. % (Figure 31.6). The lack of hydrocarbon source potential (<3.5 mg HC/g rock) combined with low hydrogen indices (HI < 50 mg HC/g TOC) indicate that the Barreirinhas shales have expelled most of their hydrocarbons. This interpretation is consistent with the observed vitrinite reflectance values that are near the overmature stage ($R_o \approx 1.35\%$) (Figure 31.6). Because the upper Paleozoic sedimentary rocks are so thin and the diabase sills so thick, this high level of thermal maturity appears to be related to these Triassic–Jurassic intrusions (Mosmann et al., 1987; Brazil, 1990; Rodrigues et al., 1991; Neves et al., 1989; Mello et al., 1991).

A thermal maturity map of the Barreirinhas source rock using vitrinite reflectance data emphasizes the association of the Juruá gas field (Figures 31.3 and 31.5) with the overmature areas ($R_o > 1.35\%$), and the Urucu oil (condensate) field with the highly mature areas ($R_o \approx 1.35\%$) (Figure 31.3) (Rodrigues et al., 1991). Based on the thermal history of the source rock, this petroleum system is gas and oil (condensate) prone.

The relationship between the time of oil generation and the formation of structures is important if petroleum is to be trapped. Based only on the burial history of the source rock, hydrocarbon generation should have occurred by latest Permian time. However, burial simulations have shown that the upper Paleozoic overburden rock was insufficient to account for the observed thermal maturity as measured in the rocks and hydrocarbons (Rodrigues et al., 1991). There is a consensus that additional heat was caused by a lithospheric thermal anomaly in the area and was associated with intrusion of igneous sills during Triassic–Jurassic time.

Biological marker data indicate a good correlation between the oils and source rock extracts (Mello et al., 1991; Rodrigues et al., 1991). Diagnostic molecular features from these samples include the following: dominance of low molecular *n*-alkanes, pristane higher than phytane, a low concentration of acyclic isoprenoids,

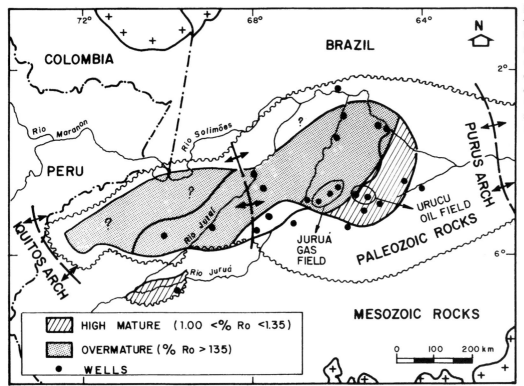

Figure 31.5. Map of thermal maturity of the Upper Devonian source rock showing the distribution of high mature and overmature stages The Juruá gas field and Urucu oil field are also shown. (Modified from Rodrigues et al., 1991.)

a high relative abundance of tricyclic terpanes, T_m higher than T_s, the presence of 28,30-bisnorhopane, and a dominance of C_{29} and C_{27} steranes over their C_{28} counterparts (Rodrigues et al., 1991; Mello et al., 1991). These geochemical data indicate that the oil in the Itaituba reservoir rock originated from the Barreirinhas source rock, so the level of certainty for the Barreirinhas–Itaituba petroleum system is known.

Events Chart

The events chart (Figure 31.7) summarizes the temporal relationship of the essential elements and processes for the Barreirinhas–Itaituba petroleum system. The hydrocarbons originated from the shallow marine black shales of the Barreirinhas Member and migrated into the eolian sandstone reservoir rocks beneath the evaporite seal rocks of the Itaituba Formation. The overburden rocks overlying the source rock include Carboniferous, Permian, Albian, and Tertiary sediments as well as diabase sills of Triassic–Jurassic age. Reconstruction of the burial and thermal history indicate that most of the generation–migration–accumulation occurred during Late Permain time, which predates formation of the Late Jurassic–Early Cretaceous traps. Therefore, hydrocarbons originally migrated into until Late Permian time, then remigrated during Late Jurassic–Early Cretaceous time into their present-day structures (Mosmann et al., 1987; Apoluceno Neto and Tsubone, 1988; Brazil, 1990; Neves et al., 1989). The critical moment was about 200 Ma when most of the hydrocarbons had already accumulated.

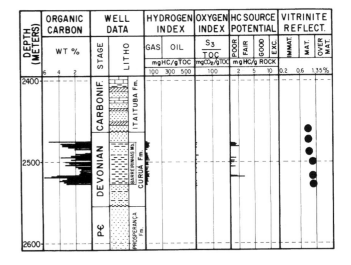

Figure 31.6. Geochemical well log of the Upper Devonian shallow marine organic-rich deposits of the Barreirinhas Member of the Curuá Formation in the Solimões basin.

The postmagmatic tectonic events probably caused hydrocarbon remobilization and cracking with partial loss of previous oil and gas accumulations. Indeed, the presence of complex gas–oil–water contacts, together with the relatively small oil columns observed in the thick reservoirs from the Itaituba and Monte Alegre formations, corroborate this hypothesis (e.g., Apoluceno Neto and Tsubone, 1988).

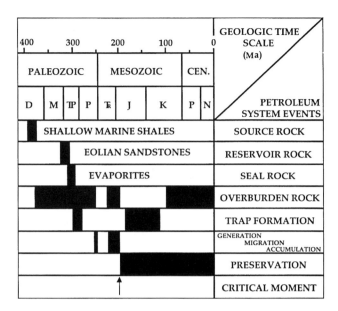

Figure 31.7. Events chart for the Barreirinhas–Itaituba(!) petroleum system.

GOMO–MARFIM(!) PETROLEUM SYSTEM

The Gomo–Marfim(!) petroleum system is an example of a system formed during the prerift and synrift evolutionary sequence (II) of the Recôncavo rift basin. This rift basin, located in northeastern Brazil, covers an area of 10,000 km^2 and is filled with Upper Jurassic–Lower Cretaceous sedimentary rocks (Figures 31.1 and 31.2).

Hydrocarbon accumulations occur throughout the sedimentary section and are distributed over most of the area; they total 680 million m^3 (4.28 billion bbl) of oil in-place (Figure 31.2) (Santos et al., 1990). Two oil fields, which together contain 1152 million bbl of oil in-place, exemplify the type of traps in this petroleum system: (1) the Água Grande oil field is representative of a prerift/synrift trap and includes the depositional sequences in the lower Candeias Formation, and (2) the Miranga oil field represents a synrift trap and includes the depositional sequences in the upper Candeias Formation and Ilhas Group (Figures 31.8 and 31.9).

Tectono-Stratigraphic Setting

The Recôncavo Basin is a structurally complex rift surrounded and floored by heterogeneous Precambrian basement rocks of the Atlantic granulitic belt. When stressed, these heterogeneous rocks fragment into many blocks of different sizes bounded by synthetic and antithetic faults. The northeast-southwest boundary faults of the rift are indicative of a regional extensional field trending N 30°–40° W (Milani and Davison, 1988). This extensional field is associated with an Early Cretaceous stretching of the continental lithosphere that eventually led to the break-up of Gondwana and to the formation of the Atlantic Ocean eastward of the rift system. The

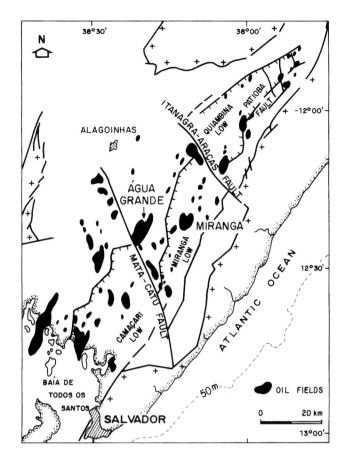

Figure 31.8. Major structural feature map showing oil fields relative to normal faults (barb on downthrown side) and strike-slip faults in the Recôncavo rift basin. (Modified from Santos et al., 1990.)

Recôncavo rift basin failed to develop into an ocean basin, but it did form a lake basin during the Early Cretaceous. The rift geometry is mainly associated with several asymmetric half-grabens controlled by master faults that dip to the west creating a ramp or a fringe zone in the western border of the basin (Figure 31.8).

Several structural features transverse to the rift axis have been interpreted as transfer or accommodation zones, which may be associated with horizontal displacement or polarity inversion along these extensional faults. Cutting across these boundary faults, several N 40° W trending lineaments have been identified as strike-slip faults or transfer zones where different rates of stretching are accommodated. The Mata–Catu fault with right-lateral displacement and the Itanagra–Araças fault with left-lateral offset cut the Recôncavo rift basin into thirds. Each third includes a structural low where the sedimentary rock thickness is greatest. The northeastern third of the basin, the Quiambina low, is a full graben, whereas the southwestern two-thirds are half-grabens, the Miranga and Camaçari lows.

The Água Grande oil field, with approximately 564 million bbl of oil in-place, is representative of the prerift/syn-rift trap style (Figures 31.2 and 31.9). Prior to rifting, a prerift depositional sequence covered the entire

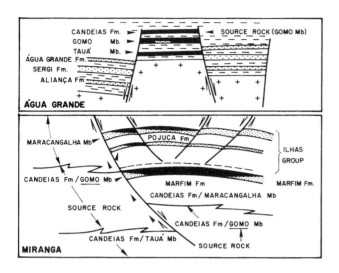

Figure 31.9. Cross sections of (a) the prerift and synrift Água Grande oil field and (b) the Miranga synrift oil field (locations of fields shown in Figure 31.8). (Modified from Santos et al., 1990.)

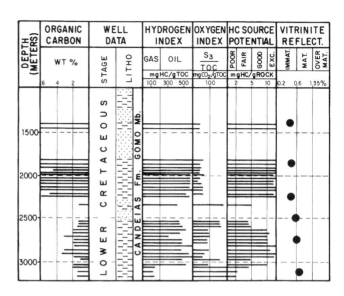

Figure 31.10. Geochemical well log showing the stratigraphic position of the Lower Cretaceous lacustrine freshwater organic-rich deposits of the Gomo Member of the Candeias Formation in the Recôncavo rift basin.

area. Within the Água Grande field, this sequence includes the Aliança, Sergi, and Água Grande formations, all of which are good reservoir rocks. The Sergi Formation, an eolian and fluvial sandstone, has reservoir rock with 18% porosity and 450 md permeability, and the Água Grande sandstone has 21% porosity and 270 md permeability. The Recôncavo rift basin formed small submerged horst blocks over which lacustrine sedimentation occurred. This prerift depositional sequence is preserved in upthrown blocks or regional horsts (Figure 31.9). After rifting, a synrift depositional sequence filled the adjacent grabens and overlapped the prerift horsts with lacustrine shales that include a source rock. In the Água Grande oil field, the prerift sequence is in direct lateral contact with the downthrown synrift lithologies of the Candeias Formation, where good source rocks in the Gomo Member have been identified (see later).

The Miranga oil field, with about 588 million bbl of oil in-place, is represented by the Candeias Formation and the Ilhas Group synrift deposits. This trap style is associated with stratigraphic trapping of hydrocarbons in turbidite sandstones of the Candeias and Marfim formations, both of which have about 18% porosity and 100 md permeability. The overlying Ilhas Group is associated with anticlinal or domal structures caused either by growth faults during rifting or by differential compaction of Ilhas Formation lithologies over older depositional sequences. A residual anticline associated with shale diapirism has played an important role in trap formation and development of the listric detached faulting. Listric faults form hydrocarbon migration pathways that connect porous lithologies of the Ilhas Group and Marfim sandstones with Gomo source rocks (Figure 31.9).

Marfim was chosen as the name for this petroleum system because the Marfim Formation contains most of the oil between the Água Grande and Miranga fields.

Source Rock and Hydrocarbon Characterization

Geochemical analyses of core and oil samples from wells drilled in the Recôncavo rift basin reveal that the main source rock for the oil accumulations in the Água Grande and Miranga oil fields are the lacustrine freshwater black shales of the lowermost Cretaceous Gomo Member of the Candeias Formation (Figure 31.10). The Gomo is characterized by a 400-m-thick succession of black shale with up to 10% TOC (Figure 31.10). In the richest intervals, the hydrocarbon source potential exceeds 60 mg HC/g rock, with HI values up to 700 mg HC/g TOC (Figure 31.10).

In general, the oil window in the Recôncavo rift basin coincides with the main structural lows where the overburden rock is thickest, such as the Quiambina, Miranga, and Camaçari lows (Figure 31.8) (Santos et al., 1990). Oil migrated from these lows along carrier beds and up listric faults, such as in the Miranga field (Figure 31.9). Sometimes the mature source rock juxtaposes the reservoir rock, such as in the Água Grande field (Figure 31.8).

Geochemical modeling of petroleum generation, timing, and intensity rates of transformation indicate that up to 80% of the petroleum had been expelled at transformation ratios $(S_1/S_1 + S_2)$ of about 0.5 and above (Soldan et al., 1987). The Gomo source rock began to generate oil in the lows during the early Aptian at about 115 Ma (Soldan et al., 1987; Daniel et al., 1989). This evidence is consistent with the observed chemical and optical thermal maturity data from vitrinite reflectance and T_{max} from Rock-Eval pyrolysis (Figure 31.10) (Gaglianone et al., 1984, Daniel et al., 1989). This geochemical log indicates that the Gomo source rock is within the oil window at 2500 m.

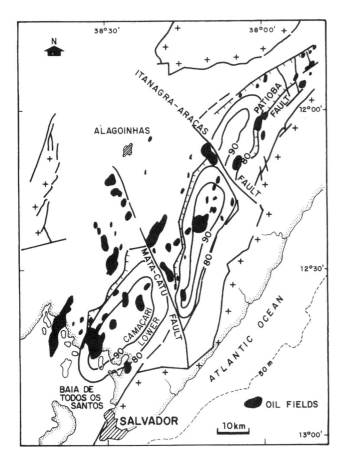

Figure 31.11. The transformation ratio (S₁/S₁ + S₂) of the Gomo Member of the Candeias Formation showing that the conversion rates of the source rock is sufficient to place it within the oil window. (Modified from Soldan et al., 1987.)

Mapping of the oil-prone source rock (Figure 31.11) emphasizes the association of the oil fields with high values of transformation ratios, which reach 90 mg HC/g of rock (Soldan et al., 1987). The geochemical parameters of the source rock indicate a type I kerogen, which is substantiated by the high volumes of oil in this petroleum system when compared to gas.

There is good correlation between biological marker data from Água Grande and Miranga field oils and from the source rock extracts of the lacustrine freshwater black shales of the Gomo Member (Gaglianone et al., 1984). Diagnostic molecular features from these samples include the following: dominance of high molecular *n*-alkanes, pristane much higher than phytane, odd–even *n*-alkane dominance, low concentration of acyclic isoprenoids, T_s higher than T_m, absence of 28,30-bisnorhopane and dinosterane, absence of C_{30} steranes, paucity of steranes with dominance of C_{29} over its counterparts, presence of gamacerane, and high hopane–sterane ratios ranging from 5 to 25 (Gaglianone et al., 1984; Mello et al., 1988; Daniel et al., 1989; Mello and Maxwell, 1990). The oils from these two fields are identical, are from the same source rock (the Gomo Member), and are in the same oil window. Therefore, the petroleum system that includes these two oil fields is the

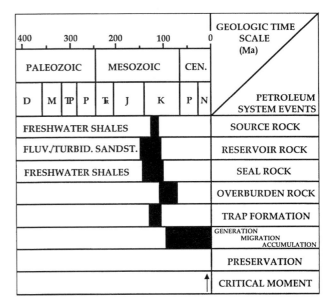

Figure 31.12. Events chart for the Gomo–Marfim(!) petroleum system.

same, and from extrapolation using the transformation ratio, this system includes all the oil fields in the Recôncavo rift basin. Based on the oil–source rock correlation, the Gomo–Marfim petroleum system is defined as a known system.

Events Chart

The events chart in Figure 31.12 summarizes the temporal relationship of the essential elements and processes of the Gomo-Marfim petroleum system. The hydrocarbons originated from the lacustrine black shales of the Gomo Member and migrated into adjacent sandstones included in the prerift and synrift sedimentary sequences. The overburden rock that overlies the source rock includes the Early Cretaceous synrift deposits and a thin veneer of postrift sediments. Traps developed as the rift formed and were essentially complete when lacustrine deposition ceased. Reconstruction of the burial and thermal history indicates that the generation, migration, and accumulation started in early Aptian time (115 Ma) and continues today in certain parts of the system. Since trap formation ceased by Early Cretaceous time, the critical moment is Early Cretaceous.

IBURA–MURIBECA(!) PETROLEUM SYSTEM

The Ibura-Muribeca(!) petroleum system is within much of the Sergipe–Alagoas basin, which is located along the coast just south of the eastern tip of Brazil (Figure 31.1). The basin, which straddles the coastline, covers an area of about 42,000 km² , including 12,000 km² onshore. Offshore the Atlantic Ocean is as much as 3000 m deep along the southeastern boundary of the basin. The petroleum system covers an area that includes 26

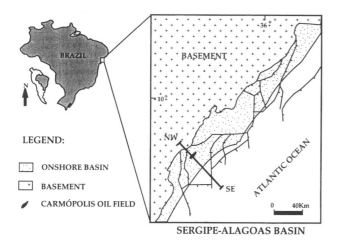

Figure 31.13. Map of the fault pattern in the basement rock underlying the Sergipe–Alagoas basin fill. The northwest-southeast cross section is shown in Figure 31.14.

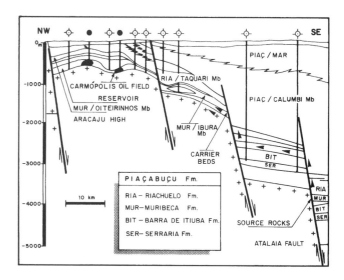

Figure 31.14. Cross section of the Carmópolis oil field in the Sergipe–Alagoas basin (location shown in Figure 31.13). (Modified from Gaglianone et al., 1991.)

known oil fields with a volume of about 380 million m^3 (2.39 billion bbl) of oil in-place. The Carmópolis oil field is the largest onshore oil field in Brazil with about 1200 million bbl of oil in-place. This field, taken as a representative trap, is a good example of the proto-marine late evolutionary stage of the rift (Figures 31.2 and 31.13).

Tectono-Stratigraphic Setting

The Sergipe-Alagoas basin includes a complex series of tectonic compartments bounded by large faults that are associated with rifting (Figure 31.13) (van der Ven et al., 1989; Aquino and Lana, 1990; Lana, 1990). The deformation is distributed along extensional faults with main orientations of N 60° W, N 43° W, N 30° E, and N-S. The most important fault system for oil migration seems to be the N 30° E trend. Regional structural highs were also formed during the rift phase, and the Carmópolis oil field is located on one of these highs, the Aracaju high (Figures 31.13 and 31.14).

The trap is mainly structural, controlled by faults that bound the block to the east and west, and a stratigraphic component is also associated with a pinch out to the north of the conglomerates and other reservoir rocks of the Carmópolis Member in the Muribeca Formation (Figure 31.14). In the western part of the Aracaju high, the Precambrian basement composed of metasedimentary rocks is highly fractured, and these fractures and vugs are hydrocarbon bearing (Azambuja Filho et al., 1980). The eastern part of the structure bears hydrocarbons in the Lower Cretaceous sedimentary rocks named the Muribeca, Barra de Itiúba, and Serraria formations (Figure 31.14). The Carmópolis accumulation is enhanced by a regional paleohigh sculptured by an erosional episode represented as a pre-Aptian unconformity. On this uncomformity, porous conglomerates and sandstones of the Muribeca Formation, which have an average porosity of 15% and permeability of up to 250 md , were deposited by alluvial fans (Azambuja Filho et al., 1990).

With progressive compaction, a large domal structure conforming to the paleotopography of the underlying basement rock was formed. Because the Carmópolis oil field is the largest and the Muribeca Formation contains most of the oil, Muribeca will be used as the reservoir rock name for this petroleum system.

Source Rock and Hydrocarbon Characterization

Detailed geochemical studies of core and oil samples from wells drilled in the Sergipe–Alagoas basin reveal that the source rocks for the oils recovered from the Carmópolis field are the protomarine hypersaline calcareous black shales of the Ibura Member within the Lower Cretaceous Muribeca Formation (Figures 31.14 and 31.15). These black shales are up to 700 m thick but average 200 m thick and have a TOC of up to 12 wt. % with an average of 3.5 wt. % (Figure 31.15). In the richest intervals, the hydrocarbon source potential exceeds 9 mg HC/g rock, and HI averages of 300 mg HC/ g TOC indicate that the organic matter is type II kerogen (Figure 31.15). This geochemical log shows that the source rock is thermally immature (R_o < 0.6%), but if it were buried greater than 2500 m, it would start to generate oil.

The oil window is offshore to the southeast where the source rock is buried deeper than 2500 m (Figure 31.16). The onshore oil fields are shallower than the oil window, whereas the source rock is within the oil window offshore (Figures 31.14 and 31.16). The pod of active source rock is shown as a cross-hatchured area offshore in Figure 31.16. It is included in the geographic extent of the petroleum system along with the distribution of the oil fields (Figure 31.16). This is long-distance oil migration of 40 km or more along unconformites and major faults from the pod of active source rock to the oil fields.

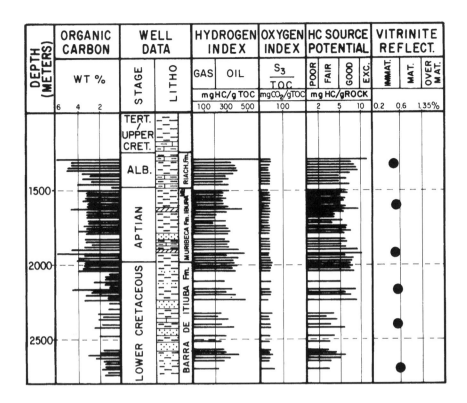

Figure 31.15. Geochemical well log of the Ibura Member within the Aptian Muribeca Formation in the Sergipe–Alagoas basin.

Geochemical modeling of the transformation ratio $(S_1/S_1 + S_2)$ and timing of oil generation, indicate that up to 80% of the organic matter has been converted to hydrocarbon. A major migration pulse has been detected for the Ibura source rock that occurred in the late Oligocene (about 26 Ma) (Gaglianone et al., 1991). Such evidence is consistent with the observed chemical, optical, and other geochemical data that indicate thermal maturation, such as vitrinite reflectance and T_{max} from Rock-Eval pyrolysis (Babinski and Santos, 1987; Gaglianone et al., 1991).

The biological marker data for the oils recovered from the Carmópolis field and the source rock extracts of the protomarine hypersaline calcareous black shales of the Ibura Member show a high degree of similarity (Mello, 1988; Gaglianone et al., 1991). Molecular features characteristic of these samples include the following: phytane higher than pristane; even–odd *n*-alkane dominance; a high concentration of acyclic isoprenoids, β-carotene, gammacerane, 28,30-bisnorhopane, C_{30} hopanes, and steranes; the presence of dinosterane and C_{30} steranes diagnostic of marine origin; T_m higher than T_s; a dominance of C_{35} hopanes over their C_{34} counterparts; a low hopane–sterane ratio; and a paucity of tricyclic and diasteranes compounds (Mello, 1988; Mello et al., 1988; Gaglianone et al., 1991). Based on the oil–source rock correlation, the Ibura–Muribeca(!) petroleum system is classified as a known system.

Events Chart

The events chart summarizes the temporal relation of the essential elements and processes for the Ibura–Muribeca petroleum system (Figure 31.17). The hydrocarbons originated from the protomarine Aptian

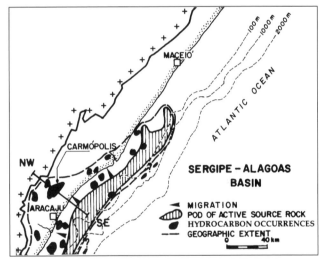

Figure 31.16. Map showing the pod of active source rock, the Ibura Member, and the geographic extent of the petroleum system. (Modified from Gaglianone et al., 1991.)

marls and calcareous black shales of the Ibura Member and migrated as far as 40 km into sandstones and coarse siliciclastics of the Muribeca Formation. The hydrocarbons have accumulated in the Lower Cretaceous alluvial fans and fan deltas, coarse siliciclastic reservoirs, and fractured Precambrian basement. The seal rocks are evaporites and marine shales deposited during Aptian–Albian time (Aquino and Lana, 1990; Gaglianone et al., 1991). The overburden rock that overlies the source rock in the offshore area includes Albian–Holocene sedimentary rocks. Traps formed as the rift developed and were essentially complete by early Paleogene time.

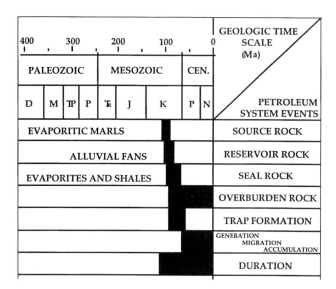

Figure 31.17. Events chart of the Ibura–Muribeca(!) petroleum system.

Reconstruction of the burial and thermal history indicates that the generation, migration, and accumulation started in late Maastrictian time (about 67 Ma) and continued to the Holocene, with a pulse in the late Oligocene (26 Ma). Since overburden rock is still being added, the critical moment is present day.

LAGOA FEIA–CARAPEBUS(!) PETROLEUM SYSTEM

The Lagoa Feia–Carapebus(!) petroleum system is one of six systems within the Campos basin, which is presently the most productive and prolific offshore Brazilian hydrocarbon province. The basin is located offshore Rio de Janeiro in southeastern Brazil and covers an area of about 100,000 km^2 from the coastline to the 3400-m isobath. The evolutionary sequence is as a rift to drift basin, and it is part of the Atlantic Ocean passive margin.

We have chosen the giant deep water Marlim oil field, which may be part of more than one system, as the representative trap for this system. The Marlim field encompasses about 152 km^2 in area and has a volume of approximately 13.9 billion bbl of oil in-place (Figures 31.2 and 31.18) (Souza et al., 1989; Guardado et al., 1990).

Tectono-Stratigraphic Setting

The Marlim oil field produces from turbidite sandstones in the deep water region of the Campos basin (Figures 31.18 and 31.19) (Lobo and Ferradaes, 1983). The reservoir rock is the Carapebus Member within the Oligocene Campos Formation. Oil is trapped in blanket turbidites that pinch out toward the west. These turbidites have an origin associated with paleocanyons that connect the deep water region with the sand-rich shelfal region. Just east of the field, three eastward-dipping listric faults affect Albian–Miocene sedimentary

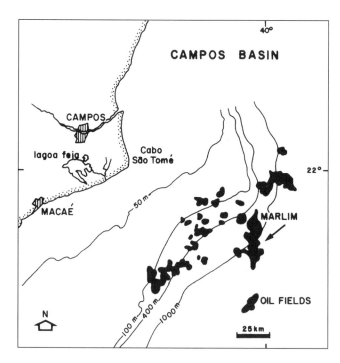

Figure 31.18. Location map of the Campos basin showing the Marlim oil field in water depths of 500–1000+ m.

rocks that show growth of sequence in the landward direction. Westward-dipping antithetic faults are associated with two of these listric faults. The westernmost listric fault in water depths of about 600 m marks the eastward boundary of the oil field (Figure 31.19). These listric faults, together with their conjugate system of antithetic faults, are controlled by halokinetic movement of the post-Albian rocks sliding over the Aptian evaporites (Figueiredo and Mohriak, 1984). Halokinesis also played a key role in the distribution patterns of the Oligocene deep water fan deposits. Salt diapirs adjacent to these listric faults can also be recognized in the seismic sections. The Lagoa Feia Formation rift sequence is identified beneath the salt layers as half-graben sedimentary wedges bounded by basement-involved planar faults (Guardado et al., 1990; Dias et al., 1990; Mohriak et al., 1990).

Hydrocarbon accumulation in the Marlim field is controlled by lateral pinchout of the sandstone turbidite reservoirs toward the west and by the regional dip toward the east (Figure 31.19). The reservoir rocks are late Oligocene fine- to medium-grained massive sandstones that are part of a huge submarine fan system, with average porosity ranging from 25 to 30% and permeabilities from 2 to 3 d (Guardado et al., 1990).

Source Rock and Hydrocarbon Characterization

A detailed geochemical investigation was carried out on core and oil samples from wells drilled in the Campos basin, and many of the oil samples came from the Marlim field (Figures 31.20 and 31.21). The results show that the source rock is lacustrine saline calcareous black

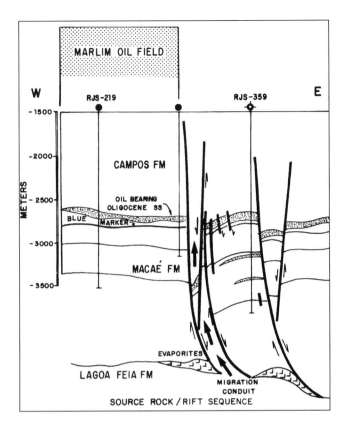

Figure 31.19. Cross section of the Marlim oil field relative to the complex of listric and antithetic faults. (Modified from Dias et al., 1990.)

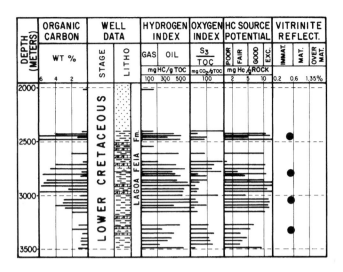

Figure 31.20. Geochemical well log of the Lower Cretaceous lacustrine saline organic-rich deposits of the Lagoa Feia Formation in the Campos basin.

shales of the Lagoa Feia Formation deposited during the late Early Cretaceous (Figueiredo et al., 1985; Mello, 1988; Mello et al., 1988; Guardado et al., 1990).

The main source rock of the Lagoa Feia Formation is about 200 m of upper Lower Cretaceous thinly laminated, calcareous black shales with a $CaCO_3$ content as high as 19%. The TOC content is 2–6 wt. % and locally as much as 9 wt. %. The HI is as high as 900 g HC/mg TOC, consistent with a type I kerogen (Figure 31.20). Organic petrology shows a predominance of lipid-rich organic matter, mainly of algal and bacterial origin, that averages 90% amorphous organic matter (Mello, 1988; Mello et al., 1988; Guardado et al., 1990). Rock-Eval pyrolysis indicates that part of the Lagoa Feia Formation is an excellent source rock, as the hydrocarbon source potential exceeds 10 mg HC/g rock.

The thermal maturity of the Lagoa Feia source rock, as shown by the geochemical log, is insufficient to generate oil ($R_o < 0.6\%$) (Figure 31.20). However, this same source rock on the west-east cross section is buried deeper than 4 km, which is undoubtedly within the oil window (Figure 31.19). Since the pod of active source rock is 2 km below the oil reservoir of the Marlim field, the oil must have migrated up the fault zones and out of the oil window into the oil-bearing Oligocene sandstones. The areal distribution of the pod of active source rock is southeast of the Marlim oil field (Figure 31.21).

The API gravity of the oils in the Marlim field ranges from 17° to 24° API. The Marlim oil composition is a mixture of biodegraded and normal oils resulting from several migration and biodegradation events that occurred during successive stages of reservoir filling (Trindade and Carminatti, 1987; Soldan et al., 1990). Geochemical modeling together with biological marker, chemical Rock-Eval pyrolysis, and petrographic evidence suggest that the source rocks of the Marlim oils are located eastward in areas with water depth exceeding 500 m (Figure 31.21). Based on burial history diagrams, the upper part of the Lagoa Feia source rock in the Campos basin started to generate oil about Coniacian–Santonian time, reaching peak oil generation during the Miocene, but it is still generating liquid hydrocarbons today (Mohriak et al., 1990; Soldan et al., 1990). The hydrocarbon migration pathway model for the Marlim oil field involves migration from the Lower Cretaceous source rock to Oligocene turbidite reservoirs along pre-salt normal faults that have kept windows open in the Aptian evaporites, along regional unconformities, and up listric normal faults (Figure 31.19).

Marlim oils and the source rock extracts of the organic-rich sections of the Lagoa Feia Formation show an identical set of biological marker characteristics (Soldan et al., 1990). These include the dominance of low molecular weigth n-alkanes with a slight odd–even predominance, pristane higher than phytane, the presence of β-carotane, a paucity of steranes, a high concentration of C_{30} αβ-hopane, and the presence of gammacerane, 28,30-bisnorhopane, and abundant tricyclic terpanes up to C_{35} (Mello, 1988; Mello et al., 1988; Soldan et al., 1990). These biological markers are consistent with a lacustrine saline environment of deposition for the source rocks (Mello et al., 1988). The Lagoa Feia–Carapebus petroleum system is thus classified as a known system on the basis of this oil–source rock correlation.

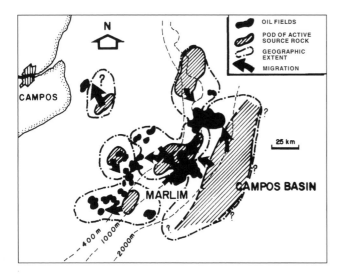

Figure 31.21. Map showing six pods of active source rock and the possible geographic extent of their respective petroleum systems. The only system discussed (Lagoa Feia–Carapebus) is the one farthest offshore, which is responsible for only part of the oil reserves in the Marlim oil field. The organic-rich deposits within the Lagoa Feia Formation form the source rock for all six of the petroleum systems in the Campos basin, and the Carapebus Member turbidite sandstones are the main reservoir rocks.

Events Chart

The events chart (Figure 31.22) summarizes the temporal relationship of the essential elements and processes of the Lagoa Feia–Carapebus petroleum system. Hydrocarbons started to migrate from the Lower Cretaceous Lagoa Feia source rock, which are calcareous shales deposited in a saline lacustrine environment, during the Miocene. Movement of the listric fault system was controlled by halokinetic movement of post-Albian rocks sliding over the Aptian evaporites. This fault system acted as a migration pathway, and in some cases as a trap, for the oil generated in the pre-salt sequence. This oil accumulated in the deep water turbidite sandstones of late Oligocene age. The trap includes both structural and stratigraphic components that are related to the evolution of the late Oligocene deep sea fan complex, which deposited the reservoir rock, and of the Oligocene–Miocene deep water marine shales, which act as seal rocks. The presence of a mixture of biodegraded and normal oils, with apparently different thermal maturity profiles, indicates the occurrence of more than one migration and biodegradation event during successive stages of reservoir filling. Such episodes appear to have been related to major sea level changes, which would have controlled the influx–reflux cycles of meteoric waters in the reservoirs (Soldan et al., 1990). The overburden rock that overlies the source rock offshore includes Lower Cretaceous–Holocene sedimentary rocks. Reconstruction of the burial and thermal history indicate that generation, migration, and accumulation started in Miocene time and are presently ongoing. Since overburden rock is still being added, the critical moment is present day.

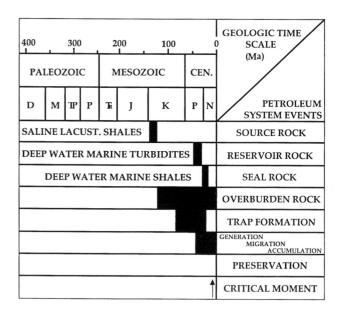

Figure 31.22. Events chart for the Lagoa Feia–Carapebus(!) petroleum system.

CONCLUSIONS

The characterization of the major petroleum systems in the Brazilian sedimentary basins was undertaken using a multidisciplinary approach involving geochemical, sedimentologic, geophysical, and microbiostratigraphic research. The integration of these data allowed the characterization, in time and space, of the petroleum pathways from source to trap of some of the most representative petroleum systems in Brazil.

Four major petroleum systems were selected as representative of 90% of the hydrocarbons (volume of oil-in-place) discovered in Brazilian basins: (1) the intracratonic sequence in the Solimões basin in the Amazon region; (2) the prerift and synrift sequence in the Recôncavo basin near the eastern tip of Brazil; (3) the protomarine sequence in the Sergipe basin in northeastern Brazil, and (4) the drift sequence in the Campos basin, offshore Rio de Janeiro in southeastern Brazil.

This type of petroleum system investigation emphasizes the genetic relationships between a particular pod of active source rock and the related hydrocarbons in the reservoir rock, focusing all geochemical, stratigraphic, and structural research on essential elements and processes (Magoon, 1990). Such an approach might open a new era in the hydrocarbon exploration of sedimentary basins of all ages.

Acknowledgments *The authors would like to thank L. B. Magoon for his helpful comments, suggestions, and modifications during the review of this manuscript. We also extend our thanks to Petrobrás, Rio de Janeiro, for permission to present and publish this paper; to the Geochemistry Sector of the Petrobrás Research Center CENPES for all the geochemical analyses; to N. C. de Azambuja Filho, L. A. F. Trindade, and*

C. F. Lucchesi for their useful suggestions; and to B. F. da Silva for his helpful assistance in editing the manuscript. We are also grateful to G. O. Estrella for presenting this paper in 1991 at the technical sessions of the AAPG Annual Meeting, Dallas, Texas.

References Cited

Apoluceno Neto, A. F., and K. Tsubone, 1988, A descoberta de petróleo do Rio Urucu, bacia do Solimões: XXV Congresso Brasileiro de Geologia, Belem, Brazil, Anais, v. 6, p. 2416–2427.

Aquino, G. S., and M. C. Lana, 1990, Exploração na bacia de Sergipe–Alagoas: O estado da arte: Boletim de Geociências da Petrobrás, v. 4 1, p. 75–84.

Asmus, H. E., and F. C. Ponte, 1973, The Brazilian marginal basins, *in* A. E. Nair and F. G. Stehli, eds., The ocean basins and margins, the South Atlantic: New York, Plenum Press, v. 1, p. 87–132.

Azambuja Filho, N. C., C. J. Abreu, P. M. Horschutz, A. Candito, and E. M. Ramos, 1980, Estudo sedimentológico, faciológico e diagenético dos conglomerados do campo petrolífero de Carmópolis: XXXI Congresso Brasileiro de Geologia, Camburiú, Anais, v. 1, p. 240–250.

Babinski, N. A., and R. C. R. dos Santos, 1984, Origem e classificação dos hidrocarbonetos da bacia Sergipe–Alagoas: Boletim de Geociências da Petrobrás, v. 11, p. 87–96.

Brazil, I. R., 1990, O potencial petrolífero e as perspectivas exploratórias da Bacia do Solimões—Norte do Brasil: Boletim de Geociências da Petrobrás, v. 41, p. 85–93.

Caputo, M. V., and O. B. Silva, 1990, Sedimentação e tectônica da bacia do Solimões, *in* G. P. Raja Gabaglia and E. J. Milani, eds., Origem e evolução de bacias sedimentares: Petróleo Brasilero S.A., Rio de Janeiro, p. 169–193.

Daniel, L. M. F., E. M. Souza, and L. F. Matos, 1989, Geochemical and hydrocarbon migration models for the Rio do Bu: integration with the northeastern sector of the Recôncavo basin, state of Bahia: Boletim de Geociências da Petrobrás, v. 33, p. 201–214.

Dias, J. L., J. C. Scarton, L. R. Guardado, F. R. Esteves, and M. Carminatti, 1990, Aspectos da Evolução tectono-sedimentar e a ocorrencia de hidrocarbonetos na bacia de Campos, *in* G. P. Raja Gabaglia and E. J.Milani, eds., Origem e evolução de bacias sedimentares: Petróleo Brasileiro S.A., Rio de Janeiro, p. 333–360.

Estrella, G., M. R. Mello, P. C. Gaglianone, R. L. M. Azevedo, K. Tsubone, E. Rossetti, J. Concha, and I. M. R. Brüning, 1984, The Espírito Santo basin (Brazil) source rock characterization and petroleum habitat, *in* G. Demaison and R. J. Murris, eds., Petroleum geochemistry and basin evaluation: AAPG Memoir #35, p. 253–271.

Figueiredo, A. M. and W. U. Mohriak, 1984, A tectônica salífera e as acumulações de hidrocarbonetos na Bacia de Campos: XXXIII Congresso Brasileiro de Geologia, Rio de Janeiro, Anais, p. 1380–1394.

Figueiredo, A. M., F. M. Pereira, W. Mohriak, and L. A. F. Trindade, 1983, Salt tectonics and oil accumulation in Campos basin, offshore Brazil: AAPG Bulletin, Abstracts, v. 69, p. 255.

Gaglianone, P. C., L. A. F. Trindade, L. M. F. Daniel, and L. P. Magnavita, 1984, Avaliação geoquímica do Recôncavo: Internal Report, Petrobrás/CENPES/DIVEX/SEGEQ, Rio de Janeiro, 130 p.

Gaglianone, P. C., E. K. Castro, H. P. Alves Filho, C. V. Araujo, E. S. T. da Frota, H. A. F. Chaves, F. C. Castro, G. P. Hamsi, Jr., and B. F. da Silva, 1991, Caracterização das novas fronteiras petroliferas da bacia de Sergipe–Alagoas: Internal Report, Petrobrás/CENPES/DIVEX/SEGEQ, Rio de Janeiro, 75 p.

Guardado, L. R., L. A. P. Gamboa, and C. F. Lucchesi, 1990, Petroleum geology of the Campos basin, Brazil, a model for a producing Atlantic type basin, *in* J. D. Edwards and P. A. Santogrossi, eds., Divergent/passive margin basins: AAPG Memoir #48, p. 3–80.

Lana, M. C., 1990, Bacia de Sergipe–Alagoas: uma hipótese de evolução tectono-sedimentar, *in* G. P. Raja Gabaglia and E. J. Milani, eds., Origem e evolução de bacias sedimentares: Petróleo Brasileiro S.A., Rio de Janeiro, p. 311–332.

Lobo, A. P., and J. O. Ferradaes, 1983, Reconhecimento do talude e sopé continentais da bacia de Campos: Internal Report, Petrobrás/DEPEX, Rio de Janeiro, 29 p.

Magoon, L. B., 1988, The petroleum systems—a classification scheme for research, exploration, and resource assessment, *in* L. B. Magoon, ed., Petroleum systems of the United States: U.S. Geological Survey Bulletin 1870, p. 2–15.

Magoon, L. B., 1990, Identified petroleum systems within the United States, *in* L. B. Magoon, ed., Petroleum systems of the United States: U.S. Geological Survey Bulletin 1912, p. 2–10.

Mello, M. R., 1988. Geochemical and molecular studies of the depositional environments of source-rocks and their derived oils from the Brazilian marginal basins: Ph.D. dissertation, Bristol University, Bristol, U.K., 240 p.

Mello, M. R., and J. R. Maxwell, 1990, Organic geochemical and biological marker characterization of source-rocks and oils derived from lacustrine environments in the Brazilian continental margin, *in* B. J. Katz, ed., Lacustrine basin exploration—case studies and modern analogs: AAPG Memoir #50, p. 77–98.

Mello, M. R., N. Telnaes, P. C. Gaglianone, M. I. Chicarelli, S. C. Brassel, and J. R. Maxwell, 1988, Organic geochemical characterization of depositional paleoenvironments of source-rocks and oils in Brazilian marginal basins, *in* L. Matavelli and L. Novelli, eds.: Advances in Organic Geochemistry 1987, v. 13, p. 31–45.

Mello, M. R., E. V. Santos Neto, G. R. Cerqueira, R. Rodrigues, and T. T. Gonçalves, 1991, The petroleum systems in the Brazilian Paleozoic basins: a biological marker approach, *in* D. A. C. Manning, ed., Organic geochemistry: Advances and Applications in Energy and the Natural Environment, Manchester University Press, Manchester, U.K., p. 76–78.

Milani, E. J., and I. Davison, 1988, Basement control and transfer tectonics in Reconcâvo—Tucano–Jatoba rift, northeast Brazil: Tectonophysics, v. 154 1/2, p. 40–70.

Mohriak, W. U., M. R. Mello, J. F. Dewey, and J. R. Maxwell, 1990, Petroleum geology of the Campos Basin, offshore Brazil, *in* J. Brooks, ed., Classic petroleum provinces: Geological Society of London Special Publication, n. 50, p. 119–141.

Mosmann, R., F. U. H. Falkenhein, A. Gonçalves, and F. Nepomuceno Filho, 1987, Oil and gas potential of the Amazon Paleozoic basins: AAPG Memoir #27, p. 207–241.

Neves, C. A. O., et al., 1989, The Amazonas basin: potential prospects and exploration priorities: Boletim de Geociencias da Petrobrás, v. 4, n. 1, p. 95–104.

Ojeda, H. A. O., 1982, Structural framework, stratigraphy, and evolution of the Brazilian marginal basins: AAPG Bulletin, v. 66, p. 732–749.

Porsche, E., 1985, Tectônica da faixa de dobramentos do Juruá, bacia do Alto Amazonas—um modelo estrutural: Master's thesis, Universidade Federal de Ribeiraõ Preto, Ouro Preto, Brazil, 124 p.

Rodrigues, R., J. A. Trigüis, C. V. Araújo, and I. Brazil, 1991, Geoquímica e faciologia orgânica dos sedimentos da Bacia do Solimões: Internal Report, Petrobrás/CENPES/ DIVEX/SEGEQ, Rio de Janeiro, 87 p.

Santos, C. F., J. A. Cupertino, and J. A. E. Braga, 1990, Síntese sobre a geologia das bacias do Reconcâvo, Tucano e Jatobá, *in* G. P. Raja Gabaglia and E. J. Milani, eds., Origem e evoluçäo de bacias sedimentares: Petroleo Brasileiro S.A., Rio de Janeiro, p. 235–268.

Soldan, A. L., L. C. Freitas, P. C. Gaglianone, H. A. F. Chaves, and J. R. Cerqueira, 1987, Quantitative estimation of original hydrocarbon source-rock potential: a statistical model of behavior: Thirteenth International on Organic Geochemistry, Abstracts, Venizia, Italy, p. 166.

Soldan, A. L., J. R. Cerqueira, J. C. Ferreira, J. C. Scarton, and C. A. G. Cora, 1990, Aspectos relativos ao habitat do óleo dos campos de Marlim e Albacora–bacia de Campos: Internal Report, Petrobrás/CENPES/DIVEX/SEGEQ, Rio de Janeiro, 170 p.

Souza, J. M., J. C. Scarton, A. Candido, C. E. Souza Cruz, and C. A. G. Cora, 1989, The Marlim and Albacora fields: geophysical, geological, and reservoir aspects: 21st Annual Offshore Technology Conference, Houston, Texas, p. 109–118.

Trindade, L. A. P., and Carminatti, M., 1987, Estudo da migraçio secundária nos Campos de Marlim e Albacora, Bacia de Campos: Internal Report, Petrobrás/CENPES, Rio de Janeiro, 157 p.

Tsubone, K., A. Neto, and I. R. Brazil, 1988, Tectonics and sedimentation of the Solimões basin, northern Brazil: Internal Report, Petrobrás/DENOC, Belém, 90 p.

van der Ven, P. H., C. Cainelli, and J. F. Fernandes, 1989, Bacia de Sergipe–Alagoas: geologia e exploração: Boletim de Geociências da Petrobrás, v. 3, n. 4, p. 307–319.

Magoon, L. B, and W. G. Dow, eds., 1994, The petroleum
system—from source to trap: AAPG Memoir 60.

Chapter **32**

Petroleum Systems in the Neuquén Basin, Argentina

Carlos M. Urien
Consultant
Buenos Aires, Argentina

Juvenal J. Zambrano
Consultant
San Juan, Argentina

Abstract

The foreland backarc Neuquén basin in southwestern Argentina includes four sedimentary cycles of Jurassic–Eocene age. (1) The Cuyo cycle includes black, organic-rich shales overlain by coastal and fluvial siliciclastics. (2) The Lotena–Chacay cycle comprises excellent siliciclastic reservoir rocks overlain by thick evaporites, all deposited on a platform. (3) The Andic cycle includes hydrocarbon-bearing basal alluvial fan deposits and transgressive sandstones that are overlain by organic-rich shaly carbonates, the main hydrocarbon source rock. This cycle also has platform to coastal carbonates overlain by fluvial deltaic clastics and neritic black shales. Evaporitic facies complete this important cycle. (4) Finally, the Rio Grande cycle comprises fluvial and alluvial siliciclastics, evaporites, and coastal or shallow platform shales and carbonates. These four sedimentary cycles represent most of the basin fill.

The western area of the basin shows a belt of north-south trending thrust cut folds built in the original foredeep basin during Andean tectonic phases. The eastern area comprises a platform, hinge line, and deep embayment separated from the western area by a megasuture.

Three petroleum systems are in two sedimentary cycles, the Cuyo and the Andic, of Jurassic–Early Cretaceous age. The second petroleum system within the lower Andic cycle contains the most hydrocarbons. All systems in the eastern area reached their critical moment during the late Eocene, and in the western area during the late Tertiary. Destruction of parts of these petroleum systems occurred through abnormal heat flow from volcanism and by erosion. Although the heat flow destroyed some hydrocarbons, in other areas it enhanced kerogen maturation and thermally cracked oil to gas. Destruction by erosion was important in uplifted areas.

INTRODUCTION

The Neuquén basin, recognized as one of the leading producers of hydrocarbons among the petroleum provinces of Argentina, is located in the southernmost segment of the sub-Andean orogen of South America. Other basins in Argentina that are related to this orogen, which extends the full length of the Pacific margin from Trinidad to the Malvinas (Falkland) plateau, include the most prolific South American petroleum provinces (Table 32.1).

The Neuquén basin is located south of the Cuyo basin, west of the San Rafael uplift, north of the North Patagonia massif, and east of the main orogenic belt of the principal Cordillera (Figures 32.1 and 32.2A). For the purpose of discussion, the Neuquén basin is divided into three areas: western, transition, and eastern (Figure 32.2B). Each area is further divided into provinces. The western area includes the following provinces: the main orogenic belt, the Loncopué trough, the Cordillera de

Table 32.1. Cumulative Production and Remaining Reserves of Oil and Gas in Argentina by Sedimentary Basin

Basin	Oil (MMbbl)		Gas (10^{12} ft^3)	
	Cum[a]	Err[b]	Cum	Err
Northwest				
Tarija & Oran-Metan	254	211	2.22	5.19
Central West				
Cuyo	1351	298	0.195	0.073
Neuquén	1568	2044	6.0	12.34
Patagonia				
San Jorge	3083	890	2.95	0.98
Magallanes (Austral)	227	264	3.25	4.33

[a]Cum = cumulative production.

[b]Err = estimated remaining reserves.

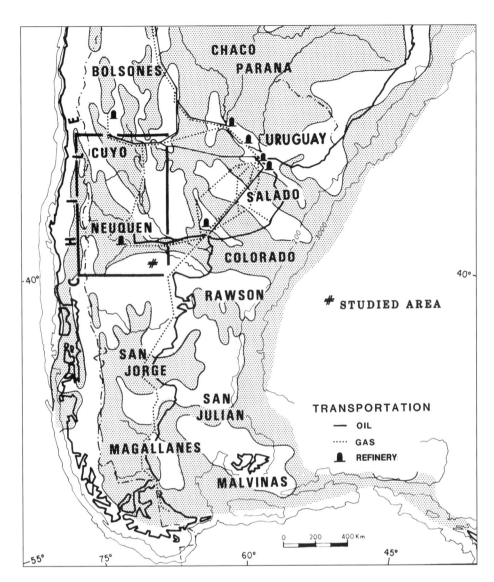

Figure 32.1. Sedimentary basins of southern South America. The rectangle outlines the study area (covered by the following figures). Key: solid lines, oil pipelines; dotted lines, gas pipelines; stippled areas, sedimentary basins; white areas, uplifts.

Viento (Viento C.), and the Agrio–Chos Malal and South Mendoza fold belt (Table 32.2). The transition area is one province, the Chihuidos–Huantraico–Reyes–Llancancelo folded zone, and is bounded on the east by a megasuture.

The eastern area includes the embayment, hinge line, and northeastern platform, which are all between the megasuture and the northeastern basin boundary adjacent to the San Rafael uplift. One province, the southern embayment, is located south of the embayment and hinge line provinces and is bounded on the north by the dorsal shear zone and on the south by the North Patagonia massif, which forms the southern basin boundary. The eastern area, sometimes referred to as extra-Andean, is undeformed by Andean tectonism, in contrast to the western and transition areas which are deformed (Table 32.2).

Only in southern South America in the Neuquén basin are there four well-preserved Mesozoic–early Tertiary transgressive–regressive sedimentary cycles. Two of these cycles, the Cuyo and Andic, contain thick intervals of good to excellent source rocks. The relationship between source rocks and reservoir rocks, as well as

the time of generation, migration fairways, and areas of accumulation, have been broadly established.

As of 1990, 6741 wells have been drilled in this basin fill, of which 2619 wells have been producing oil and gas from 185 fields. These fields cover an area of 194,700 Ha (481,100 acres) and have a cumulative production of 1568 million bbl of oil. Remaining recoverable reserves of oil are estimated at 2044 million bbl (Table 32.1). Based on its area and amount of oil production, the Neuquén basin is rated as the third highest oil-producing basin in Argentina, but it should be rated first on the basis of its exploration possibilities.

The Neuquén basin is an excellent place to study the petroleum system because it has good seismic and well data coverage, its stratigraphic record is almost complete, and hydrocarbons are present. From the investigation of these sedimentary rocks and discovered hydrocarbons, it is possible to tentatively identify three petroleum systems. This chapter provides an overview of the stratigraphic and structural features of the Neuquén basin and describes these speculative systems.

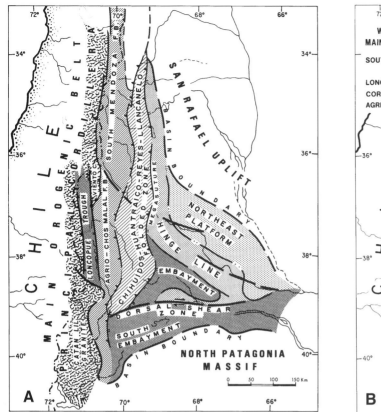

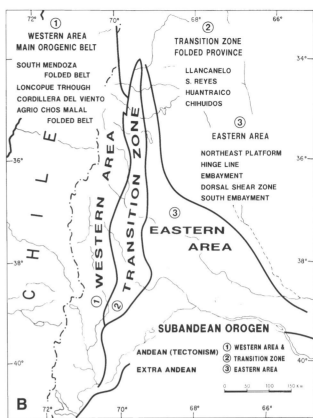

Figure 32.2. (A) Provinces of the Neuquén basin. The megasuture separates the Andean (western) and the extra-Andean (eastern) areas of the basin. The embayment is a depocenter separated from the southern embayment by the dorsal shear zone. The hinge line is the transitional flexure between the embayment and the northeastern platform. The megasuture was shifted to the west in the southern embayment as a result of activity in the dorsal shear zone. **(B)** Generalized zonation of Neuquén basin. The western area and transition zone are affected by Andean compressional tectonics, whereas ancient tensional tectonics prevail in the eastern area.

Table 32.2. Areas and Provinces of the Neuquén Basin

Deformed by Andean tectonism

Provinces in the western area
- Principal Cordillera (main orogenic belt)
- Loncopué trough
- Cordillera de Viento (Viento C.)
- Tromen–Payun volcanic uplift (Figure 32.4)
- Agrio–Chos Malal and South Mendoza folded belts

Province in transition area
- Chihuidos-Huantraico-Reyes-Llancanelo folded zone

Undeformed by Andean tectonism

Provinces in eastern area
- Northeastern platform
- Hinge line
- Embayment
- Dorsal shear zone
- Southern embayment

EXPLORATION HISTORY

Yrigoyen (1983), in his historical review of this area, informs us that hydrocarbons were mentioned in nineteenth century literature. During the 1880s, the first researcher described Cretaceous and Tertiary sedimentary deposits in the Neuquén basin. In 1905, the National Direction of Mining, Geology, and Hydrology started a systematic geologic reconnaissance of the Argentine territory. From 1900 to the late 1920s, Keidel, Wichmann, Groeber (1929), and Windhausen (1931) made significant advances in the geologic knowledge of the Neuquén basin. This knowledge led to the drilling in 1918 of the well that discovered oil in the Plaza Huincul structure. As a result, intensive exploration began by the National Direction of Mining, Geology, and Hydrology and by private oil companies.

In 1922, the Argentine state-owned petroleum enterprise, the Yacimientos Petroliferos Fiscales, was created, which subsequently began surface and subsurface geologic work. This exploration activity resulted in discoveries along the dorsal shear zone which provided information that complemented the stratigraphic and structural surveys to the north in the South Mendoza

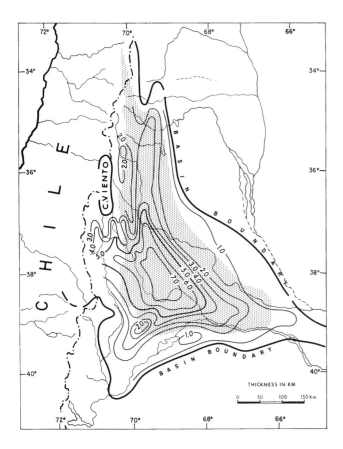

Figure 32.3. Isopach map of Mesozoic and Cenozoic sedimentary rocks and their relationship to the petroleum systems (stippled).

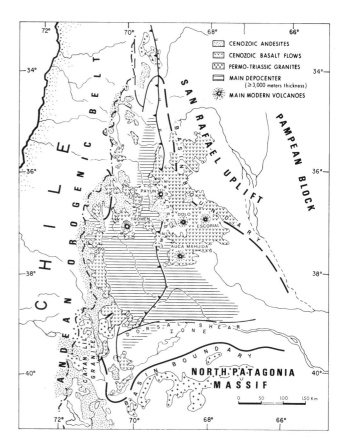

Figure 32.4. Areal distribution of Cenozoic basalts and andesites in relation to sedimentary rocks thicker than 3 km. Areas related to these volcanic centers are nonconventional heat sources, which affected the size of the pod of active source rock.

fold belt. This fold belt was investigated by Groeber, who in 1929 made the first geologic synthesis of the basin. The concepts of time–rock stratigraphic units and sedimentary cycles were, for the first time, applied in this basin (Groeber et al., 1953).

During the 1940s and 1950s, new oil and gas fields continued to be discovered in the south Mendoza fold belt and the dorsal shear zone. From the 1960s, exploration extended toward the northeasernt platform, where commercial oil was found along a regional structural trend. Recently, in areas distant from the traditional oil- or gas-bearing trends, new producing zones were identified in the northeastern platform and South Mendoza fold belt. Since 1970, more oil and gas fields have been discovered in the Agrio–Chos Malal fold belt.

BASIN BOUNDARIES

The Neuquén basin lies along the sub-Andean orogen in west-central Argentina. From north to It extends from 34° 40' to 40° south latitude and from 66° to 70° 20' west longitude. The Neuquén basin outline approximates a right triangle, with its hypotenuse trending toward the northeast. It has an area of about 137,000 km², of which more than 100,000 km² are prospective for hydrocarbons. In the central part of the basin where the basin fill is greatest, the sedimentary rocks are more than 7 km thick

(Figure 32.3). Igneous rocks of Cenozoic age cover about one-third of the basin (Figure 32.4).

Subsurface data are needed to determine the northeastern and southern boundaries, which are placed by most authors along the pinchout line of the Andic sedimentary cycle, which is Kimmeridgian–Albian in age (Figure 32.5; Table 32.3). The northeastern basin boundary, the San Rafael uplift, is a positive area defined by faults and covered with Cenozoic volcanic and sedimentary units (Figure 32.4). Southeast of the Cenozoic volcanic units, the boundary is ill-defined, as the only available information consists of some old refraction seismic data. These data suggest that to the east, a thin layer of Cretaceous or possibly Jurassic or Triassic sedimentary rocks could occur in the subsurface. This could represent a connection between the Neuquén and Colorado basins during Jurassic or Early Cretaceous time (Figure 32.1). The southern border, also defined by subsurface information, is the wedgeout line of the Andic sedimentary cycle against the Permian–Triassic granites exposed in the North Patagonia massif.

The western boundary, generally covered by Cenozoic basalt flows and andesites, is mostly erosional as observed along the eastern slope of the Andean orogenic belt (Figure 32.4). North of 39° south latitude, the western boundary is poorly defined except where the

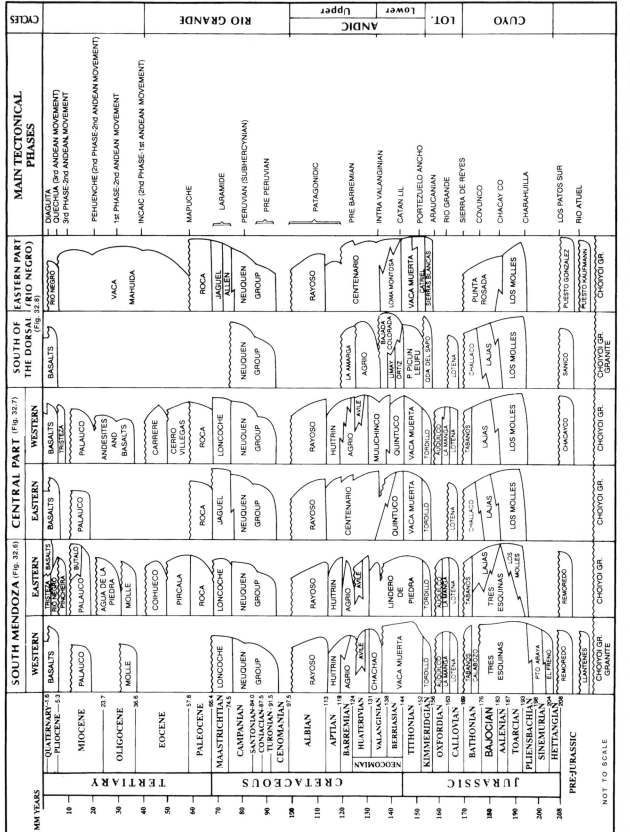

Figure 32.5. Neuquén basin stratigraphic correlation chart showing main tectonic phases. The eastern South Mendoza column compares with Figure 32.6, the western central part with Figure 32.7, and the eastern part (Rio Negro) with Figure 32.8. The unconformities that continue from column to column form the boundaries of the stratigraphic cycles.

Table 32.3. Sedimentary Cycles Separated by Unconformities (shown on Figure 32.5)

Sedimentary Cycle	Age
Rio Grande	Cenomanian or Turonian–early Eocene
Andic	Kimmeridgian–Albian
Lotena	Middle Callovian–ate Oxfordian
Cuyo	Hettangian–early Callovian

pre-Jurassic basement rock crops out. Elsewhere it is covered by Cenozoic volcanic and sedimentary rock units, such as on the Loncopué trough. Near the Chilean border, outcrops of marine Jurassic sedimentary rocks indicate that the basin extends into this country, but here it is affected by Mesozoic and Cenozoic magmatic events.

The northern end of this boundary on the South Mendoza fold belt is related to faults and uplifted blocks in the orogenic belt. Here, the Mesozoic sequences are eroded and mixed with volcanic and pyroclastic material to form discontinuous outcrops that are traceable along these mountains into Chile. In this area, the basin limit had been formerly placed along a thrust fault zone. However, in recent years, the exploration for hydrocarbons has extended into the Andean orogenic belt, where some oil fields have been found. Hence, the western boundary here is poorly defined at the surface and, for convenience, is placed near the international border between Chile and Argentina.

REGIONAL GEOLOGIC SETTING

The Neuquén basin was formed in latest Triassic or earliest Jurassic time and continued as a depositional area over a stable craton until the early Tertiary, at which time the first Andean movements closed its evolution. The western and transition areas of the basin are tectonically deformed, whereas the eastern area is undeformed (Figure 32.2; Table 32.2). The Neuquén basin consists of an eastern stable faulted platform, a hinge line, a foredeep, and a western folded belt. The eastern part overlays a Precambrian–late Paleozoic basement complex of metamorphic, submetamorphic, intrusive, and extrusive rocks. This basement complex, which already existed when the Neuquén basin was formed, extends over central and western Argentina and northern Patagonia.

The stratigraphic column for the Neuquén basin in Figure 32.5 is summarized for six areas. Stratigraphic columns are shown for both the western and eastern parts of the South Mendoza fold belt. Columns for the central part of the basin are represented by the eastern and western parts of the hinge line andnortheastern platform. The column for south of the dorsal trend shows the stratigraphy of the southern embayment, and the column for the eastern part (Río Negro) is representative of the stratigraphy at the easternmost part of the southern embayment. The four sedimentary cycles (Table 32.3) are bounded by unconformities that extend from column to column (Figure 32.5).

Basement Rock

The basement rock of pre-Jurassic age consists of several stratigraphic units exposed along the western rim of the basin (Choiyoi Group of Figure 32.5). These metamorphic rocks are probably Precambrian or lower Paleozoic (Digregorio, 1972; Digregorio and Uliana, 1980). Low-grade metamorphic to highly indurated sedimentary rocks are exposed in the southwest and are believed to be lower Paleozoic or Devonian. Similar units occur on the San Rafael uplift (Horqueta Group). In the northwest, Carboniferous–Lower Permian pyroclastics and fossiliferous marine sedimentary rocks crop out. The Permian–Triassic acid intrusives, such as those exposed in the western volcanic arc and part of the South Mendoza folded belt, also crop out in the San Rafael uplift and as part of the nuclei of some outcropping anticlines in the western folded area. The Permian–Triassic volcanic, pyroclastic, and sedimentary complex that makes up the basement rock in the subsurface of nearly the entire basin is commonly known as the Choiyoi Group (Figure 32.4) (Digregorio, 1972).

Sedimentary Basin Fill

For ease of discussion, the sedimentary basin fill has been divided into three parts. First, the two pre-Cuyo sequences were deposited into a block-faulted terrane. Second, four sedimentary cycles—the Cuyo, Lotena, Andic, and Río Grande—were deposited over a stable craton and are the focus of this chapter. Third, Tertiary rocks were deposited in a nonmarine foreland basin. In Quaternary time, volcanic activity occurred throughout most of the area.

Pre-Cuyo Sequences

Middle–Late Triassic sedimentary rocks, mostly continental clastics with tuff and volcanic intercalations, are partly developed in the basement half-grabens. These units have also been found in the subsurface. Various formations of this age have been recognized: Llantenes, Barda Alta, Paso Flores, Puesto Kaufman, and others (Figure 32.5). These rock units accumulated in small, separate fault blocks. Some of these units are reservoir rocks since they locally contain oil, which probably migrated from a younger mature source rock. The possibility of finding indigenous oil and gas in these so-called basement rocks cannot be disregarded (Robles, 1984; Digregorio and Uliana, 1980).

Another set of deposits consist of redbeds that accumulated in alluvial fans or fluvial plains. These include the Remoredo Formation in South Mendoza, the Chacayco Formation in the central part (western) of the basin, and the Planicie Morada Formation in the subsurface of the northeastern platform, among others (Figure 32.5). Lithology and seismic data show that these redbeds were deposited in grabens or half-grabens from latest Triassic (Norian or Rhaetian) to earliest Jurassic (Hettangian) time.

Cuyo Sedimentary Cycle

During Hettangian time, a general subsidence took place in what is now the Neuquén basin. The first marine transgression came from Chile toward the area of the South Mendoza fold belt (Digregorio, 1972; Legarreta and Gulisano, 1989; Volkheimer, 1978). By Pliensbachian time, this transgression progressed southward and covered most of the basin. Along the eastern margin,

alluvial plains developed. The marine and fluvial sedimentary rocks deposited during this transgression are known as the Cuyo Group (Digregorio, 1972). After Bajocian time, the transgressive phase was followed by a regressive phase that ended during the early Callovian, thus closing the Cuyo cycle.

The basal transgressive unit of this cycle (Los Molles Formation) (Figures 32.6–32.8) consists mainly of basinal

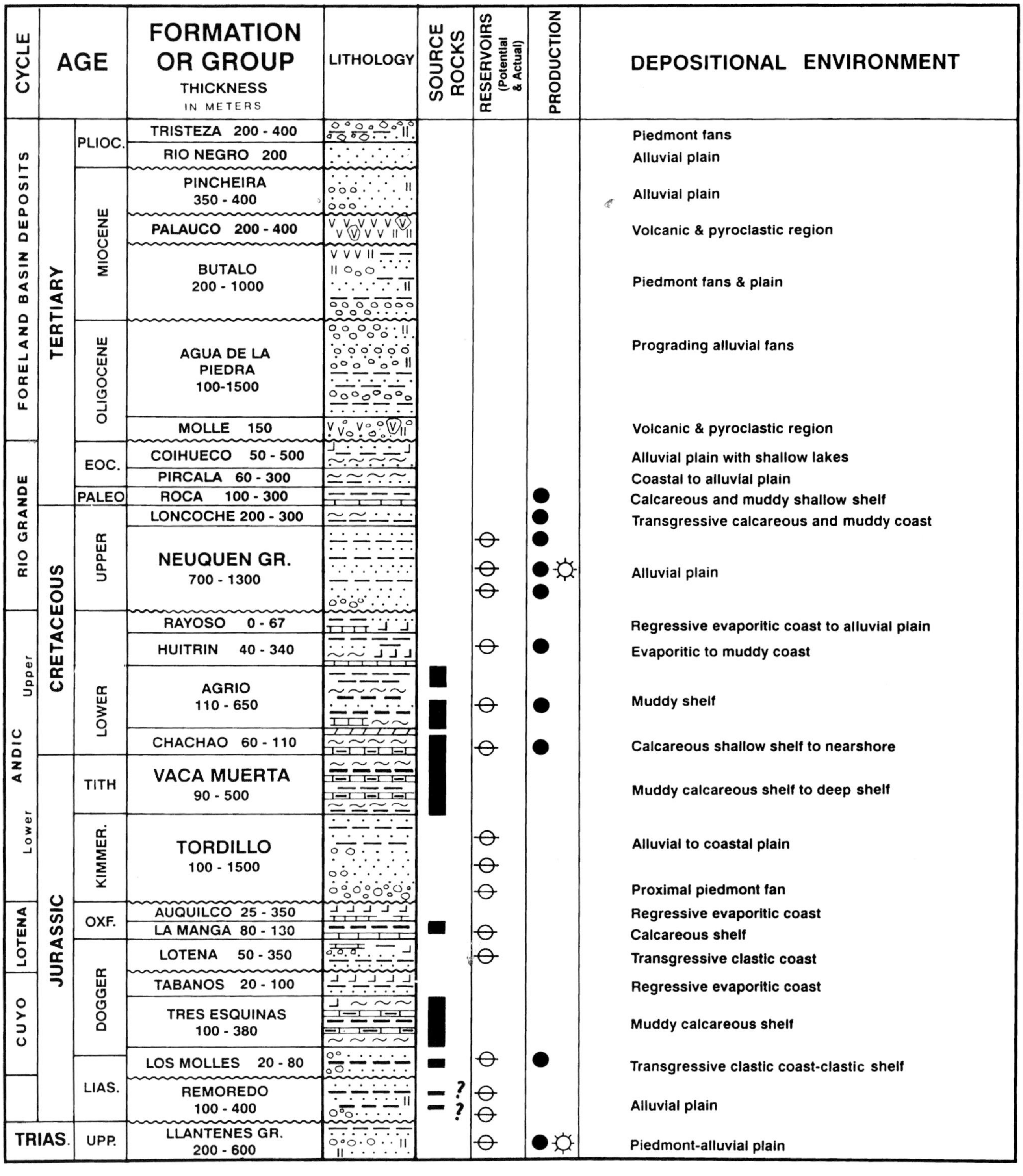

Figure 32.6. Composite stratigraphic column of the northern Neuquén basin showing rock unit thickness, lithology, producing reservoir rocks, and depositional environments.

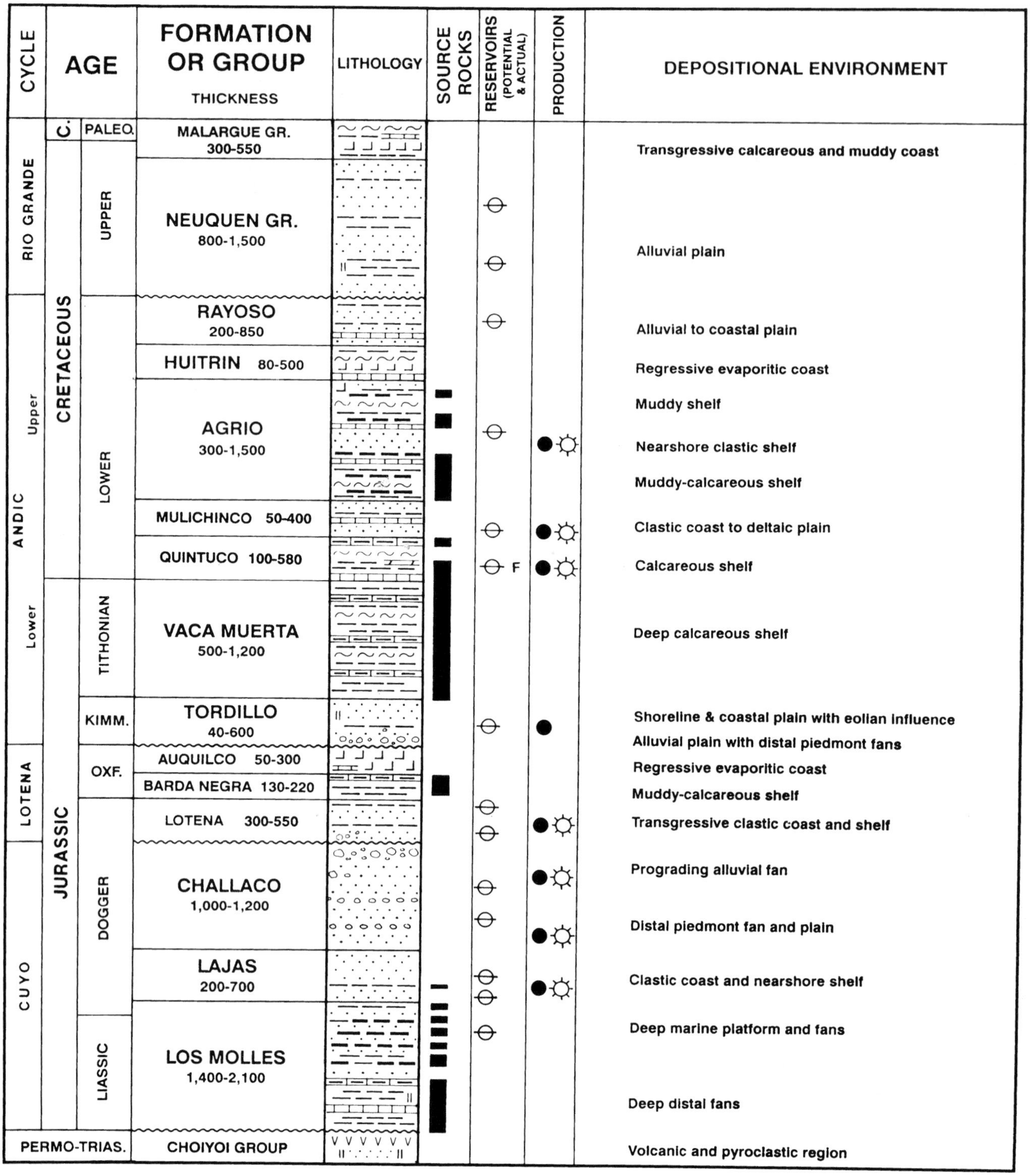

CYCLE	AGE	FORMATION OR GROUP THICKNESS	LITHOLOGY	SOURCE ROCKS	RESERVOIRS (POTENTIAL & ACTUAL)	PRODUCTION	DEPOSITIONAL ENVIRONMENT
C.	PALEO.	MALARGUE GR. 300-550					Transgressive calcareous and muddy coast
RIO GRANDE	UPPER (CRETACEOUS)	NEUQUEN GR. 800-1,500			⊕ ⊕		Alluvial plain
ANDIC / Upper	Lower CRETACEOUS	RAYOSO 200-850			⊕		Alluvial to coastal plain
		HUITRIN 80-500		■			Regressive evaporitic coast
				■			Muddy shelf
		AGRIO 300-1,500		■	⊕	●☼	Nearshore clastic shelf
				■			Muddy-calcareous shelf
		MULICHINCO 50-400		■	⊕	●☼	Clastic coast to deltaic plain
		QUINTUCO 100-580			⊕ F	●☼	Calcareous shelf
Lower	TITHONIAN	VACA MUERTA 500-1,200		■			Deep calcareous shelf
	KIMM.	TORDILLO 40-600			⊕	●	Shoreline & coastal plain with eolian influence
							Alluvial plain with distal piedmont fans
LOTENA	OXF.	AUQUILCO 50-300					Regressive evaporitic coast
		BARDA NEGRA 130-220		■			Muddy-calcareous shelf
		LOTENA 300-550			⊕ ⊕	●☼	Transgressive clastic coast and shelf
CUYO / JURASSIC	DOGGER	CHALLACO 1,000-1,200			⊕ ⊕	●☼	Prograding alluvial fan
						●☼	Distal piedmont fan and plain
		LAJAS 200-700		■	⊕ ⊕	●☼	Clastic coast and nearshore shelf
	LIASSIC	LOS MOLLES 1,400-2,100		■ ■ ■	⊕		Deep marine platform and fans
				■			Deep distal fans
	PERMO-TRIAS.	CHOIYOI GROUP	V V V V V				Volcanic and pyroclastic region

Figure 32.7. Composite stratigraphic column of the central Neuquén basin showing rock unit thickness, lithology, producing reservoir rocks, and depositional environments.

black to bluish shales, partly turbiditic. Locally, coarser siliciclastics are found at the base (e.g., El Freno Formation in South Mendoza) (Volkheimer, 1978). Sandstones tend to be more common in the upper part of this formation.

The Cuyo sedimentary cycle is progradational, as the Los Molles marine shales grade upward into shallow water deltaic facies consisting mainly of sheetlike sandbodies known as the Lajas Formation (Figure 32.7). In eastern South Mendoza, the Los Molles Formation grades upward into calcareous, marly, and clay-rich marine deposits, the Tres Esquinas Formation (Stipanicic, 1969). Farther east (Rio Negro), the Los Molles Formation grades laterally and upward into alluvial deposits of the

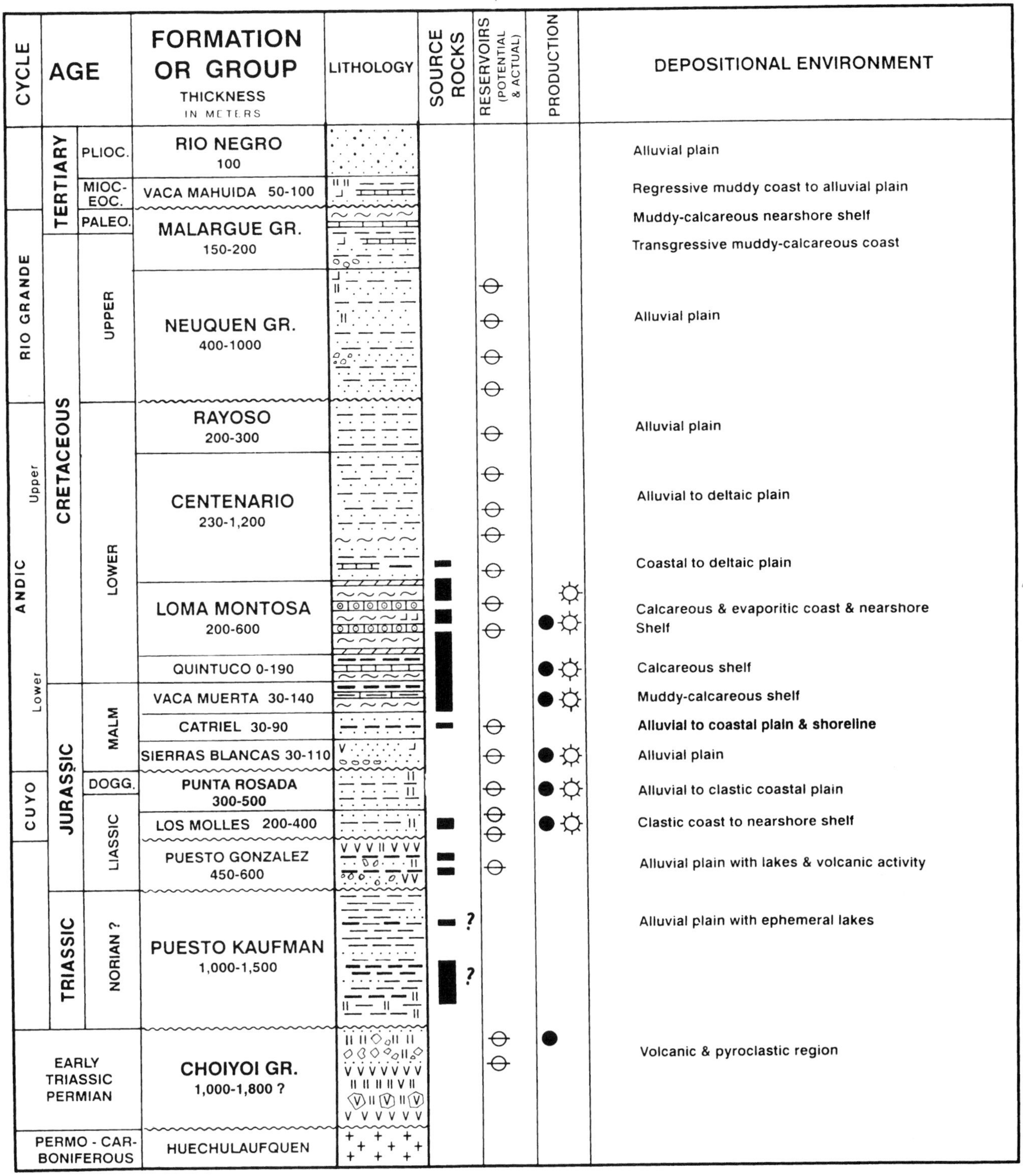

CYCLE	AGE		FORMATION OR GROUP THICKNESS IN METERS	LITHOLOGY	SOURCE ROCKS	RESERVOIRS (POTENTIAL & ACTUAL)	PRODUCTION	DEPOSITIONAL ENVIRONMENT
	TERTIARY	PLIOC.	RIO NEGRO 100					Alluvial plain
		MIOC- EOC.	VACA MAHUIDA 50-100					Regressive muddy coast to alluvial plain
								Muddy-calcareous nearshore shelf
RIO GRANDE		PALEO.	MALARGUE GR. 150-200					Transgressive muddy-calcareous coast
	CRETACEOUS Upper	UPPER	NEUQUEN GR. 400-1000			⊖ ⊖ ⊖ ⊖		Alluvial plain
ANDIC		LOWER	RAYOSO 200-300			⊖		Alluvial plain
			CENTENARIO 230-1,200			⊖		Alluvial to deltaic plain
	CRETACEOUS Lower				■	⊖		Coastal to deltaic plain
			LOMA MONTOSA 200-600		■	⊖	● ☼	Calcareous & evaporitic coast & nearshore Shelf
			QUINTUCO 0-190		■		● ☼	Calcareous shelf
	JURASSIC	MALM	VACA MUERTA 30-140		■		● ☼	Muddy-calcareous shelf
			CATRIEL 30-90		■	⊖		Alluvial to coastal plain & shoreline
CUYO			SIERRAS BLANCAS 30-110			⊖	● ☼	Alluvial plain
		DOGG.	PUNTA ROSADA 300-500			⊖	● ☼	Alluvial to clastic coastal plain
		LIASSIC	LOS MOLLES 200-400		■	⊖	● ☼	Clastic coast to nearshore shelf
			PUESTO GONZALEZ 450-600		■	⊖		Alluvial plain with lakes & volcanic activity
	TRIASSIC	NORIAN ?	PUESTO KAUFMAN 1,000-1,500		■ ? ■ ?			Alluvial plain with ephemeral lakes
	EARLY TRIASSIC PERMIAN		CHOIYOI GR. 1,000-1,800 ?			⊖ ⊖	●	Volcanic & pyroclastic region
	PERMO - CAR- BONIFEROUS		HUECHULAUFQUEN					

Figure 32.8. Composite stratigraphic column of the eastern Neuquén basin showing rock unit thickness, lithology, producing reservoir rocks, and depositional environments.

Punta Rosada Formation, a green, red, or brown sandstone and shale unit. South of the dorsal shear zone, the Lajas Formation grades upward into partially conglomeratic, red alluvial fan deposits, the Challacó Formation.

In the South Mendoza and western central parts of the basin, the Cuyo sedimentary cycle ends with the deposi-

tion of an evaporite, the Tábanos Formation (Legarreta and Gulisano, 1989). A regional erosional surface is present at the top of Cuyo cycle (Figure 32.5).

The Cuyo sedimentary cycle ranges in age from Hettangian to early Callovian (Figure 32.5; Table 32.2) and is up to 1.5 km thick in the south (Figure 32.9). In the north, this cycle is about 1 km thick. Except for four accu-

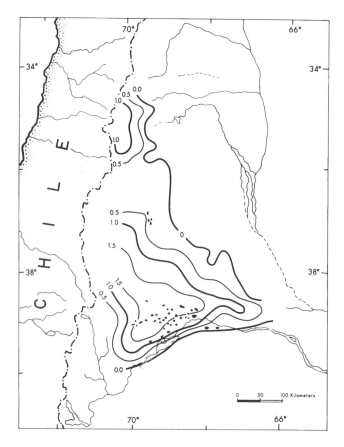

Figure 32.9. Isopach map of the Cuyo Group (Los Molles, Lajas, and Punta Rosada formations), with oil and gas fields reservoired in Liassic–Oxfordian units. (Thickness contours in kilometers.)

mulations along the hinge line, most of the oil and gas accumulations within this interval are in the southern embayment and dorsal shear zone.

Lotena Sedimentary Cycle

The Lotena sedimentary cycle began during the middle Callovian as a marine transgression and ended in late Oxfordian time. This transgression failed to reach the eastern part of the basin (Digregorio, 1972). In the southern embayment, the Lotena Formation is continental, mostly fluvial and eolian siliciclastic deposits, which grade upward into marginal marine siliciclastics (Digregorio and Uliana, 1980; Groeber et al., 1953). In the South Mendoza fold belt, the Lotena Formation grades into deep marine turbidite facies, such as those exposed in Chacay Melehue near Cordillera del Viento (Groeber et al., 1953; Digregorio, 1972).

Above the Lotena Formation are the La Manga Formation in northern Neuquén basin (Figure 32.6) and the Barda Negra Formation in the central part of the basin (Figure 32.7). These two correlative Oxfordian units were deposited on a carbonate platform and contain some organic-rich intervals.

Regressive facies are represented by the Auquilco Formation evaporites (gypsum and anhydrite) that developed in the central and northern parts of the basin

(Figures 32.6 and 32.7). Laterally, these evaporites are interbedded with limestones and red beds. They extend northward into the main Cordillera trough in the Chilean Andes as far as southern Perú (Groeber et al., 1953). The Lotena sedimentary cycle ended with the Intermalmic (or Araucanian) orogenic phase at about the end of Oxfordian or earliest Kimmeridgian time (Figure 32.5).

Andic Sedimentary Cycle

After the intermalmic orogenic phase, a new transgressive–regressive cycle occurred over nearly the entire extent of Neuquén basin. This cycle, given the name "Andico" by Groeber et al. (1953), lasted until the end of Albian time. (Figure 32.5).

The basal unit of the Andic cycle, the Tordillo Formation, consists of alluvial fan redbeds and conglomerates. Eastward, the Tordillo basal transgressive siliciclastic rocks grade up into predominantly reddish eolian alluvial and playa lake claystones of the Sierras Blancas Formation (Digregorio, 1972). Mantling the Tordillo and Sierras Blancas formations lies a uniformly thick blanket of greenish immature sandstones and conglomerates, the Catriel Formation (Figure 32.8). This unit comprises the upper part of the basal transgressive sandstone, which was deposited in beach and dune fields situated in a low-relief alluvial and coastal plain.

Overlying these siliciclastic rocks with a sharp contact is the Vaca Muerta Formation (Figures 32.6–32.8). This unit consists of organic-rich black to dark brown shales and lime mudstones, and it is the most important source rock in the basin. The Vaca Muerta Formation is mostly Tithonian and was deposited in an euxinic environment on a shelf and slope. In the deep basin (western South Mendoza, Figure 32.5), the deposition of the Vaca Muerta continued into the Valanginian (Leanza, 1973).

Above the Vaca Muerta lies a shallow water carbonate sequence, the Quintuco Formation, which was deposited over a platform during the Berriasian. Upward and laterally the Quintuco grades into the Loma Montosa Formation, which is a marginal marine, oolitic limestone interbedded with evaporites and fine-grained clastics. In the eastern part of the Neuquén basin, this is an important oil- and gas-bearing interval (Figure 32.8).

In Valanginian time, carbonate sedimentation was replaced by the siliciclastic deposition of the Mulichinco Formation, which consists of greenish sandstones interbedded with limestones and claystones deposited in a deltaic to coastal plain environment. Toward the basin margin, both the Mulichinco and Loma Montosa formations are replaced vertically and laterally by the Centenario Formation, fluvial red and green sandstones deposited in Valanginian–Aptian time. In South Mendoza, carbonate sedimentation continued with the oolitic limestones of the Chachao Formation, which produces oil and gas from fractured carbonates.

Above the Mulichinco Formation in the central part of the Neuquén basin lies the marine Agrio Formation, which consists of dark gray to black organic-rich shales deposited on an outer shelf. Eastward, the Agrio grades laterally into the middle part of the Centenario Formation. The Agrio Formation was deposited as a

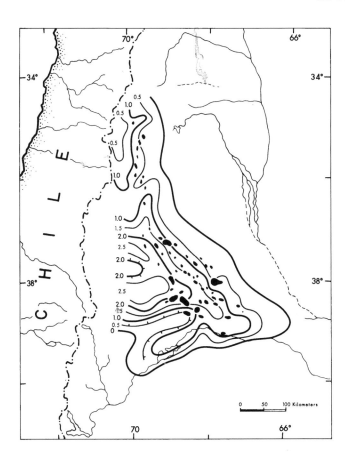

Figure 32.10. Isopach map of lower Andic cycle, Kimmeridgian–Berriasian (Tordillo, Vaca Muerta, Quintuco, and Loma Montosa formations) with oil and gas fields reservoired in these units. (Thickness contours in kilometers.)

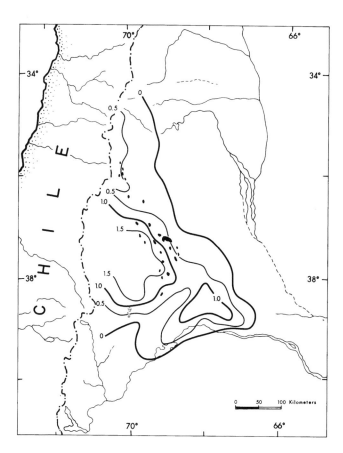

Figure 32.11. Isopach map of upper Andic cycle, Valanginian–Albian (Mulichinco, Agrio, Centenario, Huitrín, and Rayoso formations) with oil and gas fields reservoired in these units, mostly in the Avilé Member. (Thickness contours in kilometers.)

transgressive shale during the Hauterivian–Barremian. This transgression had a short-lived regressive oscillation when the Avilé Member was deposited. This is an important reservoir rock in South Mendoza and the central part of the basin (Figure 32.5).

The upper part of the Agrio, also shaly, passes into a regressive sandstone (Troncoso Member, not shown) overlain in turn by the marginal marine evaporites and carbonates of the Huitrin Formation. This formation was probably deposited over tidal flats of a restricted sea or hypersaline lake. These marginal marine sequences are overlain by the continental redbeds of the Rayoso Formation.

Isopach maps of the lower and upper units of the Andic sedimentary cycle are separated to show their distribution and the oil and gas fields for each unit (Figures 32.10 and 32.11). The lower Andic cycle ranges in age from Kimmeridgian to Berriasian and includes the Tordillo, Vaca Muerta, Quintuco, and Loma Montosa formations. Most of the oil and gas, by volume, are included in this interval, which reaches 2.5 km in thickness. The upper Andic cycle contains fewer oil and gas fields and is up to only 1.5 km in thickness. The rock units, which range in age from Valanginaian to Albian, are the Mulichinco, Agrio, Centenario, Huitrin, and Rayoso formations.

Río Grande Sedimentary Cycle

Upper Cretaceous–Eocene alluvial, fluvial, coastal, and shallow marine sedimentary rocks were deposited during the Río Grande cycle. The basal rock units began to accumulate in late Cenomanian or early Turonian time (Legarreta and Gulisano, 1989). The lower unit is the Neuquén Group, which consists of redbeds, mostly sandstones, siltstones, and claystones, in fining upward cycles. Deposition ended during the Campanian or early Maastrichtian (Digregorio, 1972; Legarreta and Gulisano, 1989). The Neuquén Group grades upward into fine-grained shallow marine siliciclastics with carbonate and evaporite intercalations, which are designated the Allen, Jaguel, and Loncoche formations (Figure 32.5). These basal marine deposits are Maastrichtian (Digregorio, 1972) or late Campanian (Legarreta and Gulisano, 1989) in age.

The next overlying unit is the Roca Formation of Paleocene age, composed of shallow marine claystones, evaporites, and carbonates. Overlying this unit is a coastal and fluvial redbed sequence called the Pircala Formation in eastern South Mendoza and the Cerro Villegas Formation in the western central part of the basin (Figure 32.5). Above these respectively lie greenish fluvial sandstones and shales of the Coihueco and

Carrere formations. They are ascribed to late Paleocene or Eocene (Yrigoyen, 1979), thus ending the Río Grande cycle (Figure 32.4).

Post–Río Grande Sedimentary Cycle

The Pyrenaic orogeny (Mapuche, Incaic, or Pre-Incaic phases) ended the stratigraphic evolution of Neuquén basin. From Oligocene to Quaternary time, thick (up to 3.5 km) Andean piedmont siliciclastics accumulated in parts of the foothills in eastern South Mendoza as a result of the uplift of the Cordillera (Figure 32.5). These units and some the underlying sedimentary cycles are important overburden rocks.

STRUCTURE

Three main structural areas occur in the Neuquén basin. First, the Andean zone in the west was most influenced by Andean tectonism from Oligocene time onward (Figure 32.2). This area encompasses the Loncopué trough, the Cordillera del Viento, and the Agrio–Chos Malal and South Mendoza fold belts. Second, a transition area, the Chihuidos–Huantraico–Reyes–Llancanelo folded zone (Herrero Ducloux, 1946), has only a moderate influence from Andean tectonism. Third, the extra-Andean area in the east shows structural deformation that was chiefly the result of Mesozoic tectonism. This last area includes the northeastern platform and hinge line, the embayment, the dorsal shear zone, and the southern embayment. The western and transition areas are deformed by Andean tectonism, whereas the eastern area lacks deformation (Table 32.2).

Andean or Western Area

The Andean area includes three provinces that contain up to 6 km of sedimentary rock (Figure 32.3) deformed from Oligocene time on. Parts of this area are covered by Cenozoic sedimentary, volcanic, and pyroclastic rocks (Figure 32.4). To the north in the South Mendoza fold belt, Mesozoic sedimentary rocks and the Permian–Triassic igneous basement rocks form extensive outcrops due to successive Andean tectonic pulses.

Structural trends in the Andean area run predominantly from north to south. A northwest-southeast lineament, which offsets the Agrio–Chos Malal and South Mendoza fold belts, extends through the transition area and into the extra-Andean area (Ramos, 1978). In the South Mendoza fold belt, lineaments extend over distances greater than 800 km and may be a surface expression of basement faults.

The most outstanding structures in the Andean area are thrust faults, parallel to the Andean orogenic belt. The main fault surfaces dip to the west, although antithetical east-dipping faults are common. In the Mesozoic sedimentary rock sequences, northward-trending anticlines are cut on their east flanks by reverse faults. These anticlines vary from a few to several tens of kilometers long. Some of them, especially in areas with Jurassic outcrops, are box shaped (steep limbs and flat culminations).

The Loncopué trough is a grabenlike depression (Ramos, 1978) about 200 km long and 20–30 km wide that is located near the Chilean border (Figure 32.2). Northeast of this trough is the Cordillera del Viento structural high (Viento C. on Figure 32.2). Here, upper Paleozoic sedimentary rocks crop out, and because of abnormally high heat flow, the Los Molles organic-rich shale is an anthracite. Eastward on a relatively uplifted block is the Tromen volcanic massif (Figure 32.4) (Ramos, 1978).

East of Loncopué trough is the Agrio–Chos Malal and South Mendoza fold belts, where Jurassic and Cretaceous sedimentary sequences are visibly folded and thrusted. Here, the strongly folded rocks form elongate, asymmetric anticlines with sharp culminations, frequently grouped in anticlinoria. The eastern flanks of the anticlines are generally bounded by western-dipping listric thrust faults. This Andean zone extends southward to about 40° south latitude. Here, structures still trend northward, but their deformation seems to be less severe than in the north.

Transition Area

The transition area, or the Chihuidos–Huantraico–Reyes–Llancanelo folded zone, is between the Andean area on the west and the extra-Andean area on the east and was influenced by Andean compressive tectonism. Its eastern boundary coincides with a megasuture (Figure 32.2) that extends from the South Mendoza fold belt to the dorsal shear zone. South of the Neuquén River, it is offset westward by the dorsal shear zone.

The transition area can be divided as three segments. (1) The northern segment, the Llancanelo foredeep, is partially covered with basalts and andesites. Structural features, such as moderately folded asymmetric anticlines, have been delineated here mostly by reflection seismic data. The flanks of these anticlines are cut by thrust faults dipping to the east. Many oil and gas fields of various sizes have been found here. (2) The Huantraico central segment is separated from the Llancanelo foredeep by the Payún volcanic plateau (Figure 32.4). These Quaternary volcanic flows cover oil and gas fields. This segment contains the Sierra de Reyes and Huantraico synclinorium, where oil and gas fields occur. The southern boundary is the southeast-trending lineament. (3) The southern segment is the Chihuidos anticlinorium, which has folds of regional extent. This anticlinorium contains internal anomalies, such as smaller anticlines and synclines.

Extra-Andean or Eastern Area

The extra-Andean area is east of the transition area and is the part of the Neuquén basin that contains most of the oil and gas fields. This zone is further divided into the northeastern platform, hinge line, embayment, dorsal shear zone, and southern embayment (Figure 32.2).

The northeastern platform is about 100 km wide and extends as far north as the San Rafael uplift. Most of its surface is covered by Cenozoic basalts, which in many

Table 32.4. Important Oil and Gas Fields in the Los Molles–Tres Esquinas(?) Petroleum System

Field			Producing Formation					Cumulative Prod.	
Name	Year	Area (ha)	Name	Age[a]	Depth (m)	Gravity (°API)	GOR (ft3/bbl)	Oil (MMbbl)	Gas (10⁹ ft3)
Aguada Toledo	1958	3700	Lajas	Trc	2837	35	5533	34.2	485.3
Al Norte de la Dorsal	1978	2170	Lajas	Trc	1480	33	—	9.4	17.5
Al Sur de la Dorsal	1978	3796	Lajas	Trc	1500	24	—	12.3	11.3
Centenario	1961	5330	Lajas	Trc	2864	36	26	49.9	247.3
Cerro Bandera	1952	520	Lajas	Trc	1287	28	84	47.8	20.6
Challaco	1940	1817	Lajas	Trc	1050	24	840	29.9	6.6
El Sauce	1957	850	Lajas	Trc	1191	31	106	26.4	9166
Veinticinco de Mayo	1964	2500	Lajas	Trc	1493	34	—	76.6	66.7

[a]Trc = Toarcian.

Data from Urien & Associates.

places mask the eastern boundary of the basin (Figure 32.4). This platform has several oil and gas fields in anticlines with gently dipping flanks that are controlled by normal faulted basement blocks.

The hinge line is a flexured area controlled by basement normal faults that trend to the northwest and separate the northeastern platform from the embayment. Anticlines here are also controlled by down to the basin faults oriented parallel to this regional trend. Most of the oil and gas fields of the extra-Andean area are in the hinge line.

The embayment is located between the hinge line and the dorsal shear zone, where up to 7 km of sedimentary rocks are found in the basin axis (Figure 32.3). Parallel to this axis, there are deep anticlinal closures, some of which contain the largest oil and gas fields found in the basin, such as Aguada San Roque, Loma de la Lata/Lindero Atravesado, and Centenario–Río Neuquén/Campo Grande (Table 32.4). South of the axis, structures are parallel or subparallel to the dorsal shear zone. The main structures here are north-dipping faults that make up a series of antithetic basement blocks and rollovers in the sedimentary cover where numerous oil and gas fields are located.

The dorsal shear zone, formerly considered to be a complex horst (Digregorio, 1972; Ramos, 1978), was reinterpreted some years ago as a right lateral wrench fault zone (Orchuela et al., 1981) on the basis of modern seismic data. This shear zone, which can be traced over a distance of nearly 300 km, has several hundred meters of vertical downthrow to the north (Digregorio, 1972). En echelon faulted anticlines are aligned on both sides of the dorsal shear zone and trend predominantly east-west. Many of these structures are oil or gas bearing and thus form an important petroleum trend.

The southern embayment contains slightly deformed anticlines that trend toward the west-southwest or west and are similar to the anticlines in the northeastern platform, as they are related to normal faults in the basement rocks. Some structures contain oil and gas accumulations. Along the western boundary of the southern embayment, the right lateral displacement of the dorsal shear zone has shifted the boundary between the Andean and extra-Andean areas to the west over the transition zone (Figure 32.2).

PETROLEUM SYSTEMS

The presence of oil and gas in the Neuquén basin proves the presence of at least one petroleum system. On the basis of the regional geology and geochemistry of the sedimentary rocks that have been penetrated or that crop out in this area, at least three speculative petroleum systems are defined. The strongest evidence for the existence of three petroleum systems is that three different thermally mature source rock intervals exist that are apparently associated with oil and gas accumulations. Oil and gas fields are associated with the Cuyo sedimentary cycle (Figure 32.9), the lower Andic cycle (Figure 32.10), and the upper Andic cycle (Figure 32.11).

Further studies, such as oil–oil and oil–source rock correlation work, will be needed to better define each system and to raise the level of certainty for these petroleum systems from speculative to known. However, a great deal can be described about the three source rock intervals and their level of thermal maturity, such that the pod of active source rock can be generally located. The stratigraphic extent of each petroleum system can be determined because (1) the migration fairway from the pod of active source rock toward the basin boundary has remained essentially the same from Jurassic time on, (2) there are no prominent unconformities, and (3) there are no significant differences in the structural deformation of the Mesozoic and lower Cenozoic sequences in most of the basin.

The only areas where a large difference in the deformation of the three intervals probably affected migration is in the northern part of the Agrio–Chos Malal and South Mendoza fold belts, as well in the piedmont zone where these sequences crop out. Here the evaporites (Tábanos, Auquilco, and Huitrín formations), which acted as gliding or décollement surfaces as well as regional seal rocks, caused strong deformational differences in the sedimentary sequences (Ploszkiewicz, 1987). Thus, these differences most likely controlled the migration and entrapment of hydrocarbons in this area and probably affected the geographic extent of each petroleum system.

The critical moment, or the time when maximum burial depth of the source rock occurred, is different in the west than in the east. In the west, trap formation and hydrocarbon migration were completed at the end of the Pliocene, whereas in the east, this occurred by the end of the Eocene. Subsequent tectonic activity in the eastern zone was insufficient to cause previously formed hydrocarbons accumulations to migrate.

The three petroleum systems located in the Neuquén basin are discussed according to their essential elements and processes, including source rocks, reservoir rocks, seal rocks, overburden, and traps. From oldest to youngest, the petroleum systems are the Los Molles–Tres Esquinas(?), the Vaca Muerta–Sierras Blancas(?), and the Agrio(?) (Table 32.5).

Source Rocks

Triassic

The Upper Triassic–Lower Jurassic sedimentary rocks (pre-Cuyo) lack a source rock, save some limited black shales in the northeastern platform (Figure 32.8). These lacustrine shales are in the Puesto Kaufman Formation of Triassic age, but because geochemical data are lacking, they are eliminated from this discussion as a source rock for hydrocarbons in this petroleum province.

Jurassic

The black shale of the Los Molles Formation, which ranges from 20 to 2100 m thick, is a potential source rock within the Cuyo sedimentary cycle (Figures 32.6–32.8; Table 32.5). The organic matter in this shale is predominantly amorphous and occasionally herbaceous. Woody material or inertinite have been reported from a few localities. Along the outcrop belt of the southern embayment, geochemical data indicate that the organic matter is immature. Downdip, where the Los Molles is buried deeper, it probably generated small amounts of hydrocarbons (Figure 32.9). In the southern prolongation of the Agrio–Chos Malal fold belt, thermal maturity of this formation is still low, so expulsion and migration of hydrocarbons probably took place in small volumes, probably during the late Tertiary. In the central part of the basin, the Los Molles is deeply buried and is thus overmature. Hence, this source rock probably generated oil that migrated to the southern embayment as it was being buried, after which gas or condensate was generated.

The La Manga and Barda Negra formations within the Lotena sedimentary cycle contain organic-rich black shale and lime mudstone, but are restricted only to the northern and central parts of the basin (Figures 32.6 and 32.7). The volume of these organic-rich beds is lower than that of the Cuyo cycle.

Geochemical data for these Jurassic source rocks include total organic carbon (TOC), C_{15+} bitumen data, kerogen maceral type, thermal alteration index, and vitrinite reflectance, and are named as the Los Molles for the three areas (Table 32.5). The TOC values are variable, with the highest reported value of 5.13 wt. % in the transitional area. In the western zone, the highest value, to our knowledge, is 3.7 wt. %, whereas values in the embayment are generally lower but near 1.0 wt. %. The Jurassic rocks include several source rocks, too many to

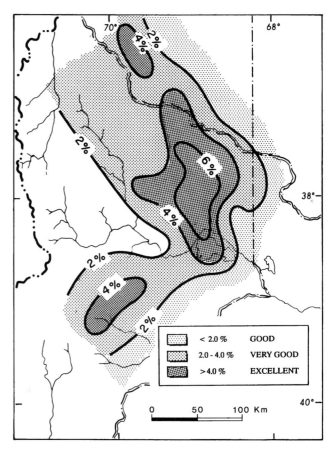

Figure 32.12. Source rock richness map (contoured in wt. % TOC) for the Vaca Muerta and Quintuco formations, which are the main source rocks in this petroleum province.

use in a petroleum system name, so the thickest and richest formation is used to represent this interval, the Los Molles Formation.

The fine-grained sandstones interbedded with organic-rich shales in the Lotena sedimentary cycle act as reservoir and seal rocks (and perhaps as a minor source rock). This cycle ends with an evaporite facies that covers most of the basin, which is the regional seal that isolates the accumulations in the Los Molles–Tres Esquinas petroleum system.

Kimmeridgian–Berriasian

The Kimmeridgian–Berriasian sequence, which encompasses the lower part of the Andic sedimentary cycle, contains two source rocks: the Vaca Muerta and Quintuco formations (Figures 32.6–32.8; Table 32.5).

The Vaca Muerta Formation, which ranges in thickness from 30 to 1200 m, contains the largest volume of organic matter of any petroleum system in the basin. It consists of thermally mature black shales, marls, and lime mudstones and is the richest and, hence, the main petroleum source rock in the Neuquén basin. The organic matter found in this formation is predominantly amorphous. Subordinate algal or herbaceous organic matter has been reported in some localities. The TOC values are generally 2–3 wt. %, but can go up to 8 wt. %

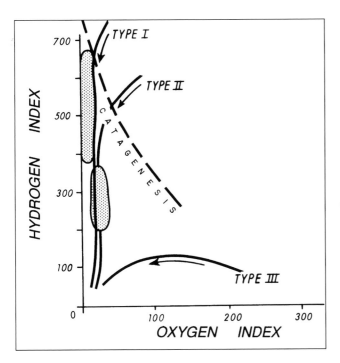

Figure 32.13. Vaca Muerta Formation kerogen types plotted on a modified van Krevelen diagram. Notice that most organic matter (stippled) is type I or II (mainly oil prone) and within catagenic stage.

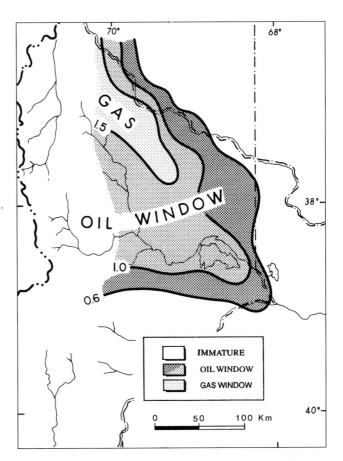

Figure 32.14. Vitrinite reflectance contour map showing the top (0.6 % R_o) and bottom (1.5 % R_o) of the oil window for the Vaca Muerta and Quintuco formations. When this map is overlain on the source rock richness map (Figure 32.12), the pod of active source rock is outlined (Figure 32.18).

(Figure 32.12) (Di Lena et al., 1989). Based on Rock-Eval pyrolysis data, the hydrogen indices range from 200 to 675 (mg HC/g TOC) (Figure 32.13). When plotted on a modified van Krevelen diagram, the Vaca Muerta Formation contains type I and II kerogen. This formation can be rated as a very good to excellent source rock. The areas with the best concentrations are the basin center and the Chihuidos folded zone.

The Quintuco Formation, which ranges up to 580 m thick, contains black shales and lime mudstones and occurs in the same area. In the eastern part of the basin (Rio Negro), the Loma Montosa Formation (up to 600 m thick) is correlative with the Quintuco Formation. The type of organic matter is similar to that of the Vaca Muerta Formation, but higher in woody or herbaceous matter. Values for TOC are also high, so that the Quintuco and Loma Montosa formations can also be rated as very good to excellent source rocks.

The contour map of TOC for the Vaca Muerta, Quintuco, and Loma Montosa formations indicates that these units are 2 wt. % or higher over most of the basin (Figure 32.12) and that they are within or below the oil window (Figure 32.14). Since the Vaca Muerta Formation is the thickest and richest of the three units, it will be used in the petroleum system name.

Valanginian–Albian

The Valanginian-Albian interval covers the upper part of the Andic sedimentary cycle and contains one important source rock—the Agrio Formation (Figures 32.6 and 32.7). However, several thinner source rocks deserve mention. The Chachao Formation is as thick as

110 m in the northern Neuquén basin (Figure 32.6), and there are some thin organic-rich rocks in the lower part of the Centenario Formation in the eastern Neuquén basin.

In the northern and central Neuquén basin, the Agrio Formation is up to 1500 m thick. The TOC is between 0.3 and 1.9 wt. % (Figure 32.15; Table 32.5). The organic matter is predominantly woody or herbaceous and has reached thermal maturity in the central part of the basin (Figure 32.16). Hydrocarbon generation possibilities for the Agrio Formation can be rated as fair to good; this generation is responsible for oil and gas accumulations in the central part of the basin (Figure 32.11). However, the volume of organic-rich sediments is low in comparison to underlying formations.

The thickest and probably the richest source rock unit in this interval is the Agrio Formation, which will be used in the petroleum system name.

Reservoir Rocks

In the Neuquén basin, oil and gas has accumulated in reservoir rocks that range in age from Permian–Triassic to Tertiary. However, most of the commercial hydrocar-

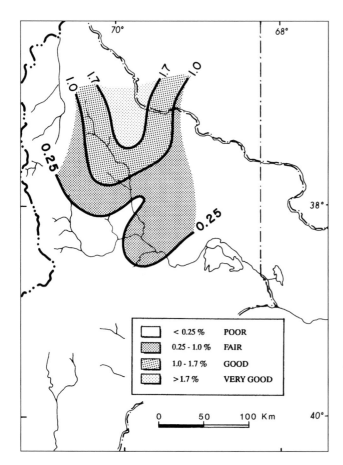

Figure 32.15. Source rock richness map (contoured in wt. % TOC) for the Agrio Formation. Note that the richest area has shifted to the northwest when compare to the Vaca Muerta and Quintuco formations (Figure 32.12), which is related to the regressive stage of the Andic sedimentary cycle.

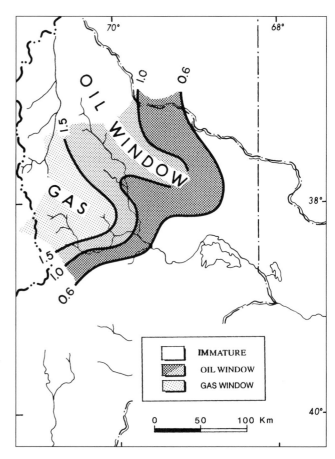

Figure 32.16. Vitrinite reflectance contour map showing the top (0.6 % R_o) and bottom (1.5 % R_o) of the oil window for the Agrio Formation. When this map is overlain on the source rock richness map (Figure 32.15), the pod of active source rock is outlined (Figure 32.19).

bons are being extracted from reservoir rocks of Jurassic and Cretaceous age. Only a few fields have yielded commercial production from sandstones and conglomeratic intervals of Triassic age (the Barda Alta and Planicie Morada formations) in the eastern part of the northeastern platform.

Jurassic

The Los Molles Formation has some permeable sandstones interbedded with the black shales which have produced oil and gas in the northeastern platform and dorsal shear zone (Figure 32.9). The upper part of the Cuyo sedimentary cycle includes regressive marginal marine and continental sandstones (Lajas and Challacó formations) (Figure 32.7; Table 32.5) that are important oil- and gas-bearing reservoir rocks in fields situated near or along the dorsal shear zone. These fields include the Plaza Huincul, Barda González, Guanaco, and Challacó. The Lotena Formation, a transgressive sandstone, also produces oil and gas in the same areas. For all these units, the porosity is variable (5–26%) because of regional and local variations in cementation and the presence of detrital matrix. Permeabilities can reach 150 md.

Of the Jurassic reservoir rocks, the unit that contains the most oil and gas is the Challacó Formation. Since the major reservoir rock for the petroleum system name is designated as the one with the largest volume of oil and gas, Challacó is part of the system name (Table 32.4).

Kimmeridgian–Berriasian

Of all three petroleum systems, the one within the Kimmeridgian–Berriasian interval has generated the greatest amount of oil and gas. It has accumulated in sandstone reservoirs of the Sierras Blancas and Catriel formations at the base of the Andic sedimentary cycle (Figure 32.10). Both units are the main producers in the hinge line fields (Cerro Los Gatos–Kaufman trend) and in fields located near the basin center where the largest concentrations of gas are found, such as in the Loma La Lata and Rio Neuquén fields. However, these sandstones can be tight due to the presence of a shaly matrix, with porosity varying from 2 to 19%. Commercial production in these sandstones is favored by the development of secondary porosity and permeability.

Since most of the oil is in the Sierras Blancas Formation, this is the reservoir name used for this petroleum system (Tables 32.6 and 32.8).

Table 32.5. Geochemical Data for Source Rocks of the Neuquén Basin by Petroleum System

Petroleum System (and Source Rocks)	Area[a]	Organic Matter Richness			Visual Kerogen Type[b]	Thermal Maturity	
		TOC (wt. %)	C$_{15+}$ HC (ppm)	C$_{15+}$ bitumen (ppm)		Kerogen Alteration	R$_o$ (%)
Agrio(?)							
(Agrio, Centenario, Mulichinco)	W	0.24–0.70	17–27	140–157	H–W, Am	2– to 4–	3.66
	T	0.29–1.90	22	146	W, H, Am	1+ to 2	0.39
	E	0.20–1.16	—	—	I, Am	1– to 2+	—
Vaca Muerta–Sierras Blancas(?)							
(Vaca Muerta, Quintuco)	W	0.51–2.17	32–2797	160–3807	Am, H, W	2+ to 3	0.75–1.32
	T	0.84–6.41	17–223	112–533	Am, Al, H, W	1+ to 3	0.39–1.52
	E	0.32–>6.0	—	—	Am–H	1+ to 3-	—
Los Molles–Tres Esquinas(?)							
(Los Molles)	W	0.24–3.72	17–58	123–538	W–H, I–Am	3 to 4–	0.25–2.67
	T	1.41–5.13	37–2067	419–4982	Am–W, H–I	1+ to 2+	0.25–2.93
	E	0.37–0.50	—	—	W, Am, I	2– to 4+	—

[a]W = western area; T = transition area; E = eastern area.
[b]Am = amorphous; Al = algal; H = herbaceous; I = inertinite; W = woody.

Table 32.6. Important Oil and Gas Fields in the Vaca Muerta–Sierras Blancas(?) Petroleum System

Field			Producing Formation					Cumulative Prod.	
Name	Year	Area (ha)	Name	Age[a]	Depth (m)	Gravity (°API)	GOR (ft^3/bbl)	Oil (MMbbl)	Gas (10^9 ft^3)
Area Entre Lomas	1960	1580	L. Montosa	Brs	2439	31	—	105.6	439.3
El Medanito	1963	555	L. Montosa	Brs	985	46	168	129.2	90.4
El Medanito	1964	4472	Sas. Blancas	Kmg	1367	32	7	128.7	90.2
E. Fernandez Oro	1969	2332	L. Montosa	Brs	2307	35	2845	15.1	228.4
E. Fernandez Oro	1974	2515	Tordillo	Kmg	2510	58	91,000	3.3	165.2
Loma la Lata	1978	7606	Quintuco	Brs	1984	45	3349	11.1	21.7
Loma la Lata	1978	43,267	Sas. Blancas	Kmg	3025	57	—	33.7	1189
Medianera	1965	1750	L. Montosa	Brs	1701	32	—	14.1	16.3
Rio Neuquén	1972	7737	Quintuco	Brs	2086	37	39,800	31.3	344.9
Rio Neuquén	1975	3164	Sas. Blancas	Kmg	2700	58	67,500	13.7	203.9
Senal Picada	1965	6100	L. Montosa	Brs	1348	31	39	80.3	42

[a]Brs = Berriasian; Kmg = Kimmeridgian.
Data from Urien & Associates.

Valanginian–Albian

In the upper Andic sedimentary cycle, the sandstones within the Mulichinco and Agrio formations are commercial reservoirs in the northeastern platform, such as the Avilé and Troncoso Members (Figure 32.5). The main production occurs in the Puesto Hernández–Chihuido de la Sierra Negra area (Table 32.7), which represents the opening of a new producing trend in the northern Neuquén basin (Figure 32.11). In this area, some oil and gas also occurs in Lower Cretaceous continental sandstones of the Rayoso Formation, as well as in the Huitrín Formation. The Late Cretaceous Neuquén Group and the Loncoche Formation also produce some oil and gas from sandstone reservoirs in the South Mendoza fold belt. Permeable intervals in carbonates have also produced oil and gas in fractured lime mudstones of various formations: the Barda Negra, Quintuco, Vaca Muerta, Chachao, and Agrio (Figures 32.6 and 32.7).

Since most of the oil, by volume, is associated with the Agrio Formation, it is used in the petroleum system name (Tables 32.7 and 32.8).

Seal Rocks

Seal rocks occur throughout the Mesozoic sedimentary column, as indicated in the stratigraphic columns (Figures 32.6–32.8).

In the Jurassic units of the Cuyo and Lotena sedimentary cycles, seal rocks are generally of regional extent, such as the clayey intervals in the Los Molles and Punta Rosada formations. The claystones and marls of the Barda Negra and La Manga formations and the evaporites of the Auquilco Formation are also efficient seal rocks for Jurassic reservoirs.

In the Kimmeridgian–Albian units in the Andic sedimentary cycle, various units form efficient seals throughout these systems. The blanketlike reservoirs are sealed by Vaca Muerta lime mudstones and shales. The

Table 32.7. Important Oil and Gas Fields in the Agrio(?) Petroleum System

Field			Producing Formation					Cumulative Prod.	
Name	Year	Area (ha)	Name	Age[a]	Depth (m)	Gravity (°API)	GOR (ft3/bbl)	Oil (MMbbl)	Gas (109 ft3)
Chihuido de la Sa. Negra	1979	800	Avilé	Htv	1296	41	1221	12.8	17
Puesto Hernandez	1972	3763	Agrio	Htv	815	—	1812	11.4	24.9
Puesto Hernandez	1970	5207	Avilé	Htv	1037	34	1859	116.9	277.3
Puesto Hernandez	1977	500	Rayoso	Alb	730	—	3162	1.8	6.3
Puesto Rojas	1975	1151	Agrio	Htv	1270	30	1375	22.7	29.3
Puesto Rojas	1975	1151	Chachao	Vlg	1445	30	1375	22.7	21.6
Rincon Chico	1982	55	Mulichinco	Vlg	1816	42	5603	0.3	1.7

[a]Alb = Albian; Htv = Hauterivian; Vlg, = Valanginian.
Data from Urien & Associates.

Table 32.8. Cumulative Oil Production from Oil Fields in each Petroleum System

Petroleum System	Age[a]	Gravity (°API)	GOR (ft3/bbl)	Oil (MMbbl)	Gas (109 ft3)	BOE (MMbbl)	Total (MMbbl)	Percent (%)
Agrio(?)	Alb	—	3162	1.8	6.3	1.1	2.9	1
	Vlg	30–42	1375–5603	23.0	23.3	3.9	26.9	11
	Htv	30–41	1221–1859	163.8	348.5	58	222	88
Vaca Muerta–Sierras Blancas(?)	Brs	31–46	39–39,800	386.7	1183	124	405	47
	Kmg	32–58	7–91,000	179.4	1648	275	454	53
Los Molles–Tres Esquinas(?)	Trc	24–36	26–840	286.5	10,021	1670	1957	100

[a]Alb = Albian; Brs = Berriasian; Htv = Hauterivian; Kmg = Kimmeridgian; Trc = Toarcian; Vlg = Valanginian.

Lower Cretaceous oolitic carbonates and packstones of the Loma Montosa Formation are sealed by lime mudstones, claystones, or less commonly, evaporites in the eastern Neuquén basin. The Huitrín Formation, a gypsum and salt interval, forms a regional seal over the Agrio Formation in central and northern Neuquén basin.

Overburden Rocks

Near the central Neuquén basin, the present-day basin fill is up to 7 km thick (Figure 32.3). However, only that portion of the basin fill overlying a source rock is responsible for thermally maturing it. Generally, the overburden rock varies from 3 to 5 km thick, but locally it can be up to 6 km for the deeper Jurassic horizon. Toward the basin boundary, it is considerably thinner, up to 2 km. In the extra-Andean area, overburden in the past should not have been much higher than it is today, even over structural highs, because of the moderate to low amount of erosion in Jurassic and Cretaceous time.

The Tertiary overburden is generally a few hundreds of meters thick and increases eastward. Only near faults related to important uplifts, such as some parts of the dorsal shear zone, could erosion have reduced the paleo-overburden by some hundreds of meters. Thus, Orchuela et al. (1981) consider that Aptian–Albian (Cretaceous) tectonic events caused the erosion of important thicknesses of Andic deposits along the dorsal shear zone. But this should be regarded as an exception in the extra-Andean area.

During the Cenozoic, Andean tectonism caused the erosion of considerable thicknesses of Jurassic and Creta-

ceous deposits and the accumulation of thick Oligocene–Recent sediments only over the foothills and piedmont plains of South Mendoza and probably in Loncopué Trough (Figure 32.2). These processes, and Cenozoic magmatic activity, destroyed some petroleum accumulations or transformed them into asphaltites. Nevertheless, some economic fields have been found in these areas. Therefore, thermal maturation and eventual overcooking were caused by abnormal localized heat flow.

Traps

In Neuquén basin, a variety of types of hydrocarbon traps have been described, which can be summarized as follows:

1. Stratigraphic trapping occurred as a result of hydrocarbons migrating toward the basin rims and their subsequent entrapment by lateral and vertical permeability barriers. The migration processes probably started to work early, presumably as a result of the subsidence produced after the early Kimmeridgian (Araucanian) phase. However, it is likely that such migration began earlier, since during the accumulation of the Cuyo Group, the subsidence of the central part of the basin was probably enough for the formation and expulsion of hydrocarbons.

2. Migration occurred through faults and trapping was created by permeability barriers. In the extra-Andean part of the basin, fault reactivation began no later than Callovian–Oxfordian time (Sierra de

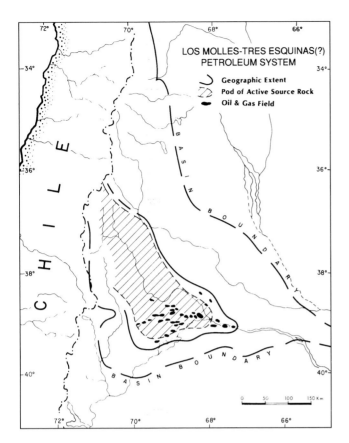

Figure 32.17. The geographic extent of the Los Molles–Tres Esquinas(?) petroleum system showing the outline of the pod of active source rock and related oil and gas fields.

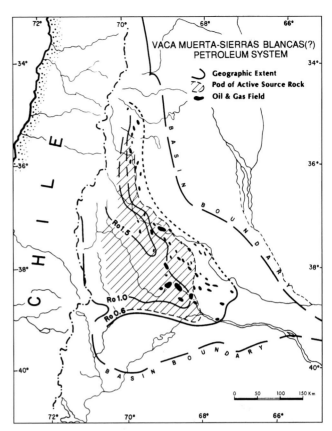

Figure 32.18. The geographic extent of the Vaca Muerta–Sierras Blancas(?) petroleum system showing the outline of the pod of active source rock (from Figures 32.12 and 32.14) and related oil and gas fields (from Figure 32.10).

Reyes phase) and continued during the subsequent Mesozoic and Cenozoic events. Hydrocarbons migrating and being trapped in pre-Jurassic intervals can be ascribed to these fault formation or reactivation events.

3. Trapping occurred in secondary porosity reservoirs, mostly produced by fracturing of brittle mudrocks or by dolomitization or dissolution of carbonates. Such processes took place during Mesozoic time, since fracturing is related mainly to Jurassic and Cretaceous flexuring tectonic events, in the extra-Andean part of the basin. In the Andean part, this could also be a result of Cenozoic Andean folding.

4. Some migration was into anticlines that were closed as a result of differential compaction or because the sedimentary cover responded to vertical oscillation and fault reactivation of fractured basement during Jurassic, Cretaceous, and early Tertiary tectonic events. This occurred in the hinge line and northeastern platform.

5. Oil migrated and was trapped in en echelon anticlines related to the dorsal shear zone, mostly in Jurassic and Cretaceous time, especially after the early Kimmeridgian and late Early Cretaceous events. According to Orchuela et al. (1981), the dorsal shear zone subsequently experienced only minor adjustments.

6. In areas affected by Andean tectonism, petroleum was trapped in anticlines formed as a result of Cenozoic folding.

Geographic and Stratigraphic Extent

The geographic extent of each petroleum system is based on the areal distribution of oil and gas accumulations that emanate from a particular pod of active source rock. The extent of the Los Molles–Tres Esquinas petroleum system (Figure 32.17) is determined from the distribution of the oil fields within the Cuyo sedimentary cycle (Figure 32.9). The pod of active source rock is located down dip beneath the thick overburden rock above the Los Molles source rock (Figure 32.3). The northwest extent of this petroleum system is unknown for lack of information.

The extent of the Vaca Muerta–Sierra Blancas petroleum system is determined from the location of the oil and gas fields in the lower unit of the Andic sedimentary cycle (Figure 32.10) and from the distribution and thermal maturity of the Vaca Muerta source rock (Figures 32.12 and 32.14). Since the Vaca Muerta extends beyond the 0.6 % R_o contour line, the location of the pod of active source rock is determined from this isoreflectance line (Figure 32.18). The extent of this petroleum system on the west is unknown for lack of information.

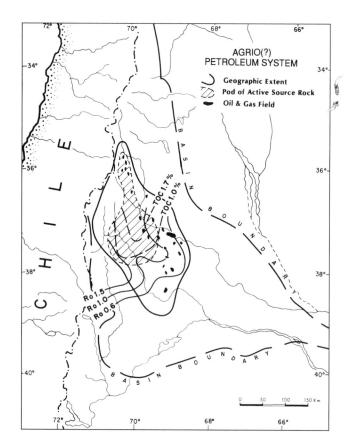

Figure 32.19. The geographic extent of the Agrio(?) petroleum system showing the outline of the pod of active source rock (from Figures 32.15 and 32.16) and related oil and gas fields (from Figure 32.11).

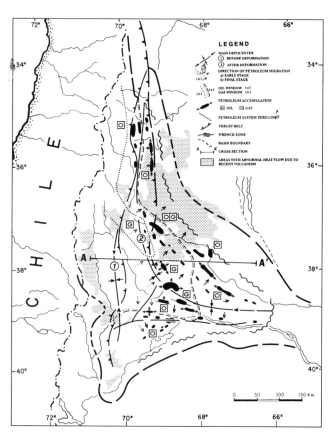

Figure 32.20. Petroleum map showing basin depocenter shifting from (1) Jurassic to (2) Tertiary time. Pathways of two hydrocarbon migration phases are indicated by two sets of arrows. The second phase was induced by Andean tectonism. Shading shows areas subjected to high heat flow from Cenozoic volcanism. (Cross section A–A' is shown in Figure 32.21.)

The extent of the Agrio petroleum system (Figure 32.19) is based on the areal distribution of the oil fields in the upper unit of the Andic sedimentary cycle (Figure 32.11) and of the pod of active Agrio source rock. This pod is limited by the amount of Agrio source rock greater than 1.0 wt. % TOC (Figure 32.15) since the thermal maturity of 0.6 % R_o for this source rock extends beyond these TOC values (Figure 32.16). Together these maps outline the pod of active Agrio source rock and the geographic extent of this petroleum system.

The stratigraphic extent of the three petroleum systems are summarized on the map in Figure 32.20 and the cross section in Figure 32.21. The cross section extends from the Andean to the extra-Andean areas in the southern part of the Neuquén basin and shows the fold belt, fold zone, and platform. Oil and gas fields are shown in structural traps, such as anticlines and fault-related traps, and in stratigraphic traps. Regional seal rocks are evaporites, carbonates, and some siltstones. The deepest source rock in the folded belt, the Los Molles Formation (type I kerogen), is the deepest limit for the stratigraphic extent of the Los Molles–Tres Esquinas petroleum system, which includes all the overlying rock units. In the same folded belt, the Vaca Muerta is the lower limit for the Vaca Muerta–Sierras Blancas

petroleum system. The Agrio source rock is just west of the megasuture in the folded zone and is the lower limit for the Agrio petroleum system.

Events Chart

An events chart for each system is included in which it is possible to appreciate the evolution of the three petroleum system (Figures 32.22A–C). The critical moment of each petroleum system varies with its stratigraphic position. However, because the Agrio petroleum system was connected with areas affected by Tertiary and Quaternary volcanism, its critical moment was influenced by abnormal thermal conditions that advanced oil generation. It is also noteworthy that source rocks and reservoir rocks in all three of the systems are usually in direct contact, and in some cases, the reservoir rock is within the source rock. Thus, most of the oil in some sectors of the basin is autochthonous, such as in the central embayment and dorsal shear zone. However, some oils have migrated a fair distance and are a mixture of oils, such as in the South Mendoza folded belt and the northeastern platform.

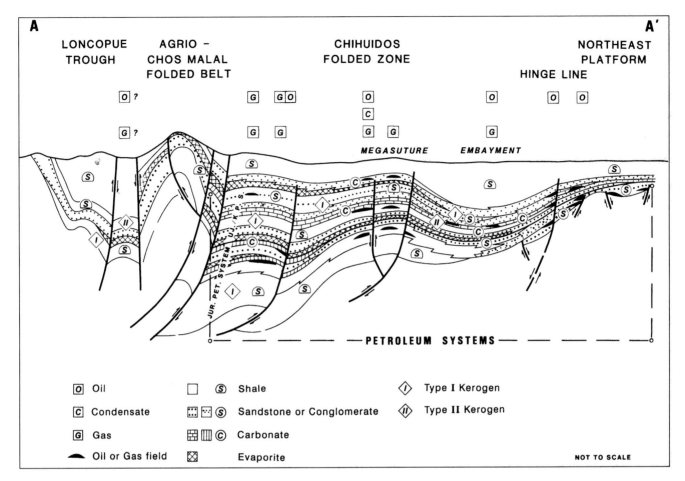

Figure 32.21. Schematic cross section (location in Figure 32.20) showing distribution of oil and gas fields in relation to source rocks (indicated by their kerogen types), main lithologic types, and structure. Trapping occurred in anticlines, against faults, and at stratigraphic permeability barriers.

References Cited

Digregorio, J. H., 1972, Neuquén, *in* A. F. Leanza, ed., Geología Regional Argentina: Córdoba, Academia Nacional de Ciencias, p. 439–505.

Digregorio, J. H., and M. A. Uliana, 1980, Cuenca Neuquina, in J. C. M. Turner, coord., Simposio Geología Regional Argentina, Córdoba, v. 2, p. 985–1032.

Di Lena, J. P., H. G. Marchese, and R. Blocki, 1989, Evaluación de rocas generadoras en la Cuenca Neuquina: Actas I Congreso Nacional de Exploración de Hidrocarburos, Mar del Plata, April, v. 1, p. 311–343.

Groeber, P., 1929, Líneas fundamentales de la Geología del Neuquén, sur de Mendoza y regiones adyacentes: Dirección General de Minería, Geología e Hidrología: Publicación 58, p. 1–105.

Groeber, P., P.N. Stipanicic, and A. Mingramm, 1953, Mesozoico, in Geografía de la República Argentina: Soc. Arg. de Estudios Geográficos GAEA, T. II (pt. 1).

Herrero Ducloux, A., 1946, Contribución al conocimiento geológico del Neuquén Extraandino: Boletín Informaciones Petrolera, Año 23, n. 271, p. 245–281.

Leanza, H., 1973, Estudio sobre los cambios faciales de los estratos limítrofes jurá sicocretá cicos entre Loncopué y Picún Leufú, provincia de Neuquén, República Argentina: Revista de la Asociación Geologica Argentina, XXVIII, v. 2, p. 97–132.

Legarreta, L., and C. A. Gulisano, 1989, Análisis estratigráfico secuencial de la cuenca Neuquina (Triásico Superior–Terciario inferior), in G. A. Chebli and L. A. Spalletti, eds., Cuencas sedimentarias Argentinas: Universidad Nacional de Tucumán, Instituto Superior de Correlación Geológica, Serie Correlación Geológica, S.M. de Tucumán, Argentina, n. 6, p. 221–243.

Orchuela, I. A., J. V. Ploszkiewicz, and R. F. Viñes, 1981, Reinterpretación estructural de la denominada "Dorsal Neuquina": Actas VIII Argentina Geological Congress, San Luis, T. III, p. 281–293.

Ploszkiewicz, J. V., 1987, Las zonas triangulares de la faja fallada y plegada de la cuenca Neuquina, Argentina: Actas X Argentina Geological Congress, Tucumán, T. I, p. 177–180.

Ploszkiewicz, J. V., I. A. Orchuela, J. Vaillard, and R. F. Viñes, 1984, Compresión y desplazamiento lateral en la zona de falla Huincul, estructuras asociadas: Actas IX Argentina Geological Congress, Bariloche, T. II, p. 163–168.

Ramos, V. A., 1978, Estructura: relatorio geología y recursos naturales del Neuquén: Actas VII Argentina Geological Congress, Neuquén, p. 99–118.

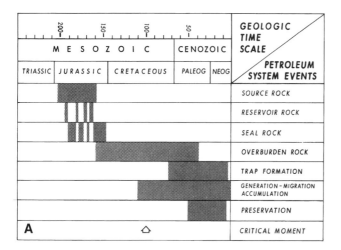

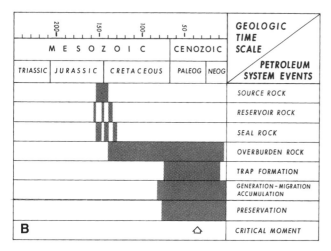

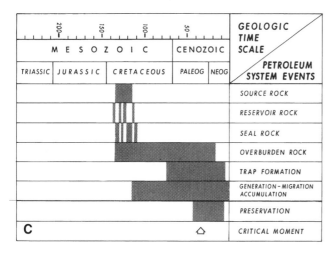

Figure 32.22. Events charts for the petroleum systems in this petroleum province: (A) Los Molles–Tres Esquinas(?), (B) Vaca Muerta–Sierras Blancas(?), and (C) Agrio(?).

Robles, D., 1984, Yacimientos de hidrocarburos: Relatorio geología y recursos naturales de la Provincia de Río Negro: Actas IX Argentina Geological Congress, Bariloche, p. 675–691.

Stipanicic, P. N., 1969, El avance de los conocimientos del Jurásico argentino a partir del esquema de Groeber: Revista de la Asociacion Geologica Argentina, XXIV, v. 4, p. 367–388.

Volkheimer, W., 1978, Descripción geológica de la hoja 27 b Cerro Sosneado: Servicio Geológico Nacional Boletín, v. 151.

Windhausen, A., 1931, Geología Argentina, Segunda Parte: J. Peuser Ltd. Editores.

Yrigoyen, M. R., 1979, Cordillera principal, in J. C. M. Turner, ed., II Simposio de Geología Regional Argentina, Córdoba: Academia Nacional de Ciencias, v. 1, p. 651–694.

Yrigoyen, M. R., 1983, Reseña sobre los conocimientos y la exploración de hidrocarburos en Argentina antes de 1907: Petrotecnia, Revista Instituto Argentina del Petróleo, March, p. 32–38, and April, p. 36–41.

Part VI

Case Studies—
Eastern Hemisphere

Magoon, L. B., and W. G. Dow, eds., 1994, The petroleum
system—from source to trap: AAPG Memoir 60.

Chapter **33**

Mandal–Ekofisk(!) Petroleum System in the Central Graben of the North Sea*

Chris Cornford

Integrated Geochemical Interpretation Ltd.
Devon, U.K.

ABSTRACT

The Mandal–Ekofisk(!) petroleum system in the Central Graben of the North Sea contains 3292 million m^3 of in-place oil, 110 million m^3 of in-place condensate, and 1167 billion m^3 of in-place gas in Devonian–Tertiary reservoirs. The major reservoir is the Upper Cretaceous to basal Paleogene chalk of the Ekofisk area in the southeastern part of the graben, with 607 million m^3 (46%) producible oil and gas as oil equivalent. Here, chalk is the seal except where synsedimentary slumping coupled with an early influx of oil creates reservoir rock. Permeability mainly results from on-structure halokinetic fracturing. The second most important reservoir, with 457 million m^3 (35%) producible oil equivalent, occurs in Paleocene sandstone where fan turbidites are excellent reservoir rocks in the Forties–Montrose and Gannet areas. Surrounding mudstones form the seal. A less significant reservoir rock, with 231 million m^3 (18%) producible oil equivalent, occurs at the Upper Jurassic level in the shallow marine Fulmar and Ula sandstones immediately underlying the source rock horizon (seal) on both the eastern and western flanks of the Central Graben. Additional reserves are found in Permian and Devonian reservoir rocks.

The oil, condensate, and gas originated from the Upper Jurassic–Lower Cretaceous organic-rich marine mudstones of the Mandal Formation (equivalent to the Kimmeridge Clay). Geochemical oil–source rock correlation has been established and is backed up by the regional distribution of fields relative to mature source rocks. Source rock thicknesses range from less than 100 m on flanks and highs, to greater than 1200 m in the axis of the Central Graben. Thermal maturity modeling indicates that oil generation was initiated by late Early Cretaceous in the mid-graben. Under steadily increasing sedimentation rates, generation continues to the present day over about 112,750 km^2 of the Central Graben.

Expulsion efficiency from the Mandal Formation source rock is approximately 60%. Secondary migration is mainly vertical, the oil and gas moving through salt- and fault-related fractures into a variety of reservoir rocks. The generation–accumulation efficiency of 0.56% is obtained using Schmoker's calculation for the petroleum system. The major control on the petroleum system efficiency is the strong vertical component of secondary migration through low permeability strata plus undiscovered reserves.

INTRODUCTION

The greater North Sea petroleum province, which includes the offshore areas of Denmark, Germany, and the Netherlands, lies mainly between the United Kingdom and Norway (inset, Figure 33.1). This province has been subjected to more than 30 years of intensive exploration by numerous companies, resulting in a substantial amount of publicly available technical information. For the greater North Sea province, about 5.56 billion m^3 (35 billion bbl) of oil, condensate, and natural gas liquids (5.56 billion m^3) and about 7.67 trillion m^3 (271 trillion ft^3) of gas (7.15 billion m^3 or 45 billion bbl of

oil equivalent) have been discovered as producible hydrocarbons (updated from Brennand et al., 1990). Most of this oil and gas originates from three major petroleum systems: a dry gas system in the south and at least two oil systems in the north.

The dry gas system in the southern North Sea petroleum province involves a gas-prone source rock, the Upper Carboniferous (Westphalian) Coal Measures, that charged mainly Lower Permian sandstone reservoirs. This system is located in the Sole Pit Trough and Broad Fourteens Basin about 100 km south of the Central Graben and contains over 4.1 trillion m^3 (145 trillion ft^3, or about 24 billion bbl oil equivalent) of nonassociated gas (Glennie, 1990b).

537

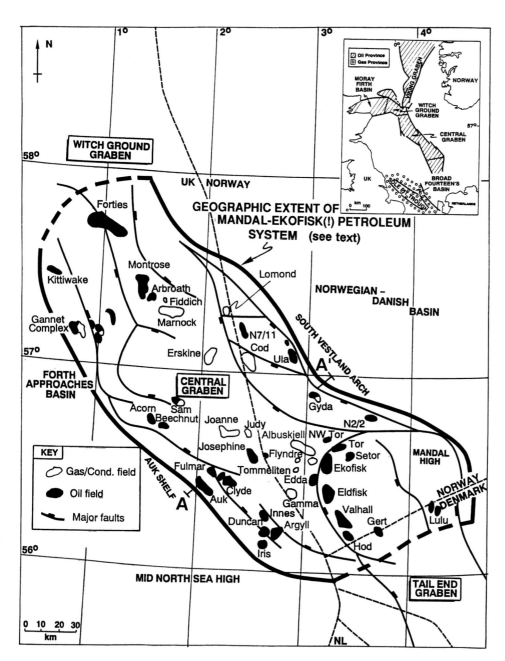

Figure 33.1. Location of the Central Graben within the North Sea area showing the gas–condensate and oil fields listed in Table 33.1. Inset map shows the location of other grabens, basins, and a trough.

The northern North Sea petroleum province involves the Viking, Witch Ground, and Central grabens, which straddle the U.K.–Norway offshore boundary. The oil systems in the northern North Sea extend from the Central Graben north to the Viking Graben and include a thick, rich Upper Jurassic to basal Cretaceous oil-prone source rock (Cornford, 1990) that charged mostly Upper Cretaceous–Paleocene reservoir rocks in the Central Graben and Jurassic reservoirs in the Viking Graben (Brown, 1991). The source rock is named the Draupne Formation in northern Norwegian waters, the Mandal and Farsund formations in Norwegian and Danish waters, and the Kimmeridge Clay Formation in U.K. waters. Since the name Mandal Formation is more widely used in the Central Graben, it is adopted as the preferred nomenclature in this paper. Exploration of these northern North Sea oil systems have identified

some 4.77 billion m³ (30 billion bbl) of recoverable oil and natural gas liquids and 3.57 trillion m³ (126 trillion ft³, or about 21 billion bbl oil equivalent) of gas (Chew and Stephenson, 1986). The North Sea has yielded a wide variety of hydrocarbons from heavy oil to dry gas, with most production being a low sulfur, medium gravity crude oil.

The geographic extent of the Mandal–Ekofisk petroleum system in the Central Graben is defined as the area that includes the hydrocarbon accumulations originating from the pod of mature Mandal Formation source rock in the Central Graben as well as the pod of active source rock itself (Figure 33.1). The oil-prone source rock, the Mandal Formation, is eroded just north of the Forties field and is preserved in the Central Graben. To the southeast, the boundary adopted here for the system is arbitrary since both source rock and maturity extend into the Tail End Graben in Danish waters (Thomsen et al., 1987). The adoption of this arbitrary boundary is justified, as in this southeastern end of the Central Graben, hydrocarbons move with a strong vertical component following halokinetic or tectonic fracture conduits.

The level of thermal maturity of this source rock varies as shown by Thomas et al. (1985b), who identified the Cod, Albuskjell, and Ekofisk "kitchens" in the Central Graben area. These kitchens were named after the nearest rather than the most significant hydrocarbon occurrence. However, the source rock between these kitchens is thermally mature and has contributed petroleum to the overlying reservoir rocks. On this basis, all of the kitchens are part of the same petroleum system. Although the same thermal maturity pattern continues into the Witch Ground Graben, Viking Graben, and Moray Firth basin, the break in the source rock north of the Forties oil field determines the geographic extent of this system.

The name adopted for this system is Mandal–Ekofisk because the Mandal Formation (or Kimmeridge Clay Formation on the U.K. side) comprises the oil-prone source rock, and the Ekofisk Formation within the Chalk Group, which contains 62% of the system's reserves, is the major reservoir rock. An excellent oil source rock correlation based on molecular and isotopic correlations and source rock maturity relationships confirms the genetic association between the reservoired oils and condensates and source rock bitumen, bestowing the (!) symbol on this system.

A general stratigraphic review of North Sea geology has been reported in Glennie (1990a), and details are provided by Ziegler (1982, 1988). Synoptic reviews of most Norwegian fields are found in Spencer et al. (1987) and of many U.K. fields in Abbotts (1991). A general account of hydrocarbon genesis in the Central Graben has been given by Cayley (1987) and Spencer et al. (1986b).

EXPLORATION HISTORY

The oil and gas fields of the Mandal–Ekofisk petroleum system in the Central Graben are listed in Table 33.1 with their discovery date, operator, and most accessible and recent published description. Figure 33.2 shows the history of exploration in terms of the annual discovery of volumes of in-place oil, condensate, and gas from 1968 to the present. Based on the discovery well, early explorers discovered the vast majority of reserves. However, this is misleading because of individual field size growth. For example, the first of the five separate acccumulations in the Gannet complex was discovered in 1972, but substantial reserves have been added by subsequent drilling in the period 1972–1982 (Armstrong et al., 1987) and these are all attributed to 1972.

Exploration in the offshore North Sea started with speculative wells sparked by the Shell–Esso discovery of the Groningen gas field in the Netherlands during

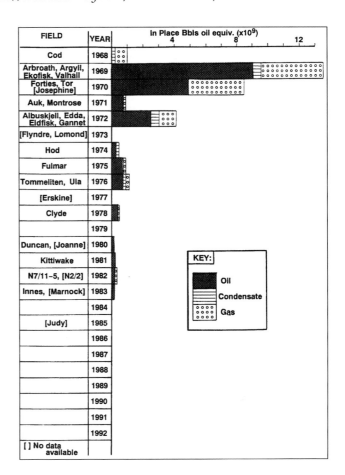

Figure 33.2. Exploration history of the Central Graben by discovery year of in-place reserves. The year is the spud date of the discovery well (Table 33.1), and the reserves relate to the data presented in Table 33.5.

1959–1963. Additional successes in the southern gas province in the 1960s soon followed (Brennand et al., 1990). These discoveries, coupled with technological advances in offshore drilling, led to the first major oil discovery by the Phillips Norway group in December 1969 in the Central Graben (Pekot and Gersib, 1987). Oil was recovered from the Danian Chalk Group, which was later to become the Ekofisk field. A year later on the U.K. side, BP discovered oil in Paleocene sandstone to identify the Forties field, further galvanizing exploration (Carman and Young, 1981).

In fact, the discovery of the Ekofisk field was predated by encouragement from drill-stem tests that recovered oil from the Danian Chalk Group in the Anne (now Kraka) field in the Danish offshore area in 1966 and the Valhal field in the Norwegian offshore area in 1967. In 1968, gas was recovered from Paleocene deep water sandstone reservoir rock in the Cod field that straddles the U.K. and Norway offshore boundary. The diversity of age and lithology of reservoir rocks in this novel petroleum province was hinted at in this early stage by the discovery in 1971 of oil in Permian and Devonian rocks in the Auk and Argyl fields, respectively. Few new field discoveries have been made in the last decade.

Table 33.1. Oil Fields of the Mandal-Ekofisk(!) Petroleum System, Central Graben, North Sea: Reservoir Ages, Lithologies and Depths, Temperatures, and Hydrocarbon Bulk Properties

Field Name	Quad/Block Designation[a]	Reference	Operator	Year Discovered	Reservoir Age
Acorn	UK29/8	No published data		—	—
Albuskjell	N1/6;N2/4	D'Heur, 1987a	Shell/Phillips	1972	Maastrichtian–Danian
Arbroath	UK22/17,18	Crawford et al., 1991	Amoco	1969	Paleocene
Argyl	UK30/24	Robson, 1991; Pennington, 1975	Hamilton	1969	U. Permian; Devonian
Auk	UK30/16	Trewin & Bramwell, 1991	Shell/Esso	1971	Permian; Cretaceous
Beechnut	UK29/9	No published data		—	—
Clyde	UK30/17b	Stevens & Wallis, 1991	Britoil/BP	1978	U. Jurassic
Cod	N7/11	D'Heur, 1987b	Phillips	1968	Paleocene
Duncan	UK30/24	Robson, 1991	Hamilton	1980	U. Jurassic
Edda	N2/6, 7	D'Heur & Michaud, 1987	Phillips	1972	Maastrichtian–Danian
Ekofisk	N2/4	Pekot & Gersib, 1987	Phillips	1969	Maastrichtian–Danian
Eldfisk	N2/7	Michaud, 1987	Phillips	1972	Maastrichtian–Danian
Erskine	UK23/26	No published data		1977	Paleocene–Jurassic
Flyndra	N1/5	No published data		1973	Maastrichtian–Danian
Forties	UK21/10;22/6	Wills, 1991	BP	1970	Paleocene
Fulmar	UK30/16, 11	Stockbridge & Gray, 1991	Shell/Esso	1975	U. Jurassic
Gannet	UK21/24, 25	Armstrong et al., 1987	Shell/Esso	1972	U. Jur, Paleoc–Eocene
Gert	DK5603/27	No published data			
Gyda	N2/1	No published data			Oligocene
Hod	N2/11	Norbury, 1987; D'Heur, 1986	Amoco	1974	U. Cretaceous–Danian
Innes	UK30/24	Robson, 1991	Hamilton	1983	L. Permian
Joanne	UK30/7	No published data		1980	Paleocene
Josephine	UK30/13	No published data	Phillips	1970	Triassic
Judy	UK30/8	No published data		1985	U. Jurassic
Kittiwake	UK21/18	Glennie & Armstrong, 1991	Shell/Esso	1981	U. Jurassic; U. Triassic
Lomond	UK23/21, 22	No published data		1973	Paleocene
Lulu (Harald)	DK5604/22	Thomsen et al., 1990		—	
Marnock	UK22/24	No published data		1983	Triassic–Jurassic
Montrose	UK22/17, 18	Crawford et al., 1991	Amoco	1971	Paleocene
N7/11-5	N7/11	Strand & Slaatsveen, 1987	Norsk Hydr	1982	U. Jurassic
N2/2 Struct.	N2/2	Gabrielsen et al., 1985, 1986	Saga	1982	U. Jurassic
Sam	UK29/4, 5	No published data			
Tommeliten	N1/9	D'Heur & Pekot, 1987; D'Heur, 1986	Statoil	1976	Maastrichtian–Danian
Tor	N2/4,5	D'Heur, 1987c	Phillips	1970	Maastrichtian–Danian
Ula	N7/12	Home, 1987; Larter et al., 1990	Conoco/BP	1976	U. Jurassic, Triassic
Ula Trend	N7/8–2/1	Spencer et al., 1986b	Mainly BP	—	U. Jurassic, Triassic
Valhal	N2/8,11	Leonard & Munns, 1987; D'Heur, 1986	Amoco	1969	Maastrichtian–Danian
Fiddich	UK22/19	No published data		—	
West Ekofisk	N2/4	D'Heur, 1987d	Phillips	1970	Maastrichtian–Danian

[a]UK, United Kingdom; N, Norway; DK, Denmark.

BASIN SETTING

The Central Graben developed as a failed rift during the Late Triassic and Jurassic and lies between the Fenno–Scandian shield to the east and the U.K. Caledonides to the west. Prior to this time, continental sedi-mentary rocks were deposited over basement rocks. This basement is poorly defined, but drilling to date has identified no significant trapped hydrocarbons in pre-Caledonide (pre-Devonian?) rocks. Well penetrations to Devonian strata on the Central Graben flanks have encountered reservoir rocks.

Table 33.1 *(continued)*

Reservoir Lithology	Top Reservoir Depth (msl)		Reservoir Temp.	HC Phase	Gravity	Density	GOR	
	(m)	(ft)	(°C)		(° API)	(g/cm³)	(ft³/bbl)	(m³/m³)
—	—	—	—	Oil	—	—	—	—
Chalk	3070	10072	138	Oil	48	0.79	158-301	890-1600
Sandstone	2448	8030	118	Oil	40	0.82	490	87
Carb; ss	2621	8600	—	Oil	37	0.84	1180	210
Ss; dolo; chlk	2236	7337	102	Oil	38	0.83	190	34
—	—	—	—	Oil	—	—	—	—
Sandstone	3673	12050	147	Oil	37	0.84	340	61
Sandstone	2870	9416	132	Oil	55	0.76	13219	2353
Sandstone	2804	9200	—	Oil	38	0.83	1404	250
Chalk	3063	10049	132	Oil	39	0.83	1725	307
Chalk	2888	9475	131	Oil	36	0.84	1551	276
Chalk	2700	8858	119	Oil	38	0.84	1483–2118	264–377
Sandstone	—	—	—	Cond	—	—	—	—
Chalk	—	—	—	Cond	—	—	—	—
Sandstone	2030	6660	96	Oil	37	0.84	303	54
Sandstone	3018	9900	140	Oil	40	0.82	614	109
Sandstone	Varies	Varies	—	Oil	Varies	—	Varies	—
—	—	—	—	Oil	—	—	—	—
Sandstone	—	—	—	Oil	—	—	—	—
Chalk	2575	8448	100	Cond	77	0.68	876	156
Sandstone	3658	12000	—	Oil	45	0.80	2247	400
Sandstone	—	—	—	Cond	—	—	—	—
Sandstone	—	—	—	Oil	—	—	—	—
Sandstone	—	—	—	Oil	—	—	—	—
Sandstone	2979	9773	118	Oil	38	0.83	340	61
Sandstone	—	—	—	Oil	—	—	—	—
—	—	—	—	Oil	—	—	—	—
Sandstone	—	—	—	Oil	—	—	—	—
Sandstone	2451	8040	125	Oil	40	0.82	700	125
Sandstone	4040	13254	161	Oil	39	0.83	1500	267
Sandstone	3360	11023	—	Oil	44	0.81	500	89
—	—	—	—	Oil	—	—	—	—
Chalk	3000	9842	124	Oil	35–50	0.78–0.85	13107	2333
Chalk	2872	9422	136	Oil	43	0.82	1461	260
Sandstone	3400	11155	143	Oil	39	0.83	500	89
Sandstone	Varies	Varies	—	Oil	39	0.83	750	134
Chalk	2400	7874	—	Oil	37	0.84	1298	231
—	—	—	—	Cond	—	—	—	—
Chalk	3065	10056	131	Oil	44	0.81	4107	731
Averages	2923	9590	127		42	0.82	2200	392

The basement rock of the Central Graben is the pre-Devonian metamorphic rocks. The basin fill contains sedimentary rocks that range in age from Devonian to Holocene and are divided into three sequences: a Devonian–Middle Jurassic prerift sequence, an Upper Jurassic–basal Cretaceous synrift unit, and a Lower Cretaceous–Holocene postrift sequence (Figure 33.3).

Figure 33.4 shows the source and reservoir rocks of the Mandal–Ekofisk petroleum system relative to the stratigraphy and lithology of the Central Graben. The source rock is the Upper Jurassic to basal Cretaceous Mandal Formation marine shales, and the major reservoir rock is chalk of the Upper Cretaceous and basal Tertiary Chalk Group, of which the Ekofisk Formation is

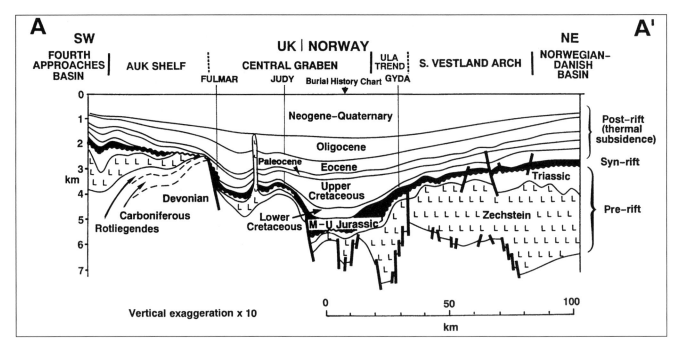

Figure 33.3. East-west cross section A–A' across the Central Graben (GECO line CGT-81-09 after Spencer et al., 1986a). See Figure 33.1 for location of cross section and Figure 33.10 for the burial history chart. Pre-rift, syn-rift, and post-rift sedimentary rocks are shown on the right.

the most productive example. The reservoir sandstones of the Paleogene and Upper Jurassic are the next most important, while minor reservoir rocks range in age from Devonian to Triassic–Lower Cretaceous.

The seals are often intraformational. For example, the seal rock for the chalk reservoirs is the same Upper Cretaceous and basal Tertiary chalk, but in an impermeable facies. The Paleogene fan and turbidite sandstones are sealed by the surrounding coeval shales. The Upper Jurassic sandstones are sealed by the Upper Jurassic mudstones of the Mandal and Farsund formations, while the Devonian and Permian reservoirs of the Auk and Argyll area are sealed by an unconformable layer of Upper Cretaceous chalk. Given a single source rock of Late Jurassic and earliest Cretaceous age and subsequent continuous sedimentation, the overburden rock was deposited from the Early Cretaceous to Holocene.

Structural History

When the Central Graben formed is still debated (Ziegler, 1982, 1988; Kooi et al., 1989). Generally, it is thought that the crust thinned and domed in the Middle Jurassic, from which a graben developed in the Late Jurassic. The thermal sag phase controlled sedimentation from the Early Cretaceous to the present day (Figure 33.3). This simple case of rift evolution was used by McKenzie (1978) to develop a general crustal-stretching model, later tested and refined by Sclater and Christie (1980), Wood and Barton (1983), and Barton and Wood (1984). A palinspastically restored stratigraphic section is presented by Thorne and Watts (1989). Subsequent models claim the rift formed earlier, in the Triassic (Fisher and Mudge, 1990), in Permian (Glennie, 1990c) or

in the Carboniferous (Haszeldine and Russell, 1987). However, all these models accept that the major graben developed during the Jurassic and that the thickest Permian–Triassic lay to the east of the younger Central Graben (Figure 33.3).

Structurally, the graben itself is simple, but because of periodic salt movements during the Early Triassic, Late Jurassic, Late Cretaceous, and Tertiary, the graben fill is complex (Taylor, 1990). The oil fields in Upper Cretaceous chalk reservoirs in the southern part of the Central Graben have developed over salt swells and pillows, with most fields in the entire Central Graben being affected to some degree by halokinesis. The unusual reservoir geometry in the Clyde and Fulmar oil fields on the southwestern flank of the graben demonstrates a subtle influence of halokinesis (Stevens and Wallis, 1991), while the Ula oil field trend on the northeastern flank contains structural domes associated with salt swells and diapirs (Spencer et al., 1986b). The structure of the Tertiary sandstone reservoir of the Cod gas field also formed in response to underlying salt piercement (D'Heur, 1987b).

Based on reflection seismic profiles, a boundary fault occurs along the southwestern margin of the Central Graben which displaces sedimentary rocks of Early Cretaceous age and older. Where this boundary fault is displaced by a series of offset (transfer) faults, oil-bearing structural traps are found, such as in the Auk and Argyl fields (Gibbs, 1989). The northeastern Central Graben margin has less definition at the basal Cretaceous because this flank of the graben is formed by flexure plus a series of smaller dip-slip faults rather than a single major fault. To the northwest, the fault-bounded intra-graben horst of the Forties–Montrose High has produced

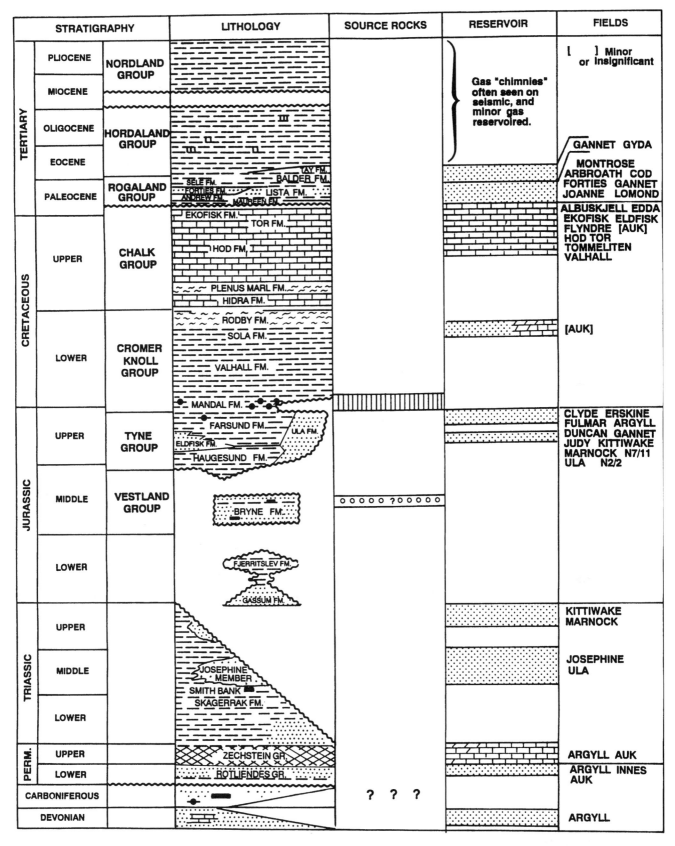

Figure 33.4. Summary of Central Graben stratigraphy showing rock units, lithology, source rocks, reservoir rocks, and fields. In most cases, seals are coeval impervious sedimentary rocks (chalk for the chalk fields and mudstones for the sandstone fields). The fields are listed adjacent to major reservoir horizons. The basement rocks, presumed to be pre-Devonian Caledonian low-grade metamorphics, are not shown. Note that in U.K. waters, the Eldfisk Formation includes the Fulmar sands and the Mandal and Farsund formations are equivalent to the Kimmeridge Clay.

structural traps, or drape closure, at the Paleogene stratigraphic level.

Today, the geologic development of the Central Graben is incomplete. As pointed out by Nielsen et al. (1986), the average sedimentation rates of 14 m/m.y. in the Paleocene and 23 m/m.y. in the Eocene–Miocene have accelerated to 100 m/m.y. in the Pliocene–Pleistocene and to 148m/m.y. in the Quaternary. The differences in shape of the burial history curves in the various grabens farther north in the North Sea are described by Cornford and Brooks (1989) in terms of a southward migration of the locus of deposition with time. This ever increasing thickness of overburden rock impacts oil and gas generation by controlling the movement of the oil-prone source rock into and through the oil and gas windows. By modifying basin geometry, it changes migration paths and trap configurations.

Stratigraphy

Figure 33.4 shows a generalized stratigraphic column for the Central Graben with the source rocks, reservoir rocks, and field names (see also Table 33.1). In terms of reservoir rocks, the fields of the Mandal–Ekofisk petroleum system fall into three main groups: (1) Jurassic, Permian, and Devonian sandstones and carbonates (pre- and synrift); (2) Upper Cretaceous–Lower Paleocene chalk (postrift); and (3) Upper Paleocene–Eocene sandstones (postrift). Given the widespread source rock for this petroleum system, the essential elements and processes controlling the distribution of oils in these three reservoirs are presented in a temporal way (Figure 33.5).

Basement Rock

Pre-Devonian basement rocks are not penetrated by wells in the Central Graben. By analogy with the flanking rocks in the United Kingdom and southern Norwegian onshore area, the basement rocks are pre-Cambrian, Cambrian–Ordovician, and Silurian sedimentary rocks that were metamorphosed during the Caledonian orogeny and intruded by late Caledonian granite.

Prerift Sedimentary Rocks

The prerift stratigraphy of the Central Graben comprises mainly nonmarine Devonian siliciclastics and Carboniferous sandstones and mudstones, together with Lower Permian sandstones of the Rotliegendes Group and Upper Permian evaporites (salts, anhydrites, etc.) of the Zechstein Group. The Auk and Argyl fields on the southwestern flank of the rift graben have reservoir rocks of Permian age with ancilliary reserves of Devonian and Cretaceous age.

The Triassic sequence is dominantly red-bed mudstones and siltstones, with some sandstones. The Lower Triassic Skagerrak Formation contains minor reservoir sandstones in the oil fields within the Ula trend (Home, 1987). In the area of the Josephine oil field, the sandstone in the Middle Triassic Josephine Member is reported as a good-quality reservoir (Fisher and Mudge, 1990).

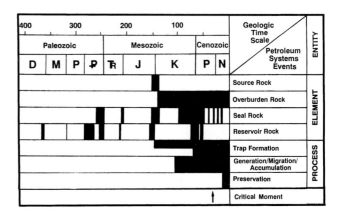

Figure 33.5. Events chart showing the timing of essential elements and processes within the Mandal–Ekofisk(!) petroleum system.

Except for the locally preserved Gassum and Fjerritslev formations, the Lower Jurassic appears to be missing over most of the area either due to nondeposition or to erosion. During the Middle Jurassic, the Central Graben was at least one provenance area for the deltaic Brent sandstone, the major reservoir rock in the Viking Graben. Within the Central Graben, it is represented locally by the Bryne Formation, which may contain a gas-prone source rock.

Synrift Sedimentary Rocks

When the up-doming collapsed and active rifting began in the Upper Jurassic, the synrift sedimentary rocks accumulated. The significance of the synrift sediments is that they include the only significant hydrocarbon source rock in the Mandal–Ekofisk petroleum system (Figure 33.5). From the way they infill the extensional paleotopography, the Upper Jurassic sequence are considered the beginning of the synrift sequence (Figure 33.3). Where thin (covering the footwalls of the rotated graben blocks), the Upper Jurassic appears to be a condensed mudstone sequence, rather than having been uplifted and eroded.

The rift formed a deep water basin that filled with mudstone of the Upper Jurassic Haugesund, Farsund, and Mandal Formations (Heather and Kimmeridge Clay Formations of the United Kingdom; Stow and Atkin, 1987). This mudstone unit includes the only significant oil-prone source rock recognized in the Central Graben (Cornford, 1990). Source rock deposition during the Late Jurassic and earliest Cretaceous resulted from the fortuitous combination of high sedimentation rates of clay-sized siliciclastic material, high planktonic productivity in the near-surface water, and development of an anoxic environment at the sediment–water interface (Figures 33.6A and C).

The closing of the oxygenated seaway connecting the Tethyan sea to the southeast and the Boreal sea to the north resulted in the development of anoxia during the Late Jurassic within the North Sea grabens and flanking basins (Figure 33.6B). Evidence for the break in the Tethyan–Boreal connection from Kimmeridgian to

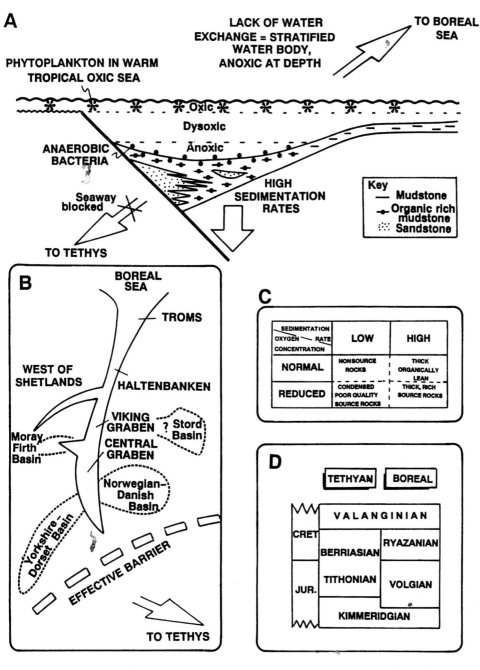

Figure 33.6. (A) An east-west section and (B) map of a developing graben system during the Late Jurassic that show the factors affecting the deposition of the Upper Jurassic–basal Cretaceous source rock in the North Sea. (C) Closure of the seaway connecting the Boreal and Tethyan seas caused anoxia in the deep water trough where sediments and organic matter accumulated as well as sedimentation rate. (D) Because of closing of the seaway, stratigraphic provincialism developed.

Valanginian time is found in the development of separate stratigraphies (Figure 33.6D). Cessation of inter-ocean exchange, coupled with deepening of the water in the graben and flank basin areas, facilitated development of stratified, stagnant water favoring organic matter preservation.

Locally derived Upper Jurassic coarse-grained siliciclastic sandstones of the Eldfisk Formation (informally called the Fulmar sandstones in the United Kingdom) constitute locally important reservoir rocks on the southwestern flank of the newly formed rift (Table 33.1). Examples are the Fulmar (Helm et al., 1990; Stockbridge and Gray, 1991), Duncan (Robson, 1991), and Clyde oil fields (Stevens and Wallis, 1991). On the Norwegian rift margin, the Ula trend contains shallow marine sandstones of the Upper Jurassic Ula Formation (Spencer et al., 1986b; Home 1987; Larter et al., 1990).

Postrift Sedimentary Rock

Subsidence due to cooling of the basement rock along the North Sea graben axis during the Early Cretaceous reconnected the Tethyan and Boreal water masses, recreating an oxygenated seaway. During this subsidence, organic-lean mudstone and siltstone with some sandstone accumulated. Although reservoir rock of this age is found north of the Central Graben, no significant commercial accumulations have been reported in the Valhall, Sola, or Rodby formations. Minor oil production, however, is attributed to an unusual Albian–Aptian carbonate breccia in the Auk field (Trewin and Bramwell, 1991).

In the Late Cretaceous–early Paleocene, rising sea level, active phytoplankton (*Globigerina*) growth in the surface waters, and continued broad regional subsidence favored deposition of chalk over the entire Central Graben area. These rocks constitute the most important reservoir in the Mandal–Ekofisk petroleum system.

A fine-grained carbonate ooze accumulated on the sea floor and, where unstable on the basin flanks, slumped down from the northeast into the deep water axis of the graben, where autochthonous, slump, debris flow, and turbidite facies are recognized (Kennedy, 1987; Taylor and Lapre, 1987). These chalks are major reservoir rocks (Table 33.1), particularly in the greater Ekofisk area where synsedimentary slumping fostered the preservation of primary porosity. Other chalk reservoirs are the Tommeliten, Albuskjell, and West Ekofisk gas–condensate fields, and the Edda, Ekofisk, Eldfisk, Hod, Tor, and Valhal oil fields, which all lie in the southeastern part of the Central Graben (D'Heur, 1986). In addition, the Chalk Group is an important part of the overburden rock, as its deposition initiated generation of petroleum from the underlying source rock in the deepest parts of the Central Graben.

The Rogaland Group, deposited during the remainder of the Paleocene and into the early Eocene, marks a major change in sedimentation from the chalk. Marine siliciclastic sandstone with some fine mud, often in the form of submarine fans, was introduced sporadically from the west and northwest into the graben (Lovell, 1990). Thus, fields with a Rogaland Group sandstone reservoir all lie in the northwestern part of the Central Graben (Figure 33.1). It has been suggested that these fans are related to the updoming or rejuvenation of the Greenland–Caledonian hinterland prior to the opening of the North Atlantic (Thompson and Gibson, 1991). The sandstones in these fans are the second most important reservoir horizon of the Mandal–Ekofisk petroleum system. In addition, the Rogaland Group created additional overburden rock, burying a wider area of the Mandal Formation and hence increasing the volume of mature source rock.

A deep water submarine fan has long been accepted as the depositional model for the Rogaland Group sandstone reservoir rocks. Recognized fan facies include marine deltaic, shelf–slope, and upper, middle, and lower fan assemblages (Stewart, 1987). An example of this association is the Forties field where, paradoxically, the thickest upper and middle fan deposits unconformably overlie the Forties–Montrose High, presumably a subdued structure during the Paleogene. Near the base of the section, the Forties field reservoir sandstone is a turbidite fan that grades to a debris flow toward the top (Wills and Peattie, 1990). This field developed structural closure from two processes: (1) rejuvenation of the tectonically positive Forties–Montrose High, which formed a drape over the previously deposited fan, and (2) differential compaction of the dominantly interfan mud sequence around the thick pod of sand (Wills, 1991). The Montrose field represents a middle fan facies of a stratigraphically older fan system (Crawford et al., 1991), while the Cod field accumulated in a more distal fan facies (D'Heur, 1987b). These fields have reservoirs in submarine fans that run down the axis of the Central Graben. A separate, lateral submarine fan contains the upper reservoir rocks of the Gannet field pools, with the South Gannet pool in a proximal position and the Central and North Gannet pools in middle fan facies (Armstrong et al., 1987).

The Hordaland Group was deposited during the Eocene–Oligocene. This dominantly mudstone unit provides additional thickening to the overburden rock and acts as a seal to the Rogaland Group reservoirs. Oil shows (but no significant accumulations) in the coarser units of the Hordaland Group attest to limited vertical migration possibilities. The top of the Hordaland Group is marked by a regionally extensive Miocene unconformity (Figures 33.3 and 33.4) (Nielsen et al., 1986). From the late Miocene to the Holocene, the sedimentation rates of mudstone have continued to increase (Nielsen et al., 1986). These mudstones have significantly thickened the overburden rock, substantially broadening the area and hence the volume of mature source rock.

MANDAL–EKOFISK(!) PETROLEUM SYSTEM

No previous workers have attempted to discuss the North Sea in general or the Central Graben in particular in terms of a petroleum system, although Demaison and Huizinga (1991) in their general review of petroleum system types established the Central Graben as a vertically drained, high impedance system. Damtoft et al. (1987) described most elements of the petroleum system in the Danish Central Trough (Tail End Graben) to the south.

The earliest volumetric calculations were published by Fuller (1975, 1980) for the entire North Sea petroleum province, and in particular, for basins and grabens in the northern North Sea. In a paper describing the Valhall oil field, Leonard and Munns (1987) defined a drainage area and thickness for the Mandal Formation source rock underlying the field. Using an average of 5–6 wt. % TOC, they estimated post–middle Miocene generation of 3.5 billion m³ of oil, giving an overall efficiency factor for the field of 8% for expulsion, migration, and entrapment. The temporal relationship of the elements of and processes in the Mandal–Ekofisk system are discussed later (Figure 33.5).

Petroleum Source Rock

The only significant petroleum source rock recognized in the Central Graben is the organic-rich shale of the Mandal Formation. In the Central Graben, the organic-rich facies ranges in age from late Volgian to Ryazanian, representing the upper part of the Kimmeridge Clay–Draupne Formation farther north (Dore et al., 1985) and being stratigraphically higher than the Kimmeridge Clay of the U.K. onshore. A study of the Central Graben by Hall and Bjorøy (1991) suggests that the Farsund and Haugesund formations are part of the same source rock interval (Figure 33.4).

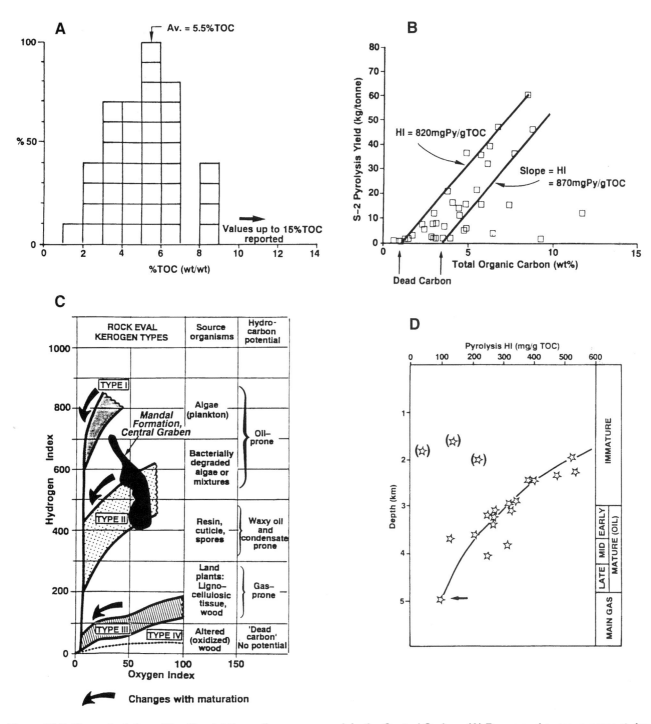

Figure 33.7. Characteristics of the Mandal Formation source rock in the Central Graben. (A) Range and average present-day TOC values. (B) Rock-Eval pyrolysis S₂ yield relative to TOC, showing the average HI (slope) and dead carbon content (intercept on the TOC axis). (C) Kerogen type of the Mandal Formation as defined on a modified van Krevelen diagram. (D) Decrease in HI with depth during oil generation. (After Cornford, 1990, with additional data.)

The Mandal Formation was deposited in an arm of the northern Boreal sea at a time when a combination of high surface water productivity, anoxia at depth, and high sedimentation rate produced an excellent source rock (Figure 33.6). In the graben areas, the organic matter in this source rock is mainly type II kerogen (Demaison et al., 1984; Cooper and Barnard, 1984; Cornford 1990) and

consists mostly of bacterially degraded algal debris with minor amounts of terrestrial debris, some oxidized. The oil-prone nature of the organic matter decreases rapidly outside the main Central Graben area, in particular toward the northeastern Norwegian–Danish flank, where the more stratigraphically restricted Tau Formation is the only oil-prone unit (Thomsen et al., 1983).

Organic Matter Richness and Type

A histogram showing the range of total organic carbon (TOC) values reported in the literature on the Mandal Formation of the Central Graben has an average TOC of 5.5 wt. % (Figure 33.7A). An average TOC of 5–6 wt. % is reported for a thick mudstone underlying the Valhall field (Leonard and Munns, 1987), while Cayley (1987) reports an average TOC of 8 wt. % with a maximum of >15 wt. % for the Central Graben as a whole. Damtoft et al. (1987) contoured average TOC values in excess of 5 wt. % for the northern sector of the adjacent Danish Tail End Graben. TOC values reported for deep wells can be substantially lower because expulsion of oil and gas reduces the residual TOC level, thus a correction must be made (as discussed later).

The local term "hot shale" is used to describe the most organic rich units of the Upper Jurassic mudstones and is derived from the high natural gamma ray wireline log response (often in excess of 200 API units). In the Mandal Formation, this has been shown to originate from the high uranium, thorium, and potassium contents, with uranium up to 40 ppm in the Central Graben (Stow and Atkin, 1987). Bjorlykke and Finstad (1975) noted contributions to the total natural gamma ray response of 61% from uranium (5.27 ppm), 33% from thorium (10.46 ppm), and 6% from potassium (1.34 ppm) in the Mandal Formation shales of the Valhall field well N2/11-1.

Discrete TOC values can be generalized across the entire source rock section using wireline log responses (Cornford, 1990). A plot of natural gamma ray response and measured TOC values from Central Graben wells shows a lower gamma ray response per unit TOC than in the Viking Graben (Cornford, 1990). However, from the present author's experience, the gamma (or spectral gamma) log response correlates well with TOC but poorly with kerogen type.

Kerogen type can be determined from the S_2 peak from Rock-Eval pyrolysis and TOC, which are used to calculate the hydrogen index (HI). Plotting the S_2 peak with TOC produces a plot that has a slope of the HI and an intercept on the TOC axis (Figure 33.7B). While the slope of the lines represents the inertinite-free HI, the intercept has been found to represent the amount of dead carbon or inertinite (plus residual carbon in postmature samples) rather than the sorptive capacity of the mineral matrix, as claimed by Langford and Blanc-Valeron (1990). Here, the Mandal Formation kerogens contain 1–3 wt. % dead carbon.

The modified van Krevelen diagram indicates that most Mandal Formation samples are type II kerogen, with some type I (Figure 33.7C). This designation is confirmed by organic petrography of the Mandal Formation and other Upper Jurassic North Sea kerogens, where abundant amorphous liptinite occurs together with minor particulate algal debris, vitrinite, and inertinite (Cornford, 1990).

The average pyrolysis HI of the Mandal Formation source rock in the Central Graben is in the range of 500–600 mg/g TOC when immature (<2 km) and falls below 100 mg/g TOC by about 5 km (16,400 ft) burial

when exhausted (Figure 33.7D). Maps have been produced of original source rock richness based on organic petrography and kerogen type (e.g., Demaison et al., 1984; Cooper and Barnard, 1984), but correction for the effects of maturation on these parameters is not always made. In some field studies, kerogens are described as type III when they are probably late mature type II.

A study of the Mandal Formation by Bailey et al. (1990) at 3700–3800 m depth in a single well in the Ekofisk area shows average pyrolysate values of about 20 kg/t, with values as high as 70 kg/t. Using the previous information, an average immature HI of 550 mg/g TOC and an average TOC value of 5.5 wt. % give an average potential yield of 30.25 kg/t. To a first approximation, this pyrolysate yield can be taken to represent the gross hydrocarbon yield of the Mandal Formation source rock.

Source Rock Thickness

The thickness of the source rock interval is difficult to assess because the sediment filled in the irregular topography produced by the pull-apart and the movement of the underlying evaporites (Figure 33.8). The rapid changes in source rock thicknesses are best observed on seismic profiles because wells are drilled mainly on structural highs and tend to penetrate the thinner sequences (Figure 33.3). The isopach map of Spencer et al. (1986b) combines the Upper and Middle Jurassic, but the majority of the section is source rock (Figure 33.8). For example, Well N2/11-1 encountered about 1200 m (3940 ft) of organic-rich shale (average 5–6 wt. % TOC) at the south end of the graben axis (Leonard and Munns, 1987). Also, at the north end of the graben axis to the east of the Gannet field, the source rock reaches at least 922 m (3025 ft) in thickness. The isopach map of the Kimmeridge Clay and the Heather Formation of Cayley (1987) shows a major thickening underlying the Joanne field in the U.K. sector. The southern extension of this source rock is mapped as the Farsund Formation in the Danish Tail End Graben by Damtoft et al. (1987), where thicknesses up to 1419 m (4656 ft) have been penetrated with the drill bit still in the formation.

Maturation and Generation

The thermal maturity at the top of the Mandal Formation source rock is best mapped using the near basal Cretaceous seismic reflector and well control. Detailed thermal maturity maps in the Central Graben have been made by Barnard and Cooper (1981), Spencer et al. (1986b), Cayley (1987), and Buhrig (1989). A synthesis of this information was used to construct the thermal maturity map in Figure 33.9). This map is based on relating oil and gas generation levels to vitrinite reflectance values (Table 33.2) using peak oil generation of 0.6–0.9% R_o. Extrapolation of maturity levels from well locations are estimated using reflection seismic data (Figure 33.3)and Platte River's BasinMod® modeling software. Such modeling requires stratigraphic, litho-

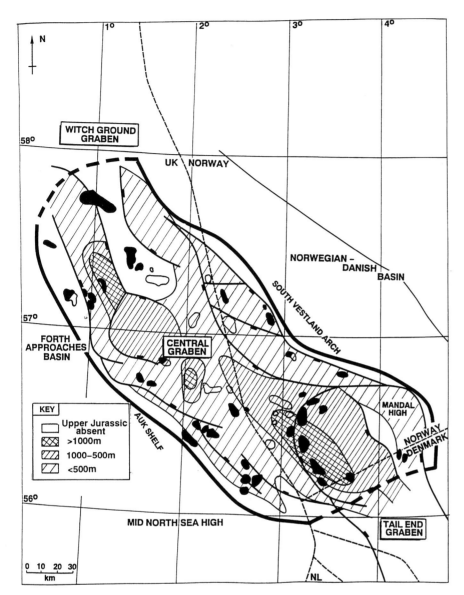

Figure 33.8. Isopach map of the Mandal Formation source rock in the Central Graben. The isopach contours are based on seismic reflectors near the basal Cretaceous and the Middle Jurassic unconformity. Thickness of this interval where penetrated by a well is often anomalously thin due to halokinetic highs. (Modified from Spencer et al., 1986a; Cayley, 1987; and individual well penetrations.)

logic, geothermal, and thermal maturity information. Stratigraphy and lithology are combined to generate a burial history diagram (Figure 33.10A). Before maturity can be calculated, the burial history plot must have a thermal grid superimposed (Figure 33.10A).

Present-Day Heat Flow

For the Central Graben, the present-day geothermal gradient of 40°C/km is known from drill-stem tests and reservoir temperature measurements and represents a heat flow of 53 mW/m² (Figure 33.10B; Table 33.1). This value is consistent with a generalized set of matrix thermal conductivities attributed to the various lithologies using an exponential compaction algorithm (Sclater and Christie, 1980).

The present-day geothermal gradient does vary within the Central Graben area (Cornford, 1990), with values ranging from 35° to 45°C/km. Reworking old data, Thorne and Watts (1989) attributed values of 1.2–1.4 HFU (heat flow units, μcal/cm² sec, equal to 50–59 mW/m²) to the Central Graben area. Leadholm et

al. (1985) contoured heat flow in the northern part of the Central Graben at greater than 1.6 HFU (67 mW/m²) and geothermal gradients of 35°–40°C/km. These values imply a very low mean thermal conductivity of 1.67–1.91 W/m °C for the overall sediment column since heat flow (mW/m²) equals thermal conductivity (W/m °C) times the geothermal gradient (°C/km).

Spencer et al. (1986b) report heat flows of 40–45 mW/m² on the northeastern flank, increasing to 50 mW/m² in the Central Graben, while much higher values (62–80 mW/m²) have been reported for the Sole Pit Trough gas area south of 55°N latitude (Oxburgh and Andrews-Speed, 1981). To the south in the Tail End Graben, low values of 1.10 HFU (46 mW/m²) are modeled for the Lulu-1 well for the present day, with lower values in the past (Thomsen et al.,1990). Since it is temperature and hence gradient that is measured, the discrepancies between the regional heat flow values appear to relate to the wide range of bulk thermal conductivities used for individual lithologies or for the whole sedimentary column. On the basis of oxygen isotopes, sea floor temperatures in the North Sea have

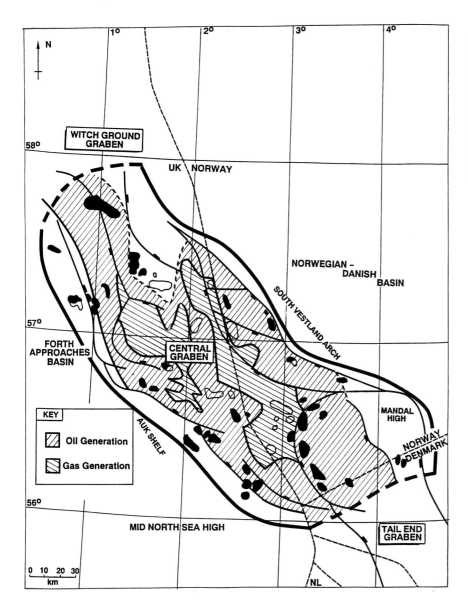

Figure 33.9. Thermal maturity map near basal Cretaceous (top source rock) in the Central Graben. Oil generation (oil window) occurs between 0.7 and 1.1% R_o, and gas generation (gas window) above 1.1% R_o. These boundaries are broadly in agreement with those reported by Larter et al. (1990), as detailed in Table 33.2. (Modified from Thomas et al., 1985a; Spencer et al., 1986a; Cayley, 1987; and other sources.)

Table 33.2. Levels of Thermal Maturity in Terms of Vitrinite Reflectance (R_o) and Depth for the Norwegian Ula Area[a]

Levels of Thermal Maturity	R_o (%)	Depth (m)
Immature (oil and gas)	0.55	3350
Early mature (oil)	0.60	3550
Peak oil generation	0.80	4000
Late mature (oil)	0.90	4200
Early (wet) gas	1.10	4500
Main (dry) gas	1.30	?

[a]Cayley's (1987) study of the U.K. Central graben quotes level of organic metamorphism values without reference to depth. From Larter et al. (1990).

Table 33.3. Surface Temperature and Heat Flow Values Used To Make the Model in Figure 33.10

Age (Ma)	Sea Floor (°C)	Heat flow (mW/m2)	Comments
Present	6	45	
15	18	45	Warm Oligo–Mio climate
65	15	45	
100	12	45	
120	15	60	Thermal decay
144	10	75	Rifting, deeper water
163	20	90	Thermal updoming

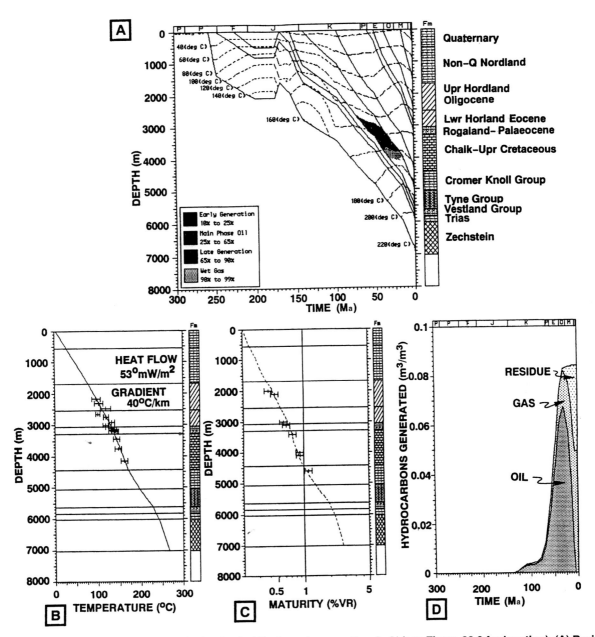

Figure 33.10. Thermal maturity modeling in the Central Graben along section A–A' (see Figure 33.3 for location). (A) Burial history diagram showing isotherms and kinetic generation windows for the Mandal Formation (BasinMod®). (B) Reservoir temperatures against depth with a best fit line of 53 mW/m² heat flow. (C) Thermal maturity calibration of measured and modeled vitrinite reflectance. (D) Generation (m³ oil and gas per m³ of source rock) versus time for the Mandal Formation source rock at this location. The time of peak generation (~30 Ma) at the location of the burial history chart defines the critical moment for this petroleum system.

changed considerably from the Neogene (18°C) to subzero temperatures in the Quaternary (Ice Ages), and finally to 6°C for the present-day interglacial (Table 33.3) (Cornford, 1990).

Paleoheat Flow

The paleogeothermal gradient and heat flow are more problematic to establish than present-day heat flow, but a decreasing heat flow with time from the Late Jurassic crustal thinning and rift event is thought to have occurred. As concluded later, a lower heat flow value is used for the Late Cretaceous and most of the Tertiary to

obtain a calibration with measured thermal maturity values. The model allows the high heat flow of the Middle Jurassic to dissipate over 60 m.y. (Table 33.3). Due to rapid and accelerating burial, the present-day thermal maturity of the source rock is insensitive to pre-Tertiary heat flow and tectonic events. The role of salt (with a high thermal conductivity) in perturbing a simple heat flow model is poorly understood, although thermal anomalies have been noted adjacent to salt diapirs.

Calibration with measured thermal maturity parameters is obtained by taking vitrinite reflectance values from the trends of a number of wells and relating them by depth to the section modeled with BasinMod (Figure

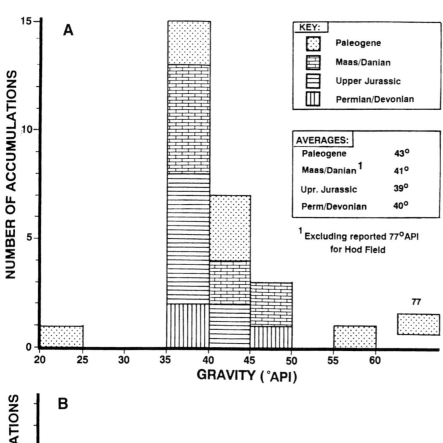

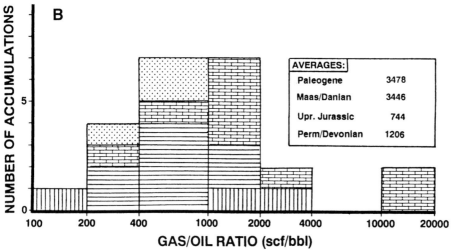

Figure 33.11. Bulk properties of oils and gas condensates of the Central Graben: (A) gravity (°API) and (B) gas–oil ratios. Data are given in Table 33.1. Individual fields may produce hydrocarbons with a range of API and GOR values.

33.10C). No acceptable calibration can be obtained using a heat flow of 53 mW/m² during the Tertiary. A plausible (but not unique) calibration is obtained by reducing the heat flow to 45 mW/m² from the late Miocene to the middle Cretaceous. The depth to the top of the oil window (~3000 m) (Figure 33.10A) is generalized over the basin fill using a seismically generated depth map of the near basal Lower Cretaceous (Spencer et al., 1986a).

As there is little present-day uplift and erosion in the Central Graben, any level of thermal maturity within the basin fill results from Tertiary and Quaternary overburden rock (Figure 33.10A). The onset of oil generation in an area where the source rock is at its deepest burial in the Central Graben is modeled in Figure 33.10A. The timing of generation at this middle basin location is shown to be 70–10 Ma (Figure 33.10D), with generation expressed in terms of cubic meters of hydrocarbon per

cubic meter of rock. This information is displayed on the generation, migration, and accumulation track in the petroleum system events chart of Figure 33.5.

Hydrocarbon Types

Bulk Composition

The typical Central Graben crude oil is a low sulfur, medium gravity oil with a napthenoparaffinic composition (Figures 33.11 and 33.12). In general, the reservoir rocks are buried to an average depth of 2923 m (9590 ft) and contain oil that averages 42° API with an average gas–oil ratio (GOR) of 392 m³/m³ (2195 scf/bbl) (Figures 33.11A and B). The average oil densities increase progressively from 43° API (0.81 g/cm³) for fields with Rogaland Formation sandstone to 41° API (0.82 g/cm³) for the Chalk Group fields and finally to 39° API (0.83 g/cm³)

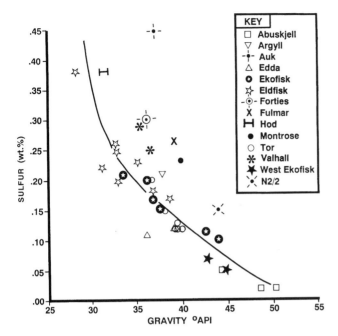

Figure 33.12. For oils from the Central Graben, API gravity decreases as the sulfur content increases. (Data from Hughes et al., 1985; Gabrielsen et al., 1985; and published industry assay data, e.g., Aalund, 1983.)

for the fields with Upper Jurassic reservoir rocks. This minor but consistent decrease in density with reservoir age may represent a degree of fractionation during migration away from the Mandal Formation source rock.

The GOR data discriminates to some extent (but not exclusively) between oil fields and gas–condensate fields (Table 33.1). Considerable variation can exist within a single field. For example, within the giant Forties oil field, three compositional (and pressure) compartments have been identified: (1) a high GOR in the southeast; (2) a less gassy crude oil in the west; and (3) an intermediate GOR in the central part (Wills and Peattie, 1990; Wills, 1991). While the authors attribute these variations to increasing thermal maturity of the source rock flanking the Forties high, another explanation is that the oil and gas have migrated first vertically from a more distant source rock out of the main graben and then laterally in the Paleogene sandstone from the southeast (Cornford, 1990). The variation in the Forties field may thus result from the influx of later more mature high-GOR liquids into the southeastern compartment of the field.

Both vertical and lateral variation in oil properties have been identified in the Ula field where, for example, the oil in the Upper Jurassic Ula Formation sandstones has a GOR of 672 scf/bbl compared with 487 scf/bbl in the Triassic reservoir. On the basis of detailed molecular ratios, the differences are attributed to the thermal maturity of the source rock charging the two compartments; a low rate of mixing is proposed (Larter et al., 1990). In addition, the Ula trend in the Norwegian Block 2/2, an upper Oligocene gas reservoir appears to contain a mixture of biogenic and thermogenic gas (Ekern, 1986; Gabrielsen et al., 1985). The thermal gas speculatively comes from overmature Mandal source rock, or from the

gas-prone Middle Jurassic source rocks (Figure 33.4).

The gas–condensate fields contain wet gas (typically 20–30% C_2–C_4/C_1–C_4), with a density range of 0.83–0.96 g/L, and yield a rich condensate fraction. Based on their density and chemistry, the liquids condensing from the gas phase in many Central Graben gas–condensate reservoirs are nearer the composition of oil and represent oil dissolved in wet gas.

With the exception of a single compartment of the Gannet field complex (Armstrong et al., 1987), the bulk properties of the commercial Central Graben hydrocarbons are in line with the kerogen type and range of thermal maturity of the Mandal Formation source rock. The presence of intermediate–heavy oil (21° API) in the South Gannet field is indicative of mixed biodegraded and nonbiodegraded oil. Bacterially degraded oil is only expected in the relatively shallow Paleogene fields.

Molecular Composition

A large number of proprietary studies of single wells, fields, and groups of fields have analyzed Central Graben oils. Given the presence of a single relatively homogeneous source rock unit, the major variation in the bulk, molecular, and isotopic properties of Central Graben oils results from differences in thermal maturity of the Mandal Formation source rock that charges each field. The molecular and isotopic properties of the oils in the Ekofisk area have been described by Hughes et al. (1985), and the properties of the Forties oil are given by Wills and Peattie (1990). Cayley (1987) illustrates whole oil gas chromatograms of Auk, Fulmar, and Gannet crude oils, while Larter et al. (1990) have detailed some properties within the Ula field.

The triterpanes (m/z 191) in the Central Graben oils show the typical bacterially degraded algal distribution of C_{27}–C_{35} pentacyclic molecules (hopanes and moretanes), and minor C_{23}–C_{30} tricyclic diterpanes common to most North Sea oils (e.g., Figures 33.13A and B). The major control on the relative abundance of the triterpanes is the thermal maturity of the Mandal Formation source rock. The relative abundance of trisnorhopane (T_m), normoretane, and moretane is characteristic of oils deriving from low maturity source rocks, while trisnorneohopane (T_s), norneohopane, and C_{30} diahopane are abundant in late mature source rock products (Figures 33.13A and B) (Cornford et al., 1983). Such mixtures of stable and unstable molecules reflect the progressive filling of the reservoir as the source rock was progressively buried (Figure 33.14).

The C_{28} bisnorhopane is lower in relative concentration in Central Graben oils compared to the more northern basins, either because it is lacking in the source rock or because it is thermally degraded in the more mature source rock (Hughes et al., 1985; Cornford et al., 1986; Hall and Bjorøy, 1991). The high relative abundance of C_{28} bisnorhopane in the Hod oil that originated from less mature source rock at this rim location of the Chalk Group fields suggests the latter.

From the m/z 217 fragmentogram, the full range of regular steranes, isosteranes, and diasteranes are found in the C_{27}–C_{29} homologous series (Figure 33.13A), with

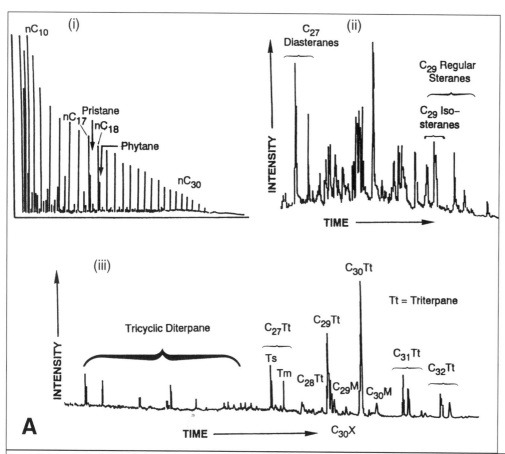

A

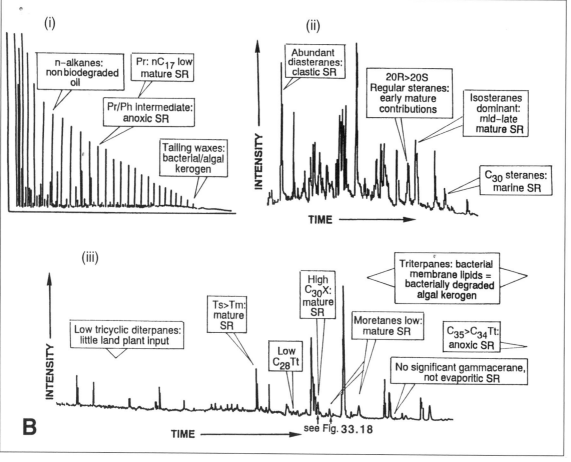

B

Figure 33.13. Molecular properties of oils from the Central Graben. (A) Identification and (B) interpretation of peaks. For parts (A) and (B): (i) the whole oil gas chromatogram of 39° API Fulmar oil (Cayley, 1987); (ii) sterane fragmentogram (*m/z* 217); and (iii) terpane fragmentogram (*m/z* 191) of the Ekofisk N2/4-3 oil (Hughes et al., 1985). Abreviations: Pr, pristane; Ph, phytane; 20R and 20S, regular sterane isomers; Tt, triterpane; M, moretane; Ts, trisnorneohopane; Tm, trisnorhopane; C_{28}Tt, bisnorhopane; C_{30}X, diahopane; and SR, source rock.

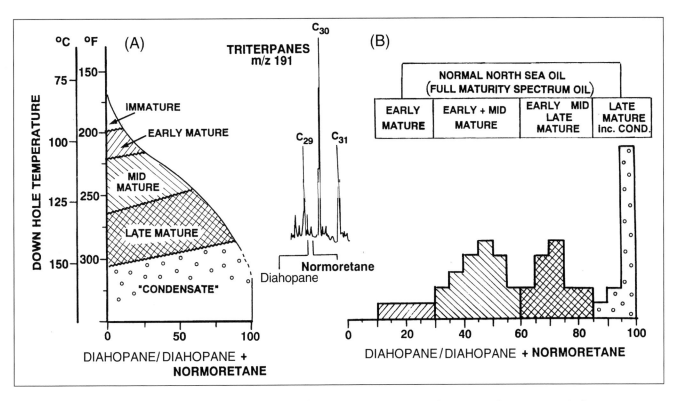

Figure 33.14. When a diahopane ratio is used to determine the thermal maturity of source rock extracts and oils, an oil–source rock correlation of samples from the Central Graben indicates the following: (A) an increase in the ratio of the source rock extract with depth, which correlates favorably with (B), the values for 62 North Sea oils. The ratio is of the thermally stable C_{30} diahopane and the thermally unstable C_{29} normoretane (Cornford et al., 1986). Oils in reservoir rocks generally represent a cumulative mix of different maturity products. Note that wireline log temperatures are corrected to reservoir temperatures ($+15°C$).

minor amounts of C_{30} steranes confirming a source rock containing organic matter of marine provenance. The ratio of regular steranes to isosteranes is controlled by the thermal maturity of the source rock, with the diasteranes being abundant, as expected in the products of a thermally mature noncarbonate source rock (Hall and Bjorøy, 1991). The m/z 218 fragmentogram of oils from the Central Graben indicates that the relative abundance of isosteranes is $C_{29} > C_{27} > C_{28}$ (Figure 33.15A).

The stable carbon isotope composition of the oils from the Central Graben is heavier (-27 to $-29‰$ PDB) (Hughes et al., 1985; Wills and Peattie, 1990) than the oils from the Viking Graben to the north (-27.5 to $-31‰$ PDB) (Bailey et al.,1990) (Figure 33.16). The profiles of the stable carbon isotope values of distillation fractions ($50°$ to $300+°C$) are flat and become isotopically lighter from Ekofisk to Argyll to Forties, with an anomalous profile for Montrose (Northam, 1985). Kerogen type and thermal maturity explain these variations.

Carbon isotope data of solution gas indicates that methane has values of about $-47.5‰$ PDB in the Ula oil field (Larter et al., 1990) and $-48.6‰$ PDB in the N2/2 accumulation (Gabrielsen et al., 1985). The carbon isotope values for the higher gas homologs of the gases from the Ula and N2/2 accumulations relate to source rock thermal maturity (Figure 33.17) (Clayton, 1991). The associated gases in the Mandal–Ekofisk petroleum system clearly fall in the field of generation from a post-mature oil-prone kerogen.

Geochemical Correlations

The oil–oil and oil–source rock correlation in the Central Graben, as in the rest of the North Sea, is based on a multiparameter geochemical approach (Cornford et al., 1983; Mackenzie et al., 1983). These parameters are affected by the following conditions: (1) source rock depositional environment, including oxicity and salinity; (2) kerogen type, including provenance and degree of alteration; (3) various levels of thermal maturity of the source rock; (4) extent of migration; and (5) degree of intrareservoir alteration. These correlation parameters used in the Central Graben and in the North Sea have been alluded to in the previous section and are discussed by Mackenzie et al. (1983), Cornford et al. (1983), Northam (1985), and Cornford (1990).

Early work in the Central Graben had established oil–oil correlations, and recent studies have detailed more specific correlations that emphasize the dominant role of thermal maturity of a single source rock in controlling hydrocarbon properties (e.g., Hughes et al., 1985; Northam, 1985; Larter et al., 1990; Cornford, 1990). The oil–source rock correlation in the Central Graben has to be seen in the context of numerous studies of correlation among kerogens, pyrolyzates, and rock extracts of the source rock for the North Sea oils (Cornford, 1990). Oils and source rocks of the Mandal–Ekofisk system have been included in such studies. Generally, gas chromatograms of the saturated fraction of mature source

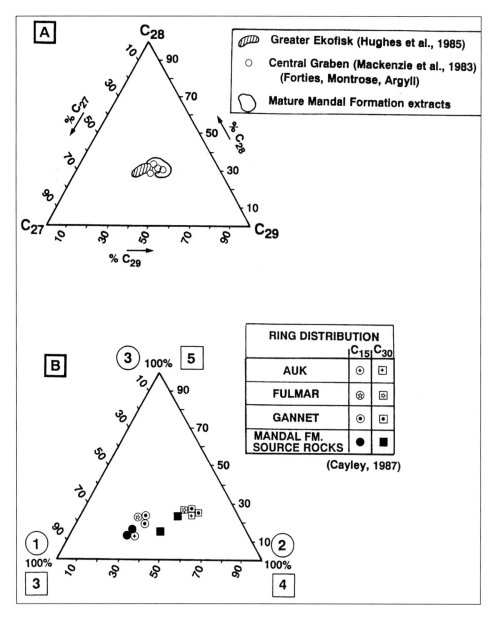

Figure 33.15. Examples of oil–source rock correlations for the Central Graben. (A) Sterane molecular weight distributions for named oils and early mature to mature Mandal Formation source rock extracts. Isosterane peak heights measured on m/z 218 mass fragmentograms. (Data from Hughes et al., 1985; and others.) (B) Shell's ring number correlation (circles = C_{15} 1-, 2-, and 3-ring compounds and squares = C_{30} 3-, 4-, and 5-ring compounds) showing close equivalence between source rock extracts (solid) and oils (open) of the Central Graben (Cayley, 1987).

rock extract, or pyrolyzates of immature Mandal Formation shales, are almost identical to those of a typical Central Graben oil.

From the low sulfur content and the middle wax napthenoparaffinic nature of the oils, the depositional environment of the source rock for the Central Graben oils is indicated as a marine shale (Figure 33.12). From microscopy (e.g., Fisher and Miles, 1983), the dominantly amorphous kerogen of the Mandal Formation is characteristic of a bacterially degraded planktonic biomass typical of a marine depositional environment. This is confirmed by macro- and microscopic fossils. The abundance of diasteranes and the lack of significant gammacerane in the oils argues against a carbonate or evaporite source rock, while the presence of significant C_{30} steranes confirms a marine origin. These latter three points are in common with the molecular signature of mature Mandal Formation shales.

Within the family of Central Graben oils, source rock maturity produces the most variation. Hughes et al.

(1985) applied factor analysis to a large data base of bulk, molecular, and isotopic properties of oils from the greater Ekofisk area. He demonstrated that the first principal component accounting for 51.4% of the variation was attributable to source rock maturity, while the second principal component at 13.0% of variation was attributable to the source rock kerogen type and/or depositional environment.

A more specific example of maturity-related oil–source rock correlation can be made using the diahopane–normoretane ratio (Cornford et al., 1986). This correlation is based on the ratio of a thermally stable molecule (C_{30} diahopane) to a thermally unstable molecule (the C_{29} normoretane) obtained from both oils and source rock solvent extracts. A general depth trend of this biomarker ratio in source rock extracts from the Central Graben is shown in Figure 33.14A. The thermal maturity correlation can be made by comparison of the source rock trend with the histogram in Figure 33.14B showing the distribution of the same ratio for the oils.

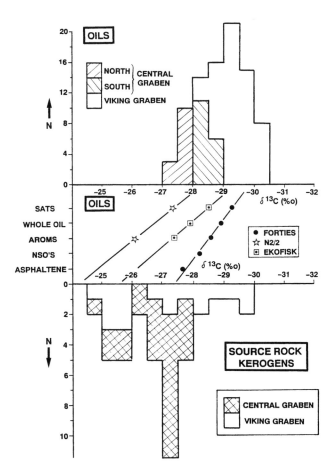

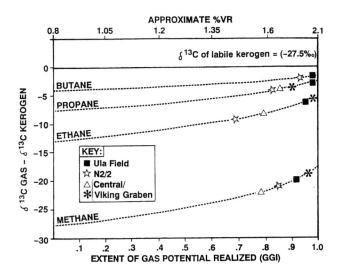

Figure 33.17. Using stable carbon isotope values of labile kerogen as a datum, similar values for methane and homologs demonstrate the thermal maturity of the source rock for the gases of the Central Graben. The cross plot of Clayton (1991) shows data from the Central and Viking grabens from the same reference, the Ula field data from Larter et al. (1990), and the N2/2 data from Gabrielsen et al. (1985). The good fit of the gas data on this plot strongly suggests that the gases were generated from an oil-prone (labile) type II kerogen. Note from Figure 33.16 that using an average source rock isotope value of –27.5 ‰ may introduce a significant error.

Figure 33.16. Stable carbon isotope data for the oils and kerogens of the Central and Viking grabens. (Central Graben oil data from Mackenzie et al., 1983; Northam, 1985; Hughes et al., 1985; Gabrielsen et al., 1985; Bailey et al., 1990; Wills and Peattie, 1990.) An oil–source correlation is implied by the alignment of the isotopic curve for the Forties and N2/2 oil fractions with the range from Mandal Formation kerogens and kerogen pyrolyzates (Bailey et al., 1990).

Where both molecules are present in abundance (relative to an unaffected molecular peak), a mixture of early and late mature source rock products is indicated, which is a common situation in the Central Graben (Figure 33.14). For example, Hughes et al. (1985), in his classic biomarker study of crude oils in the greater Ekofisk area, identified a general decrease in the thermal maturity of the source rock that charged the individual fields from the Albuskjell oil in the northwest to the Hod oil in the southeast. Northam (1985) ranked the Forties, Argyll, Ekofisk, and Montrose oils in order of increasing source rock maturity based on biomarker and isotopic profiles. Although these studies report no source rock analyses, they demonstrate that the oils of the Central Graben in general and the greater Ekofisk area in particular fall in one genetic family. They conclude that the variation in oil properties are attributable to changes in source rock maturity that correspond to local burial of the near basal Cretaceous seismic reflector and hence to Mandal Formation source rock below. This is a positive

maturity-linked oil–source rock correlation and is strong evidence for the dominance of near vertical migration in this area of the graben.

The molecular weight distribution of the steranes (based on isosterane abundances monitored at m/z 218) group the Central Graben oils into a single family with a dominance of algal and bacterial kerogen types (Figure 33.15A). In terms of sterane distribution, the Mandal Formation source rock extracts are slightly enriched in C_{29} steranes relative to the oils. Cracking or fractionation during migration may account for this shift, but the close proximity of the oils and source rock extracts again confirms a direct genetic link. The triangular plot shown in Figure 33.15B also demonstrates a close link between oils and extracts in terms of the gross carbon ring number distributions for C_{15} and C_{30} molecules, with both sample types plotting in the field for marine algal kerogen (Cayley, 1987).

In terms of kerogen type, the stable carbon isotope correlation between oils and kerogens or kerogen pyrolyzates (Bailey et al., 1990) forms the basis for an excellent correlation (Figure 33.16). In addition, the optical descriptions of the kerogen as dominantly amorphous and fluorescent and the agreement between the composition of its pyrolyzate (Larter, 1985) and the Central Graben oils further confirm the genetic link.

The stable carbon isotope ratios of the C_1–C_5 gas molecules also show a source rock maturity correlation using the approach of James (1983). Comparison with a typical kerogen stable isotope value for the Mandal

Formation of –27.5‰ PDB (e.g., Bailey et al., 1990) shows that the gases of the Central Graben (Ula and N2/2 and other fields) are consistent with generation from Mandal Formation shales in the late oil or post-oil maturity window (Figure 33.17). The kerogens of some restricted intervals are isotopically heavier (to –24‰) (Bailey et al., 1990), which would indicate gas generation at a lower maturity. There is no substantive evidence for a commercially significant ancilliary dry gas (type III kerogen) source rock in the Central Graben.

The Mandal–Ekofisk petroleum system of the Central Graben has a single well-defined source rock unit that accounts for all the hydrocarbons discovered to date.

Migration

The Upper Jurassic of the North Sea petroleum province has been one of the focal points for research on primary migration. By careful study of processes occurring at the source rock–carrier rock interface, diffusion of light hydrocarbons has been identified (Leythaeuser et al., 1987), while the heavier fractions appear to move as a discrete liquid hydrocarbon phase (Mackenzie et al., 1987; Leythaeuser et al., 1988a), probably under a pressure gradient. Lindgreen (1985, 1987) emphasized the role of micropores and microfractures in the source rock as promoting primary migration in the Upper Jurassic mudstones of the Central Graben. When a source rock is at a temperature and pressure for hydrocarbon generation, oil and gas will form a single supercritical fluid phase. Thus, in terms of mass movement, the later separating "liquid" and "gaseous" phases will have essentially the same primary migration efficiency if effects of diffusion are ignored.

Quantification of the expulsion process has been pioneered by studies of North Sea source rocks (Cooles et al., 1986; Wilhelms et al., 1990) with values of oil expulsion efficiency as high as 85% indicated. The expulsion efficiency is defined as the fraction (or percentage) of the total generated hydrocarbon that has been expelled. Experimental approaches such as pyrolysis, solvent extraction, and hydrogen mass balance based on elemental analysis have been used to establish these values. Innovative studies have focused on the analysis of early diagenetically cemented and uncemented source rocks (Wilhelms et al., 1990) and boundary effects at shale–sandstone interfaces (Mackenzie et al., 1987).

The major control on expulsion appears to be the richness and thickness of the source rock (Figure 33.18). Expulsion requires that the source rock porosity be saturated first and is thus related to richness up to a limiting value (full saturation). Source rock richness will also exert an effect (McAuliffe, 1980) if oil moves via capillary forces through a kerogen wick within the source rock. The thickness effect is best observed where source rock and carrier bed are interbedded on a small scale. In the Brae field of the southern Viking Graben, a fan conglomerate and sandstone are interbedded with the source rock; higher expulsion efficiencies are observed at a given maturity level for thinly interbedded

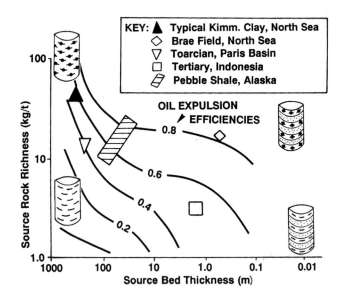

Figure 33.18. The quantity of hydrocarbons expelled from siliciclastic source rocks relative to source rock richness (after Cooles et al., 1986) and bed thickness between permeable carriers. The horizontal axis is a measure of the hydrocarbon path length before it escapes from the source rock, which in turn is related to the lithologic pathways (number of porous interbeds), diagenetic pathways (dissolution and alteration features), and fracture and fault pathways.

shales compared to the thicker, more massive shales (Leythaeuser et al., 1988a,b). Although no interbedding of source and reservoir rock is seen in the Central Graben, a high drainage efficiency is observed in fields such as Clyde and Fulmar, where the reservoir sandstones are juxtaposed against mature source rocks.

Secondary migration within the North Sea in general has been discussed in Cornford et al. (1986) and Cornford (1990), and in the specific context of the Central Graben by Cayley (1987), Hunt (1990), and Thomsen et al. (1990). These authors attribute buoyancy and pressure potential gradients as the major control on secondary migration, with the oil and gas moving as two separate phases as the hydrocarbons move away from the source rock and up to levels of lower temperature and pressure.

Overpressure in the Central Graben results from a combination of compaction, aquathermal, and hydrocarbon generation processes. The retention of overpressure in the source rock is attributed to the sealing properties of the basal Rogaland Formation. In the northern and northwestern parts of the Central Graben where coarse clastics are present in the Rogaland, near normal pressure is observed in the underlying reservoir rock intervals. Where the Rogaland is a seal rock, overpressures are in excess of 8000 psi above hydrostatic pressure (Cayley, 1987). This observation suggests two migration pathways in the Central Graben: (1) pressure-induced vertical migration via halokinetic and overpressure fractures into the Chalk Group in areas where the Rogaland is a seal (Ekofisk area); and (2) pressure-induced vertical migration via fractures through the

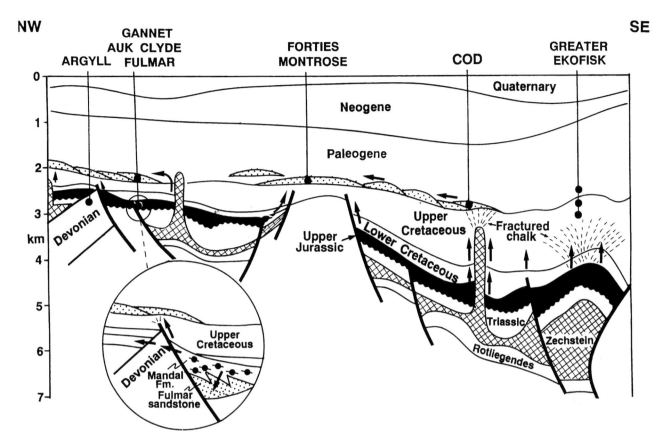

Figure 33.19. Hydrocarbon habitats in the Central Graben are illustrated with speculative migration pathways (heavy arrows). Unlike the Viking and Witch Ground grabens to the north, migration is mostly vertical through fractures produced by halokinesis. Note that wrench faulting favors vertical migration via seismic pumping.

Chalk Group into the Rogaland sandstones, then laterally through intergranular porosity into culminations within the Rogaland (feeding Forties, Montrose, Cod, etc.). The major secondary migration pathways in the Central Graben are shown (Figure 33.19).

Another migration path is via graben margin faults, particularly where an element of strike-slip movement occurs (transfer faults). This explains the filling of the fields on the southwestern graben margin (Fulmar, Clyde, and Gannet oil fields), with some migration through an unconformity or weathering profile on top of the Paleozoic in the Auk, Argyl, and Innes oil fields. For the Paleocene sandstone of the Gannet fields, the gas and light oil probably moved vertically through a fault-related fracture zone overlying the graben margin faults that penetrate the Upper Cretaceous. Near vertical migration is implied by the restricted source rock drainage area indicated as feeding the Paleocene sandstones of the Forties field (Wills and Peattie, 1990) and the Chalk Group of the Valhall field (Leonard and Munns, 1987). A more plausible charging pathway for the Forties field is via vertical migration in the main part of the graben and then laterally through the Rogaland sandstones (Figure 33.19)

Trap leakage is seen in the Central Graben where reflection seismic profiles show gas chimneys of gas-charged sediment penetrating the Tertiary section that covers the overpressured Chalk Group fields (Nordberg,

1981; Buhrig, 1989). On the floor of the North Sea, pock marks are said to result from gas escaping into the water column (Hovland and Sommerville, 1985). The presence of these features illustrates the transient nature of the traps, effectively only interrupting the inexorable escape of oil and gas to the surface. Luckily, in the Central Graben, active and accelerating subsidence has ensured the continuous replenishment of many reservoirs.

Petroleum Accumulations

The Mandal–Ekofisk petroleum system has three types of reservoir rocks based on age and lithology, which can be related to the pathway of secondary migration (Figure 33.20). These reservoirs, which range in age from Devonian to early Tertiary, are discussed in the context of the in-place and producible reserves grouped by reservoir stratigraphy in Table 33.4 and listed field by field in Table 33.5.

In the Central Graben, a distinction between a gas–condensate field and an oil field is somewhat arbitary. The term *condensate* is used when a hydrocarbon behaves as if it is in a gas phase in the reservoir but in a liquid plus gas phase at the surface, that is, the liquid has condensed while being produced. Whether a hydrocarbon exists as a liquid or a gas in the subsurface depends on its molecular composition and the reservoir temperature and pressure.

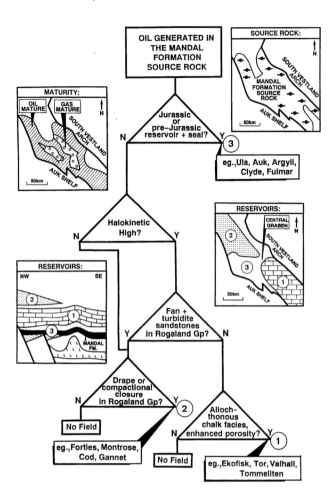

Figure 33.20. Hydrocarbon flux and final destination in the three major reservoir provinces of the Central Graben. The provinces are (1) allochthonous chalk facies to the southeast, (2) drapes or compactional closure to the northeast, and (3) Jurassic or pre-Jurassic reservoir and seal to the northwest.

Although bulk properties may be similar, the phase in the reservoir has significant implications for production. For example the middle gravity oil in the Ekofisk field has a 22% recovery factor, while the gas–condensate of the adjacent West Ekofisk field with a similar chalk reservoir has a 75% recovery factor. The bulk physical properties are not that different (36° and 44° API and GOR of 1551 and 4107 scf/bbl, respectively) (Table 33.1). Thus, in the Central Graben, three types of accumulations are found: oil accumulations (oil), oil accumulations with gas caps (oil–gas), and gas–condensate accumulations.

Devonian–Permian Reservoir Rocks

The Permian reservoir rocks on the western flank of the basin (Argyll and Auk fields) produce mainly from the basal Zechstein carbonates (dolomites), where the vuggy, fractured, and collapsed breccia porosity originated mainly from meteoric water penetration during Jurassic–Early Cretaceous (late Cimmerian) erosion and weathering (Brennand and van Veen, 1975). Average porosities of 12% (range 2–26%) and permeabilities of 53

md (range 0.1–10,000 md) are reported for the Auk field dolomites (Trewin and Bramwell, 1991). The seals for the Zechstein reservoir are the unconformity below the Chalk Group and the Upper Jurassic mudstones.

In the updip parts of the tilted blocks and in the Innes field, eolian and fluvial sandstones of the Rotliegendes Group lie within the oil column and produce optimum reservoir quality, with average porosities of 19% and maximum permeabilities in excess of 1000 md (Trewin and Bramwell, 1991; Bifani et al., 1987). The seal is the overlying Upper Jurassic shales, Upper Cretaceous chalk, and Tertiary claystones at various points in the structures. Minor occurrences of oil in the Devonian and Jurassic reservoir rocks also occur in the Argyll field (Robson, 1991). Total recoverable reserves in these two mostly Permian fields are about 29 million m³ (180 million bbl) of oil (Taylor, 1990). Given about 18% recovery factor, the in-place hydrocarbons are about 118 million m³ (740 million bbl) of oil and 9.9 billion m³ (350 bcf) of gas (Table 33.4). This comprises 3.5% of the in-place hydrocarbons in the Mandal–Ekofisk petroleum system on the basis of barrels of oil and oil equivalents. The nearby Clyde field also reports oil shows in the Rotliegendes Group (Smith, 1987).

Triassic and Jurassic Reservoir Rocks

In the Josephine field, gas and condensate are being produced from sandstones of the Josephine Member of the Middle–Upper Triassic Skagerrak Formation. Triassic sandstones are also minor reservoir rocks in the oil fields in the Ula area (Home, 1987). Information about reservoir properties and volumes in these Triassic rocks is lacking.

The Upper Jurassic Fulmar Sandstone reservoirs of the Eldfisk Formation occur along the southwestern margin of the Central Graben and include the Clyde, Fulmar, Duncan, and West Gannet fields. Together, these fields contain about 102 million m³ (640 billion bbl) of recoverable oil (Table 33.4). These reservoirs are generally deeply buried (below 3500 m) and, with average porosities in the 20% range, have benefited from a level of diagenetic porosity enhancement. Permeabilities range up to 1000 md, but for individual units the averages range from 50 to 800 md (Stevens and Wallis, 1991; Stockbridge and Gray, 1991). The seal rock for the Fulmar Sandstone reservoir is the overlying Upper Jurassic mudstone, or where eroded, impermeable chalk of the Chalk Group.

The "Ula trend" on the northeastern flank of the Central Graben produces oil from roughly equivalent fine- to medium-grained Upper Jurassic sandstone. To date, this trend has an estimated 72 million m³ (450 million bbl) of recoverable oil in nine accumulations (Spencer et al., 1986b). These reservoir rocks are deeply buried (about 3500 m), but the best reservoir zones in the Ula field still have porosities of 15–22% and permeabilities of 650–850 md (Home, 1987), even though overall average values are significantly lower (Spencer et al., 1986b). The seal rock in the Ula trend is primarily the claystones in the Mandal Formation, but in some cases, salt forms a lateral seal.

Table 33.4. Average Properties and Total Volumes of Oil Fields by Stratigraphic Interval for the Mandal–Ekofisk(!) Petroleum System, Central Graben, North Sea

Reservoir and Oil Properties

Reservoir Rock	Top Reservoir (msl) (m)	Top Reservoir (msl) (ft)	Temp. (°C)	Gravity (°API)	Density (g/cm³)	GOR ft³/bbl	GOR m³/m³	Recovery (%) Oil	Recovery (%) Gas
Tertiary	2450	8036	118	43	0.81	3678	655	39	59
Chalk Group	2848	9344	126	41	0.82	3446	613	19	38
Upper Jurassic	3325	10,908	142	39	0.83	744	132	41	43
Dev–Perm	2838	9312	102	40	0.82	1206	215	18	18
Averages	2865	9400	122	41	0.82	2268	404	29	39

Recoverable Resources

Reservoir Rock	Oil bbl (10⁶)	Oil m³ (10⁶)	Condensate bbl (10⁶)	Condensate m³ (10⁶)	Gas scf (10⁹)	Gas m³ (10⁹)	Gas BOE (10⁶)	Gas m³ (10⁶)	Total BOE bbl (10⁶)	Total BOE m³ (10⁶)	Total BOE (%)
Tertiary	2670	424	13	2	1160	33	193	31	2876	457	35
Chalk Group	2198	350	246	39	8248	244	1375	228	3819	617	46
Upper Jurassic	1320	210	0	0	800	24	133	22	1453	232	18
Dev–Perm	93	15	0	0	18	1	3	0	96	15	1
Totals	6281	999	259	41	10,226	302	1704	281	8244	1321	100

In-Place Resources

Reservoir Rock	Oil bbl (10⁶)	Oil m³ (10⁶)	Condensate bbl (10⁶)	Condensate m³ (10⁶)	Gas scf (10⁹)	Gas m³ (10⁹)	Gas BOE (10⁶)	Gas m³ (10⁶)	Total BOE bbl (10⁶)	Total BOE m³ (10⁶)	Total BOE (%)
Tertiary	5800	922	21	3	2999	85	500	79	6321	1005	23
Chalk Group	11,076	1761	671	107	34101	1015	5683	949	17,431	2817	62
Upper Jurassic	3076	489	0	0	1863	56	311	52	3387	541	12
Dev/Perm	754	120	0	0	398	11	66	11	820	130	3
Totals	20,706	3292	692	110	39,361	1167	6560	1091	27,959	4493	100

The total producible hydrocarbons in the Jurassic reservoirs of the Central Graben are thus 210 million m³ (1320 million bbl) of oil and 24 billion m³ (800 bcf) of gas, with in-place hydrocarbons estimated at 489 million m³ (3076 million bbl) of oil and 56 billion m³ (1863 tcf) of gas (Table 33.4). This comprises 12% of the in-place hydrocarbons in the Mandal–Ekofisk petroleum system on the basis of barrels of oil and oil equivalents. No data are available for the Triassic reservoirs.

Chalk Group Reservoir Rocks

The Chalk Group reservoir rocks in the Ekofisk field area are only present as a result of (1) a subtle balance between synsedimentary slumping of the chalk that led to early overpressuring, which preserved primary porosity (up to 34%), and (2) an early influx of oil into the trap, which prevented chalk diagenesis that would have destroyed reservoir porosity (D'Heur, 1984, 1986). The deposition of chalk on a paleoslope in the Late Cretaceous seaway was the initial factor that favored the preservation of reservoir properties. Normally, chalk, being a pelagic ooze, rapidly loses porosity during burial (e.g., from 60% on deposition to 30% at 1 km and 15% at 2 km). Because of the paleoslope, this process was inter-rupted by slumping that preserved anomalously high porosities because pore water was unable to escape from the slumped masses. The result is a high porosity overpressured chalk that even today effectively supports the entire lithostatic load of the overburden rock. In addition, the migration of oil from the deeply buried source rock in the Central Graben throughout the Late Cretaceous and Tertiary meant that the first oil to arrive in the overpressured near-surface chalk reservoir effectively preserved the available porosity and prevented further diagenetic reduction in pore volume. This early arriving oil must have been under an even higher overpressure to have entered the overpressured chalk (Figure 33.21).

Despite the high porosity, the measured core permeability is often very low. For example, the matrix permeability in the Ekofisk oil field chalk reservoir is up to 8 md (Pekot and Gersib, 1987). Production tests indicate *in situ* permeabilities up to 150 md, which implies a high intensity of fracturing. The intergranular (or core) permeability is thus enhanced by the connection of the pores with fractures resulting from halokinetic or tectonic activity (D'Heur, 1986) and possibly by the growth of a stylolite network (Fritzen and Corrigan, 1990). The oil fields themselves all appear to have grown over salt pillows or piercements, and are sealed either by imper-

Table 33.5. Volumes of Recoverable and In-Place Resources for the Fields of the Mandal–Ekofisk(!) Petroleum System, Central Graben, North Sea

Field Name	Quad/Block Designation	Recoverable Resources							
		Oil		Condensate		Gas		% Recovery	
		(MMbbl)	(10^6 m^3)	(MMbbl)	(10^6 m^3)	(10^9 ft^3)	(10^9 m^3)	Oil	Gas
Acorn	UK29/8	—	—	—	—	—	—	—	—
Albuskjell	N1/6; N2/4	—	—	50	8	636	18	—	75
Arbroath	UK22/17, 18	102	16	—	—	50	1	30	60
Argyl	UK30/24								
Auk	UK30/16	93	15	—	—	18	1	18	18
Beechnut	UK29/9	—	—	—	—	—	—	—	—
Clyde	UK30/17b	154	24	—	—	52	1	38	38
Cod	N7/11	—	—	13	2	293	8	—	60
Duncan	UK30/24								
Edda	N2/6, 7	25	4	—	—	78	2	22	22
Ekofisk	N2/4	1491	237	85	14	4450	126	21	21
Eldfisk	N2/7	302	48	—	—	1377	39	19	19
Erskine	UK23/26	—	—	—	—	—	—	—	—
Flyndra	N1/5	—	—	—	—	—	—	—	—
Forties	UK21/10;22/6	2470	393	—	—	748	21	57	57
Fulmar	UK30/16, 11	463	74	—	—	284	8	57	57
Gannet	UK21/24, 25								
Gert	DK5603/27	—	—	—	—	—	—	—	—
Gyda	N2/1	—	—	—	—	—	—	—	—
Hod	N2/11	38	6	—	—	33	1	16	16
Innes	UK30/24								
Joanne	UK30/7	—	—	—	—	—	—	—	—
Josephine	UK30/13	—	—	—	—	—	—	—	—
Judy	UK30/8	—	—	—	—	—	—	—	—
Kittiwake	UK21/18	70	11	—	—	24	1	40	40
Lomond	UK23/21,22	—	—	—	—	—	—	—	—
Lulu(Harald)	DK5604/22	—	—	—	—	—	—	—	—
Marnock	UK22/24	—	—	—	—	—	—	—	—
Montrose	UK22/17, 18	98	16	—	—	69	2	30	60
N7/11-5	N7/11	63	10	—	—	94	4	30	40
N2/2 Struct.	N2/2	—	—	—	—	—	—	—	—
Sam	UK29/4, 5	—	—	—	—	—	—	—	—
Tommeliten	N1/9	19	38	38	6	247	7	20	75
Tor	N2/4,5	113	18	—	—	165	15	21	21
Ula	N7/12	330	52	—	—	165	5	40	40
Ula Trend	N7/8–2/1	240	38	—	—	180	5	40	40
Valhal	N2/8, 11	211	34	10	2	273	8	15	15
Fiddich	UK22/19	—	—	—	—	—	—	—	—
West Ekofisk	N2/4	—	—	63	10	989	28	—	75.2
Sums (Averages)		6281	999	259	41	10,226	301	(30)	(42)

meable chalk or by lower Tertiary mudstone. Chalk Group fields are not found in areas where the Paleogene is arenaceous. Gas chimneys detected on reflection seismic profiles are commonly seen directly over the Chalk Group fields, indicating that both the chalk and overlying Rogaland mudstones are relatively poor seal rocks given the large overpressures recorded in the reservoirs below (Buhrig, 1989). These chalk seals are themselves frequently saturated with oil.

The lack of a clear-cut hydrocarbon–water contact in the Chalk Group fields makes the estimation of recoverable and in-place reserves an art rather than a science. Of

Table 33.5 *(continued)*

Oil		Condensate		Gas		
(MMbbl)	(10⁶ m³)	(MMbbl)	(10⁶ m³)	(10⁹ ft³)	(10⁹ m³)	Comments
—						
—	—	67	11	848	24	
340	54	—	—	83	2	Recovery estimated
218	35	—	—	257	7	
517	82	—	—	98	3	
—	—	—	—	—	—	
405	64	—	—	138	4	
—	—	21	3	489	14	
49	8	—	—	69	2	
114	18	—	—	353	10	
7099	1129	404	64	21189	600	
1589	253	—	—	7249	205	
—	—	—	—	—	—	
—	—	—	—	—	—	
4333	689	—	—	1313	37	
812	129	—	—	499	14	
800	127	—	—	1000	28	
—	—	—	—	—	—	
—	—	—	—	—	—	
236	38	—	—	207	6	
19	3	—	—	43	1	Estimated GOR
—	—	—	—	—	—	
—	—	—	—	—	—	
175	28	—	—	60	2	Average GOR used
—	—	—	—	—	—	
—	—	—	—	—	—	
—	—	—	—	—	—	
327	52	—	—	114	3	Recovery estimated
210	33	—	—	236	10	Maximum in-place reserves
—	—	—	—	—	—	
—	—	—	—	—	—	
94	15	50	8	330	9	Estimated recovery factor
539	86	—	—	788	71	
825	131	—	—	413	12	1990 reserves estimation
600	95	—	—	450	13	Average values
1405	223	66	10	1823	52	Reserves = HC pore volume
—	—	—	—	—	—	
—	—	84	13	1315	37	
20,706	3292	692	110	39,361	1167	

the Chalk Group reservoirs, production from Tommeliten, Albuskjell, and West Ekofisk gas and condensate fields has a high condensate–gas ratio in comparison with the light oils of the Edda, Ekofisk, Eldfisk, and Hod fields. Together, these fields total 321.4 million m³ (2022 million bbl) of light oil and condensate and 268.3 billion m³ (9.48 tcf) of gas as the original recoverable reserves, according to D'Heur (1986). Updated figures show 389 million m³ (2409 million bbl) of light oil and condensate and 244 billion m³ (8.2 tcf) of gas as the total producible hydrocarbons from all the Chalk Group fields, given the available data (Table 33.4).

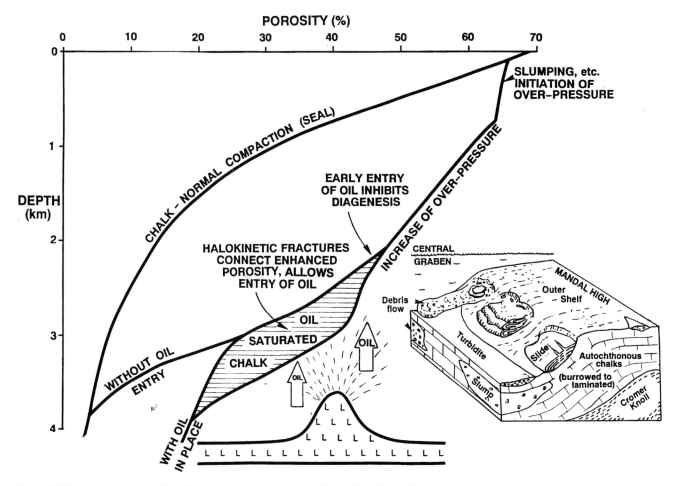

Figure 33.21. Factors controlling the porosity and permeability of the Chalk Group reservoirs of the Central Graben. Upper curve shows the normal compaction curve for chalk that acts as a seal. Lower porosity depth curve shows the effects of the rapid deposition of allochthonous chalk (slumps, mass flows, and turbidites) and the early entry of hydrocarbons and halokinetic fracturing. The lower curve shows the sedimentary processes on the basin edge, Upper Cretaceous, Central Graben. (After Taylor and Lapre, 1987.)

In the Chalk Group fields, the recovery factor for liquids is low as a result of low reservoir rock permeability. Values of 19–22% are appropriate for oils, while condensate and gas recovery is reported to average 75% in West Ekofisk (Table 33.5), a figure that is applied to the other Chalk Group condensate and gas fields. The resulting in-place oil and gas is 1868 million m³ (11,747 million bbl) of liquids (oil plus condensates) and 1015 billion m³ (34 tcf) of gas as the total in-place hydrocarbons in the Chalk fields (Table 33.4). This comprises 62% of the in-place hydrocarbons in the Mandal–Ekofisk petroleum system on the basis of barrels of oil and oil equivalents.

Tertiary Sandstone Reservoirs

The siliciclastic sandstone reservoirs of Tertiary age were deposited as deep water submarine fans that run either axial to (Forties, Montrose, and Cod) or lateral to (Gannet complex) the Central Graben trough. These excellent quality sandstone reservoirs have suffered little secondary cementation, as they are shallowly buried (Table 33.1) and hydrocarbons entered relatively early. For Forties and Gannet fields, reported porosities can be

as high as 30% with corresponding permeabilities of 1000–3000 md (Wills, 1991; Armstrong et al., 1987). Down the fan toward deeper water, reservoir quality decreases with permeabilities of 1000–2000 md in the Montrose and Arbroath fields (Crawford et al., 1991) and 15–100 md in Cod field (D'Heur, 1987b). The complexity of the reservoir sandstone distribution also increases in the distal fan lobes. The seal rock for all these Tertiary oil fields is the lateral and overlying mudstone.

The producible hydrocarbons of these Tertiary oil fields are listed individually (Table 33.5) and sum to about 457 million m³ (2876 million bbl), with the vast majority being in the Forties field. The reserves for a number of smaller Tertiary accumulations are unknown. The recovery factors for these oil fields are reported to be high, with 57% in the Forties field and 30% in Arbroath and Montrose fields, while the condensate and gas in the Cod field has a recovery factor of about 60%. Based on these recoveries, the in-place volumes are 922 million m³ (5800 million bbl) of oil and 85 billion m³ (3 tcf) of gas and comprise 22.5% of the in-place hydrocarbons in the Mandal–Ekofisk petroleum system on the basis of barrels of oil and oil equivalents.

Events Chart

The timing of key events is summarized for the Mandel-Ekofisk petroleum system in Figure 33.5. The events include deposition of the four essential elements (source, reservoir, seal, and overburden) and the three processes (trap formation, generation/migration/accumulation, and preservation).

The Mandal Formation is the only oil-prone source rock in the Central Graben. It is postmature (exhausted) in the center of the graben and is still an active source rock on the flanks. This source rock is buried by the Cretaceous and Tertiary overburden rock, which is thickest in the center of the graben along the offshore boundary between the United Kingdom and Norway. Sedimentation is continuing today, and the source rock is currently at maximum burial depth and, therefore, maximum temperature. The critical moment of the Mandal–Ekofisk petroleum system is thus today, and hence this is the time for which maps (Figures 33.1, 33.8, and 33.9) and cross sections (Figures 33.3 and 33.19) are drawn.

Generation of oil and gas is mainly the result of Tertiary–Holocene burial, there being no significant inversion in the basin (Figure 33.10). Since temperature, and not depth of burial, controls generation, the available evidence points to a relatively constant heat flow and geothermal gradient over the critical (Late Cretaceous, Tertiary, and Quaternary) time interval (Table 33.3). The resulting thermal geohistory diagram (Figure 33.10A) indicates that oil generation started about late Early Cretaceous time in the central graben area and progressed up the flanks of the graben as the overburden rock thickened. Thus, the Mandal Formation has been generating oil somewhere in the Central Graben from about 100 Ma to the present day. Viewed from the reservoir end of the migration pathway, this timing has been confirmed. Studies of the timing of fluid inclusions and diagenetic processes within the Fulmar field reservoir indicate that oil influx occurred over the last 10 m.y. (Saigal et al., 1992).

Reservoir rocks range in age from Devonian to Tertiary. Only 3.5% of the in-place oil and gas as oil equivalent has been found in reservoir rocks older than Late Jurassic (Table 33.5), while Late Jurassic reservoir rocks contain 12% of the in-place hydrocarbons. The majority (62%) of the in-place hydrocarbons are in Chalk Group accumulations that straddle the Cretaceous–Tertiary boundary, with 23% in the Paleocene–Eocene sandstone reservoirs. Reservoirs older than Late Jurassic are considered minor, whereas younger reservoir rocks are major.

The development of the seal rocks for traps is also progressive. The chalk generally acts as both reservoir and seal, augmented by the thick, dominantly fine-grained siliciclastics of the overlying Tertiary rock. The most important seal rocks are the upper tight chalk of the Chalk Group and the mudstones of the Hordaland Group. The seal for the lower Tertiary sandstone reservoirs developed as a result of the compaction of the surrounding mudstones during the late Paleogene and

Neogene, reducing the porosity and hence the permeability to a sufficient level to constitute a seal. The Zechstein Group evaporites are lithologically the best seal rock, but unfortunately underlie the active source rock so it only forms the trap seal for minor accumulations.

Trap formation occurred in three phases. First, the structural traps formed as rifting created the Central Graben in the Late Jurassic. Then the traps of the Chalk Group fields formed as salt diapirs penetrated the underlying sedimentary rocks, mainly during the Late Cretaceous and Tertiary. Finally, the clay drape structures developed as a result of differential compaction over the lower Tertiary sandstone reservoirs, with the mudstone compaction forming a seal. Some traps have composite origins, such as from Jurassic faulting coupled with salt movement for the Clyde and Fulmar fields (Stevens and Wallis, 1991) or from halokinetic doming coupled with compactional drape for the Cod field.

Alteration of petroleum in accumulations is insignificant, either by biodegradation or thermal cracking of oil. As drilling has progressed to the deeper parts of the graben, thermal alteration of deep oils has been considered. Recent work by Horsfield et al. (1991) has indicated that cracking of oil to gas cannot proceed until temperatures of 160–190°C are reached. The reservoir temperatures and oil properties given in Table 33.1 seem to confirm this trend, although Hughes et al. (1985) have explained some whole oil carbon isotope anomalies in the Ekofisk area on the basis of intrasource rock or intrareservoir cracking. It can be concluded that intrareservoir oil cracking appears to be an insignificant process in the Central Graben reservoirs and, hence, that the discovered gas–condensate fields reflect the properties of the products expelled from the source rock.

Bacterial degradation of oil is uncommon in the Central Graben. Of the reported accumulations, only the South Gannet field, with 21° API oil, has suffered bacterial degradation. With the reservoir at about 1740 m depth and hence about 75°C (40°C/km + 6°C at sea floor) this gravity is typical of mixed degraded and nondegraded oil, suggesting a period of early degradation (e.g., 15–18° API) followed by the influx of fresh oil. The fresh oil entry occurred after the reservoir was buried below the temperature for active bacterial degradation (60°C) and allows limits to be placed on the timing of this event. At a geothermal gradient of 40°C/km, the additional postdegradation burial from 60°C to 75°C is 375 m (1230 ft). Given the high average Pliocene–Pleistocene and Quaternary burial rates of 120 m/m.y., bacterial degradation ceased 3 Ma for this accumulation.

MASS BALANCE CALCULATION

The parameters discussed in the previous sections can be brought together into a mass balance equation to estimate the *generation–accumulation efficiency (GAE)* of the Mandal–Ekofisk petroleum system. In this context, the GAE is defined as the discovered in-place hydrocarbons divided by the total hydrocarbons generated times

Table 33.6. Thicknesses of Source Rock Within the Oil and Gas Windows

Thermal Maturity Level		Average Thickness (m)			
		1250	750	250	Totals
0.7% R_o					
Oil window	Area (km²)	1145	2650	7480	
	Volume (km³)	1431	1987	1870	5288
1.2% R_o					
Gas (cond?) window	Area	306	1978	745	
	Volume	383	1484	186	2053
Totals	Area	1451	4628	8225	
	Volume	1814	3471	2056	734

100. The recoverable and in-place oil and gas volumes are listed in Table 33.5 and summarized by reservoir rock, with separate sums for oil, condensate, and gas. All volumes are corrected to standard temperature and pressure, and gas is converted to oil at the energy equivalent rate of 6000 scf/bbl. The recoverable volumes are related to the in-place volumes by way of the percent recovery. The percent recovery varies within the Chalk Group fields from as low as 15% for medium gravity crude oils to 75% for gas–condensate accumulations. The excellent quality Paleocene sandstone reservoir of the Forties field produces 57% of its in-place medium gravity oil.

The estimate of the total discovered hydrocarbons is accepted as reasonably correct since missing data mainly relates to small fields often tested by only one or two wells. The following calculations are based on the total reserves reported (Table 33.5), but an additional 35% could be added to cover unreported accumulations. Speculation concerning undiscovered reserves is left to the end of this section.

The overall mass balance calculation is of the form

In-place hydrocarbons = (Hydrocarbons generated × migration efficiency) – Leakage

This balance can be established using equations of the form advocated for this volume (Schmoker, Chapter 19, this volume) and discussed by Demaison and Huizinga (1991). The thickness of the Mandal Formation, the active source rock for this system, is variable, so separate calculations are undertaken for three mapped thickness intervals (Figure 33.8 and Table 33.6). Each thickness interval was assigned the average of the contoured range, that is, 250 m for <500m, 750 m for 500–1000 m, and 1250 m for >1000 m. In addition, two thermal maturity slices were used: the presently active source rock between 0.7% and 1.1% R_o, which falls within the oil window, and the previously oil mature source rock presently buried beyond the 1.1% R_o level and hence falling within the gas window (Figure 33.9). With a rock density of 2.45 g/cm³ (t/m³), the masses of source rock are indicated for each thermal maturity window.

The weight of carbon in these masses of source rock can be determined from TOC values. As shown in Figure 33.7A, the average TOC value from conventional cores from deep wells is 5.5 wt. %. The thermal maturity of these cores is early mature, so they have lost some carbon due to the expulsion of oil. The original TOC (%TOC_o) can be calculated from the postmature TOC (%TOC_p) on the basis of a hydrogen balance from the following equation:

$$\%TOC_o = \%TOC_p/[(1 - (H/C_k))/(H/C_h)]$$

where H/C_k and H/C_h refer to the H/C atomic ratios from elemental analysis of the original kerogen ($_k$) and hydrocarbon ($_h$) product (oil or gas), respectively. This assumes that carbon is lost in the form of oil having an H/C atomic ratio of about 2 and that hydrogen is the limiting element controlling oil generation. Nomograms illustrating the correction of measured TOC for various levels of maturity are constructed by attributing transformation ratios to the levels of maturity expressed as vitrinite reflectance (Figure 33.22). Many of the wells that intersect the Mandal Formation in the Central Graben are deep, and source rocks sampled in these wells have a thermal maturity of about 0.7% R_o. Here, the TOC observed is 5.5 wt. % and would correct to a thermally immature TOC of 6.7 wt. %. In the absence of more detailed data, this value is taken as representative of the Mandal Formation over the entire Central Graben. Thus, the mass of carbon in the source rock is

Oil window:	0.067 × 12,958 billion	= 868 billion t
		= 868 × 10¹⁵ g
Gas window:	0.067 × 5010 billion	= 335 billion t
		= 335 × 10¹⁵ g

Thus, with a total mass of matured carbon (M) of 1203 × 10¹⁵ g (1203 billion t) and a late immature hydrogen index (R) of 550 mg/g TOC, the volume of hydrocarbon (pyrolyzate) generated (HCG) using Schmoker's method (Chapter 19, this volume) is

$$HCG \text{ (kg HC)} = R \text{ (mg HC/g TOC)} \times M \text{ (g TOC)}$$
$$\times 10^{-6} \text{(kg/mg)}$$
$$= 550 \times 1203 \times 10^{15} \times 10^{-6}$$
$$= 662 \times 10^{12} \text{ kg hydrocarbons}$$

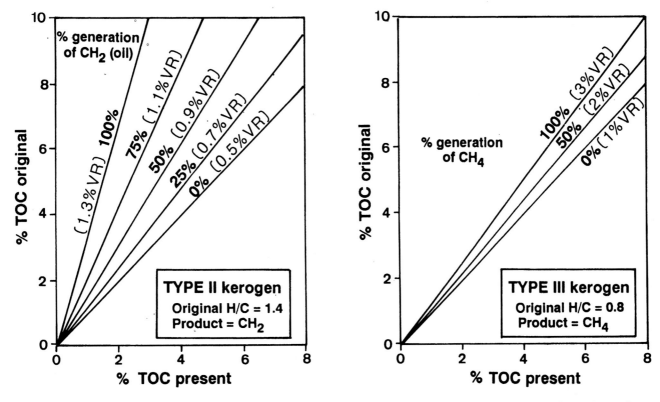

Figure 33.22. Correction of measured TOC values for the effects of oil generation and expulsion of carbon in the form of hydrocarbons from a source rock containing type II (left) and type III (right) kerogens. (Note that these graphs ignore CO_2 and H_2O loss.)

Comparison with the 3.684×10^{12} kg of in-place hydrocarbons (Table 33.5) gives a GAE for the Mandal–Ekofisk petroleum system as

$$
\begin{aligned}
\text{GAE} &= (\text{in-place}/\text{generated}) \times 100 \\
&= [(3.684 \times 10^{12})/(662 \times 10^{12})] \times 100 \\
&= 0.557\%
\end{aligned}
$$

This relatively simple calculation (based on Chapter 19) assumes that all the Rock-Eval pyrolyzate is hydrocarbon and ignores the generation of separate oil and gas phases and the effect of hydrogen mass balance and expulsion efficiency. This gross efficiency figure represents the sum of the individual efficiencies of generation and expulsion, together with losses during secondary migration and entrapment, plus the undiscovered reserves in the basin.

SUMMARY

The Mandal–Ekofisk(!) petroleum system of the North Sea Central Graben is an example of a vertically drained, high-impedance monogenetic petroleum system with a generation–accumulation efficiency of 0.56%. To date, exploration in the Central Graben has identified in-place volumes of 3292 million m³ of oil, 110 million m³ of condensate, and 1167 billion m³ of gas.

Abundant bulk, molecular, and isotopic evidence demonstrates that the Upper Jurassic to basal Cretaceous organic-rich mudstone of the Mandal Formation is the only source rock for the hydrocarbons, justifying the known (!) designation for the system. The deeply buried source rock has an average present-day TOC of 5.5 wt. % at the early mature stage, which corrects to an original TOC value of 6.7 wt. %. The source rock contains type II kerogen, with an original HI of 550 mg HC/g TOC falling to 100 mg HC/g TOC upon burial to 5000 m. This high-quality source rock resulted from accumulation under a combination of high bioproductive surface waters, anoxia at depth, and high sedimentation rates of fine siliciclastics during the development of the North Sea graben system.

A present-day average heat flow of 53 mW/m² was determined from reservoir temperature data, which is equivalent to an average geothermal gradient of 40°C/km. Modeling indicates that petroleum generation was initiated by late Early Cretaceous time and has continued to the present day under steadily increasing sedimentation rates of overburden rock. The source rock is within the oil window over most of the Central Graben area (112,750 km²) and in some areas is within the gas window (3029 km²). Source rock thicknesses range from less than 100 m to greater than 1200 m as a result of deposition during the rifting event and subsequent uplift and erosion.

On the basis of source rock richness and thickness, oil expulsion efficiency is estimated to be 60%, the remainder of the hydrocarbon potential being expelled later as gas. Most of the oil and gas has migrated vertically through halokinetic and fault-related fractures into a variety of reservoir rocks ranging from Devonian to Eocene in age. Published data show that the reserves of 8.2 Bbbl (1.3 billion m³) of oil and oil equivalent are divided among the Upper Cretaceous to basal Paleocene chalk reservoirs (46%), the Paleocene–Eocene sandstone reservoirs (35%), the Upper Jurassic sandstone reservoirs (18%), and the Devonian–Permian sandstone and carbonate reservoirs (1%).

The major reservoir in the Mandal–Ekofisk petroleum system is in the Upper Cretaceous Chalk Group where synsedimentary slumping, early oil influx, and massive overpressuring have retained anomalously high porosities, connected mainly by salt-induced fractures. The seal to the chalk fields is impervious chalk plus the overlying mudstones of the Rogaland Group. Structures have developed from the reservoir deposition onward as a result of the movement of deep Zechstein evaporites.

Where the Rogaland Group is arenaceous and no seal exists, a second major reservoir horizon is developed. This reservoir comprises upper Paleocene and Eocene sandstones deposited as axial and lateral fan turbidites. The seal to these turbidite sandstones developed on the compaction of the surrounding shales. Differential compaction as well as drape over basement highs formed trapping configurations from Eocene time onward.

A significant ancilliary reservoir occurs at the Upper Jurassic level in the Ula and Fulmar sandstones immediately underlying the source rock horizon on both the east and west flanks of the graben. A complex seal originated from Tyne and Cromer Knoll Group shales, Chalk Group chalk, and Zechstein salt. The structures developed as rotated fault blocks during graben extension and were modified and accentuated by later halokinesis.

A simple volumetric calculation indicates generation of 662 billion t of hydrocarbon and a resulting petroleum system efficiency of 0.56%. The apparent low efficiency for the Mandal–Ekofisk petroleum system must encourage future exploration since it indicates that a significant amounts of the hydrocarbons have escaped, were destroyed, or remain to be discovered.

Acknowledgments *This manuscript would have been difficult to complete without the sterling effort of my wife, Sally Cornford, who drafted all the figures. I also would like to thank Ken Glennie and Jenny Miles for commenting on an earlier draft. Peter van de Kamp, John T. Smith, Gerard Demaison, and Miner B. Long critically reviewed this paper and made many helpful suggestions.*

References Cited

Aalund, L., 1983, North Sea crudes: Flotta to Thistle: Oil and Gas Journal, June 6, p. 75–79.

Abbotts, I. L., ed., 1991, United Kingdom oil and gas fields, 25 years commemorative volume: Geological Society of London, Memoir 14, 573 p.

Armstrong, L., A. Ten Haven, and H. D. Johnson, 1987, The geology of the Gannet fields, central North Sea, UK Sector, *in* J. Brooks and K. W. Glennie , eds., Petroleum geology of NW Europe: London, Graham and Trotman, v. 2, p. 533–548.

Bailey, N. J. L., Burwood, R., and Harriman, G. E., 1990, Application of pyrolysis carbon isotope and biomarker technology to organofacies definition and oil correlation problems in North Sea basins: Organic Geochemistry, v. 16, p. 1157–1172.

Barnard, P. C., and B. S. Cooper, 1981, Oils and source rocks of the North Sea area, *in* L. V. Illing and G. D. Hobson, eds., Petroleum Geology of the Continental Shelf of North-West Europe: London, Heyden, p. 169–175.

Barton, P., and R. J. Wood, 1984, Tectonic evolution of the North Sea basin: crustal stretching and subsidence: Geophysical Journal of the Royal Astronomical Society, v. 79, p. 987–1022.

Bifani, R., G. T. George, and A. Lever, 1987, Geological and reservoir characteristics of the Rotliegend Sandstones in the Argyll field, *in* J. Brooks and K. W. Glennie, eds., Petroleum geology of NW Europe: London, Graham and Trotman, v. 1, p. 509–522.

Bjorlykke, K., and K. G. Finstad, 1975, The Kimmeridge shale, its composition and radioactivity, *in* K. G Finstad and R. C. Selly, eds., Jurassic North Sea Symposium: Geilo, Norwegian Petroleum Society, p. 12-1–12-20.

Brennand, T. P., and F. R. van Veen, 1975, The Auk oil field, *in* A. W. Woodland, ed., Petroleum and the continental shelf of north-west Europe: Applied Science, p. 275–281.

Brennand, T. P., B. Van Hoorn, and K. H. James, 1990, Historical review of North Sea exploration, *in* K. W. Glennie, ed., Introduction to the Petroleum Geology of the North Sea, 3rd ed.: London, Blackwell, p. 1–33.

Brown, S., 1991, Stratigraphy of oil and gas reservoirs: UK continental shelf, *in* I. L. Abbotts, ed., United Kingdom oil and gas fields, 25 years commemorative volume: Geological Society of London, Memoir 14, p. 9–18.

Buhrig, C., 1989, Geopressured Jurassic reservoirs in the Viking Graben: Modeling and Geological Significance: Marine and Petroleum Geology, v. 6, p. 31–48.

Carman, G. J., and R. Young, 1981, Reservoir geology of the Forties oilfield, *in* L. V. Illing and G. D. Hobson, eds., Petroleum Geology of North-West Europe: London, Heyden, p. 371–379.

Cayley, G. T., 1987, Hydrocarbon migration in the Central North Sea, *in* J. Brooks and K. W. Glennie, eds., Petroleum geology of N.W. Europe: London, Graham and Trotman, v. 1, p. 549–556.

Chew, K. J., and H. Stephenson, 1986, Exploration success offshore Norway compared with the remainder of the North Sea graben system and with other hydrocarbon provinces, *in* A. M. Spencer et al., eds., Habitat of Hydrocarbons on the Norwegian Continental Shelf: London, Graham and Trotman, p. 61–74.

Clayton, C., 1991, Carbon isotope fractionation during natural gas generation from kerogen: Marine and Petroleum Geology, v. 8, p. 232–240.

Cooles, G. P., A. S. Mackenzie, and T. M. Quigley, 1986, Calculation of petroleum masses generated and expelled from source rocks, *in* D. Leythaeuser and J. Rullkotter, eds., Advances in Organic Geochemistry 1985: Oxford, Pergamon, p. 235–246.

Cooper, B. S., and P. C. Barnard, 1984, Source rocks and oils of the central and northern North Sea, *in* G. Demaison and R. J. Murris, eds., Petroleum geochemistry and basin evaluation: AAPG Memoir 35, p. 303–314.

Cornford, C., 1990, Source rocks and hydrocarbons of the North Sea, *in* K. W. Glennie, ed., Introduction to the Petroleum Geology of the North Sea: London, Blackwell, p. 294–361.

Cornford, C., and J. Brooks, 1989, Tectonic controls on oil and gas occurrences in the North Sea area, *in* A. J. Tankard and H. R. Balkwill, eds., Extensional tectonics and stratigraphy of the North Atlantic margins: AAPG Memoir 46, p. 523–539.

Cornford, C., J. A. Morrow, A. Turrington, J. A. Miles, and J. Brooks, 1983, Some geological controls on oil composition in the UK North Sea, *in* J. Brooks, ed., Petroleum geochemistry and exploration of Europe: Geological Society of London Special Publication 12, p. 175–194.

Cornford, C., E. E. J. Needham, and L. DeWalque, 1986, Geochemical habitat of North Sea oils and gases, *in* A. M. Spencer et al., eds., Habitat of Hydrocarbons on the Norwegian Continental Shelf: London, Graham and Trotman, p. 39–54.

Crawford, R., R. W. Littlefair, and L. G. Affleck, 1991, The Arbroath and Montrose field, Blocks 211/7a, 211/12a, UK North Sea, *in* I. L. Abbotts, ed., United Kingdom oil and gas fields, 25 years commemorative volume: Geological Society of London Memoir 14, p. 211–217.

Damtoft, K., C. Andersen, and E. Thomsen, 1987, Prospectivity and hydrocarbon plays of the Danish Central Trough, *in* J. Brooks and K.W. Glennie, eds., Petroleum Geology of NW Europe: London, Graham and Trotman, v. 1, p. 403–417.

Demaison, G., and B. J. Huizinga, 1991, Genetic classification of petroleum systems: AAPG Bulletin, v. 75, p. 1626–1643.

Demaison, G., A. J. J. Holck, R. W. Jones, and G. T. Moore, 1984, Predictive source bed stratigraphy: a guide to regional petroleum occurrence: North Sea basin and eastern North American continental margin: Proceedings of the World Petroleum Congress, London, Paper PD-1(2), p. 17–29.

D'Heur, M., 1984, Porosity and hydrocarbon distribution in the North Sea chalk reservoirs: Marine and Petroleum Geology, v. 1(3), p. 211–238.

D'Heur, M., 1986, The Norwegian chalk fields, *in* A. M. Spencer et al., eds., Habitat of Hydrocarbons on the Norwegian Continental Shelf: London, Graham and Trotman, p. 77–89.

D'Heur, M., 1987a, Albuskjell, *in* A. M. Spencer et al., eds., Geology of the Norwegian oil and gas fields: London, Graham and Trotman, p. 39–50.

D'Heur, M., 1987b, Cod, *in* A. M. Spencer et al., eds., Geology of the Norwegian oil and gas fields: London, Graham and Trotman, p. 51–62.

D'Heur, M., 1987c, Tor, *in* A. M. Spencer et al., eds., Geology of the Norwegian oil and gas fields: London, Graham and Trotman, p. 129–142.

D'Heur, M., 1987d, West Ekofisk, *in* A. M. Spencer et al., eds., Geology of the Norwegian oil and gas fields: London, Graham and Trotman, p. 165–175.

D'Heur, M., and F. Michaud, 1987, Edda, *in* A. M. Spencer et al., eds., Geology of the Norwegian oil and gas fields: London, Graham and Trotman, p. 63–72.

D'Heur, M., and L. J. Pekot, 1987, Tommeliten, *in* A. M. Spencer et al., eds., Geology of the Norwegian oil and gas fields: London, Graham and Trotman, p. 117–128.

Dore, A. G., J. Vollset, and G. P. Hamar, 1985, Correlation of the offshore sequences referred to the Kimmeridge Clay Formation—relevance to the Norwegian sector, *in* B. M. Thomas et al., eds., Petroleum Geochemistry in Exploration of the Norwegian Shelf: London, Graham and Trotman, p. 27–38.

Ekern, O. F., 1986, Late Oligocene gas accumulations, Block 2/2, Norway, *in* Habitat of Hydrocarbons on the Norwegian Continental Shelf: London, Graham and Trotman, p. 143–149.

Fisher, M. J., and J. A. Miles, 1983, Kerogen types, organic maturation and hydrocarbon occurrences in the Moray Firth and South Viking Graben, North Sea basin, *in* J. Brooks, ed., Petroleum Geochemistry and Exploration of Europe: Geological Society of London Special Publication 12, p. 195–201.

Fisher, M. J., and D. C. Mudge, 1990. Triassic, *in* K. W. Glennie, ed., Introduction to the Petroleum Geology of the North Sea: London, Blackwell, p. 191–218.

Fritzen, A., and T. Corrigan, 1990, Establishment of a geological fracture model for dual porosity situations on the Ekofisk field, *in* A. T. Buller et al., eds., North Sea Oil and Gas Reservoirs—II: London, Graham and Trotman, p. 173–184.

Fuller, J. G. C. M., 1975, Jurassic source rock potential and hydrocarbon correlation, North Sea, *in* Proceedings of the Symposium on Jurassic—Northern North Sea: Geilo, Norwegian Petroleum Society Meeting.

Fuller, J. G. C. M., 1980, An untitled note by John Fuller, *in* J. M. Jones and P. W. Scott, eds., Progress report on fossil fuels—exploration and exploitation: Proceedings of the Yorkshire Geological Society, v. 42, p. 581–593.

Gabrielsen, R. H., S. Ulvoen, A. Elvsborg, and O. Fredrik, 1985, The geological history and geochemical evaluation of Block 2/2, offshore Norway, *in* B. M. Thomas et al., eds., Petroleum Geochemistry in Exploration of the Norwegian Shelf: London, Graham and Trotman, p. 165–178.

Gabrielsen, R. H., O. F. Ekern, and A. Edvardsen, 1986, Structural development of hydrocarbon traps, Block 2/2, Norway, *in* A. M. Spencer et al., eds., Habitat of Hydrocarbons on the Norwegian Continental Shelf: London, Graham and Trotman, p. 129–141.

Gibbs, A. D., 1989, Structural styles in basin formation, *in* A. J. Tankard and H. R. Balkwill, eds., Extensional tectonics and stratigraphy of the North Atlantic margins: AAPG Memoir 46, p. 81–93.

Glennie, K. W., ed., 1990a, Introduction to the Petroleum Geology of the North Sea, 3rd ed.: Blackwell, London, 402 p.

Glennie, K. W., 1990b, Outline of the North Sea history and structural framework, *in* K. W. Glennie, ed., Introduction to the Petroleum Geology of the North Sea, 3rd ed.: London, Blackwell, p. 34–77.

Glennie, K. W,. 1990c, Lower Permian—Rotliegend, *in* K. W. Glennie, ed., Introduction to the Petroleum Geology of the North Sea, 3rd ed.: London, Blackwell, p. 120–152.

Glennie, K. W., and L. A. Armstrong, 1991, The Kittiwake field, Block 21/18, UK North Sea, *in* I. L. Abbotts, ed., United Kingdom oil and gas fields, 25 years commemorative volume: Geological Society of London Memoir 14, p. 339–345.

Hall, P. B., and M. Bjorøy, 1991, Biomarkers and organic facies of source rocks and oils of the North Sea Central Graben, *in* D. Manning, ed., Organic geochemistry, advances in applications in energy and the natural environment: Manchester, U.K., Manchester University Press, p. 192–194.

Haszeldine, R. S., and M. J. Russell, 1987, The late Carboniferous northern North Atlantic ocean: implications for hydrocarbon exploration from Britain to the Arctic, *in* J. Brooks and K. W. Glennie, eds., Petroleum Geology of NW Europe: London, Graham and Trotman, v. 2, p. 1163–1175.

Helm, A. A. van der, D. I. Gray, M. A. Cook, and A. M. Schulte, 1990, Fulmar—the development of a large North

Sea field, *in* A. T. Buller et al., eds., North Sea Oil and Gas Reservoirs—II: London, Graham and Trotman, p. 25–45.

Home, P. C., 1987, Ula, *in* A. M. Spencer et al., eds., Geology of the Norwegian Oil and Gas Fields: London, Graham and Trotman, p. 143–151.

Horsfield, B., H. J. Schenk, N. Mills, and D. H. Welte, 1991, Closed-system programmed temperature pyrolysis for simulating the conversion of oil to gas in a deep petroleum reservoir: compositional and kinetic findings (abs.): 15th International Organic Geochemistry Meeting, Abstracts, Manchester, U.K., p. 56.

Hovland, M., and J. H. Sommerville, 1985, Characteristics of two natural gas seepages in the North Sea: Marine and Petroleum Geology, v. 2, p. 319–326.

Hughes, W. B., A. G. Holba, D. E. Miller, and J. S. Richardson, 1985. Geochemistry of the greater Ekofisk crude oils, *in* B. M. Thomas et al., eds., Petroleum Geochemistry in the Exploration of the Norwegian Shelf: London, Graham and Trotman, p. 75–92.

Hunt, J. M., 1990, Generation and migration of petroleum from abnormally pressured fluid compartments: AAPG Bulletin, v. 74, p. 1–12.

James, A. T., 1983, Correlation of natural gas by the use of carbon isotope distribution between hydrocarbon components: AAPG Bulletin, v. 67, p. 1176–1191.

Kennedy, W. J., 1987, Sedimentology of Late Cretaceous–Paleocene chalk reservoirs, North Sea Central Graben, *in* J. Brooks and K. W. Glennie, eds., Petroleum Geology of NW Europe: London, Graham and Trotman, v. 1, p. 469–481.

Kooi, H, S. Cloetingh, and G. Remmelts, 1989, Intraplate stress and the stratigraphic evolution of the North Sea Central Graben: Geologie en Mijnbouw, v. 68, p. 49–72.

Langford, F. F., and M.-M. Blanc-Valeron, 1990, Interpreting Rock-Eval pyrolysis data using graphs of pyrolizable hydrocarbons vs. total organic carbon: AAPG Bulletin, v. 74, p. 799–804.

Larter, S. R., 1985. Integrated kerogen typing in the recognition and quantitative assessment of petroleum source rocks, *in* B. M. Thomas et al., eds., Petroleum Geochemistry in Exploration of the Norwegian Shelf: London, Graham and Trotman, p. 269–286.

Larter, S., K. Bjorlykke, D. Karlsen, T. Nedkvitne, T. Eglinton, P. Johansen, D. Leythaeuser, and G. A. Newcombe, 1990, Determination of petroleum accumulation histories: examples from the Ula field, Central Graben, Norwegian North Sea, *in* A. T. Buller et al., eds., North Sea Oil and Gas Reservoirs—II: London, Graham and Trotman, p. 319–330.

Leadholm, R. H., T. T. Y. Ho, and S. K. Sahai, 1985, Heat flow, geothermal gradients and maturation modelling on the Norwegian continental shelf using computer methods, *in* B. M. Thomas et al., eds., Petroleum Geochemistry in Exploration of the Norwegian Shelf: London, Graham and Trotman, p. 131–144.

Leonard R. C., and J. W. Munns, 1987, Valhall, *in* A. M. Spencer et al., eds., Geology of the Norwegian Oil and Gas Fields: London, Graham and Trotman, p. 153–163.

Leythaeuser, D., R. G. Schaefer, and M. Radke, 1987, On the primary migration of petroleum: Proceedings of the 12th World Petroleum Conference, Houston, v. 2, p. 227–236.

Leythaeuser, D., R. G. Schaefer, and M. Radke, 1988a, Geochemical effects of primary migration of petroleum in Kimmeridge source rocks from Brae field area, North Sea, Part I: Geochimica Cosmochimica Acta, v. 52, p. 701–703.

Leythaeuser, D., M. Radke, and H. Willsch, 1988b, Geochemical effects of primary migration of petroleum in Kimmeridge source rocks from Brae field area, North Sea,

Part II: Geochimica Cosmochimica Acta, v. 52, p. 2879–2891.

Lindgreen, H., 1985, Diagenesis and primary migration in Upper Jurassic claystone source rocks, North Sea: AAPG Bulletin., v. 69, p. 525–536.

Lindgreen, H., 1987, Experiments on adsorption and molecular sieving and interferences on primary migration in Upper Jurassic claystone source rocks, North Sea: AAPG Bulletin, v. 71, p. 308–321.

Lovell, J. P. B., 1990, Cenozoic, *in* K. W. Glennie, ed., Introduction to the Petroleum Geology of the North Sea: London, Blackwell, p. 273–293.

Mackenzie, A. S., J. R. Maxwell, and M. L. Coleman, 1983, Biological marker and isotope studies of North Sea crude oils and sediments: Proceedings of the World Petroleum Congress, London, Section PD1(4), p. 45–56.

Mackenzie, A. S., D. Leythaeuser, P. Muller, M. Radke, and R. G. Schaefer, 1987, The Expulsion of petroleum from Kimmeridge Clay source rocks in the area of the Brae oilfield, UK continental shelf, *in* J. Brooks and K. W. Glennie, eds., Petroleum Geology of North-West Europe: London, Graham and Trotman, v. 1, p. 865–877.

McAuliffe, C. D., 1980, Oil and gas migration: Chemical and physical constraints, *in* W. H. Roberts III and R. J. Cordell, eds., Problems of petroleum migration: AAPG Studies in Geology 10, p. 89–107.

McKenzie, D. P., 1978, Some remarks on the development of sedimentary basins: Earth and Planetary Science Letters, v. 40, p. 25–32.

Michaud, F., 1987, Eldfisk, *in* A. M. Spencer et al., eds., Geology of the Norwegian Oil and Gas Fields: London, Graham and Trotman, p. 89–105.

Nielsen, O. B., S. Sorensen, J. Thiede, and O. Skarbo, 1986, Cenozoic differential subsidence of the North Sea: AAPG Bulletin, v. 70, p. 276–298.

Norbury, I., 1987, Hod, *in* A. M. Spencer et al., eds., Geology of the Norwegian Oil and Gas Fields: London, Graham and Trotman, p. 107–116.

Nordberg, H. E., 1981, Seismic hydrocarbon indicators in the North Sea: Norwegian Symposium on Exploration, Norwegian Petroleum Society, p. 8.1–8.40.

Northam, M. A., 1985, Correlation of northern North Sea oils: the different facies of their Jurassic source, *in* B. M. Thomas et al., eds., Petroleum Geochemistry in the Exploration of the Norwegian Shelf: Graham and Trotman, London, p. 93–99.

Oxburgh, E. R., and C. P. Andrews-Speed, 1981, Temperature, thermal gradients and heat flow in the southwest North Sea, *in* L. V. Illing and G. D. Hobson, eds., Petroleum Geology of the Continental Shelf of North-West Europe: London, Heydon, p. 141–151.

Pekot, L. J., and G. A. Gersib, 1987, Ekofisk, *in* A. M. Spencer et al., eds., Geology of the Norwegian Oil and Gas Fields: London, Graham and Trotman, p. 73–87.

Pennington, J. J., 1975, The geology of the Argyll field, *in* A. W. Woodland, ed., Petroleum and the Continental Shelf of North West Europe, Vol. 1: Geology: London, Applied Science, p. 285–291.

Robson, D., 1991, The Argyll, Duncan and Innes fields, Blocks 30/24, 30/25a, UK North Sea, *in* I. L. Abbotts, ed., United Kingdom oil and gas fields, 25 years commemorative volume: Geological Society of London Memoir 14, p. 219–225.

Saigal, G. C., K. Bjorlykke, and S. Larter, 1992, The effects of oil emplacement on diagenetic processes—examples from the Fulmar reservoir sandstones, central North Sea: AAPG Bulletin, v. 76, p. 1024–1033.

Sclater, J. G., and P. F. A. Christie, 1980, Continental stretching: an explanation of the post-middle Cretaceous subsidence of the Central North Sea basin: Journal of Geophysical Research, v. 85, n. B7, p. 3711–3739.

Smith, R. L., 1987, The structural development of the Clyde field, *in* J. Brooks and K. W. Glennie, eds., Petroleum Geology of North West Europe: London, Graham and Trotman, v. 1, p. 523–531.

Spencer, A. M. et al., eds., 1986a, Habitat of Hydrocarbons on the Norwegian Continental Shelf: London, Norwegian Petroleum Society, Graham and Trotman, 354 p.

Spencer, A. M., P. C. Home, and V. Wiik, 1986b, Habitat of hydrocarbons in the Jurassic Ula trend, Central Graben, Norway, *in* A. M. Spencer et al., eds., Habitat of Hydrocarbons on the Norwegian Continental Shelf: London, Graham and Trotman, p. 111–127.

Spencer, A. M. et al., eds., 1987, Geology of Norwegian Oil and Gas Fields: London, Graham and Trotman, 493 p.

Stevens, D. A., and R. J. Wallis, 1991, The Clyde field, Block 30/17b, UK North Sea, *in* I. L. Abbotts, ed., United Kingdom oil and gas fields, 25 years commemorative volume: Geological Society of London Memoir 14, p. 279–285.

Stewart, I. J., 1987, A revised stratigraphic interpretation of the early Paleogene of the Central North Sea, *in* J. Brooks and K. W. Glennie, eds., Petroleum Geology of North West Europe: London, Graham and Trotman, v. 1, p. 557–576.

Stockbridge, C. P., and D. I. Gray, 1991, The Fulmar fields, Blocks 30/16, 30/11b, UK North Sea, *in* I. L. Abbotts, ed., United Kingdom oil and gas fields, 25 years commemorative volume: Geological Society of London Memoir 14, p. 309–316.

Stow, D. A. V., and B. Atkin, 1987, Sediment facies and geochemistry of Upper Jurassic mudrock in the Central North Sea area, *in* J. Brooks and K. W. Glennie, eds., Petroleum Geology of North West Europe: London, Graham and Trotman, v. 2, p. 797–808.

Strand, J. E., and D. I. Slaatsveen, 1987, 7/11-5 Discovery, *in* A. M. Spencer et al., eds., Geology of the Norwegian Oil and Gas Fields: London, Graham and Trotman, p. 177–183.

Taylor, J. C. M., 1990, Upper Permian—Zechstein, *in* K. W. Glennie, ed., Introduction to the Petroleum Geology of the North Sea, 3rd ed.: London, Blackwell, p. 153–190.

Taylor, S. R., and J. F. Lapre, 1987, North Sea chalk diagenesis: its effect on reservoir location and properties, *in* J. Brooks and K. W. Glennie, eds., Petroleum Geology of NW Europe: London, Graham and Trotman, v. 1, p. 483–495.

Thomas, B. M. et al., eds., 1985a, Petroleum Geochemistry in the Exploration of the Norwegian Shelf: London, Graham and Trotman, 337 p.

Thomas, B. M., P. Moeller-Pedersen, M. F. Whitaker, and N. D. Shaw, 1985b, Organic facies and hydrocarbon distribution in the Norwegian North Sea, *in* B. M. Thomas et al., eds., Petroleum Geochemistry in the Exploration of the Norwegian Shelf: London, Graham and Trotman, p. 3–26.

Thompson, R. N., and S. A. Gibson, 1991, Subcontinental mantle plumes, hotspots and pre-existing thinspots: Journal of the Geological Society, v. 148, p. 973–977.

Thomsen, E., H. Lindgreen, and P. Wrang, 1983, Investigation on the source rock potential of Denmark: Geologie en Mijnbouw, v. 62, p. 221–239.

Thomsen, E., K. Damtoft, and C. Andersen, 1987, Hydrocarbon plays in Denmark outside the Central Trough, *in* J. Brooks, and K. W. Glennie, eds., Petroleum Geology of North West Europe: London, Graham and Trotman, v. 1, p. 375–388.

Thomsen, R. O., I. Lerche, and J. A. Kostgard, 1990, Dynamic hydrocarbon predictions for the northern part of the Danish Central Graben: an integrated basin analysis assessment: Marine and Petroleum Geology, v. 7, p. 123–137.

Thorne, J. A., and A. B. Watts, 1989, Quantitative analysis of North Sea subsidence: AAPG Bulletin, v. 73, p. 88–116.

Trewin, N. H., and M. G. Bramwell, 1991, The Auk field, Blocks 30/16, UK North Sea, *in* I. L Abbotts, ed., United Kingdom oil and gas fields, 25 years commemorative volume: Geological Society of London Memoir 14, p. 227–236.

Wilhelms, A., S. R. Larter, D. Leythaeuser, and H. Dypvik, 1990, Recognition and quantification of the effects of primary migration in a Jurassic clastic source rock from the Norwegian continental shelf, *in* B. Durand and F. Behar, eds., Advances in Organic Geochemistry 1989: Oxford, Pergamon, v. 16, p. 103–113.

Wills, J. M., 1991, The Forties field, Blocks 21/10, 22/6a, UK North Sea, *in* I. L. Abbotts, ed., United Kingdom oil and gas fields, 25 years commemorative volume: Geological Society of London Memoir 14, p. 301–308.

Wills, J. M., and D. K. Peattie, 1990, The Forties field and the evolution of a reservoir management strategy, *in* A. T. Buller et al., eds., North Sea Oil and Gas Reservoirs: London, Graham and Trotman, p. 1–23.

Wood, R., and Barton, P., 1983. Crustal thinning and subsidence in the North Sea: Nature, v. 305, p. 136–136.

Ziegler, P. A., 1982. Geological Atlas of Western and Central Europe: Amsterdam, Shell International Petroleum Maatschappi/Elsevier, 130 p and maps.

Ziegler, P. A., 1988. Evolution of the Arctic–North Atlantic and the western Tethys: AAPG Memoir 43, 198 p.

"Any good athlete will tell you winning is, finally, mental attitude. It is a dedication to excellence; and a grim, steely determination. Not easy—but kind of simple."

—John A. Masters

Passage from Masters, J. A., 1986, Winning: delivered at a convention of petroleum landmen, Vancouver, British Colombia.

Magoon, L. B, and W. G. Dow, eds., 1994, The petroleum
system—from source to trap: AAPG Memoir 60.

Chapter **34**

Petroleum Systems of the Lower Saxony Basin, Germany

Franz Kockel

Hermann Wehner

Peter Gerling

Federal Institute for Geosciences and Natural Resources (BGR)
Hannover, Germany

ABSTRACT

The Lower Saxony basin (LSB) is a highly differentiated graben filled with marine, lacustrine, and hypersaline sedimentary rocks of Late Jurassic and Early Cretaceous age. The basin inverted in Late Cretaceous time and was intruded by large laccoliths. Based on the occurrence of three oil types in close association with two source rocks, two petroleum systems are identified in this hydrocarbon province. The LSB Jurassic (!) petroleum system includes the first and oldest source rock, the Posidonia Shale (lower Toarcian), which is present throughout the entire Lower Saxony basin except for the westernmost part. Oils originating from it are characterized by a $\delta^{13}C$ value of –29‰ (type X). The LSB Lower Cretaceous (!) petroleum system includes the second and younger source rock, the "Wealden" papershale of Berriasian age, which occurs only in the western half of the basin. Its oil is characterized by a $\delta^{13}C$ value of –32‰ (type Z). A mixture of both oil types may occur (type Y) where both source rocks are present in a thermally mature stage and where reservoir rocks (Valanginian sandstone) are above the Wealden papershale.

Reservoir rocks are sandstones and limestones of Late Triassic (Rhaetian) to Early Cretaceous age. The most important reservoirs are Middle Jurassic sandstones, Upper Jurassic sandstones and limestones, and Lower Cretaceous sandstones. Traps are either facies and unconformity traps of pre-Turonian age or structural traps that originated during the Late Cretaceous basin inversion. Two periods of oil generation are recognized. Most oil generated during the first period from both source rocks in the central part of the basin during Albian–Turonian time (120–83 Ma). This oil—except for asphalt traces found—is quantitatively lost, as the traps have been destroyed during the Late Cretaceous (Santonian) inversion phase and the source rocks were overmatured due to additional heating by intrusion of deep-seated Late Cretaceous laccoliths.

Recoverable oil accumulations, now concentrated along the northern, western, and eastern borders of the basin, were less affected by these Late Cretaceous events. These oil ocurrences are limited to those areas where the vitrinite reflectance of the source rocks are presently in the range of 0.5–0.9% R_o. This second period of oil generation started with the end of basin inversion and may still be going on (83–0 Ma). From thermal maturity and structural considerations, short and mainly vertically directed migration paths are assumed. Cumulative production and proven reserves indicate that 3–10% of the hydrocarbons generated during the second period of oil formation actually accumulated in adjacent traps.

INTRODUCTION

The Lower Saxony basin is located in northwestern Germany (Figure 34.1) and contains numerous commercial oil and gas accumulations. Although oil was generated from Mesozoic source rocks and is trapped in Upper Triassic, Jurassic, and Cretaceous reservoir rocks, most gas originates from the underlying Upper Carboniferous coal seams and is trapped in Carboniferous, Permian, and Lower Triassic reservoir rocks. This deeper petroleum system is not the subject of this study but rather the two petroleum systems that include the two source rock horizons and the three oil types in various Mesozoic reservoirs.

Several oil seeps or asphalt deposits have been known in this area since the Middle Ages. In 1858, the first drill hole was successfully completed, which led to the first oil boom in the 1880s and 1890s. From 1934 onward, systematic exploration was carried out with government financial support using geophysical methods for the first time. In 1945, a total of 18 oil fields were known in the post-Permian sedimentary sequence, and progress had been made in the understanding of the stratigraphy, facies development, and structures of the basin fill (Bentz, 1947).

In 1965, nearly all of the now known 95 oil fields had been discovered, 64 of which are still being produced. Production of crude oil in 1968 amounted to 6.4 million t/yr (47.7 million bbl/yr). Since then, the yearly output has shrunk to 2.6 million t/yr (19.38 million bbl/yr) in 1990, which represents 72% of the total production of oil in Germany. In many cases, oil recovery is enhanced by secondary and tertiary processes. Cumulative production from the Lower Saxony basin totals about 182 million t (1356.45 million bbl), and estimated remaining reserves are about 41.8 million t (310 million bbl). Gas from Mesozoic sources is exclusively produced in three of the petroleum deposits, but methane, wet gas, and condensate are by-products in many oil fields. The original gas–oil ratio depends on the thermal maturity of the source rocks in the vicinity of the deposit and can vary between 8 m³ gas/m³ oil in immature areas to more than 750 m³/m³ in areas of higher maturity source rocks.

Publications on various aspects of the petroleum geology of the Lower Saxony basin are numerous. Summaries and comprehensive references are given by Bentz (1947), Guzman (1956), and especially Boigk (1981). A modern genetic synthesis of the basin was published by Betz et al. (1987). The results of recent work on oil–source rock relationships, thermal maturity investigations of source rocks and products, as well as structural aspects of oil generation and migration are given by Binot et al. (1993).

SEDIMENTARY BASIN SETTING

Structural Setting

The Lower Saxony basin is a special Jurassic–Lower Cretaceous basin within the greater North Sea–German–Polish basin that is filled with Carboniferous, Permian, Mesozoic, and Tertiary sedimentary rocks. This greater basin is bounded on the north by the East North Sea high and the Ringkøbing–Fyn high (southern Jutland, Fyn island), on the northeast by the southwest border of the East European platform (Baltic shield), and on the southwest and south by the London–Brabant high (massif) and the Rhenish and Bohemian massifs. Within this greater basin, the Lower Saxony basin is a graben, which subsided rapidly in Kimmeridgian–Aptian time. Structural inversion occurred in Late Cretaceous time. This graben is bordered on the north by the Pompeckj block or swell, on the west by the Central Netherland high, and on the

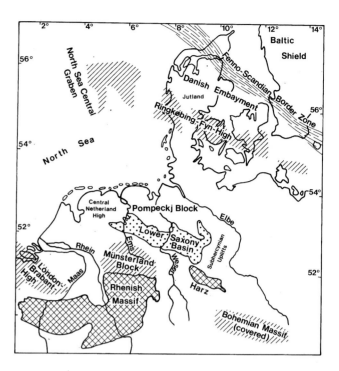

Figure 34.1. Index map of the Lower Saxony basin relative to the North Sea, central European rivers, and several geologic features.

east by the "subhercynian uplifts." The southern border is formed by the Münsterland block and the Harz mountains. The high margins of the basin are characterized by reduced thicknesses of Upper Jurassic–Lower Cretaceous sedimentary rocks.

The differentiation of the Lower Saxony basin from the greater North Sea–German–Polish basin started in Late Triassic (Rhaetian) time. The NNE-SSW striking ridges, troughs, horsts, and grabens that dominated the paleogeographic pattern of the Early Permian–Late Triassic became overprinted by WNW-ESE trending features that, for the first time, indicated the regional strike of the Lower Saxony basin (Figure 34.2). Only along the eastern margin of the basin does the NNE-SSW trend of the older structures persist. This incipient Lower Saxony basin persisted until Callovian–Oxfordian time.

From the Kimmeridgian through the Early Cretaceous (Berriasian), a complex series of WNW-ESE striking horsts and grabens developed. These grabens were filled with a very thick sequence of sedimentary rocks whose depositional environment changed from marine, to shallow marine–deltaic, to hypersaline, and finally to lacustrine. During this time, the surrounding horsts were deeply eroded. The Hauterivian again flooded the high grounds that surrounded the basin and covered these high grounds with a thin layer of sediments, whereas in the interior of the basin, the taphrogenetic subsidence continued and received thick layers of sediments.

During the late Aptian, the subsidence of these fault-controlled grabens diminished in intensity and a broad sink developed, reducing the rate of sedimentation substantially. This broad sink was filled with Albian,

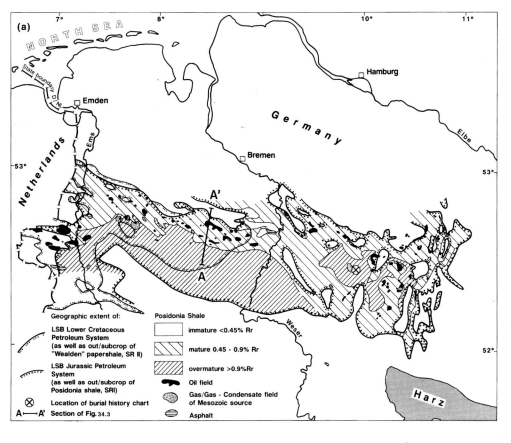

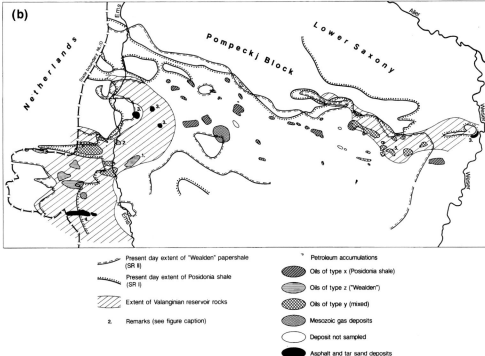

Figure 34.2. (a) Map showing the geographic extent of the LSB Jurassic(!) and LSB Lower Cretaceous(!) petroleum systems; Mesozoic oil, gas, and asphalt deposits; distribution and thermal maturity of the Posidonia Shale; distribution of the Wealden papershale; and location of cross section A–A' and burial history chart. (b) Distribution of oil types in the western Lower Saxony basin (west of the Weser River). Oil type Z accumulations are concentrated in the area west of the Ems River, where the Wealden papershale source rock extends beyond the Posidonia Shale. Type Y oil (mixed oil) is found where both source rocks are thermally mature and Valanginian reservoir rocks exist. Type X (Posidonia Shale) occurs in all oil fields where both source rocks are mature but Valanginian reservoirs are lacking. There are several exceptions: (1) Posidonia Shale source rock is overmature and produces only gas, which has been traced within the oil type Z. (2) Oil type X is found in Jurassic reservoir rocks, oil type Z in Valanginian reservoir rocks, and the mixed oil type is lacking. (3) Tar sands indicate immaturity of the source rocks. (4) Residual asphalt deposits indicate paleo-oil seep in pre-Paleogene time. (5) Oil type Y is contaminated with associated gases, which stem from type III kerogen, most likely Wealden coal seams.

Cenomanian, and Turonian sedimentary rocks that are thicker than those on the adjacent highs (bottom cross section on Figure 34.3).

At the beginning of the Coniacian, the Lower Saxony basin as a whole and all the individual graben-in-graben features were inverted. Former normal boundary faults were transformed into reverse or overthrust faults. Marginal troughs, which formed on the former graben shoulders, were filled with thick Late Cretaceous sedimentary rocks, the detritus of which was eroded from the crests of the individual rising inversion structures. In the central axis of the former Lower Saxony basin, laccol-

(a)

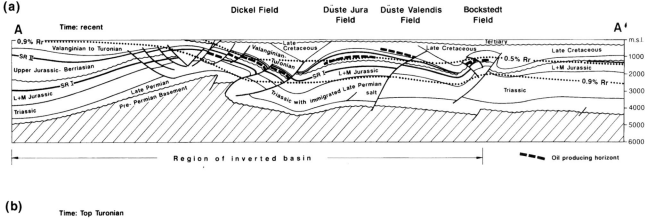

(b)

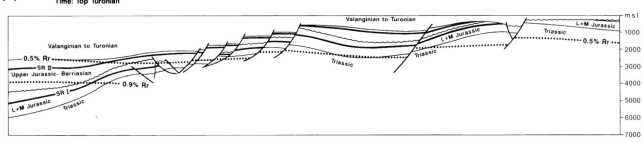

Figure 34.3. (a) Cross section A–A' (located on Figure 34.2a) is reconstructed for the end of Turonian time through the northern part of the Lower Saxony basin west of the Weser River. It shows the structural style, stratigraphic units, and level of thermal maturity (modified from Best, 1989, unpublished data). SR I is the Posidonia Shale and SR II is the Wealden paper-shale. Thick dashed lines are oil accumulations. Dotted lines indicate the upper and lower boundary of the oil window. (b) Same cross section but for present day (back stripped to the end of Turonian time when basin inversion began). Signatures as in part (a).

iths (massifs of Bramsche, Vlotho, Uchte, and Neustadt–Heessel) intruded the sedimentary rocks, causing intense organic metamorphism in the overlying sedimentary rocks and injection of hydrothermal fluids. The chemical composition of these laccoliths is unknown, as they have only been identified by indirect methods (gravity, magnetics, and coalification).

This fault-controlled inversion phase terminated in Campanian time, but feeble uplift lasted until the end of the Cretaceous. Thin Tertiary sedimentary rocks were deposited on the northeastern and western margins of the former basin and were partly removed again in Oligocene and Miocene time when the entire area, including the adjacent Pompeckj swell, was tilted toward the north (top cross section on Figure 34.3).

Stratigraphic Section

A highly simplified stratigraphic column for the entire Lower Saxony basin from the Late Triassic to Tertiary is given in Figure 34.4. This figure displays neither the small-scale facies differentiations nor the numerous local discordances and thickness variations that resulted from the contemporaneous taphrogenetic subsidences of this complex graben-in-graben system and from the halokinetic movements of the salt domes astride the basement fractures.

Considering the structural history of the basin, we can

divide the sedimentary column into six intervals that are often separated by nearly basinwide unconformities:

1. Pre-Rhaetian interval (Permian–Norian)
2. Incipient basin formation interval (Rhaetian–Oxfordian)
3. Graben basin formation interval (Kimmeridgian–Aptian)
4. Internal sag interval (Albian–late Turonian);
5. Inversion interval (Coniacian–Campanian)
6. Postinversion interval (Paleocene–Miocene)

Pre-Rhaetian Interval

The base of the sedimentary section discussed here is formed by the basal Rhaetian (Upper Triassic) or in parts by the "Steinmergelkeuper" (Norian) unconformity, or the so-called Early Kimmerian unconformity. As far as is known, the strata underlying this unconformity comprise the following: Dinantian shales and platform carbonates, Visean and lower Namurian (Variscian) flysch, upper Namurian–upper Westphalian (Variscian) molasse sedimentary rocks with coal seams, Stefanian and Lower Permian continental red beds, Upper Permian evaporites (which have been halokinetically mobilized, especially in the eastern part of the basin), Lower Triassic (Buntsandstein) red beds and sabkha sediments, marine Anisian–Ladinian Muschelkalk and sabkha sediments of Carnian and Norian age (lower and

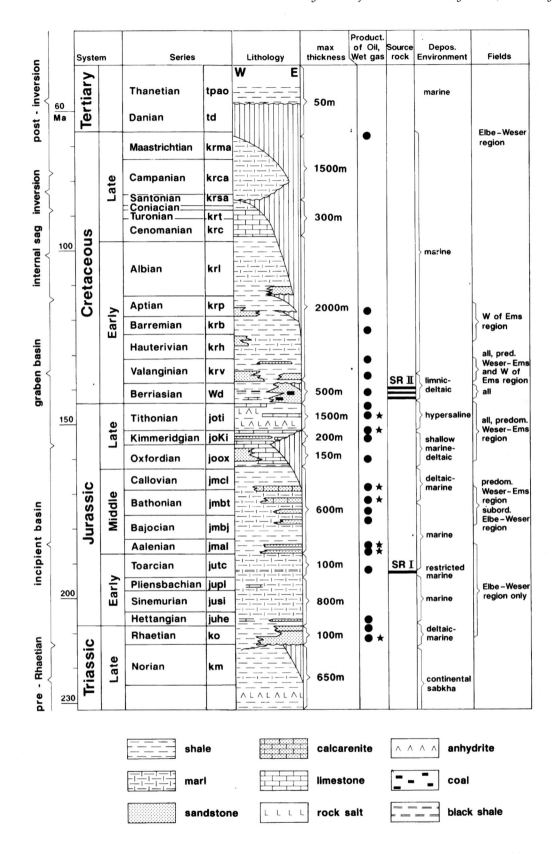

Figure 34.4. Generalized stratigraphic column for the Lower Saxony basin showing lithologies, maximum thicknesses, intervals that produce oil (solid circles) and wet gas (solid stars), oil source rock intervals (SR I = Posidonia Shale, SR II = Wealden papershales), depositional environments, and producing intervals according to regions. Important unconformities in the lithology column separate the six intervals discussed in the text.

middle Keuper) with intercalated salt deposits. Late Scythian and Norian synsedimentary movements formed generally NNE-striking (but also some WNW-striking) ridges, troughs, horsts, and grabens, which are covered by the Early Kimmerian unconformity.

Incipient Basin Formation Interval

In early Rhaetian time, the structural reorientation occurred, forming the incipient Lower Saxony basin. The deltaic sandstones of Rhaetian age are the lowermost reservoir rocks and are up to 100 m thick in the east but nonexistent in the west. These delta deposits were shed from the southeast and northeast and are intercalated by dark gray marine claystone containing type III kerogen. The Rhaetian deposits are overlain by up to 800 m of a Lower Jurassic marine sequence that is uniform in the west, but shows a mixed lithology in the east. In the west, dark gray claystones and marlstones prevail, whereas in the east, sandstones, sedimentary iron ores, and limestones indicate a nearshore environment.

Within a 100-m sequence of Toarcian sedimentary rocks, the Posidonia Shale, a calcareous bituminous shale with an average thickness of 25 m, was deposited under restricted marine conditions over the entire basin. It is the main oil source rock in this petroleum province (SR I).

During the early Middle Jurassic (Aalenian), near-shore bar and estuarine sands were derived from the east and deposited along the eastern border of the basin. In Bajocian time, the paleogeographic configuration changed entirely. Delta fans of Bajocian, Bathonian, and Callovian age prograded from the rising eastern border of the North Sea Central Graben into the central northern part of the basin. Only the eastern and western marginal parts do not contain these important reservoir rocks. The Middle Jurassic rock sequence locally attains a total thickness of 600 m. The Lower–Middle Jurassic sedimentary rocks are also locally preserved in sinks on the Pompeckj block under the Lower Cretaceous unconformity in the northern part of the basin.

At the beginning of the Late Jurassic (Oxfordian), marine sedimentation was confined to the Lower Saxony basin. A total of 150 m of shallow water limestones with intercalated sedimentary iron ores are found in the east, whereas west of the Weser River, they are replaced by less than 50 m of shallow marine or deltaic sands derived from the west and south.

Graben Basin Formation Interval

Shallow water conditions, alternating with periods of deltaic or hypersaline sedimentation (maximum thickness 200 m), continued during the Kimmeridgian. A middle Kimmeridgian transgression can be observed on top of local ridges and along the northern and western margin indicating a widening of the basin compared with the Oxfordian distribution. This trend continued into later Kimmeridgian time.

In Tithonian time, the Lower Saxony basin was completely cut off from the open sea and hypersaline as well as lacustrine environments prevailed, leading to the deposition of rock salt layers up to 1500 m thick. Intercalated within these layers are serpulid calcarenite bars that are good reservoir rocks. These thick evaporite deposits are the best hydrocarbon seal in the region. During the Tithonian, the taphrogenetic movements in the basin reached their peak, leading to extreme variations in facies and thickness over short distances.

At the beginning of the Early Cretaceous (Berriasian), the basin was occupied by a freshwater to brackish water lake (Bückeberg formation or "Wealden" in German terminology) in which fluvial deltaic deposits were derived from the southeast. Swamps developed between the subdeltas in the eastern part of the basin, giving rise to coal deposits. West of the Weser River, a lake remained open where dark claystones and bituminous papershales intercalated with Cyrena shell horizons were deposited. These bituminous Wealden papershales are the second, younger source rock of the petroleum system (SR II).

In Valanginian–Hauterivian time, the basin was again occupied by the sea, which also progressively flooded the high grounds north of the basin (Pompeckj block). Two siliciclastic sands of different Valanginian ages (maximum 100 and 40 m, thick, respectively) and of Hauterivian age (maximum 50 m thick) were transported into the basin from the western and northern margins. Argillaceous sediments prevailed in the late Early Cretaceous, representing another seal rock, except at the southeastern margin, where sedimentary iron ores accumulated. A minor influx of sand occurred from the south and west during the Aptian. Taphrogenetic block-faulting continued during the entire Early Cretaceous, producing a highly complex isopach pattern. The intensity of the fault movements migrated from the center of the basin to its northern margin.

Internal Sag Interval

Active faulting ceased in early Aptian time. Albian claystones (maximum 500 m thick) with minor sand influx from the southeast, along with Cenomanian and Turonian limestones (maximum 300 m thick), are deposited in a nonfaulted basin differentiated into ridges and troughs reflecting the former horst and graben features. From Valanginian to early Cenomanian time, up to 2300 m of marine, mainly argillaceous sediments were deposited in the central part of the basin. They represent an important overburden rock prior to inversion of the Lower Saxony basin.

Inversion Interval

In late Coniacian–Campanian time, during and shortly after the inversion phase, marine marlstones, calcarenites, and chalk, commonly with sedimentary iron ores at the base, were deposited. Also, olisthostromes and flysch-like sediments have been observed. Sedimentation was generally restricted to the marginal troughs in front of the inversion structures. Maastrichtian deposits occur only locally.

Postinversion Interval

In early–middle Paleocene time, a general low stand of sea level caused a regional truncation of all structures originated during the inversion act. Tertiary sedimentary

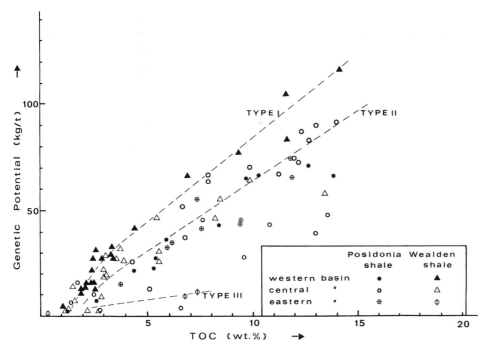

Figure 34.5. Relationship between genetic potential (S_1 + S_2) (Espitalié et al., 1985) and total organic carbon (TOC) content of the Posidonia Shale (SR I) and the Wealden paper-shale (SR II) source rocks in the Lower Saxony basin. The dashed lines indicate type I, II, and III kerogens. Within the Wealden papershale, the kerogen type ranges from I to II from the western to central areas of the basin.

rocks (upper Paleocene–Oligocene) are found only in the northern and northeastern parts of the basin in a marginal position. They consist of interbedded sandstones within a dark claystone sequence. These marine sedimentary rocks are up to 50 m thick and unconformably overlie the older sedimentary rock sequences. Transgressive Miocene deposits are only locally preserved due to a general uplifting and tilting of northwestern Germany toward the north in Pliocene time.

THE PETROLEUM SYSTEM

Based on the occurrence of three oil types in close association with two source rocks, two petroleum systems are identified in this hydrocarbon province. The LSB Jurassic(!) petroleum system includes the first and oldest source rock, the Posidonia Shale (lower Toarcian), which is present throughout the entire Lower Saxony basin except for the westernmost part. Oils originating from it are characterized by a $\delta^{13}C$ value of –29‰ (type X). The LSB Lower Cretaceous(!) petroleum system includes the second and younger source rock, the Wealden papershale of Berriasian age, which occurs only in the western half of the basin. Its oil is characterized by a $\delta^{13}C$ value of –32‰ (type Z). A mixture of both oil types may occur (type Y) where both source rocks are present in a thermally mature stage and where reservoir rocks (Valanginian sandstone) are above the Wealden papershale.

Petroleum Source Rocks

There are two source rocks in this hydrocarbon province, which can clearly be correlated geochemically and isotopically with different oils in the adjacent reservoir rocks.

The older source rock (SR I) is the lower Toarcian Posidonia Shale. This marine sedimentary sequence was deposited in an extremely restricted environment and is distributed over the entire basin (Figure 34.2) except for marginal parts west of the Ems River (Figure 34.2a). Its thickness varies from 15 to 30 m, the average value being 25 m. The organic matter consists of algal remains. The amount of total organic carbon (TOC) is variable; a mean content of 8 wt. % seems reasonable, but values as high as 20 wt. % west of the Ems River are possible (Figure 34.5). The genetic potential (S_1 + S_2) can be as high as 140 kg HC/t rock and averages about 60 kg HC/t rock. Over the entire basin, most of the organic matter in this source rock is classified as type II kerogen (Figure 34.5). The thermal maturity of this source rock varies from immature (<0.5 % R_o) along the eastern border of the basin to overmature (>0.9% R_o) in the center of the basin (Figure 34.2).

The younger source rock (SR II) is the bituminous Wealden papershale horizon within the lacustrine Berriasian sequence ("Bückeburg Formation"). This source rock is restricted to the western part of the Lower Saxony basin (west of the river Weser, Figure 34.2). At the western margin, it oversteps the Posidonia Shale distribution area west of the Ems River. The amount of organic matter is highly variable. Mean TOC values are 7 wt. % in the western area and 4 wt. % in the area just west of the Weser River. However, values as high as 14 wt. % are reported. The genetic potential can be as high as 120 kg HC/t rock, but it averages about 40 kg HC/t rock. The kerogen is type I in the western part of the basin, but tends toward type II as the Weser River is approached (Figure 34.5). The mean thickness of the source rock is about 25 m (Wiesner, 1983). The thermal maturity ranges from immature (<0.5% R_o) along the northern margin of the basin to overmature (>0.9% R_o) in the basin center (Figure 34.2a).

Table 34.1. Oil and Wet Gas Fields Relative to the Ems and Weser Rivers in the Lower Saxony Basin[a]

Item (Units)	West of the Ems	Between Ems & Weser	East of the Weser
Number of producing fields	9	23	30
Number of exhausted fields	2	4	2
Years of discovery	1945–1984	1945–1965	1857–1960
Producing rock unit[b]	jmcl, joti, Wd, krv, krh, krp	jutcu, jmalo, jmbi, jmbt, jmcl, joox, joki, joti, Wd, krv	ko, juhe, jutcu, jmalo, jmbj, jmbt, joox, joki, joti, WD, krv, krma
Producing depth (m)	700–1300	0–2000, ave., 1200–1500	—
Trap type (number of fields)	Facies (1), structure + mixed (10)	Facies (1), structure (26)	Facies (2), discordancy (12), structure (38)
Cumulative oil production (t)[c]	62,388,182	49,272,414	70,701,069
Remaining oil reserves (t)	25,270,000	10,894,000	4,990,000

[a]From internal reports of the Geological Survey of Lower Saxony; detailed data on individual fields not permitted to be published.
[b]Rock unit abbreviations as in Figure 34.6 caption.
[c]No data for gas available

Reservoir Rocks

The reservoir rocks of this petroleum province are mostly siliciclastic or calcareous sandstones (Figures 34.3, 34.4, and Table 34.1), although carbonate reservoir rocks are also productive. The oldest reservoir rocks containing oil in the Lower Saxony basin are Rhaetian deltaic sandstones developed only in the eastern part of the basin. Most of the oil reserves are in the Aalenian sandstones, which furnish most of the production in the eastern basin and are absent west of Braunschweig. Between the Weser and Ems Rivers, the Bajocian, Bathonian, and Callovian sandstones are the most important reservoir rocks, together with Oxfordian and Kimmeridgian sandstone and limestone reservoir rocks. Upper Jurassic carbonate rocks are also productive in this region as well as in the area west of the Ems River.

The economically most important reservoir rocks along the northern and western fringe of the western basin are Valanginian sandstones (Figure 34.2b), which wedge out to the east and south toward the center of the basin. The Posidonia Shale source rock itself, Wealden sandstones and coquinites, and Hauterivian and Aptian reservoir rocks west of the Ems River yield minor production.

Seals and Overburden Rocks

Seal rocks for the oil accumulations are the Lower–Middle Jurassic shales, the Tithonian evaporites, and the thick Hauterivian–Albian claystone sequence (Figures 34.6a and b). These rocks played the role of overburden before and after the inversion in pre-Coniacian time. Along the western, northern, and northeastern margins, Tertiary claystones play an additional role of overburden rock (Figures 34.4 and 34.6). In the central part of the basin, the seal quality of the Mesozoic claystones is considerably reduced due to "baking" by Late Cretaceous laccolith intrusions.

Traps

The nature of the traps is variable (Figure 34.6). Facies traps have a synsedimentary origin in some Aalenian sandstones (estuarine "shoestring" sands) in the eastern basin and by wedging out of the Valanginian sandstones in the western basin. Unconformity traps prevail in the northeastern and southeastern parts of the basin, where transgressive Valanginian–Albian sedimentary rocks truncate the Jurassic reservoir rocks. The most widespread trap type, especially west of the Weser River, is of structural origin. These traps were either formed at the flanks or on the tops of salt diapirs (predominantly in the eastern basin) or in roll-over structures. Complicated anticlines linked to overthrusts that originated during the inversion predominate the western part of the basin (Figure 34.3).

Oil Field Examples

Due to the great variety of reservoir rocks and trap types, no typical oil field can be named. Thus, three examples are given in Table 34.2 to demonstrate the wide range of oil field characteristics. These fields are located west of the Ems, between the Ems and Weser, and east of the Weser (see Table 34.2 for details).

Oil Types and Oil–Source Rock Relationships

Crude oils found east of the Weser River have nearly identical isotopic compositions and biological marker patterns regardless of the age or structural position of their reservoir rocks (Figures 34.7 and 34.8), a strong indication for the existence of only one source rock. The only exceptions are highly mature oils from two accumulations. Based on the type of organic matter and richness, the Posidonia Shale (SR I) is considered to be the only source rock in the area. Figure 34.7 illustrates the excellent agreement of the sterane and triterpane

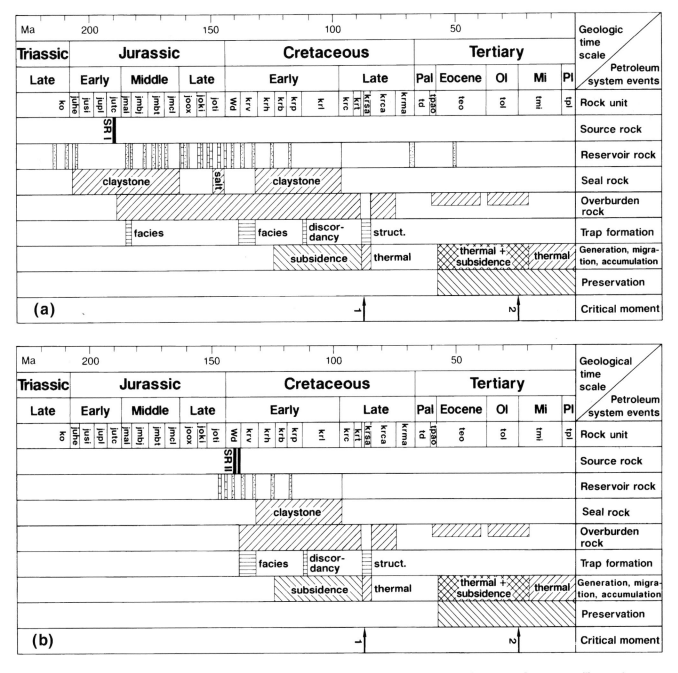

Figure 34.6. The events chart for (a) the LSB Jurassic(!) petroleum system and (b) the LSB Lower Cretaceous(!) petroleum system. The geologic time scale is after Palmer (1983). The rock unit abbreviations are ko, upper Keuper; juhe, Hettangian; jusi, Sinemurian; jupl, Pliensbachian; jutc, Toarcian; jmal, Aalenian; jmbj, Bajocian; jmbt, Bathonian; jmcl, Callovian; joox, Oxfordian; joKi, Kimmeridgian (in local sense); joti, Tithonian; Wd, Berriasian; krv, Valanginian; krh, Hauterivian; krb, Barremian; krp, Aptian; krl, Albian; krc, Cenomanian; krt, Turonian; krcc, Coniacian; krsa, Santonian; krca, Campanian; krma, Maastrichtian; td, Danian; tpao, upper Paleocene; teo, Eocene; tol, Oligocene; tmi, Miocene; and tpl, Pliocene.

patterns of a crude oil (type X) and a Posidonia Shale extract. The δ13C values of Posidonia Shale kerogens and crude oil aromatics are about –29‰ and are essentially identical. Moreover, with only one exception, oil accumulations were discovered only in that area where the Posidonia Shale occurs in a thermal maturity range of 0.5–0.9% R_o.

West of the Ems River, the Wealden papershales extend beyond the Posidonia Shale (Figure 34.2a). The oils found here (type Z) can clearly be distinguished from the type X oil. Based on biological marker fingerprints (Figure 34.9) and isotope ratios (Figure 34.8) of kerogens and crude oil aromatics (about –32‰), a good correlation with the Wealden papershales is observed (Figure 34.9).

In the middle part of the basin, roughly between the Ems and Weser Rivers, both source rocks are thermally mature (Figure 34.2a). A third oil (type Y) occurs, which

Table 34.2. Characteristics of Largest Fields with Oil Types X, Y, and Z Located Relative to the Ems and Weser Rivers in the Lower Saxony Basin

Item (Units)	West of the Ems	Between Ems & Weser	East of the Weser
Field(s)	Scheerhorn	Rühle, Rühlermoor, Rühlertwist	Hankensbüttel
Trap type	Fractured anticline, originated during Santonian inversion	Fractured anticline, originated during Santonian inversion	Faulted unconformity belowAptian–lower Albian
Reservoir lithology	1. Upper Kimmeridgian shelly limestone (gigas beds) 2. Tithonian shelly limestone (serpulit) 3. Berriasian Ostracodal limestone ("Wealden") 4. Valanginian "Bentheim sandstone" 5. Upper Hauterivian "Gildehaus sandstone"	Middle Valanginian Bentheim sandstone	Aalenian bar sands and estuarine sands
Thickness (m)			
Upper reservoir	Reservoirs 1–3: <10	10–31	18–28
Lower reservoir	Reservoirs 4–5: <60	4–26	2–7
Porosity (%)			
Upper reservoir	—	24–30	27
Lower reservoir	Reservoirs 4–5: 20–30	24–29	25
Permeability (md)			
Upper reservoir	—	10–20,000	5420
Lower reservoir	Reservoirs 4–5: <10,000	10–7,000	648
Height of closure (m)	Reservoir 5: 65	300	56
Pool cover (km^2)	9.4	24	6
Source rock(s)	Wealden papershale	Wealden papershale, *Posidonia* shale	*Posidonia* shale
Oil			
Type	Z	Y	X
Specific gravity	0.875	—	0.89–0.91
Paraffin (%)	—	—	2.02–4.44
Viscosity (Pa)	0.0297	0.07	0.011–0.0022
Percentage sulfur (%)	—	—	0.75
GOR (m^3/m^3)	27	21	23
Reservoir temperature (˚C)	Reservoir 5: 48	42	—
Cumulative production (t)	7,379,703 (Res. 4: 6,729,667)	25,057,200	13,310,500
Number of wells	169	370	56
Year of start of production	1949	1945	1956
Reserves (t)	2,750,000	14,680,000	1,177,000

is most likely a mixture of type X and Z oils, as deduced from the carbon isotope ratios (Figure 34.8) and biological marker patterns. However, its occurrence in oil accumulations is bound to the presence of a reservoir rock younger than the Wealden papershale source rock (SR II), which in most cases is a Valanginian sandstone. Only in these sandstones is the type Y oil (a mixture of types X and Z) present. If Cretaceous reservoir rock is absent, only the type X oil is found in the Jurassic reservoirs. The Wealden papershale loses its excellent source rock character toward the eastern part of the basin (Figure 34.2) due to the influx of delta sands and interbedded coal seams, whereas that of the Posidonia Shale remains constant. This is the reason why only type X oil is found in the eastern part of the basin.

Based on the excellent oil–source rock correlations,

oil–oil correlations, and the distribution of oil types relative to the distribution of their source rocks, two petroleum systems exist with a known level of certainty.

Oil-Associated Gas

Molecular and isotopic compositions of associated hydrocarbon gases provide certain additional information. Bacterially generated methane is present in all oil fields. In addition to the oil-associated gaseous hydrocarbons, which are the main gas constituents, coal gas from the underlying Carboniferous coal beds was found as a third mixing partner in a few petroleum deposits.

Values for $\delta^{13}C$ from ethane and propane are useful for making thermal maturity estimates (Faber, 1987). For example, these gas maturities lead to the conclusion that

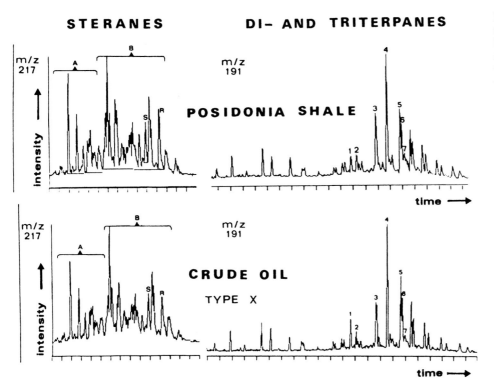

Figure 34.7. Example of an oil source rock correlation using biological markers. Crude oil (type X) and source rock, both from the Suderbruch field in the eastern part of the Lower Saxony basin, show identical sterane and triterpane mass chromatogram patterns. On the *m/z* 217 fragmentogram, the peaks under A are rearranged steranes and under B are regular steranes. The S's and R's are 20S- and 20R-5-$\alpha\alpha$-ethylcholestanes, respectively. On the *m/z* 191 fragmentogram, the numbered peaks are as follows: (1) and (2) C_{27}-hopanes, (3) norhopane, (4) hopane, (5) and (6) 22S- and 22R-homohopane, and (7) gammacerane.

oil generation from the Posidonia Shale ceased when it exceeded a thermal maturity of 0.9% R_o. At higher maturities, expulsion of wet gas, condensate, and finally dry gas occurred. In addition, methane carbon isotope ratios are effective in identifying the facies changes of the Wealden papershale (type I/II to type III kerogens) from west to east.

Thermal Maturation and Migration History

West of the Weser River, the Posidonia Shale and Wealden papershale source rocks became thermally overmature and mature, respectively, during pre-Turonian subsidence (south end of bottom cross section, Figure 34.3). East of the Weser, this overmaturity (deduced from numeric modeling) occurred 65 Ma

(Figures 34.2 and 34.10a). These areas suffered an extreme thermal impact by the laccolithic bodies intruded during or shortly prior to the Santonian inversion. This combination of subsidence and magmatic thermal maturation led to the first generation of hydrocarbons, which either were trapped in existing facies, discordancy, or structural traps or were evaporated before or during the inversion act between about 120 and 83 Ma. The oil accumulated in these preinversion structures became released when the traps were rearranged or destroyed during the inversion tectonics. In our view, there was little chance that oils generated and migrated could reaccumulate in structural traps that formed contemporaneously to the inversion act. The widespread occurrence of asphalts indicates that the oils were quantitatively lost. The still existing preinversion

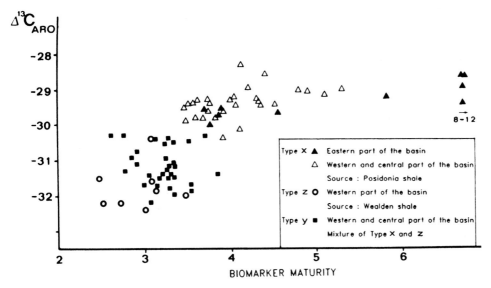

Figure 34.8. Comparison of carbon isotope and biological marker data of oils from the Lower Saxony basin. The three different groups defined by their biomarker patterns (see Figures 34.7 and 34.9) can also be identified by means of isotope values. Biomarker maturity is calculated from the ratio of certain biomarkers which are identified in Figure 34.7. Biomarker maturity = 1:2 + 3:4 + 7:4 + 5:6 + S:R + A:B. A, B = total counts on the mass chromatograms of A and B areas in Figures 34.7 and 34.9.

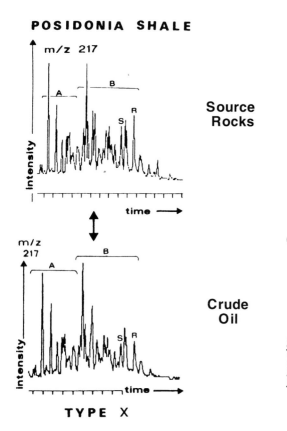

POSIDONIA SHALE

Source Rocks

TYPE X

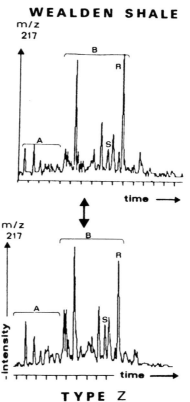

WEALDEN SHALE

Crude Oil

TYPE Z

Figure 34.9. Example of two oil–source rock correlations based on biological markers from oils in the western Lower Saxony basin. Type X is identical to the oils from the Posidonia Shale, occurring in the eastern Lower Saxony basin. Type Z oils originate from the Wealden papershale and have a different biomarker pattern. Type Y, not shown here, resembles type Z, but the distribution of the C_{27}-steranes, moretanes, and tricyclic diterpanes is different. Type X oil and Posidonia Shale are from the Annaveen field, and type Z oil and Wealden papershale are from Emlichheim field. (For identification of peaks, see Figure 34.7.)

traps along the northeastern margin of the basin had not been filled until the end of the Santonian. The source rock in the vicinity was immature at that time and the influence of the intrusive bodies did not affect these areas.

During the middle–late Santonian, the entire basin (except the marginal parts) was uplifted and thus oil generation ceased for a certain period. A second period of oil generation started after the inversion and filled the structural traps formed in Santonian time. In the areas of present-day hydrocarbon accumulations, located almost exclusively near the basin margins, the oil window for both source rocks was reached during the Late Cretaceous–early Tertiary (83–55 Ma). The heat source in these uplifted areas was either a continuing slight heating in the periphery of the large Late Cretaceous intrusions or a general elevation of the regional heat flow since Tertiary time. The elevated heat flow (70–90 mW/m2, according to Brink et al., 1992) has been measured, but the reason for it remains unknown (alteration of crustal composition in the course of the inversion?). At the northeastern margin of the basin, subsidence during the Tertiary was sufficient to bring the previously immature source rock into the oil window. In most areas, measured source rock maturity differs positively from that calculated from mere subsidence assuming a "normal" temperature gradient of 33°C/km, demanding additional heat aside from the mere subsidence maturation. Because the variations of heat flow in the past 83 Ma cannot be determined with sufficient exactitude, it is difficult to give a reasonable age for the beginning of this second oil generation period.

Figure 34.3 shows this development in greater detail. Note that none of the present-day traps existed in pre-Turonian time. The source rocks below the present day oil fields at this time were still thermally immature. A thick overburden rock matured to overmatured both source rocks at the southern (left) end of the cross section. Subsequent uplift has brought these overmature source rocks to the surface (part a, left) today. Oil (type X) in the Dickel and Düste Jura fields is from Posidonia Shale (SR I), due to the lack of Lower Cretaceous reservoir rocks, and in the Bockstedt field, due to the lack of the Wealden papershale (SR II).

Geochemical maturity of the accumulated hydrocarbons coincides with the present-day thermal maturity of the source rocks in the immediate surroundings, whereas the source rocks in the adjacent synclines around the traps normally are more mature or overmature compared with the geochemical maturity of the oils. This implies that oils being produced today originate from source rocks directly underlying the traps. Thus, migration paths can be assumed to be very short (<2 km) and mostly vertical. Hydrocarbon generation is presently ongoing, as the geochemical maturity of the oils and the thermal maturity of the source rocks are similar.

Efficiency of the System

The occurrence of one or two source rocks with variable TOC values and hydrogen indices requires separate calculation of the efficiencies for the two parts of the basin (Table 34.3). In the western part of the basin, oil type Y (a mixture of types X and Z) occurs in a number

Figure 34.10. (a) Burial history chart for the LSB Jurassic(!) petroleum system. SR I generated oil over a 40-m.y. period from 105 to 65 Ma. (b) Burial history chart for the LSB Lower Cretaceous(!) petroleum system. SR II equivalents were in the oil window from 92 to 56 Ma. The events charts show the stratigraphic units penetrated from the Aptian down to the Rhaetian (and further) and the essential elements for both systems (see text for details). The drill hole used for the charts is situated in the eastern part of the basin in a wet gas producing area (see Figure 34.2) and does not contain the Wealden papershale source rock; the charts show the burial history of its facies equivalent. The oil window (obliquely hatched) is 0.5–0.9% R_o, the gas window (horizontally hatched) is above 0.9% R_o for the only source rock present. The MASCAL calculation program, developed by DEMINEX, has been used. (For rock unit abbreviations, see Figure 34.4.)

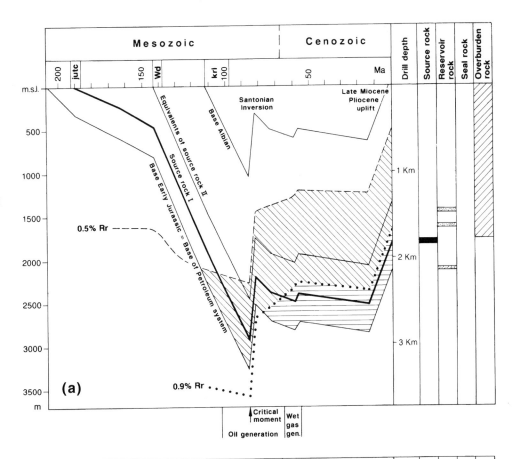

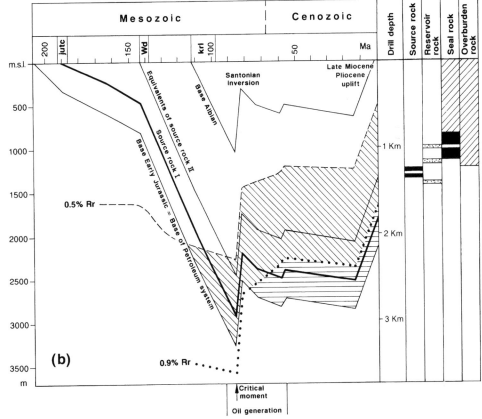

Table 34.3. Generation–Accumulation Efficiency Calculation for Both Petroleum Systems in the Lower Saxony Basin

| Items (units) | West of the Weser | | East of the Weser |
| | Source rock I | Source rock II | Source rock I |
	Posidonia	*Wealden*	*Posidonia*
Area (m²) (0.5–0.9% R_o)	2.06 billion	2.73 billion	2.9 billion
Thickness (m)	25	25	25
Density (t/m³)	2.3	2.3	2.3
TOC (wt. %)	8	4.5	8
HI_{im}–HI_m (g/g TOC)	0.3	0.37	0.3
Amount of generated hydrocarbons (t)	2.85 billion	2.6 billion	4.0 billion
Petroleum in place plus reserves (t)[a]	0.089 billion	0.267 billion	0.206 billion
Generation–accumulation efficiency (%)	3.1	10.2	5

[a]Assuming 35% recovery of crude oil and 80% recovery of gas.

of deposits. Here, the amount of parent oils was estimated using the varying carbon isotope values of the mixed oils and the constant isotope value for type X (–29‰) and type Z (–32‰).

The volume of the source rocks and the amount of generated hydrocarbons were calculated by using Schmoker's formula (Chapter 19, this volume). Only those areas of the basin were considered where the source rocks are at present in the thermal maturity range of 0.5–0.9% R_o. Thus, areas with overmature source rocks due to preinversion burial or heating are excluded from the calculations because the amount of trapped oil in preinversion time cannot be reconstructed.

Because knowledge of the thickness of the Wealden papershale and its average TOC content is limited, calculations for this source rock are estimates only. According to these calculations (Table 34.3), about 3–10% of all hydrocarbons generated are actually accumulated.

Acknowledgments   *This study relies partially on unpublished reports by Baldschuhn, Best, Binot, Frisch, and Hiltmann (all of the Federal Institute for Geosciences and Natural Resources) and on internal reports of the Geological Survey of Lower Saxony. We thank these colleagues for their assistance and the Federal Ministry of Research and Technology, as well as the German Association of Oil and Gas Producing Companies (WEG), for sponsoring us and for permission to publish.*

References Cited

Bentz, A., ed., 1947, Erdöl und Tektonik in NW Deutschland: Hannover-Celle, Amt für Bodenforschung, p. 1–387.

Betz, D., F. Führer, G. Greiner, and E. Plein, 1987, Evolution of the Lower Saxony basin: Tectonophysics, v. 137, p. 127–170.

Binot, F., P. Gerling, W. Hiltmann, F. Kockel, and H. Wehner, 1993, The petroleum system of the Lower Saxony basin, *in* A. M. Spencer, ed., Generation, accumulation and production of Europe's hydrocarbons, III: Special Publication of the European Association of Petroleum Geologists, v. 3, p. 121–139.

Boigk, H., 1981, Erdöl und Erdölgas in der Bundesrepublik Deutschland, Erdölprovinzen, Felder, Förderung, Vorräte, Lagerstättentechnik: Stuttgart, Enke Verlag, 330 p.

Brink, H. J., H. Dürschner, and H. Trappe, 1992, Some aspects of the late and post-Variscian development of the Northwest German basin: Tectonophysics, v. 207, p. 65–95.

Espitalié, I., G. Deroo, and F. Marquis, 1985, La pyrolyse Rock-Eval et ses applications, deuxieme part: Revue de l'Institut Francais du Petrole, v. 40, p. 755–784.

Faber, E., 1987, Zur Isotopengeochemie gasförmiger Kohlenwasserstoffe: Erdöl, Kohle, Erdgas, v. 103, p. 210–218.

Guzman, E., ed., 1956, Symposium sobre yacimientos de Petroleo y gas—Tom V: Europa, Mexico City, p. 1–162.

Palmer, A. R., 1983, The decade of North American geology, 1983 geologic time scale: Geology, v. 11, p. 503–504.

Wiesner, M. G., 1983, Lithologische und geochemische Faziesuntersuchungen an bituminösen Sedimenten des Berrias im Raum Bentheim-Salzbergen, Emsland: Ph.D. dissertation, University of Hamburg, Hamburg, Germany, 113 p.

Magoon, L. B, and W. G. Dow, eds., 1994, The petroleum
system—from source to trap: AAPG Memoir 60.

Chapter **35**

Tótkomlós–Szolnok(.) Petroleum System
of Southeastern Hungary

J. L. Clayton

C. W. Spencer

Branch of Petroleum Geology
U.S. Geological Survey
Denver, Colorado, U.S.A.

I. Koncz

Nagykanizsa, Hungary

Abstract

Several petroleum provinces in southeastern Hungary are part of the greater late Miocene–Pliocene Pannonian basin of central Europe. The Pannonian basin formed as a tensional basin in early–middle Miocene time (17–12 Ma) when thick (<1250 m) marine bioclastic carbonates were deposited. Pre-Miocene basement rocks are composed of lithologically and structurally complex rocks of Precambrian to Mesozoic age. Overlying the basement rocks and the marine carbonates are thick (<4500 m) lacustrine Pannonian rocks of late Miocene and Pliocene age. Gas production with some oil and condensate is predominantly from structural and combination traps. Part of one petroleum system present in southeastern Hungary consists of middle–upper Miocene source rocks and reservoir rocks. Fractured Precambrian rocks are the next most important reservoir rocks. Gas and oil generation began less than 6 Ma and is continuing today.

Overpressuring is regionally present in rocks at drill depths greater than 2500 m. The overpressuring is caused by a combination of undercompaction (incomplete sediment dewatering) and active hydrocarbon generation from middle–upper Miocene source rocks. Some overpressuring may be caused by thermally generated CO_2 yielded during metamorphism of Paleozoic carbonate basement rocks. Vertical fracturing and sandstone carrier beds cause hydrocarbons from the overpressured source rocks to migrate into basement rocks and Miocene age reservoir rocks. The overpressuring has caused the gas and oil to be forced downward, upward, and laterally. At depths shallower than 2500–1800 m, the hydrocarbons (and CO_2) migrated mostly by buoyancy.

More than 26 oil and gas fields have been discovered in mostly structurally controlled accumulations. These fields have an estimated original in-place oil of 35.3 million t and in-place gas of 66.2 million m^3. The amount of undiscovered resources is unknown but only a few deep (>5000 m) exploratory tests have been drilled, and exploration has just begun for stratigraphic traps.

INTRODUCTION

We have divided southeastern Hungary into six provinces using depth to the pre-Miocene basement rock as a guide (Figure 35.1). These provinces, located within the greater Pannonian basin, include several lows (Makó trough, Békés basin, and Földes trough) and highs (Endröd shelf, Furta high, and Battonya high). Petroleum exploration began in 1918, although the first important discovery (Pusztaföldvár field) was not made until 1958. More than 26 oil and gas fields have been discovered in mostly structurally controlled accumulations (Table 35.1). These fields have an estimated original in-place oil of 35.3 million t and in-place gas of 66.2 billion m^3 (Table 35.2). About 3.4 million t of oil and 18.6 million m^3 of gas had

been produced by about 1985. Original recoverable reserves for these fields is estimated to be 10 million t of oil and 53 billion m^3 of gas. The amount of undiscovered resources is unknown but only a few deep (>5000 m) exploratory tests have been drilled, and exploration has just begun for stratigraphic traps. The exploration history of this and other parts of Hungary is discussed by Dank (1985, 1988).

Currently, southeastern Hungary produces mostly gas and gas condensate with secondary amounts of oil. Most of the gas and oil fields have been discovered in structural and combination (structural–stratigraphic) traps whose reservoir rocks are the basement rock or the overlying sedimentary rocks. The reservoir rocks range in age from Precambrian to Pliocene, but most produc-

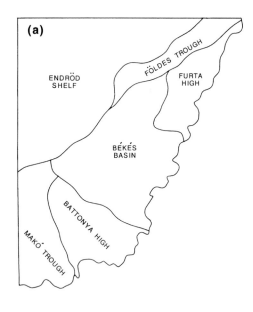

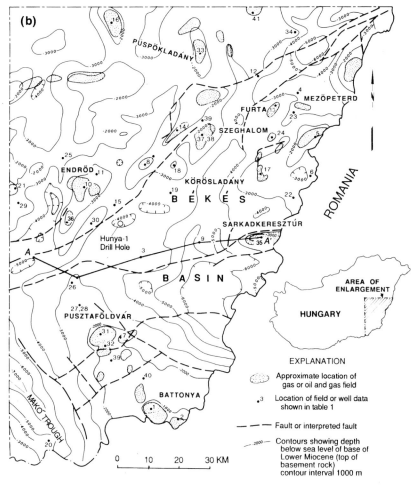

Figure 35.1. (a) Map showing southeastern Hungary divided into regions based on structural elements and present-day depth to basement. (b) Map of southeastern Hungary showing approximate locations of oil and gas fields. Numbers refer to locations of fields listed in Table 35.1. Structural contours are on top of pre-Miocene (basement) rocks. Selected field names and location of Hunya-1 drill hole are shown.

tion is from the upper Miocene. The pre-Miocene basement rocks consist of a variety of lithologies including igneous and metamorphic rocks with fracture permeability and some solution porosity (Table 35.1). Middle Miocene shales and basal clay–marl and upper Miocene marl are believed to be the major source rocks for most of the gas and oil (Clayton et al., 1990; Clayton et al., in press). Thinner, less organic rich, and therefore minor, source rock intervals are also found in the overlying upper Miocene Szolnok and Algyö formations. Thermal maturation of the major source rocks is believed to have begun in latest Miocene time (<6 Ma) and continues to the present (Szalay, 1988).

There are several essential elements of the petroleum system responsible for all of the thermal gas (with some condensate) and oil being produced to date in the area. (1) The source rocks are middle–upper Miocene shale, clay–marl, and marl. (2) The major reservoir rocks include pre-Miocene basement through upper Miocene Szolnok Sandstone Formation. (3) The seal rocks are the clay–marls throughout the section. (4) The overburden rocks range in age from late Miocene to Holocene. Some shallow gas deposits interpreted to be of microbial origin (Clayton et al., 1990) come from a separate petroleum system. This chapter will discuss only the petroleum system responsible for the thermal gas, condensate, and oil.

PANNONIAN BASIN SETTING

Structural Setting

The Pannonian basin formed as a consequence of the continental collision that formed the Carpathian arc starting in early–middle Miocene time with attendant crustal stretching and thinning (Sclater et al., 1980). Normal faulting during this lithospheric extension led to the development of smaller troughs such as the Makó trough or smaller basins such as the Békés basin (Figure 35.1) (Horvath and Royden, 1981). Each of these small, deep troughs or basins is separated by basement highs. Based on present-day structural contours on the base of the lower Miocene rocks (top of the basement rocks), the basin fill in the Makó trough is over 7 km thick and in the Békés basin over 6 km thick (see the southern half of map in Figure 35.1). Between the Békés basin and the Makó trough, Tertiary–Quaternary sedimentary rocks thin (about 2000 m or less thick) over the top of the Battonya high (Figure 35.1).

Displacement along basement faults occurred before and during deposition of the unconformity-bounded lower–middle Miocene rocks (Figure 35.2). The structural contour map and the cross section show both periods of fault movement. Where the 4000-m contour lines intersect the basement fault at the western end of section A–A', no offset of the contours are indicated on the map,

Table 35.1. Gas, Condensate, and Oil Accumulations of the Tótkomlós–Szolnok(.) Petroleum System[a]

Map No.	Field or Well Name	Year Disc'd	Producing Rock Unit	Reservoir Lithology	Gas Type	Oil Gravity (API)	Prod. or Test Depth (m)
1.	Battonya	1959	Pz, L Pan, U Pan	ml, ss, cgl	T, CO_2	42	1000
2.	Battonya-E	–	L Pan	ml	M	43	700–1100
3.	Békés	–	Szolnok Fm	ss	T, CO_2, M	42	2500–3000
4.	Berettyószentmárton	–	–	–	CO_2, M	–	2200–2500
5.	Biharkeresztes	–	br	mt	T, CO_2	32	1500–1700
6.	Biharugra	–	Mz	ls	T, CO_2	44	2300
7.	Csanádapaca	1982	L Pan	ml	T, CO_2	35	1800–2000
8.	Dévaványa		PreC–Mio	varies	T	35–44	1900–2500
9.	Doboz-1	–	–	–	T, CO_2	–	4300–4600
10.	Endröd	–	Pz – L Pan	mt, ml	T	29–57	2100–2600
11.	Endröd-Észak	–	PreC	mt	T, M	29–36	1000–2900
12.	Földes	–	–	–	T	–	2100–2700
13.	Furta	–	–	–	T, CO_2	–	2300
14.	Füzesgyarmat	–	Mio	–	T, CO_2	–	1800–1900
15.	Gyoma	–	L Pan	mt	T	35	3100
16.	Kevermes	–	–	–	T, CO_2	–	1700
17.	Komádi	–	PreC–L Pan	mt, ml, ss	T	26–47	1800–3100
18.	Körösladány	–	–	mt	T	48	2600–2900
19.	Köröstarcsa	–	Mio–L Pan	ml	T, CO_2	42	3300–3400
20	Makó-1	–	Mio–L Pan	ml	T	46	4100–4900
21.	Martfü	–	–	–	T	–	1700–2100
22.	Mezögyán	–	Mio	cgl, ss	T	32	2300
23.	Mesöpeterd	–	–	–	T	41	2100–2800
24.	Mezösas	–	PreC	mt	T	40	2300–2800
25.	MezötúrC-3	–	Mio–L Pan	cgl, ml	T	32	2300–2900
26.	Nagyszénás	–	–	–	T	–	2900–3100
27.	Orosháza	–	–	–	C	–	2500–2800
28.	Orosháza-DNY	–	–	–	C	–	2500–2600
29.	Öscöd	–	–	–	T	–	2200
30.	Örménykut	–	Szolnok Fm	ss	T	46	2100–3100
31.	Pusztaföldvár	1959	br–U Pan	varies	T, CO_2	27–30	1600–1800
32.	Pusztaszöllös	1961	Mz–U Pan	ls, dol, ss	T, M	30	1500–1800
33.	Püspökladány	–	–	–	T	–	200–2100
34.	Sáránd	–	–	–	T	–	2000
35.	Sarkadkeresztúr	1978	PreC–L Pan	mt, ss	T	42–51	2500–3000
36..	Szaruas	–	Szolnok Fm	–	T, CO_2	24–55	2200–2400
37.	Szeghalom	–	PreC	mt	T	31–46	1800–2200
38.	Szeghalom-E	–	PreC–Mio	mt	T	45	1700–2300
39.	Tótkomlós	–	Tr–L Pan	dol, ml	CO_2, M	31–44	960–1900
40.	Végegyháza-NY	–	–	–	T, C	–	1400–1500
41.	Hajduszoboszló	–	–	–	T, M	–	900–1200

[a]Map numbers correspond to locations on Figure 35.1. Symbols: br, basement rock; cgl, conglomerate; dol, dolomite; L Pan, lower Pannonian; ls, limestone; Mio, pre-Pannonian Miocene; ml, marls; mt, metamorphic; M, microbial gas; Mz, undifferentiated Mesozoic; PreC, Precambrian; Pz, Paleozoic; ss, sandstone; T, thermally derived hydrocarbon gas; Tr, Triassic; U Pan, upper Pannonian.

but at the eastern end of A–A', the 4000-m basement contour is offset (Figure 35.1b). Rock units vary in thickness within the lower–middle Miocene (section A–A', Figure 35.2) from 1200 m on the east near the Doboz-1 well to only several meters thick near the Nagyszenas-2. Based on this, and the broken structural contour lines on the map (Figure 35.1b), pre-Miocene movement of basement faults are suspected. Movement of these same basement faults prior to late Miocene time is also shown on section A–A', as the faults do not displace late Miocene and younger sedimentary rocks. However, the upper Miocene "basal clay–marl and marl" (Tótkomlós+ Formation, unit 1 in Figure 35.3) also varies in thickness from a few meters in the Nagyszénas-2 well to about 500 m between the Doboz-1 and Sarkad-keresztúr-4 wells. This interpretation of fault movement and variations in sedimentary rock thickness indicate that early–middle Miocene rocks filled in a block-faulted terrain of high relief, while late Miocene and younger rocks were deposited over lower but persistent relief.

Table 35.2. Oil and Gas Production in Southeastern Hungary

	Oil	
	In–place (million t)	Production to 1985 (million t)
	35.3	3.4
	Gas	
Vol. of Combustible Gas (average %)	(million m³)	(milion m³)
85	40,285	11,175
60	3,399	2,405
40	14,670	4,740
20	158	1
5	7,654	4
Totals	66,166	18,325

Continuous deposition occurred from late Miocene (end of Sarmatian) to Pliocene time and is referred to as the Pannonian rock sequence (Juhász, 1991). These sediments onlapped and buried pre-late Miocene undulating hills, which locally had more than 1000 m of topographic relief. Differential compaction of overlapping sediments is interpreted to be the mechanism that caused the broad anticlines to form over these pre-late Miocene hills.

Much of the gas, condensate, and oil production from pre-Miocene rocks is from Precambrian to Paleozoic igneous and metamorphic rocks that are highly fractured owing to extensional tectonics and associated faulting during development of the Pannonian basin. These fractured rocks provide not only suitable reservoir properties but also serve as conduits for secondary migration of hydrocarbons from the thermally mature source rocks (Szalay, 1988; Clayton et al., in press; Spencer et al., in press). For example, at the east end of section A–A', the source rock interval is thin in the Sarkadkeresztúr-4 well but is up to 400 m thick in the Doboz-1 well. This interval is thermally mature in both wells, and gas and condensate were recovered from the underlying basement rocks. These hydrocarbons are interpreted to have migrated updip through the pre–upper Miocene rocks (Figure 35.2).

High heat flow associated with crustal thinning (up to about 120 mW/m²) during development of the Pannonian basin (Dövény and Horváth, 1988) is an important element in the thermal maturation of relatively young (Miocene–Pliocene) source rocks in southeastern Hungary, as well as in other parts of the Pannonian basin.

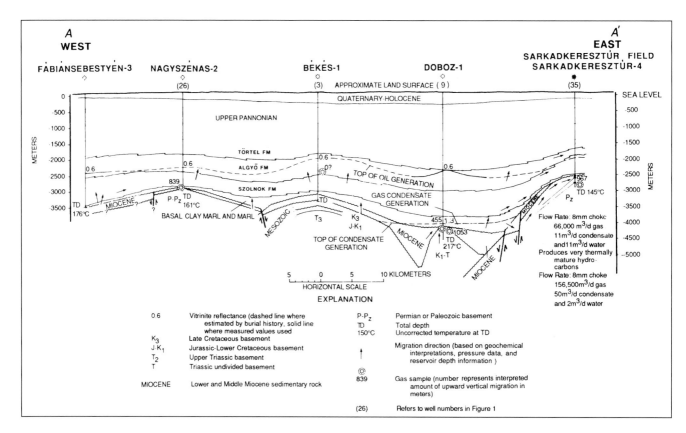

Figure 35.2. West–east cross section A–A' across Békés basin (see Figure 35. 1 for location). The Tótkomlós–Szolnok(.) petroleum system consists of fractured basement reservoir rocks including lower–middle Miocene units unconformably overlain by basal clay–marl and marl source rocks (Tótkomlós Formation). Sandstone reservoirs are in the Szolnok Formation. Overburden rocks include sequences from the Szolnok Formation up to the Holocene.

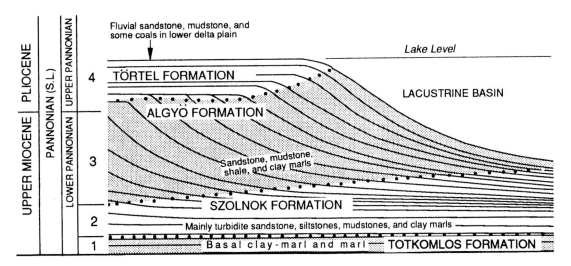

Figure 35.3. Typical Pannonian prograding lacustrine deltaic sequence showing the time-transgressive character of deposition. The main petroleum system source rocks are the basal clay–marl and marl (unit 1 in Table 35.3) at the base of the lower Pannonian. The Törtel and younger rocks are composed predominantly of sandstone and do not contain good seals. Some bacterial gas occurs in shallow water wells in youngest Pliocene and Quaternary strata. The contact between the Törtel and Algyö formations varies in age from late Miocene to Pliocene. (Modified from Molenaar et al., in press.)

Stratigraphy

The Pannonian basin is a young (17–10 Ma) extensional basin containing more than 7000 m of Miocene–Holocene sedimentary fill. The stratigraphic section can be divided into four intervals as follows: (1) pre-Miocene basement rocks; (2) lower–middle Miocene shallow marine bioclastic and shale or marl sedimentary rocks; (3) upper Miocene–Pliocene lacustrine and fluvial–terrestrial rocks of the Pannonian basin; and (4) Quaternary–Holocene terrestrial sedimentary rocks.

The pre-Miocene basement rocks are structurally and lithologically complex and include Proterozoic and Paleozoic metamorphic and metasedimentary rocks as well as Mesozoic sedimentary rocks (Dank and Kókai, 1969). Unconformably overlying thes basement rocks are the lower–middle Miocene rocks.

During extensional tectonics that formed the Pannonian basin from 17 to 10 Ma, the block faulted terrain was the site of shallow marine deposition. A light-colored bioclastic (primarily rudistid debris) material was deposited in a high-energy, wave- and current-dominated, shallow marine enviroment (Juhász, 1991; Phillips et al., in press). Where this unit thickens into the grabens, it consists of dark-colored, organic-rich marine sediments. Based on section A–A', the thickness is variable and ranges from a few meters to 1300 m. Although this marine unit is displaced by basement faults, an apparent gradational contact (shown as an unconformity on Figure 35.2) occurs in places with the overlying lacustrine basal clay–marl and marl source rocks, the first of the Pannonian basin fill. As discussed later, the major source rocks in this petroleum system are shales, clay–marls, and marls of the middle Miocene sequence and lower Pannonian Tótkomlós Formation.

The major portion of the Pannonian basin fill consists of upper Miocene–Pliocene sedimentary rocks (Figure

35.3), which form the lower–upper Pannonian sequence. According to Juhász (1991) and Mattick et al. (in press), infilling of the basin resulted from a major cycle of deltaic sedimentation starting in Sarmatian (12 Ma) or earliest Pannonian time, with water depths in this large freshwater lake up to 1000 m. The lowermost unit is the middle–upper Miocene basal clay–marl and marl source rocks (that is, pre-Pannonian Miocene to lower Pannonian) deposited into an anoxic environment that was followed by extensive basin filling by many deltas prograding into and across the lake basin. This deposition was followed by marsh and fluvial conditions. Figure 35.3 shows the prograding and time-transgressive nature of these delta plain to basinal lacustrine deposits.

The prograding Pannonian basin fill can be divided into four stratigraphic units based on their interpreted depositional environments, of which the lowermost three are lacustrine (lower Pannonian) and the fourth is fluvial–terrestrial (upper Pannonian) (Phillips et al., in press). The first or lowermost unit, the basal clay–marl and marl source rocks, ranges from a few meters up to 500 m thick (Figure 35.2) and has numerous stratigraphic names (Tótkomlós Lime Marl Formation, Dorozsma Marl Formation, Vásárhely Marl Formation, and Nagykörü Clay Marl Formation) assigned to it (Figure 3 in Phillips et al., in press). The underlying middle Miocene shale and marl contains the richest source rocks in the basin (TOC as high as 5.0 wt. %). Source rocks of the lower Pannonian sequence (Tótkomlós Formation) and the overlying Szolnok Formation have slightly lower TOC contents (as high as about 2.0 wt. %) and are probably quantitatively less important than the pre-Pannonian rocks of middle Miocene age. The pre-Pannonian (middle Miocene) rocks are difficult to distinguish from lowermost Pannonian strata of the Tótkomlós Formation by lithology or seismic stratigraphy. Because the Tótkomlós Formation contains some source rocks

Table 35.3. Depositional Environment, Depositional Sequence, and Formation Name of Pannonian Rock Units Shown on Figure 35.3

No.	Depositional Environment	Depositional Sequence	Lithologic Description	Formation Name
4	Fluvial–terrestrial	Delta plain	Fluvial sandstone, mudstone, and some coals in lower delta plain	Törtel Formation
3	Lacustrine	Delta slope	Sandstone, mudstone, shale, and clay marls	Algyö Formation
2	Lacustrine	Prodelta	Mainly turbidite sandstone, siltstone, mudstones, and clay marls	Szolnok Formation
1	Lacustrine	Basinal	Basal clay–marl and marl source rock	Tótkomlós Formation

and because it is difficult to distinguish between the middle Miocene and Pannonnian source rocks, Tótkomlós is arbitrarily chosen for convenience as part of the name of this petroleum system. It should be emphasized, however, that the source rocks occur over a much broader depth and age interval, as noted earlier.

The second unit overlying this basal rock unit is the prodeltaic Szolnok Formation, which ranges in thickness on section A–A' from 400 to 800 m and contains numerous turbidite sandstones that are petroleum reservoir rocks. The third unit is the Algyö Formation, which is a deltaic slope facies that overlies the prodeltaic facies and ranges in thickness from 200 to 600 m. Finally, the fourth and uppermost Pannonian rock unit comprises the fluviodeltaic rocks deposited on a delta plain and fluvial flood plain (Phillips et al., in press). The Törtel Formation is a potential sandstone reservoir rocks and is in the basal few hundred meters of this rock unit. The total thickness of this uppermost unit varies in thickness from 1700 to 2000 m. Table 35.3 and Figure 35.3 show the stratigraphic relationships of these four units.

The last sequence of sedimentary rocks is the Quaternary–Holocene terrestrial sedimentary rocks that overlies the Pannonian basin fill. These youngest rocks are relatively thin and seldom exceed 400 m in thickness.

TÓTKÓMLÓS–SZOLNOK(.) PETROLEUM SYSTEM

Essential Elements

Source Rocks

Certain parts of the stratigraphic section in southeastern Hungary can be eliminated as potential source rocks on the basis of lithology, depositional environment, and thermal history. The pre-Miocene basement rocks are mostly metamorphic and therefore not considered as possible source rocks for the hydrocarbons in the area. The lower Miocene rocks can be eliminated as they are light-colored bioclastic limestones. Within the Pannonian rock units, the fluviodeltaic rocks of Pliocene age, the only potential source rocks for hydrocarbons are coal beds and some associated coaly shales; in fact, these may be the source rocks for the microbial gas in the upper Pannonian rock units (Clayton et al., 1990). However, these rock units, along with the Quaternary–Holocene units, can be eliminated as source rocks for thermal gas

and oil based on their low levels of thermal maturity (Figure 35.2). The most likely stratigraphic interval that contains oil- and gas-prone source rocks is the middle (pre-Pannonian) to upper Miocene (lower Pannonian) sequence.

The lower Pannonian sequence consists of genetically related rocks deposited in a relatively freshwater lake in late Miocene time. This lake started out at the size of the Pannonian basin, which covered most of Hungary and adjacent countries. Southeastern Hungary was at the most distal area to prograding deltas that were gradually filling in the lake basin. Here, the basal clay–marl and marl unit, the Tótkomlós Formation, was deposited above the middle Miocene rocks, which included both bioclastic (organic-lean) and clastic (organic-rich shale and marl) rocks. The middle Miocene unit and the Tótkomlós Formation contain as much as 5.0 and 2.0 wt. % TOC, respectively, and mostly type III kerogen, with secondary amounts of type II kerogen according to Rock-Eval pyrolysis results. Micropaleontology indicates that the organic-rich rocks contain few fossils or evidence of bioturbation, suggesting that this lake bottom was anoxic most of the time. The provenance of the organic matter was predominantly from inflowing streams (terrestrial). A few of the rocks contain higher hydrogen (type II) organic matter, although in much smaller amounts than the type III organic matter. This thick sequence, which includes middle Miocene rocks and upper Miocene basal clay–marl and marl (lower Pannonian, Tótkomlós Formation), is the major source rock sequence for the hydrocarbons (mostly gas) in this area (Figures 35.3 and 35.4).

Progressing up through the lower Pannonian prodeltaic and deltaic slope facies, we encounter other thinner source rocks (e.g., in the Szolnok Formation). These are considered minor source rocks because they were deposited in closer proximity to the delta, where sediment dilution was a factor and bioturbation was more prevalent. These source rocks are expected to be more discontinuous and thinner (Figure 35.4) and are not believed to have generated and expelled significant quantities of oil or gas.

Because this study was restricted to southeastern Hungary, the geographic extent of the major source rocks (middle Miocene and Tótkomlós Formation) is not well documented, and the geographic extent of this petroleum system has not been determined at the present time. Source rocks of Miocene age are known in other parts of Hungary, such as in the Zala basin of

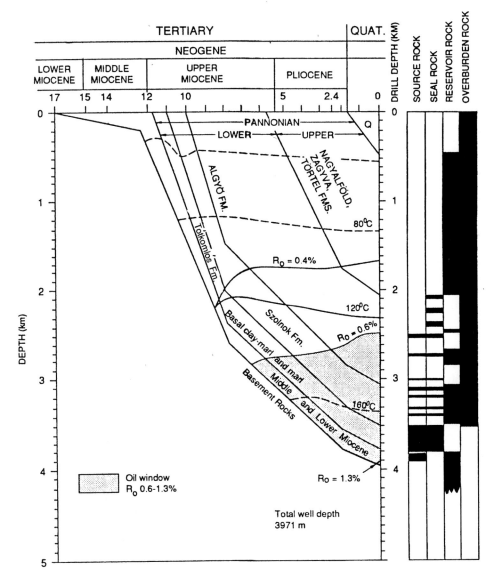

Figure 35.4. Burial history chart of basement to Pliocene rocks. Owing to the time-transgressive character of the Pannonian, the age of any given facies varies slightly in different parts of the basin. Vitrinite reflectance values are based on present-day measurements and extrapolated back through time. The essential elements of the Tótkomlós–Szolnok(.) petroleum system are shown on the right. (This figure is substantially modified from a burial curve of Horvath et al., 1986.)

western Hungary (Clayton and Koncz, 1994), but geologic and geochemical data presently available are insufficient to show that the same petroleum system extends across this broad area.

Reservoir Rocks and Accumulations

The pre-Miocene basement and lower–middle Miocene are reservoir rocks. In most cases, these reservoirs are characterized by fracture permeability and secondary porosity. Precambrian rocks also form reservoirs in seven fields (Table 35.1). Fractured Paleozoic metasedimentary rocks with some igneous rocks are reservoir rocks in two fields, and fractured Mesozoic carbonates form reservoirs in the Biharugra and Tótkomlós fields. Seven fields produce from lower–middle Miocene bioclastic carbonate reservoir rocks. The two most common pre–upper Miocene reservoir rocks are Precambrian and lower–middle Miocene.

The remainder of the reservoir rocks are within the upper Miocene and Pliocene Pannonian units. Fifteen fields have reservoir rocks in the lower Pannonian and

three fields have upper Pannonian reservoir rocks. In two fields, discontinuous lower Pannonian conglomerate reservoir rocks occur in the basement and are locally present beneath the basal clay–marl and marl. Thick (10–50 m) sandstones are present in the Szolnok Formation (Phillips et al., in press). D. L. Gautier (pers. comm., 1988) observed that most Pannonian sandstones in the Szolnok and Algyö formations are litharenites. The sandstones may have up to 25% porosity at 2250 m depth but average no more than 5% porosity at 3400 m; however, porosities as high as 11% at 3400 m were observed in one core sample.

Dank (1985) notes that most of the oil and gas fields produce from structural closures. As of about 1985, approximately 3.4 million t of oil and 18.3 billion m^3 of gas have been produced from more than 41 fields discovered in southeastern Hungary. Data for individual fields are not publicly available so only general observations are possible here. Of these 41 fields (Table 35.1), 35 contain thermally derived hydrocarbon gas, 7 contain microbial gas, and 13 contain CO_2 in concentrations over 50% (Clayton et al., 1990). If an API gravity of 40° is used to distinguish between oil (<40°) and condensate (≥40°), then 7 fields contain oil, 7 contain oil and condensate, and 11 contain condensate.

Gas–oil ratios (GORs) can be used to determine whether southeastern Hungary is predominantly an oil, condensate, or gas province. Generally, GORs less than 200 (m³/m³) in produced hydrocarbons are characteristic of oil provinces, and GORs greater than 3600 (m³/m³) indicate a gas province. GORs in between these two values are condensate provinces. Since cumulative hydrocarbon gas production from this area is 18.3 billion m³ and oil production is 3.4 million t or 3.96 million m³ (Table 35.2), the GOR is 4600. Therefore, southeastern Hungary is a gas province.

Most of the hydrocarbon accumulations are in lower Pannonian rocks (Table 35.1). Unfortunately, the name of the rock units that act as reservoir rocks for most of these accumulations is undesignated. Lack of sandstone in the source rocks and deltaic slope rocks (Phillips et al., in press) suggests unfavorable reservoir facies. In contrast, the sandstone-rich turbidites of the prodelta (Phillips et al., in press) could provide favorable reservoirs, especially since they are in close proximity to the source rocks. Thus, the stratigraphic name of the prodeltaic rocks, the Szolnok Formation, is used as the reservoir rock name in this petroleum system. It is worth noting that on some basement highs in the basin, sandstones are present in the Szolnok Formation overlying unconformities and are apparently derived from reworking of lower Pannonian sandstones and conglomerates.

Seal Rocks

The only regional seal rocks are the basal clay–marl and marl source rocks that were important to the seven hydrocarbon accumulations in the Precambrian reservoir rocks and the seven in the lower–middle Miocene mentioned earlier. The other accumulations in the lower Pannonian require secondary seals. Secondary seals can be interpreted where the reservoir rocks are within traps or where oil and gas has accumulated. As mentioned earlier, 15 oil fields or traps produce from lower Pannonian reservoir rocks.

Carbon dioxide is present in a number of fields and, where present, occurs in highest concentrations in basement rocks. Spencer et al. (in press) compiled core-measured horizontal and vertical permeabilities of shale and clay–marl. They found that these fine-grained rocks become good barriers to vertical migration at depths of 2000 m and deeper and help trap CO_2 of deep basement origin.

Overburden Rocks

The overburden rocks are those sedimentary rocks that overlie the source rocks, and if they get thick enough, thermally mature the source rocks. The overburden rocks in southeastern Hungary are upper Miocene–Holocene sedimentary rocks (Figures 35.2 and 35.4). Figure 35.4 shows a burial curve for a typical moderately deep well in the Békés basin (Hunya-1 drill hole, Figure 35.1b). The basal Pannonian clay–marl and marl source rocks began the main pulse of oil generation (0.6% R_o) about 6 Ma. The Tótkomlós Formation source rocks and Szolnok Formation reservoir rocks (turbidite sandstones) entered the oil window about 5 Ma.

The burial history chart was constructed from core data and other well data from the Hunya-1 drill hole located just north of section A–A′ (Figure 35.1b). The pre–upper Miocene rocks penetrated in this well are of no consequence to the thermal maturity of the overlying basal clay–marl and marl source rocks (Tótkomlós Formation). The source rocks were about 350 m thick when they were deposited 11.7–11 Ma. Deposition of the overburden rocks followed from 11 Ma to the present day. If we use 0.6 % R_o as the top of the oil window, the base of the source rocks entered the oil window slightly before 6 Ma. At this location, the source rocks never reached the gas window (1.35 % R_o).

Processes

Traps

The formation of hydrocarbon traps began when the source rocks were deposited because the source rocks formed a seal for the pre–upper Miocene basement rocks. These structural traps persist to the present day. Combinations traps formed in the early Pannonian during deposition over basement topographic highs. The chronology of formation of these traps is shown on the Tótkomlós–Szolnok petroleum system events chart in Figure 35.5).

Migration and Accumulation

Migration occurred both laterally and vertically. Studies of oils by Clayton et al. (in press) show that some oils have migrated vertically more than 3000 m. Gas analyses by Clayton et al. (1990) indicate that gas has migrated vertically as much as 3500 m. Lateral migration distances of 1–2 km for oil seem likely based on relationships of geochemical, stratigraphic, structural, and pressure data (Figure 35.2). Gas migration was at least this far vertically and laterally.

The main migration routes include fractured basement rocks, lower–middle Miocene units, and Pannonian sandstones and conglomerates. The Szolnok Formation contains many thick, permeable sandstones that have acted as carrier beds. Local (short distance) migration seems to have occurred in Algyö Formation sandstones.

Abnormally high pressure is present at depths deeper than about 2500 m throughout most of the basin (Spencer et al., in press). The shallowest abnormally high pressure is found at about 1800 m in several wells. Figure 35.6 shows pressure versus depth for wells in the southeastern part of Hungary. These data are from the Békés and adjacent provinces. Spencer et al. (in press) has interpreted that the shallow (1800–2500 m) overpressures were caused by undercompaction (incomplete sediment dewatering) and that the overpressuring deeper than 2500 m was most likely caused by presently active hydrocarbon generation (mostly gas) and generation of

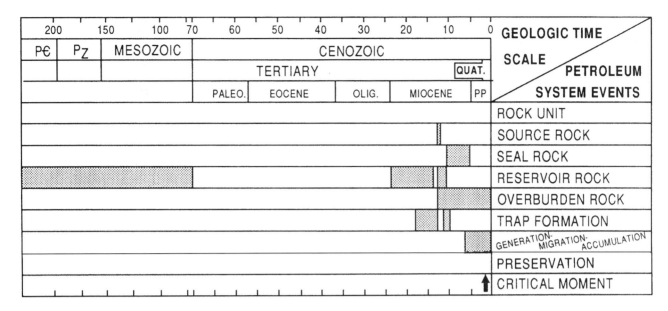

Figure 35.5. Events chart for the Tótkomlós–Szolnok(.) petroleum system. PP, Pliocene and Pleistocene (includes Holocene).

CO_2 from thermal destruction of carbonates during metamorphism of Paleozoic sedimentary rocks deep in the basement. Overpressuring in deep rocks provides a mechanism for expulsion of hydrocarbons from source rocks into carrier beds, where they could migrate by pressure differential in the lower permeability rocks and by bouyancy in very permeable reservoirs.

Level of Certainty

The level of certainty for a petroleum system expresses the degree to which the available geologic and geochemical data support the hypothesis that hydrocarbons in the major reservoir rocks orginated from the designated source rocks. We conclude that the thermal gas and associated oil and condensate all originated from the same middle Miocene and Tótkomlós Formation source rock sequence, although gas–source rock correlations are untested. This source rock sequence contains several organic-rich sequences separated by organic-lean rocks.

With the data presently available, it is not possible to determine the exact thicknesses or areal extent of any individual organic-rich source rock stratum contained within the middle Miocene and Tótkomlós Formation sequence. Therefore, the source rocks are indicated schematically in Figure 35.4 by a series of individual units of uncertain thickness ranging in age from the latest middle Miocene to late Miocene (Szolnok Formation). Geochemical characterization of the oils produced from the basin has shown that at least two genetically distinct oil types are present and that these oil types can be correlated with extracts obtained from organic-rich rocks within the source rocks interval (Clayton et al., in press). However, the source rocks have been cored in only a few wells, and very few wells have been drilled in the central part of the basin. Therefore, it is unknown to what extent the organic matter varies in content and composition within any given narrow stratigraphic interval across the basin. This problem is exacerbated by the fact that the rocks are time-transgressive and intertonguing of various lithologies occurs, which precludes stratigraphic correlations at the level of thin (few meters thick) organic-rich intervals that occur within the thicker sequence. Accordingly, it is unclear to what degree minor variations in oil composition result from organic matter variation (or thermal maturity differences) within a single stratigraphic unit or are caused by contribution of oil from more than one stratigraphic unit within the thick source rock sequence.

The oil–source rock correlations are reasonably well established, at least to the extent that organic-rich rocks of the middle Miocene and Tótkomlós Formation correlate with oils produced in the basin (Clayton et al., in press). However, correlations between source rocks and the gases have not been unequivocally established. Furthermore, although there is sufficient evidence that organic-rich rocks of middle Miocene age and within the Tótkomlós Formation are the source of the oils, genetic relationships among *individual, thin source rock units* within the middle Miocene and Tótkomlós Formation are uncertain. Therefore, the level of certainty for the Tótkomlós–Szolnok (.) petroleum system is hypothetical.

This discussion illustrates some of the difficulties of applying the petroleum system concept. First, the level of detail, or "resolution," with which oil–source rock relationships are determined from geochemical and geologic studies may vary considerably. Therefore, the level of certainty that is assigned to the petroleum system depends entirely on the scale used to study the system. For example, in southeastern Hungary, relatively few samples of Miocene or Pliocene shale and marl were cored and are available for analysis, even though these units are thick and widespread in the basin. Very few

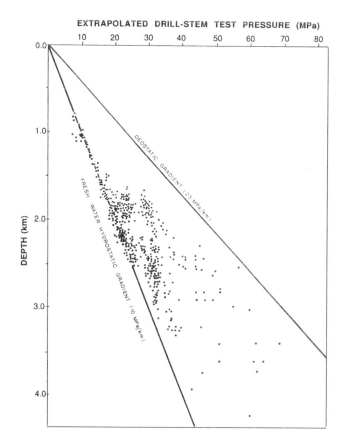

EXTRAPOLATED DRILL-STEM TEST PRESSURE (MPa)

Figure 35.6. Reservoir pressure (MPa) versus depth of burial for the southeastern part of the Great Hungarian Plain, including the Békés basin.

single source rock interval containing several organic facies, provides valuable insight into petroleum generation and migration in the province and is of considerable importance in exploration. For example, currently very little exploration has been directed toward stratigraphic traps in basinward, off-structure positions, and our studies indicate a high potential for oil and gas trapped on the flanks of the structural highs bordering the basin.

Petroleum System Name

The name of this petroleum system is the Tótkomlós–Szolnok(.) system. The source rock name is to be chosen from numerous stratigraphic names from the same interval, but Tótkomlós was chosen because much of the type III kerogen is contained within this unit. The more organic-rich middle Miocene rocks do not have a commonly recognized stratgraphic name. Based on geologic and geochemical data presently avaliable, the thin, discontinuous source rocks overlying the Tótkomlós are not considered to contribute substantially to this petroleum system.

The reservoir rock name, Szolnok Formation, was chosen because most of the fields produce from lower Pannonian rock units (Table 35.1) and because most of the sandstone is within the prodeltaic unit, which is the depositional environment of this unit. If the volumetric data for all of the fields in this petroleum system become available and it is found that more hydrocarbon is in a different stratigraphic interval, then the reservoir rock name will have to be revised.

Stratigraphic and Geographic Extent

The stratigraphic extent of the Tótkomlós–Szolnok system is quite specific, but the geographic extent is not well known. Because the overburden rocks are at maximum burial depth over most of the area, the stratigraphic extent of this system is measured from the surface to the base of the source rocks or where hydrocarbon accumulations are present within the basement rocks; it is at the base of the hydrocarbon column or just below the migration path (Figure 35.2).

The geographic extent is unknown because this petroleum system goes beyond the area of study. The geographic extent of a petroleum system is controlled by the area of active source rocks and the distribution (in reservoirs) of hydrocarbons that have been expelled from those active source rocks. The Tótkomlós–Szolnok system in southeastern Hungary extends beyond this area because the source rocks apparently blanket the entire area and are within the oil window or, if deep enough, the gas window as its burial depth is between 3000 and 4000 m (Figures 35.2 and 35.4). In other words, the source rocks are actively generating hydrocarbons throughout southeastern Hungary, so it is logical to assume that the petroleum system extends beyond this area. To determine the actual size of this petroleum system, the thermal maturity and extent of the source rocks must be mapped and the outermost edge of the migrating hydrocarbons must be identified. This may include the entire Pannonian basin fill.

wells have been drilled in the deeper parts of the basin, so limited numbers of source rock samples are available in the areas where the source rock interval is the thickest.

Moreover, petroleum exploration in the basin is aided by a general understanding of the effective source rock distribution. More detailed oil–source rock correlations between oils and each individual organic-rich stratum within the Neogene source rock sequence are not critical, unless a much more detailed exploration approach is undertaken in which variations in organic richness and expulsion efficiencies on a local scale are considered in prospect evaluations. Accordingly, source rock data have come from samples taken at relatively few locations in the province and at fairly widely separated depth intervals in any given well (Clayton et al., in press). We can, however, assign a high degree of certainty to our conclusion that the Miocene and Pliocene rocks are the source of most of the basin's oil and gas (Clayton et al., in press). However, if we wish to establish more specific correlations between source rocks and individual oil subtypes, the level of certainty decreases to only hypothetical.

As a practical matter, the scale used to define a petroleum system depends on the application. In the case of southeastern Hungary, an understanding of the petroleum system previously defined, in which the Miocene–Pliocene source rock sequence is taken as a

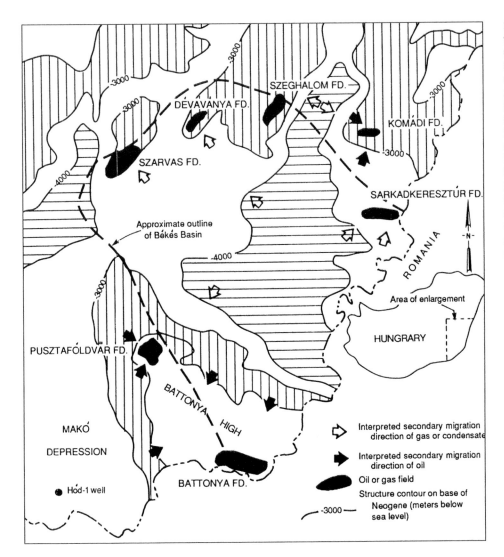

Figure 35.7. Generalized structural contour map on the base of Neogene rocks (datum is sea level). Vertical hatchured area shows interpreted generation zone of least mature oils from Miocene source rocks (0.35–0.60% R_o). Horizontal hatchures indicate generation depths of more mature oils. Unhatchured areas represent a transition between these two maturity zones. Solid arrows indicate migration directions for oil. Open arrows indicate migration of condensate and gas. (From Clayton et al., in press.)

For example, reservoirs on structural highs separating two subbasins (e.g., the Battonya structure forming the boundary between the Békés basin and Makó trough, Figure 35.1a) are charged from two directions (Figure 35.7) (see Sajgó, 1984). Because the active source rocks are present in both the Makó trough and Békés basin, the reservoirs producing on the west side and top of the Battonya high were charged by the active source rocks in the Makó trough or even from the south in the Romanian part of the Pannonian basin (Figure 35.1b). Reservoir rocks located on the Békés basin side of the Battonya arch (or other structural highs located along the margins of the Békés basin) could not have been charged by source rocks other than those located within the Békés basin. Most of the fields in the study area were likely charged from source rocks within the Békés basin because the main phase of oil generation and expulsion commenced about 6–7 Ma, after the structural and topographic development of the Békés basin. This would preclude migration of oil or gas from outside the area except along structurally high positions separating subbasins.

SUMMARY

Many fields considered to be structurally controlled are actually combination (structural–stratigraphic) traps. A few deep (>4000 m) test wells have been drilled with mixed success into deep, seismically mapped closures. Areas of potential stratigraphic and structural–stratigraphic traps are relatively unexplored on the flanks of the basement highs. These traps should have good potential for economic resources of hydrocarbons. Most will probably be found at depths of >3000 m.

The Tótkomlós–Szolnok petroleum system in the Békés basin is different from petroleum systems in other areas in that fractured basement (pre-Pannonian age) rocks play a major role. The basement rocks are conduits for regional hydrocarbon migration and are some of the most important reservoir rocks in the system. Many of the basement rocks possess both solution porosity and fracture porosity.

The basement rocks in the structurally low areas are covered by more than 6000 m of lower–middle Miocene rocks as well as upper Miocene–Pliocene lacustrine sediments that include turbidite, delta slope, delta front, delta plain, and fluvial deposits.

The pre–upper Miocene surface had locally more than 3000 m of pre-Pannonian topographic relief. These hills or highs were inundated by fluviolacustrine deposits. Facies changes, differential compaction, and some post-depositional structural movement formed the structural and structural–stratigraphic closures that control most of the presently discovered accumulations (Figure 35.1b). Most of these accumulations produce from depths of 1000–3000 m.

Gas is the dominant hydrocarbon, but many oil and gas condensate fields have been found. Neogene shales and clay marls are the only source beds for the hydrocarbons. Overpressuring, caused by several mechanisms, occurs throughout the basin at depths greater than 2500 m. Vertical migration of hydrocarbons exceeds 3000 m in some areas, and most of the production in the basin is from rocks that never reached a thermal maturity of 0.6% R_o. Some short-distance migration of low-maturity oils occurs locally.

Future exploration of this petroleum system will likely concentrate on stratigraphic traps and structural–stratigraphic traps on the flanks of the basement highs. Much of the system is relatively unexplored at depths greater than 3500 m.

References Cited

Clayton, J. L., and I. Koncz, 1994, Petroleum geochemistry of the Zala basin, Hungary: AAPG Bulletin.

Clayton, J. L., C. W. Spencer, I. Koncz, and A. Szalay, 1990, Origin and migration of hydrocarbon gases and carbon dioxide, Békés basin, southeastern Hungary: Organic Geochemistry, v. 15, p. 233–247.

Clayton, J. L., I. Koncz, J. D. King, and E. Tatar, in press, Generation and migration of oil in the Békés basin, southeastern Hungary, *in* P. G. Teleki, R. E. Mattick, and J. Kókai, eds., The Békés basin, a study in basin analysis: USGS Professional Paper.

Dank, V. E., 1985, Hydrocarbon exploration in Hungary: VIIIth RCMNS Congress, Neogene Mineral Resources in the Carpathian Basin, Budapest, p. 107–213.

Dank, V. E., 1988, Petroleum geology of the Pannonian basin, Hungary: an overview, *in* L. H. Royden and F. Horváth, eds., The Pannonian basin—a study in basin evolution: AAPG Memoir 45, p. 319–331.

Dank, V. E., and J. Kókai, 1969, Oil and gas exploration in Hungary, *in* P. Hepple, ed., The Exploration for Petroleum in Europe and North Africa: London, Institute of Petroleum, p. 131–145.

Dövényi, P., and F. Horváth, 1988, A review of temperature, thermal conductivity, and heat flow data from the Pannonian basin, *in* L. H. Royden and F. Horváth, eds., The Pannonian basin—a study in basin evolution: AAPG Memoir 45, p. 195–233.

Horváth, F., and L. Royden, 1981, Mechanism for the formation of the intra-Carpathian basins: a review: Earth Evolutionary Science, v. 1, n. 3-4, p. 307–316.

Horvath, F., P. Dövényi, A. Szalay, and L. H. Royden, 1986, Subsidence, thermal, and maturation history of the Great Hungarian Plain, *in* L. H. Royden and F. Horvath, eds., The Pannonian basin—a study in basin evolution: AAPG Memoir 45, p. 355–372.

Juhász, Gy., 1991, Lithostratigraphical and sedimentological framework of the Pannonian sedimentary sequence in the Hungarian Plain (Alföld), Eastern Hungary: Acta Geologica Hungarica, v. 34, p. 53–72.

Mattick, R. E., J. Rumpler, B. Szanyi, G. Márton, and A. Ujfalusy, in press, Subtle traps interpreted from seismic stratigraphy, Békés basin, *in* P. G. Teleki, R. E. Mattick, and J. Kókai, eds., The Békés basin, a study in basin analysis: USGS Professional Paper.

Molenaar, C. M., I. Gajdas, A. Kovács, B. Szanyi, and I. Révész, in press, Stratigraphic framework and sandstone facies distribution of the Pannonian sequence, Békés basin, *in* P. G. Teleki, R. E. Mattick, and J. Kókai, eds., The Békés basin, a study in basin analysis: USGS Professional Paper.

Phillips, R. L., I. Révész, and I. Bérczi, in press, lower Pannonian deltaic-lacustrine processes and sedimentation, *in* P. G. Teleki, R. E. Mattick, and J. Kókai, eds., The Békés basin, a study in basin analysis: USGS Professional Paper.

Sajgó, Cs., 1984, Organic geochemistry of crude oils from southeastern Hungary, *in* P. A. Schenck and J. W. de Leeuw, eds., Advances in Organic Geochemistry 1983: Organic Geochemistry, v. 6, p. 569–578.

Sclater, J. G., L. Royden, F. Horváth, B.C. Burchfiel, S. Semken, and L. Stegana, 1980, The formation of the intra-Carpathian basins as determined from subsidence data: Earth and Planetary Science Letters, v. 51, p. 139–162.

Spencer, C. W., Á. Szalay, and E. Tatar, in press, Abnormal pressure and hydrocarbon migration in the Békés basin, southeastern Hungary, *in* P. G. Teleki, R. E. Mattick, and J. Kókai, eds., The Békés basin, a study in basin analysis: USGS Professional Paper.

Szalay, J., 1988, Maturation and migration of hydrocarbons in the southeastern Pannonian basin, *in* L. H. Royden and F. Horváth, eds., The Pannonian basin—a study in basin evolution: AAPG Memoir 45, p. 347–354.

Magoon, L. B, and W. G. Dow, eds., 1994, The petroleum
system—from source to trap: AAPG Memoir 60.

Chapter **36**

Northern Delta Depobelt Portion of the Akata–Agbada(!) Petroleum System, Niger Delta, Nigeria

C. M. Ekweozor
Petroleum Geochemistry Research Group
University of Ibadan
Ibadan, Nigeria

E. M. Daukoru
Nigerian National Petroleum Corporation
Lagos, Nigeria

Abstract

The northern depobelt portion of the Akata–Agbada(!) petroleum system corresponds geographically and stratigraphically to the northernmost of six depobelts recognized in the Niger delta. This portion of the system has a total surface area of 7675 km^2 and contains about 3 billion bbl of mostly light waxy crude oil and over 7 trillion scf of gas. These hydrocarbons, whose source rocks are both the Akata and Agbada formations, accumulated in sandstone reservoirs of the Agbada Formation within a depth interval of 1000–4000 m. The total cumulative production from 11 oil fields within the northern depobelt is about 500 million bbl.

The organic matter in the Niger delta is never concentrated in continuous mappable source rock layers but is instead randomly distributed through the stratigraphic sequence. Thus, two points summarize the approach adopted to quantify the hydrocarbons generated. First, the source rock interval is identified as that part of the section presently within the oil window and the part that was within the oil window at the time of growth fault displacement but has since been buried deeper. Second, a statistical average of 2.2 wt. % TOC calculated from the literature was applied to the net thickness of clay to represent the source rock interval. Where this interval is thermally mature to overmature, it is the active source rock. This active source rock interval straddles the lower Agbada and upper Akata formations and corresponds to 43–39 Ma (middle–late Eocene). The oils from this petroleum system can be unequivocally correlated with their presumed source rocks by biological marker analysis.

Traps were created by synsedimentary tectonics that started about 41 Ma, at which time the active source rock was buried to about 2500 m. Significant primary migration of hydrocarbons presumably occurred continously until stabilization of the depobelt, which took place nearly 22 Ma. Therefore, the pod of active source rock in the Northern delta depobelt was active from 41 to 22 Ma.

The efficiency of this petroleum system is only about 1.0%. The extent to which this efficiency is representative of the rest of the Akata–Agbada petroleum system cannot yet be judged until more studies of this kind in other depobelts have been conducted. However, the efficiency in the Northern delta depobelt may be relatively low because of perceived deficiencies in trapping conditions, such as ratty sands and prevalence of hanging wall fault closures.

INTRODUCTION

The Niger delta basin, situated at the northeastern margin of the Gulf of Guinea on the west coast of Africa, is one of the most prolific hydrocarbon provinces in the world. The sedimentary basin fill occupies a total area of 75,000 km^2 and is at least 12 km thick in the central part. Estimates of ultimately recoverable hydrocarbons for the entire Niger delta are about 20 billion bbl of oil and 30 tcf

of gas, giving one of the highest concentrations of petroleum per unit volume of basin fill.

Following a major marine transgression in the Paleocene, the paleo–Niger delta started to prograde to the southwest into the equatorial Atlantic Ocean. This sediment build-up was accompanied by growth fault tectonics normal to the direction of progradation which resulted in a series of seven parallel fault-bounded depositional belts (depobelts). These depobelts are succes-

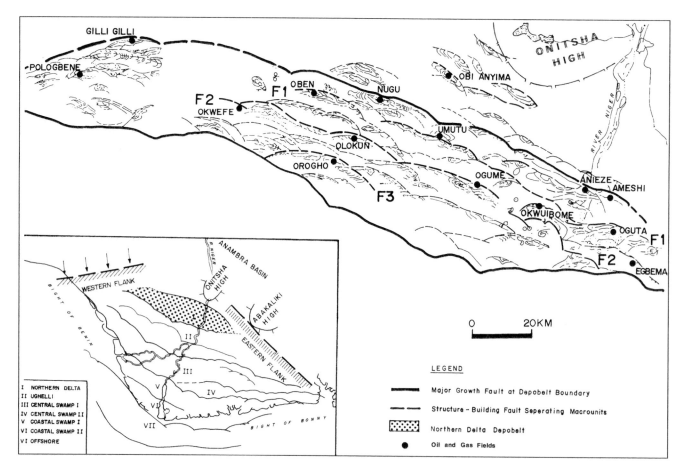

Figure 36.1. Map of the Northern delta depobelt portion of the Akata–Agbada(!) petroleum system showing the major oil fields, some of which are yet to be developed. F1, F2, and F3 are fault trends that outline macrostructural units. The inset shows the other depobelts of the Niger delta.

sively younger from north to south (Figure 36.1, inset). Overprinting the entire architecture of these depobelts is the same stratigraphic sequence that consists of three thick rock units, which from shallowest to deepest are

1. The Benin Formation, which is composed mostly of sandstones deposited in a fluvial and coastal environment
2. The Agbada Formation, which is interbedded sandstones and shales deposited in a transitional to marine paralic environment
3. The Akata Formation, which is mostly massive marine shale (Figure 36.2).

As much as a 1-km thickness of Benin Formation unconformably overlies the Agbada and Akata formations, which together are at least 3 km thick.

Each depobelt is considered to be a distinct entity or cell with respect to sedimentation, structural deformation, and hydrocarbon generation and accumulation, with the exception of depobelts V and VI, which act as a single cell (Evamy et al., 1978). Small amounts of hydrocarbons probably move between depobelts, but for the purpose of this discussion, the amount is insignificant.

Although the Akata–Agbada(!) petroleum system

making up the total Niger delta hydrocarbon habitat covers a much larger area, only the Northern delta depobelt is discussed here. Since all the oils of the Niger delta have a similar composition (Doust and Omatsola, 1990; Evamy et al., 1978), they are presumed to originate from the same pod of active source rocks, which are divided into six depobelts. Because each of the six depobelts is partitioned with respect to generation, migration, and accumulation, each cell or depobelt can be studied independently of the other (Figure 36.1).

The organic matter for both the Akata and Agbada formations is geochemically similar (Bustin 1988). Both rock units are responsible for most or all of the oil in the Niger delta. Exploratory wells have penetrated only the upper part of the Akata Formation, and this part is more thermally mature than and usually comparable in organic richness to the overlying lower Agbada Formation. For this reason, the Akata Formation is used as the source rock in the petroleum system name. Also, because most of the oil and gas is being produced from the Agbada Formation, it is considered the major reservoir rock.

The gas–oil ratio (GOR) of the Northern delta depobelt (Table 36.1) is typical of an oil province (2000 ft^3/bbl), and the source rock sampled to date is both oil

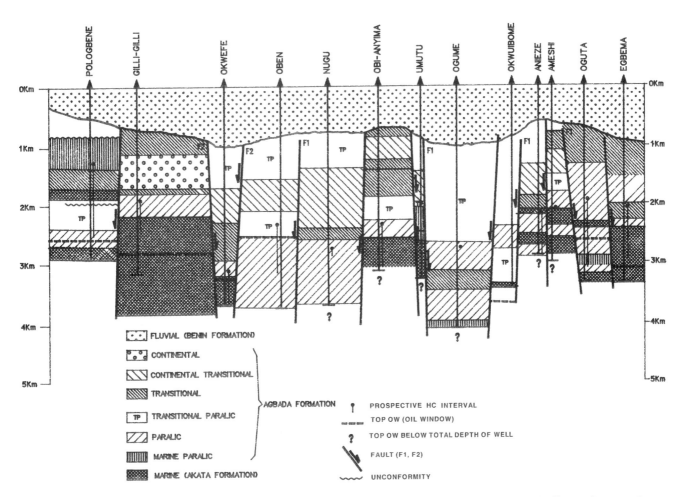

Figure 36.2. West–east cross section across the Northern delta depobelt portion of the Akata–Agbada (!) petroleum system showing the top of the oil window, accumulation depths, and other present-day geologic features. Note that the top of the oil window is presently at various depths in the fault blocks because the sedimentary rocks were displaced by synsedimentary tectonism from their initial positions during the phase of active oil generation and migration. Field locations shown on Figure 36.1.

and gas prone (hydrogen index 100–300 mg HC/g TOC). The oil–source rock correlation is positive, and the level of certainty of this petroleum system is known. Thus, the name of the petroleum system in the Niger delta hydrocarbon habitat is the Akata–Agbada(!).

Oil exploration in the Niger delta started after World War II, with the first well drilled by Shell D'Arcy (now The Shell Petroleum Development Company of Nigeria Limited) in 1950. Earlier wells had been drilled and extensive geologic and geophysical investigations conducted in the Cretaceous rock sequences at the periphery of the post-Paleocene Niger delta. To date, 980 exploratory wells have been drilled, resulting in the discovery of 173 producing oil fields and at least half as many smaller or economically marginal discoveries that are yet to be developed.

The petroleum geology of the Niger delta oil province has been described in several major publications, including Frankl and Cordry (1967), Short and Stauble (1967), Weber and Daukoru (1975), Evamy et al. (1978), and Doust and Omatsola (1990). In addition, many publications have dealt with specific aspects of the delta. Of these, the most signifi-

cant are by Stoneley (1966) and Burke et al. (1972), who attempt to estimate from gravity and magnetics the total thickness of basin fill and the nature of the Niger delta basement. Hospers (1965, 1971) deduced the basement configuration from geophysical data, and Burke (1972) dealt with the relationship of longshore drift, the location of modern submarine canyons in the delta, and the possible occurrence of submarine fans in the pre-Tertiary rock sequences of the delta.

Knox and Omatsola (1989) have described in detail the processes by which the depobelts succeed each other in time and space. The stratigraphic evolution of the Tertiary Niger delta and the adjoining Cretaceous rocks for a number of typical Nigerian oil fields is analyzed in Weber (1971). Allen (1965) and Oomkens (1974) discussed the recent sedimentation and physiography of the delta.

The geochemistry of the sedimentary organic matter, including the crude oils, has been studied extensively (e.g., Evamy et al., 1978; Ekweozor et al., 1979a, b; Udo et al., 1986; 1988a, b; Bustin, 1988; Doust and Omatsola, 1990). There is a consensus that the organic matter origi-

Table 36.1. Hydrocarbon Accumulation in the Northern Delta Depobelt of the Akata–Agbada(!) Petroleum System

Field name	Production Depth (m)	Oil Gravity (°API)	Cumulative Oil production[a] (MMbbl)	Oil STOIP[b] (MMbbl)	Gas STGIP[c] (billion scf)	STOIP (million BOE)	Total Oil In-Place (million BOE)
Oben/Oben N.	2661–3030	37–46	125.3	444	1896	327	771
Oguta	—	—	128.4	610	2619	452	1062
Egbema /Egbema W.	—	—	52.3	528	117	203	731
Izombe/Ossu	—	—	44.2	176.9	—	—	177
Ugada, Okpai, Akri, Gilli-gilli (combined)	—	—	83.9	444.5	—	—	445
Estimated unconnected fields/prospects (combined)	—	—	—	827.3	1620	270	1097
Totals			434.1	3030.7	7312	1252	4283

[a]Data from the Nigeria National Petroleum Corporation, Lagos; Shell Petroleum Development Co. Nig. Ltd..
[b]STOIP, stock tank oil in-place.
[c]STGIP, stock tank gas in-place.

nated mainly from terrestrial and nearshore marine paleoenvironments. Petrologically it consists primarily of vitrinite, plant liptinites, and some amorphous material probably derived from bacterial reworking. Autochthonous marine input is generally low or absent. This organofacies corresponds to the type IIB–IIIA kerogen that is considered to be both oil and gas prone. An important feature of the organic matter occurrence is that it is generally widely disseminated throughout the sedimentary rock column rather than being concentrated within any mappable stratigraphic rock unit.

The primary oil of the delta is light and waxy and is biodegraded at temperatures lower than 80°C to yield a medium-weight, nonwaxy, naphthenic oil. Molecular evidence confirms that the oils were derived mainly from land plant debris. The oil habitat is the paralic Agbada Formation, where it is usually trapped in rollover anticlines associated with growth faults.

Evamy et al. (1978) concluded from observations of the physical properties and distribution of the oils and their relationship with geotemperatures and the presumed source rock that generation and migration of hydrocarbons occurred close to the attainment of present-day overburden. But Knox and Omatsola (1989) contradicted this late generation–migration hypothesis and instead inferred, from their escalator regression model, that primary migration and accumulation occurred long before the present overburden was attained, perhaps even earlier than the time of early Benin Formation deposition.

Another controversy has centered on whether the source rock for this crude oil is located mainly in the deeply buried continuous shales of the Akata Formation or in the interbedded sandstone and shale of the Agbada Formation. Generation in the former would have required fairly long-range migration of the crude oil via growth faults, whereas only short-distance updip

movements would have been necessary for *in situ* Agbada generation.

Ekweozor and Okoye (1980) presented analytical data favoring the deeply buried lower parts of the paralic sequence and the uppermost strata of the continuous marine shales as the main source rock. This was challenged by Lambert-Aikhionbare and Ibe (1984), who claimed that Agbada shales were thermally mature at depths as shallow as 1800 m and therefore should be the source rock for the crude oil found in the adjacent sandstone reservoir rocks. This viewpoint was supported by Ejedawe (1986) who postulated the existence of a shallow expulsion zone that corresponded to 0.3–0.6% R_o in the Agbada Formation. Ekweozor and Daukoru (1984) reiterated the preference for a deeply buried source rock by means of geochemical fingerprinting techniques, which show a positive correlation between the shallow oil and the deep shale and a negative correlation between the same oil and the shallow shale.

Modeling studies of the evolution of the oil window have generally shown that available source rocks for this oil exist mainly in the lower Agbada and upper (where penetrated) Akata formations (Evamy et al., 1978; Ejedawe et al., 1984a,b). This is also the conclusion of other analytical studies (Nwachukwu and Chukwurah, 1986; Udo et al., 1986; 1988 a,b). More recently, Ekweozor and Udo (1988), Udo and Ekweozor (1990) and Ekweozor and Telnaes (1990) precisely determined, by the oleanane parameter, that the top of the oil window corresponds to an average vitrinite reflectance of 0.55% R_o. Therefore, in this chapter, the top of the oil window is defined at 0.6% R_o, which excludes substantial parts of the Agbada Formation (except the lower sequences) from the pod of active source rock and includes the upper parts of the Akata Formation. This assumes the operation of a deep rather than a shallow migration zone in the delta.

GEOLOGIC SETTING

Niger Delta

The Niger delta is flanked on the northwest by a thick outcrop of uppermost Cretaceous sedimentary rocks which in turn rest unconformably on an extensive Precambrian basement complex. A narrow step-faulted hinge zone trending northwest-southeast marks the transition from Niger delta Tertiary growth fault tectonics to the uniformly dipping beds of the Upper Cretaceous delta (Figure 36.1).

The eastern and northeastern flank of the Upper Cretaceous delta is tectonically and sedimentologically more varied. The most prominent feature is the Abakaliki high, which includes a succession of Aptian–Santonian siliciclastic rocks that were subjected to compressive deformation near the end of the Santonian. Because of this deformation, the center of deltaic deposition was displaced westward to fill the Anambra basin (Murat, 1972).

Throughout the post-Santonian period to the Paleocene, the Anambra basin was the center of deposition for several prodelta cycles until a major northward marine transgression took place. The Imo Shale was deposited during this transgression. At the end of this transgression, the progradation that formed the present-day Niger delta was initiated.

The Niger delta represents a typical offlap sequence in which the Benin, Agbada, and Akata formations are time-equivalent, proximal to distal, prograding facies units. This progradation was influenced by synsedimentary growth faults whereby the rate of forward advance of the sandy Benin Formation was temporarily retarded when a major growth fault was activated at the delta front. The downthrown part of this active boundary fault became the new focus of Agbada or paralic facies deposition until subsidence in front of the fault was stabilized or filled to near sea level. The sandstone of the Benin Formation then resumed its rapid oceanward advance over the newly established depobelt. This mechanism, called the *escalator regression model* (Knox and Omatsola, 1989), postulates that the base of the Benin Formation in any of the six depobelts is coeval with the base of the Agbada Formation in the adjacent depobelt to the south. This principle implies an abrupt shift in the age of the base of the Benin Formation across the bounding faults of depobelts and has been used to define the northern limit of the Northern delta depobelt.

Northern Delta Depobelt

The vertical and lateral extent of the Northern delta depobelt of the Akata–Agbada petroleum system has been derived from the principle of escalator regression. The southern boundary of the depobelt is delineated with reasonable certainty except at the eastern and western extremes. These extremes are marked by a transition to the Cretaceous rocks where growth fault tectonics cease. The northern limit is more subtly expressed because of the lack of pronounced northern

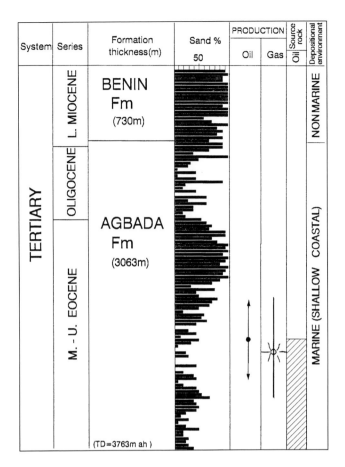

Figure 36.3. Stratigraphic column of Oben-1 well, which is typical of the Northern delta depobelt. The location of the Benin and Agbada formations and the source rock and hydrocarbon-producing intervals are shown. The Akata Formation was not penetrated, but its estimated top position here is at a depth of 4250 m (see Figure 36.4c).

dips into the bounding growth fault system. However, by comparing the shift in stratigraphic position of the base of the Benin Formation in wells outside the Northern delta depobelt (such as the Obi Anyima) with others inside the depobelt (such as Oben-1), it is possible to delineate the northern limit of the Northern delta depobelt with reasonable confidence. The depobelt covers a total surface area of 7675 km[2] (Figure 36.1).

Figure 36.2 is a west–east cross section across 12 oil fields, from Pologbene to Egbema fields, within the depobelt to show the important stratigraphic and structural features. The Obi Anyima oil field is outside the Northern delta depobelt to the north. In all fields, wells penetrate up to 1.0 km of the Benin Formation. The continuous marine shale sequence of the Akata Formation is penetrated only at the western and eastern extremities and in Obi Anyima situated updip of the depobelt. Elsewhere, most of the wells just penetrate the paralic sequence of the Agbada Formation, especially at the central region where it is thickest.

Three important faults (F1, F2, and F3 on Figure 36.1 and F1 and F2 on Figure 36.2) have significant displacements and delimit large structural units within the depobelt, thereby contributing to stratigraphic complexity. This complexity makes it difficult to correlate reservoir–seal rock pairs across faults.

The depth to the top of the oil window corresponds to 0.6% R_o and was determined for various wells by reconstructing their burial and thermal histories using a Shell computer program, BURMAG. Although vitrinite reflectance was measured in only a few wells, the calculated thermal maturity threshold values correlated well with the measured vitrinite reflectance data for the Pologbene-1, Gilli-Gilli-1, and Oben-1 wells. In this way, the present top of the oil window was established at 2500–3500 m in seven wells (Figure 36.2). The depth to 0.6% R_o is shallower at the flanks of the depobelt relative to the central blocks, which is in agreement with the trend of increasing sand percentage or decreasing geothermal gradient.

Figure 36.3 illustrates a typical sedimentary rock column penetrated in the Northern delta depobelt. Here, the Oben-1 well penetrates 730 m of nonmarine sandstone in the Benin Formation and 3063 m of interbedded sandstone and shale in the Agbada Formation. The Akata Formation is beyond the total depth (3763 m) of this well and is estimated to commence at a depth of 4250 m. Based on literature Rock-Eval pyrolysis data for Gilli-Gilli-1 and Pologbene-1 wells (Udo et al., 1988a,b; Udo and Ekweozor, 1988), it can be inferred that the lower 1000 m of this unit is an oil-prone source rock. Above this source rock lies the sandstone reservoirs from which oil is produced. However, the oil-prone source rock is restricted to the bottom of the well, which judging by the low percentage of sandstone, represents a transition to the Akata Formation.

ESSENTIAL ELEMENTS

Source Rock

A first constraint in Niger delta hydrocarbon habitat studies has been to understand the role of the dispersed organic matter. To date, a distinct source rock with a mappable top and bottom is unidentified. Rather, the entire sedimentary sequence (particularly clay beds, whether massive as in the Akata Formation or intercalated as in the Agbada Formation) appear to be the source rock, provided they are within or below the oil window. From geochemical analysis done to date, the vertical and horizontal distribution of total organic carbon in individual wells is observed to be inconsistent. However, Bustin (1988) noted a broad but consistent decrease in the quantity of organic matter with decreasing age for the entire Tertiary Niger delta, while Doust and Omatsola (1990) have emphasized environmental control of organic matter occurrence. Because the source rock richness cannot be mapped, another way must be used to determine the volume of the pod of active source rock.

A second constraint applied in the determination of source rock volume is the depth of the oil window, i.e., the volume of source rock within the oil window. The

top of the oil window is frequently penetrated at or near total depth of exploratory wells, but the greatest depth of the source rock that could have generated oil can only be estimated from reflection seismic information.

A third constraint is determining the time when reservoir sands were deposited and structures formed. Obviously, any hydrocarbons generated before a rollover anticline or other potential trap was formed could not have contributed to the volume of accumulated hydrocarbons. Based on the escalator regression principle, the time (41 Ma) of retardation of the progradation of the Benin Formation as inferred from wells north of the northern delta depobelt was that moment when faults displaced and structures began to form. Because of insufficient well control, it is impossible to validate this age by using that time when the sedimentary section within the depobelt expanded.

It should be remembered that by the time structures began to form, a pod of active source rock already existed. The source rock at that time, T_1, could be defined by marker beds M_1 and M_2 representing the bottom and top of the oil window, respectively, while the overlying marker, M_3, corresponded to the initial horizon of fault displacement or structuration (Figures 36.4a and b). At subsequent times T_2 and T_3, the oil window was defined by the marker beds M_2–M_3 and M_3–M_4, respectively, while it is now defined by markers M_4 and M_5. Thus, the strata that may have generated hydrocarbons are within and below the present-day oil window because the whole section has moved through the oil window since time T_1, that is, the aggregate interval M_1–M_5.

A fourth constraint is to discount that portion of the source rock sequence that was already within the oil window before the activation of the depobelt on the grounds that its expelled hydrocarbons were presumably dissipated before traps were created. Thus, the initial paleotop of the oil window (M_2) practically delimits the base of the source rock sequence. On the basis of these considerations, it is thought that the M_2–M_1 portion of the source rock interval that is presently buried to a depth of 6.1–6.9 km within the massive marine shales of the Akata formation in the Oben area is unlikely to have contributed significantly to the pooled oil (Figure 36.4c). It is therefore discounted from the aggregate source rock sequence to give an effective or active source rock interval bracketed by the marker beds M_2 and M_5, that is, lying between the initial paleo- and present-day top of the oil window. This interval has a gross thickness of 3.3 km and consists of 1.45 and 1.85 km, respectively, of the Agbada and Akata formations (Figures 36.4b and c).

Measured total organic carbon (TOC) concentration and hydrogen index (HI) values of the paralic and prodelta sedimentary rocks are available for two key wells, the Pologbene-1 and Gilli-Gilli-1 (Udo et al., 1988a, b; Udo and Ekweozor, 1988). In addition, Bustin (1988) reported a statistical average TOC of 2.2 wt. % and an HI of 90 mg HC/g TOC for the depobelt. Bustin's TOC average of 2.2. wt. % appears reasonable and is adopted for the volumetric calculations here because it is similar to the average TOC obtained by Udo and Ekweozor

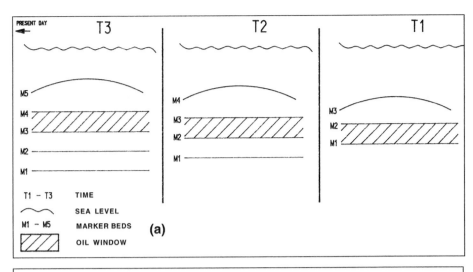

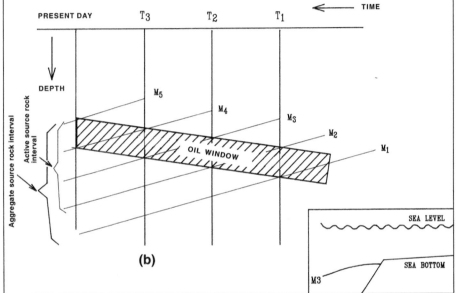

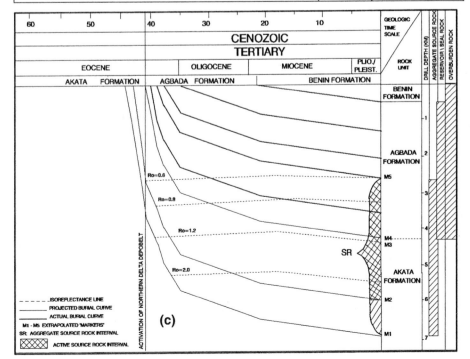

Figure 36.4. (a) Conceptual model for evolution of the source rock as it passed thought the oil window in the Niger delta. (b) Dynamic relationship between subsidence and the oil window at times T_1, T_2, T_3, and present day in the Niger delta. (c) Burial history graph for the Oben-1 well in the Northern delta depobelt showing the evolution of the top of the oil window, peak oil generation, the top of the gas window and commencement of the zone of metagenesis corresponding to 0.6, 0.8, 1.2, and 2.0% R_o, and the stratigraphic depths of the source, seal–reservoir, and overburden rocks. Projected depths below the well's total depth (3763 m) help to determine the aggregate source rock interval thickness. Marker beds as follows: M_1, estimated base of the aggregate source rock interval, M_2, base of the active source rock interval, M_4, top of the Akata Formation, M_5, top of the aggregate source rock interval. Most of the oil was generated and accumulated by 22 Ma.

(1988) for Agbada–Akata shales from Pologbene-1 (2.5 wt. %) and Gilli-Gilli-1 (2.3 wt. %).

However, Bustin's HI average (90 mg HC/$_g$ TOC) is too low and, in our opinion, does not reflect the petroleum potential of the source rock in this depobelt. This is supported by our comparison of HI data from whole-rock and pre-isolated kerogens from Pologbene-1 and Gilli-Gilli-1 wells (Figure 36.5). This shows that for both the paralic and marine rock sequences penetrated in the two wells, HI values from whole-rock (cuttings) pyrolysis (Rock-Eval) lie mainly between 30 and 300 mg HC/g TOC, whereas the values for the corresponding pre-isolated kerogens range between 100 and 350 mg HC/g TOC. This apparent improvement in HI values must mean that the low values from pyrolysis of whole rock were due to mineral matrix effects that are known to be common in deltaic sedimentary rocks (Espitalie et al., 1980). This conclusion is supported by high values of the oxygen index, 70–300 (mg CO_2/g TOC) from Rock-Eval pyrolysis of the whole-rock samples of the same shales (Udo et al., 1988b). Note that Bustin's HI values were from whole-rock pyrolysis.

From the kerogen pyrolysis data for Gilli-Gilli-1, the only well that traversed virtually the entire present-day oil window, we have determined an average HI of 232 and 161 mg HC/$_g$ TOC for the immature and mature–supermature shales, respectively (Udo et al., 1988a, b).

From Figure 36.5, we conclude that the paralic and prodelta shales in the depobelt wells are both oil and gas prone since they contain mostly mixtures of type IIB and IIIA kerogen.

Reservoir and Seal Rocks

Potential reservoir rocks have been penetrated from 1000–3900 m in the depobelt and are deepest at the center of the depobelt. Reservoir rocks are typically on the order of 30–46 m in thickness, with multiple reservoir–seal rock pairs in any given oil field. The sandstone reservoirs are in the Agbada Formation and are heterogenous, being a mixture of barrier bar and channel sands, with occasionally deep water turbidites in the transitional sequence into the Akata Formation (e.g., Egbema field). Porosities vary with depth from 25 to 15%, while permeabilities are high at about 1–2 d.

The oil is medium to light with API gravities ranging from 30 to 45°. The few crude oils that have relatively heavy API gravity show evidence of freshwater washing and bacterial transformation. The lighter crude oils, which typically occur deeper than 3500 m, are volatile and have GORs ranging from 180 to 1600 (ft³/bbl). Sulfur content is low (0.1–0.4 wt. %), and the average pristane–phytane ratio is high (2.7).

Geochemically, the Niger delta oils are similar, although two subfamilies can sometimes be distinguished depending on which of the two end-members of the corresponding source rock kerogens was preponderant. In the case of the Northern delta depobelt, the oils are identical at the molecular level as evidenced by biologic marker comparisons of two oils from the Pologbene and Egbema fields in the eastern and western

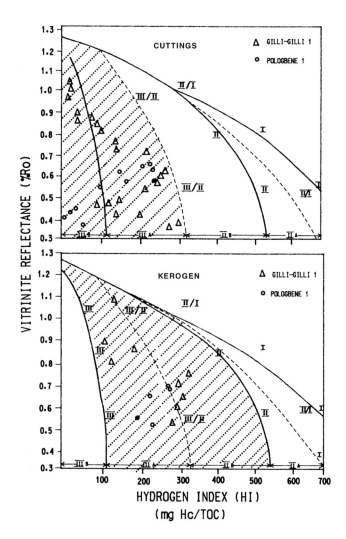

Figure 36.5. Classification of the sedimentary organic matter in the Northern delta depobelt as illustrated by plots of vitrinite reflectance versus HI from Rock-Eval pyrolysis of whole rock (cuttings) and the corresponding pre-isolated kerogens from Gilli-Gilli-1 and Pologbene-1 wells. (Boundaries of kerogen types are from D. Leythaeuser, personal communication, 1983; data from Udo et al., 1988b.)

flanks of the depobelt (Figure 36.6). The composition of both the pentacyclic triterpanes and triaromatic steranes are identical. Therefore, both oils originated from similar organic facies at about the same level of thermal maturity.

The largest oil fields in this petroleum system are Gilli-Gilli, Oben, Oguta, and Egbema. Together with expected recovery from undeveloped discoveries and prospects, the total oil in-place is about 4 billion bbl (Table 36.1). Although there are some gas fields, most of the gas in this petroleum system is associated with oil.

Overburden Rock

The *overburden rock* is the sedimentary sequence that buries the source rock deep enough to become thermally mature to generate oil. In all cases, the Benin Formation

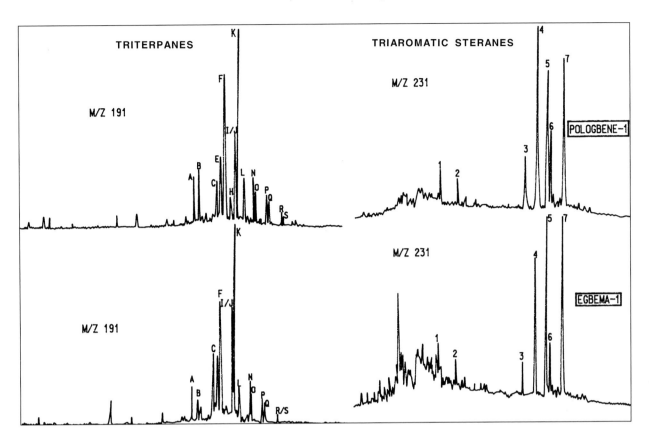

Figure 36.6. Oil–oil correlation of whole crudes from Pologbene-1 and Egbema-1 wells by means of *m/z* 191 and *m/z* 231 fragmentograms. Peaks correspond to the following derivatives of triaromatic steranes (from Mackenzie, 1984): 1, C_{20}; 2, C_{21}; 3, C_{27} (20S); 4, C_{27} (20R)/C_{28} (20S); 5, C_{28} (20S); 6, C_{27} (20R); 7, C_{28} (20R). (See Ekweozor et al., 1979a, for identification of triterpanes.)

contributes up to 1 km of overburden. The upper part of the Agbada Formation also contributes 1–2 km, as in the Oben-1 well (Figure 36.4c). The remainder of the overburden rock is the source rock itself wherever it is more than a few hundred meters thick.

PROCESSES

Trapping Styles

Hydrocarbons are mainly trapped in rollover anticlines which, in the Northern delta depobelt, are characteristically simple (unfaulted) structures with a single growth fault as compared to their more severely deformed counterparts farther south (Evamy et al., 1978). The fault plane of these single growth faults associated with the structures contain alternating clay and sandstone streaks that can act as seals or conduits (Weber and Daukoru, 1975; see Downey, Chapter 8, this volume). The smeared-in clay as well as lateral juxtaposition of sandstone to clay layers account for the fault traps observed in some oil fields in this depobelt. Sandstone pinchouts and channel truncation features also constitute important stratigraphic traps in the flanks, such as in Egbema and Pologbene fields.

Generation, Migration, and Accumulation of Oil

The burial history graph for the Oben-1 well drilled in the Oben oil field is reconstructed by BURMAG and is typical for the Northern delta depobelt (Figure 36.4c). To assess the thermal history for marker beds within the Agbada Formation but below the total depth of this well, BURMAG has also drawn burial curves for these deeper markers and has calculated the corresponding vitrinite reflectance values (0.6, 0.8, 1.2, and 2.0% R_o) from the estimated age and depth of the markers and sandstone percentages. From this reconstruction, it is evident that the depths 2800 and 4500 m represent the present-day positions for the tops of the oil (0.6%) and gas (1.2%) windows, respectively.

The M_2 marker of the source rock interval was at the top of the oil window at a depth of approximately 2900 m when oil traps began to form about 41 Ma (Figure 36.4c). Oil generated before that time probably had little chance to be pooled in this depobelt. This marker is inferred to have subsided at first very rapidly then slowly from 22 Ma (when basin stabilization was initiated) to its present depth of 6100 m. Most of the oil would have been generated during the period of rapid burial (41–22 Ma). Similar burial scenarios have been

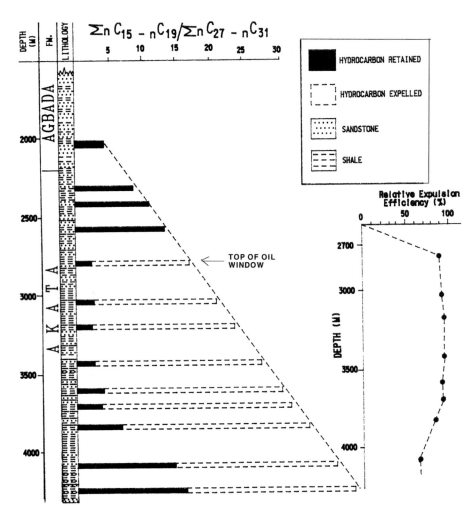

Figure 36.7. Hydrocarbon generation–expulsion profile of the Gilli-Gilli-1 well from depth trend plot of the abundance ratio of medium *n*-alkanes (nC_{15}–nC_{19}) to their heavier counterparts (nC_{27}–nC_{31}) from gas chromatography of total saturated alkanes fraction of rock extractives. Inset is a plot of the variation, with depth of the relative expulsion efficiency of the alkanes, assuming a regular increase in total generated hydrocarbons with burial depth.

reconstructed for the other marker beds, M3–M5 (Figure 36.4c). The critical moment coincided with maximum hydrocarbon generation, roughly the average of the interval from 41 to 22 Ma, or 32 Ma, which was during the time of intense creation of new trapping opportunities.

The burial and thermal history reconstructed using other important wells such as Pologbene-1, Orogho-1, and Egbema-1 is similar to that of Oben-1, suggesting that the thermal maturity pattern given here is typical of the entire depobelt. However, for each fault block, the thermal maturity thresholds for the tops of the oil and gas windows (0.6 and 1.2% R_o, respectively) correspond to different depths because the uplift for each block is different and the throw across the growth faults vary. It can be seen from Figure 36.2 that 2500 m is about the shallowest depth position for the present-day top of the oil window. In fact, in the central part, it is as deep as 4000 m.

For the burial history of the Oben-1 well, the active source rock interval is the section from 6100 m up to the top of the present-day oil window at 2800 m (Figure 36.4c). This includes nearly 1.45 km of the lower Agbada and 1.85 km of the upper Akata. Thus, the gross interval that is presently in or has moved through the oil window since structural traps began to form and is judged to have been capable of expelling the generated hydrocarbons is 3300 m thick.

Since much of the gas window is probably in the overpressured sections of the Akata Formation far below potential reservoirs, the bulk of the pooled gas in the Northern delta depobelt is assumed to have generated in association with the oil.

Adequate drainage of the source rock situated in the paralic Agbada Formation, such as in the Oben-1 well, is not in doubt in view of the availability of interbedded sandstones that should have provided suitable migration pathways and reservoir facilities. But the possibility of effective drainage of the massive shale of the Akata Formation is a more controversial matter. To test the drainage capability of the Akata source rocks, we have carried out a semi-quantitative evaluation of hydrocarbon generation and expulsion in the Gilli-Gilli-1 well which penetrated a >2-km-thick Akata section still within the present-day oil window. We used the well-known fact that the medium-weight alkanes, such as the nC_{15} to nC_{19} members, are expelled faster into the geosphere than their heavier counterparts, the nC_{27} to nC_{31} homologs (e.g., Leythaeuser et al., 1983). Thus, the abundance ratio

$$\frac{\sum (nC_{15} \text{ to } nC_{19})}{\sum (nC_{27} \text{ to } nC_{31})}$$

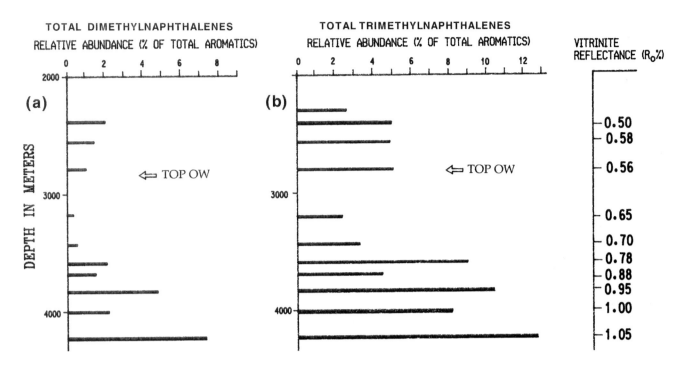

Figure 36.8. Hydrocarbon generation–expulsion profile of Gilli-Gilli-1 well from depth trend plots of the combined relative abundances of (a) dimethylnaphthalenes and (b) trimethylnaphthalenes from gas chromatography of the total aromatic alkanes fraction of rock extractives. The measured vitrinite reflectance values of the corresponding whole rock are shown (OW, oil window).

determined from the *n*-alkanes distribution in rock extract and plotted against the corresponding burial depth presents a hydrocarbon generation–expulsion profile. Figure 36.7 shows the depth trend for the Gilli-Gilli-1 well. Values for the relative expulsion efficiency (REE) are deduced from the relationship

$$REE\ (\%) = \frac{HC_g - HC_r}{HC_g} \times 100$$

where HC_g and HC_r are equivalent total *n*-alkanes generated and retained, respectively. These REE values are plotted against burial depth to produce an expulsion curve (Figure 36.7 inset). It is evident from this that the least REE value, about 60%, corresponds to the most deeply buried parts of the source rock sequence (depth >4 km). Above that horizon and up to the present-day top of the oil window (at 2800 m), the average REE is as much as 90%. Note that the entire source rock sequence here is all within the Akata Formation.

An independent support for the deduction that the Akata shales have expelled their generated hydrocarbons is provided by the depth trend plot of the abundances of dimethylnaphthalenes and trimethylnaphthalenes. These compounds appear to be expulsion-sensitive aromatic biomarkers. Figures 36.8a and b show the trends for the same section of Gilli-Gilli-1 well that was analyzed previously. The close similarity of Figures 36.7 and 36.8 confirms that adequate source rock drainage was possible in thermally mature sections of the Akata Formation despite their undercompaction and possibly

overpressure at the time of active subsidence. This is consistent with the earlier arguments of Weber and Daukoru (1975) and Ekweozor and Daukoru (1984) that overpressure does not inhibit oil migration.

PETROLEUM SYSTEM EVENTS CHART

The events chart summarizes the temporal extent of the essential elements and processes that occur within the petroleum system (Figure 36.9). In this case, the events chart is based on the Oben-1 well, which is representative of the Northern delta depobelt of the Akata–Agbada petroleum system.

The aggregate source rock interval encompasses the Agbada and Akata formations ranging in age from 44 to 39 Ma (middle–late Eocene). The Agbada Formation provides the seal and reservoir rocks dated at 41–22 Ma. The overburden rock includes the Agbada and Benin formations and ranges in age from Eocene to Holocene (41–0 Ma). Trap formation (41–22 Ma) initiated by growth fault activity occurred contemporaneously with oil generation that peaked at approximately 32 Ma, which is the critical moment. This means that in this system, the key to the determination of source rock volume and yield is closely related to the timing of trap creation.

The events chart shows that, contrary to the assertion of Evamy et al. (1978), generation and migration of hydrocarbons was largely completed long before the present overburden was attained, although minor amounts of hydrocarbon are still being generated.

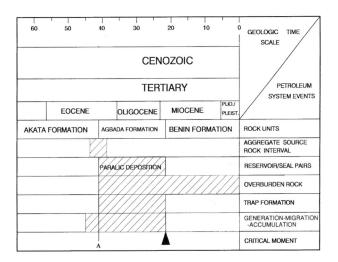

Figure 36.9. An events chart showing the time that the four essential elements were deposited and when the two processes (trap formation and hydrocarbon generation–migration–accumulation) took place for the Northern delta depobelt portion of the Akata–Agbada petroleum system (A = activation of Northern delta depobelt). The critical moment occurred after most of the oil was generated and is based on Figure 36.4c.

LEVEL OF CERTAINTY

The level of certainty indicates the confidence that a particular source rock generated a particular oil. An oil–oil correlation of the oils from the eastern and western flanks of the Northern delta depobelt indicate that they are geochemically similar and are therefore assumed to come from the same pod of active source rock in the Niger delta area (Figure 36.6). Indeed, it is possible by means of diagnostic biological markers to determine, approximately, the burial depth of the source rock of a specific accumulation within an oil field and infer the equivalent thermal maturity (% R_o) of the oil. This is demonstrated here for the Pologbene-1 well (Figure 36.10).

The m/z 191 fragmentogram of the saturated hydrocarbon fraction of an oil recovered from a depth of 1614 m in the well is compared to those from the presumed source rock at four depth intervals averaging 2264, 2577, 2703, and 2880 m. Table 36.2 shows the values for the oil and shales of three thermal maturity-sensitive biological marker indices: T_s/T_m, C parameter, and L parameter.

A consistent pattern of variation in the values calculated for the source rock emerges in going from the shallowest (2264 m, 0.53% R_o) to the deepest (2880 m, 0.64% R_o). The corresponding thermal maturity values for the oil best compare with those of a source rock in the Akata Formation between the depths of 2703 and 2880 m (average depth 2792 m). Similarly, an average equivalent 0.63% R_o for the source rock can be inferred for the expelled oil. Therefore, based on biological markers and other data, there is a high degree of confidence that the oils in the system originated from the source rocks at the top of Akata Formation and the bottom of the Agbada Formation.

EFFICIENCY OF SYSTEM

The *generation–accumulation efficiency* of a system is a quantitative estimation of the fraction of the total generated hydrocarbons that were trapped and preserved. It is calculated according to the method of Schmoker (Chapter 19, this volume). The values used to calculate the system efficiency for this study are as follows: (1) the area of the pod of active source rock of the Northern delta depobelt of the Akata–Agbada petroleum system is 7675km²; (2) the gross thickness of the active source rock is 3.3 km, which discounted 30% for sand layers, leaves a net thickness of 2.31 km of clay; (3) the average total organic carbon is 2.2 wt. %; and (4) the density of the source rock is 2.6 g/cm³. Therefore, the total mass of organic carbon is

$$HC_{mass} = 2.31 \times 0.022 \times 2.6 \times 76.75 \times 10^{17} \text{ g}$$
$$= 10.14 \times 10^{17} \text{ g}$$

The average HI of thermally mature to overmature source rocks determined from kerogen pyrolysis data from the Gilli-Gilli-1 well (Udo et al., 1988a,b) is 161 mg HC/g TOC, and the average HI of the immature source rock is 232 mg HC/g TOC. Therefore, the mass of hydrocarbons generated and expelled per gram of organic carbon is

$$232 - 161 \text{ mg } = 71 \text{ mg}$$

Therefore, the total mass of hydrocarbons generated is

$$HC_{mass} = 71 \times 10.14 \times 10^{17} \times 10^{-6} \text{ kg}$$
$$= 719.94 \times 10^{11} \text{ kg}$$
$$= 517 \times 10^9 \text{ bbl of oil}$$

From Table 36.1, the total in-place oil plus oil equivalent of in-place gas is 4.283 billion bbl of oil. This is equal to the total hydrocarbons accumulated in known traps.

Therefore, the efficiency of the system is

$$\text{Efficiency } = [(4.283 \times 10^9)/(517 \times 10^9)] \times 100$$
$$= 0.8\%$$

This means that approximately 1% of all the hydrocarbons generated was trapped in an oil field. If 5% is considered the average efficiency for a petroleum system, it thus appears as if the Northern delta depobelt portion of the Akata–Agbada petroleum system is inefficient. This apparent inefficiency may, in part, be due to the following three reasons.

First, many structures in the Northern delta depobelt rely on a hanging wall fault seal which is statistically a less efficient trapping mechanism than dip closures common in the younger depobelts of the central and southern delta. Second, a characteristic feature of the

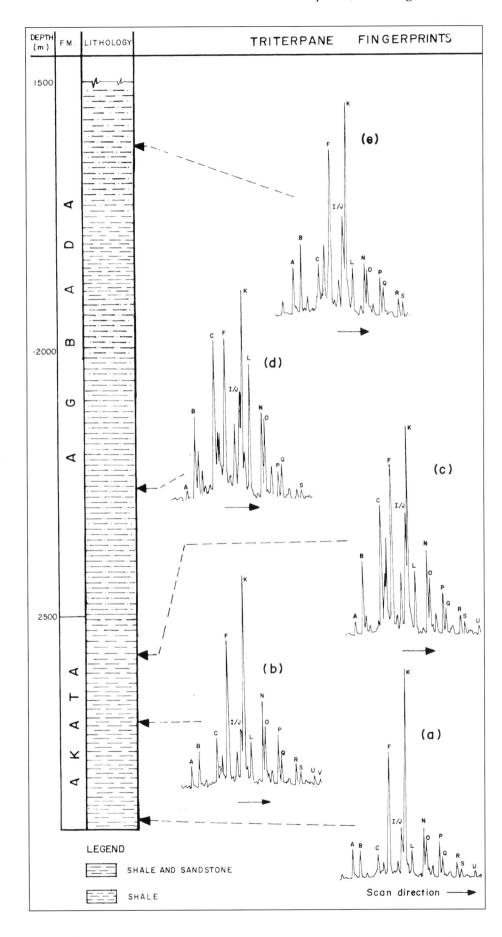

Figure 36.10. The litholog of Pologbene-1 well and the salient features of the *m/z* 191 fragmentograms (triterpanes fingerprint) of the saturates fraction of rock and oil samples from the following depths: (a) 2880 m, shale; (b) 2703 m, shale; (c) 2577 m, shale; (d) 2264 m, shale; (e) 1614 m, oil. (Peaks are numbered according to Ekweozor et al., 1979a.)

Table 36.2. Biomarker Indices[a] from *m/z* 191 Fragmentograms of Saturated Hydrocarbon Fraction of an Oil and Presumed Source Rocks in Pologbene-1 well

Type	Sample Depth (m)	Vitrinite Reflectance (% R_o)	T_s/T_m[b]	C Parameter[c]	L Parameter[d]
Oil	1614	0.60	0.7	0.2	0.2
Shale	2264	0.53	0.1	0.7	0.6
Shale	2577	0.58	0.2	0.6	0.3
Shale	2703	0.61	0.6	0.2	0.2
Shale	2880	0.64	1.0	0.1	0.1

[a]Biomarker indices determined from peak height ratios (see Ekweozor et al., 1979a, for peak identification).
[b]T_s/T_m is C_{27} hopane–II/(C_{27} 17a(H)–hopane).
[c]C parameter is C_{30} triterpane (C)/(C_{30} 17a(H)–hopane).
[d]L parameter is C_{30} moretane (L)/(C_{30} 17a(H)–hopane).

Niger delta is that the sequence is thickest in the central region, thinning toward the Northern delta and offshore. As a result, the number of reservoir–seal pairs are relatively few in the Northern delta depobelt when compared to the central and coastal swamp depobelts (II–VI on Figure 36.1 inset), further contributing to inefficiency of hydrocarbon trapping. Finally, it may be that the estimate of oil and gas expectation in undrilled prospects is low. However, even if future discoveries were as great as those found to date, the system efficiency would still be low.

In the light of this, it is unlikely that the Northern delta depobelt portion of the Akata–Agbada petroleum system typifies the overall efficiency of hydrocarbon formation and preservation for the entire system. More studies are needed to verify whether that portion of the system farther south is more efficient.

SUMMARY AND CONCLUSIONS

A petroleum system forms when hydrocarbon fluid moves outward from a pod of active source rocks to any nearby trap. If a trap is absent, the hydrocarbons seep to the surface and are destroyed. The purpose of this study was to map the geographic, stratigraphic, and temporal extent of the Northern delta depobelt portion of the Akata–Agbada petroleum system using oil accumulations and shows that migrated from the pod of active source rocks. In effect, we were mapping the oil plumbing system, and the exercise was restricted to the Northern delta depobelt.

Because most of the oil generated before 41 Ma migrated to the surface for lack of traps and because little oil was generated after 22 Ma, the temporal extent of this petroleum system ranges from 41 to 22 Ma. The Northern delta depobelt portion of the system covers an area of 7675 km² toward the northern fringe of the Tertiary rocks of the Niger delta and contains approximately 3 billion bbl of oil and over 7 trillion ft³ of gas in sandstone reservoir rocks deposited as barrier bars, channel sandstones, and turbidites, all of which are emplaced within the 1000–4000 m depth interval of the Agbada Formation.

The aggregate source rock for this petroleum system has a gross thickness of 4100 m and an earliest age of 44

Ma. If we discount the most deeply buried part because it expelled oil prior to the formation of traps, we obtain a 3300-m-thick active source rock sequence. This corresponds to the upper Akata and lower Agbada formations. From reconstruction of its thermal history, it is evident that the pod of active source rock was at the top of the oil window when traps began to form and has since subsided to approximately 6100 m.

Thus far, all the oils analyzed from the system can be unequivocally correlated with their presumed source rocks. Evidently, some of the biomarkers in the oils were expelled at maturities equivalent to 0.6% R_o, which means that they were formed close to the top of the oil window. The generation–accumulation efficiency of this petroleum system is computed to be about 1.0% from total generated hydrocarbons of 517 billion bbl and in-place hydrocarbons of 4.3 billion bbl. This low value signifies an inefficient petroleum system thought to result mainly from deficiencies in trapping conditions (leaky traps) that characterize the Northern delta depobelt.

Acknowledgments   The technical assistance and useful comments of P. S. Omuku and K. O. Ladipo are gratefully acknowledged. We thank the Shell Petroleum Development Company of Nigeria Limited and the Nigeria National Petroleum Corporation for providing the oil and rock samples and for granting permission to publish. John T. Smith and Peter van de Kamp are also gratefully acknowledged for their critique of the manuscript.

References Cited

Allen, J. R. L., 1965, Late Quaternary Niger delta, and adjacent areas—sedimentary environments and lithofacies: AAPG Bulletin, v. 49, p. 547–600.
Burke, K, 1972, Longshore drift, submarine canyons, and submarine fans in development of Niger delta: AAPG Bulletin, v. 56, p. 1975–1983.
Burke, K, T. F. J, Dessauvagie and A. J. Whiteman, 1972, Geological history of the Benue valley and adjacent areas, *in* Proceedings of First Conference on African Geology, 1970: Ibadan, Nigeria, Ibadan University Press, p. 287–305.

Bustin, R. M., 1988, Sedimentology and characteristics of dispersed organic matter in Tertiary Niger delta: origin of source rocks in a deltaic environment: AAPG Bulletin, v. 72, p. 277–298.

Doust, H., and E. Omatsola, 1990, Niger delta, *in* J. D. Edwards and P. A. Santagrossi, eds., Divergent/passive margin basins: AAPG Memoir 45, p. 201–238.

Ejedawe, J. E., 1986, The expulsion criterion in the evaluation of the petroleum source beds of the Tertiary Niger delta: Journal of Petroleum Geology, v. 9, p. 439–450.

Ejedawe, J. E., S. J. L. Coker, D. O. Lambert-Aikhionbare, K. B. Alofe, and F. O. Adoh, 1984a, Evolution of oil-generative window and oil and gas occurrence in Tertiary Niger delta basin: AAPG Bulletin, v. 68, p. 1744–1751.

Ejedawe, J. E., D. O. Lambert-Aikhionbare, and C. Okorie, 1984b, Time of hydrocarbon expulsion in Niger delta basin: Nigerian Association of Petroleum Explorationists Bulletin, v. 1, p. 1–10.

Ekweozor, C. M., and E. M. Daukoru, 1984, Petroleum source bed evaluation of the Tertiary Niger delta: reply: AAPG Bulletin, v. 68, p. 390–394.

Ekweozor, C. M., and N. V. Okoye, 1980, Petroleum source bed evaluation of Tertiary Niger delta: AAPG Bulletin, v. 64, p. 1251–1259.

Ekweozor, C. M., and N. Telnaes, 1990, Oleanane parameter: verification by quantitative study of the biomarker occurrence in sediments of Niger delta: Organic Geochemistry, v. 16, p. 401–413.

Ekweozor, C. M., and O. T. Udo, 1988, The Oleananes: origin, maturation and limits of occurrence in Southern Nigeria sedimentary basin: Organic Geochemistry, v. 13, p. 131–140.

Ekweozor, C. M., J. I. Okogun, D. E. U. Ekong, and J. R. Maxwell, 1979a, Preliminary organic geochemical studies of samples from the Niger delta, Nigeria: Part 1, analysis of crude oils for triterpanes: Chemical Geology, v. 27, p. 11–28.

Ekweozor, C. M., J. I. Okogun, D. E. U. Ekong, and J. R. Maxwell 1979b, Preliminary organic geochemical studies of samples from the Niger delta, Nigeria: Part 2, analyses of shales: Chemical Geology, v. 27, p. 29–37.

Espitalie, J., M. Madec, and B. Tissot, 1980, Role of mineral matrix in kerogen pyrolysis: influence on petroleum generation and migration: AAPG Bulletin, v. 64, p. 59–66.

Evamy, B. D., J. Haremboure, P. Kamerling, W. A. Knaap, F. A. Molloy, and P. H. Rowlands, 1978, Hydrocarbon habitat of Tertiary Niger delta: AAPG Bulletin, v. 62, p. 1–39.

Frankl, E. J., and E. A. Cordry, 1967, The Niger delta oil province—recent developments onshore and offshore: Seventh World Petroleum Congress, Mexico City, Proceedings, v. 1B, p. 195–209.

Hospers, J., 1965, Gravity field and structure of the Niger delta, Nigeria, West Africa: Geological Society of America Bulletin, v. 76, p. 407–422.

Hospers, J., 1971, The geology of the Niger delta area, *in* The geology of the East Atlantic continental margin: Great Britain, Institute. Geol. Science Report 70/16, p. 121–142.

Knox, G. J., and E. M. Omatsola, 1989, Development of the Cenozoic Niger delta in terms of the "escalator regression" model and impact on hydrocarbon distribution, *in* W. J. M. van der Linden et al., eds, 1987, Proceedings, KNGMG Symposium on Coastal Lowlands, Geology, and Geotechnology: Dordrecht, Klumer Academic Publishers, p. 181–202.

Lambert-Aikhionbare, D. O., and A. C. Ibe, 1984, Petroleum source bed evaluation of Tertiary Niger delta: discussion: AAPG Bulletin, v. 68, p. 387–394.

Leythaeuser, D., A. S. Mackenzie, R. G. Schaefer, F. J. Altebäumer, and M. Bjorøy, 1983, Recognition of migration and its effects within two core holes in shale/sandstone sequences from Svalbard, Norway, *in* M. Bjorøy et al., eds., Advances in Organic Chemistry: New York, John Wiley, p. 136–146.

Mackenzie, A. S., 1984, Applications of biological markers in petroleum geochemistry, *in* J. Brooks and D. Welte, eds., Advances in Petroleum Geochemistry: London, Academic Press, p. 115–214.

Murat, R. C., 1972, Stratigraphy and paleogeography of the Cretaceous and lower Tertiary in southern Nigeria, *in* Proceedings of First Conference on African Geology, 1970: Ibadan, Nigeria, Ibadan University Press, p. 251–266.

Nwachukwu, J. I., and P. I. Chukwurah, 1986, Organic matter of Agbada Formation, Niger delta, Nigeria: AAPG Bulletin, v. 70, p. 48–55.

Oomkens, E., 1974, Lithofacies relations in the late Quaternary Niger delta complex: Sedimentology, v. 2, p. 195–222.

Short, K. C., and A. J. Stauble, 1967, Outline of geology of Niger delta: AAPG Bulletin, v. 51, p. 761–779.

Stoneley, R., 1966, The Niger delta region in the light of the theory of continental drift: Geological Magazine, v. 105, p. 385–397.

Udo, O. T., and C. M. Ekweozor, 1988, Comparative source rock evaluation of Opuama Channel Complex and adjacent producing areas of Niger delta: Nigerian Association of Petroleum Explorationists Bulletin, v. 3, n. 2, p. 10–27.

Udo, O. T., and C. M. Ekweozor, 1990, Significance of oleanane occurrence in shales of Opuama Channel Complex, Niger delta: Energy and Fuels, v. 4, p. 248–254.

Udo, O. T., J. I. Okogun, and C. M. Ekweozor, 1986, Petroleum Geochemistry of an ancient clay-filled canyon in the western Niger delta, Nigeria: 191st American Chemical Society National Meeting, Division of Geochemistry, Book of Abstracts, p. 41.

Udo, O. T., C. M. Ekweozor, and J. I. Okogun, 1988a, Petroleum Geochemistry of an ancient clay-filled canyon in the western Niger delta, Nigeria: Nigerian Association of Petroleum Explorationists Bulletin, v. 3, n. 1, p. 8–25.

Udo, O. T., C. M. Ekweozor, and J. I. Okogun, 1988b, Organic petrographic and programmed pyrolysis studies of sediments from the northwestern Niger delta, Nigeria: Journal of Mining and Geology (Nigeria), v. 24, p. 85–96.

Weber, K. J., 1971, Sedimentological aspects of oil fields in the Niger delta: Geologie en Mijnbouw, v. 50, p. 559–576.

Weber, K. J., and E. M. Daukoru, 1975, Petroleum geology of the Niger delta: Proceedings of the Ninth World Petroleum Congress, Tokyo, v. 2, p. 209–221.

"The more uncertainty attends a given prospect, the more a systematic expression of subjective probability is needed."

—Peter R. Rose

Passage from Rose, P. R., 1992, in Steinmetz, R., ed., The business of petroleum exploration: AAPG, p. 71.

Magoon, L. B, and W. G. Dow, eds., 1994, The petroleum
system—from source to trap: AAPG Memoir 60.

Chapter **37**

Cambay–Hazad(!) Petroleum System in the South Cambay Basin, India

S. K. Biswas

Director KDMIPE
Oil & Natural Gas Commission
Dehradun, India

M. K. Rangaraju

J. Thomas

S. K. Bhattacharya

KDMIPE
Oil & Natural Gas Commission
Dehradun, India

Abstract

The Cambay–Hazad(!) petroleum system in South Cambay basin, India, has original in-place oil and gas reserves of 395 million t. The system covers 9320 km^2 encompassing 20 different oil and gas accumulations. Sedimentary rocks in this petroleum province range in age from Paleocene to Recent and were deposited in a Tertiary rift basin. Carbon isotopic and biological marker data indicate that the low sulfur, high API gravity oil originated from the lower–middle Eocene Cambay Shale source rock. Burial and thermal history reconstructions indicate that oil generation and migration occurred from Miocene (21 Ma) to Recent time. The overburden rocks are over 3 km thick and range in age from middle Eocene to Recent. The principal reservoir rocks are sandstone units of the Hazad and Ardol members of the Ankleshvar Formation.

The essential elements of the petroleum system, consisting of the source, reservoir, seal, and overburden rocks, were deposited from early Eocene to Recent time and the critical processes of generation, migration, trap formation, and accumulation occurred from the Miocene to Recent.

The mass of hydrocarbons generated by the Cambay Shale was calculated and compared to the estimated in-place oil and gas reserves to determine the efficiency of the petroleum system. On the basis of an average organic carbon content of 2.6%, a difference between the original and present-day hydrogen index of 28 mg HC/g TOC, and a 4057.5-km^3 volume of mature source rock, it is estimated that about 7.61×10^{12} kg hydrocarbons were generated. Estimated in-place oil and gas reserves in accumulations within the system are 3.95×10^{11} kg hydrocarbons. These calculations indicate that about 5.2% of the generated hydrocarbons have accumulated in known fields.

INTRODUCTION

South Cambay basin, an integral part of the Cambay rift, is located in the southern part of Gujarat State in western India. The geographic boundary of this basin is outlined on the north by the mouth of the Mahisagar River at the town of Cambay, on the west by the Gulf of Cambay, on the south by the Tapti River, and on the east by the headwaters of the Narmada River (Figure 37.1).

The Cambay rift is a complex Tertiary graben filled with more than 7 km of sedimentary rocks. These rocks overlay the Deccan Trap (volcanic) basement rock. This rift is bounded by north-south boundary faults both on the eastern and western margins. Right lateral strike-slip faults that trend northeastward break the rift into smaller basins. The South Cambay basin is located at the south end of the Cambay rift.

Geologic and geophysical surveys carried out in the late 1950s led to the identification of the Ankleshvar structure, and the well drilled in 1960 resulted in the first oil discovery in the South Cambay basin. Up to 1990, a total of 20 oil and gas fields had been discovered in the South Cambay basin, and all of them are included in the Cambay–Hazad(!) petroleum system.

The history of petroleum exploration, geology, tectonics, and stratigraphy of the Cambay rift have been covered by several workers (Mathur et al., 1968; Raju, 1968; Chandra and Choudhary, 1969; Rao, 1969; Sudhakar and Basu, 1973; Bhandari and Choudhary, 1975; Mehrotra and Ramakrishna, 1980; Misra and Pati, 1980; Biswas, 1982; Bhasin et al., 1985; Biswas 1987; Mohan, et al., 1987) and in several unpublished reports of the Oil and Natural Gas Commission of India. The hydrocarbon prospects of South Cambay basin are discussed by Dhar et al. (1989).

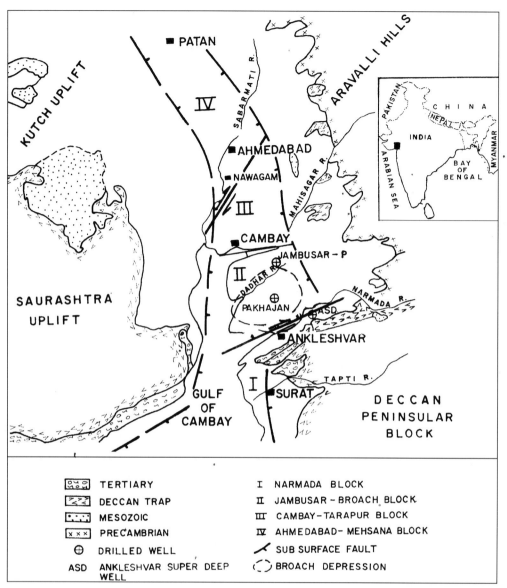

Figure 37.1. Map of the Cambay rift showing the Precambrian, Mesozoic, Deccan Trap (Cretaceous–Tertiary boundary), Tertiary rock outcrops, and various geographic features and cities. The subsurface normal faults that form the rift graben and right lateral strike-slip faults that form the blocks (I–IV) are indicated. The Broach depression and the Pakhajan, Ankleshvar super deep, and Jambusar-P wells are also shown. The inset shows the location of the Cambay rift relative to India.

Legend:

⊡ TERTIARY		I	NARMADA BLOCK
⊡ DECCAN TRAP		II	JAMBUSAR - BROACH BLOCK
⊡ MESOZOIC		III	CAMBAY-TARAPUR BLOCK
x x x PRECAMBRIAN		IV	AHMEDABAD- MEHSANA BLOCK
⊕ DRILLED WELL		⟋	SUB SURFACE FAULT
ASD ANKLESHVAR SUPER DEEP WELL		⌐⌐	BROACH DEPRESSION

Orlov (1965), mainly from geologic evidence, considered the Eocene Cambay Shale to be the source rock for hydrocarbons in the Ankleshvar field. Subsequently, Chandra et al. (1983) and Yalcin et al. (1987) have confirmed the petroleum potential of the Cambay Shale from extensive geochemical analyses. Correlation index and stable carbon isotopic ($\delta^{13}C$) values reported by Singh et al. (1987) reveal that oils in different pools of the South Cambay basin are genetically similar and that the mass spectrometric fingerprints of the Cambay Shale and those of the oils bear resemblance. Banerjee et al. (1990) used $\delta^{13}C$ values with percentage of ethane and $i\text{-}C_4/n\text{-}C_4$ ratios of Gandhar oils to consider the likelihood of contributions from sources in addition to the Cambay Shale for the accumulation at Gandhar. Nonassociated gas deposits are also present in Neogene reservoir rocks at shallower depths (Figures 37.2 and 37.3). Carbon isotopic ratio studies of some of these gas accumulations reveal that the gas is neither bacterial nor metagenetic in origin but thermogenic. Therefore, the most likely source of this gas is the Cambay Shale.

SEDIMENTARY BASIN SETTING

The tectonic evolution of the Cambay rift in the northwestern part of the Indian Peninsula is closely related to the origin and evolution of the western margin of the Indian plate. The Cambay rift is 425 km long, 40–60 km wide, and oriented in a meridional to submeridional direction. The rift is located between the Kutch and Saurashtra uplifts on the west and the Deccan uplift and Aravalli hills on the east (Figure 37.1). This rift system formed at the end of the Mesozoic and was accompanied by extensive eruption of continental flood basalts.

The Deccan Trap volcanic episode at the Cretaceous–Tertiary boundary is also related to the break up of the Seychelles Islands from the Indian plate and the subsequent northward drift of the Indian subcontinent. The flood basalts form the basement rock of the Cambay rift. The rift is divided into several discrete tectonic blocks or grabens with transfer zones delineating the blocks. The tectonic blocks from south to north are the Narmada block, the Jambusar–Broach block, the Cambay–Tarapur

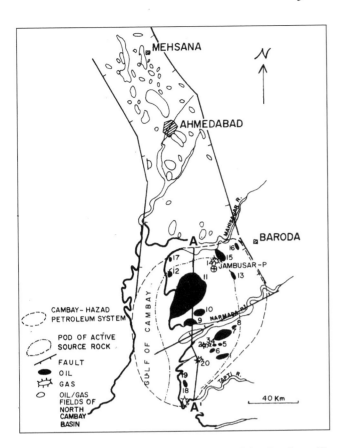

Figure 37.2. Map of the oil and gas fields of the Cambay rift. The oil and gas fields of the North Cambay basin are outlined north of the Mahisagar River. The oil fields (black) and gas fields (barbed) within the geographic extent of the Cambay–Hazad(!) petroleum system (dashed line) are shown. The pod of active source rock (dash-dot line) is the Cambay Shale. Location of cross section A–A' (Figure 37.3) and the Jambusar-P well are also shown. Oil and gas fields are numbered as follows: (1) Kosamba, (2) Elao, (3) Kudara, (4) Sisodra, (5) S.W. Motwan, (6) W. Motwan, (7) Ankleshvar, (8) Andada, (9) Dahej, (10) Pakhajan, (11) Gandhar, (12) Nada, (13) Matar, (14) Gajera, (15) Dabka, (16) Padra, (17) S. Malpur, (18) Hazira, (19) Bhandut, and (20) Olpad.

block, and the Ahmedabad–Mehsana block (Figure 37.1). The Cambay–Hazad petroleum system in the South Cambay basin encompasses the first two blocks.

The Jambusar–Broach block is characterized by a deep depression called the Broach depression with more than 7 km of Cenozoic sedimentary rock. The depocenter was located around the Pakhajan well during the Paleogene. It shifted toward the northwest during the Neogene. The Broach depression hosts the thickest development of the thermally mature source rock, the Eocene Cambay Shale, and the largest oil and gas field discovered to date in the South Cambay basin.

Structural Setting

The South Cambay basin is bound by the Saurashtra uplift on the west and the Deccan Peninsular block on the east. Toward the north, the Nawagam shear, a right-

lateral transfer zone of the Cambay rift, delimits the basin. The Cambay rift evolved during the Late Cretaceous as a consequence of the initiation of the western margin of the Indian plate. The structural style is intimately controlled by primordial tectonic (structural) trends and influenced by two major conjugate shear rift systems, namely, the Narmada (near Ankleshvar) and Nawagam, which cross each other south of the Saurashtra uplift in the offshore area. The Cambay rift appears to have been displaced westward by right-lateral Narmada tear and continues southward offshore parallel to the west coast of India (Biswas, 1987). The Deccan Trap continental flood basalts, which form the basement rock for the Tertiary sedimentary rock fill of the South Cambay basin, are closely associated with this tectonic evolution.

Structural entrapment styles within the South Cambay basin are intimately related to the interaction of the Cambay rift fault system and Narmada shear zone and to the intragraben transfer zones (toward the north). In addition to the resulting structural entrapment styles, the depositional systems within the basin have several other stratigraphic and combination traps on the flanks of the basin and over intrabasinal highs (Figure 37.2). Cross section A–A' in Figure 37.3 has been constructed across the South Cambay basin to illustrate the stratigraphic section and generalized structural style. The section was constructed using reflection seismic and well data. The top of the oil window shown on the section is based on vitrinite reflectance data.

Stratigraphic Section

A stratigraphic column of the South Cambay basin encompasses the Upper Cretaceous–Recent (Figure 37.4). The Deccan Trap basalt flows, dated as late Maastrichtian–early Paleocene, form the basement rock for the Tertiary sediment fill of the South Cambay basin. The Trap is several hundred meters thick along the east and west flanks of the basin. In the Ankleshvar super deep (ASD) well drilled near Ankleshvar (Figure 37.1), more than 3200 m of basalt was penetrated without encountering the Precambrian basement or the Mesozoic sedimentary rock. Evidence indicates the presence of Lower Cretaceous sedimentary rock below the Deccan Trap along the western and eastern margins of the basin.

During Late Cretaceous rifting, faults formed numerous topographic lows and scarps. The nonmarine sedimentary rocks of the Olpad Formation were deposited as coalescing and stacked alluvial fans along the fault scarps. The Olpad Formation is several hundred meters thick and comprises weathered volcanics, conglomerates, trap wacke, and other volcanic derivatives, including silty ferruginous clays deposited in fluvial environments. The formation is unfossiliferous, and a Paleocene age is inferred from the overlying fossiliferous marine Cambay Shale. The Olpad Formation, where penetrated, is a poor source rock. However, some rock intervals have good reservoir characteristics in which a few hydrocarbon accumulations have been discovered.

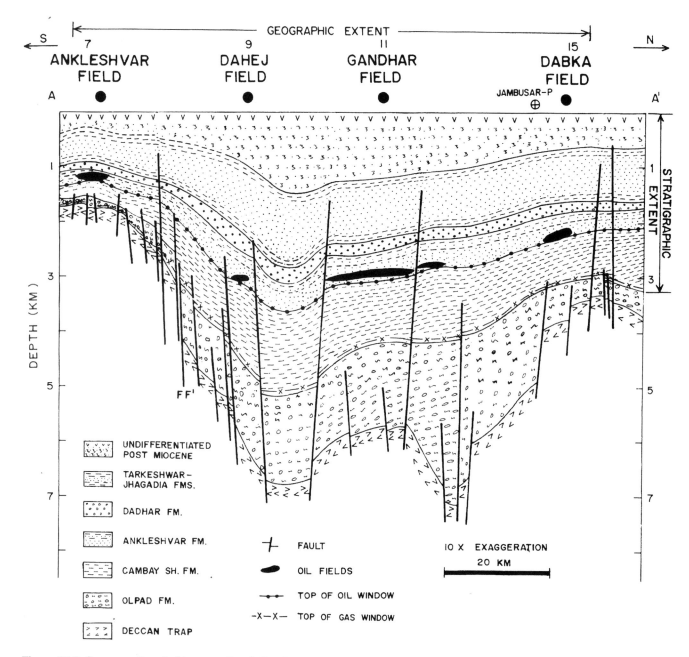

Figure 37.3. Cross section A–A' across South Cambay basin showing the geographic and stratigraphic extent of the Cambay–Hazad(!) petroleum system. The top of the oil window (0.6% R$_o$) and gas window (1.3% R$_o$) are also shown. Locations of oil fields, cross section A–A', and the Jambusar-P well are shown on Figure 37.2.

The Cambay Shale unconformably overlays the Olpad Formation. This shale represents the first major marine transgressive episode in the basin. The shale is gray to dark gray, fissile, often carbonaceous, and rich in disseminated organic matter. Geochemical analysis of the Cambay Shale has demonstrated that it is an excellent source rock. Faunal control has established that the major part of the Cambay Shale is of early Eocene age, although the upper part may extend into the middle Eocene. Besides being a shale, some silty layers within the Cambay Shale have commercial oil accumulations.

The Cambay Shale is conformably overlain by the Ankleshvar Formation, which represents a major regressive phase. It comprises four members, from oldest to

youngest: the Hazad, Kanwa, Ardol, and Telwa. The Hazad Member is mainly a sandstone deposited as a prograding deltaic facies. It forms the major reservoir rock with almost 85% by volume of the hydrocarbon accumulations in the Cambay–Hazad petroleum system. Hazad reservoirs are effectively capped by the marine transgressive Kanwa Shale Member of middle Eocene age. Ardol deltaic facies conformably overlie the Kanwa Shale, and this delta prograded more toward the basin than did the Hazad. The Ardol Sandstone Member has fairly good reservoir rock characteristics and accounts for about 15% by volume of the accumulated hydrocarbons within this petroleum system. The Telwa Shale Member, which represents another rapid marine transgressive

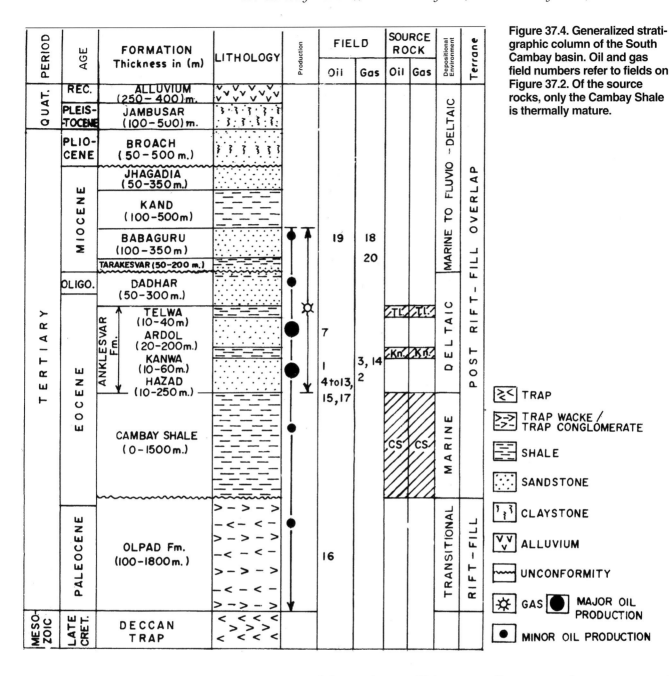

Figure 37.4. Generalized stratigraphic column of the South Cambay basin. Oil and gas field numbers refer to fields on Figure 37.2. Of the source rocks, only the Cambay Shale is thermally mature.

phase in the late Eocene, conformably overlies the Ardol member and is an effective cap for the Ardol accumulations.

The Dadhar Formation was deposited conformably over the Telwa Member and is a widespread prograding deltaic sandstone unit of late Eocene–early Oligocene age. To the south of the Narmada megashear (along the Narmada River on Figure 37.1), a fossiliferous limestone band (containing *Nummulites fichteli*) of early Oligocene age marks the end of the deltaic activity and is followed by a hiatus due to complete withdrawal of the sea from the basin.

The Neogene section is represented by marine to fluviodeltaic interbedded shale and sandstone. The Neogene includes the Miocene Tarakeshwar, Babaguru, Kand, and Jhagadia formations. The Miocene–Pliocene boundary is again marked by an unconformity.

Pliocene–Pleistocene sedimentary rocks are represented by the Broach and Jambusar formations consisting of claystone and sandstone. Recent alluvium covers the entire basinal area except the outcrops along the eastern margin. The entire Neogene section is immature for hydrocarbon generation, but it is part of the overburden rock necessary to create thermal maturity in the Cambay Shale.

The Cenozoic stratigraphy of the South Cambay basin indicates cyclic deposition, that is, many marine transgressions followed by deltaic regressions. This cyclic deposition indicates alternating periods of subsidence and stability. This resulted in the deposition of alternating sandstone and shale sequences that ideally provided reservoir–cap rock combinations for Eocene–early Oligocene traps. However, faunal control is meager for correlating transgressive events with major

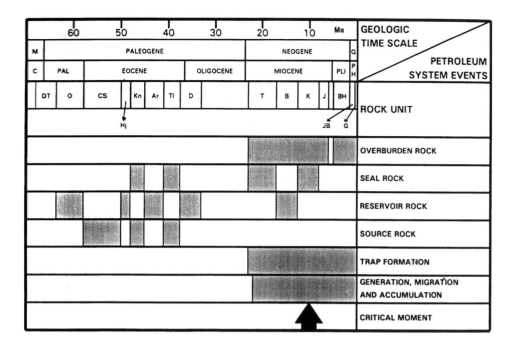

Figure 37.5. Cambay–Hazad(!) petroleum system events related to time. Abbreviations of rock units: DT, Deccan Trap; O, Olpad Formation; CS, Cambay Shale; Hj, Hazad Member; Kn, Kanwa; Ar, Ardol; Tl, Telwa; D, Dadhar Formation; T, Tarakeshwar Formation; B, Babaguru Formation; K, Kand Formation; J, Jhagadia Formation; BH, Broach Formation; JB, Jambusar Formation; G, Alluvium. Geologic time scale: M, Mesozoic; C, Cretaceous; PH, Pleistocene–Holocene.

worldwide eustatic sea level changes. During the Neogene, a renewed phase of subsidence resulted in the deposition of thick marine to fluviodeltaic sedimentary rocks by the paleodrainage network of the proto-Mahisagar, Dadhar, and Narmada rivers.

THE CAMBAY–HAZAD(!) PETROLEUM SYSTEM

Analysis of the petroleum system in the South Cambay basin is related to structural styles and the pod of active source rock. The events and processes that make up the petroleum system are described here and shown relative to the geologic time scale in Figure 37.5.

Petroleum Source Rock

Potential source rocks in the South Cambay basin include the Cambay Shale and the Kanwa and Telwa shale members of the Ankleshwar Formation (Figure 37.4). The shale members of the Ankleshvar Formation are adequately rich in organic matter, with total organic carbon (TOC) varying from 1 to 2 wt. %. However, throughout the South Cambay basin, these shale members are immature, except along the western part of Broach depression where they are in the very early catagenetic stage as indicated by vitrinite reflectance values of 0.5–0.6% R_o.

The source rock for the commercial accumulations of oil and gas in the South Cambay basin is the lower–middle Eocene Cambay Shale, which extends across the entire South Cambay basin including the Gulf of Cambay. The maximum thickness of Cambay Shale penetrated is 1500 m in the Jambusar-P well (Figure 37.1).

The amount and type of organic matter and its level of thermal maturity indicate that the Cambay Shale is a good oil and gas source rock. Extensive TOC measurements and Rock-Eval pyrolysis data on Cambay samples from the drilled wells have been generated. TOC measurements of more than 600 samples from 20 wells indicate that the average TOC is 2.6 wt. %. Rock-Eval pyrolysis data from 9 wells indicate a present-day average hydrocarbon index (HI) of 93 (mg HC/g TOC). Geochemical data from the Paleogene sequence in wells of the Broach-Jambusar block in South Cambay basin (presented by Banerjee and Rao, 1993) further confirm the generation potential of Cambay Shale as a major hydrocarbon source rock.

The immature HI of the Cambay Shale has been computed using the following steps. The paleo-geothermal gradient during Cambay Shale deposition was computed using the Sweeney and Burnham (1990) vitrinite evolution model. The paleogeothermal gradient so computed was used as input in the Tissot and Espitalie (1975) generation model to compute the extent of transformation of the organic matter at the base and top of the Cambay Shale. The HI before onset of generation (HI$_o$) is given by the formula

$$HI_o = HI_p \times 100 / (100 - Tr \%)$$

where HI$_p$ is the average present day HI and Tr % is the computed percent transformation. The average HI of the sequence before onset of generation will then be the mean of the computed immature hydrogen indices at the top and bottom of the sequence. The immature HIs of the Cambay Shale were computed at different locations following these steps. The mean HI for these is 121 (mg HC/g TOC). The difference between the average immature HI and the average present-day HI is 28 (mg HC/g TOC).

A plot of hydrogen index against oxygen index for several wells of the South Cambay basin is shown in Figure 37.6. This plot indicates that the bulk of the

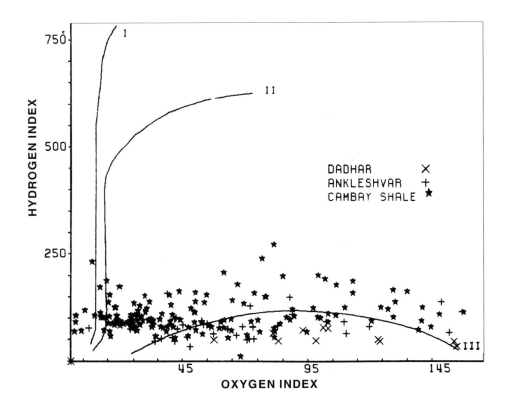

Figure 37.6. Hydrogen index versus oxygen index plot of source rocks in the South Cambay basin. The HI of the Cambay Shale is as high as 250.

organic matter of potential source rocks are type III, with some contribution from type II. Vitrinite reflectance measurements, T_{max} data, and TTI computations indicate that the bulk of the Cambay Shale is in the catagenetic stage.

A Lopatin diagram was constructed for the deepest well, Jambusar-P (Figures 37.1 and 37.2), to show the time and depth at which oil and gas generation from the Cambay Shale occurred (Figure 37.7). The data on age, depth, and thickness of the rock units penetrated in this well are taken from the study of Mohan (1988). For the Cambay Shale source rock, the TTI of 10 corresponding to the top of the oil window (0.6% R_o) occurred during the early Miocene and the TTI of 180 corresponding to the top of the gas window (1.3% R_o) occurred during the Pliocene (2 Ma). The critical moment is at 10 Ma because this corresponds to peak hydrocarbon generation from the Cambay Shale in most of the area circumscribed by the pod of active source rock. For the last 21 m.y., the Cambay shale has continuously generated oil and gas.

Reservoir Rocks and Accumulations

Most hydrocarbon-bearing reservoir rocks in the South Cambay basin are deltaic sandstones that were deposited by the proto-Narmada, Mahisagar, and Dadhar river systems during a regressive phase in the middle Eocene–early Oligocene. These reservoir rocks are capped by marine shales deposited during short transgressive episodes. Other reservoir rocks include the trap wackes of the Paleocene Olpad Formation, siltstones within the Cambay Shale, and lower Miocene sandstones of the Babaguru Formation.

About 85% by volume of the in-place oil and gas accumulations are confined to the Hazad Member and the remaining 15% in the Ardol Member of the Ankleshvar Formation. Minor amounts are also present in the Paleocene Olpad Formation, Eocene Cambay Shale, upper Eocene–lower Oligocene Dadhar Formation, and basal Miocene sandstones.

The largest oil and gas field in the Cambay–Hazad petroleum system is Gandhar (field 11 on Figure 37.2) with in-place reserves of 210 million t. The Gandhar accumulation occurs in multiple pay sands in a combina-

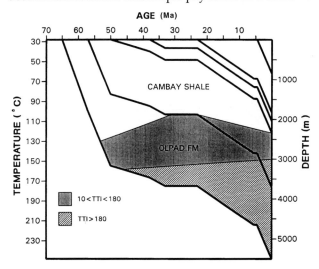

Figure 37.7. Lopatin reconstruction of burial and thermal history at Jambusar-P well location (Figures 37.1 and 37.2). The critical moment is 10 Ma. Oil generation has been continuous since the Miocene (21 Ma).

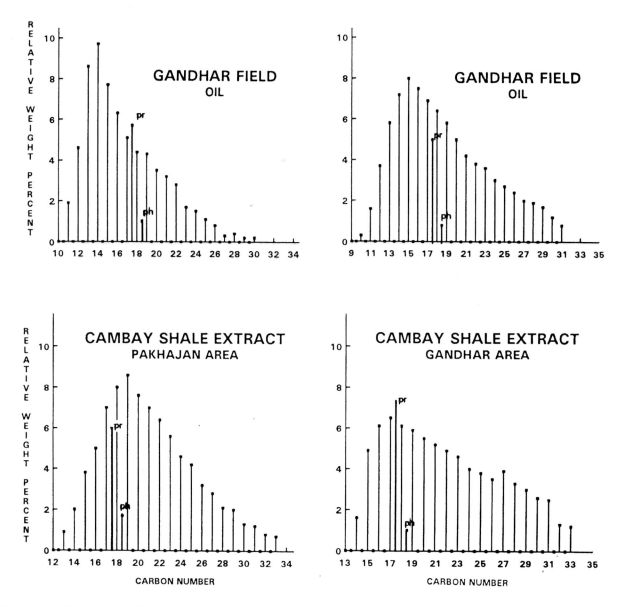

Figure 37.8. The *n*-alkane distribution of representative oils and source rock extracts of the Cambay Shale. The pristane (pr) and phytane (ph) peaks are labeled.

tion trap. The field extends over an area of 175 km² and has a net pay thickness of 57 m. The API gravity of the oils range from 42° to 55°. The reservoirs occur over a depth range of 2750–3020 m, and porosities vary from 12 to 22%. The average initial reservoir pressure ranges from 285 to 342 kg/cm². The initial gas-oil ratio (GOR) ranges from 147 to 748 (vol/vol).

The second largest field in this system is Ankleshvar (field 7 on Figure 37.2) with in-place oil and gas reserves of 153 million t. The structure is a doubly plunging faulted anticline with the oil pools occurring at an average depth of about 1250 m. The field extends over 30 km² and has a net pay thickness of 46 m. The multiple sandstone reservoirs have an average porosity of 23% and an average permeability of 250 md. The oils range in API gravity from 45° to 50°. The sulfur content is negligible, and the wax content ranges from 5 to 12%.

Level of Certainty

The level of certainty indicates the confidence level in correlating the oil and gas accumulations to a particular active source rock. GC-MS, carbon isotopic, and biological marker data on oils and source rock extracts (Datta et al., 1987; Mathur et al., 1987; Singh et al., 1987) show good correlation between the oils in South Cambay basin fields and the Cambay Shale. Studies on the organic matter of the Cambay and the shales of the Ankleshvar Formation have indicated the predominance of terrestrial organic matter deposited under relatively oxic environments. Figure 37.8 shows the distribution of *n*-alkanes in two oils from the Gandhar field and two extracts of Cambay Shale. The source rock extracts exhibit C_{18}–C_{20} maximum, and the oils show maximum in C_{14}–C_{16}. The distribution of the isoprenoids pristane and phytane in

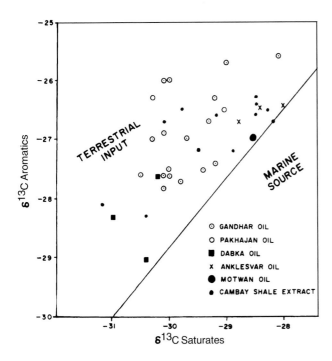

Figure 37.9. Carbon isotopic ratios of saturated versus aromatic hydrocarbons in oils and rock extracts from the South Cambay basin.

the oils and extracts exhibit a good match. The carbon isotopic ratios of saturate versus aromatic hydrocarbons for 20 oil samples and 13 rock extracts from the Cambay Shale are nearly identical, as shown in Figure 37.9. The $\delta^{13}C$ for the aromatic hydrocarbons in the 13 rock extracts range from –26.3 to –27.6‰, a 1.3‰ difference, and for the 20 oils from –25.71 to –28.95‰, a 3.24‰ difference.

Based on biological markers, particularly the ratio of pristane and n-C_{17} to phytane and n-C_{18}, the oils with a range of 1.5–2.03 show a good correlation with the Cambay Shale extracts with values of 1.7–1.8. A few rock extracts from the Kanwa and Telwa shales of the Ankleshvar Formation have also shown fairly good correlation with a few oils.

Geographic and Stratigraphic Extent

The geographic extent of the Cambay–Hazad petroleum system includes the pod of active source rock and the oil fields that were charged from that pod (Figure 37.2). The Lopatin diagram (Figure 37.7) indicates that the top of the Cambay Shale is the top of the oil window and that the base of the shale is within the gas window. Projecting the oil window across the South Cambay basin on the basis of vitrinite reflectance data indicates that the pod of active source rock is smaller than the outline of the petroleum system (Figure 37.2).

The accumulations charged by the Cambay Shale are shown in Figure 37.2. The Cambay Shale extends to North Cambay basin where it is also in the mature stage, but the oil accumulations of North Cambay basin exhibit different characteristics. Data are inadequate for oil to source correlation in North Cambay basin.

The stratigraphic extent of the petroleum system includes all the rock units that are essential elements and processes of the system (Figures 37.2–37.5 and 37.7). The essential elements of the Cambay–Hazad petroleum system (Figure 37.5) are as follows:

1. The source rock is lower–middle Eocene Cambay Shale.
2. The reservoir rocks are the middle Eocene Hazad and Ardol members of the Ankleshvar Formation, the upper Eocene–lower Oligocene Dadhar Formation, and lower Miocene basal sandstone of the Babaguru Formation.
3. The seal rocks are the middle Eocene Kanwa Shale, the upper Eocene Telwa Shale Member of the Ankleshvar Formation, the lower Miocene Tarakeshvar Formation, and the upper Miocene Kand Formation.
4. The overburden rocks are the middle Eocene–Recent units that overlie the source rock.

Trap formation started in early Miocene (23 Ma) before oil generation commenced (20 Ma), and both continue to the present day.

EFFICIENCY OF THE SYSTEM

The efficiency of the petroleum system is determined by a comparison of the in-place oil and gas reserves to the amount of oil and gas generated by the pod of active source rock, and it is expressed as a percentage. The amount of hydrocarbons generated from the Cambay Shale has been computed following the method of Schmoker (Chapter 19, this volume).

The average TOC content of Cambay Shale from 20 wells is 2.6 wt. %, and its average density determined from density logs is 2.55 g/cm^3. The area of the active source rock pod is 5410 km^2 and its rock volume is 4057.5 km^3. The mass of organic carbon (M) is calculated according to equation 1 of Schmoker:

$$M \text{ (g TOC)} = 2.6/100 \times 2.55 \times 4.1 \times 10^{18}$$
$$= 2.72 \times 10^{17} \text{ g TOC} \qquad (1)$$

The mass of hydrocarbons generated per unit mass of organic carbon (R) for the Cambay Shale is calculated as follows:

$$R \text{ (mg HC/g TOC)} = HI_o \text{ (mg HC/g TOC)}$$
$$- HI_p \text{ (mg HC/g TOC)}$$
$$R \text{ (mg HC/g TOC)} = 121 - 93 = 28 \qquad (2)$$

where HI_o is the original hydrogen index and HI_p is the present-day hydrogen index. The total mass of hydrocarbons generated (HCG) is thus equal to the result of equation 2 times the result of equation 1 times 10^{-6}:

$$HCG \text{ (kg HC)} = 28 \times 2.72 \times 10^{17} \times 10^{-6}$$
$$= 7.61 \times 10^{12} \text{ kg HC}$$

The in-place reserves of oil and gas discovered thus far in the system total 395 million t. Thus, the generation–accumulation efficiency of the system is 5.2%.

CONCLUDING REMARKS

The Cambay–Hazad(!) petroleum system in south Cambay basin covers 9320 km² and contains 20 proven oil and gas fields totaling 395 million t of original in-place petroleum reserves. The system belongs to Tertiary sediments in which the essential elements were deposited from early Eocene to Recent time. The critical processes occurred from Miocene onward. The amount of generated hydrocarbons are estimated to be 7.61×10^{12} kg showing 5.2% efficiency for the proven accumulated hydrocarbons.

Acknowledgments   *The authors are grateful to P. K. Chandra, Vice-Chairman, Oil and Natural Gas Commission, for permission to publish this paper. The authors acknowledge the assistance of Nuzhath J. Thomas in calculation of immature HI used in generation modeling and in preparation of Figures 37.5 and 37.7. They are grateful to J. Kundu for providing the cross section shown in Figure 37.3.*

References Cited

Banerjee, A., S. R. Dalal, and J. P. Thapliyal, 1990, Geochemical evaluation of Gandhar oils and gases: Unpublished Oil and Natural Gas Commission report, Baroda, India.

Banerjee, A., and K. L. N. Rao, 1993, Geochemical evaluation of part of the Cambay Basin, India: AAPG Bulletin, v. 77, p. 29–48.

Bhandari, L. L., and L. R. Choudhary, 1975, Stratigraphic analysis of Kalol and Kadi formations: AAPG Bulletin, v. 59, p. 856–871.

Bhasin, A. L., S. P. Painuly, S. P. S. Baghel, B. N. Sharma, G. Lal, and B. S. Ghosh, 1985, Paleodelta exploration model for South Cambay basin: Unpublished Oil and Natural Gas Commission report, Dehradun, India.

Biswas, S. K., 1982, Rift basins in the western margin of India and their hydrocarbon prospects: AAPG Bulletin, v. 66, p. 1497–1513.

Biswas, S. K., 1987, Regional tectonic framework, structure, and evolution of the western marginal basins of India: Tectonophysics, v. 137, p. 307–327.

Chandra, P. K., and L. R. Choudhary, 1969, Stratigraphy of Cambay basin: Oil and Natural Gas Commission Bulletin, v. 6, p. 35–50.

Chandra, K., R. K. Kumar, C. Prakash, M. R. Mali, P. K. Saxena, P. Dwivedi, M. C. Sharma, G. C. Datta, S. Rao, and V. Gupta, 1983, Geochemistry and genesis of Cambay basin crudes: Unpublished Oil and Natural Gas Commission report, Dehradun, India.

Datta, G. C., S. P. Das, P. Dwivedi, V. Gupta, V. Banerjie, and R. K. Kumar, 1987, Stable carbon isotopic studies of crude oils of Cambay basin, in Kumar et al., eds., Petroleum Geochemistry and Exploration in Afro-Asian Region: Balkema, Rotterdam, p. 483–486.

Dhar, P. C., M. K. Mukherjee, M. Jain, S. Chawla, and A. Sood, 1987, Hydrocarbon prospects of the Broach depression, Cambay basin: Oil and Natural Gas Commission Bulletin, v. 24, p. 39–58.

Mathur, L. P., K. L. N. Rao, and A. N. Chaube, 1968, Tectonic framework of Cambay basin: Oil and Natural Gas Commission Bulletin, v. 5, p. 7–28.

Mathur, S., V. K. Jain, G. K. Tripathi, J. K. Jassal, and K. Chandra, 1987, Biological marker geochemistry of crude oils of Cambay basin, India, in Kumar et al., eds., Petroleum Geochemistry and Exploration in Afro-Asian Region: Balkema, Rotterdam, p. 459–473.

Mehrotra, R. B., and V. Ramakrishna, 1980, A re-look at the stratigraphy and hydrocarbon occurrences of North Cambay Basin with special reverence to Kadi Formation: Unpublished Oil and Natural Gas Commission report, Ahmedabad, India.

Mishra, P. C., and P. B. Pati, 1980, Stratigraphic and paleotectonic analysis of Paleogene sediments with special reference to Cambay Shale and hydrocarbon prospects, South Cambay basin, Gujarat: Unpublished Oil and Natural Gas Commission report, Dehradun, India.

Mohan, M., 1988, Stratigraphy and source rock potential of the Paleogene strata met with in well Jambusar-P-1: Unpublished Oil and Natural Gas Commission report, Baroda, India.

Mohan, M., S. K. Bhattacharya, D. C. Sharma, C. L. Choudhary, and M. Shanmukhappa, 1987, Environmental reconstruction and depositional modelling of the Hazad pay sands in Gandhar: Unpublished Oil and Natural Gas Commission Report, Baroda, India.

Orlov, V. S., and G. I. Sovirn, 1965, Analysis of pressure and conditions of ways to improve development of Ankleshvar oil field: Unpublished Oil and Natural Gas Commission report, Dehradun, India.

Raju, A. T. R., 1968, Geological evolution of Assam and Cambay Tertiary basins of India: AAPG Bulletin, v. 52, p. 2422–2437.

Rao, K. L. N., 1969, Lithostratigraphy of Paleogene succession of Southern Cambay basin: Oil and Natural Gas Commission Bulletin, v. 6, p. 24–37.

Singh, S. P., M. Mathur, J. G. Saxena, and J. P. Thapliyal, 1987, Geochemical characteristics of oils occurring in the multi-layered reservoirs of the Broach syncline, Cambay basin: Oil and Natural Gas Commission Bulletin, v. 24, p. 191–213.

Sudhakar, R., and D. N. Basu, 1973, A reappraisal of the Paleogene stratigraphy of southern Cambay basin: Oil and Natural Gas Commission Bulletin, v. 10, p. 55–76.

Sweeney, J. J., and A. K. Burnham, 1990, Evaluation of a simple model of vitrinite reflectance based on chemical kinetics: AAPG Bulletin, v. 74, p. 1559–1570.

Tissot, B., and J. Espitalie, 1975, Thermal evolution of organic matter in sediments: Applications of a mathematical simulation: Review Insititute Français du Pétrole, v. 30, p. 743–777.

Yalcin, M. N., D. H. Welte, K. N. Misra, S. K. Mandal, K. C. Balan, K. L. Mehrotra, B. L. Lohar, S. P. Kumar, and G. S. Mishra, 1987, 3-D computer aided basin modelling of Cambay basin, India—A case history of hydrocarbon generation, in Kumar et al., eds., Petroleum Geochemistry and Exploration in Afro-Asian Region: Balkema, Rotterdam, p. 417–450.

Magoon, L. B., and W. G. Dow, eds., 1994, The petroleum
system—from source to trap: AAPG Memoir 60.

Chapter 38

Bampo–Peutu(!) Petroleum System, North Sumatra, Indonesia

Steven P. Buck

Mobil Exploration Norway
Stavanger, Norway

Thane H. McCulloh

Dallas, Texas, U.S.A.

Abstract

The Bampo–Peutu(!) petroleum system occurs near the northern end of the island of Sumatra, Indonesia. This system, which is within the larger North Sumatra basin, includes 10 gas and gas–condensate discoveries and has produced more than 9.5 tcf of gas and 500 MMbbl of condensate and natural gas liquids (C_2–C_{4+}) as of May 1991. Original discovered reserves are estimated at 15 tcf of gas and 1.0 Bbbl of condensate and natural gas liquids. Source rock analytical data and carbon isotopic analyses indicate that the Oligocene Bampo Formation is the principle source of hydrocarbons in the system, with shales of the Miocene Peutu Formation a potential secondary source. These strata are lean in organic matter (TOC < 1 wt. %) and contain primarily type III kerogen. However, this lean source rock is offset by the substantial volume of mature to overmature, fine-grained rock in the deeps. Miocene reefal carbonates of the Peutu Formation constitute the primary reservoir strata, while overpressured shales of the Baong, Peutu, and Bampo formations provide excellent seals. Most accumulations occur in structural–stratigraphic traps. Reefs developed preferentially on paleotopographic highs and were later encased in impermeable shales. Multiple migration pathways, including basal coarse clastics, several unconformity surfaces, and localized faults, all provide conduits for hydrocarbon migration from the mature source rocks to the adjacent reefs. The timing of peak migration is estimated at 12–4 Ma. A trapping efficiency of 3.6% is calculated for the entire petroleum system by comparing volumetric estimates of hydrocarbons generated to the amount trapped in known discoveries. A much higher trapping efficiency (40–70% range) characterizes the Arun gas field. Ideal geologic conditions, including centripetal migration from several flanking depocenters, explain this high migration efficiency.

INTRODUCTION

The Bampo–Peutu(!) petroleum system of North Sumatra is situated near the northwestern tip of the Indonesian archipelago and extends from onshore Sumatra into the Andaman Sea (Figure 38.1). Situated between the Indian Ocean and the Thailand–Malaysia peninsula, this system represents the northern termination of a chain of prolific petroleum systems that extend along the northeastern side of the island of Sumatra.

Exploration History

Petroleum exploration in North Sumatra has a long, colorful history beginning in the late nineteenth century. Initial exploration of the region began in the 1880s when a local tobacco farmer located several oil seeps and recognized the implications for potential subsurface accumulations. Exploratory drilling commenced soon afterward in 1883, with the first commercial discovery occurring at Telaga Tunggal in 1885 (van Bemmelen, 1970). Three additional fields were discovered by the turn of the century, and with this success came the birth of the local petroleum industry and the beginnings of what would later become one of the world's largest oil companies, Royal Dutch Shell.

Exploration in North Sumatra continued into the early 1940s as Dutch and Indonesian explorationists conducted geologic field investigations followed by torsion balance and first generation seismic reflection and refraction surveys. Several of the largest and most prospective structural features were recognized during these early field studies (Meyer, 1942), but Japanese occupation of Indonesia during World War II terminated these early efforts. Following the war, Indonesia's struggle for independence and subsequent internal political conflicts further postponed new exploration in the country. It was not until the mid-1960s that new political stability encouraged the Indonesian petroleum industry to resume full operations and begin exploring

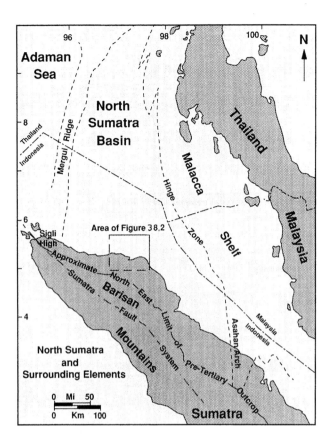

Figure 38.1. Map showing geographic location and present-day boundary (dashed line) of the North Sumatra Tertiary basin. Light shading is water and darker shading is land. Location of Figure 38.2 is shown.

once again. As a consequence of this long drilling hiatus, all 10 gas–condensate fields that define the Bampo–Peutu petroleum system have been discovered since 1971 (Table 38.1).

Previous Investigations

Economic interest in the geology of Sumatra has stimulated much research on various aspects of the petroleum systems of North Sumatra (Graves and Weegar, 1973; Kamili and Naim, 1973; Kamili et al, 1976; Houpt and Kersting, 1978; Kingston, 1978; Cameron et al., 1980; McArthur and Helm, 1982; Situmorang et al., 1983; Soeparjadi, 1983; Aziz and Bolt, 1984; Weathers and Helm, 1984; Burnaman et al., 1985; Thamrin, 1985; Situmeang and Davies, 1986; Sosromihardjo, 1988; Kjellgren and Sugiharto, 1989; Wang et al., 1989; Davies, 1990; Rory, 1990; Sunaryo and Djamil, 1990). Several commendable efforts have been made to use geochemical data to link specific source intervals to reservoired hydrocarbons (Kingston, 1978; Situmeang and Davies, 1986; Kjellgren and Sugiharto, 1989), and the present study complements the results of these earlier works. In particular, we build upon the published source–oil correlations of Situmeang and Davies (1986) and Kjellgren and Sugiharto (1989). With new geochemical data of our

own, we distinguish two separate petroleum systems for North Sumatra: the Bampo–Peutu system, which refers primarily to the gas condensate fields (A–J on Figure 38.2) of North Sumatra, and a second petroleum system that includes the oil fields (1–7 on Figure 38.2). The Bampo–Peutu petroleum system is the focus of this chapter, and the reader is referred to earlier publications for information on the oil fields in the other petroleum system (Situmeang and Davies, 1986; Kjellgren and Sugiharto, 1989).

SEDIMENTARY BASIN SETTING

The Bampo–Peutu petroleum system is contained within the large tectonic depression known as the North Sumatra basin. The margins of this basin are defined by the Mergui Ridge to the west, the Malacca platform to the east, the Barisan Mountains to the south, and the convergence of the Mergui Ridge and Malacca platform to the north (Figure 38.1). The basin spans almost 300,000 km^2 and contains over 6 km of mostly fine-grained Tertiary sedimentary rocks in several of the deepest depocenters. The Tertiary strata record an early history of extensional rifting to form the basin, followed by a period of stable sedimentation, and lastly, a period of compression starting in middle Miocene time but culminating in the Plio-Pleistocene that uplifted the Barisan Mountains. The portion of the North Sumatra basin that contains the Bampo–Peutu petroleum system is shown on Figure 38.2.

Structural Setting

The North Sumatra basin is characterized by a series of alternating structural highs and deeps with an approximate north-south orientation. The east-west schematic cross section in Figure 38.3 transects several important features, including the Arun and Alur Siwah highs, the Jawa and Lho Sukon deeps, and the Malacca shelf. This cross section is based on integrated interpretations of reflection seismic and well data. The structural configuration of the basin is interpreted as a series of north-south trending horsts (highs) and grabens (deeps) and/or half-grabens whose orientation may be related to a preexisting basement structural grain (ASCOPE, 1985). Early sedimentation in these deeps was influenced by this north-south structural grain, as the basal sedimentary units are generally restricted to these paleodepressions.

Sedimentation and subsidence continued without interruption in the deeps from early Oligocene to Holocene time. Elsewhere, sedimentation was interrupted by local uplifts, depositional hiatuses, or regional erosion, as several angular unconformities are observed over many of the structural highs. Basement faults that bound the highs locally extend upward into Pliocene strata indicating movement into at least Pliocene time.

During late Tertiary time, the North Sumatra basin was dominated by a compressional event that caused uplift of the southwestern margin of the basin and elevation of the Barisan Mountains. This deformation is

Table 38.1. Reserve Estimates and Production Statistics as of May 1991 for Gas–Condensate Accumulations in the Bampo–Peutu(!) Petroleum System[a,b]

	Well Name	Year Disc'd	Res Fm	Res Lith	Producing Status	Res Depth (m)	Cond Gravity (API)	Cum Production Cond (× 10⁶ bbl)	Cum Production Gas (bcf)	Ultimate Reserves Cond (× 10⁶ bbl)	Ultimate Reserves Gas (bcf)
A	Arun	1971	Peutu	Ls	Producing	2900	56°	530	9500	960	13,900
B	S. Lho Sukon A	1972	Peutu	Ls	Shut-in	2600	—	–	–	—	300
C	Alur Siwah	1972	Peutu	Ls	Shut-in	2800	—	—	—	—	—
D	S. Lho Sukon B	1980	Peutu	Ls	Shut-in	2425	—	—	—	—	30
E	N. Lho Sukon A	1981	Peutu	Ls	Shut-in	1300	—	—	—	—	100
F	Pase	1983	Peutu	Ls/Ss	Shut-in	2000	—	—	—	—	120
G	Rayeu C	1983	Peutu	Ls	Shut-in	1950	—	—	—	—	75
H	Cunda A	1984	Peutu	Ls	Shut-in	3650	—	—	—	—	80
I	Peusangan B	1985	Peutu	Ls	Shut-in	1975	—	—	—	—	40
J	S. Lho Sukon D	1991	Peutu	Ls	Shut-in	2450	—	—	—	—	385

[a]Abbreviations: Res, Reservoir; Lith, lithology; Cond, condensate; Cum, Cumulative.

[b]Only the Arun gas field has significant condensate reserves; others are primarily dry gas discoveries. All trap types are combined structural–stratigraphic. See Figure 38.2 for location of wells lettered A–J. Data from Soeparjadi (1983), Jordan and Abdullah (1987), and unpublished Mobil internal company reports.

related to the current tectonic setting of Sumatra at the southeastern margin of the Eurasian plate. The plate boundary is marked by the Sunda or Java trench where the Indian plate is actively subducting beneath the Eurasian plate. Plate convergence and subduction along this boundary have been associated with uplift and an associated magmatic arc, the Barisan Mountains. The compression that formed this mountain front has influenced regional sedimentary patterns and produced many of the present-day compressional features found in the North Sumatra basin.

Stratigraphic Section

The oldest sedimentary rocks identified within the North Sumatra basin are synrift siliciclastic strata of early Oligocene age. The youngest are siliciclastic sediments being deposited today on the floor of the Andaman Sea. Multiple regional unconformities and depositional hiatuses subdivide the intervening thick Tertiary sedimentary rocks that fill the basin (Figure 38.4).

Coarse siliciclastic strata (local fanglomerate, metamict conglomerate, and sandstone) of the Bruksah Formation are at the base of the sedimentary section. The Bruksah unconformably overlies a deeply eroded metamorphic basement of diverse pre-Tertiary rocks that form the basin floor. Basement lithologies are highly variable and include metasedimentary schist, phyllite, calcareous slate, metagraywacke, recrystallized carbonate, and rare Mesozoic plutonic and basaltic rocks. Composition of some coarse clasts within the Tertiary strata match the underlying basement lithologies, implying local derivation. This first phase of sedimentation began in topographic depressions or deeps initially of local extent (ASCOPE, 1985; Blevins et al., 1990). The coarse clastic strata of the Bruksah Formation grade upward and interfinger laterally with bioclastic limestones of the Jeuku Limestone and shales and claystones of the Bampo Formation, the latter of which locally contains deep

water foraminifera and rare nannofossils of early–late Oligocene age.

The name Jeuku Limestone has been applied to shallow water bioclastic limestone of Oligocene age that occurs locally in a few wells (Jeuku #1 and wells over the Cunda high) and equivalent outcrops in the Barisan Mountains. This limestone signifies that reefal and platform carbonate sedimentation occurred simultaneously with deposition of Bruksah coarse clastics and/or

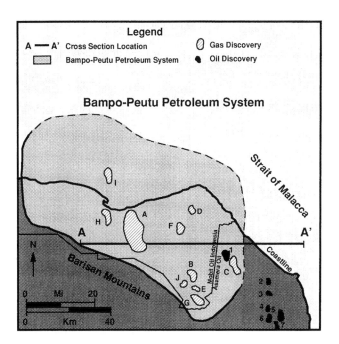

Figure 38.2. Geographic extent of the Bampo–Peutu(!) petroleum system showing locations of gas condensate field discoveries (A–J on Figure 38.4 and Table 38.1). The dashed portion of the boundary line reflects the uncertainty in its placement. Oil accumulations (1–7 on Figure 38.4) are in the other North Sumatra petroleum system. Cross section A–A' is shown in Figure 38.3.

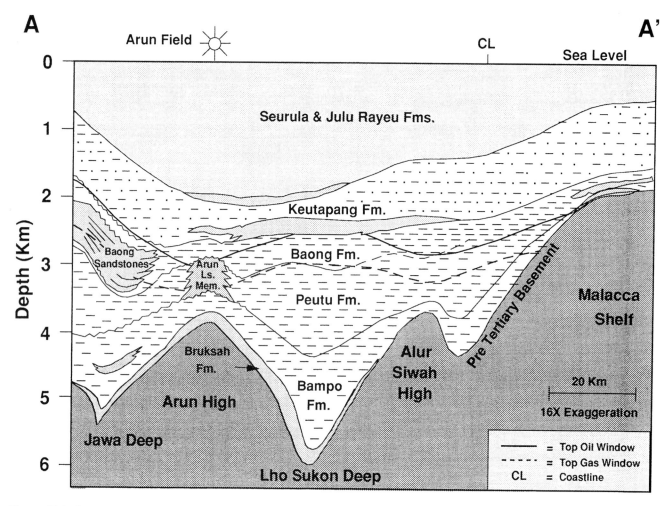

Figure 38.3. Cross section A–A' transecting key structural features of the North Sumatra basin. Location of Arun gas field and top of oil (0.6% R_o) and gas (1.2% R_o) window are shown.

Bampo basinal shales west of the Arun high. Nummulitic foraminifera accompanied by algae and coralline debris suggest clear, warm waters and shallow banktop environments. The regional extent of this limestone facies is poorly known, but an approximate north-south depositional trend is suggested by the known distribution of this facies from the Cunda high in the north, through the Jeuku #1 well, and to the south where it crops out in the Barisan Mountains southwest of the Arun gas field (north of Lake Laut Tawar).

The Bampo Formation consists of upper Oligocene fine-grained strata (claystone, mudstone, and black shale) which conformably overlies and interfingers with the coarser basal clastics of the Bruksah Formation. Diagnostic fossils in the Bampo are uncommon but, where present, indicate deep marine sedimentation that may have been oxygen deficient. Organic matter in this unit is mainly humic with a total organic carbon (TOC) content ranging from 0.3 to 0.7 wt. % for immature rocks. Nevertheless, geochemical evidence presented here indicates that the Bampo is the primary source for most of the hydrocarbons in the Bampo–Peutu system. Overpressured Bampo shales also provide an impermeable

bottom seal for overlying Peutu reservoir rocks.

The Bampo Formation and, in some places, the Bruksah Formation are bounded above by a regional unconformity that is locally angular, indicating that more than 1000 m of section has been uplifted and eroded. For example, notice the missing section beneath the Arun gas field in Figure 38.3. This erosional event was followed by an early Miocene transgression and deposition of the Peutu Formation.

Thick shales and marls of the Peutu Formation were deposited in the deeps. These lithologies interfinger with platform carbonates and with local reefal carbonates or bioclastic buildups where the metamorphic basement was high. These reefal carbonate facies comprise the primary reservoirs for the Bampo–Peutu petroleum accumulations such as the Arun gas field, while the flanking Peutu shales provide an overpressured lateral seal. Peutu basinal shales may also locally represent a secondary hydrocarbon source.

A regional unconformity of middle Miocene age is present at the top of the Peutu Formation (Abdullah and Jordan, 1987; Jordan, 1989; Jordan and Abdullah, 1992). The amount of erosion on this unconformity is variable

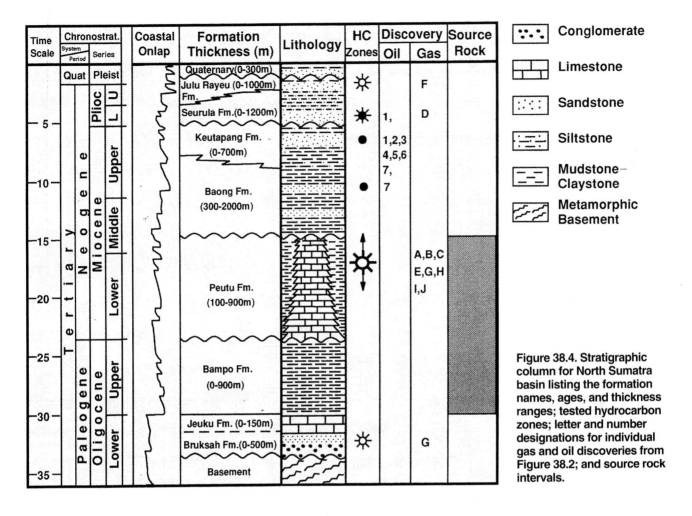

Figure 38.4. Stratigraphic column for North Sumatra basin listing the formation names, ages, and thickness ranges; tested hydrocarbon zones; letter and number designations for individual gas and oil discoveries from Figure 38.2; and source rock intervals.

across the North Sumatra basin, with basement highs exhibiting the greatest amount of removal. Subaerial exposure and meteoric water influx during this erosional event enhanced the reservoir characteristics of the Peutu reefs by creating a significant amount of secondary porosity. Most Peutu reefs that lack this secondary porosity also lack sufficient primary porosity to be adequate petroleum reservoirs.

A third cycle of submergence and sedimentation began with deposition of the Baong Formation. This cycle began some places as early as 15 Ma, but it is locally as late as 9 Ma. The Baong comprises mostly of shales and mudstones that are typically overpressured. In this petroleum system, these lithologies provide an excellent top seal for gas–condensate accumulations in the underlying Peutu reservoir rocks. Locally, sandstones are present in the Baong Formation along the southern edge of the North Sumatra basin. In the Jawa deep area, such sandstones are interpreted as deep water turbidites. However, to the southeast, Baong strata are thought to be mostly deltaic sedimentary rocks with local fine-grained facies being the source rock for the light oil accumulations of the Baong–Keutapang/Seurula petroleum system found in this portion of the basin (Figure 38.2).

The Baong Formation grades upward into the Keutapang Formation as a series of regressive claystone,

mudstone, siltstone, and minor sandstone strata. The base of the Keutapang is clearly diachronous across the basin, ranging from 11 to 4 Ma. These minor sandstone units sometimes contain gassy oils that are compositionally different from hydrocarbons of the Bampo–Peutu petroleum system.

Marine claystones and silty sandstones of the Pliocene Seurula Formation overlie the Keutapang Formation, in some places gradationally and in other places unconformably. Sandstone within the Seurula Formation is one of the primary reservoir rocks for the other North Sumatra petroleum system (Situmeang and Davies, 1986), but Seurula reservoir rock quality is variable and uneconomic in many locations.

Late Pliocene and younger units of the Julu Rayeu Formation and undifferentiated Quaternary sediments succeed the Seurula Formation. These units are composed of sandy claystones and sandstones deposited in marine environments ranging from nearshore neritic to outer neritic open marine conditions. The contact between the Seurula and the Julu Rayeu formations can be gradational or locally marked by a minor transgressive unconformity. Sandstones of the Julu Rayeu Formation locally contain hydrocarbon gas, but it is uncertain whether these gas accumulations are commercial under current economic conditions.

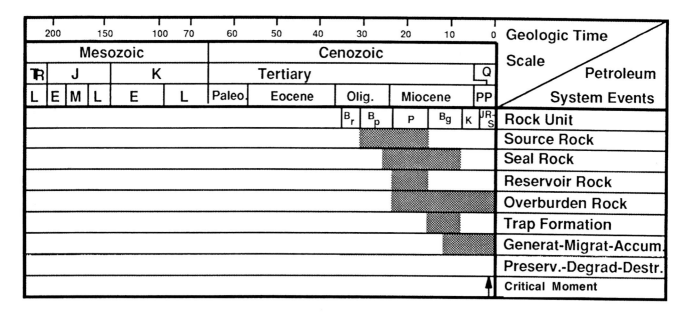

Figure 38.5. Events chart for the Bampo–Peutu(!) petroleum system. Rock unit abbreviations: Br, Bruksah Formation (Jeuku Limestone); Bp, Bampo Formation; P, Peutu Formation; Bg, Baong Formation; K, Keutapang Formation; JR-S, Julu Rayeu–Seurula Formations.

THE PETROLEUM SYSTEM

The petroleum system defines all the geologic elements and processes that are essential to petroleum accumulations (Magoon, 1989). Understanding the temporal relationships of these processes is necessary to fully evaluate the petroleum system and its historical development. Figure 38.5 defines the timing of all petroleum system events for the Bampo–Peutu petroleum system of North Sumatra. A more detailed discussion of the essential elements is presented here.

Petroleum Source Rock

Hydrocarbons in North Sumatra originated from multiple source rock units, including shales and claystones within the Bampo Formation, basinal shales and marls within the Peutu Formation, and shales within the Baong Formation (Kingston, 1978; Situmeang and Davies, 1986; Kjellgren and Sugiharto, 1989; Blevins et al, 1990). Each of these units is both laterally and vertically heterogeneous in terms of lithofacies, organic matter content, and level of thermal maturity. As far as is known, all of these source rocks were deposited in marine environments in the northern North Sumatra basin. Nevertheless, as discussed later, most of the kerogen is type III in composition.

Geochemical oil–source correlations presented here indicate that the shale and mudstone of the Bampo Formation are the principle source rocks for the gas–condensate accumulations of North Sumatra, with the Peutu Formation a potential secondary source. Baong shales in the deeps surrounding the Arun gas field (Jawa and Lho Sukon deeps) have little to no hydrocarbon generative capacity due to a local dearth of organic matter and to the hydrogen-poor composition of the

organic matter that is present (unpublished analytical data). However, source rock analytical data, both published and unpublished, show that the capacity of Baong shales to generate oil increases toward the eastern and southeastern margins of the North Sumatra basin. In this part of the basin, the Baong Formation is regarded as the major source of oil for the accumulations in the other North Sumatra petroleum system (Figure 38.2).

The geologic boundary separating the Bampo–Peutu petroleum system from the other North Sumatra petroleum system appears to be influenced by lateral changes in depositional and paleobathymetric patterns through time, which in turn affects the ability of each source rock to generate particular types of hydrocarbons. Based on available source rock data and regional geology, the feature delineating these two systems is tentatively interpreted as the Alur Siwah high (Figure 38.3), with the exception of oil field 1 (Figure 38.2) which demonstrates some overlap between the two systems. The discussion here focuses on the source rock potential of the Bampo and Peutu formations.

Basinal facies of the Bampo and Peutu formations are composed of a thick sequence of marine shale and mudstone lean in organic matter which contain predominantly type III kerogens plus a small yet variable fraction of hydrogen-rich sapropelic kerogen. Petrographic data of organic matter confirm that most of this organic matter was derived from land plants, with minor amounts of algal and amorphous kerogens. Broad regional trends in total organic carbon from well and outcrop samples suggest that the principal sources of this plant detritus were from the southwest, especially in Miocene strata (Blevins et al., 1990). Mapped patterns of shale thickness, and of source rock richness and kerogen facies, indicate that organic accumulation was controlled by depositional environments and paleobathymetry.

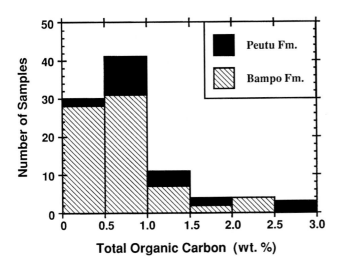

Figure 38.6. Total organic carbon (TOC) measurements (wt. %) of 101 outcrop and well (core and cuttings) samples for Peutu and Bampo shales and mudstones. No analytical data are included from wells drilled with oil-based muds due to severe contamination problems. Samples with highest TOC values are primarily located in deeps.

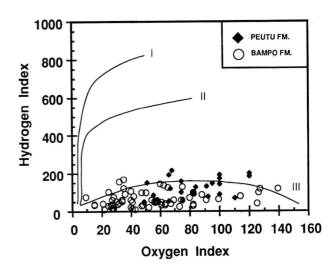

Figure 38.7. Modified van Krevelen diagram based on Rock-Eval pyrolysis data of the same outcrop and well samples as those shown in Figure 38.6. Visual kerogen analyses demonstrate that most organic matter is terrestrial (humic) type III kerogen.

Preservation of organic matter was concentrated in the paleobathymetric deeps where sedimentation was most rapid and sea bottom waters were least oxidizing. Minor amounts of more hydrogen-rich marine kerogen are locally present, especially in the deepest depocenters.

Source rock richness and kerogen type have been evaluated using standard LECO combustion, Rock-Eval pyrolysis, and visual kerogen analyses of the least mature rock samples available. Samples from onshore wells that used oil-based drilling muds were avoided because of severe contamination problems. Even after multiple cleanup attempts by solvent extraction, mud contaminants remaining in rock chips posed a vexing interpretive problem. Figure 38.6 shows the range and frequency of TOC measurements in weight percent for uncontaminated well cores and cuttings and for outcrop samples from the Bampo and Peutu formations. Figure 38.7 displays the low hydrogen index (HI) values for these same samples and the interpreted humic (type III kerogen) composition of the organic matter. Visual kerogen analyses support these interpretations and, along with the previous data, demonstrate a poor to moderate hydrocarbon generative capacity for both source intervals. The original generative capacity of these samples was probably greater than the present-day measured values due to a minor amount of thermal conversion of even the most virgin samples available. Nevertheless, the original TOC and HI content were probably of marginal source quality; this interpretation is based on generative potential reconstructions using mass balance calculations and comparisons with completely immature kerogens of similar composition from other petroleum systems worldwide.

The exceptionally lean organic composition of Bampo and Peutu source rocks is partially offset by the substantial thickness of fine-grained rocks found in the deeps.

Estimates of source rock thickness have been made using regional seismic data tied to well penetrations where available. Few exploration wells have been drilled into the deeps, but seismic data show a significant thickening of the source units into these structural lows (Figure 38.3). Thickness estimates of the source rock intervals range from 0 m over some basement highs (as a consequence of depositional thinning plus erosional truncation) to roughly 1800 m in the deepest depocenters for the combined Bampo and Peutu sections.

Maturation modeling of the Bampo and Peutu source horizons was conducted using an internally developed computerized maturation modeling system. Figure 38.8 shows the interpreted burial and maturation history for the Lho Sukon deep, located east and southeast of the Arun gas field. Modeling runs used (1) burial history data interpreted from seismic and nearby deep well data, (2) present-day geothermal gradients extrapolated from drill stem and logging temperatures, (3) paleogeothermal estimates derived from vitrinite reflectance, (4) thermal alteration index and apatite fission track data, and (5) kerogen kinetics from published (Tissot et al, 1987) and in-house kinetic models that assume a mixed type II/III kerogen (to account for humic and sapropelic components). The boundaries for the oil and gas windows labeled on Figure 38.8 are interpreted from vitrinite reflectance interpretations and basin modeling results that estimate the fraction of source kerogen converted to hydrocarbons through time, using the previous assumptions.

Multiple sensitivity analyses were conducted to evaluate the uncertainty of all input assumptions, and a three-dimensional study was conducted over the entire system to assess spatial variations. Results from the three-dimensional study are similar to the one-dimensional results shown in Figure 38.8; Bampo and Peutu

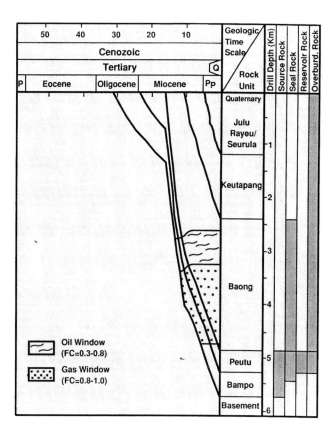

Figure 38.8. Burial and maturation history diagram for the southern end of the Lho Sukon deep. Stratigraphy and thermal history for the deep are interpreted from nearby seismic and well data. Essential elements are shown. Gas and oil windows are based on estimates of source rock fractional conversion (FC, 0.3 = 30%) from modeling studies.

source rocks in the deeps are presently overmature in most locations, with peak generation occurring in late Tertiary time (~12–4 Ma). Rapid conversion of the source kerogen was caused by substantial late Tertiary sedimentation and unusually high geothermal gradients (average 46.8°C/km from 113 wells). Rapid conversion of the source kerogen and the resultant pulse of hydrocarbon generation may have enhanced the migration efficiency of the system because of the unusual brevity of the heating and the migration episode. Hydrocarbons were generated and migrated after trap formation over a relatively short time interval. Thus, there was less time for migrating hydrocarbons to escape the system and a better chance for them to accumulate in preexisting structural–stratigraphic traps.

Exploration and modeling results indicate that gas–condensate hydrocarbons are the primary migratory (expulsion) products of thermal decomposition of the Bampo and Peutu type III kerogens. The volumes of potentially liquid hydrocarbons generated from such lean and gas-prone source rocks presumably were sufficiently limited so that they dissolved in the volumetrically dominant gas phase to be carried out of the source rocks as a subordinate part of a gas–condensate phase (Durand, 1988; Claypool, 1991).

Reservoir Rocks and Accumulations

Local carbonate reefs of the Peutu Formation were constructed by Miocene organisms that flourished in clear, tropical waters over shallow basement horst blocks. These carbonate buildups comprise the primary known reservoir rock for gas–condensate accumulations of the Bampo–Peutu petroleum system. Isolated patch reefs attained thicknesses exceeding 300 m and grade laterally into fine-grained clastic facies in the adjacent structural lows. Reservoir porosity and permeability were locally enhanced by secondary carbonate dissolution when the reefs were emergent and meteoric waters percolated through the subaerially exposed carbonates (Jordan, 1989). Effective seals and stratigraphic traps were created where lateral interfingering of the carbonates with basinal Peutu shales occurred and where a thick shale cover (Baong Formation) subsequently blanketed them, both of which are now overpressured (~0.72 psi/ft shale pressure gradient) (Aziz and Bolt, 1984; Blevins et al, 1990). Overpressured shales in the Bampo Formation also provide an impermeable bottom seal for overlying reservoir rocks in the Peutu Formation. Formation pressures measured in many of these reservoirs are significantly higher than would occur if normal hydrostatic conditions prevailed. (Reservoirs exhibit a normal gas pressure gradient but high absolute pressures due to the overpressured gradient in the overlying shale of the Baong Formation.) Therefore, the overpressured (~0.72 psi/ft gradient) shale of the Bampo Formation provides a crucial bottom seal to prevent hydrocarbons from leaking downward from the reservoir rock. This excellent sealing capacity and the recent timing of hydrocarbon generation together help explain how large gas accumulations are preserved in this actively deforming basin.

Multiple pathways exist to facilitate migration of hydrocarbons from the deeps to the carbonate reefs. Basal clastic units of the Bruksah Formation, local unconformities at the base of and within the Peutu Formation, and extensional fault surfaces all provide migration routes that focus buoyancy-driven hydrocarbons updip into carbonate reefs on the adjacent structural highs.

The Arun gas field is presently the only producing gas–condensate field of the Bampo–Peutu petroleum system, but future production from several smaller discoveries is virtually assured. The carbonate reservoir rock at Arun exceeds 300 m in thickness with an average net pay thickness of 152 m. Reservoir conditions at Arun include an initial abnormally high reservoir pressure of 7100 psi (49 MPa) and reservoir temperature of 178°C at 3048 m, average porosity of 16.2%, and an average water saturation of 17.0%. The average composition of gas produced from the Arun field is 67.3% C_1, 12.7% C_2–C_{7+}, 13.8% CO_2, 5.9% H_2O, and 0.3% N_2. The methane in gas from Arun field has a carbon isotopic $\delta^{13}C$ value of –41‰ (Kingston, 1978). Condensate is produced at an approximate ratio of 50 bbl/MMscf of gas, with an average API gravity of 56° (all Arun production data from Soeparjadi, 1983). Estimates of the reserve and production statistics for all discoveries in the Bampo–Peutu system are listed in Table 38.1.

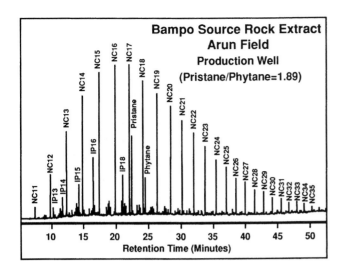

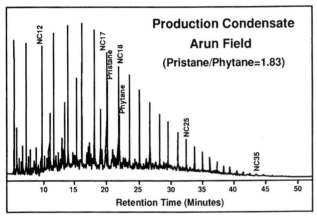

Figure 38.9. Gas chromatographs of a Bampo source rock extract and condensate from the Arun gas field, North Sumatra.

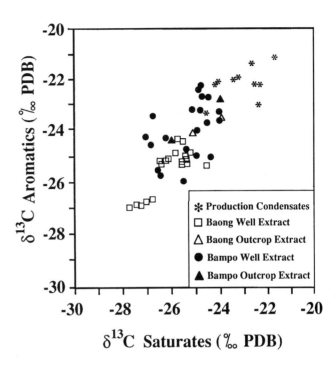

Figure 38.10. Carbon isotopic composition plot of the aromatic and saturate fractions for 10 condensates and 43 source rock extracts. Samples are identified by their sample type and stratigraphic location. Condensate data overlap the Bampo source rock extracts, while the Baong extracts do not overlap.

Level of Certainty

Identification of the fine-grained basinal facies of the Bampo and Peutu formations as the source rock for gas–condensate accumulations in North Sumatra is based on both geochemical and geologic evidence. Chemical and isotopic comparisons between Arun gas–condensate and organic matter extracted from Bampo–Peutu source rocks are consistent with a possible genetic relationship. Moreover, the lack of any other organic carbon-containing rock units of significant thickness in the immediate area supports this correlation by process of elimination.

Representative gas chromatographic profiles of an Arun gas field condensate and a Bampo source rock extract are displayed in Figure 38.9. While the hydrocarbon distributions of such high maturity liquids are limited in diagnostic character, there are general geochemical similarities. Both samples have a predominance of monotonically decreasing normal alkanes and similar pristane–phytane ratios (1.83 versus 1.89). The Bampo source rock extract has a remnant odd-numbered normal alkane predominance (CPI = 1.16), which

supports derivation or contribution from terrestrial (humic) organic matter. The differences between the hydrocarbon distributions shown in Figure 38.9 are partially due to differences in thermal maturity. The source rock sample analyzed was from a depth of 10,248 ft (3124 m) and has a thermal maturity of about 0.7% R_o. The condensate is largely derived from laterally equivalent source rocks in the deep where thermal maturity levels are presently in the range of 1.6–3.0% R_o.

Carbon isotopic compositions of saturate and aromatic fractions of 10 condensates from producing wells and 43 extracts from subsurface and outcrop source rock samples are plotted in Figure 38.10. The $\delta^{13}C$ values of the condensate hydrocarbon fractions range from –25 to –22‰ for the saturate fraction and from –22.5 to –21‰ for the aromatic fraction. The comparable fractions for the Bampo rock extracts range from –27 to –24‰ and from –26 to –22‰, respectively. The overlap in isotopic composition, although limited, is consistent with a genetic relationship between the Arun condensates and the Bampo rock extracts. The condensates are isotopically heavier than the source rock hydrocarbons because the condensates are residual liquids from more extensive thermal cracking processes occurring in the deeps. In contrast, the $\delta^{13}C$ values of the Baong rock extracts are on average 3–4/mL lighter than those of the condensates, a difference that argues against the Baong shales being a significant source for the condensates. Analytical data for isotopic characterization of the Peutu Formation shales are lacking.

The isotopic composition of the methane and the chemical composition of the gas produced from the Arun gas field ($\delta^{13}C = -41\%_0$, $C_1/C_{1-5} = 0.84$) is consistent with being thermally derived from shales low in organic matter containing dispersed type III kerogen (Schoell, 1983; Johnson and Rice, 1990). The provenance of this organic matter deposited in a marine environment is terrestrial (humic).

As previously discussed, additional support for this oil (condensate)–source rock correlation is the stratigraphic distribution of the organic matter. Source rock analytical data indicate that shales of the Bampo and Peutu have poor to moderate generative potential but are found in sufficient volume and maturity levels in the deeps to have generated substantial quantities of hydrocarbons. In contrast, available samples from the Baong Formation are too lean, hydrogen poor, and locally immature to have generated the gas–condensate accumulations of the Bampo–Peutu petroleum system.

The greatest uncertainty in our oil (condensate)–source rock correlation arises from the limited availability of uncontaminated and immature source rock samples from the deeps where the richest source rock facies might be anticipated. It is conceivable that better quality source rocks of the Baong and Peutu formations, with carbon isotopic compositions similar to those of the reservoired hydrocarbons, have been accidentally missed by those exploration wells drilled without oil-based muds. However, based on currently available geochemical and geologic data, the Bampo Formation is considered the dominant source for hydrocarbons of the Bampo–Peutu petroleum system.

Geographic and Stratigraphic Extent

The geographic extent of the Bampo–Peutu petroleum system is defined as the area encompassing the region of mature source rock and all known accumulations, which covers 7600 km² (Figure 38.2). Vitrinite reflectance, thermal alteration index (TAI), and maturation modeling results indicate that the Bampo and Peutu source intervals are mature to overmature across much of the North Sumatra basin (Figure 38.3). Hence, the boundaries of this system are not really constrained by maturity but instead by the geographic limits of organic matter preservation. Mapped patterns of shale thickness, source rock richness, and kerogen facies indicate that organic matter accumulation, and therefore the system boundaries, were controlled by Bampo and Peutu depositional environments and paleobathymetry. The dashed system boundaries shown in Figure 38.2 are designated to reflect the uncertainty in their placement. Limited well penetrations to the north and northeast and restricted sample availability to the southeast increase the uncertainty of the exact placement of system boundaries in these two areas.

The stratigraphic extent of the system encompasses all rock units that are essential elements to the system, specifically, all Tertiary strata that overlie metamorphic basement and are up to 6 km thick. These include (1) Bampo and Peutu source rocks, (2) Peutu carbonate reservoir rocks, (3) Baong, Peutu, and Bampo shale seal rocks, (4) Peutu to Quaternary overburden rocks, and (5) Bruksah conduit rocks (and associated unconformities and/or faults) that facilitate hydrocarbon migration.

EFFICIENCY OF SYSTEM

The efficiency of this petroleum system is calculated by comparing the volume of hydrocarbons generated to estimates of the volume of hydrocarbons trapped in known discoveries. The volume of hydrocarbons generated was calculated using Schmoker's method (Chapter 19, this volume). Estimates of the amounts trapped at individual discoveries are listed in Table 38.1.

The amount of hydrocarbons generated is calculated by the following series of steps. First, the mass of organic carbon (M) is calculated for each source rock unit as follows:

$$M \text{ (g TOC)} = [\text{TOC (wt. \%)}/100] \times \rho(\text{g/cm}^3) \times V \text{ (cm}^3) \tag{1}$$

where ρ (rho) is the average formation density and V is the volume of the source unit.

The average organic carbon contents, based on data in Figure 38.6, are calculated at 0.87 and 0.74 wt. % for the Peutu and Bampo source rocks, respectively. Based on well log data, the estimated density of the formations in the depocenters is 2.55 and 2.66 g/cm³, respectively. The areal extent of mature source rock with generative potential for both source formations (outline from Figure 38.2) is 7600 km², or 7.6×10^{13} cm². The average source rock thickness estimated from computer gridded depth–structure maps is 345 m for the Peutu and 460 m for the Bampo. The volumes of mature source rock are then calculated at 2.62×10^{18} cm³ and 3.50×10^{18} for the Peutu and Bampo, respectively. Inserting these values into equation 1, we obtain the following:

$$
\begin{aligned}
M_{\text{Peutu}} &\text{ (g TOC)} \\
&= [(0.87 \text{ wt. \% TOC})/100] \times 2.55 \text{ g/cm}^3 \\
&\quad \times 2.62 \times 10^{18} \text{ cm}^3 \\
&= 5.82 \times 10^{16} \text{ g TOC}
\end{aligned}
$$

$$
\begin{aligned}
M_{\text{Bampo}} &\text{ (g TOC)} \\
&= [(0.74 \text{ wt. \% TOC})/100] \times 2.66 \text{ g/cm}^3 \\
&\quad \times 3.50 \times 10^{18} \text{ cm}^3 \\
&= 6.89 \times 10^{16} \text{ g TOC}
\end{aligned}
$$

The mass of hydrocarbons generated per unit mass of organic carbon (R) for the Peutu and Bampo source units are calculated as follows:

$$
\begin{aligned}
R &\text{ (mg HC/g TOC)} \\
&= \text{HI}_o \text{ (mg HC/g TOC)} - \text{HI}_p \text{ (mg HC/g TOC)}
\end{aligned} \tag{2}
$$

where HI_o is the original hydrogen index and HI_p is the present-day hydrogen index.

The original HI is roughly estimated at 200 for both source units based on mass balance considerations. Average mature HI_p values were calculated from data in Figure 38.7 as 100 and 70 for the Peutu and Bampo source rocks, respectively. These values were used to solve equation 2 as follows:

$$R_{Peutu} \text{ (mg HC/g TOC)}$$
$$= 200 \, HI_o \text{ (mg HC/g TOC)}$$
$$- 100 \, HI_p \text{ (mg HC/g TOC)}$$
$$= 100 \text{ (mg HC/g TOC)}$$

$$R_{Bampo} \text{ (mg HC/g TOC)}$$
$$= 200 \, HI_o \text{ (mg HC/g TOC)}$$
$$- 70 \, HI_p \text{ (mg HC/g TOC)}$$
$$= 130 \text{ (mg HC/g TOC)}$$

A minimum estimate for the total mass of hydrocarbons generated (HCG) is calculated using Schmoker's equation 3 (Chapter 19, this volume):

$$HCG \text{ (kg HC)}$$
$$= R \text{ (mg HC/g TOC)} \times M \text{ (g TOC)}$$
$$\times (1 \text{ kg}/10^6 \text{ mg)} \qquad (3)$$

Inserting the results from equations 1 and 2 into equation 3, we get

$$HCG_{Peutu} \text{ (kg HC)}$$
$$= R \text{ (mg HC/g TOC)} \times M \text{ (g TOC)}$$
$$\times (1 \text{ kg}/10^6 \text{ mg)}$$
$$= 100 \text{ (mg HC/g TOC)} \times [5.82 \times 10^{16} \text{ (g TOC)}]$$
$$\times (1 \text{ kg}/10^6 \text{ mg)}$$
$$= 5.82 \times 10^{12} \text{ kg HC}$$

$$HCG_{Bampo} \text{ (kg HC)}$$
$$= R \text{ (mg HC/g TOC)} \times M \text{ (g TOC)}$$
$$\times (1 \text{ kg}/10^6 \text{ mg)}$$
$$= 130 \text{ (mg HC/g TOC)} \times [6.89 \times 10^{16} \text{ (g TOC)}]$$
$$\times (1 \text{ kg}/10^6 \text{ mg)}$$
$$= 8.96 \times 10^{12} \text{ kg HC}$$

The total mass of hydrocarbons generated for both source units is then the sum of the two separate estimates, or 1.48×10^{13} kg HC. The total amount of discovered hydrocarbons in-place is calculated from the estimates of recoverable hydrocarbons listed in Table 38.1 using an 80% recovery factor for gas and condensate. From Table 38.1, total recoverable reserves are estimated at 1.503×10^{13} ft^3 of gas and 9.6×10^8 bbl of condensate. Using the 80% recovery factor, in-place reserves are estimated at 1.88×10^{13} ft^3 of gas and 1.2×10^9 bbl of condensate. Converting these values to

kilograms gives in-place hydrocarbons of 3.81×10^{11} kg of gas (2.03×10^{-2} kg/ft^3) and 1.5×10^{11} kg of condensate (125.0 kg/bbl). The combined total is then 5.31×10^{11} kg HC in-place.

To conclude this exercise and estimate the efficiency of the petroleum system, the in-place reserves are contrasted to the amount generated using the following equation:

$$PS_{efficiency} \text{ (\%)}$$
$$= [\text{in-place (kg HC)/generated (kg HC)}] \times 100$$
$$= [(5.31 \times 10^{11} \text{ kg HC})/(1.48 \times 10^{13} \text{ kg HC})] \times 100$$
$$= 3.6\% \qquad (4)$$

This calculation implies that only 3.6% of all hydrocarbons generated in the entire system were trapped in known discoveries, or alternately, that 96.4% were lost or retained in the source. Considerably larger trapping efficiencies are calculated if estimates are made on specific drainage areas (and volumes) for individual accumulations (40–70% efficiency range). In particular, the central location of the Arun gas field reservoir rock, astride the structurally high block between the two major deeps of the system, is ideally located to efficiently trap products migrating from the pod of active source rock. These same deeps also contain the best quality source rock facies identified within the system and overpressured shales that provide superb sealing capacity. In all, the ideal geologic conditions present within and near the Arun gas field have contributed to its extraordinary trapping efficiency, estimates that range from 40 to 70% for the drainage area (range reflects uncertainty in initial source rock generative potential and volume across the system).

Efficiency estimates for the entire petroleum system will change if future discoveries are made, but considering the extent of exploration drilling to date, these changes are likely to be minor unless some fundamentally different trap (prospect) and play concept is found fruitful. Therefore, although the spatial limits of the system itself are constrained by the preservation of organic matter, trapping efficiency estimates demonstrate that hydrocarbon charge is not the factor that limits large accumulations in the system. Instead, adequate reservoir and/or trapping mechanisms are the critical parameters constraining the overall efficiency of the Bampo–Peutu petroleum system.

SUMMARY

The Bampo–Peutu petroleum system encompasses 10 gas and gas–condensate discoveries that have estimated original discovered reserves of 15.0 tcf of gas and 1.0 Bbbl of condensate and natural gas liquids and is entirely within the North Sumatra basin. Only one discovery, the Arun gas field, is currently producing, and it has produced over 9.5 tcf of hydrocarbon gas and more than 500 MMbbl of condensate and natural gas liquids. Essential elements of the system include the Bampo and

Peutu source shales and marls; the Peutu carbonate reservoir rocks; the Baong, Peutu, and Bampo shale seal rocks; Bruksah clastic migration conduits; and overburden strata ranging from the Peutu Formation through Quaternary deposits. Unconformities and propitiously located extensional faults are also important conduits.

Geographically the system covers 7600 km[2] and stratigraphically includes up to 6 km of Tertiary sedimentary rocks. Most traps were formed in Miocene time, and the generation–migration–accumulation of hydrocarbons started in middle Miocene and is still ongoing. The time duration of the system extends from early Oligocene to Holocene time, with the critical moment of peak migration culminating in late Tertiary time (12–4 Ma).

Three-dimensional basin modeling results demonstrate that substantial late Tertiary sedimentation and unusually high geothermal gradients caused rapid conversion of kerogen and a brief pulse of hydrocarbon migration. A trapping efficiency of 3.6% is calculated for the entire petroleum system by comparing volumetric estimates of the total mass of hydrocarbons generated to the mass in discovered traps. Trapping efficiency estimates indicate that hydrocarbon charge is not the limiting factor for large accumulations to occur in the system, but instead, that adequate reservoir and/or trapping mechanisms are the critical parameters constraining the overall efficiency of the Bampo–Peutu petroleum system. The exceptionally high trapping efficiency calculated for the Arun accumulation (40–70% range) is indicative of a very large and efficient trap centered between two adjacent depocenters that jointly provide a large fetch area covering two efficiently drained lobes of the pod of active source rock.

Acknowledgments *The authors wish to thank both Mobil Oil Indonesia and Pertamina for approval to publish this summary. This report is an outgrowth from a regional evaluation recently conducted by Mobil Oil Indonesia. To our coworkers of this evaluation, J. Y. Blevins, S. P. Brown, and R. K. Foster, we owe our sincere appreciation for their vital contributions to our compilation. Special thanks are also expressed to the exploration managers at Mobil Oil Indonesia, especially Z. A. Kamili, and to A. Aziz, K. R. Dihardjo, L. R. High, S. Suwardi, Y. F. Wang, and the entire exploration and support staff at Mobil Oil Indonesia, for their assistance throughout this study. Contributions by R. J. Enrico, J. R. Flannery, J. R. Gormly, M. A. Northam, M. B. Ray and numerous others at the Mobil Dallas Research Laboratory and Mobil Exploration and Producing Services, Inc., are also gratefully acknowledged. This paper was significantly improved through critical reviews by G. E. Claypool, K. R. Dihardjo, E. P. Dion, S. Sosromihardjo, J. W. Stinnett, A. Sulaeman, and S. Suwardi.*

References Cited

Abdullah, M., and C. F. Jordan, 1987, The geology of the Arun field Miocene reef complex: Proceedings of the 16th Indonesian Petroleum Association Annual Convention, Jakarta, Indonesia, p. 65–96.

ASCOPE, 1985, The stratigraphic correlation study of the Andaman Sea–Strait of Malacca: Technical Paper TP/4, ASCOPE Secretariat, Jakarta, Indonesia, 28 p.

Aziz, A., and L. H. Bolt, 1984, Occurrence and detection of abnormal pressures from geological and drilling data, North Sumatra basin: Proceedings of the 13th Indonesian Petroleum Association Annual Convention, Jakarta, Indonesia, p. 195–215.

Blevins, J. Y., S. P. Brown, S. P. Buck, R. K. Foster, and T. H. McCulloh, 1990, The North Sumatra Task Force final report: Unpublished internal company report, 119 p.

Burnaman, M. D., R. B. Helm, and C. R. Beeman, 1985, Discovery of the Cunda gas field, B Block, North Sumatra: an integrated geologic/seismic stratigraphic case history: Proceedings of the 14th Indonesian Petroleum Association Annual Convention, Jakarta, Indonesia, p. 453–460.

Cameron, N. R., M. C. G. Clarke, D. T. Aldiss, J. A. Aspden, and A. Djunddin, 1980, The geologic evolution of northern Sumatra: Proceedings of the Ninth Indonesian Petroleum Association Annual Convention, Jakarta, Indonesia, p. 149–186.

Claypool, G. E., 1991, Petroleum retention in source rocks and the effect on timing and volume of petroleum expelled: Unpublished internal company report, Mobil Exploration and Producing Services Inc., 5 p.

Davies, P. R., 1990, Tectonics of North Sumatra (abst.): Sixth Geology, Mineral, and Hydrocarbon Resources of Southeast Asia (GEOSEA VI) Regional Conference, Jakarta, July 1987, v. 4, p. 77.

Durand, B., 1988, Understanding of HC migration in sedimentary basins (present state of knowledge): Advances in Organic Geochemistry 1987, Organic Geochemistry, v. 13, p. 445–459.

Graves, R. R., and A. A. Weegar, 1973, Geology of the Arun gas field, North Sumatra: Proceedings of the Second Indonesian Petroleum Association Annual Convention, Jakarta, Indonesia, p. 23–51.

Houpt, J. R., and C. C. Kersting, 1978, Arun reef, B Block, North Sumatra: Proceedings of the Indonesian Petroleum Association Carbonate Seminar, Jakarta, Indonesia, Sept. 12–19, 1976, p. 42–60.

Johnson, R. C., and D. Rice, 1990, Occurrence and geochemistry of natural gases, Piceance basin, northwest Colorado: AAPG Bulletin, v. 74, p. 805–829.

Jordan, C. F., Jr., 1989, The geology of the Arun reservoir: depositional and diagenetic history of a Miocene patch reef complex, North Sumatra, Indonesia: Unpublished internal company report, Mobil Oil Indonesia, 67 p.

Jordan, C. F., Jr., and M. Abdullah, 1992, Arun field—Indonesia North Sumatra basin, Sumatra, *in* N. F. Foster and E. A. Beaumont, eds., Stratigraphic traps III, atlas of oil and gas fields: AAPG Treatise of Petroleum Geology, p. 1–39.

Kamili, Z. A., J. Kingston, Z. Achmad, A. Wahab, S. Sosromihardjo, and C. V. Crausaz, 1976, Contribution to the pre-Baong stratigraphy of North Sumatra: Proceedings of the Fifth Indonesian Petroleum Association Annual Convention, Jakarta, Indonesia, p. 91–108.

Kamili, Z. A., and A. M. Naim, 1973, Stratigraphy of lower and middle Miocene sediments in North Sumatra basin: Proceedings of the Second Indonesian Petroleum Association Annual Convention, Jakarta, Indonesia, p. 53–72.

Kingston, J., 1978, Oil and gas generation, migration, and accumulation in the North Sumatra basin: Proceedings of the Seventh Indonesian Petroleum Association Annual Convention, Jakarta, Indonesia, p. 75–104.

Kjellgren, G. M., and H. Sugiharto, 1989, Oil geochemistry: a clue to the hydrocarbon history and prospectivity of the southeastern North Sumatra basin, Indonesia: Proceedings of the 18th Indonesian Petroleum Association Annual Convention, Jakarta, Indonesia, p. 363–384.

Magoon, L. B., 1989, The petroleum system–status of research and methods, 1990: U.S. Geological Survey Bulletin 1912, 88 p.

McArthur, A. C., and R. B. Helm, 1982, Miocene carbonate buildups, offshore North Sumatra: Proceedings of the 11th Indonesian Petroleum Association Annual Convention, Jakarta, Indonesia, p. 126–146.

Meyer, H., 1942, A compilation of the results of geological and geophysical exploration work done during recent years in the Tertiary basin of North Sumatra: Unpublished contractor report, Mobil Oil Indonesia, 51 p.

Rory, R., 1990, Geology of the South Lho Sukon 'A' Field, North Sumatra, Indonesia: Proceedings of the 19th Indonesian Petroleum Association Annual Convention, p. 1–40.

Schoell, M., 1983, Genetic characterization of natural gases: AAPG Bulletin, v. 67, p. 2225–2238.

Situmeang, S., and P. R. Davies, 1986, A geochemical study of Asamera's Block 'A' production sharing contract area, North Sumatra basin: Proceedings of the 15th Indonesian Petroleum Association Annual Convention, Jakarta, Indonesia, p. 321–340.

Situmorang, B., Siswoyo, M. Thamrin, B. Yulianto, 1983, Heat flow variation on western Indonesian basinal areas: implication on basin formation and hydrocarbon potential: Proceedings of the 12th Indonesian Petroleum Association Annual Convention, Jakarta, Indonesia, p. 157–169.

Soeparjadi, R. A., 1983, Geology of the Arun gas field: Journal of Petroleum Technology, v. 35, p. 1163–1172.

Sosromihardjo, S. P. C., 1988, Structural analysis of the North Sumatra basin with emphasis on synthetic aperture radar data: Proceedings of the 17th Indonesian Petroleum Association Annual Convention, Jakarta, Indonesia, p. 187–209.

Sunaryo A. C., and A. H. Djamil, 1990, Development of Arun east flank, onshore North Sumatra: Proceedings of the 19th Indonesian Petroleum Association Annual Convention, Jakarta, Indonesia, p. 517–546.

Thamrin, M., 1985, An investigation of the relationship between the geology of Indonesian sedimentary basins and heat flow density: Tectonophysics, v. 121, p. 45–62.

Tissot, B. P., R. Pelet, and P. H. Ungerer, 1987, Thermal history of sedimentary basins, maturation indices, and kinetics of oil and gas generation: AAPG Bulletin, v. 71, p. 1445–1466.

van Bemmelen, R. W., 1970, The Geology of Indonesia: Economic Geology: The Hague, Netherlands, Martinus Nijhoff, 267 p.

Wang, Y. F., F. M. Budijanto, M. L. Johnson, and R. S. A. Siringoringo, 1989, Neogene seismic sequences and structural styles in B and Peusangan blocks, North Sumatra basin, Indonesia: Proceedings of the 18th Indonesian Petroleum Association Annual Convention, Jakarta, Indonesia, p. 339–362.

Weathers, L. R., and R. B. Helm, 1984, Stratigraphic delineation of the Baong sandstone by high resolution acoustic inversion in the North Sumatra basin: Proceedings of the 13th Indonesian Petroleum Association Annual Convention, Jakarta, Indonesia, p. 443–459.

*"Profitable exploration requires wise
investment of risk capital in people's ideas."*

—Marlan W. Downey

Passage from Downey, M. W., 1992, in Steinmetz, R., ed., The business of petroleum exploration: AAPG, p. 201.

Petroleum System Calculation Sheet

Petroleum system name:

Petroleum provinces:

API gravity: $\qquad$ GOR (ft^3/bbl; m^3/m^3) =

Mass of petroleum accumulated (recoverable and in-place oil and gas):

Recoverable oil (bo)	=	bo
In-place oil (bo)	=	bo
$\times$ 139.3 kg/bo	=	kg oil

Recoverable gas (cfg)	=	cfg
In-place gas(cfg)	=	cfg
$\times$ 2.03 x 10^{-2} kg/cfg	=	kg gas

Totals

Recoverable oil and gas	=	kg oil and gas
in-place oil and gas	=	kg oil and gas

Mass of petroleum generated in source rock:

Given: Average TOC (wt. %)   =

Source rock density (ρ)   =

Volume (V = A $\times$ h) (cm^3)   =

M (g TOC)=[TOC (wt. %)/100] $\times \rho$ (g/cm^3) $\times$ V (cm^3) =   (1)

Given: HI$_o$ (original, mg HC/g TOC)   =

HI$_p$ (present-day, mg HC/g TOC)   =

R (mg HC/g TOC) = HI$_o$ (mg HC/g TOC) – HI$_p$ (mg HC/g TOC) =   (2)

HCG (kg HC) = R (mg HC/g TOC) $\times$ M (gTOC) $\times$ 10^{-6} (kg/mg) =   (3)

Generation–accumulation ratio (GAE):

GAE = (in-place/generated) $\times$ 100   =   %

Standard Abbreviations and Units

ABBREVIATIONS AND ACRONYMS

AFTA	apatite fission track annealing
BHT	bottom-hole temperature
bbl	barrel
bbo	billion barrels of oil
bo	barrels of oil
boe	barrels of oil equivalent (1 bo = 6000 cfg)
cfg	cubic feet of gas (see scfg)
CGR	condensate–gas ratio
DST	drill-stem test
FID	flame ionization detection
FPD	flame photometric detection
ft	feet
GAE	generation–accumulation efficiency
GC	gas chromatography
GC-MS	gas chromatography–mass spectrometry
GOR	gas–oil ratio
Gt	Gigaton
HC	hydrocarbon
HPLC	high-performance liquid chromatography
HI	hydrogen index from Rock-Eval pyrolysis
H/C	hydrogen/carbon ratio from elemental analysis
km	kilometer
M	thousand
m	meter
m^3	cubic meter
mi	mile
m.y.	million year time interval
Ma	million years ago or million years of age
mW	microwatt
OI	oxygen index from Rock-Eval pyrolysis
O/C	oxygen/carbon ratio from elemental analysis
PI	production index from Rock-Eval pyrolysis
scfg	standard cubic feet of gas (at standard temperature and pressure, STP)
t	metric ton (tonne)
TAI	thermal alteration index
TOC	total organic carbon from Leco analyzer or carbon analyzer attached to Rock-Eval pyrolysis
tcfg	trillion cubic ft of gas
Tg	teragram
TOC	total organic carbon
TR	transformation ratio
TTI	time–temperature index
wt. %	weight percent

UNIT CONVERSIONS

Energy

1 boe	= 6000 cfg (energy equivalent)

Length

1 m	$= 1 \times 10^2$ cm
1 ft	= 0.3048 m

Area

1 acre	$= 0.004046875$ km^2
1 mi^2	$= 2.589998$ km^2
1 km^2	$= 1 \times 10^{10}$ cm^2

Volume

1 bo	= 42 gal (U.S.)
1 bo	= 0.158987 m^3
1 m^3	= 6.28994 bo
1 m^3	= 35.314 ft^3
1 km^3	$= 1 \times 10^{15}$ cm^3
1 ft^3	= 0.028317 m^3
1000 tcf	$= 28.3 \times 10^{12}$ m^3
1000 tcf	$= 2.0 \times 10^{16}$ g CH$_4$
1000 tcf	= 2000 Tg CH$_4$

Mass

1 Gt	$= 10^{15}$ g
1 Tg	$= 10^{12}$ g
1000 tcf	$= 28.3 \times 10^{12}$ m^3 = 2.0×10^{16} g CH$_4$ = 2000 Tg CH$_4$
CH$_4$ at STP	= 20.3 g/ft^3 = 2.03×10^{-2} kg/ft^3
30° API oil	= 306.43 lbs/bbl = 139.30 kg/bbl
40° API oil	= 288.54 lbs/bbl = 131.15 kg/bbl
50° API oil	= 272.58 lbs/bbl = 123.90 kg/bbl

GOR

ft^3/bo	= 0.178 m^3/m^3
m^3/m^3	= 5.614 ft^3/bo

Glossary of Terms
Applicable to the Petroleum System

compiled by

Jennifer A. Miles
Optimisers Limited
Fordwells, Oxon, U.K.

active source rock A source rock that generates petroleum, either biogenically or thermally. If a source rock was active in the past, it is either inactive or spent today.

basin A depression into which sediment is deposited. Also refers to the basin fill. Sometimes used to mean petroleum province and sedimentary basin.

burial history chart A burial history curve or geohistory diagram constructed to show the time over which hydrocarbon generation occurs. Depicts the essential elements and the critical moment for the system.

critical moment The time that best depicts the generation–migration–accumulation of hydrocarbons in a petroleum system. A map and cross section drawn at the critical moment best shows the geographic and stratigraphic extent of the system.

effective source rock A source rock that is generating or has generated and expelled petroleum.

essential elements The source rock, reservoir rock, seal rock, and overburden rock of a petroleum system. Together with the processes, essential elements control the distribution of petroleum in the lithosphere.

events chart A chart for a petroleum system showing when the essential elements and processes took place as well as the preservation time and critical moment of the system.

generation–accumulation efficiency The ratio, expressed as a percentage, of the total volume of trapped (in-place) petroleum for the petroleum system to the total volume of petroleum generated from the pod of active source rock.

generation–migration–accumulation One petroleum system process that includes the generation and movement of petroleum from the pod of active source rock to the petroleum show, seep, or accumulation. The time over which this process occurs is the age of the petroleum system.

geographic extent The area over which the petroleum system occurs defined by a line that circumscribes the pod of active source rock and all the discovered petroleum shows, seeps, and accumulations that originated from that pod. The geographic extent is mapped at the critical moment; also called the **known extent**.

inactive source rock A source rock that has stopped generating petroleum, although it still shows some petroleum generating potential.

level of certainty The measure of confidence that petroleum from a series of genetically related accumulations originated from a specific pod of active source rock. Three levels used are known (!), hypothetical(.), and speculative(?), depending on the level of geochemical, geophysical and geologic evidence.

overburden rock The sedimentary rock above which compresses and consolidates the material below. In a petroleum system the overburden rock overlies the source rock and contributes to its thermal maturation because of higher temperatures at greater depths. An essential element of the petroleum system.

petroleum A mineral oil occurring in subsurface rocks and at the surface which is a naturally occurring mixture of hydrocarbon and nonhydrocarbon compounds. It may occur in the gaseous, liquid, or solid state depending on the nature of these compounds and existent conditions of temperature and pressure. Commonly used synonyms are **hydrocarbon** and **oil and gas**.

petroleum province A geographic location, frequently named, in which petroleum occurs; also referred to as a petroleum basin or basin. Examples include the Williston basin, Zagros thrust belt, and the Paris basin.

petroleum–source rock correlation   A comparison of chemical properties and relative abundances of individual chemical compounds present in source rocks and petroleum with the purpose of establishing a genetic relationship between the petroleum and its source rock.

petroleum system   The essential elements and processes as well as all genetically related hydrocarbons that occur in petroleum shows, seeps, and accumulations whose provenance is a single pod of active source rock. Also called **hydrocarbon system** and **oil and gas system**.

petroleum system age   The time over which the process of generation–migration–accumulation of hydrocarbons in the system takes place on the events chart.

petroleum system investigation   An investigation that identifies, names, determines the level of certainty, and maps the geographic, stratigraphic, and temporal extent of a petroleum system. It includes petroleum–petroleum and petroleum–source rock geochemical correlation, petroleum system map, cross section, burial history and events charts, table of hydrocarbon accumulations, and a mass balance calculation.

petroleum system logic   The thought process required to develop an integrated interpretation of the process of petroleum generation–migration–accumulation. In exploration, it is used to evaluate an exploration opportunity or prospect.

petroleum system name   A compound name that includes the source rock in the pod of active source rock, the reservoir rock containing the largest volume of petroleum, and the level of certainty of a petroleum system; for example, the Mandal–Ekofisk(!) petroleum system.

petroleum system processes   The two processes of trap formation and generation–migration–accumulation of petroleum. The preservation, degradation, and destruction of petroleum is omitted as a process because it generally occurs after a petroleum system is formed (preservation time). Together with the essential elements, the processes control the distribution of petroleum in the lithosphere.

petroleum system recovery efficiency   A ratio, expressed as a percentage, of the ultimately conventionally recoverable barrels of oil equivalent to the barrels of oil equivalent that could have been generated from a pod of active source rock if the source rock were completely spent.

pod of active source rock   A contiguous volume of source rock that is generating and expelling petroleum at the critical moment and is the prove-nance for a series of genetically related petroleum shows, seeps, and accumulations in a petroleum system. A pod of mature source rock may be active, inactive, or spent.

potential source rock   A source rock that contains adequate quantities of organic matter to generate petroleum, but only becomes an effective source rock when it generates biogenic gas at low temperatures or it reaches the proper level of thermal maturity to generate petroleum.

preservation time   The time after generation–migration–accumulation of petroleum takes place that encompasses any changes to the petroleum accumulations up to present day.

reservoir rock   A subsurface volume of rock that has sufficient porosity and permeability to permit the migration and accumulation of petroleum under adequate trap conditions. An essential element of the petroleum system.

seal rock   A shale or other impervious rock that acts as a barrier to the passage of petroleum migrating in the subsurface; it overlies the reservoir rock to form a trap or conduit. Also known as **roof rock** and **cap rock**. An essential element of the petroleum system.

source rock   A rock unit containing sufficient organic matter of suitable chemical composition to biogenically or thermally generate and expel petroleum. An essential element of the petroleum system.

spent source rock   A source rock that has generated and expelled all of its petroleum and is now overmature, with no further potential for generation.

stratigraphic extent   The span of lithologic units that encompasses the essential elements within the geographic extent of a petroleum system. It can be displayed on the burial history chart and cross section drawn at the critical moment.

thermal maturity   Sufficient thermal alteration in a source rock, either present day or in the past, to generate petroleum. Three levels are early or low, peak or mid-, and late or high. The record of thermal maturity determined for a source rock seldom reflects its current state of petroleum generation, as thermal maturation levels are irreversible on cooling.

trap   Any geometric arrangement of rock regardless of origin that permits significant accumulation of oil or gas, or both, in the subsurface and includes a reservoir rock and an overlying or updip seal rock. Types are stratigraphic, structural, and combination traps. Trap formation is one of the petroleum system processes.

Index